D1176496

HISTORY OF SCIENCE SOCIETY PUBLICATIONS

NEW SERIES IV

A HISTORY OF MAGIC AND EXPERIMENTAL SCIENCE

VOLUMES V AND VI

THE SIXTEENTH CENTURY

VOLUME VI

A HISTORY OF MAGIC AND EXPERIMENTAL SCIENCE

VOLUMES V AND VI

THE SIXTEENTH CENTURY

By LYNN THORNDIKE

VOLUME VI

COLUMBIA UNIVERSITY PRESS

NEW YORK AND LONDON

First printing 1941
Fourth printing 1966

Printed in the United States of America

CONTENTS

XXXI. POST-COPERNICAN ASTRONOMY 3

The *Prutenic Tables* — Maestlin concerning them — Tables of Femelius — Attitude of elementary textbooks in astronomy — Plan of the rest of this chapter — Gesner — Dodoens, *Cosmography* — Bicardus — Peucer — Constantinus — Gemma Frisius — Stadius, *Ephemerides*, 1556 — Recorde, *Castle of Knowledge* — Schreckenfuchs — Feild and Dee — Garcaeus — Biesius — Pena — Mesmes — Offusius — Pontus de Tyard — Dee, *Propaedeumata* — Maurolycus — Piccolomini — Stadius, *Tabulae Bergenses* — Santbech — Neander — Cornelius Gemma — Valerius — Stanhufius — Peletier — Theodoricus — Nunes — Crusius — Schreckenfuchs on the *Sphere* — Besson — Brucaeus — Digges — Nabod — Witekind — Forster — d'Anania — Bodin, *Republic* — Giuntini — Leoninus and Lonicerus — Freige — Clavius — Maestlin — Dodoens, edition of 1584 — Barozzi — The Aristotelians: Pendasio, Giannini, Meurer — Other philosophers: Benedetti, Bruno — Tycho Brahe and his correspondents — Raymarus Ursus — Magini — Galluccio — Origanus — Christmann — Gilbert — Galileo — Minerva — Summary

XXXII. THE NEW STARS 67

The star of 1572 — More startling than *De revolutionibus* — Effect on Tycho Brahe — His interest in astrology — But absorption in astronomy — Pena holds that the air extends to the fixed stars — Thaddeus Hagecius — Digges and Dee — Praetorius on the disappearance of the star of 1572 — Tycho's re-estimate of it — Helisaeus Roeslin — — Maestlin on the comet of 1577 — His astrology — Roeslin's letter to Maestlin — Maestlin on the comet of 1580 — Varied shadings and combinations of opinions — Maestlin's *Ephemerides* — His *Epitome of Astronomy* — Sacrobosco shines on — Adoptions of Pena's theory — Tycho still maintains the incorruptibility of the heavens — Brucaeus questions the expenditure of time on comets — Inconsistency of the Aristotelian doctrine of comets with astrology — Voetius — Dasypodius — Scultetus — Caesius — Simon Grynaeus — Libri's misstatement concerning Sordi — Olaus — Persistence of Aristotelian doctrines of comets and of the incorruptibility of the heavens — Cortés — Satler — Taxil — Giannini

XXXIII. ASTROLOGY AFTER 1550 99

Some general characteristics — Gaurico — Haghen — Gemma Frisius — Garcaeus — Other genitures of famous men — Dariot — Hebenstreit — Pontus de Tyard — Offusius — Cyprian Leowitz — Hieronymus Wolf — Leowitz continued — Bodin's criticisms of him — Taisnier — Stadius — Nabod — Speroni — Siderocrates — Paduanius — Scevolini — Geuss — Levinus Battus — Cerreto — Placido Foschi — Schylander — Pianero — Mizauld — Petrus de Peramata — Juan de Carmona — Baccius Baldinus — Giuntini — Winckler — Ranzovius — Benedetti — Rossi on climacteric years — Finck — Henricus à Lindhout — Henri de Monantheuil — Henisch — Peter Ryff — Satler

XXXIV. THE CATHOLIC REACTION: INDEX, INQUISITION AND PAPAL BULLS 145

Introduction — Inquisition and Witchcraft — the *Index* — Spanish Index — Council of Trent — Papal Inquisition — Experiences with it, of Cardan, Barozzi, Aldrovandi, Bruno, Porta — Bull of Sixtus V — Were annual predictions decreasing in Italy? — Gallucius — Rizza Casa — Padovanius — Ingegneri — Porta, *Coelestis physiognomia*, 1603 — *Chirofisonomia* — Magini — Astrology at Salamanca — Cortés — Johannes Franciscus Leo — Taxil — Bouchel — Bartolini — Bull of Urban VIII — Petrus Antonius — Campanella — Morin

XXXV. ADVERSARIES OF ASTROLOGY 179

Mercator not a consistent opponent — Alessandro Piccolomini — Fulke — Lucilio Maggi — Adam ab Invidia — Quenay of Evreux — Squarcialupus — Freige — Dudith — Buonsegni's translation of Savonarola — Jacques Fontaine — Nicodemus Frischlin — Sixtus ab Hemminga — Juan de Carmona — Sisto da Siena — Otto Casmann — George of Ragusa — Guy Coquille — Alexander de Angelis, 1615 — Giannini, 1618

XXXVI. MEDICINE AFTER 1550 207

Plan of the chapter — Rapard on bathing — Falloppia on medicated waters — Pest tracts: Oddus de Oddis, Michele Mercati, Johann Bokel, Petrus Salius Diversus, Georgius Rivettus, Horatius Augenius — Campi, *De morbo arietis* — Controversies: Nola, Cuneus, Philalethes, Sclanus — Gómez Pereira — *Secrets* of Alessio of Piedmont — Mizauld's *Arcana* — Fioravanti, *Capprici* — Bairo, *Secreti* — Isabella Cortese — *Secrets* ascribed to Falloppia — Guinther of Andernach — Quacks and impostors: Simon Forman — Popular errors: Joubert, Bachot, Mercurio, Aldana, Primrose — Theses at Montpellier — Mattioli — Spirits of the body: Argenterius, Bertacchi, Cureus on Trincavelli — Salomo Alberti — Olmo on occult virtue — Fienus on imagination

XXXVII. LIBAVIUS AND CHEMICAL CONTROVERSY 238

Libavius and the controversy between Ramists and Peripatetics — His tracts on weapon ointment and the bleeding corpse — Relation to Paracelsanism — Alchemical or chemical textbook — Reproaches against Paracelsus — Interest in medieval alchemy — Guibert's two treatises against alchemy — *Defense of Alchemy* by Libavius — Porta and alchemy — Guibert, *De interitu alchemiae* — Duchesne — Turquet de Mayerne — Extension of the controversy: Riolan, Bauchinet, Harvet, Libavius — Duchesne's arguments — Anonymous reply, probably by Riolan — Duchesne's rejoinder — Harvet's arguments — Palmarius — Libavius on the comet of 1604

XXXVIII. THE SIXTEENTH CENTURY NATURALISTS 254

Dioscorides, nomenclature and botanizing — Early works on animals — Figulus and Longolius — Later publications culminating in the tomes of Aldrovandi — His list of naturalists — Efforts in the direction of botanical method by Figulus and Maranta — Medieval knowledge of herbs compared with that of the sixteenth century — Botany not ranked high as a university subject — Attempted classification in a manuscript of 1573 — Correspondence and cooperation — Specimens and museums — Limits to scientific observation — Science often subsidiary to other interests — Question of arrangement — Relation to medieval works and to humanistic studies — Ryff on

Ruelle's translation of Dioscorides — Reaction against expenditure of time over classical names — Interest in flora and fauna of one's own country and vernacular — Interest in flora and fauna of the New World and the Far East — But compilation still the prevalent method — Retention of other characteristics from the medieval enyclopedias — Aldrovandi on the eagle — Unsatisfactory standards of credibility — Indiscriminate use of past authors — Aldrovandi's unsuccessful effort to omit nugae — How far were extraordinary assertions tested? — Scaliger on Cardan — Further examples of credulity, hesitancy and scepticism — Monsters — L'Ancre on the bizarreness of nature — Barnacle geese — The biped dragon of 1572 — Spontaneous generation — Marvelous works of God — Fossils — No correlation or inverse ratio between science and superstition — Occult tendencies — Doctrine of signatures — Gathering herbs on Midsummer Night — Spirits in wells and mines — Summary — Buffon on Aldrovandi

XXXIX. THE LORE OF GEMS 298

Camillo Lunardi — Petrus Arlensis de Scudalupis — Early editions of Marbod on gems — Erasmus Stella — Rueus — Kentmann's catalogue of minerals — Gesner's work of 1565 — Encelius — Menabenus and Ricardus on bezoar stones — Lodovico Dolce — Garcia da Orta and Fragoso — Bacci and Gabelchover — Gilbert, *De magnete* — De Boodt, 1609 — Albinius, 1611

XL. CESALPINO'S VIEW OF NATURE 325

Career of Cesalpino — His *Peripatetic Questions* — Did he anticipate Harvey in the discovery of the circulation of the blood? — *Alpes caesae* of Taurellus — Cesalpino as a botanist — His *De metallicis* — His *Daemonum investigatio Peripatetica*

XLI. EFFORTS TOWARDS A CHRISTIAN PHILOSOPHY OF NATURE 339

Numerous publications showing a general interest in nature — Bigot's *Prelude to Christian Philosophy* — Postel's conception of nature — The Holy Land, universal monarchy and astrology — Effect of the voyages of discovery — Daneau's *Christian Physics* — Nicolaus Contarenus, *De perfectione rerum* — Scribonius, *Methodical*

Doctrine of Nature — Four past schools of physics — Vallesius, *Sacra philosophia* — Nature of the heavens — Words and numbers — Astrology and divination — Belot's *Flowers of Christian and Moral Philosophy*

XLII. FOR AND AGAINST ARISTOTLE 363

Alessandro Piccolomini — Landi, *Paradossi* — Cureus, *Libellus physicus* — Meurer, *Meteorologia* — Vimercati — Zabarella — Mercenarius — Telesio — Honoratus de Robertis — Benedetti — Francesco Patrizi — Zuccolo — Francesco Piccolomini — Gilbert, *Nova philosophia* — Chassinus, *De natura*, 1614 — Basso against Aristotle, 1621 — Abiding influence of Aristotle

XLIII. NATURAL PHILOSOPHY AND NATURAL MAGIC . . . 390

Introduction — Alonso de Fuentes — John Dee — Levinus Lemnius — Biesius: career, *De universitate* (1556), *De natura* (1573) — Maffei, *Scala naturale* — Georg Pictorius: career; works here considered, mostly second-hand; physical questions; ceremonial magic; demons and witches — Cornelius Gemma, *De arte cyclognomica* — *De naturae divinis characterismis* — Pererius on physics and magic: alchemy, dreams, astrology — Huarte Navarro — Aevolus on sympathy and antipathy — Theses proposed by Mairhofer on natural magic, etc. — Porta on natural magic — Original and enlarged editions — His credulity and scepticism — Experiments — *Phytognomonica* — Giordano Bruno — His vagabond career — Attitude towards nature and magic — Reasons for his execution — Tommaso da Ravenna — Cortés, 1601 — Obicius, 1605 — Pietro Passi, 1614 — Alsted's encyclopedia

XLIV. MYSTIC PHILOSOPHY: WORDS AND NUMBERS . . . 437

Scope of this chapter — Continued activity of Lefèvre, Reuchlin and Trithemius — Lazzarelli, *Crater Hermetis* — Correspondence of Ganay and Trithemius — Visit of Bouelles to Trithemius — *De septem secundadeis* — Bouelles on numbers — Gesner's estimate of him — Clichtowe on mysticism and numbers — Beheim to Reuchlin — *De arte cabalistica* — Galatinus — Hochstraten — Paul Riccio — Hieroglyphics: Horapollo and Piero Valeriano — Hermetic corpus — *Theology* of Aristotle — Francesco Giorgio on the harmony of the universe — Tenaud on the

Cabala — A cabalistic manuscript — Constantinus on the Cabala — Postel — Paul Skalich — John Dee, *Hieroglyphic Monad* — Arbatel — Bungus on numbers — l'Apostre on the number seven — Bruno on numbers and figures — *Prognostica* of Orpheus or Hermes — Patritius, *Magia philosophica* — Jessenius, *Zoroaster* — Johann Pistorius — Attacked by Heilbronner — Albinius, 1611 — Rheticus and Kepler — Bodin

XLV. DIVINATION 466

Giovanni Francesco Pico della Mirandola, *De rerum praenotione* — Geomancy of Spirito, Rossi, Ringelberg and Geber — Fanti, *Triompho di Fortuna* — Jacobus de Panico — Gaudentius Tervisinus — Parabosco — Cattan — Bandaroy — de la Tayssonière — Geomancies in manuscript — *Nomandia* of Annibale Raimondo — Jacques Gohorry (Leo Suavius) — Dream-Book of Daniel — Artemidorus, *Oneirocritica* — Scaliger's commentary on Hippocrates, *De insomniis* — Ponzetti — Fox Morcillo — Hegendorff — Jean Thibault — Conrad Gesner — Oger Ferrier — Renting a haunted house — Argenterius — Carreri — Thomas Hill — Achmet — Celso Mancini — Nifo on auguries and weather signs — Paul Minerva on weather prediction — Portents and prodigies — Nausea's seven books of marvels — *Sibylline Oracles* — Works on fate — Peucer and Camerarius on divination — Career of Peucer — Character of his work — Natural and diabolical divination distinguished — Oracles — Rivius — Peucer's attitude towards magic, cabala, numbers, astrology, occult virtue and sympathy, spontaneous generation, alchemy — The treatise of Camerarius — Pictorius on varieties of divination — Zanchius — Boissard — Hagecius on metoposcopy — Rothmann on chiromancy and astrology — Belot, 1619 — Froger, 1622 — Franzosius on divination by dreams and prophecy, 1632

XLVI. THE LITERATURE OF WITCHCRAFT AND MAGIC AFTER WIER 515

Wier, *De praestigiis daemonum*, 1563 — Scope of this chapter — Durastantes — Diacetius — Argentinus — Grynaeus, *De incubo* — Daneau — Verini — Hemming — Nodé — Massé — Joel — Adam a Lebenwald — Bodin, *Démonomanie* — d'Anania — Vairus — Reginald Scot —

Le Loyer — Rivius — Lavater — Scherertzius— Biermann — Godelmann — Binsfeld — His attitude towards occult virtue, knowledge of the future, comets, physiognomy, alchemy — Codronchi — Werwolves denied — *Daemonologie* of James I — Cicogna — Boquet — Fontaine — Literature of exorcism: Menghi, Polidoro, Porri, etc. — Caranta, 1624

XLVII. THE SCEPTIC AND THE ATHEIST: FRANCESCO SANCHEZ AND LUCILIO VANINI 560

Sanchez and Vanini at Toulouse — Career of Francesco Sanchez — Character of his *Quod nihil scitur* — His personal experience — Scope of and limits to his scepticism — Criticism of contemporary learning — Failure to develop a better scientific method — His later career and writings — Character of Vanini's works — His admiration for Pomponazzi and Cardan — His science antiquated and faulty — His limited scepticism as to natural marvels — Faith in the influence of the stars — The true avenue of scientific progress

XLVIII. SUMMARY AND BY-PRODUCTS 574

Dramatis personae — Citation of the classics — Of Arabic and Jewish authors — Of medieval Latin writers — Where the scene has been laid — Leading intellectual centers — Italy and Germany compared — Paris in the sixteenth century — Local physicians — Humanistic form and veneer — Germs of scientific societies — Centers of printing — Comparison of things and topics mentioned in our different volumes: their number and classification

APPENDICES

4. Genitures of Men of Learning 595
5. Zimara and the *Trinum magicum* 599
6. Printers of the Sixteenth Century 603

GENERAL INDEX 615
INDEX OF MANUSCRIPTS 762
INDEX OF INCIPITS 765

ABBREVIATIONS

Art ancien	L'Art Ancien S.A., Dealers in Rare Books, Manuscripts etc., Zurich.
BB	Boncompagni's *Bullettino di bibliografia e di storia delle scienze matematiche e fisiche*, Rome, 1868-1887, Vols. I-XX.
BL	Bodleian Library, Oxford.
BM	British Museum, London.
BMsl	British Museum, Sloane Manuscripts.
BN	Bibliothèque Nationale, Paris.
BNna	Bibliothèque Nationale, nouvelles acquisitions manuscrits.
Brunet	J. C. Brunet, *Manuel du libraire et de l'amateur de livres*, 1860-1880, 8 vols.
BU	Bologna, University library.
Bulaeus	see Du Boulay.
Bullarium romanum	*Bullarum diplomatum et privilegiorum sanctorum romanorum pontificum Taurinensis editio*, 1857-1872, 24 vols. and Appendix.
c	century.
c.	circa.
Carafa	Josephus Garafa (or, Giuseppe Caraffa), *De gymnasio Romano et de eius professoribus*, Romae, 1751-1752, 2 vols.
Chevalier	Ulysse Chevalier, *Répertoire des sources historiques du moyen âge, Bio-Bibliographie*, Paris, 1905-1907, 2 vols.
CGM	Codex graecus Monacensis, Bayerische Staats-Bibliothek, München.
CLM	Codex latinus Monacensis, Bayerische Staats-Bibliothek.
Col	Columbia University Library, New York.
ColR	Rotograph, Columbia University Library.
comm.	Commentary on, Commentarius, commentator.
Copinger	W. A. Copinger, *Supplement to Hain's Repertorium bibliographicum*, London, 1895-1902, 2 vols. in 3.
CR	*Corpus reformatorum*, ed. K. G. Bretschneider und H. E. Bindsell, 98 vols. to 1935.

CU	Cambridge University.
Dallari, *Rotuli*	Umberto Dallari, *I rotuli dei lettori legisti e artisti dello studio bolognese dal 1384 al 1799,* Bologna, 1888-1924, 4 vols.
De balneis (1553)	*De balneis omnia quae extant apud Graecos Latinos et Arabes,* Venice, 1553.
Dedic	Dedication, Dedicated to, etc.
DES (1917)	David Eugene Smith, "Medicine and Mathematics in the Sixteenth Century," *Annals of Medical History,* 1917, pp. 125-40.
DNB	*Dictionary of National Biography,* London, 1885-1901, 63 vols.
Doppelmayr (1730)	Johann Gabriel Doppelmayr, *Historische Nachricht von den Nürnbergischen Mathematicis und Künstlern,* Nürnberg, 1730.
Du Boulay	C. E. du Boulay, *Historia universitatis Parisiensis,* Paris, 1665-1673, 6 vols.
Duhem I (1906), Duhem II (1909)	Pierre Duhem, *Etudes sur Léonard de Vinci: ceux qu'il a lus et ceux qui l'ont lu,* Paris, 1906, 1909.
Duhem III (1913)	Pierre Duhem, *Etudes sur Léonard de Vinci: les précurseurs parisiens de Galilée,* Paris, 1913.
Duhem I (1913) Duhem II (1914) Duhem III (1915) Duhem IV (1916) Duhem V (1917)	Pierre Duhem, *Le système du monde,* 5 vols., Paris, 1913-1917.
DWS	Dorothea Waley Singer, *Catalogue of Latin and Vernacular Manuscripts in Great Britain and Ireland dating from before the sixteenth century,* Brussels, 1928-1931, 3 vols.
ed.	edited by, edition, printed.
Ep.	Epistola.
et seq.	et sequuntur.
Eubel	C. Eubel, *Hierarchia catholica medii aevi,* Münster, 1898-1910, 3 vols.
f. or fol.	folio, leaf
Ferguson	John Ferguson, *Bibliotheca Chemica: a catalogue of rare alchemical, chemical and pharmaceutical books, manuscripts and tracts . . . in the collection of J. Young,* Glasgow, 1906.
FL	Florence, Laurentian Library (R. Biblioteca Medicea Laurenziana).

FN	Florence, Biblioteca Nazionale.
FR	Florence, Riccardian Library.
fr.	français or French.
Gaurico (1552)	Lucas Gauricus, *Tractatus astrologicus in quo agitur de praeteritis multorum hominum accidentibus per proprias eorum genituras . . .* , Venetiis, 1552.
Gesner (1545)	Conrad Gesner, *Bibliotheca universalis,* Tiguri, 1545.
Grabmann II (1936)	Martin Grabmann, *Mittelalterliches Geistesleben: Abhandlungen zur Geschichte der Scholastik und Mystik, Band II,* Munich, 1936.
Graesse	Jean George Théodore Graesse, *Trésor de libres rares et precieux, ou, Nouveau dictionnaire bibliographique,* Dresden, 1859-1869, 7 vols.
GW	*Gesamtkatalog der Wiegendrucke,* Leipzig, 1925- In process.
Hain	Ludwig Hain, *Repertorium bibliographicum in quo libri omnes ab arte typographica inventa usque ad annum MD typis expressi ordine alphabetico vel simpliciter enumerantur vel adcuratius recensentur,* Stuttgart, 1826-1838, 4 vols.
Hansen (1900)	Joseph Hansen, *Zauberwahn Inquisition und Hexenprozess im Mittelalter,* Munich and Leipzig, 1900.
Hansen, *Quellen*	Joseph Hansen, *Quellen und Untersuchungen zur Geschichte des Hexenwahns und der Hexenverfolgung im Mittelalter,* Bonn, 1901.
Hellmann (1914)	G. Hellmann, *Beiträge zur Geschichte der Meteorologie,* Berlin, 1914.
Hellmann (1917)	G. Hellmann, "Die Wettervorhersage im ausgehenden Mittelalter," *Beiträge z. Gesch. d. Meteorologie,* II, 169-229, Berlin, 1917.
Hellmann (1924)	G. Hellmann, "Versuch einer Geschichte der Wettervorhersage im XVI Jahrhundert," 54 pp. *Abhandlungen d. preussischen Akademie d. Wissenschaften,* Jahrgang 1924, Physikalisch-Mathematische Klasse, Berlin, 1924.
HL	*Histoire littéraire de la France,* Paris, 1733- . In process.
Hoefer	J. C. F. Hoefer, *Nouvelle biographie générale depuis les temps reculés jusqu'à nos jours,* 1853-1870, 46 vols.
Houzeau et Lancaster	J. C. Houzeau et A. Lancaster, *Bibliographie générale de l'astronomie,* Bruxelles, 1882-1889, 2 parts in 3 vols.

Jobst (1556)	Wolfgang Jobst (Guolph. Justus), *Chronologia sive temporum supputatio omnium illustrium medicorum tam veterum quam recentiorum*, Francoph. ad Viadrum, 1556, 8vo.
Jöcher	Ch. G. Jöcher, *Allgemeines Gelehrten Lexicon*, Leipzig, 1750-1751, 4 vols.
Klebs (1938)	Arnold C. Klebs, *Incunabula scientifica et medica.* Short Title List. Bruges, 1938. Reprinted from *Osiris*, Vol. IV.
Kobolt	Anton Maria Kobolt, *Baierisches Gelehrten-Lexicon*, Landshut, 1795.
Libri	Guil. Libri, *Histoire des sciences mathématiques en Italie depuis la Renaissance jusqu'à la fin du XVIII*[e] *siècle*, 1838-1841, 4 vols.
Manget	J. J. Manget, *Bibliotheca chemica curiosa*, Geneva, 1702, 2 vols.
Mazzuchelli	Gianmaria Mazzuchelli, *Scrittori d'Italia*, Brescia, 1753-1763.
Michaud	M. M. Michaud, *Biographie universelle ancienne et moderne*, Deuxième édition, 45 vols.
MS and MSS	Manuscript and Manuscripts.
Muratori, *Scriptores*	*Rerum Italicarum scriptores ab anno aerae christianae 500 ad 1500*, ed. L. A. Muratori, 1723-1751. New edition in process since 1900.
n.	note or footnote.
n.d.	no date given.
Panzer	G. Wolfgang Panzer, *Annales typographici ab artis inventae origine ad annum MDXXXVI*, Nürnberg, 1793-1803, 11 vols.
Pellechet	M. Pellechet, *Catalogue général des incunables des bibliothèques publiques de France*, Paris, 1897-1909, 3 vols.
Pèrcopo	Erasmo Pèrcopo, "Luca Gaurico, ultimo degli astrologi: notizie biografiche e bibliografiche," *Società Reale di Napoli, Atti della Reale Accademia di archeologia, lettere e belle arti*, XVII (1893-1896), ii, 3-102.
Proctor	Robert Proctor, *An index to the early printed books in the British Museum*, London, 1898-1903.
pr	printed or printer.
Reichling	Dietericus Reichling, *Appendices ad Hainii-Copingeri Repertorium bibliographicum*, Monachii et monasterii Guestphalorum, 1905-1914, 8 vols.

Renaudet (1916)	A. Renaudet, *Préréforme et humanisme à Paris pendant les premières guerres d'Italie (1494-1517)*, 1916.
Reusch (1886)	Franz Heinrich Reusch, *Indices librorum prohibitorum des sechzehnten Jahrhunderts*, Tübingen, 1886.
Richter	J. P. Richter, *The Literary Works of Leonardo da Vinci*, 1883, 2 vols.
Sbaralea	*Supplementum et castigatio ad Scriptores trium ordinum S. Francisci a Waddingo aliisque descriptos*, original edition, Rome, 1806, 2 vols.; revised edition, 1908, 1921.
Schreiber	W. L. Schreiber, *Die Kräuterbücher des XV und XVI Jahrhunderts*, München, 1924.
Sitzb.	Sitzungsberichte.
Sudhoff (1894)	Karl Sudhoff, *Versuch einer Kritik der Echtheit der Paracelsischen Schriften*, Berlin, 1894.
Sudhoff (1902)	Karl Sudhoff, *Iatromathematiker vornehmlich im 15. und 16. Jahrhundert*, Breslau, 1902.
T I, II, III, IV	Lynn Thorndike, *A History of Magic and Experimental Science*, New York, 1923 and 1934, 4 vols.
T (1929)	Lynn Thorndike, *Science and Thought in the Fifteenth Century*, New York, 1929.
T (1937)	Lynn Thorndike and Pearl Kibre, *A Catalogue of Incipits of Medieval Scientific Writings in Latin*, 1937.
Thuanus	Augustus Thuanus (Jacques Auguste de Thou), *Historiarum sui temporis ab anno domini 1543 usque ad annum 1607 libri cxxxviii*, Francofurti, 1625-1628, 4 vols. in 2. The notices of learned men in the years of their deaths were printed separately by Teissier, *Les eloges des hommes savants tirez de l'histoire de M. de Thou avec des additions* etc., Leida, 1715.
Tiraboschi	Girolamo Tiraboschi, *Storia della letteratura italiana*, usually cited from the edition of Milan, 1822-1826.
Tiraqueau	Andrea Tiraquellus, *Commentarii de nobilitate et iure primigenitorum*, usually cited from the edition of Venice, 1574.
Tomasini	Jac. Phil. Tomasini, *Illustrium virorum elogia iconibus exornata*, usually cited from the edition of Padua, 1630.
Toppi	Nicolò Toppi, *Biblioteca Napoletana et apparato agli huomini illustri in lettere di Napoli e del Regno, delle famiglie, terre, città e religioni che sono nello stesso regno*, Napoli, 1678.

tr	translated, translation, translator
Trithemius	*Liber de scriptoribus ecclesiasticis,* Basel, 1494.
VA	Bibliotheca Apostolica Vaticana.
VI	Vienna, National-Bibliothek.
Will	Georg Andreas Will, *Nürnbergisches Gelehrten-Lexicon,* 1755-1758, 4 vols.
ZB	*Zentralblatt für Bibliothekswesen.*
Zedler	J. Zedler, *Grosses Vollständiges Universal Lexicon aller Wissenschaften und Künste,* Halle and Leipzig, 1732-1750, 64 vols.
Zetzner	Lazarus Zetzner, *Theatrum chemicum,* Strasburg, 1659-1661, 6 vols., is the edition usually cited.
Zinner (1925)	Ernst Zinner, *Verzeichnis der astronomischen Handschriften des deutschen Kulturgebietes,* Munich, 1925.
Zinner (1934)	Ernst Zinner, *Die fränkische Sternkunde im 11. bis 16. Jahrhundert,* Bamberg, 1934.
Zinner (1936)	Ernst Zinner, "Johannes Müller von Königsberg (Regiomontanus)," *Philobiblon, eine Zeitschrift für Bücherfreunde,* IX (1936), 89-97.
Zinner (1938)	Ernst Zinner, *Leben und Wirken des Iohannes Müller von Königsberg genannt Regiomontanus,* Munich, 1938.

A HISTORY OF MAGIC AND EXPERIMENTAL SCIENCE

THE SIXTEENTH CENTURY

CHAPTER XXXI

POST-COPERNICAN ASTRONOMY

Copernicus . . . omnia in re astronomica invertit
—SCHRECKENFUCHS

Erasmus Reinhold, whom we saw looking forward in 1542 to the publication of *De revolutionibus,* as a result of the appearance of that work composed new astronomical tables, which were first printed at Tübingen in 1551. They were called *Prutenic Tables* in honor of Albert, duke of Prussia and margrave of Brandenburg, to whom they were dedicated.[1] In the preface Reinhold states that observations, made for many years past by leading astronomers, have shown that the old tables can no longer be used as a basis for calculating the positions of the heavenly bodies. We therefore, Reinhold continues, owe much thanks to that great man, Nicolaus Copernicus, for having freely communicated to the studious his observations, won by the vigils of many years and by assiduous labor, and for having by the publication of *De revolutionibus* restored the theory of movements, which was in a state of almost total collapse. In geometry Copernicus was supreme, but in numerical reckoning he sometimes made slips. Reinhold has compared the observations of Copernicus with those of Ptolemy and others very accurately, and, except for the bare observations and demonstrations, has "taken nothing else" from Copernicus but has worked out the canons anew and in some cases in a totally different way. Reinhold presently reiterates that that very learned man, Copernicus, who was a second Atlas or Ptolemy, although he most eruditely set forth demonstrations and the causes of movements on the

[1] *Prutenicae Tabulae Coelestium motuum autore Erasmo Reinholdo Salveldensi, cum gratia et privilegio Caesareae et Regiae Maiestatis,* Tubingae per Ulricum Morhardum anno MDLI Copy used: BM 8560.cc.6.(1.).

basis of his observation, yet so shunned this labor of constructing tables, that a computation based upon his canons does not agree with his own observations. To this laborious task of constructing tables Reinhold has given seven years, to the detriment of his private fortune, which he might have been augmenting by paying undertakings and divinations. It thus appears that the *Prutenic Tables* were not merely a tabulation of the results of Copernicus, although both then and since they were often referred to roughly as Copernican, or by some such phrase as "according to the calculation of Copernicus," as if his canons and reckoning and those of Reinhold were identical.

These *Prutenic Tables* found favor with many persons who either did not accept the Copernican hypotheses in their entirety, feeling that they required some modification, or who had less interest in such theoretical and revolutionary proposals than in practical tables which gave the positions of the planets more accurately than the tables of the past and so would serve as a safer basis for prediction from the stars. The *Prutenic Tables* were reissued at Tübingen in 1572 and at Wittenberg in 1585 by G. Strubius. They appear to have been well received from their first appearance and to have been supplanted only by the *Rudolphine Tables* of Kepler, whereas the Copernican theory won general acceptance only in the next century after it had been modified and further developed by the discoveries of Kepler and others. Tycho Brahe, however, while calling Reinhold an "illustrious astronomer of our age," remarked that he had been chiefly occupied with demonstrations and numerical calculations, and had observed the stars little, using a poor wooden quadrant and borrowing largely in this respect from Copernicus.[2]

Maestlin, although a defender of the Copernican system, when discussing in 1596 the dimensions of the celestial orbs and spheres, preferred to use the *Prutenic Tables* of Erasmus Reinhold rather than *De revolutionibus*, "although these (figures) might have been excerpted and copied without labor partly

[2] Tycho Brahe, *Opera*, ed. Dreyer, III (1916), 146.

from Copernicus himself and partly from Ptolemy." For as Reinhold himself had stated in the preface to the *Prutenic Tables*, he discussed the observations and demonstrations proposed by Copernicus much more exactly and more accurately than Copernicus himself.[3] Maestlin more than once expressed regret that Reinhold's untimely death had prevented his producing the commentary upon the books of Copernicus or upon his own *Prutenic Tables* which he had planned.[4] On the other hand, we are told by a modern writer that the lack of recent observations against which the positions derived from older works could be checked "made Reinhold's tables only slightly more accurate than the Alfonsine tables or those of Regiomontanus."[5]

Indeed, Maestlin himself had in 1586 criticized those who were responsible for the reformed Gregorian calendar for having used the *Prutenic Tables* instead of working out new ones from more recent observations. In this connection he stated that the Alfonsine and Prutenic were the only tables available, and that it was a common complaint of all mathematicians that the calculations of neither corresponded exactly with the sky.[6] Previously, in his *Ephemerides* of 1580 Maestlin had noted that the *Prutenic Tables*, although much nearer the truth than others, were sometimes two degrees wrong for the position of Mars and as much as an hour off for lunar eclipses. He ascribed these defects, not to the absurdity of their underlying hypotheses, "as it seems to some," nor to bad construction of the tables, but to the observations used "in demonstrating the appearances of the anomalies."[7]

In 1599 Christopher Femelius, professor of mathematics at

[3] *De dimensionibus orbium et sphaerarum coelestium iuxta Tabulas Prutenicas ex sententia Nicolai Copernici. Appendix M. Michaelis Mestlini mathematum in Tubingensi Academia professoris:* reprinted in Kepler, *Prodromus diss. cosmographicarum*, 1621, p. 149.

[4] *Idem* and p. 93 of the same volume, in Maestlin's preface to the *Narratio prima* of Rheticus.

[5] Francis R. Johnson, *Astronomical Thought in Renaissance England*, Baltimore, 1937, p. 112.

[6] Michael Maestlin, *Alterum examen novi pontificialis Gregoriani kalendarii . . .*, Tubingae apud Georgium Gruppenbachium, 1586, p. 4. Copy used: BM 531.k.3.(2.).

[7] Michael Maestlin, *Ephemerides novae ab 1577 ad 1580*, Tubingae, 1580, Praefatio.

Erfurt, published synoptic tables for finding the true places of the planets, derived from the *Prutenic Tables* but disposed in Ptolemaic form, together with an investigation of fixed days and movable feasts of both the Julian and Gregorian calendars.[8] In the preface Femelius states that although the Prutenic canons are judged to be nearer the truth than others, yet many complain of their difficulty and prolixity. He has therefore made a selection for the use especially of beginners, and invokes the authority of Ptolemy and Virdung as well as Reinhold and Stadius. The last named is quoted that this world has never seen the superior of Copernicus, whose penetrating and concise brevity and the sharpness and subtlety of whose demonstrations preclude their use to many.[9] Femelius, however, often cites and follows him.[10] Thus he presents the *Prutenic Tables* and Copernican demonstrations in diluted form, without ceasing to maintain a respectful attitude towards Ptolemy.

Next to astrological predictions, elementary textbooks after the manner of the *Sphere* of Sacrobosco seem to have been the most frequent publication in the astronomical field in the sixteenth century. Apparently almost every university had at least one elementary astronomical text produced for local consumption during this period. Their authors seldom reached the theory of the planets, the intricacies of which they usually postponed to a future volume which never appeared. The intricacies of

[8] *Synopticae tabulae eliciendi vera loca planetarum ex tabulis Prutenicis derivatae et forma Ptolemaica dispositae una cum investigatione dierum fixorum et festorum mobilium utriusque calendarii Iuliani et Gregoriani auctore M. Christophoro Femelio mathematum professore,* Witebergae Impensis Samuelis Selfisch Bibliopolae, 1599. Copies used: BN V.8421-8421 ter; BM 531.k.3.(3.).

[9] "Copernico nihil hic orbis vidit aut exquisitius aut concinnius cuius arguta concisaque brevitas imo demonstrationum acumen subtilitasque plerisque usum praecludit."

[10] Among the Praecepta which precede his tables are: xxix, ". . . Nos in hac quoque parte Copernici viam secuti prosthaphaereses orbis tantum ad eccentrici apogeon et perigeon supputavimus"; xxxi, "Verum hanc varietatem ex motuum calculo removendam censuit summus vir Copernicus"; xxxii, "Prudenter Copernicus omnes motus coelestes numerat a prima stella asterismi Arietis velut a certo et fixo principio"; xl, "Ideo ad Copernici imitationem canonem aequalis motus longitudinis in tribus superioribus negleximus"; xlv, "Luna nova et plena secundum Copernicum est proxima centro primi epicycli sive ipsius anomaliae epicycli."

the Copernican theory likewise were eschewed by such writers as beyond the reach of the beginning students for whom they wrote. They commonly adhered strictly to the Ptolemaic system, both as customary and as presenting the heavens the way they looked to an observer on the earth. This dead weight of pedagogical tradition and inertia did far more to delay the spread and general acceptance of the Copernican hypothesis than any religious opposition to it. Galileo might have done better to write a systematic textbook than his provocative dialogues. Hardly a single elementary textbook was written on the Copernican basis. Usually a passing sentence or two was all the recognition given to it. After examination of such textbooks had given me this idea, I found my impression confirmed by Hortensius in the preface to his Latin translation of Blaeu's *Institutio astronomica* in 1668. He states that, if the Copernican theory had been graphically presented sooner, as it had been recently by Blaeu, it would not have been condemned as absurd before it had been seen how it saved the phenomena, and that more probably than any other system. But because Copernicus himself was "too obscure in his writings to be understood by everyone," and because the use of the Copernican sphere and hypothesis was not explained in a popular way by any astronomer,[11] many condemned it as false without understanding it. Although there had been much controversy whether the earth moved or was at rest, this had enlightened the average reader very little.[12]

One would have thought that it might have occurred to the minds of sixteenth century teachers that the very persons who would be most likely to grasp readily the rudiments of the Copernican theory, if only it were put before them simply and

[11] ". . . neque ab ullo astronomo populariter explicatus est."

[12] See *Hortensius ad lectorem* and Blaeu's own *Praefatio* in Guilielmi Blaeu *Institutio astronomica de usu globorum et sphaerarum caelestium ac terrestrium duabus partibus adornata: una secundum hypothesin Ptolomaei per terram quiescentem, altera iuxta mentem N. Copernici per terram mobilem. Latine reddita a M. Hortensio in ill. Amsterdamensium schola matheseos professore,* Amstelaedami apud Ioannem Blaeu, 1668, 8vo. Copy used: BM 8561.aa.14.

According to Zedler the first Dutch edition was in 1640, two years after Blaeu's death.

clearly, would be young students whose minds were open to new ideas and not prejudiced or preoccupied by some other astronomical theory. They had not, like their teachers, been long accustomed to the Ptolemaic theory. But so persistent were these early modern educators in seeing a mote in the student's eye, when it was really a beam in their own, that even Blaeu in the seventeenth century, who is said by his Latin translator, Hortensius, to have been the first to construct a Copernican sphere, and who himself accepted the Copernican hypotheses, thought it advisable to offer beginners a Ptolemaic sphere first, so that they would have less difficulty with the other.[13]

I shall now illustrate in some detail the attitude—favorable, hostile or negligent—towards the Copernican theory in the half century or so following its enunciation. This will be done by a survey, primarily chronological, of a number of books and authors. Many will be astronomical textbooks of the type already mentioned, others will be *Ephemerides* or more advanced works in astronomy, while others will border on the domain of astrology. The last will not be found least favorable to the new theory. Some attention will also be given to commentaries on Aristotle. An exhaustive survey is not attempted either of such literature or of allusions to Copernicus. Many works of which I have the titles have become rare and inaccessible. But I believe that those which I have examined and which are here presented give a fair representation and sufficient cross section for illustrative purposes of opinion then in the circles that should have been the most informed and intelligent. Also that the picture thus offered of the spread or failure to spread of the Copernican theory is fuller and more accurate than any hitherto attempted.

Conrad Gesner, in his *Universal Library* of 1545, although Rheticus had once been his schoolmate at Zurich under Myconius, gave only a brief notice either of the *Narratio prima* or

[13] The same dubious pedagogical principle still prevails today in some planetariums.

De revolutionibus. Under the name of Rheticus he remarks that Copernicus asserts that the earth is moved about the sky, "as will be stated more fully in its place."[14] But he appears to have forgotten this promise when he came to treat of Copernicus, since he merely repeats that in *De revolutionibus* it is asserted that the earth is moved about an immobile sky.[15] Presumably Gesner meant that the earth moved or is moved about *in* the sky, but he does not seem to say so. In any case he would appear to offer the reader a sufficiently startling, if an inaccurate or inadequate, notion of the revolutionary character of Copernicus's work. At the same time that Gesner gave Rheticus only a half dozen lines, and Copernicus less than four, he devoted a page and a half to Vesalius—the half page to quotation from the preface of *De humani corporis fabrica*. He also gave a page and a half to Osiander, but without noting the editorial preface to *De revolutionibus*. As for Reinhold, he was not included at all in the 1545 edition of the *Universal Library*.

Dodoens, although more celebrated as a botanist than as an astronomer, wrote a little work on *Cosmography* in four books devoted respectively to the universe, heavens, earth and motion. It was completed and passed by the censor in 1546, and was printed at Antwerp in 1548.[16] Dodoens adheres to the view that the sun moves about the earth, which is at rest at the center of the universe with the same center and axis as the eighth sphere. He specifically denies that the earth can revolve about this axis, which would be contrary to the movement in a straight line otherwise characteristic of the four elements. Moreover, parts of the universe nearest to the axis move either not at all or very slowly, while, if any motion is to be ascribed to the earth, it would have to be daily in twenty-four hours.[17] Dodoens

[14] Gesner (1545), fol. 269v, ". . . narratio prima de libris revolutionum Nicolai Copernici Torannaei quibus terram circa coelum moveri asseritur."

[15] *Ibid.*, fol. 518v, ". . . nuper scripsit Revolutionum libros quibus terram circa coelum immobile moveri asseritur."

[16] *Cosmographica in astronomiam et geographiam isagoge per Rembertum Dodonaeum Malinatem medicum et mathematicum*, Antwerpiae ex officina Ioannis Loēi, anno MDXLVIII. Pages unnumbered. Copy used: BM 531.e.1.

[17] *Ibid.*, III, 5. In the revision of 1584 this last argument was omitted and the wording of the other was altered.

does not mention Copernicus in this connection, although he elsewhere cites him several times. None of these citations, with perhaps a single exception,[18] have reference to the Copernican theory. One states that Copernicus, like Proclus and others, employs the terms, Arctic and Antarctic, instead of Boreus and Austrinus. Another affirms that in the fourth book of *De revolutionibus* he has calculated the relative magnitudes and distances from earth of the sun and moon most neatly by geometry from observation of their parallaxes and apparent diameters. In a third place he is cited as to longitude and latitude; in a fourth, as to morning and evening stars; in a fifth, with Peurbach as to whether the eighth sphere moves sometimes faster and again more slowly.[19] Incidentally it may be noted that even in this introductory work Dodoens affirms that the planets by their movements reveal the future.[20] Like most of our sixteenth century authors, he says that earth and water form one globe.[21]

The *New Questions on the Sphere* of Ariel Bicardus are a set of simple questions and answers, intended as a textbook for adolescents. This brief and elementary booklet was printed at Venice in 1549 and at Wittenberg in 1550, but seems to have found most use at Paris, where Houzeau and Lancaster list five editions between 1551 and 1562, while I have used a still later one of 1569.[22] The book has some new features from the standpoint of presentation and pedagogy, but its astronomy remains Ptolemaic and Sacroboscan. I did not notice any mention of Copernicus. The preface of January 1, 1549, written before the *Prutenic Tables* had appeared, expresses the hope that Reinhold

[18] This is the rather cryptic utterance with which IV, 11 opens: "Ad diurnam etiam revolutionem ut Copernicus inquit facere videntur ortus et occasus non illi de quibus modo diximus sed quibus matutina et vespertina sydera fiunt."

[19] *Ibid.*, II, 14; III, 7, 9; IV, 11, 13. Copernicus of course actually transferred the motion of the eighth sphere to the earth.

[20] *Ibid.*, I, 8.

[21] *Ibid.*, III, 3.

[22] *Quaestiones novae in libellum de sphaera Ioannis de Sacro Bosco in gratiam studiosae iuventutis collectae ab Ariele Bicardo ac nunc denuo recognitae figuris mathematicis et tabulis illustratae quae in reliquis editionibus antehac desiderabantur*, Parisiis, Apud Gulielmum Cavellat in pingui gallina ex adverso collegii Cameracensis, 1569, 70 fols., small octavo. Copy used: BM 8561.aaa.23.(2.).

will write as good a commentary on the *Sphere* as he has written on Peurbach's *New Theories of the Planets.* This remains unaltered in the edition of 1569.

Despite the appearance of the *Prutenic Tables* in 1551, Nicolaus Pruckner, editor of Firmicus Maternus and defender of astrology to Edward VI, issued astronomical tables at Basel in 1553 which were still based upon the *Alfonsine Tables.*[23]

Caspar Peucer of Wittenberg dedicated to duke Augustus of Saxony on June 1, 1551, *Elements of Doctrine concerning the Celestial Circles and First Motion.*[24] That Peucer had a high opinion of Copernicus as an astronomer is indicated by his closing a list of great *astrologi* at the beginning of the book with his name and giving somewhat more details about him than others. After the Arabic astronomers in this list come Alfonso the Wise, Witelo, Guido Bonatti, William of St. Cloud.[25] Then, after a gap of a century, follow John of Gmunden, Peurbach, Bianchini, Regiomontanus, Bernard Walther, Dominicus Maria of Bologna "whom Copernicus heard and helped," Werner, Stoeffler, and last Copernicus himself. Schöner, Rheticus and Reinhold are not mentioned: Copernicus stands out alone. Towards the end of the book Peucer also gives the Copernican revision of the Ptolemaic estimates of the relative size of sun, earth and moon.[26] Yet Peucer puts the earth in the center of the universe. He says that Aristarchus of Samos made it revolve between Mars and Venus about an immobile sun, and that Copernicus, "greatest of all writers on astronomy since Ptolemy," has adopted similar hypotheses to his demonstrations. But Peucer omits them in order not to offend or disturb beginning students (*tyrones*) by their novelty.[27] Later on he asserts that both the Bible and physical reasons prove that the earth does not move but rests fixed and immovable at the center of the universe and

[23] Tycho Brahe, *Opera*, ed. Dreyer, VIII (1925), 461.

[24] *Elementa doctrinae de circulis coelestibus et primo motu, autore Casparo Peucero,* Wittebergae ex officina Cratoniana, 1551, 8vo, pages unnumbered, signatures A to T. Copy used: BM 529.a.2.

[25] Disguised as "Guilhelmus de S. Godialdo."

[26] *Ibid.*, fols. (S 8) verso-T recto.

[27] *Ibid.*, fol. G verso.

repeats biblical passages and physical arguments to prove this.[28] He also holds that planets and stars are affixed to their orbs and moved by these.[29] Houzeau and Lancaster were therefore in error in saying of Peucer's work, "C'est le premier livre d'une certaine valeur écrit dans les idées de Copernic."[30] Their further statement that the works of Peucer were put on the *Index expurgatorius,* although literally true, is equally misleading, if they mean to suggest that this was because of his supporting the Copernican theory, which he did not do. Like Dodoens and most of his contemporaries, however, he abandoned the attempt to make the sphere of the element water enclose that of the earth, affirming instead that earth and water were spherical bodies which by their mutual embrace constituted one globe and one convex surface.[31] So much of a dent the voyages of discovery had made in the Aristotelian doctrine of heavy and light, of natural place, and of spheres of the elements. Peucer's textbook was reprinted at Wittenberg a number of times before the close of the century.

The *Nomenclator of Illustrious Writers* of Robert Constantinus, published at Paris in 1555, is a brief bibliography, arranged topically, which usually merely lists authors and titles. In six pages devoted to astronomical works it is said of Copernicus that he wrote *Books on Revolutions* in which he showed that the sun stands still, while the earth is one of the planets and is moved by a triple motion—a notice as favorable as it is succinct.[32] It will be noticed incidentally, however, that the Aristotelian doctrine of moved and mover and of movers of the spheres died hard, since even a pro-Copernican spoke of the earth as being moved rather than moving.

[28] *Ibid.,* fol. G 3· verso.

[29] *Ibid.,* fol. (C 8) verso.

[30] J. C. Houzeau et A. Lancaster, *Bibliographie générale de l'astronomie,* Brussels, I(1887), 584. I have not seen the "editio recognita et aucta" of 1558, but do not imagine that the presentation was made more Copernican in it. At least the passage in Houzeau et Lancaster makes no distinction in that respect between the different editions of Peucer's work.

[31] Peucer, *op. cit.,* fol. F 3 verso.

[32] Robertus Constantinus, *Nomenclator insignium scriptorum quorum libri extant vel manuscripti vel impressi ex bibliothecis Galliae et Angliae,* Paris, 1555, 8vo, 189 pp., p. 92. Copy used: BM 619.a.1.

Gemma Frisius, at his death in 1555, left incomplete a treatise on the astrolabe which was finished by his son, Cornelius Gemma, and published in 1556.[33] Noting that Ptolemy had estimated the progress of the fixed stars at a rate of one degree in a hundred years, while they had moved since at an average of a degree every sixty-seven years, Gemma held, like Copernicus, that the observations of the ancients upon which the estimate by Ptolemy was based were not to be rejected "but embraced as fundamentals of the art." An anomaly or inequality in the movement of the fixed stars must therefore be admitted, and no one had drawn up equations for it better than Copernicus, whose canons Gemma therefore followed in preference to any previous ones.[34] It is remarkable that Gemma should have hit upon one of the few points in which Copernicus was mistaken as a reason for accepting his calculations. Mixed motives were involved in accepting or rejecting the Copernican hypotheses, and those who accepted them were not necessarily or always right.

In a letter penned during the last year of his life Gemma Frisius urged Stadius to publish his *New Ephemerides* for the years 1554-1570, and not to be deterred by fear of being accused of believing that the earth is moved, while the sun stands still in the center of the universe, or by fear of criticism for having abandoned the *Alfonsine Tables* and Peurbach and having followed the *Prutenic Tables* and his own observations. The *Alfonsine Tables* had been a new departure in their day. Now they should be replaced by the Prutenic, "most exquisite of all that the world has yet seen." This was the aim of Copernicus,

[33] Gemma Frisius, *De astrolabio catholico*, Antwerp, 1556. Copy used: BM 531.f.7.

[34] *Ibid.*, cap. 21. fol. 34r-v; van Ortroy, *Bio-bibliographie de Gemma Frisius*, 1920, pp. 23-24, n.3. In the 1583 revision and abbreviation by Martin Euerarthus the passage has been altered. The estimates of 100 and 67 years are repeated, but the sentence defending the accuracy of the ancient observations is omitted, and the chapter closes with the brief statement: "Hence it is evident that there is some inequality of motion in the fixed stars which so far no one has better equated than Copernicus." Gemma's acceptance of the Copernican canons and further personal remarks are omitted. Probably these changes were merely the result of an attempt to abbreviate, since the Ptolemaic estimate and Copernican canons are not questioned. *De astrolabio catholico*, Antwerp, 1583, p. 24. Copy used: BM 1395.f.14.

and towards it Gemma himself had made many observations and infallible demonstrations. Now Reinhold had with tireless industry based his most elaborate *Prutenic Tables* on *De revolutionibus*. The movement of the earth and immobility of the sun were not stated as absolutely necessary assumptions, but as not utterly absurd, conformable to nature, and accounting for the positions of the stars—past, present, and future. Although the hypotheses of Ptolemy at first sight were more plausible, yet they involved not a few absurdities too, and did not offer so evident explanations of the phenomena as Copernicus did. However, if anyone wished, he could refer those movements of the earth which Copernicus assumed, except the two first, to the heavens and yet employ the same canons of calculation. But Copernicus had not wished to invert the whole order of his hypotheses, resting content with those which would suffice to true finding of the phenomena.

This was a vigorous defense of the Copernican theory, but there seem to have been few like it in the years immediately following Gemma's death. Stadius published Gemma's letter with his *Ephemerides* the next year.[35] but did not show himself so outspoken in favor of the movement of the earth and immobility of the sun.

In his preface to Philip II of August 15, 1556, Stadius noted, like Ptolemy, that the movements of Saturn, Jupiter and Mars so agreed with the access and recess of the sun that they were always at the top of their epicycles when in conjunction with it and at the bottom of them when it was farthest off. Venus and Mercury darted to and fro about the sun as if executing its commands and were always in the apogee or perigee of its epicycle, Venus being never farther distant than 47 degrees, 35 minutes, and Mercury no more than 27 degrees, 37 minutes. He added that the theory of motions required correction, that Copernicus had happily begun the task and Reinhold completed it. He fol-

[35] *Ephemerides novae et exactae Ioannis Stadii Leonnouthesii ab anno 1554 ad annum 1570*, Coloniae Agrippinae apud haeredes Arnoldi Birckmanni, anno MDLVI, fols. a recto-a ii verso. Copy used: BM 532.c.9.

lowed in their footsteps, since observations had convinced him that existing *Ephemerides* did not agree with the sky. He had based his new ones for the sixteen years from 1554 to 1570 upon the *Prutenic Tables* and had tested them for two years[36] before publication, not trusting merely in his own observations in this checking up, but also using those of Gemma Frisius and Philip Montegius for the fixed stars.

In the ensuing text which is introductory to the *Ephemerides* themselves Stadius again speaks of the movement of the sun and of the planets retrograding. But he cites Copernicus and Reinhold for the anomaly in the precession of the equinoxes and refers the reader for further information to the *Narratio prima* of Rheticus.[37] He describes his canon of the equation of natural days as collected from the doctrine of Copernicus and recent observation, and that for the latitude of the moon as from the *Prutenic Tables,*[38] which are cited again subsequently.[39] He also informs us that Copernicus followed Ptolemy in reckoning the latitude of the moon from the northern limit, while the *Alfonsine Tables* reckon it from the head of the dragon.

These *Ephemerides* of Stadius were as much astrological as Copernican. In the preface to Philip II the control by the planets of the weather and of fatal downfalls of kingdoms was asserted. It was added that the captivity of Francis I had been predicted to the day and hour by a Franciscan of Mechlin, who had likewise forecast the death of the prince of Orange at the early age of twenty-six, and that Paris Caeresarius had predicted to Farnese his accession to the papacy as Paul III. In the subsequent text the horoscope of the aforesaid prince of Orange, Renatus Challonius, is discussed at length.

Robert Recorde's *Castle of Knowledge,* published in 1556, is said by a recent writer to be "a far more accurate and compre-

[36] Those for 1554-1557 appear to have been published separately, or perhaps annually, since in a collection of *Ephemerides* (BM 532.c.6) they manifest slight typographical variations from the edition of 1556, although otherwise apparently identical with those dedicated to Philip II.

[37] *Ibid.,* fols. c 2 r-v, (f 4) r.

[38] *Ibid.,* fol. d verso.

[39] *Ibid.,* fols. (g 4) v, h recto.

hensive introduction to astronomy" than either Proclus or Sacrobosco on the sphere.[40] It certainly is wordier. Yet he represented the earth as at rest and refused to discuss the Copernican theory at present as "too difficult for this first Introduction,"[41] although he hinted that there might be some truth in it.[42]

A long and elaborate commentary on the *New Theories of the Planets* of Peurbach was published in 1556 by Erasmus Oswald Schreckenfuchs[43] (1511-1579) who already in 1551 had edited the *Almagest* of Ptolemy with a preface and annotations.[44] Schreckenfuchs, an Austrian who had studied at Ingolstadt, Leipzig and Basel, taught school a while at Memmingen and then mathematics and Hebrew—into which language he translated the New Testament—at Tübingen and Freiburg-im-Breisgau, towns where the dedications to his works of 1551 and 1556 are respectively signed. In the preface to his edition of the *Almagest* he complained that there had recently arisen a new kind of theologian who deterred the young from astronomy, called astronomers astrologers, and confused both with pyromancy, hydromancy, nigromancy and geomancy. In the commentary on Peurbach Ptolemy is the other author most cited, and the Ptolemaic system is followed with especial attention to the construction and use of astronomical tables. The recent *Prutenic Tables* nevertheless seem not to be mentioned, and the first reference to Copernicus appears to come only at page 388 of the folio volume. At page 61, however, his observations of the three total

[40] Francis R. Johnson, *Astronomical Thought in Renaissance England,* 1937, pp. 10-11, n.7.

[41] *Ibid.*, pp. 126-27.

[42] I cannot agree with Johnson, *op. cit.*, p. 128, that "Recorde clearly shows in this passage that he believes the Aristotelian and Ptolemaic arguments against the earth's rotation to be entirely fallacious."

[43] *Eras. Oswaldi Schreckenfuchsii Commentaria in Novas Theoricas Planetarum Georgii Purbachii quas etiam brevibus tabulis pro eliciendis tum mediis tum veris motibus omnium planetarum item tabulis coniunctionum et oppositionum ac eclipsium luminarium ad summum illustravit . . . His quoque accesserunt varia exempla et demonstrationes quibus astronomiae studiosus suo marte omnis generis tabulas secundorum mobilium facile conficiet . . . Praeterea elegantes singulorum planetarum sphaerae.* Basileae per Henrichum Petri, mense Septembri anno MDLVI, folio, 424 pp. Copy used: BM 533.i.3.(5.).

[44] Copy used: BM 531.n.21, same printer. Schreckenfuchs had also edited Abraham ben Chija, *Sphaera mundi,* Basel, 1546, but I have not seen this.

lunar eclipses of October 6, 1511, September 5, 1522, and August 25, 1523, are presented without acknowledgement, so that further investigation might detect a similar surreptitious use of the *Prutenic Tables*. In the passage where Copernicus is named, Schreckenfuchs, after alluding to the theory of Thebit as to the motion of the eighth sphere and the Alfonsine addition of a ninth, also mentions, "lest I omit anything," the recent explanations of Werner and Copernicus. Either, he admits, seems closer to the truth than the opinions of their predecessors.[45] Werner, to account for the diversity of the equinoxes and of the sun's greatest declination, added yet another eleventh sphere to the ninth and tenth which medieval astronomy had superimposed upon the eight spheres of Ptolemy. Copernicus, "that miracle of nature, . . . just as he turned everything else in astronomy upside down, so he did in the case of the eighth sphere, which he makes fixed and immobile as it were and beneath it imagines that the equinoxes, whether mean or true, are moved from the first star of Aries contrary to the order of the signs." But since this hypothesis requires more space for its discussion than is now available, Schreckenfuchs says no more of it.

Schreckenfuchs shows his interest in astrology by giving Peurbach's horoscope in his preface. Towards the close of his work he affirms that it would be easy to improve astronomy, if financial support were forthcoming. For scientific observations childish instruments will not suffice. Great astronomical machines are required which will remain fixed in the same spots for ages and be tested by many astronomers. Every university should have such an observatory. But while Tübingen has a few traces of such instruments, Nürnberg is the only city whose government has done much for men like Regiomontanus, Schöner and Werner.

In 1556 was printed at London an *Ephemeris* for 1557 according to the canons of Copernicus and Reinhold by John Feild with a brief introductory letter by John Dee. Dee says that the

[45] *Commentaria in novas theoricas,* 1556, pp. 388-89.

old astronomical tables and canons no longer agree with the phenomena. He hopes that others know of the writings or at least the names of Copernicus, Rheticus and Reinhold. This is not the place to dissert concerning the Copernican hypotheses, but his labors in restoring astronomy have been Herculean and divine. Dee censures those who continue to issue *Ephemerides* based on antiquated canons which are ten, twelve or thirteen degrees wrong as to the position of Mercury. Feild repeats the same criticism, remarking that he realizes more and more each day in how many and varied ways those err who in astrological judgments follow the *Ephemerides* of Stoeffler, Pitatus, Simi, Mizauld and others who use "the hypothesis of Alfonso," by which he presumably means the *Alfonsine Tables*. Feild has therefore prepared this new *Ephemeris* based upon Copernicus and Reinhold, not because of superior ability on his part, but because no one else has done so. In closing, however, he states that the *Ephemerides* of Ioannes Stadius have appeared while his own *Ephemeris* was in press. But he regards them as erroneous, although he cherishes Stadius for his talent and great learning. He wishes that Gemma Frisius had lived to correct them before they were published. Thus two persons who alike professedly followed in the footsteps of Copernicus and Reinhold might disagree with one another as well as with earlier tables and calculations. The interest of Feild in astrology is further shown by a Table for drawing up a figure of the constellations which accompanies his *Ephemeris*.[46]

In a brief treatise on this same theme of erecting figures of

[46] *Ephemeris anni 1557 currentis iuxta Copernici et Reinhaldi*(sic) *Canones fideliter per Ioannem Feild Anglum supputata ac examinata ad meridianum Londinensem qui occidentalior esse iudicatur a Reinhaldo*(sic) *quam sit Regii Montis per horam i scr. 50. Adiecta est etiam brevis quaedam Epistola Ioannis Dee qua vulgares istos Ephemeridum fictores merito reprehendit. Tabella denique pro coelesti themate erigendo iuxta modum vulgariter rationalem dictum per eundem Ioannem Feild confecta Londinensis poli altitudini inserviens exactissime.* Excussum Londini in aedibus Thomae Marshe, 1556. Copy used: BM 718.g. 61.

Actually the letter of Dee comes first, then the *Tabella,* and last the *Ephemeris*.

Dee's letter has already been summarized in English by Francis R. Johnson, *Astronomical Thought in Renaissance England*, 1937, pp. 134-35.

the sky, of which the dedication is dated July 18, 1556,[47] Johann Garcaeus referred to Copernicus as "the outstanding artificer of our age." He was not, however, speaking of the heliocentric theory but of the Copernican perpetual canons of mean motions and equations which might be accommodated backward and forward to any observations. Fundamental to this doctrine were the *Prutenic Tables,* "a divine work, most worthy of perpetual memory."[48] Later Garcaeus noted that, while the Alfonsine tables computed movements from the equinoctial point, which observations had shown to undergo alteration, Copernicus instead imagined a mean equinox and reckoned all movements from the first fixed star in Aries and a certain beginning in the eighth sphere.[49]

Nicolaus Biesius, in a work on the universe or natural philosophy of 1556, without committing himself to support of the Copernican theory, said that Copernicus gave an exact calculation and explanation of the celestial motions. Biesius thought that it made little difference whether we say that the planets are carried in epicycles or in eccentrics or partly in one way and partly in the other, since their positions and virtues remain the same. This would not be the case, however, if we should adopt a system of concentric spheres.[50]

Jean Pena, royal professor of mathematics at Paris, certainly could not be accused of being afraid of new and revolutionary theories, as his denial of the substantiality of the celestial spheres,[51] statement that air filled the heavens, and explanation of comets show. Writing in 1557 a preface to his edition of Euclid's *Optics,* he spoke of Copernicus as "most famous" and "a man certainly of marvelous sagacity."[52] Pena did not, however,

[47] I have used the edition of 1573: Johann Garcaeus, *Tractatus brevis . . . de erigendis figuris coeli . . .*, Witebergae, 1573. Copy used: BM 718.d. 27.(2.).

[48] *Ibid.*, fol. (E 8) r-v.

[49] *Ibid.*, fol. F 2 recto.

[50] *De universitate libri tres quibus universa de natura philosophia continetur,* Antwerp, 1556, p. 73. At p. 69, note e, with reference to the movement of trepidation he had said, "Haec optime explicantur a Nicolao Copernico in libris revolutionum."

[51] Averroes, however, had long since held that the heavenly bodies and spheres were pure form.

[52] *Euclidis Optica et Catoptrica,* Paris, 1557: Ioannis Penae regii mathematici de usu optices praefatio ad

accept the triple motion which Copernicus assigned to the earth, although he interpreted the varying distance of the fixed stars at different periods as proof that the earth altered its position slowly with the progress of time.[53] He upheld Ptolemy's estimates of the greatest and least distances of the moon from the earth against the criticism of Copernicus.[54] On the other hand, he maintained that according to optics the sun, Venus and Mercury all seemed to be in the same orb. Also, so far as optics was concerned, that the earth might either be in the center of the universe, with the epicycles of Venus and Mercury having the sun for their center as all three revolved about the earth,[55] or the earth might be making an annual revolution about the sun, at rest in the center of the universe, "and the same epicycles of Mercury and Venus have the sun as their center."[56]

Jean Pierre de Mesmes published at Paris in 1557 *Astronomical Institutions* in French which were much the usual treatise on the *Sphere* in four books and with the closing chapter on the eclipse at the time of the crucifixion, like Sacrobosco.[57] The author proposed to write a further work on the theory of the planets and put off to it the discussion even of the eighth sphere in its entirety.[58] Mesmes cites many authors, classical, Arabic, medieval Latin and more recent from the *Perspective* of Witelo to the *Physics* of Melanchthon. He believes in recent progress in astronomy. In one passage he says that Pico della Mirandola, before criticizing Firmicus for misplacing Mercury, should have

---

illustrissimum principem Carolum Lotharingum cardinalem, fols. (aa iv) recto, bb recto.

[53] *Ibid.*, fol. (aa iv) r-v.

[54] *Ibid.*, fol. bb recto.

[55] In this it will be seen that Pena anteceded Tycho Brahe and his emulators in the main point of their theories.

[56] *Ibid.*, fols. aa iii verso-(aa iv) recto.

[57] Jean Pierre de Mesmes, *Les institutions astronomiques contenans les principaux fondements et premières causes des cours et mouvemens celestes. Avec la totale revolution du ciel et de ses parties, les causes et raisons des eclipses tant de la lune que du soleil. A Monsieur de Roissy conseiller du roy, maistre des requestes, ordinaire de son hostel.* A Paris de l'imprimerie de Michel de Vascosan. demeurant en la rue S. Iaques, à l'enseigne de la fontaine. MDLVII. Avec privilege du Roy. Copy used: BN V.1708.

The dedication to the author's father, Iean Iaques de Mesmes, seigneur de Roissy is dated at its close Thursday December 10, 1556.

[58] *Ibid.*, p. 96.

taken into account that "the doctrine of the natural courses of the planets was still in its infancy" in the days of Firmicus and Pliny.[59] In another passage, after listing Thales, Sulpitius Gallus, Hipparchus and Ptolemy as ancient expounders of eclipses, and devoting a whole paragraph to Alfonso the Wise, he says that finally during the last 150 years the great Governor of the celestial bodies and of human hearts, has made appear on earth the rare and admirable spirits of Bianchini, Peurbach, Regiomontanus, Copernicus, Schöner, Apian, Stoeffler, Reinhold, Gaurico, Cardan, Cyprian Leowitz, "our Oronce," and still others.[60] In a third passage he notes how moderns like Reinhold, Oronce Finé, and Peucer have enlarged Ptolemy's table of climes.[61] But despite the criticism of the *Alfonsine Tables* by Regiomontanus, Rheticus and Reinhold, Mesmes advises the reader to continue to follow them until God sends another Alfonso to encourage astronomers to solve the difficulties of the third movement of the eighth sphere.[62]

As for the Copernican theory, already in his preface Mesmes says that he will not avail himself of the reasons and arguments of Copernicus to do away with the ninth sphere and to trouble or discourage tender and rude minds by new theories. He repeats this attitude in the chapter on the immobility of the earth, in which he cites Archimedes as to the opinion of Aristarchus of Samos and adds that Copernicus, "another second Ptolemy," uses this absurd opinion to support his own demonstrations and celestial revolutions, which would be totally null without such a false hypothesis.[63]

A recent sales catalogue, in which de Mesmes' work is listed, makes the questionable statement that he "is the first French astronomer who dealt with Copernicus's new theory of the movement of the earth, and then adds, "It was still, no doubt, dangerous to discuss this revolutionary theory." Mesmes displays no

[59] *Ibid.*, p. 43.
[60] *Ibid.*, p. 285 (IV, 4).
[61] *Ibid.*, p. 141 (II, 19).
[62] *Ibid.*, p. 97.
[63] *Ibid.*, p. 56 (I, 19). In yet another place, p. 267 (IV, 3), Mesmes gives the differing estimates of Ptolemy and Copernicus for the length of the earth's shadow.

fear of any such danger from ecclesiastical quarters. On the contrary, after listing biblical passages that represent the sun as moving and the earth as immobile, he expresses the fear that "perhaps some will ridicule astronomy for thus availing itself of divine authority."[64] Moreover, in his discussion of the darkening of the sun at the time of the crucifixion, Mesmes, while admitting the possibility of divine miracles *ad libitum,* as in the case of Joshua stopping the sun, adopts the somewhat unusual position that the eclipse at the crucifixion was local in order to give the Jews a sign and not universal.[65]

Already in his preface Mesmes cited mystical authors like Philo Judaeus and the *Pimander* of Hermes, and affirmed his belief in astrology as well as astronomy.[66] He gives the properties of the planets in his chapters on them. Eclipses not merely enable us to reckon the distance and proportions of the heavenly bodies but are messengers of universal causes and of sad and tragic events to monarchies, empires and kingdoms.

Mesmes gives the same overestimate of the distance of the clouds which we shall hear from Meurer, saying that many maintain that they vary in distance from 772,000 paces or 386 French leagues to 288,000 paces or 144 leagues. He has noted, however, that Witelo proved by his optical lines that the clouds were 52,000 paces or 26 French leagues from the earth's surface, and he adds that Pliny, citing Posidonius, gave the distance as only 5,000 paces.[67]

Also at Paris were published *Ephemerides* for 1557 by Iofrancus Offusius, a German who issued this work there lest he seem entirely ungrateful in leaving France which had nourished him, a wanderer.[68] His *Ephemerides* purported at least to differ from

[64] *Ibid.*, p. 58: "Peult estre qu'aucuns se moqueront de l'astronomie pour ce qu'il s'ayde des divines auctoritez; toutefois nous trouvons fort honeste d'accorder la Philosophie celeste avec les sentences divines et s'ayder d'icelles pour eclaircir et confirmer le iugement des hommes."

[65] *Ibid.*, pp. 310-13 (IV, 8).

[66] *Ibid.*, preface to book IV.

[67] *Ibid.*, p. 2.

[68] *Ephemerides anni salutis humanae 1557 ex recenti theoria eiusque tabulis supputatae quae omnia post plurium observationem edidit Iofrancus Offusius Germanus Philomates animadvertens quasque alias Ephemerides errore scatentes adnexa diaria tabella aeris mutationi praevidendae omnino necessaria. Subsequitur et tabula cardinalis cuique*

the common reckoning and from the most recent tables and to be based on many observations of the heavens extending over some years. Offusius contends that the *Alfonsine Tables* and *Ephemerides* based upon them, together with the superstitious inventions of the Indians, Arabs, Egyptians and Persians, have made solid astrological prediction practically impossible. After fourteen years or more of vain labors he almost despaired of the art with Pico della Mirandola. Then, warned by the counsels of Regiomontanus, he abandoned the Alfonsine reckoning, made his own observations, and—so he flatters himself—came to conclusions quite contrary to the ravings of deluded astrologers. No eclipse of sun or moon will occur in the year 1557 but there will be a meeting of the sun and Mercury. The opaque body of the smaller planet will be visible interposed between us and the sun. It will look like a sunspot and should be observed through two flat pieces of glass of different colors. Offusius does not give the hour for this phenomenon and will be content if he has the day right, since he must confess that he has not completely mastered the true movement of Mercury, although he has no doubt that his estimate is far more accurate than others. He has indicated a transit of Mercury for April 4 and September 19, 1557, by the Julian calendar, or about April 14 and September 29 by the present Gregorian calendar. Since we are told that transits of Mercury can take place only near the dates May 7 and November 9, his estimate seems far from correct. The date of the first accurately observed transit of Mercury is said to have been at noon, November 7, 1677,[69] so that Offusius perhaps deserves some credit for at least trying to predict one. He does not mention the *Prutenic Tables,* raising the problem whether he was ignorant of their existence, or whether he utilized them without admitting it. His own work, which was for but one year, does

---

recte philosophanti de divina astrorum facultate omnino contemplanda cum praeceptis. Parisiis ex officina Ioannis Royerii typographi regii, Jan. 30, 1557 Copy used: BM 531.g.8.(1.).

[69] *Encyclopedia Britannica,* 14th edition, article, "Mercury." Two transits have not been observed in a single year. My impression is that it was unusual to predict transits of Mercury in *Ephemerides* and annual predictions, although solar and lunar eclipses were quite commonly given. But the matter might well be investigated farther.

not seem to have been generally known, although Pontus de Tyard refers to it, while Tycho Brahe cited another work by Offusius. The *Ephemerides* of Stadius, which were for Antwerp while Offusius's were for Fontainbleau, also indicate that there would be no eclipse in 1557 "for our horizon," but indicated only conjunctions of the sun and Mercury, not transits, and these on the different dates, April 1 and September 8. The positions given by Offusius for the sun around these dates make a fairly close approach to those of Stadius, but for Mercury vary on the average about ten minutes of a degree from those of Stadius.

Pontus de Tyard in his work in French on the universe, published at Lyons in 1557,[70] noted that some had thought that the earth moved while the sky stood still, others that both heavens and earth moved, but that the opinion most favored by authority and reason was that the sky moved and not the earth.[71] He gave, however, Copernicus's determination of the apogee of the sun and estimates of the relative magnitudes of sun, moon and earth.[72] In recording observations made by Jacques Peletier and himself of Jupiter shining so brightly as to cast a shadow, he stated that the planet according to the *Alfonsine Tables* was about the fourth degree and 23 minutes of Capricorn, or, as the *Prutenic Tables* more truly reckon, in the fifth degree and 53 minutes of Capricorn.[73] The common opinion, stated by Iunctinus in 1577 in his commentary on the *Sphere* (II, 152) was that only the sun, moon and Venus could cast a shadow.

Later on, in considering the element earth, Pontus gave a number of arguments for its moving, which are of the scholastic and Peripatetic variety rather than Copernican. For example, it is more fitting for a corruptible element to move than the incorruptible heavens, and for earth to move in order to receive their influence than for them to move in order to bestow it.

[70] Pontus de Tyard, *L'Univers ou discours des parties et de la nature du monde*, a Lion par Ian de Tournes et Guil. Gazeau, 1557, 156 pp. and index. On the verso of the title-page is a bearded likeness of the author at the age of 31.

[71] *Ibid.*, p. 15.

[72] *Ibid.*, pp. 39, 44-45.

[73] *Ibid.*, p. 35.

Movement is local, while the heavens are infinite. The earth, enveloped by slippery air and water, can move readily; its weight is conducive to movement; in the microcosm the heart which occupies the center of the body moves. But Tyard concludes that these arguments are insufficient to outweigh the inconveniences which the diversified movements of the stars raise, and which are not met by the Copernican comparison of an observer on earth to a man in a boat to whom the shores of the stream seem to move. Pontus adds, however, that the demonstrations of Copernicus are ingenious and his observations exact. But whether his disposition of the heavenly bodies is true or not does not affect our knowledge of the nature of the earth as an element.[74] Which is rather dodging the question.

Pontus more boldly affirms that he sees no reason to prevent one from believing that the stars themselves move and are not carried by their spheres, and that the ethereal matter is liquid and quite permeable.[75] The seven planets are disposed at varying distances, not lodged each in a particular heaven. Since epicycles and other such circles are admittedly imaginary, the planet would have to move itself within its own sphere in any case. For were these circles real, they would conflict.[76]

This work of Tyard takes the form of a dialogue between himself and Le Curieus and Hieromnine, who find him in his study or observatory assembling the parts of a meteoroscope, by which word is presumably meant an astrolabe or planisphere.[77] Of these interlocutors Hieromnine advances the religious objections, and besides those based upon the Bible, is made to represent the views of Hebrew Talmudists and Cabalists. At one point he interrupts to say that one cannot piously deny that the eternal prison of the damned is in the center of the earth. "I do not wish," he says, "to confess myself too superstitiously

[74] *Ibid.*, pp. 96-100.

[75] *Ibid.*, pp. 51-52.

[76] *Ibid.*, p. 53: "Car les corps des astres choqueroient et entrebresoient les cercles l'un de l'autre."

[77] See Barozzi, *Cosmographia*, Venice, 1585, Praefatio, "In Meteoroscopia vero nobis extant," where all the works listed are concerning such astronomical instruments. A fair sample is, "Ioannis Schoneri Planisphaerium sive Meteoroscopium."

credulous and would not rest the truth on a story or two. But Holy Scripture . . . seems to me to state this too definitely to be deemed fabulous."[78] At another point in the discussion he claims that the movements of trepidation and from west to east of the heavens are set forth figuratively in various passages of the Bible, as the rabbis have explained.[79] Le Curieus is true to his name and inclined to raise objections and note inconsistencies, while Pontus plays the rôle of the judicious scientific observer. One wonders if Galileo in his dialogues on the Ptolemaic and Copernican systems was influenced by this earlier slightly sceptical and malicious discourse of Pontus de Tyard, which, however, concludes quite orthodoxly by affirming the creation of the world and its final consumption by fire.[80]

John Dee has been represented as one of the earliest advocates of the Copernican theory and, as we have seen, spoke well of it in his letter of 1556. Yet in his *Propaedeumata Aphoristica* concerning the powers of nature, published in 1558, he speaks of the *primum mobile* as a concave spherical mirror so solid that no ray of the stars can penetrate it, of that swiftest of all celestial motions, the revolution of the heavens westward in twenty-four hours, and of the movement of the sun.[81] Copernicus is mentioned merely as having demonstrated that the sidereal solar year is in the sixteenth century about twenty seconds different than the estimate of Thebit ben Corat.[82] Astrological dicta, a further development of Roger Bacon's multiplication of species, and stress upon the harmony of the universe and sympathy and antipathy in nature are other characteristics of the work. In any case Dee, with his mystical inclination towards every form of the occult, would hardly bring the Copernican party into good repute by his accession to its ranks. And he believed in so many things that were wrong, that we could not give him personally any high credit, even if in this one instance he believed in something that happened to be right.

[78] *L'Univers*, 1557, pp. 69-70.

[79] *Ibid.*, p. 21.

[80] *Ibid.*, pp. 135, 155.

[81] John Dee, *Propaedeumata Aphoristica de praestantioribus quibusdam naturae virtutibus*, London, 1558, Aph. 22, 58, 65-66. Copy used: BM 717.g.-13.(1.).

[82] *Ibid.*, Aph. 67.

Maurolycus, in his work on the *Sphere* published in 1558,[83] said that the ignorance of antiquity must give way, to which the huge islands and immense regions recently discovered were unknown, and that stupidity must yield ground, which had supposed different spheres of earth and sea or different centers thereof. Yet he clung to the notion that the center of the earth was identical with that of the universe, and that the earth did not move. Against its revolving upon its axis he urged that clouds and birds would be left to the west, and that a stone thrown vertically into the air would not drop to the same spot. Yet he had just rebutted the cognate notion that men in the Antipodes would fall off the earth or stand on their heads. He does not seem to have named Copernicus in this connection, although Freige, writing in 1579, states that Maurolycus judged Copernicus deserving of a scourging rather than reprehension.[84] Perhaps Maurolycus said so in another work.

Nor does Alessandro Piccolomini mention Copernicus in his work on the theory of the planets, published in Italian the same year.[85] Indeed, except for vague reference to "the astronomers," his citation seems limited to Ptolemy and his own *Sphere* of 1548.[86] Both these works of Piccolomini were commended highly by Giuntini in 1577,[87] but his *Della grandezza dell' acque e della terra*, published in 1557, was more original and influential.[88] Piccolomini gives us to understand that astronomers are not much concerned whether the circles and motions which they

[83] Maurolycus, *De sphaera sermo*, 7 unnumbered pages preceding a collection of treatises on Spherics by such authors as Theodosius, Menelaus and Autolycus, including his own, and upon kindred topics. Messanae in freto Siculo impressit Petrus Spira mense Augusto MDLVIII. The dedication is to Charles V, "Messanae Iulio mense MDLVI." Copy used: BM 8534.f.15.

[84] Jo. Thomas Freigius, *Quaestiones physicae*, 1579, p. 183: "Sed Copernicum scutica potius aut flagello quam repraehensione dignum iudicavit Maurolycus."

[85] *La prima parte de le theoriche ò vero speculationi dei pianeti*, Vinegia, 1558, appresso Giordano Ziletti all' insegna della stella. Dedicated to Cosimo de' Medici, duke of Florence. Copy used: BM 718.e.8.(2.).

[86] *De la sfera del mondo libri quatro in lingua toscana. De le stelle fisse libro uno*, Venice, 1548, 4to.

[87] F. Iunctini, *Comm. in Sphaeram J. de Sacro Bosco*, 1577, II, 291.

[88] Concerning it see Roberto Almagià, "Il primo tentativo di misura del rapporto quantitativo fra le terre emerse e i mari, *Archivio di storia della scienza*, II (1921), 51-64.

assume to save the appearances are real, which they leave to natural philosophers to determine,[89] being themselves satisfied with a basis for calculation of the positions and movements of the planets and for prediction therefrom.[90] Piccolomini tells of an astronomical observation which he made at Padua years ago with an instrument like a quadrant, with a radius of at least four feet, in the presence of Federigo Delfino, professor of astronomy at Padua who died in 1547, and a skilled maker of metal instruments named Berarodino.[91] This may be compared with Jean de Murs' observation over two centuries before with a kardaga with a radius of fifteen feet.[92]

In 1560 John Stadius, who now styles himself both royal mathematician and mathematician to the duke of Savoy, and whose likeness at the age of thirty-two adorns the title-page, issued a stately folio volume of some two hundred pages under the title, *Tabulae Bergenses*.[93] The work is further described as essential for astronomers, astrologers, physicians, politicians, economists, poets, theologians, historiographers and grammarians. The adjective Bergenses has reference to Robert de Bergis, the prince-bishop of Liège, to whom the work is dedicated. In the dedicatory epistle Stadius professes to follow in the footsteps of Copernicus and Reinhold, but to offer a compendium more readily usable and intelligible than the concise brevity and subtle acumen of *De revolutionibus* or the most scrupulous and exact

[89] *La prima parte de le theoriche* etc., 1558, cap. 10, fols. 22r-23r, "Per modo di digressione si discorre se le immaginationi fatte da gli Astrologi per salvar' le apparentie de i pianeti sono fondate nel vero dela Natura."

[90] *Ibid.*, fol. 22v.

[91] *Ibid.*, cap. 3, fol. 5r.

[92] T III, 294-95.

[93] *Tabulae Bergenses aequabilis et adparentis motus orbium coelestium ad illustrissimum reverendissimumque principem D. Robertum de Bergis Leodii episcopum Bullionii ducem comitem Lossensem etc. per Ioannem Stadium regium et ducis Sabaudiae mathematicum quae decem canonibus ad omnium seculorum memoriam planetarum et siderum vera loca ante Christum et retro cum observationum historiis congruentia suppeditant. Item de fixis stellis commentarius . . .*, Coloniae Agrippinae, Apud haeredes Arnoldi Birckmanni, Anno a virgineo partu 1560. Copy used: BM 533.i.6.(5.).

The pagination is faulty. Some intervening sub-title pages are left unnumbered, while from p. 148 we pass to those numbered 185-245, with no pp. 149-84.

Delambre, *Histoire de l'astronomie du moyen âge*, Paris, 1819, pp. 447-49, has given some account of the work.

but troublesome and laborious calculus of the *Prutenic Tables.* More particularly he praises Copernicus for having demonstrated that the apse of the sun is descending towards the earth, which should revive the torpor and decay of this world's extreme old age but eventually produce the final conflagration at a time exactly in accord with the prophecy of Elias as to the world's duration. These passages are suggestive of the attitude of Stadius throughout the work. His real love is astrological prediction, to which he makes frequent reference in a commentary on the fixed stars which fills the last third of the volume.[94] He has made some observations of his own, rejects the *Alfonsine Tables,* more particularly as regards the eighth and ninth spheres, and welcomes Copernicus's observations and his suggestion of an anomaly in the precession of the equinoxes as a thread leading out of the labyrinth.[95] But Stadius still speaks throughout of the eighth sphere and of the movement of the sun.

Copernicus and his observations and tables (as well as the Prutenic) are mentioned favorably several times in the *Astronomical Problems* of Daniel Santbech of Nimwegen.[96] He is said to have impugned the old theory of the moon by very strong arguments and to have demonstrated another in exquisite agreement with recent observations.[97] But the Copernican theory as to the earth and sun is passed over in silence. Santbech alludes to observations of his own in 1559 at Nimwegen and Cologne and to others of March 10, 1538, at Tübingen and of April 13, 1538, by Cardan,[98] whom he cites oftener than Copernicus and calls *facile princeps* of all the philosophers of his time.[99] Sant-

[94] Its astrological character is revealed by its full title (not to mention those of several chapters): *Item de fixis stellis Commentarius quo perpetua loca illarum demonstrantur et ortus et occasus earundem ad quodlibet clima tum ex iisdem calamitatis sterilitatis valetudinis anniversariae et geniturarum praenotiones minime aberrantes edocentur.*

[95] *Ibid.,* p. 23, at the close of the *Astronomiae Historia.* Also pp. 183, 187-88, in *De fixis stellis,* caps. 1 and 2.

[96] *Problematum astronomicorum et geometricorum sectiones septem . . . autore Daniele Santbech Noviomago,* Basileae, per Henrichum Petri et Petrum Pernam, MDLXI. Copy used: Col 515.01 R26. See De observationibus ton phainomenon, Propositions v, xiii, xiv, xxxi; pp. 11, 46, 52, 95.

[97] *Ibid.,* Prop. xii, p. 44.

[98] *Ibid.,* Prop. x, xiv, xxxi; pp. 33, 50, 95.

[99] *Ibid.,* Prop. xi, p. 38.

bech was not averse to astrology and gives genitures of Filelfo and Walter Corbett to illustrate tables of revolutions.[100]

Neither the Copernican theory nor astrology found a place in the textbook on the *Sphere* which Michael Neander (1529-1581) published at Basel in 1561.[101] From 1551 on he had taught mathematics and Greek at Jena until in 1560 he became professor of medicine.

The interest and activity in the field of astrological prediction of Cornelius Gemma were even more intense and prolonged than those of his father, Gemma Frisius, while his intellectual ability and scientific aptitude were distinctly inferior.[102] In his *Meteorological Ephemerides* for the year 1561 he recounts how he came gradually to abandon the Alfonsine for the Prutenic Tables.[103] In working out his new method of weather prediction, partly on the basis of records kept for thirty years by his father, he at first followed the *Alfonsine Tables* but found that weather prediction based upon them was often incorrect, and that they did not correspond to the present positions of the stars. This last his father had already observed and in recent years Cornelius had seen it with his own eyes and attested it by experience with the radius. He therefore turned to the *Prutenic Tables,* having admired the divine genius of Copernicus, and worked out his cases of correspondence between the weather and the stars all over again. He recognized, however, that the Copernican calculations were often at fault as to the movements of Mars and Mercury.[104] But his finding the Ptolemaic theory of the planets

[100] *Ibid.,* Prop. xi, pp. 42-43.

[101] *Elementa sphaericae doctrinae seu de primo motu in usum studiosae iuventutis methodice et perspicue conscripta a Michaele Neandro ex valle Ioachimica,* Basileae, per Ioannem Oporinum, 1561.

[102] Cornelius thought that his father turned away from astrological weather prediction, at least, as being too uncertain: *Ephemerides meteorologicae anni 1561,* fol. A 2 verso.

[103] *Ephemerides meteorologicae anni MDLXI ad directionem horizontis Brabantici ceu latit. 51 grad. institutae per Cornelium Gemmam Louan. medicum,* Excudebat Ioannes Withagius ad insigne Falconis anno MDLXI, fols. A verso-A 3 recto.

[104] *Ibid.,* fol. A 3 recto, "Nam nec ipsa Copernici ratio suis undique numeris est absoluta cum in motu Martis atque Mercurii frequentior error sit deprehensus." Van Ortroy, *Bio-Bibliographie de Gemma Frisius,* p. 136, n.2, after quoting at length Cornelius's criticism of the *Alfonsine Tables* and praise of Copernicus, omits this rather important qualification.

in error led him also to question the Ptolemaic principles of casting nativities and predicting the weather, and to try to evolve a new art or method of astrological judgment. Thus Cornelius Gemma was induced in the first instance to deviate from the old system because of its failure in astrological application. Then astronomical observation confirmed this and led him further to deviate from the Ptolemaic brand of astrology. But astrological interest was the leitmotif throughout. His interest in the Copernican theory as such was almost nil.

In the dedicatory preface of February 13, 1561, to his manual on the *Sphere* and first rudiments of astronomy, Cornelius Valerius or Wouters,[105] professor of Latin in the trilingual college at Louvain, says that it was composed twenty-four years ago, when he was a youth. The few changes he had made since in this brief booklet of thirty-three small leaves,[106] comprise no allusion to Copernicus or his theory. The volume would therefore hardly deserve to be mentioned here at all, were it not for the fact that nine more editions of it appeared before the close of the century,[107] showing how many persons who could read Latin remained content with this sort of meager and antiquated treatment, and how slight a ripple the publication of *De revolutionibus* had left upon the surface of general education. In his similarly terse and trite text on natural philosophy, of which the dedication is dated five years later on May 27, 1566, Valerius is a little fuller on the question whether the earth moves. He declares that it has been proved by sure arguments that it does not move, "although there were those who thought that the heavens stand still and that the earth is moved, whose quite false opinion it is not necessary to refute."[108] This work, too,

[105] C. Valerius, *De sphaera et primis astronomiae rudimentis* etc., Antverpiae ex officina Christophori Plantini sub circino aureo, anno MDLXI. Copy used: BM 8560.aa.4.(1.).

[106] *Ibid.*, pp. 4-36, followed at pp. 37-43 by Brevia quaedam de geographia praecepta.

[107] See Houzeau et Lancaster. They also list an edition of Antwerp, Plantin, 1558, 8vo. Valerius can hardly be alluding to this edition when he says in the dedication of 1561 that he has been told that the work has been printed somewhere in Germany, but that if so, it has been without his knowledge.

[108] *Physicae seu de naturae philosophia institutio perspicue et breviter explicata a Cornelio Valerio Ultraiecti-

was reprinted at least once, in 1593. It is the briefest résumé of the natural philosophy of Aristotle that I remember to have seen, occupying only a hundred odd small pages—much shorter than the *Margarita philosophica* or *Parvulus philosophiae*—suggesting once again that reliance on compendiums was no medieval monopoly, and that the time devoted to natural philosophy in the curriculum had decreased since the middle ages. Valerius would not attribute too much to the influence of the stars and opposes extreme genethlialogy.

Michael Stanhufius, in his two books of meteorology, printed at Wittenberg in 1562, waxed indignant at the most serious madness and insanity of some who, relying upon he knew not what authority, propounded this paradox, that the sun stands still, while the earth is revolved and moved. Of this opinion was Aristarchus of Samos, who is said by Suidas to have left two sons who were both fools. Judging from this absurd opinion, he had little brains himself. Although among more recent men some have tried to defend the same theory, it is established by the most certain demonstrations that the sun is moved, while the earth is immobile.[109] Later on Stanhufius more mildly remarks that the sun occupies the middle place in the order of the planets. "For we follow now Ptolemy, Pliny, Cicero, and the custom of the schools."[110] Copernicus remains unmentioned. Even in stating the magnitude of the sun, no later estimate is given than that of Ptolemy.[111] Although he was so emphatic in rejecting the Copernican theory or anything like it, Stanhufius in his second book approached the discussion of the rainbow with professed trepidation.[112]

---

no . . ., Antwerpiae ex officina. Christophori Plantini architypographi regii, 1574, p. 17. Copy used: BM 536.d.14. This is presumably not the first edition, since the dedication is dated May 27, 1566.

[109] *De meteoris libri duo quorum prior tradit de aethere et elementis, posterior complectitur omnium fere meteororum prolixam explicationem . . . a M. Michaele Stanhufio Franco,* Vitebergae, MDLXII, fols. (C 6) v-(C 7)r. Copy used: BM 538.a.3.(2.). In the reprint of Wittenberg, 1577, the passage occurs at the same place.

[110] *Ibid.*, fol. E 5 recto.

[111] *Ibid.*, fol. (E 8) verso.

[112] *Ibid.*, fol. (M 7) recto.

Jacques Peletier of Le Mans[113] (1517-1582),[114] whose version of Euclid's *Elements* was sharply criticized by Buteo,[115] and who accompanied the marshal de Brissac to Piedmont as his physician and adviser concerning fortifications, presents an interesting complex of attitudes in matters mathematical, astronomical and astrological. He regarded himself as a tireless and eminent mathematician who had squared the circle and given a double demonstration that two lines could be drawn in the same plane which would not be parallel and yet never meet.[116] He was not merely a firm but an old-fashioned adherent of astrology, maintaining the old method of determining the twelve houses by equal division of the zodiac against the newer method of Regiomontanus by projection of equal segments from the equator. Peletier regarded it as a remarkable indication of the validity and virility of astrology that it had been able to survive disagreement on this fundamental matter, and that astrologers had so often predicted truly despite this serious handicap. He promised to defend astrology against its opponents in another place.[117] Yet in the very treatise in which he discussed this astrological problem of the correct way to draw up the horoscope, he not merely affirmed that there was room for the Copernican theory, since even a false hypothesis in astronomy might lead to the knowledge of truth, but he also said that while in the present treatise he followed Ptolemaic doctrine, elsewhere he would with God's help illustrate the view of Copernicus with beautiful arguments.[118] Conservative and cautious where he was convinced that an innovation in astrological technique was sapping the

[113] Abbé Clément Jugé, *Jacques Peletier du Mans (1517-1582); essai sur sa vie, son oeuvre, son influence*, Paris, 1907, pp. 6, 15, and 449, with a six page chronological list of Peletier's works.

[114] In his *Commentarii tres . . . De constitutione horoscopi*, Basel, 1563, p. 69, Peletier gives a *figura coeli* for his own geniture at 4 A.M. on July 25, 1517. Copy used: BM C.80.e.3.(1.).

[115] *Io. Buteonis Annotationum liber in errores Campani, Zamberti, Orontii, Peletarii, Io. Penae interpretum Euclidis,* printed following his *De quadratura circuli libri duo,* at pp. 207-83, Lugduni apud Gulielmum Rovillium, 1559. Copy used: BM 714.a.29.

[116] Peletarius, *De constitutione horoscopi*, 1563, pp. 69-70.

[117] *Ibid.*, p. 50.

[118] *Ibid.*, p. 52.

truth of that art, he was open-minded and progressive with reference to the new astronomical hypothesis and ready to further it.

In 1564 Sebastian Theodoricus of Winsheim, professor of mathematics at Wittenberg, composed *New Questions on the Sphere, that is, Concerning the Celestial Circles and Primum mobile,*[119] although in the dedicatory epistle he praised the previous and similar work of Peucer as including all that was necessary and having a good method. His own manual of 320 small pages in four parts is arranged in the form of questions and answers, with the former set off in heavy type and with considerable use of the syllogistic form of proof in the answers. For example, having demonstrated for seven pages that the earth is exactly in the center of the universe, Theodoricus adds the following "Proba" that it does not move.[120] Whatever Holy Scripture affirms is true beyond doubt. Holy Scripture affirms that the earth is immobile and fixed. Therefore the earth is at rest at the center of the world and does not move. Not only does Theodoricus give no recognition to the Copernican theory, he will not even accept the ninth sphere which the "Alphonsini" had inserted between the Ptolemaic eighth sphere and the *primum mobile.*[121] He affirms still that the sky is a simple body and so moves circularly, that the sphere is the first and most perfect figure, and that all the stars are moved by the motion of their orbs, to which they are fixed.[122] But even he has abandoned the opinion of the Peripatetics that there is ten times as much water as earth, and holds that water does not enclose the earth spherically but forms one globe with it.[123] He cites Copernicus as well as Ptolemy for the relative magnitudes of earth and sun. He gives Copernicus's figures for the maximum and minimum declination of the sun, and his estimate that this movement of

[119] I have used the edition of 1570: *Novae quaestiones sphaerae hoc est de circulis coelestibus et primo mobili in gratiam studiosae iuventutis scriptae a M. Sebastiano Theodorico Winshemio mathematum professore,* Witebergae, MDLXX, Excudebat Iohannes Crato. Copy used: BM 8530.aaa.43.

[120] *Ibid.,* pp. 116-17.

[121] *Ibid.,* pp. 77-78, "Etsi Alphonsini decem numerant orbes tamen nos contenti sententia Ptolemaei tantum novem recitabimus."

[122] *Ibid.,* pp. 68-76.

[123] *Ibid.,* pp. 106-7.

the ecliptic approaching and receding from the equator is completed in 1717 years.[124] Jejune, attenuated and superannuated as the textbook of Theodoricus may seem to the modern reader, it appears to have been inflicted on the students at Wittenberg for several decades, since further editions appeared in 1567, 1570, 1578 and 1605. Theodoricus contended that elementary spherics such as his own were necessary for all students of the liberal arts and not merely for those who were to go on in astronomy.[125] He included some astrological matter in his manual.

Neither Regiomontanus nor Copernicus escaped criticism in the treatise *On the Art of Navigation* by the Portuguese mathematician, Pedro Nunes.[126] Regiomontanus was said to have transferred a day from B.C. to A.D. in the reckoning of the *Alfonsine Tables,* and his opinion concerning the equinoxes was unacceptable to Nunes. Copernicus was charged with error in propositions concerning spherical and rectilinear triangles.[127] He was so intent, remarks Nunes sarcastically, on revamping the well-nigh forgotten astronomy of Aristarchus of Samos concerning the movement of the earth, and immobility of the sun and eighth sphere, by the method, roots and demonstrations of Ptolemy, that he paid little attention to this property of the sides and angles of a triangle.[128] In another place Nunes notes that Werner suggested a double trepidation to make his observations agree with those of Alfonso, Albategni and Ptolemy, while Copernicus offered another method to attain the same object but did not mention Alfonso's findings in this connection. Again Nunes comments ironically that he does not know whether to follow

[124] *Ibid.,* pp. 90, 144-45.

[125] *Ibid.,* Ep. dedic., opening sentence.

[126] Pedro Nunes, *De arte atque ratione navigandi libri duo,* Conimbricae in aedibus Antonii a Mariis Universitatis typographi anno 1573, cum facultate inquisitoris. The dedication by the printer gives the impression that there had been an earlier faulty edition.

The work seems to be included with a differently worded title in the Basel, 1566, edition of *Opera* of Nunes, and again in 1592. Some writers have placed the first edition at Coimbra in 1546: see Rodolphe Guimarães, *Sur la vie et l'oeuvre de Pedro Nunes,* Coimbra, 1915, pp. 47-48.

[127] These criticisms of Regiomontanus and Copernicus are included in the summary, "Praecipuae sententiae posterioris libri," which precedes the text and are further developed in the corresponding passages of the second book.

[128] *Ibid.,* p. 66, col. 2.

Werner or Copernicus, since their observations do not agree.[129] Nunes defended both the *Alfonsine Tables* and Ptolemy against certain recent criticisms, holding, for example, that the *Alfonsine Tables* indicated the equinoxes correctly, and that hence the length of year which they gave was exact.[130]

The aforesaid treatise *On the Art of Navigation* is followed in the edition of 1573 by *Annotations on the Theories of the Planets of George Peurbach*[131] which had already appeared in the *Opera* of 1566. In this work Nunes limits himself to matters which had not been sufficiently or correctly explained by previous commentators. This appears to involve no recognition of the existence even of the Copernican theory. Reinhold is twice criticized[132] but apparently for statements in his commentary on Peurbach and not in the introduction to the *Prutenic Tables.*

As its title, *Doctrine of the Revolutions of the Sun,*[133] shows, this work of 1567 by Paul Crusius of Coburg does not advocate the movement of the earth. Yet it takes its point of departure from the statement by Copernicus in his preface to *De revolutionibus* that at the time of the Lateran Council he saw that the calendar could not then be successfully reformed, because the

[129] *Ibid.*, p. 31, col. 2.

[130] *Ibid.*, p. 30, col. 2.

[131] *Ibid.*, pp. 127-201: *In theoricas planetarum Georgii Purbachii annotationes aliquot per Petrum Nonium Salaciensem.*

[132] "Praecipua ex eis quae in theoricas planetarum Georgii Purbachii annotavimus," at the front of the volume; also pp. 154-55, 180, col. 2.

[133] *Doctrina revolutionum solis tam aequalium quam apparentium methodica ratione fideliter conscripta pro explanatione trium praeceptorum quae sunt numero 21, 22 et 23 in tabulis Prutenicis Reinholdi. Cum tabulis mediarum conversionum temporis et motuum solis in annis tropicis et sidereis. His adiecti sunt perpetui canones magnitudinis apparentis anni pro inveniendis novo modo veris revolutionibus. Item canones temporarii et generales apparentium revolutionum ad normam aequalitatis accomodati. Postremo canon introitus solis in quatuor cardines seu tropica signa zodiaci ad annos 200. Paulo Crusio Coburgensi autore.* Ienae ex officina Thomae Rebarti, anno 1567.

Copy used: BM 531.k.6.(3.), which once belonged to John Dee, as the words, "Ioannes Dee 1568," written on its title page, indicate.

The work is found in manuscript form in BM Sloane 14, 16th century, fols. 45-63v, of which fols. 51v-63v are occupied by tables.

In the same MS are such other astrological tracts as horoscopes for the year 1578, and a work on directions by Baldwinus Thorellus to Torsianus the astrologer: BM Sloane 14, fols. 36r-37r, De ratione dirigendi, opening, "Inter astrologica iudicia scire tempora accidentium . . ."

movements of sun and moon, and the length of years and months had not yet been sufficiently calculated. Regiomontanus, says Crusius, would no doubt have solved these difficulties, had he lived longer. As it was, Copernicus by his lucubrations made whole an almost collapsed astronomy. His observation of the autumnal equinox of 1515 is also cited. Reinhold too is in the estimation of Crusius no less worthy of praise. But inasmuch as in the *Prutenic Tables* he explained the revolutions of the sun and length of the apparent year briefly, Crusius will develop the matter more fully. He further gives a twofold method of finding true conversions of the sun according to the *Alfonsine Tables*.[134] Crusius also wrote a chronological work upon epochs and empires.[135] He died January first, 1572.

After lecturing on the *Sphere* of Sacrobosco at Freiburg for eighteen years,[136] Schreckenfuchs, whose commentary on Peurbach's *Theory of the Planets* has been already noticed, published that on the *Sphere,* a folio volume of some 300 pages.[137] Anent the teaching of Sacrobosco that the earth is motionless at the center of the universe, Schreckenfuchs said that the mobility of the earth might be defended, as it had been by Nicolaus Copernicus, a man of incomparable genius whom he might call a miracle of the universe, if he did not fear to offend certain men who were most tenacious of philosophy hallowed by antiquity, and not unjustly so. Not to enter now into long arguments and explanations in a doubtful matter, he promised—much as he had done in 1556—to treat it most fully and manifestly in his *Commen-*

[134] The foregoing statements are found in the preface to Johann Wilhelm, duke of Saxony.

[135] *Liber de epochis seu aeris temporum et imperiorum omnium facultatum studiosis utilissimus,* edited by Ioan. Thom. Freigius, Basel, [1578]. Copy seen: BM 718.c.12.(1.).

[136] So he says in the dedicatory epistle, which would indicate that he left Tübingen in 1551, after dating his preface to Ptolemy's *Almagest* there.

[137] *Erasmi Oswaldi Schreckenfuchsii Commentaria in Sphaeram Ioannis de Sacrobusto accuratissima quibus non solum ea quae in autoris contextu sunt sed alia etiam ad sphaericam doctrinam necessaria explicantur tabularumque constructio . . . docetur. His adiecti sunt eiusdem autoris Canones quibus usus tabularum quae operi ex libro Directionum Ioannis Regiomontani passim inseruntur . . . continetur.* Basileae ex officina Henricipetrina mense Septembri anno MDLXIX. Copy used: BM C.73.d.11.

The commentary ends and Canons begin at p. 290.

taries on Copernicus, if the fates permitted.[138] But although he was to live ten years longer, he seems not to have finished this proposed work. He was said, however, by Tycho Brahe to have possessed a model of the Copernican system.[139]

We have already heard Besson, writing in French in 1569 on a different subject—the discovery of underground waters—crave leave to speak as a mathematician rather than a physicist or theologian, since others before him had employed hypotheses which may have been false but helped them in arriving at truth. Thus Ptolemy had saved the phenomena by the supposition of eccentrics and epicycles which do not exist in nature, while Copernicus postulated something wholly repugnant to nature, that the earth moves and sun and planets (*sic*) stand still, yet had thereby succeeded in often tracing the celestial movements and positions more accurately than Ptolemy.[140] This position of Besson probably was the most prevalent attitude among men of science towards the Copernican theory in the later sixteenth century.

The curiosity as to the Copernican theory which Henry Brucaeus (1531-1593)[141] was to manifest in a letter of 1584 would never be suspected from his *De motu primo*, a textbook written to replace the *Sphere* of Sacrobosco in courses at the university of Rostock, either in its first printing of 1573[142] or the

[138] *Ibid.*, p. 36.

[139] Tycho Brahe, *Opera*, ed. Dreyer, VII, 79.

[140] Jacques Besson, *L'art et science de trouver les eaux et fontaines cachées soubs terre*, Orléans, 1569, I, 2.

[141] Henricus Brucaeus was born at Alost in Flanders, went to school at Ghent and then to the university of Paris, taught a grammar school for a while at Bruges, took the M.D. degree at Bologna, practiced medicine in Alost, became a Protestant and fled to Rostock, where he was made professor of medicine—and apparently of mathematics. Besides this astronomical textbook he composed medical treatises: *De scorbuto*, *De syphilide*, etc. Carl F. Heusinger, *Comm. de J. Cureo summo saec. XVI medico theologo philosopho historico*, 1853, pp. 33-34. Melchior Adam, *Vitae Germanorum medicorum*.

According to Valerius Andreas, *Bibliotheca Belgica*, Lovanii, 1643, p. 343, Brucaeus lived a long time at Rome and was on friendly terms with Turnebus and Ramus at Paris before teaching medicine and mathematics for twenty-five years at Rostock.

[142] Henricus Brucaeus, *De motu primo libri tres*, Rostochii excudebat J. Lucius, 1573, 8vo, 99 pp. Copy used: BN V.20672. Houzeau et Lancaster, I (1887), 595-96, misdate this edition as 1570, and add another of 1584 which I have not seen. Valerius Andreas lists an edition of 1580.

posthumous edition of 1604 by Erasmus Stocmann,[143] another professor there. It still represents the earth as a sphere at rest in the center of the universe, and the stars as not moved of themselves but with the spheres in which they are set.[144]

Thomas Digges, writing in 1573, admired the genius and singular industry of Copernicus and put him above all who had written on spherical triangles, although in discussing them he had omitted some elementary matters.[145] Digges was further opposed to the Ptolemaic or pre-Copernican astronomy as a disfiguration of the most beautiful anatomy and absolute symmetry of the universe, which it represented "by repugnant and mutually colliding eccentric orbs and epicycles revolving irregularly about their own centers, and many other most absurd hypotheses." This was the chief cause why Copernicus employed other hypotheses and tried to construct a new anatomy of the celestial machine. Digges made the rather wild further suggestion that the movement of the earth might account for the apparent diminution in magnitude of the new star of 1572.[146] In offering this suggestion he was apparently unmindful of the great distance at which Copernicus had placed the sphere of the fixed stars. In closing Digges urged all those interested in astronomy to seize the occasion of examining whether "the monstrous system of celestial globes invented by the ancients" had been "absolutely corrected and emended by that divine Copernicus of more than human genius," or whether more still remained to be done. The only way to settle this was, in his opinion, by most precise observations of this new star of 1572 and other moving stars from different points on the earth's surface.[147] Three years later Digges appended a description of the Copernican system, under the title, "A perfit description of the caelestial orbes," to a revision of the *Prognostication Euerlastinge* of his father,

[143] *Henrici Brucaei artium et medicinae doctoris De motu primo libri tres recogniti a mendis typograph. repurgati a M. Erasmo Stocmanno Hambургensi naturalis philosophiae professore publico.* Rostochii excudebat Stephanus Myliander anno MDCIV. Copy used: BM 533.a.10.

[144] *Ibid.*, fols. 4v, 24v.

[145] Thomas Digges, *Alae seu scalae mathematicae*, London, 1573. Praefatio ad lectorem and fol. (H 3) verso.

[146] *Ibid.*, Praefatio ad lectorem.

[147] *Ibid.*, fol. L 2 verso.

Leonard Digges. They appeared together in at least six more editions by 1605.[148]

In his elementary textbook of astronomy Valentin Nabod gave the system of Martianus Capella in which Mercury and Venus revolve about the sun. He added that Copernicus had taken occasion from this to make Saturn, Jupiter and Mars, and indeed everything included within the sphere of the moon, revolve about the sun as center of the universe, while the sun and fixed stars remained unmoved. Copernicus had thus "with so small a number of spheres" saved all the phenomena of the sky through the ages, as no one before him had done, with the greatest praise and admiration of the learned. Nabod then presented a figure of the Copernican system, which, as we have seen, was an unusual thing to do in an elementary textbook. He remarked that no one should be greatly offended by the movement of the earth and quiet of the sun. If, however, anyone preferred to consider the earth at rest and the sun as in motion, he could reach the same results by practically the same demonstrations, as was understood by all who knew anything about mathematics.[149] We treat in another chapter of Nabod's devotion to astrology, by which art he was said to have predicted his own death.

In the preface to his textbook on the sphere, addressed to young students of the liberal arts, Hermann Witekind admitted that there had long since been enough and too many works, old and new, on the elements of astronomy and geography, and that an increase in the number of readers of such books was more to be desired than that the multitude of writers should be augmented. Yet he wrote another. This most beautiful subject was now neglected and despised in the extreme in the schools. He

[148] See "Thomas Digges, the Copernican System, and the Idea of the Infinity of the Universe in 1576," by Francis R. Johnson and Sanford V. Larkey, *The Huntington Library Bulletin,* No. 5, April, 1934, pp. 69-117; and Francis R. Johnson, *Astronomical Thought in Renaissance England,* 1937, Chapter 6.

[149] Valentinus Naiboda, *Astronomicarum institutionum libri III quibus doctrinae sphaericae elementa methodo nova . . . traduntur,* Venetiis, 1580, fols. 41r, 42r. Copy used: BM 531.f.13.

The work seems to have first appeared in 1573 with the title, *Primarum de coelo et terra institutionum quotidianarumque mundi revolutionum libri tres,* Venetiis, 1573.

had been giving instruction in it to some students at his house, and the present manual is the outcome. It was printed first at Heidelberg in 1574, then at Neustadt an der Hardt in the Palatinate in 1590.[150] Witekind became professor of mathematics at Neustadt in 1581. In an inaugural lecture on May 22 at 7 A.M. in the new public auditorium he spoke several times of organs, automata or machines of the movements of the planets and celestial orbs. For one of these machines, Charles V had given Iohannes Homelius (Hummel), professor at Leipzig, a thousand gold pieces.[151] In his textbook Witekind accepts the ninth sphere and a single sphere of earth and water. He cites Copernicus that the eighth sphere moves one degree in seventy years against Ptolemy's estimate of one in a hundred years, and also on the distance of the planets from the earth. But he "proves" that the earth is situated at the center of the universe and that it does not move. He gives the stock arguments with those from the Bible last.[152]

An odd mixture of allusions to current astronomical—and astrological—publications and opinions is encountered in the *Meteorographical Ephemerides* of Richard Forster, doctor of arts and medicine, published at London in 1575.[153] In the dedicatory preface to Robert, earl of Leicester, baron of Denbighe and chancellor of Oxford, Forster expresses the wish that Hippocrates had noted the state of the heavens together with his cases, and the hope to publish another opuscule on larger matters, such as comets and unusual apparitions, according to Ptolemy in the *Almagest* and *Quadripartitum*. Later he gives the beginnings of the four monarchies, first according to modern

[150] I have used the later edition: *De sphaera mundi et temporis ratione apud christianos Hermanni Witekindi*, Neostadii Palatinorum excudebat Matthaeus Harnisch, MDXC. Copy used: BM c.75.a.11.

[151] *Hermanni Witekindi Oratio de doctrina et studio astronomiae*, Neapoli Nemetum excudebat Matthaeus Harnisch, 1581, 4to minori. Copy used: BM 8561.c.55.

[152] *De sphaera mundi* etc., 1590, pp. 79, 11, 80, 109, 93, 99 respectively.

[153] *Ephemerides Meteorographicae Richardi Forsteri Londinensis artium ac medicinae doctoris ad annum domini 1575 et positum finitoris Londini emporii totius Angliae nobiliss. diligenter examinatae.* Londini excudebat Ioannes Kyngstonus typographus. Copy used: BM 533.a.31.(2.).

authorities and the *Prutenic Tables,* then according to the ancients and the *Alfonsine Tables.* He closes with the statement that with tireless industry he has brought this work to a conclusion, "following in this matter Ptolemy and my observations and those of certain very learned men." Then, with a very complimentary reference to Cornelius Gemma, is appended a treatment of a solar eclipse of the past November and its effects. Incidentally Leowitz is criticized for following the Arabs rather than Ptolemy in his prediction from it. Finally Forster states that astronomy, which in England first began to revive and emerge from darkness into light through the efforts of John Dee, keen champion of new hypotheses and Ptolemaic theory, will, as a result of the interference of unskilled persons, go to ruin "with the heavens of Copernicus and Reinhold," unless Dee again interposes his Atlantean shoulders. Apparently Forster drew no sharp line between the Ptolemaic and Copernican theories.

In the prohemium of the geographical work of Giovanni Lorenzo d'Anania, dedicated from Naples on July 22, 1575, to Caterina Iaggelone Sforza d'Aragonia, princess of Poland and queen of Sweden, and printed at Venice in 1576,[154] the earth is described as the heaviest element and immobile at the center of the universe. Yet from the geographical standpoint the work of d'Anania had considerable merit, not only devoting one of its four books to the new world, but including laws and customs, trees, herbs and medicines and inventors, as well as provinces, cities, mountains, seas, lakes, rivers and fountains. It gave a two page list of rather unusual and mainly recent authorities. It was reprinted at Venice in 1582 and again in 1596.

The learned Bodin in his *Republic* raised several objections to the Copernican theory. One was that it required the earth to

[154] Gio. Lorenzo d'Anania della Città di Taverna, *L'Universale Fabrica del Mondo overo Cosmografia. Divisa in quattro Trattati ne i quali distintamente si misura il Cielo e la Terra e si discrivono particolarmente le Provincie Città Castella Monti Mari Laghi Fiumi e Fonti e si tratta delle Leggi e Costumi di molti Popoli de gli Alberi e dell'Herbe e d'altre cose pretiose e Medicinali e de gl'Inventori di tutte le cose. Di nuouo posta in luce con privilegio.* In Venetia Ad instantia di Aniello San Vito di Napoli, MDLXXVI. Copy used: BM 1295.l.9.

move, another that it involved the stranger absurdity of putting the sun in the center of the world and the earth 50,000 leagues away from the center, and of making part of the sky and planets mobile and part immobile. Ptolemy had rebutted the theory of Eudoxus by arguments which seemed true but which Bodin admitted Copernicus had answered well, to which in turn Melanchthon's only reply had been to quote scripture. Bodin had a further objection to the Copernican theory which he regarded as new and not yet used by anyone against Copernicus, namely, that a simple body could have only one movement of its own, whereas Copernicus had assigned three movements to the earth.[155] Four years later in the *Démonomanie* Bodin still adhered to the Ptolemaic system, speaking of the eighth sphere as moving 133,000,000 leagues a day. Incidentally he displayed his ignorance of the past literature of astronomy by classing Campanus as an Arabic writer along with Alfraganus, Thebit and Albategni.[156]

Commentaries on the *Sphere* of Sacrobosco were carried to an extreme of length by Iunctinus or Giuntini. His two volume work of 1577 devoted over 300 pages to Sacrobosco's first chapter alone, quoting profusely and introducing much astrological and other extraneous matter selected with little discrimination from authors of very varying merit.[157] In the course of this farrago he complimented Copernicus for having with supreme skill and ingenuity shown not only the reasons why the apparent tropical year was unequal, but the way by which the length of the natural year could be determined at any given time. For this, however, Iunctinus cited not *De revolutionibus* but the 21st precept of the *Prutenic Tables*.[158] He also used them for Copernicus's determination of the apogee of the sun in 1515.[159] In an-

[155] *Les six livres de la republique de I. Bodin Angeuin*, Paris, 1576, p. 442 (IV, 2). Dorothy Stimson, *The Gradual Acceptance of the Copernican Theory of the Universe*, 1917, pp. 45-47, has quoted a passage of like tenor from Bodin's later work, *Universae Naturae Theatrum*.

[156] Bodin, *Démonomanie*, 1580, fol. 248r.

[157] Duhem, *Les origines de la statique*, II (1906), 99, noted that Giuntini copied entire pages of Albert of Saxony without acknowledgement.

[158] *F. Iunctini Comm. in Sphaeram Ioannis de Sacro Bosco*, 1577, I, 341.

[159] *Ibid.*, II, 285.

other passage Iunctinus misrepresented the view of Copernicus, saying that Alfonso king of Spain, Peurbach, Regiomontanus and Nicolaus Copernicus added another sphere to those of the planets, fixed stars and *primum mobile,* calling the last the tenth sphere and introducing a new ninth sphere or *mobile secundum.*[160] In the Italian version of his commentary on the *Sphere,* published at Lyons in 1582, Giuntini gave a brief summary of the Copernican theory with a rude diagram, although he himself with Sacrobosco still described the earth as immobile at the center of the universe.[161] In his *Speculum astrologiae* of 1573 Giuntini had included *Tabulae resolutae* for estimating the move-

[160] *Ibid.,* I, 35.

[161] *La sfera del mondo,* Lyon, 1582. I have not seen this edition, but it has been discussed, with a facsmile of the passage and diagram in question, by Grant McColley, "Francesco Giuntini and the Copernican Hypothesis," in *Popular Astronomy,* XLV (1937), 70-73.

Professor McColley, perhaps by a misprint, gives the date of Giuntini's birth as 1522 rather than 1523. He also, I believe, misinterprets the diagram when he says that "the space below the moon, now extending to the central sun, remains the sublunary region." What is denominated "Orbis deferens terrę lunęque et regionis sublunaris" in the diagram includes only the region between the spheres of Mars and Venus. The sublunar region is clearly comprised entirely within this orb and constitutes as usual the spheres of fire, air, water and earth. The only space "below the moon" is that between it and the earth. Neither Copernicus nor Giuntini thought that sublunar objects would fall towards the central sun rather than towards the earth.

There is however, a curious feature of Giuntini's summary of the Copernican theory which McColley has not remarked. It says that next to the sun at the center of the world comes the sphere of the moon, then that of Mercury, etc., although presently it speaks again of the moon as revolving about the earth. I quote the Italian:

"Conforme à questa opinione è quella di Niccolo Copernico, il quale facendo muouere la terra pone il Sole nel centro del mondo & doppo il Sole doue segue il cielo della Luna" (no such sphere of the moon is shown in the diagram, however) "vi pone quel di Mercurio & poi quello di Venere sopra il quale mette la terra nel orbe del Sole" (i.e. in the place where the sphere of the sun was usually located) "alle quale da tre moti. Il primo è il moto diurno, il secondo quello di ogni cento anni vn grado: & il terzo quello della declinatione. Et attorno alla terra in vn piccolo cerchio vi pone la Luna: la quale girando attorno alla terra in ventisette giorni & un terzo, è hora congiunta & hora opposta al Sole. Seguono poi i cieli di Marte, Gioue, & Saturno: i quali tutti fa muouere nel tempo ordinario, & sopra i pianeti pone l'ottaua sfera immobile, la quale chiama luogo del mondo doue si girano gli altri cieli. Et questa opinione tenne ancora Aristarco Samio, che fu auanti lo aduenimento di Christo saluator nostro anni 1800(*sic*). Et per intelligenza della quale opinione habbiamo posto la sopra scritta figura."

ments of all the planets according to the observations of Copernicus.[162]

Houzeau and Lancaster (No. 2723) ascribe to A. Leoninus or van Leeuwen a *Theory of the Celestial Motions According to the Doctrine of Copernicus,* published in octavo at Cologne in 1578 and again in 1583, but I have not found the work. It is not comprised among eight titles which Zedler, following the Belgian bibliographies of Swertius and Andreas, attributed to Albertus Leoninus or Leeuwen of Antwerp, who lived into the seventeenth century, although these titles include a treatise on the true quantity of the tropical year and the restoration of the calendar, addressed to Gregory XIII and printed at Cologne in octavo in 1578, and an *Epitome orbis.* Andreas further lists a treatise against the *genethliaci* by Leoninus and a commentary on the doctrine of the precession of the equinoxes and obliquity of the zodiac but says nothing of the Copernican title. Houzeau and Lancaster (No. 2756) further ascribe to M. A. Lonicerus a *Theory of Celestial Motions According to the Hypothesis of Copernicus,* Cologne, 1583, in quarto, of which I have found no other trace.

Freige, in his *Physical Questions* of 1579, used determinations by Copernicus of the apogees of the three superior planets to determine their perigees in his own time.[163] In discussing the question whether astronomers agree as to the situation and number of orbs, Freige gave a very brief résumé of the Copernican system, and cited Maurolycus, as we have noted, to the effect that Copernicus deserved a thrashing.[164]

The Jesuit astronomer, Clavius of Bamberg, in the fourth edition of his voluminous *Commentary on the Sphere of Sacrobosco,*[165] praised Copernicus as "the eminent restorer of as-

[162] McColley, *op. cit.,* notes neither these *Tabulae* nor the *Speculum astrologiae,* Lugduni, Phil. Tinghi, 1573, 4to.

[163] Jo. Thomas Freige, *Quaestiones physicae,* Basel, 1579, lib. xvi, p. 340.

[164] *Ibid.,* pp. 183-84.

[165] I have used the edition of Lyons, 1593, which appears to be a reprint of that of Rome, 1581, which are the place and date given in the dedication to Wilhelm, count Palatine of the Rhine and duke of Bavaria. An edition of Rome, Victor Helianus, 1570, is listed by the Librairie J. Thiébaud, Paris, Catalogue 69, June, 1939, Item 1182.

tronomy in our times whom all posterity will ever gratefully celebrate and admire as another Ptolemy."[166] But what Copernicus is particularly praised for is the suggestion of four movements for the eighth sphere—which of course he really regarded as motionless. Clavius utterly rejected the Copernican method of explaining the four movements and his "absurd hypotheses" of a stable sun and mobile earth. Indeed, he regarded the Copernican explanation of two of the four movements in question as scarcely intelligible and involving contrariety. Clavius alluded again to the Copernican theory in the course of a long argumentative defense of eccentrics and epicycles.[167] He remarked that Copernicus had not rejected eccentrics and epicycles but rather, aided by previous calculations based upon them, had tried to show that their arrangement was not such as Ptolemy had suggested. And if the position of Copernicus involved no falsity or absurdity, it would be a question whether to adhere to the Ptolemaic or Copernican theory. But the fact that Copernicus advocated such absurdities as that the earth was not in the middle of the firmament and moved with a triple motion—whereas philosophers agreed that a simple body could have but a single movement—and that he contradicted many passages of Scripture made his hypotheses unacceptable to Clavius.[168] Although Clavius made these allusions to Copernicus, he does not seem to have adverted to the *Prutenic Tables* nor to have cited either Reinhold or Rheticus, perhaps because they were under a stigma of Protestantism which Copernicus was not.

Michael Maestlin, although his observation of the comet of 1577 had already led him to favor the Copernican hypothesis, in his elementary textbook of astronomy, dedicated in 1582 to the duke of Wurtemberg, still followed the method of Sacrobosco whom he praised highly. He added, however, an eccentric of the eccentric to save the phenomenon of the unequal approach of the apogee of the sun which Copernicus was supposed to have demonstrated from observations, and censured the authors of

[166] *Ibid.*, p. 67, in an excursus first added in the fourth edition.

[167] *Ibid.*, pp. 499-525.

[168] *Ibid.*, pp. 519-20.

the *Alfonsine Tables* for having here, as in other places, "too boldly differed from Ptolemy."[169] But when Maestlin came to the eighth sphere, he adopted an Alfonsine explanation, although it deviated from the truth in many respects, and it would be more convenient to embrace the demonstrations of Copernicus. "But since these are the more difficult and require a fuller explanation than can be given at present, we could not present them here."[170]

In the revised edition of his *Cosmography* which Dodoens issued in 1584[171] he described it as primarily introductory to Ptolemy but also to the *De revolutionibus* of Copernicus, a most learned man who dissented from Ptolemy in some hypotheses. In this later edition Dodoens inserts a denial of the movement of access and recess or trepidation, and the consequent supposition of a ninth sphere between that of the fixed stars and *primum mobile.* This ninth sphere, he says, neither Ptolemy nor Copernicus recognized.[172] Apart from this, there are only slight changes in the new edition, and all the mentions of Copernicus which we noted in the edition of 1548 remain the same in that of 1584.

On the other hand, Barozzi retained the Alfonsine ninth sphere in his *Cosmography* of 1585. He further held that the earth was immobile and the opinion of Aristarchus and Copernicus, false.[173]

For more than half a century after the publication of *De revolutionibus* Aristotelian works on the heavenly bodies continued to appear as if nothing had happened. These expositions were normally purely theoretical and argumentative. They were not only unruffled by any extended reference to the Copernican theory, but for that matter to the Ptolemaic. They cited a wealth

[169] Michael Maestlin, *Epitome astronomiae,* edition of 1597 (BM 531.f.15), pp. 303-8.

[170] *Ibid.,* pp. 488, 499-500.

[171] *De sphaera sive de astronomiae et geographiae principiis cosmographica isagoge olim conscripta a Remberto Dodonaeo medico nunc vero eiusdem recognitione locupletior facta.* Antwerpiae apud Christophorum Plantinum, MDLXXXIV. Copy used: BM 533.b.9.

[172] *Ibid.,* I, 7; p. 19.

[173] *Cosmographia . . . ad magnam Ptolemaei mathematicam constructionem ad universamque astrologiam instituens Francisco Barocio Iacobi filio patritio Veneto autore,* Venetiis, 1585. Copy used: BM 533.b.10.

of past philosophical opinion from Plato down through Alexander of Aphrodisias, Philoponus, Themistius, Plotinus, Proclus, Eustratius, through Avicenna, Avicebron, Averroes, and other Arabic commentators, even through Latin schoolmen such as Aquinas, Aegidius, Occam, Capreolus and Cajetan, to recent writers like Ficino, Achillini and Zimara. But they seldom utilized anyone who possessed a first-hand knowledge of astronomy, and should therefore be regarded as largely ignoring astronomy and observation of any sort, rather than as opposing or neglecting the work of Copernicus in particular.

Of this attitude many examples might be noted from the work on the nature of the celestial bodies by Federico Pendasio,[174] published at Mantua in 1555,[175] to that on the substance of the heavens, printed at Venice in 1618, by Thomas Giannini, professor of philosophy in the university of Ferrara.[176] In the latter are cited such intervening authors as Philalthaeus, Mercenarius, Telesio, Vimercati, with whom as well as Pendasio Giannini did not always agree. It was the interpretation of Aristotle in which most of these works were primarily, even exclusively, interested. They disagree among themselves rather than oppose Copernicus or any other outsider. If Giannini cites Telesio, it is not for the latter's own philosophy, but for his attempt to show from passages in Aristotle that the sky is made of fire.[177] Pendasio, I believe, does not mention Copernicus. Giannini twice refers to him as having revived the obsolete opinion of Nicetas and Aristarchus as to the earth's motion.[178] In one of these passages Copernicus is called an indeed remarkable observer of the celestial movements. In the other he is said to have detected that

[174] There seem to have been two men of this name: one who attended cardinal Erolo at the Council of Trent and died at Rome in 1562—see Bettinelli, *Ragionamenti delle lettere e delle arti mantovane,* 1774, p. 119; the other, confused with the former by Bettinelli, who taught at Padua until 1571 (Riccoboni, *De gymnasio Patavino,* 1598, fol. 33v), and then at Bologna until 1603-1604 (Dallari, *I rotuli,* cf. Index).

[175] Pendasius, *De natura corporum coelestium*, Mantua, 1555. Copy used: BM 8562.a.9.

[176] Thomas Gianninius, *De substantia caeli et stellarum efficientia disputationes Aristotelicae,* Venetiis apud Robertum Meiettum, 1618.

[177] *Ibid.*, p. 41.

[178] *Ibid.*, pp. 37, 63.

the phenomena had not been quite correctly explained by previous astronomers and to have added an eleventh sphere(!).

Wolfgang Meurer (1513-1585), recipient of many of George Fabricius's letters,[179] had a distinguished career at the university of Leipzig, where he held all possible offices of administration, honor and dignity, and taught first Aristotelian philosophy, then medicine.[180] In his *Meteorology,* published two years after his death by his son Christopher,[181] Meurer adheres closely to Aristotelian doctrine, no doubt because the work is an outgrowth of his past lectures on the natural philosophy of Aristotle. It is true that his son represents it as the product of life-long private study and industry, but it had been far enough advanced for his friends to urge him to publish it long before his death. At any rate, it seems unaffected either by the Copernican theory or by the celestial phenomena of 1572, 1577, 1580 and 1585, unless we may detect a slight trace of Copernican influence in his calling the ninth sphere that of mutation of apogees. He retains the conception of incorruptible heavens and four inferior elements of which the heavens are the efficient cause. Many persons deny that fire is an element but for insufficient reasons which he has elsewhere refuted and will not now repeat, merely warning youth not to depart rashly from received opinions unless forced to by the thing itself or persuaded by the most solid reasoning.[182] His bibliography does not include either Rheticus or Copernicus, although it lists king Alfonso and Sacrobosco, and such recent writers as Camerarius, Melanchthon, Milich, Julius Caesar Scaliger, Rondelet, Sebastian Fox-Morcillo, Vimercati, Fernel,

[179] *Georgii Fabricii Chemnicensis Epistolae ad Wolfg. Meurerum et alios aequales. Maximam partem ex autographis nunc primum edidit Detl. Carolus Guil. Baumgarten-Crusius,* Lipsiae, 1845.

[180] A very interesting account of his scholastic career is given in a Vita of considerable length by Bartholomaeus Walther, which is prefixed to Meurer's *Meteorologia.*

[181] *Wolfgangi Meureri medici ac philosophi Meteorologia quaestionibus informata et explicationibus dilucidis illustrata olim in celeberrima academia Lipsensi publice tradita nunc vero primum in lucem edita a M. Christophoro Meurero filio mathematum professore publico. Huic prefixa est narratio de curriculo vitae eiusdem autoris studio M. Bartholomaei. Waltheri,* Lipsiae, 1587.

[182] *Ibid.*, p. 21.

Lucillus Philalthaeus, Leowitz and Mizauld. These last names suggest that Meurer was more attentive to recent occult and astrological doctrine than to new astronomical theory.

Meurer accepts the Ptolemaic order of the planetary spheres but makes a single globe of earth and water, stating that the phenomena show this clearly.[183] On the other hand, while he repeats the "common opinion" that no cloud is more than nine miles above the earth, and that sometimes clouds are not more than a half mile distant, based on the fact that an observer on a mountain like Vesuvius sees clouds on his level or even below him, he rejects it for the opinion of those "who are accustomed to measure the distance of places more exactly." Thereupon he cites the estimate of Witelo that the clouds are 52,000 paces or 13 German miles above the earth's surface, and another estimate that the lowest clouds are 288,000 paces or 72 German miles distant, while the highest clouds attain an altitude of 772,000 paces or 193 German miles. He therefore places clouds in the middle rather than the lower region of the air.[184] Perhaps he thought this reconcilable with the fact that some mountain peaks rise above the clouds, since in a later passage he says that the reason why no snow or rain or wind occurs on the top of Mount Olympus is that it is so high that it transcends the middle region of the air where snow is produced.[185]

We turn from followers of Aristotle to an opponent. In 1585, in the same volume in which Benedetti attacked the Aristotelian physics and cosmology, he published a letter which may have been composed some years before, in which he made brief but not unfavorable allusion to the opinion of Aristarchus of Samos and Nicolaus Copernicus, as he called it.[186] He mentioned it, however, only incidentally in order to support his argument that the heavens did not exist merely for the sake of so vile a body

[183] *Ibid.*, pp. 6, 21.

[184] *Ibid.*, pp. 249-50.

[185] *Ibid.*, p. 303. On the tendency towards excessive estimates of the height of mountains in early modern times see my "Measurement of Mountain Altitudes," *Isis,* IX (1927), 425-26, and Florian Cajori, "History of Determinations of the Heights of Mountains," *Isis,* XII (1929), 482-514.

[186] Giov. Batt. Benedetti, *Diversarum speculationum* . . . , 1585: *Epistolae,* pp. 255-56.

as our earth. For, if the earth served as a center of the moon's greater epicycle, as Aristarchus and Copernicus thought, why should not Saturn, Jupiter, Mars, Venus and Mercury revolve about other bodies similar to our globe? Having given the Copernican theory this rather strange twist, Benedetti added that the immense velocities with which the sun, Saturn and other heavenly bodies were supposed to travel could be avoided by a simple revolution of the earth about its axis. This would reduce the movement of the sun to an annual orbit about the earth. Or it would suffice, if the earth similarly revolved about the sun; for the arguments adduced by Ptolemy against the earth's moving were not accepted by the Copernicans, who maintained that the surrounding water and air would move with the earth. Benedetti did not state these views as his own, however. In another letter of September 30, 1581, we find him defending the *Alfonsine Tables* and *Ephemerides* based upon them, apparently in terms of the Ptolemaic system, although he mentions the *Almagest* and *De revolutionibus* together as authoritative works. He criticizes the *Prutenic Tables,* however, as involving especially laborious calculation on the part of one using them.[187]

The appropriation of the Copernican theory for his own purposes of speculation by so fanciful and wayward a genius as the unorthodox wanderer over the face of western Europe, Giordano Bruno, poet and philosopher, can hardly have done much to recommend the new hypotheses either to sober men of science or to staid contemporary public opinion.[188]

That other men of the sixteenth century should not be censured too sharply for failing to accept the Copernican hypothesis is indicated by the fact that Tycho Brahe, the most assiduous observer of the heavenly bodies during that period, could not bring himself to believe that the earth moved, much less to ac-

[187] *Ibid.,* pp. 228-48, Defensio Ephemeridum ad illustr. D. Bernardum Trottum, especially pp. 235 and 242.

[188] Especially when he made such absurd overstatements as that Copernicus had understood more in two chapters than Aristotle and all the Peripatetics in all their study of nature. *Opera,* I, i, 17 (Naples, 1879), *Oratio valedictoria habita in academia Witebergensi,* 8 March, 1588.

cept three different simultaneous motions for it. He more than once stated in so many words that the Copernican system was false and involved absurdities.[189] Indeed, Copernicus himself in his preface to Paul III had admitted that his view seemed absurd,[190] and Maestlin still employed that word in 1596 when defending the Copernican theory.[191] That much used textbook of the sixteenth century, the *Margarita philosophica,* contained the statement that one could scarcely say anything more absurd in Physics or Astronomy than that the center of the universe was not in the interior of the earth.[192] Tycho for his part admitted more than once that the Copernican hypothesis of a triple motion of the earth was ingenious and explained the celestial phenomena fairly well.[193] But it was not true, rather against all physical truth.[194] Why make our opaque, gross, slow, heavy earth a star and more revolved than the others?

This and other physical reasons for not accepting the movement of the earth were not Tycho's only criticisms of Copernicus and his theory. He seems to have felt with Peucer that Copernicus had not performed as many observations of the heavens as were required in constructing so great a work.[195] Tycho further charged Copernicus with errors in observation which were perhaps due to use of defective instruments. Thus

[189] *Opera* ed. Dreyer, III, 63, "non tantum dubia sed plane falsa et absurda." At VII, 293, in a letter to Magini he states that his own system avoids both Ptolemaic superfluities and Copernican absurdities.

[190] "Et quamvis absurda opinio videbatur. . . ."

[191] In his preface to his reedition of Rheticus's *Narratio prima,* as printed in Kepler, *Prodromus dissertationum cosmographicarum,* 1621, p. 90: "Quod si quem sicut hactenus non paucos Copernici hypothesium a multis illegitime condemnata et praeter rationem diffamata absurditas offendit. . . ."

[192] Cited by Pierre Duhem, *Les origines de la statique,* II (1906), 65-66.

[193] Tycho Brahe, *Opera,* ed. Dreyer, VII, 294-95; III, 179.

[194] *Ibid.,* VII, 295, "nequaquam in rei veritate constare"; III, 179, "contra omnem physicam veritatem"; III, 63, "imo id ita se nequaquam habere suo loco luculenter ostendemus."

[195] *Ibid.,* VII, 189, Peucer writes, "nec tantum observationum habuisse quantum operi tanto conficiundo fuit opus." Tycho notes four times that Copernicus had not observed Mercury: *Ibid.,* II, 89, 445; V, 109, 323. In view of this it is rather odd that in drawing up horoscopes in 1577 and 1583 for king Christian and prince John respectively he should have followed Copernicus rather than the *Alfonsine Tables* or his own observations only for the planet Mercury: *Ibid.,* I, 189, 262.

by mismeasurement of the elevation of the pole at Frauenburg he had fallen into a great error as to the apogee and eccentric of the sun.[196] Again he had made the sun about 162 times as large as the earth, while Tycho's calculation was that it was only a little over 139 times as great as our globe.[197] Or for the length of the year Tycho preferred the Alfonsine tables to the Prutenic based upon Copernicus.[198]

In his work of 1573 on the new star of 1572 Tycho affirmed that by frequent observation he had found that the Copernican calculations were closer to the truth than the Alfonsine or any other astronomical tables. In another passage, however, he preferred his own observations of the moon in preceding years to either the Alfonsine or Copernican tables, and noted that the winter solstice occurred ten hours later than stated in the Alfonsine tables and five hours earlier than the Prutenic tables. For the summer solstice the Alfonsine tables were four hours off, the Prutenic two hours at fault. For the recent great conjunction of Saturn and Jupiter in 1563 his observations showed that the Alfonsine tables misdated it by a whole month, while the Prutenic tables, although more exact as to the motion of these planets, were almost an entire day off. But in a tract on the lunar eclipse of 1573 he calculated the time of its appearance from the Prutenic tables, "founded on the Copernican hypotheses." In 1584 he found the Alfonsine tables more accurate for the recent vernal equinox but Copernicus more exact for the movement of the moon.[199] Also the solar eclipse of 1598 occurred an hour behind the Prutenic tables and was less obscure than they indicated.[200]

If nothing else showed the absurdity of the Copernican theory, it would be enough to condemn it in Tycho's eyes that it required so immense and useless a starless space between the orbit of Saturn and the sphere of the fixed stars.[201] Tycho notes that

[196] *Ibid.*, II, 29-32. For other errors ascribed by Tycho to Copernicus see Dreyer's Index in vol. XV.

[197] *Ibid.*, II, 416, 422.

[198] *Ibid.*, VII, 382, letter to Ranzovius.

[199] *Ibid.*, VII, 78: Tycho to Brucaeus.

[200] *Ibid.*, VII, 251.

[201] *Ibid.*, III, 63.

Copernicus had observed the fixed stars little.[202] And in his catalogue of the fixed stars Tycho did not leave a single one as either the Alfonsine tables or Copernicus had placed it.[203] Moreover, he contended that observations of comets refuted the notion of an annual circular movement of the earth.[204] Finally, Tycho resorted not merely to physical and mathematical, but to biblical and theological arguments against the Copernican theory.[205] If an astronomer of such standing employed biblical and theological as well as physical and mathematical reasons, we need not take it amiss if less scientific minds and more theological and miscellaneous writers did so to a still greater degree. It should, however, be recognized that in Tycho's case jealousy of the Copernican achievement may have operated subconsciously to incline Tycho to belittle it, and that *amour propre* may have had something to do with his devising his own *Systema mundi* which he held avoided both the Ptolemaic superfluities and the Copernican absurdities. The attitude of Tycho shows further that mere assiduity and painstaking accuracy in accumulating and tabulating scientific observations does not necessarily make one any more broad-minded and open to new ideas, or less conservative and attached to old predilections, just as it did not necessarily result in freedom from astrological and occult notions.

On the other hand, the inquiries which Tycho received from correspondents as to the relative merits of the Alfonsine and Prutenic tables, or of the Ptolemaic and Copernican hypotheses, indicate that they were alive to the importance and significance of the new theory. Johannes Pratensis, professor of medicine at Copenhagen, wanted to know which was preferable: the Ptolemaic system as corrected by Tycho, the Copernican, or some third system.[206] Brucaeus wished to know where he could

[202] *Ibid.*, III, 337.

[203] *Ibid.*, VII, 293. Tycho believed that the latitudes of the stars changed by reason of the altered inclination of the ecliptic, and that neither Werner nor Copernicus had noted this: *ibid.*, p. 295.

[204] *Ibid.*, VII, 295.

[205] *Ibid.*, III, 179, "sed et repugnante sacrarum litterarum autoritate quae praecipua esse debet"; VII, 295, "suo loco et tempore a nobis irrefragabiliter non saltem theologice et physice sed etiam mathematice convincetur."

[206] *Ibid.*, VII, 24.

find a machine or planetarium showing the Copernican system, which he never had been able fully to grasp from a simple delineation.[207] The only such model of which Tycho could think was a small one he had once seen in the possession of Schreckenfuchs and which was supposed to illustrate both the Ptolemaic and Copernican hypotheses. But as he thought it over afterwards, it seemed to him defective.[208] Intelligent interest in the problem and reluctance to ascribe movements to the earth were also shown by several persons who attempted to claim as their own Tycho's solution of having Mercury and Venus revolve about the sun as it revolved about the earth.[209] Magini in his *Theory of the Planets* had reduced the Copernican speculation more nearly to Ptolemaic form than before in his resolution of astronomical tables from the Prutenic.[210]

To his *Fundamentum astronomicum,* published at Strasburg in 1588, Nicolaus Raymarus Ursus Dithmarsus added *New and True Hypotheses of the Motions of the Mundane Bodies.*[211] This claim has recently been allowed by Grant McCollcy,[212] who has even credited Raymarus Ursus with a fourth system of the world to rank with the Ptolemaic, Copernican and Tychonian. Dreyer, on the other hand, affirms that Raymarus not only published as his own those prosthaphaeretic formulae which Paul Wittich had discovered in 1580, but, what was much more serious, claimed and published the Tychonian system as his own.[213]

[207] *Ibid.,* VII, 85: letter to Tycho of June 12, 1584.

[208] *Ibid.,* VII, 79. Although placed before it in Dreyer's edition, this would seem to be Tycho's reply to the letter mentioned in the preceding note. Schreckenfuchs is not mentioned in Dr. Dorothy Stimson's *Gradual Acceptance of the Copernican Theory.*

[209] *Ibid.,* VIII, 206: Tycho mentions Ursus, Duncan Liddelius, and Roeslin as having plagiarized his hypotheses or claiming that they had suggested them to him.

[210] *Ibid.,* VII, 296: Tycho to Magini.

[211] *Nicolai Raymari Ursi Dithmarsi Fundamentum astronomicum, id est nova doctrina sinuum et triangulorum. . . . Cui adjunctae sunt: Hypotheses novae ac verae motuum corporum mundanorum . . .,* Strasburg, 1588, 4to: BM 8561.c.56.

[212] "Nicolas Reymers and the fourth system of the world," *Popular Astronomy,* 46 (1938), 25-31. See also the earlier paper of Siegmund Günther, "Die Kompromiss-Weltsysteme des XVI, XVII und XVIII Jahrhunderts," *Annales internationales d'histoire,* Congrès de Paris 1900, 5e section, Histoire des Sciences, Paris, 1901, pp. 121-45.

[213] Dreyer in the notes to Tycho Brahe, *Opera* VI (1919), 351-52. McColley in the above article cites only Dreyer's *Life of Tycho Brahe* and *Planetary Systems.*

He had visited Tycho at Hven in 1584, and was bitterly accused by Tycho of having stolen his ideas.[214] Christopher Rothmann, the mathematician of the landgrave of Hesse, also assailed Raymarus.[215] The latter in reply attacked both Tycho and Rothmann in a work of 1597.[216] Meanwhile, in 1593, we have an annual astrological prediction in German by him.[217]

Giovanni Antonio Magini of Padua, professor of mathematics at Bologna, in 1589 published *New Theories of the Celestial Orbs Agreeing with the Observations of Copernicus.*[218] He took the position that Copernicus had so reformed astronomy that no correction of equal motions, or a very slight one, was now required, whereas the Ptolemaic and Alfonsine calculations had been shown unsatisfactory not only by the Copernican arguments but by the daily observations of many persons. For although Copernicus had devised hypotheses which wandered far from verisimilitude, yet they corresponded closely to the phenomena. But either from a desire to display his ingenuity or convinced by his own reasoning, he had revived the opinion of Nicetas, Aristarchus and others as to the movement of the earth and had upset the received constitution of the universe. This made many question his results or at least disapprove of his hypotheses as monstrous. Magini has consequently thought it advisable to cast them aside and to associate others with the observations of Copernicus and the Prutenic tables. He has therefore collated the ideas of Ptolemy and Copernicus, adding new hypotheses of his own where they seemed necessary, and has written an introductory text or theory of the planets along these lines.[219] He asserts that there was a great demand for such a theory of the planets which would abandon the out-moded Alfonsine hypotheses and conform to recent observations with-

[214] *Opera,* VIII (1925), 204-5. Consult the Index in Vol. XV for many other passages referring to Raymarus Ursus.

[215] *Ibid.,* VI, 61 *et seq.,* 361 *et seq.*

[216] *De astronomicis hypothesibus seu systemate mundano . . . vendicatio et defensio,* Pragae, 1597: BM 8561.c.57.

[217] Hellmann (1924), p. 29.

[218] *Novae coelestium orbium theoricae congruentes cum observationibus N. Copernici, auctore Io. Antonio Magino . . .,* Venetiis Ex officina Damiani Zenarii, MDLXXXIX.

[219] From his dedicatory epistle to John Jacob Tonialus of Verona.

out such absurd hypotheses as Copernicus had imagined. He excuses himself for not accompanying his text with commentaries because of his occupation with the revision of his *Ephemerides* and his new duties in his first year as professor of mathematics at Bologna. He has had to change entirely the theories of the sun and moon but has adhered to the Ptolemaic system for the other five planets, except that he has added some new movements and orbs which seem to have escaped Ptolemy. To avoid difficulties and excessive multiplication of motions and orbs he has retained equants. When he has more time to devote to the problem, he hopes to dispense with equants for the five planets, as he already has done in the case of the sun and moon. According to his hypotheses Venus and Mercury will be found now above and now below the sun, while only the three superior planets will always be above the sun. He agrees with Copernicus so far as the diversity of angles, proportions and dispositions of the orbs and their distances from the earth are concerned. Even those very learned men who by diligent observation of the new star of 1572 and the comet of 1578 have become convinced that the Copernican theory is close to the truth should not find Magini's theories of the planets, when stripped of equants, repugnant to their observations.

Formerly, in the canons of his tables written at Rome, Magini had utilized an anonymous work which promised hypotheses agreeing with both the Alfonsine and *Prutenic Tables*. Others such as Joseph Moletius in his *Gregorian Tables* had also followed it. Magini, however, had since proved some of its hypotheses false and was thereby led to formulate his own. Its author did not understand the precession of the equinoxes. Nor did he rightly reckon the motion of the anomaly of the apogee and eccentricity of the sun. His hypotheses do not agree with Copernicus or the *Prutenic Tables*.[220]

Again in the main preface to his work Magini calls Copernicus a most erudite man and outstanding artificer who most ingeni-

[220] First preface to the studious reader.

ously thought out his hypotheses of the multiple movement of the earth and quiet of the sun and fixed stars in order to avoid a multitude of spheres. But because these hypotheses have been generally rejected, many have unjustly inveighed against so great a man, to whom astronomy owes an eternal debt. Yet hitherto no one has calculated the celestial movements more expeditely and surely than Copernicus.

In his prefatory remarks Magini further insists that the stars and planets are moved by their orbs or spheres and cannot move of themselves. He finds it necessary to insert a ninth and a tenth sphere between that of the fixed stars and the *primum mobile,* to have orbs with poles different both from those of the other orbs and those of the zodiac, and, in addition to eccentrics and epicycles, to have orbs which are not of uniform breadth or thickness but concentric on one side and eccentric on the other. He thinks of Venus and Mercury as with the sun traversing the zodiac in one year.

In the text proper Magini first considers the theory of the motion of the eighth sphere and the three spheres beyond it. He then turns to the three superior planets. In their case the eccentric which carries the epicycle is not in the plane of the ecliptic and of the extreme orbs[221] but cuts it obliquely and its axis also intersects the axis of the zodiac.[222] Nor is the epicycle in the same plane as its eccentric.[223] Next is considered the theory of the sun which requires five orbs. Magini believed that the length of the year is variable and instable because of diversity in the movement of the sun and the unequal motion of the eighth sphere.[224] Passing to the theory of Venus, we are told that its sphere has four orbs, and that its eccentric which carries its epicycle does not move, as the three superior planets do, on an axis and poles inclined to the plane of the ecliptic at a fixed angle, but on an axis and poles which sometimes approach the poles of the zodiac and sometimes depart from them.[225] We are further told that

[221] That is, the eight, ninth, tenth and eleventh spheres.

[222] *Op. cit.,* fol. 10r.

[223] *Ibid.,* fol. 16v.

[224] *Ibid.,* fol. 38v.

[225] *Ibid.,* fol. 41r.

Copernicus makes the eccentricity of Venus variable, as he does that of Mars also.[226] Mercury requires six orbs and has an unequal annual motion of the apogee of the true eccentric which carries the epicycle.[227]

The theory of the moon Magini first sets forth according to Copernicus, and then according to his own hypotheses. He agrees with Copernicus that the Ptolemaic theory of the moon does not conform to our senses and experience. But he thinks that the Copernican theory of a double epicycle would sometimes prevent our seeing the spots on the moon.[228] It takes him 24 pages to set forth the theory of the moon according to Copernicus and 27 pages to present his own, which employs eccentrics only without epicycles.

The work of Magini is profusely illustrated with figures representing the orbs and movements of the planets. Its briefer second book[229] deals, as was customary with works on the theory of the planets, with their "passions", beginning with their latitudes and closing with eclipses. Instead of reducing the number of Ptolemaic movements and orbs, as Copernicus had tried to do, Magini has increased them. In place of the simplicity and uniformity which had been the ideal at least of Copernicus, he appears to have devised a system more clumsy and complicated than either the Copernican or Ptolemaic.

Johann Richter or Praetorius (1537-1616) was born in Joachimsthal, studied at Wittenberg, from 1562 to 1568 made mathematical instruments at Nürnberg, in 1569 visited Prag and Vienna and went with Andreas Dudith to Cracow, from 1571 to 1575 taught at Wittenberg, returned to Poland, Dudith and Vienna, then in 1576 became professor of mathematics at Altdorf for the rest of his life.[230] In his lectures there, which are preserved in manuscript form, he gradually came to give some attention to the Copernican theory.[231] In his lectures for 1594 a

[226] *Ibid.*, fol. 41v.
[227] *Ibid.*, fols. 45r, 50r.
[228] *Ibid.*, fols. 69v-70v.
[229] Covering fols. 383r-115v.
[230] Will, III, 225.
[231] *Ibid.*, p. 229: *Primi mobilis et planetarum theoriae Ptolemaicae collatae cum hypothesibus Copernici, ita tamen ut supposita Ptolemaica retineantur,* 1588.

figure of the Copernican system appeared for the first time, while in his last lecture for 1613 he referred to a scrap of paper torn from a letter of Regiomontanus and once in the possession of Georg Hartmann, in which he said that it was necessary that the motion of the stars vary a little bit because of the motion of the earth. But Praetorius found no such opinion in the extant works of Regiomontanus, and no such paper exists today.[232] Will represented Praetorius as a foe of astrology, but Hellmann counts twenty annual predictions by him in German for the years 1578-1598.[233]

John Paul Gallucius in his *Theater of the World* of 1588 still listed eleven celestial spheres and four elements, but made earth and water a single sphere. Discussing the relative amount of land and sea, he says that the truth long remained hidden because navigation did not extend to many places, but that now it is evident even to the blind that the quantity of earth exceeds that of water, as Alessandro Piccolomini had demonstrated by most convincing reasoning. These remarks of Gallucius apply especially to the earth's surface, for he still placed the inferno inside the earth in ten concentric circles.[234] In his *Speculum Uranicum*, printed at Venice in 1593, the full title speaks of following the *Prutenic Tables* for the true places of the eighth sphere and seven planets at any given time. In the text Gallucius speaks of the movement of the eighth sphere and in general adheres to the Ptolemaic system.

David Origanus or Dost, professor of mathematics at Frankfurt, in 1599 issued new *Ephemerides* for the 36 years from 1595, when those of Stadius began to show great error, to 1630.

[232] Zinner (1938), pp. 37, 202-3. Zinner argues that the passage could not refer to the revolution of the earth on its axis and did refer to its movement about the sun. I should think it more likely that it had reference to something like the third motion assigned to the earth by Copernicus or to the almost imperceptible movement that some believed occurred as a result of the shifting of position of land and water on the earth's surface and in its interior and consequent changing of the center of gravity.

[233] Hellmann (1924), p. 29. See also Tycho Brahe, *Opera*, III (1916), 155, for the real attitude of Praetorius towards astrology.

[234] Jo. Paulus Gallucius, *Theatrum mundi et temporis*, Venetiis, 1588, pp. 10, 15, 38.

They were "computed with the greatest diligence from the hypotheses of Copernicus and the Prutenic canons," and were accommodated to the horizon of Frankfurt an der Oder and to either calendar.[235] Origanus, who lived from 1558 to 1628, also wrote on the comet of 1618, and a work on natural astrology and the effects of the stars which appears to have been first published after his death in 1645 at Marseilles.

Jacob Christman of Johannisberg (1554-1613), professor of logic at Heidelberg, but a student of mathematics, chronology, and oriental languages,[236] published in 1601 three books of solar observations in which he explained the true movement of the sun in the zodiac, and argued that various authors had fallen into the gravest errors because they had not observed the movement of the sun.[237] Evidently he did not accept the Copernican theory.

William Gilbert, although a firm believer in the movement of the earth and usually reckoned as one of those who did most to advance the Copernican theory, recognized the strength of the objections to it that it required a triple movement of the earth and too vast an empty space between Saturn and the eighth sphere.[238] He also declared that the inequalities of the phenomena could not be saved by any circular or uniform motion,[239] thus definitely abandoning this Copernican ideal. He further felt that

[235] *Ephemerides novae annorum xxxvi incipientes ab . . . 1595 quo Ioannis Stadii maxime aberrare incipiunt et desinentes in annum 1630 . . . supputatae a M. Davide Origano,* Francofurti ad Oderam, 1599. Copy used: BM 8562.bbb.36.

[236] He was professor of Hebrew for seven years before he became professor of logic for twenty, after which in 1608 he became extraordinary professor of Arabic: Melchior Adam, *Vitae Germanorum philosophorum.*

[237] Iacobus Christmannus Ioannisbergensis, *Observationum solarium libri tres in quibus explicatur verus motus solis in zodiaco et universa doctrina triangulorum ad rationes apparentium coelestium accomodatur . . .,* Basileae, Impensis Lazari Zetzneri, 1601, 227 pp. Copy used: BM 531.k.6.(4).

[238] *Guilielmi Gilberti Colcestrensis medici regii De mundo nostro sublunari Philosophia nova, Opus posthumum, ab authoris fratre collectum pridem et dispositum, nunc ex duobus MSS codicibus editum,* Amsterdam, 1651, II, xx, p. 193: ". . . Copernici vero ratio magis incredibilis licet minus in motuum convenientiis absurda, quod terram triplici oportebat motu agitari tum vel maxime quod nimis vastam capacitatem inter orbem Saturni et octavam sphaeram esse oportet quae prorsus sideribus vacua relinquitur."

[239] *Ibid.,* p. 194.

he could state the movement of the earth according to Copernicus more plainly than it had been described by Copernicus himself.[240] He attributed to Giordano Bruno (Nolanus) another arrangement by which the sun moved annually about the earth in the equinoctial circle, while the earth retained the other two movements ascribed to it by Copernicus.[241] He referred to the varying explanations of the moon's movements given by Ptolemy, Copernicus and Magini without deciding between them, but held that the moon was moved by the earth as the tides are moved by the moon, and that the fact that the moon always kept the same face turned towards the earth showed that it was bound to it magnetically.[242] In an over-simplified and partially incorrect résumé of the history of astronomy Gilbert said that, after Ptolemy, Alfonso X and then Peurbach and Regiomontanus discovered a third movement which they called access and recess. Ptolemy introduced the ninth sphere; Thebit added a tenth; Averroes dispensed with all but eight orbs. Alpetragi did away with eccentrics and epicycles. Copernicus recalled older opinions, inverted the order of the planets, and, like some new Atlas of astronomy, emended the movements by new hypotheses. Baptista Turrius and Fracastoro piled up homocentrics to the number of seventy-seven. Tycho Brahe, inferior to no one in this age and a great observer of the phenomena, devised a different system from that of Copernicus, Raimarus Ursus in his *Fundamentum Astronomicum* also suggested a new arrangement of the entire system of the universe.[243]

We suggested earlier in this chapter that Galileo might better have written a systematic textbook setting forth the Copernican theory than his provocative dialogues. As a matter of fact, he did compose a brief treatise on the sphere or cosmography in Italian for his disciples which circulated in manuscript from 1604 on and was printed posthumously at Rome in 1656.[244] But

[240] *Ibid.*, II, 22; p. 196: "Motus terrae iuxta Copernicum planius quam ab eo describitur sic habet. . . ."

[241] *Ibid.*, p. 199.

[242] *Ibid.*, p. 185.

[243] *Ibid.*, pp. 149-51.

[244] It is reprinted with collation of four earlier MSS in the Edizione Nazionale of *Le opere di Galileo Galilei*, Florence, II (1891), 203-55: Trattato della sfera ovvero cosmografia.

it adhered strictly to the Ptolemaic system and represented the earth as immobile at the center of the celestial sphere. Copernicus is not even mentioned, although Galileo had elsewhere shown himself favorable to the Copernican theory as early as 1597.[245]

In 1616, the year of the condemnation of the Copernican theory by the Holy Congregation, Paul Minerva of Bari, a Dominican, master of sacred theology, and "moderator and regent" of the university of Naples, dedicated to cardinal Agostino Galemini an elaborate work on weather prediction.[246] In it he adverts a number of times to Copernicus and Tycho Brahe and confutes the opinion that the earth moves. He states that he has discussed this more fully in his treatises on meteorology[247] and human opinions,[248] as well as in a special treatise *De motu terrae.* These other works I have not seen. In that of 1616 Minerva rejects the movement of the earth as false, contrary to sense, experience and reason, to Holy Scripture "which in many places declares and confesses the stability, firmness, permanence and immobility of earth," and to holy doctors expounding those passages of Scripture. Minerva further characterizes it as an opinion "undoubtedly destructive to a large part of philosophy and astrology." It is, however, probable and is useful to dispute, test and defend for the sake of exercise and to train the talents of youth. Just as Minerva as a boy used to defend the views of other ancient philosophers against Aristotle, "so this opinion about the earth's motion can be upheld." It is a very ancient tenet of the Pythagoreans, Heraclides of Pontus, Ecphantus, Philolaus, Nicetas of Syracuse, and their disciples. In recent times Coelius Calcagninus of Ferrara recalled it to light; then that most worthy astronomer, Nicolaus Copernicus, employed it to establish his hypotheses. Finally, William Gilbert of Colchester in his *Nova Physiologia*[249] and in his work on the magnet

[245] *Ibid.,* p. 206.

[246] Paulus Minerva, *De praecognoscendis temporum mutationibus iuxta triplicem viam coelestem metheorologicam et terrestrem libri tres. . . . In tertio confutatur opinio de mobilitate terrae,* Neapoli, 1616, in folio. Copy used: BM 719.m.9.

[247] *Ibid.,* p. 288, "De rebus meteorologicis."

[248] *Ibdi.,* p. 244, "De opinionibus hominum"; p. 289, "Opiniones hominum de deo et creaturis."

[249] Minerva must have had access to this work in manuscript.

defended it but, like Copernicus, fell into Scylla while trying to avoid Charybdis.[250] Minerva reviews Gilbert's arguments at some length and complains that he did not prove them.[251] To Galileo's investigations with the telescope he makes no allusion.

While Minerva thus rejected the motion of the earth, except as elevated in dry exhalations to form comets, he had no objection to utilizing the astronomical calculations of Copernicus, if they seemed to be the best available. In his preface to the reader he says that in reckonings of the fixed stars according to longitude he has embraced both methods, Alfonsine and Copernican, that nothing may be lacking to the student. For their risings and settings he has employed only the Copernican reckoning as developed by Magini, since the findings of Tycho Brahe have not yet appeared. He awaits their publication eagerly, for they will differ from the Copernican and be more trustworthy, although they too will require emendation with the passage of time. For the entry of the sun into the twelve signs Minerva used the reduction of the movement of the sun from the Copernican calculation to the Tychonic which Magini had given in his supplements to the *Isagogicae Ephemerides,* which he continued from 1610 to 1630. In this connection Minerva says that the solar reckoning and length of the year according to the *Alfonsine Tables* "always have surpassed all others, because correct and true and more in accord with observations," and that Tycho followed it rather than the Copernican calculation in this regard. Magini gave two reasons why Copernicus was less correct on this point: first, that his estimate of the movement of the eighth sphere was too slow; second, that he misplaced the apogee and eccentric of the sun. On these points he was corrected by Tycho's observations.[252]

Our survey has revealed a frank recognition—though seldom acceptance—of the main contentions of Copernicus in the years immediately following the publication of *De revolutionibus.* After the appearance of the *Prutenic Tables* comes a tendency

[250] *Ibid.,* p. 289.
[251] *Ibid.,* pp. 292-304.
[252] *Ibid.,* p. 200.

on the part of many to associate Copernicus with their findings, to praise him in vague, general terms and to specify one or two minor points based upon his observations, but to forget, ignore, or remain blind to the major conclusions and implications of the Copernican theory.

We have further seen that a chief reason for turning to the *Prutenic Tables* was dissatisfaction with the *Alfonsine Tables* or what then passed for the *Alfonsine Tables,* not with the observations or hypotheses of Ptolemy. This dissatisfaction with the *Alfonsine Tables* was not merely because they had gotten out of date and no longer corresponded to the observed position of the stars and planets, but because they had presumed to correct Ptolemy, to amend his estimate for the precession of the equinoxes, to imagine a ninth sphere beyond his eighth. This problem, which had been occupying the minds of astronomers since Thebit ben Corat, continued to intrigue almost every sixteenth century writer on the *Sphere.* It was Copernicus's solution of it by a combination of his observations with those of Ptolemy and the Arabs and Alfonso, and his theory of an anomaly in the precession of the equinoxes and in the distance between sun and earth through the ages, which attracted their attention and appealed to many of them far more than the Copernican theory as we understand it. They turned in many cases to Copernicus and the *Prutenic Tables* for a vindication of Ptolemy against the more recent medieval hypothesis of a ninth sphere, not for their own hypotheses which were tantamount to a serious modification of the Ptolemic system, if not to that complete overthrow of it which some modern historians have supposed.

Then comes a third stage, when the *Prutenic Tables* are also found to correspond none too well to the observed positions of the stars, when the sufficiency of even the observations of Copernicus is questioned by Tycho Brahe on the basis of fuller observations, when the *Alfonsine Tables* are vindicated by the judgment of the Gregorian calendar reformers as to the length of the year, but when philosophers who are intent on attacking Aristotle and founding new systems of their own find congenial encouragement in the boldness of the Copernican hypotheses. Also when astronomers like Tycho Brahe and physical scientists like William Gilbert face the full meaning of *De revolutionibus* but make modifications or new hypotheses and systems of their own, combining Ptolemaic and Copernican features.

Finally, the effect produced upon some of the more scientifically inclined minds of the time by the Copernican and Tychonian systems, as by the earlier homocentric system of Fracastoro, was one of reaction against hypotheses and of insistence upon limiting oneself to observation of the actual positions and movements of the heavenly bodies. The whole matter was much slower of settlement than one might think. A mathematical Franciscan and younger contemporary of Newton, Père Grégoire or Henri Marchand, born at Lyons in 1674 and deceased at Marseilles in 1750, is still found defending the Copernican hypothesis and writing a dissertation on the impossibility of the systems of Ptolemy and Tycho Brahe.[253]

[253] See MS Lyons 925 for these and other mathematical and astronomical treatises by him.

CHAPTER XXXII

THE NEW STARS

Then felt I like some watcher of the skies
When a new planet swims into his ken.
—KEATS

Early in November of 1572 watchers of the skies were startled by the sudden apparition of a new celestial phenomenon. It surpassed in brightness and apparent magnitude all the heavenly bodies except the sun, moon and Venus. If the sky was clear, it could be seen at any hour during the daytime as well as at night. It looked like a star rather than a comet, since it had neither tail nor hairy appearance. Its position with reference to the fixed stars did not alter, and to the most careful observers such as Maestlin and Tycho Brahe it seemed to have no parallax, diversity of aspect, or difference between its apparent and true motion. They therefore placed it not only farther off than the moon but even beyond all the planets in the sphere of the fixed stars. This meant either that it could not be a comet, or that the Aristotelian theory of comets as terrestrial exhalations in the upper air below the sphere of the moon was erroneous at least in this case. If it was not a comet but a new fixed star, or if it was a comet recently generated in the heavens, it was fatal to the hitherto generally accepted belief among philosophers that the heavens were eternal and incorruptible and that there was no generation or corruption in the sky. Indeed, if it was a new star, it would seem further to violate the statement of the theologians that God had ceased from the act of creation on the seventh day and ever since. Moreover, the only previous record of a new star, so Tycho Brahe said, was one for which Pliny cited Hipparchus and a dubious allusion by Cyprian Leowitz to another in 1264 which was probably after all a comet.[1]

[1] Tycho Brahe, *Opera,* ed. Dreyer, I, 16; II, 328.

The star of 1572 could not be identified with any previously known star or planet, since they all still occupied their old positions, while it had blazed forth in a place hitherto unoccupied. Moreover, if so large and bright a star had been previously in existence, it was hard to explain how such astronomers as Ptolemy, Alfonso and Copernicus had failed to notice it. Some persons said that it returned every hundred or four hundred years but they gave no proof of its previous occurrence at these dates. Many persisted in regarding it as a comet in the air, but the weight of scientific evidence was decidedly against them, and it was difficult to conceive how so large a body could be composed of terrestrial exhalations, as comets were supposed to be by Aristotle.

It seems safe to say that to the scientific world of the sixteenth century, and probably to the religious world also, this new star of 1572 came as a greater shock than the publication of the Copernican theory in 1543. Men had been prepared for and looking forward to the printing of the work of Copernicus, but the brightly shining apparition of 1572 flashed upon them like a thief in the night. Moreover, Copernicus had merely added another hypothesis and calculation in the attempt to explain observed and well-known facts. The star of 1572 was a new and indisputable fact which upset more than one hoary and hallowed theory. Cornelius Gemma's soul was filled with gratitude to God that this splendid phenomenon had come during his lifetime. It inspired him to construct his cosmocritical art and to compose his book on *Divine Signs in Nature*. It caught the eye of Tycho Brahe as he was on his way to his alchemical laboratory. Thereafter he devoted most of his time to astronomical observation rather than chemical experiment. The star of 1572 itself absorbed many of his hours. After it had disappeared and he could no longer observe it, he continued to occupy himself with an elaborate review and criticism of all that others had written concerning it, with the record of his own observations, and with revision of his first brief treatise on it, composed while it was still visible.[2]

[2] *Ibid.*, II, 307, 329.

So dumbfounded indeed were such leading astronomers as Maestlin and Tycho Brahe by this exception to all their preconceived notions, that at first they could offer no natural explanation for it but proclaimed it a miraculous divine new creation. This was the conclusion to which the most careful measurements and accurate mathematical calculations seemed inevitably to lead. Tycho would not even compare it with the star of Bethlehem, which was in the lower air near the earth's surface and which the Magi understood by their occult science. But this was the greatest miracle of nature since the beginning of the world or at least comparable with Joshua's ordering the sun to stand still.[3]

Nor was Tycho any less inclined to attribute significance for the future to the new star than were those who based prognostications upon it as a comet. It was a sign from God beyond all order of nature, "constituted by Himself in the beginning and now finally exhibited to a world hastening to its end." Yet Tycho ventured further to indulge in five pages of astrological judgment concerning its effects, which should exceed even those of an eclipse or greatest conjunction both in magnitude and in unusualness. Great political and religious changes were to be expected, the more so since there would be a change of triplicitas in ten years. Tycho further considered the relation to the new star of the various planets and the regions where its effects would be most felt. He then concluded with the esoteric utterance that he was passing over in silence what might be adduced from the truer and more secret fonts of another astrology, known to very few and whose mysteries it would be wrong to violate.

The greater part of Tycho's oration on the mathematical disciplines before the university of Copenhagen in September, 1574, was devoted to assertion of the influence of the stars and

[3] These passages are found in Tycho's first brief work on the star of 1572 to Iohannes Pratensis, M.D., dated at Knusdorp on May 3, 1573. It occupies pp. 9-34 in vol. I of Dreyer's edition of Tycho's *Opera.*

Maestlin's similar attitude is shown in the following passage: "Quid ergo prohibet quin dicamus totum hoc Hyperphysicum stellamque hanc novam a summo Creatore his novissimis temporibus creatam esse atque uti miraculose coepit ita miraculose desituram cuius utriusque causa omnem humanum captum effugiat," quoted by Tycho Brahe, *Opera,* 1648, p. 335.

to defense of astrology. He admitted that its principles and axioms could not compare in certainty with those of geometry and astronomy, and that the influence of the stars was less patent to the senses than their motion. But he refuted the objections of philosophers and theologians to the art.

At their birth or soon after Tycho drew up several elaborate horoscopes for members of the Danish royal family: the future Christian IV, prince John, and prince Huldaric. He took great pains to base these upon as accurate astronomical observations and calculations as possible and would not rely on existing tables. In 1577 in the geniture of the future Christian IV he followed the calculations of Copernicus rather than the *Alfonsine Tables* for the movements of the planet Mercury, and made some further corrections from his own observations. In 1583, in the horoscope for prince John, he followed neither the Alfonsine nor *Prutenic Tables,* since frequent observation with instruments had shown both to be in error, except that for Mercury, difficult to observe because so near the sun, he generally followed Copernicus. Tycho recognized the uncertainty of astrology as to various matters such as the assignment of cities and countries to different signs of the zodiac, or predicting from the child's nativity as to his parents, brothers and sisters. The latter practice he usually continued nevertheless. In the case of prince John, whose horoscope indicated that he would remain single, prediction as to his children seemed superfluous. But since he might will to marry and so overcome the contrary inclination of the stars, Tycho investigated the matter further and found that, if he did so, his offspring would be girls of weak constitution. Tycho predicted that the future Christian IV would scarcely survive his fifty-sixth or fifty-seventh year, but that monarch in fact lived past seventy.

These princely genitures in Latin remained until the present century in manuscript, as did a work by Tycho in German devoted primarily to the astrological influence of the comet of 1577. It is rather significant that this work, although intended to correct various erroneous tracts in German which had appeared upon that comet and written in the vernacular for popular consumption, was apparently not published by Tycho, whereas his longer Latin work on the same comet, in which he abstained from treating its astrological significance, was printed in his lifetime. He seems to have become so absorbed with the Latin work that the other was side-tracked, suggesting that astrology may have lost its hold on scientifically minded persons, not because they ceased to have faith in it, but because they became more intent upon positive astronomical activity for its own sake. The continued hold of astrology upon Tycho is seen in two tracts by him on the comet of 1585, one printed the year after, the other found in manuscript, but both astrological.

Years before the appearance of the star of 1572, Cardan in his *De subtilitate* of 1550, and in 1557 Jean Pena, royal mathematician at Paris, had rejected the doctrine that comets were exhalations from earth set on fire in the supreme region of air. From the fact that the tail of the comet was always turned away from the sun they inferred that comets must be transparent bodies or globes of some material like glass or crystal through which the sun's rays could be refracted and kindle fire. But through fire itself the sun makes no pyramidical refraction.[4] Pena had further held that it could be demonstrated by the principles of optics that some comets were far above the orbit of the moon.[5] He had also advanced the revolutionary idea that the space traversed by the planets was filled with air and that between the earth and them there was nothing but air—no sphere of fire and no succession of spheres moving the planets. For if light had to pass through so many different media of varying density, whether one thought of the celestial spheres as hard and solid or as more rarefied and limpid than air, there would be no possibility of certain astronomical observation and measurement, and the researches of Hipparchus, Ptolemy and Copernicus would be in vain.[6] From this optical reasoning, then,

[4] *Euclidis Optica et Catoptrica*, Paris, 1557: *Ioannis Penae regii mathematici de usu optices praefatio ad illustrissimum principem Carolum Lotharingum cardinalem*, fol. bb ii recto.

[5] *Ibid.*, fol. bb ii verso.

[6] *Ibid.*, fol. aa ii verso.

Pena rejected both the sphere of fire and the celestial spheres as well as the notion that the planets were borne along by their spheres and did not themselves move. Pena's early death prevented his promulgating this theory further, but it did not die with him, for years later we find Tycho Brahe holding him responsible for the spread of the opinion that air not merely encircled the earth but was disseminated throughout the heavens.[7]

Controversy as to the new star of 1572 waxed very hot in some quarters. Thaddeus Hagecius, whose work upon it I have not seen, refers back to it in a treatise of 1584 on another subject. He states that he was immediately dragged into the theological arena by Theodore Graminaeus and William Lindanus, bishop of Ruremond, and attacked most bitterly. Lindanus, whom he did not know and had never injured even by a word, would not even leave him a place among Christians but accused him of venerating doctrine of the devil in place of the gospel of Christ.[8] He was delayed in the preparation of an elaborate reply and after two years circulated in manuscript a sort of introduction to it.[9] This he complains his two opponents spread abroad without waiting for his full work to appear.

The appearance of the new star led Thomas Digges and John Dee to publish their treatises on the way to measure the parallax, with careful and generous acknowledgement of their mutual indebtedness.[10] Digges held that there had been no previous ade-

[7] Tycho Brahe, *Opera,* ed. Dreyer, II, 77; III, 154; VI, 135, 187, 320; VII, 121, 172, 212, etc.

[8] Thaddaeus Hagecius, *Aphorismorum metoposcopicorum lib.*, 1584, p. 24, Copy used: BM 1141.b.11.(2). Concerning Graminaeus see the index volume XV to Dreyer's edition of Tycho Brahe's *Opera* and Valerius Andreas, *Bibliotheca Belgica,* 1643, p. 828.

[9] *Ibid.*, p. 25, "ex integro meo opere Aquilonis historici levem quendam prodromum manuscriptum tertio iam decurrente anno emisi."

[10] Thomas Digges, *Alae seu scalae mathematicae quibus visibilium remotissima coelorum theatra conscendi et planetarum omnium itinera novis et inauditis methodis explorari, tum huius portentosi sideris in mundi borealis plaga insolito fulgore coruscantis distantia et magnitudo immensa situsque protinus tremendus indagari deique stupendum ostentum terricolis expositum cognosci liquidissime possit,* Londini apud Thomam Marsh, 1573, 4to, 44 fols.

Then follows, with a new title page and signatures and a preface by D Digges, Dee's *Parallaticae commentationis praxeosque nucleus quidam,* by a different printer, John Day. Copy used: BM 532.d.1.(4).

quate treatment of the subject even by Regiomontanus.[11] He further questioned whether the movement of the earth might not be the sole reason why the new star diminished in apparent magnitude,[12] which would seem to suggest that he might have utilized his own method of the parallax to more advantage. He urged most precise observations of the new star from various points on our globe.[13]

The star of 1572 proved to be less inalterable and abiding than the fixed stars and planets. Its color soon altered, its magnitude diminished, and its brightness waned. Finally, after shining all through the year 1573, it disappeared from sight early in 1574. Thus as a sign in the sky it declined in impressiveness, while it scarcely seemed classifiable as one of the eternal and incorruptible heavenly bodies. Yet it had appeared and tarried among them. Johann Praetorius, professor of mathematics at Wittenberg and then at Altdorf, in his tract on the subsequent comet of 1577, said of the star of 1572 that, while it was shining, astrologers and philosophers differed as to whether it was a fixed star, new divine creation, a comet, or something halfway between star and comet. But that after it disappeared, there was general agreement that it was a meteor rather than a star but in the ethereal region.[14] The impression which it had at first made and the problems which it had raised still inspired Tycho Brahe to review the entire literature upon it, to compare his own observations of it with those made by others, and to develop his first hasty treatment of it in 1573 into a long work intended to serve as the basis for a restoration of astronomy—*Astronomiae instauratae progymnasmata*.[15] Moreover, there came in 1577 another heavenly messenger and celestial sign to drive home the lessons of the first, to evoke another outpour of treatises and prognostications, and to keep men thinking upon the problems which the star of 1572 had raised. That of 1577 was more evidently

[11] *Ibid.*, in his Preface to Wm. Cecil.
[12] *Ibid.*, Preface to the reader.
[13] *Ibid.*, fol. L 2 verso.
[14] Tycho Brahe, *Opera*, ed. Dreyer, III (1916), 154.
[15] It fills the second and third volumes of Dreyer's edition of Tycho's works.

a comet and moved about in the sky, yet appeared to be above the moon.[16]

Reconsidering his first estimate of the star of 1572 in the light of this later phenomenon, Tycho Brahe ceased to proclaim it a marvelous new divine creation and suggested that it might have been formed out of an adjacent segment of the Milky Way. It was of celestial matter, not terrestrial exhalations, but of less perfect substance than the fixed stars, which served to explain why it had so soon dissolved and disappeared. It resembled the fixed stars as an alchemical artefact does the natural metal.[17] The comets of 1580 and 1585 confirmed Tycho in his rejection of the Aristotelian doctrine of comets, to which his observations and those by others of the phenomena of 1572 and 1577 had led. The comet of 1585, in his opinion, was undoubtedly above the sun. Rothmann had even put it in the sphere of Saturn. That of 1580, Tycho suggested, was perhaps even beyond the eighth sphere.[18]

The Jesuit astronomer, Clavius, in his *Commentary on the Sphere of Sacrobosco,* had no doubt that the new star of 1572 was in the firmament, whether it was a comet or a new creation. He quoted writings of 1572 concerning it by Paulinus Pridianus, a physician and astronomer of Antwerp, and by Maurolycus.[19]

Helisaeus Roeslin, a physician of Zabern in Alsace, wrote in 1578 on the new stars and more particularly on the comet of 1577[20] without mention, and apparently without knowledge, of

[16] C. Doris Hellman (Mrs. Morton Pepper) who published "A Bibliography of Tracts and Treatises on the Comet of 1577," *Isis,* XXII (Dec. 1934), 41-68, is working on a fuller treatment of the literature concerning the comet as a doctoral dissertation at Columbia University.

[17] *Opera,* ed. Dreyer, III, 304-8. Tycho repeated these views in a letter of 1590 to Peucer.

[18] *Ibid.,* IV, 350: *Opera,* ed. of 1648, II, 203.

[19] *Christophori Clavi Bambergensis ex societate Iesu In Sphaeram Ioannis de Sacro Bosco Commentarius nunc quarto ab ipso auctore recognitus et plerisque in locis locupletatus,* Lugduni, sumptibus fratrum de Gabiano, 1593, pp. 210-11. But, as we have seen, with a dedication of 1581.

[20] *Theoria nova coelestium METEΩΡΩΝ in qua ex plurium cometarum phoenomenis Epilogisticis quaedam afferuntur de novis tertiae cuiusdam Miraculorum Spaerae Circulis Polis et Axi: super quibus cometa anni MDLXXVII novo motu et regularissimo ad superioribus annis conspectam stellam tanquam ad Cynosuram pro-*

the views thereon of Tycho Brahe, although he praised those of Thaddeus Hagecius and Cornelius Gemma. Roeslin maintained on the one hand that the comet of 1577, like the new star of 1572, was neither elementary nor sublunar but celestial and in ethereal regions. He even attempted what he declared no one before him had tried, to show that comets moved in regular orbits with poles and an axis. On the other hand he insisted that the new star of 1572 and the comet of 1577 were not natural phenomena but miraculous apparitions and divine signs of the approaching end of the world. No greater prodigy than the star of 1572 had been seen since the beginning of the world, while the comet of 1577 was not a vulgar one but preternatural and metaphysical. Other portents in the form of meteors, balls of fire and falling stars had followed these in the years of 1575 and 1578. Thus the scientific advance over the Peripatetic doctrine of comets as terrestrial exhalations is counterbalanced by the tendency still to connect celestial phenomena with the supernatural and with divination of the future.

The new star of 1572 and comet of 1577 are identified with two signs often mentioned by the Babylonian sibyl and are further related to the Apocalypse and to the vaticinations of Joachim, Ubertino, "Theolosphorus" (or Thelesphorus), Torquato and others. As the comet of 1556 was the harbinger of disturbances in lower Germany, so it is to be feared that the recent comet means the spread of these evils to the adjoining parts of Europe. And that in these last times great changes are imminent both in church and state is confirmed on other astronomical grounds, since the sun or the center of its eccentric is now almost at the bottom of its small circle and close to the earth. Also six great conjunctions have occurred since Adam, in the days respectively of Enoch, Noah, Moses, the ten tribes of Israel, Christ and Augustus Caesar, and Charlemagne. In an appendix Roeslin adds that as man the microcosm is subject

---

gressus Harmoniam singularem undique ad Mundi Cardines habuit maxime vero medium Europae et exacte Germaniae Horizontem non sine numine certo respexit. Argentorati. Excudebat Bernhardus Iobin, 1578.

in disease to critical days, so the macrocosm or world at large in its infirm old age has certain critical years. In 1583-1584 there will be a change from the aerial to fiery triplicitas as there was in the time of Christ, while unusual eclipses will mark the forty years, 1574-1614, since the disappearance of the new star. After some reflections on the years of the synagogue of the Old Testament and the days of the prophet Daniel, Roeslin infers from the lapse of 1655 years between Adam and the flood, that the second conflagration of fire will occur in 1654 A.D. He also has something to say of perfect numbers and the four monarchies, and endeavors to solve the meaning of Daniel's "time, times and half a time" by arranging biblical history in clusters of fourteen generations each, and the emperors since Julius Caesar in groups of forty-two, to Constantine, Charlemagne and Charles V respectively.

Thus for Roeslin, instead of any warfare between science and religion such as some modern writers have tried to see everywhere in the sixteenth and seventeenth centuries, the two fields are not yet even separated. To us they seem confused in his thought; to him they seemed most happily harmonized. He may have dropped a doctrine of Aristotle; he has not lost hold of a single biblical prophecy. As a physician he is interested in astronomy. As an astronomer he not merely tries to plot the course of a comet but to demonstrate its future significance and to fit it into a scheme of world history based upon the Bible and astrology.

The comet of 1577 also elicited a treatise of no small importance from Michael Maestlin who signs himself further as "deacon of the church which is in Backnang."[21] In the preface to Louis, duke of Wurtemberg and Tech, count of Mompelgard or Montbeliard, Maestlin tells how the duke's father, Christopher, had educated him for the church from tender years.

[21] Michael Maestlin Goeppingensis, *Observatio et demonstratio cometae aetherei qui anno 1577 et 1578 constitutus in sphaera Veneris apparuit cum admirandis eius passionibus varietate scilicet motus loco orbe distantia a terrae centro etc. adhibitis demonstrationibus geometricis et calculo arithmetico cuiusmodi de alio quoquam cometa nunquam visa est.* Tubingae excudebat Georgius Gruppenbachius, 1578, 59 pp. Copy used: BM 532.e.61.

Then by the son's liberality he has been able not only to study at ease philosophy, science and mathematics, but to devote himself to the saving doctrine of the holy divine word in so far as God has given him grace. It is to mathematical studies nevertheless that he feels himself born. From boyhood they have so fascinated him that he has never tired of them. By the same token he admires Alfonso the Wise, patron of astronomy, far more than those monarchs who slew thousands and increased their power by land and sea. Today Alfonso is much more alive than they. The duke has encouraged Maestlin to go on to advanced work in mathematics. When he found that something was lacking in existing astronomical tables and calculus, he began to make and record as many astronomical observations as possible, to compare these with others, and so attempt to restore astronomical calculus to "an absolute and long expected integrity." On this account he has always given more attention to astronomy than to astrology. Here is manifest the same motive as we have seen at work in Tycho Brahe. Prediction of the future from the stars is slighted, not for the negative reason that Maestlin considers it superstitious—we shall soon see that apparently he did not—but because astronomical observation and measurement make a greater positive appeal to him.

As for "the new and dread prodigy, a comet of unusual magnitude," Maestlin finds that it does not conform to others previously observed. He tries to show on the basis of his careful observations of it and by geometrical and arithmetical demonstrations that its movement from first to last has been no less bound by most certain astronomical laws than the motion of any other star. Accompanying his text is a map of the path of the comet in the sky with its position and that of the sun at different dates. Maestlin did not find this sort of detailed measurement in the descriptions of previous comets but perhaps he was unacquainted with Toscanelli's manuscript on the comet of 1472. In any case he makes the point that astrologers predict from comets without undertaking any such careful observations and hence proceed on a quite invalid foundation.

Maestlin rejects the opinions of those who think the comet an elementary and not a celestial body. One reason that it cannot be an exhalation in the air is that Witelo and Alhazen demonstrate by optics that the earth's atmosphere cannot be but a small fraction of its diameter in height, or the sun's rays would be reflected in its vapors long after the sun was below the horizon. It is therefore absurd to locate a comet at a distance of eight times the earth's radius and yet assert it to be within the region of air. Maestlin places the comet in the sphere of the planet Venus and finds its motion equal and regular. This demonstrates that the orbit of Venus about the earth is apparently irregular. And this in turn leads him to embrace the Copernican theory, for he finds that of all the hypotheses as to the movements of the heavens, it is the only one into which the observed course of this comet will fit.

It is not with this progressive note of experimental verification of the Copernican hypothesis that Maestlin closes. We go back to astrology. His last chapter is devoted to conjecture as to the significations of this comet. It is true that he censures astrologers who abuse the art and the practice of interrogations. But he believes that true astrologers have learned from the experience of many centuries that eclipses and comets are precursors of misfortune. He does not feel qualified himself to issue a judgment or prognostication, because so far his studies have been astronomical rather than astrological. Further, he is doubtful whether this particular comet is unfavorable or favorable. Before he saw any other judgments on it, he presumed that many would put it under Saturn, and they have done so. He, however, for the reason that we have heard, would put it under Venus. It seems a sign of ill from the Turks, and this has been borne out by a Turkish attack when it first appeared. Other portents in the sky seen at Backnang on November 22 and 23, at Berlin by Thurneisser on November 25, and by Andreas Noltius on December 19, indicate disturbances which can be settled only by war, as Maestlin attempts to confirm by four historic examples. He then closes with a warning to Christians to turn to God.

After reading Maestlin's treatise on the comet of 1577 Roeslin wrote him[22] that in observing and explaining this comet he had shown himself such an artificer in illustrating prodigies of this sort as the world had not seen since its foundation. Ancient writers had left nothing of the sort, and moderns had only begun to investigate the parallaxes of comets by observations and instruments and to record their findings. Roeslin accepted Maestlin's corrections of his own tract on the comet and confessed that he had made its epicycle too small, misled by Thurneisser's asserted observation of it on October 19, which he was now inclined to reject, since Maestlin had not seen it then, although intent on observations of Saturn that very evening. He suggests that Thurneisser wished to justify his own previous prediction that some star would rise on October sixth. The observations and parallaxes of Cornelius Gemma agree with the circle and epicycle assigned to the comet by Maestlin, to whom Roeslin sends a copy of Gemma's treatise, "since I notice it had not yet come to you." Thaddaeus Hagecius had given this comet a parallax of five degrees, probably because he had accepted its apparent altitude and had observed it carelessly, but Maestlin's work should convince him of his error.

Roeslin also was much pleased by what Maestlin said of the material of the comet and what Gemma said of the form and efficient causes of its generation, since these agreed with what he had written concerning the motion of comets. He was inclined to believe that even the sublunar region of inferior comets must be put higher than the Peripatetics had hitherto placed it, but will write Maestlin further on that head later. He goes on to state that he had once abandoned "all these studies" from lack of instruments, but "the magnitude of these miracles," namely the new star of 1572 and the comet of 1577, had set him to thinking again. He believes that he has discovered that comets are subject to certain circles "of the last heaven." Of one circle in the sphere of Venus he regards Maestlin as the first discoverer.

[22] "Datae Tabernae Alsatiae 18 Octobris Anno 1578": printed with Maestlin's *Ephemerides novae ab anno 1577 in annum 1590,* Tubingae, 1580, 4to. Copy used: BM 532.d.13.

For another through the solsticial points, he gives the credit to Gemma, while he claims as his own discovery a third coinciding with the horizon of Germany. He believes that he can defend his sphere of comets from those of the years 1475, 1532, 1533, and 1556 as well as 1577, and will sometime write Maestlin further on this point.

Maestlin was only twenty-eight years old when he wrote on the comet of 1577, as is shown by a picture of him with the accompanying inscription, "Aetatis 28—1578," in a subsequent publication of which we are about to speak. This is his *Astronomical Consideration and Observation of the Ethereal Comet of 1580,* with a description of other meteorological phenomena known as "chasms" of the years 1580-1581.[23] He again dedicates his work to duke Louis of Wurtemberg. Maestlin has just become professor of mathematics at the university of Heidelberg. Previously the illness of his wife and daughter and his trips to Heidelberg in connection with the vacant chair there had interrupted his astronomical observations at Backnang.

In the preface Maestlin recognizes that comets and "chasms" are signs of future ills, trumpeters and rods of divine wrath at our sins as truly as the rainbow is God's sign of promise. In closing the text he says that, although he does not pretend to skill in astrological judgment, it is not difficult to predict the future series of events from these phenomena. This comet portends a much worse series of calamities than before. Inasmuch as the comet of 1577, although it was in the sphere of benevolent Venus, signified adversities in many places, not indeed from the Turk (as we heard Maestlin himself suggest before) but from those who are even more cruel than Turks, what shall we think of this present comet of horrid aspect, sad face, dark funereal obscurity, Saturnine visage, and pale image of death? No one should doubt that inevitable fate is at hand.

[23] Michael Maestlin, *Consideratio et observatio cometae aeterei astronomica qui anno 1580 . . . apparuit. Item descriptio terribilium . . . chasmatum quae his annis 1580 et 1581 conspecta sunt,* Heidelbergae, 1581, 4to, preface and 36 numbered pp. Copy used: BM 532.e.63. For chasmata see Aristotle, *Meteor.*, I, 5.

But Maestlin's main purpose and interest, as before, is to examine the comet's movement, place, properties and the astronomical laws governing it. As before, he concludes that it was not sublunar but shone high in the heaven. He remarks on the tortuous arguments to which opponents of the ethereal position of the new star of 1572 were forced to resort. He laments that many still uphold conjectures and the authority of old philosophy against most certain geometric demonstrations from most diligent observations in which they know there is no falsity. Speaking for himself, these three new and unusual stars of 1572, 1577 and 1580, all seen in the heavens within a period of eight years, have convinced him that the Peripatetic doctrine of comets is untenable. He has not yet had time, however, to figure out whether this last comet of 1580 is in the sphere of Saturn, Jupiter or Mars.

The case of Maestlin shows that we cannot divide men into two camps with lines sharply drawn between them, but that we ever find all sorts of intermediate shadings and combinations of opinion. He represents the most advanced methods of astronomical observation and mathematical calculation, he abandons the Aristotelian theory of comets, he embraces the Copernican hypothesis. But he still believes in astrological judgments and that comets are signs of divine wrath. It was not merely the ignorant and backward or the hidebound conservative who cherished such notions. Our young astronomer cannot be classed as a mossback. Yet for him science and astrology go together: in his mind there is not warfare but concord between science and theology.

Tycho Brahe, although the leading astronomer of his day and generation, displayed a very similar attitude. He maintained anthropocentric and religious conceptions of nature and the universe. He held that the world was made for man, and that the work of the divine hand could be seen in the vilest creatures, but especially shone forth in the sky.[24] He cited Scripture against the Copernican hypothesis and the movement of the earth, yet

[24] *Opera,* ed. Dreyer, I (1913), 35.

explained away by free interpretation the biblical mention of waters above and below the firmament as having reference merely to the sea and clouds. In another passage he inveighed against those who were all too ready to adopt unproved novelties in religion, yet continued to adhere to the Aristotelian doctrine of comets after their own observation should have demonstrated its falsity.[25]

In his *Ephemerides* for the years 1577-1590,[26] which continued those of Stadius, Maestlin noted that no one since Ptolemy, not even Copernicus, had made observations of the fixed stars. He also expressed the hope of a radical renovation of astronomy. "Relying therefore on the certitude of my observations, I am confident that this almost collapsed science of the stars . . . will be greatly amplified in its new splendor." The volume contains a list of proposed works by Maestlin, for which an imperial privilege is given in advance as they shall later be published. These proposed works comprise a compendium of astronomy to consist of a commentary on the *Sphere* and *Theories of the Planets*, an arithmetic, plane and spherical trigonometry, commentaries on Cleomedes and Theodosius, treatises on instruments, *Revolutions of the Celestial Orbs* in imitation of the *Almagest* and Copernicus, new tables in imitation of the Alfonsine and Prutenic, *Tabulae resolutae* after those of Bianchini, and new *Ephemerides* based upon the new tables. Few of these proposed works were ever published, and it was to be Tycho Brahe and Kepler, rather than Maestlin, who were to observe the fixed stars and reform astronomy.

Maestlin, however, initiated his program of publication by an *Epitome of Astronomy* dedicated to the duke of Wurtemberg in 1582[27] and corresponding to the proposed Compendium. In the preface to the reader Maestlin tells us that, since method is very important in such a work, he long deliberated as to it, especially since he found much discrepancy in existing manuals. Then he

[25] *Ibid.*, III, 56.

[26] Michael Maestlin, *Ephemerides novae ab anno 1577 ad annum 1590*, Tubingae, 1580, 4to. Copy used: BM 532.d.13.

[27] I have used an edition of 1597: *Epitome astronomiae*, BM 531.f.15.

noticed that in fundamentals most of them followed Sacrobosco. He therefore examined the *Sphere* of Sacrobosco and came to the conclusion that no better way could be devised of presenting the elements of astronomy, and that even those who censured Sacrobosco sharply could not avoid following largely in his footsteps. Yet he flourished around the years 1232 and 1256, a barbarous period in which there was a great dearth of learned men. This remark shows the historical astigmatism and illogicality of Maestlin, however acute his astronomical observations and calculations were. But what a phenomenon Sacrobosco was! The new star of 1572 and the comet of 1577 might wax and wane; Copernicus might amend Ptolemy; *Prutenic Tables* might replace Alfonsine and then receive their own share of adverse criticism; astronomy, restored by Regiomontanus, might collapse again. But the fundamental old *Sphere* of Sacrobosco went on shining, unobscured even by the classical reaction.

In previous chapters we have heard many modifications suggested of the old conception of four elements and their arrangement in successive spheres from the earth to the moon in accordance with the Aristotelian doctrine of heavy and light. The discovery of land scattered over the surface of the globe had convinced most thinking scientists that there was only a single sphere of earth and water instead of a sphere of earth enclosed in one of water. Some, like Cardan, held that water was heavier than earth and sank into it as far and in as great quantity as it could. Others, like Ramus, Cardan and Tycho Brahe, rejected both fire as an element and the existence of a sphere of pure fire between the air and the moon. As it became apparent that the new star of 1572 and the comet of 1577 were much farther away than the moon from the earth, a number of astronomers adopted the view of Pena that the spheres of the planets were not composed of a fifth essence but that the region of air extended from the earth to the fixed stars. By this theory comets might still be thought of as meteorological manifestations in the air and not as celestial bodies composed of ethereal matter like the planets and fixed stars. Among those to adopt this explanation were Johannes Praetorius in his tract on the comet of 1577, where he definitely attributed it to Pena,[28] Henry Brucaeus,[29] and Christopher Rothmann,[30] mathematician or astronomer to the landgrave of Hesse. Thus in order to save the Aristotelian doctrine of comets as terrestrial exhalations in the air, these men were ready to modify another Aristotelian theory that the heavens were eternal, incorruptible and of a fifth essence unlike the elements and to abandon the conception of planetary spheres. All of which seems very much like cutting off the baby's head in order to cure it of squinting. Incidentally it may be added that Praetorius was at the same time an astrologer, since a score of annual predictions in German by him are extant for years between 1578 and 1598.[31] Rothmann defended the Copernican hypothesis and believed that the earth moved.[32]

Tycho Brahe ultimately rejected the Aristotelian doctrine of comets and a sphere of fire. He expressed the rhetorical wish that professors and students in the universities would take occasion from the star of 1572 to open their eyes and learn from the book of nature by how many and how great errors that pagan Aristotle had fascinated them for so many centuries.[33] Nevertheless he continued to hold with the Stagirite that the heavens were free from all impurities of the elements and contained neither air nor water.[34] In his first work on the new star, dated from Knusdorp on May 5, 1573, he said that all philosophers were agreed that there was neither generation nor corruption in the heavens, and he appears to have maintained this belief throughout his life. A third opinion was that of Paracelsus that the sky is elemental fire,[35] while Caspar Peucer

[28] *De cometis qui antea visi sunt et de eo qui novissime mense Novembri apparuit narratio a Iohanne Praetorio Ioachimico,* Noribergae, 1578, 4to. I have not had access to this work but follow Tycho Brahe's account of it, *Opera,* ed. Dreyer, III (1916), 153-57. Neither Tycho nor Hagecius was able to obtain a copy: see their correspondence of May 3 and Nov. 1, 1588, and Nov. 1, 1589: *Ibid.,* VII, 120, 147, 212.

[29] Tycho Brahe, *Opera,* ed. Dreyer, VII, 143, 167.

[30] *Ibid.,* III, 155.

[31] Hellmann (1924), p. 29.

[32] Tycho Brahe, *Opera,* ed. Dreyer, VII, 238.

[33] *Opera,* ed. Dreyer, III, 141. Also at p. 56 Tycho criticizes those who believed Aristotle rather than their own eyes.

[34] *Ibid.,* VII, 229-30.

[35] Tycho adverts to it, *ibid.,* VII, 230; IV, 382.

in 1590 still argued from the literal sense of Scripture for waters above the firmament.[36] So we see again various shades and combinations of opinion, that we cannot sharply separate Aristotelians and Copernicans, that either of them is as likely to be favorable to astrology as the other, and that the holder of a modern or correct view in one respect is not saved thereby from gross error in another.

Brucaeus, writing to Tycho Brahe in 1588, could still question the advisability of expending so much time and labor over such transitory phenomena as comets, which never recurred again but perished, each comet being an individual phenomenon of which the knowledge died with the comet itself.[37] It is germane to notice not only that such discussion of comets by Tycho as seemed to Brucaeus somewhat aimless and too prolix and elaborate laid the foundation for later discovery and scientific advance, but also that this same Brucaeus had three years before expressed surprise that Tycho's students were issuing astrological calendars in view of the uncertainty, not to say impossibility, of weather prediction.[38] Thus it was the critic of astrological excesses who also was inclined to chide astronomy for useless vagaries, while the restless explorer of the heavens and scientific observer of the stars was not averse to their astrological influence. It is true that Tycho in one passage declares that even the common people are aware of the vanity and futility of weather prediction in annual prognostications. But he straightway appended an example of good weather prediction.[39] It may further be noted that Brucaeus spoke slightingly of Paracelsus, whom Tycho called "the incomparable philosopher and physician of the Germans."[40]

[36] *Ibid.*, VII, 231-32. Tycho replied that Moses was writing for the common people and merely distinguishing between the clouds and the sea. He added that the greatest absurdities would ensue from admitting the existence of supra-celestial waters.

[37] *Ibid.*, VII, 144: "Sed quid de re numquam recurrente imo intereunte tantum laboris, obiecit mihi quidam, sumimus?" VII, 167: "Quod autem scripsi totam tractationem de cometis circa individua versari quorum cognitio una cum ipso cometa intercidit verum est, cum nec motus idem nec corporis forma eadem unquam sit reditura."

[38] *Ibid.*, VII, 91-92, 100.

[39] *Ibid.*, I, 36.

[40] *Ibid.*, VI, 224; VII, 169.

Human thinking and theorizing in any sphere—political, economic, social, intellectual or religious—have seldom been consistent. The most logical *Summa,* the best-rounded philosophical system has always had some excrescence, some foreign substance, some utter anomaly that should have caused its originator or his followers the same acute discomfort that a corncob produces in one trying to sleep on a husk mattress. But so ingrained is human waywardness and perversity, so great the enthusiasm for a new social order or religion, so intense the attachment to establish economic conditions and to firmly rooted ideas, that to conservative and radical alike such misplaced and contradictory notions are cherished closer than a brother, are regarded as the seeds of the grape, the exceptions that prove the rule, the dearest wandering black sheep of the whole flock. They may even be the last of all the old notions to be relinquished, for the very good reason that there were no sufficient grounds for adopting them in the first place, and that they were not integral parts of the lost faith, abandoned system, or fallen social order. They are nuts that would break the strongest teeth, so everyone swallows them whole.

Of this sort was the position in medieval cosmology and astrology of the Aristotelian doctrine that comets are terrestrial exhalations. It did not fit in at all. The fundamental law of nature was that inferiors were ruled by superiors, that transitory, corruptible, terrestrial bodies were governed by eternal, incorruptible, heavenly bodies; that everthing beneath the moon was subject to the movements, light and influence of the planets, stars and orbs above the moon. Yet comets, described as terrestrial, combustible exhalations of transitory existence, which circulated only in the upper air or at most in the region of elementary fire beneath the moon, were believed to be sure signs, if not causes, of the death of kings and other great disasters. Moreover, this belief was to outlast, if anything, the more plausible and general doctrine of the submission of inferior to superior nature. At least it was slower to show signs of losing ground. Furthermore, no sooner was it demonstrated that comets were really celestial phenomena than astrology, which, it might have been thought, would be strengthened by this removal of an anomaly and this confirmation of its central and fundamental doctrine, sank rapidly into a state of decline and was soon rejected by science.

I am aware that the exhalations which were supposed to take fire aloft and become comets were thought of as caused by the planets, and that each comet was under the especial lordship of one or two planets whose influence it was supposed to convey. But this was a mere subterfuge and piece of sophistry. Why was not observation of the planets which were going to produce the comet enough to indicate all the coming effects, both the comet itself and the other changes associated with it? Why intrude an intermediate cause or sign? Why was it necessary or proper for astrologers to take into account in their predictions anything beneath the moon? Why should "signs in the air" be any more astrological or prophetic than earthquakes, floods and other terrestrial and aquatic phenomena, which were produced by the stars much as comets were said to be? It seems clear that for purposes of prognostication the comet was tacitly treated as a celestial cause, while for purposes of Aristotelian physics and meteorology it was classified as an earthly exhalation. This double-faced irregularity, as has been already suggested, seems rather to have been welcomed than otherwise by the writers, thinkers and observers of the time.

A rather extreme instance of the point we are making is supplied by a publication as late as 1665. In that year Gisbertus Voetius reprinted the *Declamation* of Libavius on the comet of 1604, together with an *Exercise* of his own on prognostications of comets.[41] Yet, without taking any notice of Copernicus, Galileo or observations through the telescope, Voetius still main-

[41] *Exercitatio de prognosticis cometarum,* Amsterdam, 1665, 4to, with Andreas Libavius, *Declamatio de cometa anni 1604,* Amsterdam, 1665, Copy used: BM 532.e.16.(3.).

I have also seen listed an edition of Amsterdam, 1641. Yet in the above mentioned edition the dedication to two physicians and former professors in the university of Utrecht—William Stratenus, M.D., now physician to the prince of Orange, and Arnold Senguerdius, Ph.D., now in Amsterdam—is dated at Utrecht in May, 1665.

tained the Aristotelian doctrine of comets. On the other hand, he opposed the rules of astrology and allowed only a limited prediction from comets, which he regarded as divine miracles and signs rather than natural causes. He compiled from a large number of authorities, most of whom were antiquated, and for the rest engaged in theoretical argument, apparently alike oblivious to more recent scientific hypotheses and astronomical observations. Possibly the retention of belief in comets as divine warnings may be regarded as compensatory for the abandonment of astrology, much as the stricter Puritan Sabbath served to fill the gap left by the non-observance of saints' days.

Returning to the sixteenth century, we may notice a few more examples of the literature. Conrad Dasypodius (Rauchfuss), noted as the constructor in 1574 of the astronomical clock in the cathedral at Strasburg,[42] published there in 1578 a *Brief Doctrine Concerning Comets and the Effects of Comets*[43] which was almost wholly astrological. Yet in the preface to John Sambucus (1531-1584), imperial historian and counselor, who had received the licentiate in medicine at Padua in 1555, Dasypodius spoke of editing the texts of several classical mathematicians. From an ancient codex belonging to Sambucus he had years ago printed Theodosius and Autolycus.[44] Five years since he turned over to the printer the complete works of Euclid, "corrected and emended and adorned,"—this last word perhaps indicates humanistic tampering with the style—but the printer has added delay to delay and still is holding up publication. Recently from the same manuscript Dasypodius sent to be printed scholia on Euclid's *Elements* by Isaac the monk, a Byzantine writer of the late fourteenth century.[45] "My geometric commentaries I still

[42] Schoepflin, *Alsatia illustrata*, 1751-1761, II, 292, n.5. There was an earlier clock of 1352-1354 and a third constructed by Schwilgué. See Alfred Ungerer, *L'Horloge astronomique de la cathédrale de Strasbourg*, Paris, 1922, 60 pp. with a bibliography of the previous literature of the subject.

[43] Cunradus Dasypodius, *Brevis doctrina de cometis et cometarum effectibus*, Argentorati, 1578, 4to. Copy used: BM 532.e.56. There is also a copy in the New York Public Library.

[44] At Strasburg in 1572.

[45] For an edition of 1579 see the printed catalogue of the Bibliothèque Nationale, Paris. I do not find Isaac mentioned in Krumbacher's *Byzantinische Literaturgeschichte*. But see T V, 623.

have with me, but when occasion offers, I shall publish them with my other writings. Your Hero you shall see shortly."[46] Two manuscripts of such ancient Greek texts which once belonged to Dasypodius are preserved today in the university library at Upsala. One is a sixteenth century paper copy of the *Harmonics* of Ptolemy, which, according to a note at its close, was given by Dasypodius to David Wolkenstein on St. John the Baptist's day, 1575.[47] The other, likewise of the sixteenth century and written on paper, is the *Geometry* of Joannes Pediasimus or Galenus, and bears on its first leaf the legend, "I am the property of Conrad Dasypodius and his friends."[48] Neither of these manuscripts was known to the first editors of these respective works, John Wallis[49] and Gottfried Friedlein.[50]

Dasypodius still accepts the Aristotelian doctrine of comets and regards the star of 1572 as such a comet. For the astrological influence of comets he follows Ptolemy with some citation of medieval Arabic and Latin authors—Albumasar and Leopoldus. He records past examples of influential comets, but his chronology is at times faulty, as when he dates the fall of Constantinople in 1445. Comets under the domination of the planet Venus have unusually long bright rays and are seen rarely or with the greatest change in affairs, as in the year 1470. But it is to the comet of 1477, a century ago, that Dasypodius ascribes the most specific ills. There was an unheard-of wheat famine, a plague of locusts, and a great pest in Italy. Charles the Bold and 17,000 Burgundians were killed in battle with the Swiss, while Louis XI lost 20,000 men in Burgundy. In the following year there was pest in Switzerland. Finally, the comet announced the deaths of Mary, wife of Maximilian, Casimir, son of the king of Poland, Edward IV of England, Albert of Brandenburg,

[46] The *Geometrical Vocabulary* of Hero was printed at Strasburg in 1579 and his *Mechanics* in 1580.

[47] Upsala Greek MS 45. See Charles Graux, "Notices sommaires des MSS grecs de Suède, Mises en ordre et complétées par Albert Martin," *Extrait des Archives des Missions,* 3e série, tome XV, Paris, Ernest Leroux, 1889.

[48] Upsala Greek MS 46, fol. 1, "sum Conradi Dasypodii et amicorum."

[49] Joh. Wallis, *Claudii Ptolemaei Harmonicorum libri tres ex codicibus mss. undecim nunc primum graece,* Oxonii, 1682.

[50] *Jahrbuch f. Phil. u. Paed.,* 92 (1865), 366-83.

and Matthias Corvinus of Hungary. Since the last named monarch did not die until 1490, Dasypodius seems guilty of another chronological slip. He ascribed the Peasants' War of 1525 to a comet, and many evils to the comets of 1531, 1532 and 1533. In his fifth and last chapter he finally reaches the current comet of 1577.

Tycho Brahe later remarked[51] with regard to the astrological causes of the comet of 1577 listed by Dasypodius, that, if such positions of the stars as he gave produced comets, attempts to predict their appearance would be more successful. Actually, Tycho added, no one had succeeded in predicting the appearance of a comet except by chance, whereas many had announced the coming of comets which had failed to materialize. For example, no comet had appeared between that of 1558 and that of 1577, yet almost every year in the interim a comet had been forecast by astrologers, and commonly on more plausible astrological grounds than those advanced by Dasypodius.

Bartholomaeus Scultetus, in a treatise dedicated to the senate of Görlitz and printed there in 1578,[52] located the comet of 1577 in the sublunar region, although he made at least a pretense of astronomical measurements and calculations after the manner of Tycho Brahe, with tables and figures of angles and spherical triangles. Some of his observations were "from the information of the most famous mathematician, Paul Wittich of Breslau." He then turned to "the significance and effect of this prodigious portent," following the method of Ptolemy's *Quadripartitum* in Cardan's edition and judging the comet's effects from its magnitude, color, splendor, form, duration, site, the direction of its tail, its longitude and latitude with consideration of the signs, and its relation to the fixed stars.

In connection with the comet of 1577 a catalogue and review of previous comets, which claimed to be fuller than any hitherto,

[51] *Opera*, ed. Dreyer, IV (1922), 362, in his *De mundi aetherei recentioribus phaenomenis of 1588.*

[52] Barth. Scultetus, *Cometae anno humanitatis I.C. 1577 a 10 Novembris per Decembrem in 13 Ianuarii sequentis anni continuis LX & V, D. in sublunari regione adparentis descriptio*, Görlitz, 1578

was issued by Georgius Caesius, pastor at Leutershausen, together with a judgment from the comet of 1577, and addressed to the council of Nürnberg.[53]

A curious complex of attitudes is displayed in two tracts on the nature of ignited meteors and the causes and significations of comets, with observations of that of 1577, which Simon Grynaeus addressed to Ludwig VI, elector Palatine, early in 1579 and which were printed with other tracts on comets in 1580.[54] They also are found in a Palatine manuscript now preserved at the Vatican.[55] In the preface Grynaeus says that there are two operations of nature which give rise to doubt and hesitation in human minds, namely, occult virtues and the influence of meteorological and celestial bodies. Throughout the text he airs his acquaintance with the Greek language and once discusses the definition and etymology of the terms, portent, prodigy, *ostentum* and *monstrum*. He adheres to the Aristotelian doctrine of comets and says nothing of the star of 1572 and recent opinions that comets are celestial bodies. But he recognizes the force of the argument: if comets are mere mixtures of the inferior elements and not celestial bodies, how can they signify the future? His

[53] *Catalogus numquam antea visus omnium cometarum secundum seriem annorum a diluvio conspectorum usque ad hunc praesentem post Christi nativitatem 1578 annum cum portentis seu eventuum annotationibus et de cometarum in singulis Zodiaci signis effectibus . . . a M. Georgio Caesio pastore in oppidulo Leutershausen: et eiusdem Iudicium de Cometa nuper in fine anni 77 elapsi viso.* Noribergae Excudebat Valentinus Furmannus. I own a copy. At fol. A ii verso is a bibliography of previous histories of comets.

[54] *Commentarii duo: De ignitis meteoris unus, alter de cometarum causis atque significationibus, conscripti per Simonem Grynaeum. Accessit eiusdem observatio cometae qui anno superiore 77 et ab initio 78 fulsit,* 1580, 88 pp., in *De cometis dissertationes novae.*

[55] Vatic. Palat. lat. 1072, Simonis Grynei Commentarii duo de ignitorum meteororum natura, incipit fol. 4, "Totum hoc universum . . ." In principe est Ep. dedic. ad Ludovicum comitem palatini Rheni, incipit fol. 1, "Due sunt . . ." On the title page we read: "De ignitorum meteororum natura commentarii duo quorum priore de causis impressionum ignitorum et phasmatum (chasmatum?) disseritur. Altero de cometarum causis et significatione ad illustrissimum principem dominum Ludovicum comitem Palatinum Rheni S.R.I. Archidapiferum et electorem conscripti a Simone Grynaeo doctore medico. Accesserunt eiusdem Observationes cometae qui anno 1577 aliquot mensibus et ab initio anni 78 fulsit et Disputatio de inusitata magnitudine et figura Veneris conspecta ad finem anni superioris et in initio huius 1579."

answer is that they are neither signs of calamities nor causes of future events, and he minimizes their influence on nature without denying it entirely. Reviewing the comets of 1531, 1532, 1554 and 1558, he notes that the weather effects ascribed by Aristotle to comets did mark those years. But they also were fertile years, showing the error of those who say that comets cause sterility. Grynaeus admits that indirectly comets may be a cause of pestilence, although he suggests that they would tend to purify rather than to pollute the air. He denies any connection between comets and such events as the death of kings. Nor may such diverse calamities as pest, war, floods and famine all be traced to one and the same cause. In astronomy Grynaeus is inclined to accept the suggestion of moderns that there is an eleventh sphere but he does not recognize the Copernican hypothesis and still has all the heavenly spheres revolve about the earth as their center.

Thus this backward geocentric Aristotelian, as some would call him, is opposed to prediction of the future, aside from the weather, from comets, although he agrees that they may be signs of divine wrath. He is more interested in purely astronomical observations of the comet of 1577, which he first saw at Heidelberg on November 14 of that year and of which he gives his observations at fifteen different times. It is true that he appends a physical and a theological judgment concerning the comet, but the former contains no astrology, and the latter is limited to reflections on the extreme effete old age of this world, human iniquity, and God's just wrath but vouchsafing of warning signs. The common opinion concerning the comet he opposes. This done, Grynaeus turns to further astronomical observations, this time of the unusual magnitude and shape of Venus as seen on five occasions during December, 1578. Thus Grynaeus combines the practice of repeated scientific observations with retention of an outworn doctrine which they should have disproved. He accepts comets as divine signs but not as natural causes of human and historic events. His complex of tenets illustrates once again that we find all kinds of intellectual permutations and combinations, however incongruous or unexpected they may be. Almost any assortment of ideas, conflicting or harmonious, is found in some mind or other.

Libri,—whose *History of the Mathematical Sciences in Italy from the Renaissance of Letters to the End of the Seventeenth Century,* written a century ago, combined so many excellencies with such serious defects,—said with regard to the treatise on the comet of 1577, published at Parma in 1578 by Pietro Sordi, that the author, like others of his time, thought that the return of comets could be predicted by astronomy and calculation.[56] This statement gives the impression that Sordi thought of comets as heavenly bodies with regular orbits whose re-appearance could be astronomically calculated. On turning to Sordi's own text we discover that he believed nothing of the sort. He still holds and sets forth at length the Aristotelian doctrine of comets according to which they are terrestrial exhalations which rise into the third or supreme region of air next to the sphere of fire where they become inflamed and after a few months are consumed and disappear.[57] Moreover, there is neither astronomical observation nor numerical calculation shown in Sordi's treatise. Its first part is purely argumentative, citing previous and contemporary writers like Pontano, Cardan and Piccolomini, setting forth other opinions about comets and rebutting them, then developing his own view which is that of Aristotle. The second part of the work is astrological, citing the *Flores* of Albumasar, mentioning as examples various past comets and the events which followed them, and giving the constellations connected with the recent comet of November 13, 1577, for Parma, since Sordi holds that different places are under different stars and signs. Finally, it is not the return of comets that Sordi thought

[56] Libri IV (1841), 45, citing Tiraboschi XI, 452-53 (VII, 717-18 in the Milan, 1824 edition which I usually cite). Probably Libri had not himself examined Sordi's work. However, even the quotation from it given by Tiraboschi, although it fails to bring out the fact that Sordi thought of comets as terrestrial exhalations, not as heavenly bodies, indicates only that the appearance, not the return, of a comet could be predicted.

[57] Pietro Sordi, *Discorso sopra le comete,* Parma, 1578, fol. 20v *et seq.* Copy used: BM 53.b.9.

could be astronomically predicted: it is the generation of a comet under planetary influence that he thought should be astrologically forecast. Having told of some ancient Greek who foretold that a stone would fall from the sun at a given time, he suggests that surely by the same art there must have been stated rules by which the very day of a comet's inflammation and apparition could be foretold. "But these have not come down to us." However, Felice Pacchiotto, that most excellent philosopher and *rara avis* in many sciences, had told Sordi that he had seen a book which showed by astrology and arithmetic the time of the appearance of comets. Therefore Sordi, instead of taking an astronomical step forward and being a forerunner of Halley, merely took an astrological step backward in the direction of Aristotle and Albumasar. I have dwelt upon the matter in some detail because it supplies an excellent illustration of the perils of writing a history of the mathematical sciences without taking the constant presence of astrology into account during the centuries in question, and because it further shows the faultiness of an historical method which endeavors to pick out from the writings of past authors sentences or passages in which they are supposed to have marked the first appearance of a fruitful idea or to have heralded the development of some future discovery, without estimating the meaning and value of this utterance in relation to its context and to the main aims and totality of the author's work.

The extent and limits of Sordi's belief in astrology are indicated by his statement that the celestial bodies by their virtue, light and motion govern all this inferior machine and human inclinations, but not our intellect and our will which are absolutely free.[58] Again, after stating in closing that he "ever submits to the holy judgment of our Catholic religion," Sordi adds that it is his belief that the stars do not compel or necessitate but only incline "in the manner that the holy Catholic Roman church holds."[59] Some thought it impossible that a comet should remain immobile, as Seneca and Ptolemy had stated, but Sordi suggests

[58] *Ibid.*, fol. 20r.

[59] *Ibid.*, fol. 60r-v.

that such a comet might be under the attraction of a stationary planet.[60] Two more examples may be given of Sordi's general scientific notions. He affirms what was certainly not the case, that all philosophers, astrologers, mathematicians and geometers held it for most certain that sun, moon and stars do not move themselves but "with the motion of their orbs, in which they stand fixed like knots in a wooden table," and that they are merely denser and thicker portions of their orbs.[61] In another passage Sordi says that animate bodies are generated only in earth and water, not in the other two elements. The salamander, thanks to its very cold temperament, may be able to withstand fire for a while but is not generated in it. Aristotle was quoted as to insects born in furnaces, where they flutter about in the flames and on emerging suddenly die. Sordi replies to this that Aristotle did not say that they were generated in the fire but in the furnaces or stone.[62]

Elias Olaus Cimbrus, an assistant to Tycho Brahe, put the comet of 1585 above the moon and noted that it was round and tailless. But his discussion of it was mainly astrological. He considered its relation to the conjunction of 1583, noting incidentally that a terrible pest had followed the conjunction of 1563. He further connected it with Saturn and spent eleven pages on its effects. He then continued with an astrological and meteorological diary for the ensuing year, 1586, devoting four pages to prediction as to its four seasons, and then two pages to each month in the form of an almanach with weather prediction.[63]

We may terminate this chapter by a few examples of the strong hold which the Aristotelian doctrines of comets and of incorruptible heavens maintained in the early seventeenth century despite all the observations, measurements and discussion aroused by the new stars.

Gerónimo Cortés of Valencia, although a mathematician

[60] *Ibid.*, fol. 33v.

[61] *Ibid.*, fol. 13r.

[62] *Ibid.*, fols. 18r-19v.

[63] *Diarium astrologicum et metheorologicum anni a nato Christo 1586 et De cometa quodam rotundo omnique cauda destituto qui anno proxime elapso mensibus Octobri et Novembri conspiciebatur ex observationibus certis desumta consideratio astrologica*, Uraniburgica, 1586. Copy used: BM 532.e.62.

and the author of a *Lunario y prognostico perpetuo* which ran through many editions,[64] in a chapter on comets in his composite volume on *Physiognomy and Various Secrets of Nature,* printed at Cordova in 1601, Zaragoza in 1603, and, in an enlarged edition, at Tarragona in 1609,[65] affirms that comets are nothing else than a mass of burning exhalations, some of which are generated in the first region of the air and others formed in the third. The latter are larger and move circularly with the heavens but so irregularly, and sometimes contrary to the motion of the heavens, that the falsity is evident of the opinion of certain astronomers and philosophers, that comets are engendered in the ethereal region from condensation of celestial matter.[66]

Writing in 1605 of the new star of 1572 and likewise those of 1600 and 1604, Wolfgang Satler still upheld the three regions of air, the distinction between elementary and celestial spheres, and the Aristotelian doctrine of comets. He rejected the Ramian dogma of only three elements, excluding fire. Satler maintained that meteors might be generated naturally or supernaturally. Were one to admit that natural comets appear above the moon, one might as well locate clouds and coruscations there too. The recent new stars fell into the second supernatural category and were hyperphysical, since they had appeared in the heavens, where there is no generation or corruption. Our sin was the cause of their preternatural generation, since the warnings conveyed by natural comets below the moon had failed to move us to repentance. Eclipses too, in Satler's opinion, always portended something for man. But from these supernatural stars no prediction according to astrological rules was possible.[67]

[64] The first edition of it listed by Nicolás Antonio, *Bibliotheca Hispana nova,* Madrid, 1783-1788, was at Valencia in 1598. He does not mention the *Octava y ultima impression del lunario y pronostico perpetuo,* Barcelona, G. Margarit, 1614, 8vo, 221 pp., BN V.29306. There were other printings after it.

[65] I have seen only this third edition: *Phisonomia y varios secretos de naturaleza: contiene cinco tratados de materias diferentes todos revistos y majorados en esta tercera impression a la qual se han añadido muchas cosas notables y de mucho provecho. Compuesto por Hieronymo Cortes natural de la Ciudad de Valencia con licencia.* En Tarragona por Felippe Roberto, 1609, 115 fols.

[66] *Ibid.,* V, 16; fols. 81r-82r.

[67] Wolfgang Satler, *Dianoia astrologica,* Montisbelgardi, 1605, cap. 38, pp. 289-96. Copy used: BM C.79.a.26.

Jean Taxil in 1614 praised both the Jesuit astronomer Clavius and Galileo to the skies, saying that Clavius "has spoken more clearly of astrology and all other parts of mathematics than any author of past centuries," and that Galileo is "the pearl of astrologers of this century" and "the honor and glory of our age, as he will be an object of wonder to ages to come." Yet Taxil regards the new stars of 1572 and 1605 as mere comets in the upper region of air. He contends that those astronomers who put the star of 1572 in the eighth sphere on the ground that it had no parallax were old men with weak vision whose observations must be discounted.[68]

In 1618 Giannini still affirmed the eternal, incorruptible and non-elementary nature of the heavens in the latter part of a chapter devoted to rebuttal of the arguments by which Philoponus had maintained that the heavens were of a fragile and mortal nature.[69] After stating the proofs given by the astronomers that the star of 1572 was not in the elementary region and was not one of the constellation of Cassiopeia, Giannini admits that the question is a difficult one. But he is not inclined, "because of these new stars," to desert Aristotle, whose opinion as to the nature of the sky has been approved by all the most learned masters of scholastic theology. Giannini therefore tries to discount the positions of the astronomers and to convince himself that Aristotle would have placed these new stars in the elementary region. If the astronomers feel that he has not done them justice, he reminds them of the epicycles and eccentrics with which Hipparchus and Ptolemy modified the homocentric theory of Calippus and Eudoxus, of the two new spheres added to the eighth by the medieval Arabs and Latins, and an eleventh suggested by Copernicus (*sic!*). If all these amendments and innovations have been introduced into astronomy, may not two or three stars, visible at a certain distance from the sun and

[68] Jean Taxil, *L'Astrologie et physiognomie en leur splendeur,* Tournon, R. Reynaud, 1614, 8vo. The first part, entitled, "Recueil de partie des erreurs et contradictions de l'anticometiste en son libelle," is a reply to an anonymous writer who had disagreed with Taxil as to comets. The allusions to Clavius and Galileo occur at pp. 179, 173 and 175.

[69] Tommaso Giannini, *De substantia caeli,* Venice, 1618, cap. 9, pp. 34-38.

hidden otherwise, also have been previously overlooked? Whatever may be thought of the nature of these stars, a problem still controversial; it would be unfitting on that account to reject what is confirmed by no despicable arguments and as to which there is general agreement among most eminent men. If from three new stars one may infer that the sky is of mortal nature, why from the innumerable stars in which no change in substance has been noted through all past time may not the permanence of the heavens be a much more logical conclusion? With this rhetorical and fallacious line of argument Giannini dropped the subject, and so may we.

CHAPTER XXXIII

ASTROLOGY AFTER 1550

Si quis igitur collectis rerum memorabilium locis ad ea traiectiones maximas accomodarit et regiones affici aut res publicas mutari perspexerit, tum scientiam de moribus et natura populorum efficit pleniorem, tum etiam de omni genere historiarum multo verius ac melius iudicabit.

—Bodin, *Methodus*, cap. v.

In the second half of the sixteenth century efforts to improve astrology, to make it more natural and scientific, become noteworthy. The attempt is made on several hands to gather data, to collect a large number of particular cases, and from this mass of observations by the inductive method to work out and formulate more dependable rules of prediction. This was done especially in the field of nativities, where individual horoscopes and genitures were noted in the hope of providing an experimental basis for astrological laws. Annual predictions for society at large continued, however, and conjunctions, eclipses and comets were still observed and prognosticated from. The reaction from Arabic to Ptolemaic astrology, which we have seen in the first half of the century, went on, and the problem as to which method of dividing the zodiac into houses was the best still vexed practitioners of the art. But despite the expressions of preference for Ptolemy, his *Quadripartitum* was not to be printed again after the edition of 1553, which was just about the time that the publication of the works of the Arabic astrologers began to thin out. Some astrologers did not share the urge to reform their art but went on along the old traditional lines. In the following pages we shall offer illustrations of both trends.

How great the popular faith in astrological predictions still was in the second half of the century may be inferred from a statement made by Cornelius Gemma in 1569. He tells of an astrologer who eight years earlier had made a lucky forecast of future events which won him such a reputation that thereafter the people would have believed him, had he foretold that the stars would fall from the sky. Although he was now dead, prognostications were still issued under his name.[1]

Medical men of the fourteenth and fifteenth centuries had published *Consilia,* or records of their particular cases with mention by name of famous patients. Cocles had introduced a similar practice in his work on chiromancy and physiognomy, discussing such individuals as Ludovicus Vitalis, Caesar Borgia, and Savonarola. This method was extensively employed by Luca Gaurico in a work printed at Venice in 1552 while he was bishop of Civitate.[2] This *Tractatus astrologicus* followed a different procedure from that of 1540 by the same author. Of its six books the first gave figures of the constellations at the foundation or restoration of a number of cities and buildings. The remaining five books gave the genitures of various well-known persons, usually accompanied by a sketch of the individual's life and character. The object was to lay a foundation for future prediction by a careful examination of the nativities and accidents (i.e. subsequent lives) of a number of recent cases. In some instances the horoscopes of living persons were given, and Gaurico predicted as to the remainder of their careers. The second book dealt with seven popes and twenty-nine cardinals and prelates; the third, with thirty-four secular rulers; the fourth, with forty-one men of letters and learning, nine musicians, and five artists; the fifth, with forty-six instances of violent death; the sixth, with nine persons of imperfect or mutilated physique. While laying an experimental basis for genethlialogy is the pro-

[1] Cornelius Gemma, *De arte cyclognomica,* 1569, II, 1; p. 28. Gemma is either guilty of careless overstatement in saying that the astrologer has been dead "many years" (*a multis hinc annis*), or his previous "eight years" should be a larger figure.

[2] *Lucae Gaurici Geophonensis episcopi Civitatensis Tractatus astrologicus in quo agitur de praeteritis multorum hominum accidentibus per proprias eorum genituras ad unguem examinatis, quorum exemplis consimilibus unusquisque de medio genethliacus vaticinari poterit de futuris, quippe qui per varios casus artem experientia fecit exemplo monstrante viam.* Venetiis apud Curtium Troianum Navò, MDII.

fessed aim of the book, it is probable that the sale of the volume was increased by the appeal made to general interest and curiosity by the inclusion of so many well-known names and persons in high places.

Although Gaurico noted his past successful predictions—as he claimed—in a number of the cases recorded, he failed to foresee the papal tiara for cardinal Caraffa and gave no inkling of the coming early violent death of Henry II of France, to whom he promised "a most happy and green old age."[3] Gaurico also, according to Pèrcopo, even made mistakes as to past events. He said that, when the Venetian troops entered Padua in 1509, two Paduans, whom he mentioned by name, were hanged, whereas the truth was that one of them died a natural death in that year, while the other was still living when Gaurico's work was published. His libellous statement got Gaurico into difficulties at Venice, and, rather than admit his mistake, he left the city.[4] Cardan had anteceded Gaurico in the publishing of a collection of genitures. The last of his five books on genitures, printed at Nürnberg in 1547, had collected a hundred examples of them.[5]

Valerius Andreas[6] states that Theodoric ab Haghen, a physi-

[3] Pèrcopo, XVII, ii, 39, notes, however, that, in a *Pronostico* of July 30, 1552, to the duke of Ferrara, Gaurico predicted for Henry II "some impediment from horses and tears flowing from the left eye," which the wounding of the king by a lance in 1559 was to verify.

In 1580 Ranzovius, *Catalogus imperatorum* . . . , p. 52, said that Gaurico five years before the event had warned Henry II to avoid a duel when he was about forty-one years of age, since the stars threatened then a wound in the head which would result in blindness or death.

Thus the prediction becomes more accurate as the event approaches and passes.

Aleander records a similar earlier slip by Gaurico in the case of Zenobius Acciaiolus of Florence who died in his fifty-ninth year, although Gaurico had predicted that that revolution of his nativity would be very happy. Henri Omont, "Journal autobiographique du Cardinal Jerôme Aleander (1480-1530)," *Notices et Extraits,* 35 (1897), p. 41.

[4] Pèrcopo XVII, ii, 36-37. The page in Gaurico's work which Pèrcopo cites for the passage in question, fol. 10v, was left blank in the copy of the Venice, 1552 edition to which I had access: Col 156.4 G23. Presumably this was done to satisfy the offended person and families.

[5] Hieronymus Cardanus, *Libelli quinque: I. De supplemento Almanach, II. De restitutione temporum et motuum coelestium, III. De iudiciis geniturarum, IV. De revolutionibus, V. De exemplis centum geniturarum.* Additis insuper tabulis . . . etc. Nürnberg, Joh. Petreius, 1547.

[6] *Bibliotheca Belgica,* 1643, p. 823.

cian and star-lover of Utrecht, published in 1552 an astrological *Prognosticon* from creation to recent times,[7] but I have not found the work.

One year after the death of Gemma Frisius (1508-1555) his treatise on the *Catholic Astrolabe* was published at Antwerp by his son, Cornelius Gemma (1535-1579) who added the last 19 chapters and dedicated the work to Philip II.[8] In this work it is stated that Johann Schöner followed Regiomontanus's method of dividing the astrological houses on the equator until his old age when, influenced by the opinion of certain more recent writers he changed to the method of Ptolemy and Firmicus of dividing the zodiac itself into twelve equal parts. Cardan adopted this last-named method in his early supplements to the *Almanach* and in his collection of one hundred genitures, but in his commentary upon Ptolemy's *Quadripartitum* followed the method of Regiomontanus. Cyprian Leovitius said that opinions as to the merits of the two methods differed, but that he had found that predictions based upon the method of Regiomontanus came out better in actual practice. Gemma Frisius was likewise a little inclined to side with Regiomontanus, but was of the opinion that satisfactory predictions had been made by the other method also.[9] In the closing chapters of the same work Cornelius Gemma gives a horoscope for his father and a scheme of the constellations for 1554, the year of Philip II's marriage with Mary Tudor.[10]

The dedication to John Frederick, duke of Stettin and Pomerania, by John Garcaeus Junior (1530-1575) of his *Brief Treatise on Erecting Figures of the Sky, Verifications, Revolutions and Directions* is dated July 18, 1556[11] although the edition I

[7] *Prognosticon stellare ab orbe condito usque novissimum iuxta errantium siderum habitudines . . . , inscriptum Georgio Egmondano episcopo Ultrajectino,* typis Herm. Borculoii, 1552, 4to.

[8] Reinier Gemma (Frisius), *De astrolabio catholico,* Antwerp, 1556. I have used a copy at the Academy of Medicine, New York, which once belonged to the famous Portuguese mathematician, Pedro Nunes (1502-1578). Also BM 531.f.7.

[9] *Ibid.,* cap. 52, fols. 85v-86r.

[10] *Ibid.,* cap. 97, fols. 169v-174v.

[11] Hoefer, XIX, 449-50, was therefore mistaken in dating the work at Wittenberg, 1555.

have used was printed at Wittenberg in 1573.[12] Garcaeus, who was born at Wittenberg in 1530 and became a professor at Greisswald in 1561, was also the author of works which, judging from their titles, were more purely astronomical and meteorological. In 1565 he published a *Mirror of the Firmament Which Commonly Is Called the Celestial Globe,* and treatises on time or the rising and setting of the fixed stars and the use of the celestial globe. In 1568 appeared his *Meteorology,* with tables added which embrace the entire doctrine of meteors. It was reprinted in 1584. The work on erecting figures or schemes of the sky is on the other hand essentially astrological, although involving the determination of an accurate astronomical basis for such judgments and predictions. Ptolemy is named as the supreme and safest guide in the matter of judgments, and Garcaeus expresses the request, "in the name of all the studious," that his "dearest teacher" at Wittenberg, Caspar Peucer, will sometime communicate the method of this Ptolemic doctrine to them. There also is given a poem covering a page and a half of Caspar Peucer to Garcaeus.

The phase of astrology to which the treatise of 1556 by Garcaeus is chiefly devoted is genitures and their proper determination as a basis for prediction. There is much discussion how to determine the exact moment of birth. This problem involves that difference between true and astronomical days called equation of days. It in turn has a triple form: one Ptolemaic, another that of recent astronomers and astrologers from the doctrine of Ptolemy and Copernicus, the third that of Regiomontanus. As an example of a nativity, it is stated that the elector and duke of Saxony was born July 30, 1526, at 5.38 A.M.

Like Gemma, Garcaeus also notes the current difference of opinion as to the division of the circle of the zodiac into the twelve astrological houses. How Ptolemy divided these is not certain. Regiomontanus in his work on *Directions* enumerates three methods. One is that of Campanus, "whom Gazulus fol-

[12] Johann Garcaeus, *Tractatus brevis . . . de erigendis figuris coeli,* Witebergae, 1573. Copy used: BM 718.d. 27.(2.).

lows." A second, which the contemporaries of Garcaeus generally designate as the ancient method of Ptolemy and Firmicus, is that of division of the zodiac into equal parts. The third, recommended by Regiomontanus and called the rational method, is that of Abraham Aven Ezra. It divides the equator into twelve equal parts and then projects these upon the zodiac, resulting in unequal segments there. Garcaeus mentions yet another method, that "of Alcabitius or rather John of Saxony and those astrologers who flourished before Campanus." If by this remark Garcaeus meant to date John of Saxony before Campanus, he was of course in error.

Garcaeus more than once cites the earlier work of Schöner on nativities and rehearses his verification of the moment of his birth from a fall which he had in his fifty-eighth year on New Year's day. Besides this method of ascertaining the time of birth by subsequent accidents of the person concerned, Garcaeus mentions two others: one by the conjunction or opposition preceding the true ascendent, the other by the Trutina of Hermes or length of time spent by the child in the womb.

In another work on *Method of Astrology* which Garcaeus dedicated to the elector of Saxony and published at Basel in 1576,[13] genitures of famous men of the recent past were presented on a larger scale than before. Where Gaurico in 1552 had given some one hundred and sixty such examples, Garcaeus offered over four hundred, of whom fully a fourth were men of learning, beginning with Petrarch.[14] Garcaeus professedly conformed to Ptolemaic astrological principles in drawing up his genitures. In a preface concerning astrology generally he declared that it was not against freedom of the will, and that God often acted against secondary causes (i.e. the stars). Also the devil abused nature. Thus qualified, the interest of Garcaeus in nativities seems to have aroused no ecclesiastical opposition, and he became bishop of Neu-Brandenburg.

[13] *Astrologiae methodus in qua secundum doctrinam Ptolemaei genituras qualescunque iudicandi ratio traditur*, Basileae, Henricipetri, 1576. Copy used: BM 718.k.32.

[14] I list a number of them with their dates of birth in an appendix to this volume.

The currency of such genitures of famous men at this time is further attested by manuscript additions at the back of a copy of the 1546 edition of the work of Albohali on judgments of nativities.[15] Here are written in fifty-two horoscopes of noted persons: Paul Eberus, the theologian, born on November 8, 1511, Joachim Camerarius, Melanchthon, Hermolaus Barbarus, Politian, Giovanni Jacopo de' Medici, cardinals Rudolph Pius and Marcellus Cervinus, George of Trebizond, Alciati, Joseph Justus Scaliger, Vesalius, the theologian Justus Jonas, Hieronymus Wolf, Erasmus Reinhold, Matthias Flacius Illyricus, and so on.[16] These genitures are not a mere copy of a portion of those given by Gaurico or Garcaeus, since the order is different and some names are given of persons born too late to have been noted by those authors.[17] Or, where the same person is mentioned, the date of birth is sometimes given differently.[18]

An introductory astrological manual of about the usual sort was published at Lyons in 1557 by Claude Dariot,[19] a physician of Beaune who was born at Pommard in 1530 or 1533, became a Calvinist, and died in 1594. His work was sufficiently well received to be republished in French translation the next year,[20]

[15] BN Rés. V.1300.

[16] Other names are: Christian of Denmark, Paul III, elector Augustus of Saxony, Geo. Sabinus, Io. Schosser, a poet, Cornelius Agrippa, Erasmus, Bembo, Matthias Corvinus, Maurice, elector of Saxony, John Frederick, elector of Saxony, the emperors Maximilian, Ferdinand and Maximilian II, John Rosenberger, a patrician of Augsburg, Fantinus Cornelius Venetus, Facius Cardan, and Joachim Schmitt.

[17] Such as Andreas Sartorius, professor at Frankfurt, Martin Benckendorff, professor of philosophy and law, Caleb Trygophorna, professor at Frankfurt (1563), and Hieronymus Setser (1568). I do not, however, any longer have access to the works of Gaurico and Garcaeus to make sure of this. The mention of Frankfurt professors suggests that these manuscript additions were made there.

[18] That for Paul Eberus is given as November 8, 1511, while Garcaeus (1576), p. 185, gives Nov. 7, 1511.

[19] *Ad astrorum iudicia facilis introductio Claudio Darioto Pomarcensi medico ac mathematico authore. Eiusdem tractatus de electionibus principiorum idoneorum rebus inchoandis. Quibus accessit fragmentum de morbis et diebus criticis ex astrorum motu cognoscendis eodem authore: Ad illustrissimum et eruditissimum virum dominum Anthonium Thomam Savium doctorem medicum Lugdunensem.* Lugduni apud Mauricium Roy et Ludovicum Pesnot, 1557. Copy used: BM 718.e.45.

[20] *L'Introduction au iugement des astres, Avec un traité des elections propres pour le commencement des choses* . . . , Lyon par Maurice Roy et Loys Pesnot, 1558.

and in English at the end of the century. The French version, however, omitted a supplementary tract by Dariot on knowing diseases and critical days from the stars.[21] To the English translation, on the other hand, was appended an independent work of astrological medicine by "G.C. gent."[22] Dariot translated *Die grosse Wundartzney* of Paracelsus into French and is said to have composed four treatises on judicial astrology and six on medicine, of which at least one remained unprinted.[23]

Johann Hebenstreit, a physician of Erfurt, was the author of ten annual astrological predictions, all in German, found by Hellmann, for years between 1549 and 1569.[24] He doubtless wrote others that are no longer extant. He furthermore published or re-issued at Erfurt in 1559 an *Aderlassbuch* in German, containing rules for bleeding for thirty years to come.[25]

Pontus de Tyard, Thiard or Thyard, seigneur de Bissy, was one of the Pleiad, first printing his poems in 1549, and was praised by Ronsard and others. Incidentally it may be noted that Ronsard himself was not averse to astrology, treating the influence of the stars didactically in his *Des astres* and lyrically in *La Hymne des estoiles*. Pontus de Tyard for his part was a learned man as well as a poet. He knew oriental languages well enough to be listed in the *Gallia Orientalis* of Collemesius. He was interested in theology, philosophy, history, mathematics, astronomy and astrology. He became an apostolic protonotary, a canon at Chalons-sur-Saône, and in 1578 a bishop. He passed several years at the courts of Charles IX and Henry III, and, unlike most of the clergy, opposed the League at the Estates of Blois in 1588.[26] We are at present, however, concerned with a

[21] Sudhoff (1902), pp. 60-61.

[22] "A treatise of mathematical Phisicke, . . . never before handled in this our native language, written by G. C. gent., practitioner in phisicke," appended to the English translation of Dariot, *Ad astrorum iudicia facilis introductio*, London, 1598.

[23] Abbé Gandelot, *Histoire de la ville de Beaune et de ses antiquités*, Dijon, 1772, p. 151. The Catalogue of the Bibliothèque Nationale lists a work on gout by Dariot and another on the preparation of medicaments.

[24] Hellman (1924), p. 27.

[25] BM 1175.b.19.

[26] F. L. C. Marin, *Notice sur la vie et les ouvrages de Pontus de Thiard*, 1786: BM 1103.c.4.(3.). For an autograph signature of Jan. 21, 1602, by Pontus de Tyard, owned by Professor Hugo Thieme, Ann Arbor, Mich., see CMRM II, 1130.

work which he had published thirty years earlier.

The preface of the *Mantice ou discours de là verité de divination par astrologie* is dated at Lyons, August 20, 1558, and the work was printed there the same year. It is written in an intolerably involved French prose and, to add to the reader's woes, is printed entirely in italics, causing one to sigh for Latin style and Roman type. The author states that, of all the past forms of divination or Mantice, astrology alone remains today. His work is a dialogue in which Le Curieux argues against astrology, Mantice defends the art, and the author speaks in conclusion. We have already met Le Curieux as one of three interlocutors in another work by Pontus de Tyard, *L'Univers,* where the name was spelled Curieus instead of Curieux. Le Curieux is as opposed to alchemy as to astrology, calling the alchemists "falsifiers of natural reasons" who dishonor the name of philosophy. He calls the Arabic commentator on the *Quadripartitum* of Ptolemy, "Haly, the forger of Ptolemy in a hundred passages of his own invention." Possibly this means that he ascribes the *Centiloquium* to Haly. He dislikes John of Saxony's comparison of astronomer and astrologer to apothecary and physician respectively. He attacks Guido Bonatti more than once, saying concerning his discussion of astrological elections, "Hoh, les poingnantes et solides raisons: Hoh, le bon sens et jugement admirable!" Mantice holds that Apollo, Venus, Mercury and Diana were royal or learned persons whose astronomical and astrological labors led to the planets being named after them. He also asks if Le Curieux refuses to believe that the Delphic oracle, administered by a virgin priestess, was secretly related to the celestial virgin. He asserts that Pico della Mirandola's death was foretold to the exact year, month and day by the astrologers, and that Paris of Mantua upon the death of Leo X wrote to Alessandro Farnese warning him of his accession to the papacy (as Paul III) twelve years beforehand, of peril from drowning seven years beforehand, and of his death in twenty-seven years. Whereas Le Curieux discredited alchemy, Mantice regards the truth of necromancy as proven by the witch of Endor incident, "to deny which would be worse than heresy."

Moreover, according to the secret doctrine of necromancy the dead come up feet first unless summoned for royalty, which explains why the *phytonisse* knew that Saul was king. Mantice also holds that when one remembers that the Passion and whole life of Christ were predicted by the prophets without blame, one ought not to be scandalized at His subjection in natural things to the stars, since He had previously disposed the sky according to his will.

In closing the author affirms that years ago he tried to acquire the gift of divination, sought out demons and spirits, and formed a hundred monstrous characters, but with no success. He is uncertain as to astrology but feels that present astrologers cannot predict truly because past astronomical tables do not give the true movements of the planets. Jofranc Offusien whom he met two years ago at Dieppe made some for a year only which differed from all the others. Also astrologers disagree how to draw up their schemes of the sky. Like Pigghe and other adherents of Ptolemaic astrology, Pontus objects to the hypothesis of a ninth sphere and to the basing of judgments upon it. He therefore refuses to embrace judicial astrology until the movements of the heavens are exactly known, until some invincible reason and certain experience sanction a single method of representing the twelve houses, and the old rules are amended and accommodated to our times or new ones are devised based on nature not superstition, on which judgments can be founded without fail. Despite these strictures Pontus was to publish *Ephemerides of the Eighth Sphere* in 1562, probably in an effort himself to provide the needed solid basis for prediction. The *Mantice* was reissued in an enlarged edition at Paris after about fifteen years.[27]

The Jofranc Offusien or Joannes Francus Offusius, to whom Pontus de Tyard referred, published *Ephemerides for the Year 1557*, which appear to be the very tables that Tyard mentioned,[28] although Hellmann's listing of the work implies that

[27] Deuxième édition augmentée, 4to, 114 pp. (Galiot du Pré: Paris, 1573?): BM 85.e.9.(2.).

[28] *Ephemerides anni salutis humanae 1557 ex recenti theoria eiusque tabulis supputatae quae omnia post plurium*

it also included astrological prognostication.[29] Offusius had already composed a treatise *On the Divine Power of the Stars Against a Decadent Astrology,* with a preface dedicated to the emperor Maximilian II on January 8, 1556. The work, however, remained unprinted[30] until its author's married daughter, Francisca de Feinis, sent a copy to the daughter of Maximilian, Elisabeth, queen of France and consort of Charles IX, and the work was printed at Paris in 1570.[31]

Offusius, unlike Pontus de Tyard, found the Ptolemaic astrology too childish and attempted to work out a new method based on reason, solid principles, and experience. To this end he gave up a lucrative medical practice and refused attractive positions offered by princes. In the preface to Philomates[32] which follows those to Maximilian and his daughter, he tells of his vain search for years through nearly the whole world for a capable scientific collaborator. Perhaps he was just returned from some long voyage, when Pontus saw him at Dieppe, or maybe he was about to leave France as he implies in his *Ephemerides* for 1557.

Offusius attempts to measure quantitatively the influence of the stars, which he believes they exert through the four qualities rather than occult influence. The sun warms and dries. The moon moistens and chills a little. Saturn produces cold with dryness. Mars burns and dries. Venus dispenses moisture and a little heat. Mercury dries. But the question remains: how much of a quality does each planet produce at different positions in its orbit. Its force in this respect depends on its access and recess,

observationem edidit Iofrancus Offusius Germanus Philomates . . . , Parisiis ex officina Ioannis Royerii typographi Regii, Jan. 30, 1557.

[29] Hellmann (1924), p. 33.

[30] Before the fire of 1904 there were two MSS of the work at Turin: CDII. i.II.17, 16th century (tenth year of the reign of Henry II), Gabriel Bonarino Jofrancus Offusius, *De divina astrorum facultate in larvatam astrologiam meditatio;* also in CDV.i.II.29.

[31] *De divina astrorum facultate in larvatam astrologiam,* Paris, 1570: BM 718.h.4, also at Columbia University bound with Guido Ubaldo del Monte, *Planisphaeriorum universalium theorica,* 1579. The name of Offusius does not appear in Zedler, Jöcher and other biographical dictionaries.

[32] Offusius himself is called Philomates on the title page of his *Ephemerides* of 1557.

its elevation above the horizon, the time it remains above the horizon, and so on. Offusius is further convinced, though for a long time he could not convince himself of this, that nature follows a certain numerical and geometrical order. Whereupon he engages in mystic calculations as to the regular solids of the sort later indulged in by Kepler. Hot is to dry as the pyramid to the cube, hot to cold as the pyramid to the octahedron, and cold to wet as the octahedron to the icosahedron. The sun is 576 diameters from the earth's center, and 24 is the square root of 576. The sun's apogee and perigee differ by 49 diameters, of which seven is the square root. Plato gave 24 as the numerical equivalent of the tetrahedron[33] and hexahedron, 48 for the octahedron, 120 for the icosahedron, 360 for the dodecahedron, making 576 for the sum of them all. Ptolemy, however, placed this figure at 580; Aretaeus, at 555; more recent writers, at 571; while Offusius himself has demonstrated against the first book of Cardan's *De subtilitate* that it is 579. The "corpulence of the pyramid" is to that of the hexahedron as 28 and ¼ to 84 and ¾, while the two values, 113 and 391/512 and 133 and 121/512, represent the octahedron and icosahedron respectively. These numbers total 360, a divine proportion undiscovered by anyone else so far as Offusius knows. He explains that his reason for omitting the dodecahedron from this calculation is that it corresponds so well to the sphere of the fixed stars. Not that the fixed stars are idle and without influence upon us, for nature makes nothing in vain, but Offusius thinks that they act only with and through the planets. He adds nebulae or nebulous stars to the six orders of fixed stars. He reckons those of the first order as from five to seven diameters, those of the second order as of four diameters, of the third and fourth as three and two respectively, of the fifth as one and a half diameters, and the sixth as of a single diameter. His method further requires determination of the quantity of the planets and proximate determination of the midpoint of the elemental regions of fire and air.

[33] It might seem that 7 should correspond to the tetrahedron.

The stars act by their rays, which are sometimes efficaciously united, sometimes impede one another. Offusius recognizes that judgments will be very difficult by his new method without comparison to the constellations of other times similarly examined. It will therefore be necessary to accumulate a mass of observations before astrological judgment and prediction become easy. Tycho Brahe was to speak favorably of this work of Offusius with its argument from the symmetry of the heavenly bodies and the mysteries of numbers, but adopted the estimate of 575 rather than 576 or 579 diameters as marking the distance of the earth from the sun.[34]

It seems strange that the earliest annual prediction by Cyprian Leowitz (1524[35]-1574) found by Hellmann was for 1564,[36] since that astrologer's career long antedated this year. Already in 1551 at Augsburg had been printed his *Tables of Positions.* In 1552 his *Tables of Oblique Ascensions Produced for Many Degrees of the Altitude of the Pole* had been published with the *Tables of Directions* of Regiomontanus. He had written on the comet of 1556, and in the same year at Augsburg appeared his *Accurate Description and Picture of All Eclipses from 1554 to 1606* A.D., so computed for the meridian of Augsburg as to be easily accommodated to any other, together with an explanation of the effects both general and particular for every geniture. In 1557 he issued *Ephemerides* for the years 1556 to 1606, with positions of the fixed stars from 1349 to 2029 A.D., and an *Almanach* or *Lasztafel* in German for the coming year, 1558. In that year he printed at London in Latin *A Brief and Clear Account of Judging Genitures from Physical Causes.*

Tycho Brahe gave a rather discriminating estimate of Leowitz whom he called a Bohemian. He was tireless in astronomical calculations and in working out canons and Ephemerides.

[34] *Astronomiae instauratae progymnasmata,* Pars II, cap. 7: in *Opera,* ed. Dreyer, II, 421.

[35] Garcaeus in his above-mentioned work of 1576 gave the date of Leowitz's birth as July 8, 1524, at eight minutes before midnight. The year 1514, suggested by Dreyer, *Tychonis Brahe Opera,* VIII (1925), 458, is probably a misprint for 1524.

[36] Hellmann (1924), p. 28.

His *Tables of Directions,* based on both the *Alfonsine Tables* and those of Copernicus (i.e. the Prutenic), were superior to previous ones. He had shown them to Tycho when the latter was at Lauingen, birthplace of Albertus Magnus, in 1568. His tables of the *primum mobile* had not been published but were kept in the Fuggers' library at Augsburg. On the other hand, Leowitz observed the heavens little and lacked suitable instruments except clocks. He was much given to astrological predictions and surpassed others therein, but whether his art was solid Tycho would not say. He did say, however, that he thought Leowitz too quick to jump to general conclusions from one or two particular instances. He also ventured the surmise that it might have been better had Cyprian devoted more time to astronomical observations and calculations and less to astrology, for which Sixtus ab Hemminga and Bodin had criticized him.[37]

To the work of Leowitz on genitures was prefixed an *Admonition Concerning the True and Licit Use of Astrology* in the form of a dialogue between an astrologer and his disciple. The author was Hieronymus Wolf (1516-1580), classical scholar, translator and schoolmaster. In a two page letter to Leowitz from Augsburg, dated February 20, 1557, Wolf says that astrology would never have been the object of so much hatred and envy, if it had not been abused and prostituted by unscrupulous or unqualified astrologers. He hopes that Cardan and Leowitz will restore it to its pristine dignity and authority. What his own dialogue fails to cover may be sought in the first book of Firmicus and fourth book of Manilius, in Ptolemy's preface to the *Quadripartitum,* in the writings of Lucius Bellantius, Pontano and other learned men. In the following introduction to the *Admonitio* Wolf further laments that fools or wicked men are taking possession with impunity of all disciplines. Once the doctoral degree was a barrier against this. He does not deny, however, that plausible arguments are being advanced against the art of astrology itself.

In the dialogue proper the astrologer—who appears to be more or less identified by Wolf with himself—says that the

[37] *Opera,* ed. Dreyer, III (1916), 218-24; in edition of 1602, pp. 707-9; in that of Frankfurt, 1648, p. 422.

precepts of the Chaldeans, Egyptians and Arabs often no longer apply to our times and climes. For example, if his own horoscope is interpreted according to the rules of Haly Abenragel, it appears that he should be a very fierce and warlike warrior. And perhaps he would have been, had he been born among the Arabs, a race given to robberies. But he lives in a peaceful province and therefore has turned out to be such a person as his disciple sees. "And would that I had more nerves and spirit and body, so that anyone might not think he can treat me as he pleases with impunity." Wolf therefore does not reject Arabic astrology from classical prejudice or animus but gives reasons why it should be qualified for other lands, peoples and times.

Wolf further observes that there is great controversy between the astrologers themselves, first as to drawing up the horoscope or nativity, then as to certain significations of the stars, third as to the choice of significators and many other matters. Nor can these controversies be easily settled, since reasons and authorities are about equally strong for either party. On the other hand, there are many cases of pat astrological predictions. The astrologer recounts the incident concerning Stoeffler which we have given elsewhere, and adds that he could mention some marvelous cases of his own.

The disciple adduces the argument against astrology of Erasmus. Either it is true, false, or ambiguous. If the last, there might as well be no prediction at all. If false, such delusion is injurious. If true and of happy events, you will be distracted by hope and, when the event occurs, will lose the pleasure of novelty. But if the event is sad, you will be miserable before your time and the ill will be redoubled. "For often fear is worse to bear than trouble itself." The astrologer replies that Erasmus did not put forth this argument seriously but for the sake of exercise. His other writings show that he was not without faith in astrology. He boasted that he had been relieved in the stone by an astrological image of a lion. As for the argument, the wise man is unmoved either by sudden joy or disaster but rather uses diligent preparation in bearing either fortune.

Wolf would divide astrology into three or four main parts.

First is weather prediction; second, political and religious change. Or some may prefer to combine these two under the caption of revolutions and conjunctions. Third is the fabrication of characters and images, of which he does not treat here and which many think is little different from magic or idolatry, although they are wicked indeed who do not distinguish between the use and abuse of a thing. The fourth part deals with the private fortune of the individual and subdivides into genethlialogy, elections and interrogations. No disapproval seems to be expressed or felt as to any of these.

The next year Wolf gave further evidence of his interest in astrology by publishing the Greek texts with Latin translations of anonymous commentaries, sometimes ascribed to Proclus, on the *Quadripartitum* of Ptolemy, Porphyry's introduction to the same, and an anonymous Latin translation of a work on the revolutions of nativities ascribed to Hermes.[38] In March, 1575, towards the end of his life, Wolf wrote to Tycho Brahe, urging him to refute the criticisms of Erastus and others against astrology that it was contrary to religion and divinely prohibited. To Wolf it seemed no more opposed to Christianity than did the infinite height and magnitude of the heavens. He listed, however, seven uncertainties about astrology itself which he thought had contributed to destroy faith in its predictions: namely, controversy as to the number and motion of the heavens, as to the motion of the planets, the method of constructing the horoscope, disagreement as to the effects of the stars, uncertainty as to the beginnings of kingdoms and cities and great conjunctions and trigoni, the dissimilitude between twins, and the uncertainty as to the instant of birth.[39] The story is told that Wolf forecast the day of his own death and, as it approached, gave away his belongings. When he overlived the time set, he was ashamed to take them back, but excused his error on the ground that he had not given the position of the planet Mars

[38] Hieronymus Wolfius, *Commentarii Ptolemaici et Porphyriana isagoge, cum Hermete de revolutionibus*, Basel, 1559. The fuller title of the last item is, *Hermetis philosophi de revolutionibus nativitatum libri duo incerto interprete.*

[39] Tycho Brahe, *Opera*, ed. Dreyer. VII (1924), 16.

sufficient consideration.[40] Wolf was poor and sick most of his life and, according to Will, thought himself bewitched, another indication of the hold that the occult had on his mind.[41]

We now come to the work of Leowitz on judging genitures from physical causes.[42] Thus the very title expresses the effort, so general in the later sixteenth century, to establish a natural astrology. Leowitz aims at a method which can be accommodated to considerations of almost all horoscopes, and much of his discussion is quite technical. He refers the reader to the explanation of the doctrine of directions which he gave and illustrated by examples five years before in his edition of the tables of directions of Regiomontanus. Incidentally it may be remarked that Leowitz' commentary on the *Tables of Directions* of Regiomontanus was characterized by Nabod a few years later as "ruder, verbose and extended to the extreme of tediousness." Nabod admitted, however, that Leowitz had greatly augmented the number of particular tables of positions and for this labor was to be highly commended.[43]

Leowitz repeated the three methods of rectifying the degree of the ascendent at the time of birth which we have heard from Garcaeus and which Giuntini was to give again.[44] The first method, for Leowitz, is that of Ptolemy by the Animodar, that is, the planet in the degree of conjunction or opposition of the luminaries immediately preceding the nativity. The second is the Trutina of Hermes, and the third by accidents, good or ill, that later befall the child.

Among the topics which Leowitz covers and therefore regards

[40] Iohannes Praetorius, *Unschuldige Nachrichten*, 1715, p. 20.

[41] Georg Andreas Will, *Nürnbergisches Gelehrten-Lexicon*, IV (1758), 286 *et seq.*

[42] *Brevis et perspicua ratio judicandi genituras ex physicis causis*, London, 1558.

[43] Valentin Nabod, *Commentary on the Quadripartitum of Ptolemy*, BMsl 216, fol. 178v: ". . . exposita alibi et ab ipso Regiomontano cuius traditio si cuipiam videatur succinctior aut subtilior ei forte consultum fuerit et accedat rudiorem illam et verbosam atque ad omne taedium usque extensam illarum tabularum expositionem Cypriani Leovitii qui praeterea particulares etiam positionum tabulas maximo numero auxit et hoc precipuo nomine fit istius labor commendabilis."

[44] F. Iunctinus, *Speculum astrologiae*, Lyons, 1573, fols. 12r-13v.

as predictable from the nativity are fortune and misery in general, which he illustrates by the horoscopes of Matthias Hunyadi and Maurice, elector of Saxony, great good fortune from mines, illustrated by Jacob Fugger the Elder, Weickmoser and John Rosenberger, and captivity, illustrated by the cases of Francis I, John Frederick, elector of Saxony, Philip, landgrave of Hesse, and Henry, duke of Brunswick. Other questions which he considers soluble from the nativity are whether the child will acquire riches by licit or illicit methods, whether his wealth will be durable and lasting, whether he will get a wife easily or with great difficulty, what sort of wives he will have, what regions and cities are more agreeable to him and what ones he should avoid as disadvantageous and hostile, whether his friends will be constant or mutable. But questions concerning his brothers and sisters or parents, which pertain to another person than the *natus* himself, are difficult to judge from his nativity and do not have equal certitude with other predictions. His religious life is a matter, Leowitz grants, more for theologians than astrologers to decide. But he thinks that his dreams may be considered astrologically without any conflict "with sacred letters." Leowitz also touches on elections, although that department of astrology would seem foreign to his strict theme of judging nativities. Both he and Wolf allude to a fuller, more general and exhaustive book on astrology which Leowitz is going to publish later, but he seems not to have done so, since his work of 1564 on conjunctions hardly fits that description.

The work on conjunctions[45] seems to have been composed at the request of the future emperor Maximilian II, since in a preface to him dated September 24, 1563, Leowitz says: "You have in my judgment, Maximilian, most serene Caesar, what you wished, a special history of the entire Fourth Monarchy, ac-

[45] Cyprianus Leovitius, *De coniunctionibus magnis insignioribus superiorum planetarum solis defectionibus et cometis in quarta monarchia cum eorumdem effectuum historica expositione. His ad calcem accessit Prognosticon ab anno domini 1564 in viginti sequentes annos,* Laugingae ad Danubium, 1564. Copy used: BM 718.e.8. (4.). In this edition the *Prognosticon* has a separate title page at signature (L).

I have also used the editions of 1573 and 1618.

commodated to celestial causes and to the motion of the stars." In other words, we are given an astrological interpretation of history from the beginning of the Roman empire or fourth monarchy to the present, with relation of various leading events to great conjunctions, eclipses and comets. Especial note is taken of those reigns which were marked by the passing of the conjunction of Saturn and Jupiter from one trigonus to another, that is, from watery to fiery signs, from fiery to earthy, or terrestrial to aerial. Also comparisons are instituted, for example, between the ages of Diocletian and Henry IV, the reigns of Constantine and Barbarossa, or the times of Huss and Luther. A long list of solar eclipses since the opening of the fourteenth century is given, with a briefer list of comets. Leowitz says that this has cost him a great deal of labor and that no one had done it before. This may be true of the solar eclipses, but past comets had often been reviewed, while Tannstetter's pupil Perlach had enumerated previous conjunctions.

To the work on conjunctions in the volume of 1564 was appended a prognostication for the next twenty years, including the two major conjunctions of 1564 and 1583. This prediction begins with the solar eclipse of June 20, 1563, at five P.M. in the eighth degree of Cancer, and argues repeatedly by analogy from previous eclipses what its effects will be. The present time is compared with that of Charlemagne and with the Apostolic age. A comet is predicted for 1564 and a solar eclipse for April 9, 1567, shortly after noon in the 29th degree of Aries. The conjunction of 1583 will be the last in the watery trigonus and will move on into the fiery signs. Leowitz calls Maximilian II the first Hapsburg ruler under whom a fiery triplicitas begins, and hopes that he will prove another Charlemagne. He also compares the future conjunction of 1583 with that which preceded the birth of Christ and hints that the second coming is not far off. Neither was this the case nor was Maximilian II who reigned from 1564 to 1576 to see the conjunction of 1583. In an epilogue Leowitz warns sceptics that history demonstrates the great effects of conjunctions in the past. His work appeared in German the same year, in French in 1568, and again in Latin not only at London in 1573, but even after the death of Maximilian II and passing of the conjunction of 1583 at Wittenberg in 1586 and at Marburg in 1618.[46]

Bodin in the *Republic* made a number of criticisms of Leowitz as an astrologer. One was that he still followed the *Alfonsine Tables* and consequently was a month or two off in his calculation of the time of great conjunctions.[47] Another was that he had predicted the end of the world from the conjunction of 1584, saying that it undoubtedly announced the second coming. Bodin sneered at Leowitz for having nevertheless issued *Ephemerides* for thirty years after 1584,[48] but this was not a wholly effective sarcasm, since astrologers did not usually represent the effects of a great conjunction as immediate but prolonged through the following years. Bodin further censured Leowitz for predicting the revolution of the year from the entry of the sun into Aries instead of from the autumnal equinox, when Bodin held that most great political changes had occurred.[49] He also charged Leowitz with having incorrectly predicted that the emperor Maximilian would rule all Europe and with failing to predict his defeat by the Turks the very next year.[50] Some of these criticisms of Leowitz had been made by his fellow astrologers before they were repeated by Bodin. In both his *Republic* and *Methodus ad facilem historiarum cognitionem* Bodin criticized details of astrological technique past and present, but was favorable to the influence of the stars and even to the doctrine of great conjunctions, if duly worked out upon a correct historical and natural basis.

Astrological works of 1559 and 1562 by Jean Taisnier are discussed in our chapter on him, Besson, and Palissy.

The swing away from Arabic and medieval astrology is il-

[46] Copies of the German edition, Lauingen, 1564 are BN 4° V.1284 and BM 8610.bb.12; of the edition of London, 1573, BM 8610.b.50; of that of Marburg, 1618 (with works of Goclenius), BM 718.f.26.

[47] *Les six livres de la republique de I. Bodin Angeuin,* 1576, p. 430.

[48] *Ibid.*, p. 438.

[49] *Ibid.*, p. 439.

[50] *Ibid.*, p. 440.

lustrated by Stadius. Although in 1560 still a believer in the significations of the stars, he says that he has abandoned superstitious divinations from parts of the sky supposed to give particular presages as to grain, oil, cheese, butter and the like. His father, though a simple man without learning, could predict as to the crops better than Stadius himself could from this tradition "of the Saracens and barbarians." Rustics laugh at annual astrological predictions which are based upon such delusions.[51]

In 1560 Valentin Nabod or Naiboda, ordinary professor of mathematics at Cologne, published an elementary work on astrology based upon the text of Alcabitius but collating it with Ptolemy and rejecting sortilege and absurd vulgar notions.[52] The usual commentary on Alcabitius of the fourteenth century writer, John of Saxony, whom Pontus de Tyard had classed among barbarous writers, was now omitted. In his preface to the magistrates of Cologne Nabod praises them for having preserved the city safe amid a war inflaming Europe, for having during a scarcity of crops three years since provided from their granaries not only for their own citizens but for many neighboring places, and for maintaining the university. When Nabod himself came to town and began to teach mathematics privately, because it was the only discipline not already included in the university curriculum, they not merely engaged him at an annual salary, but remunerated him for the instruction he had already given. Before in 1556 he had printed the first book of Euclid and an arithmetical work of his own. In the preface Nabod further declares that he deems the "puerile and ridiculous" charges of Pico della Mirandola against astrology unworthy of notice.

In the text much use is made of the *Tables of Directions* of

[51] *Tabulae Bergenses*, 1560, p. 207, De fixis stellis commentarius, cap. 7.

[52] *Enarratio elementorum astrologiae in qua praeter Alcabicii qui arabum doctrinam compendio prodidit expositionem atque cum Ptolemaei principiis collationem reiectis sortilegiis et absurdis vulgoque receptis opinionibus de verae artis praeceptorum origine et usu satis disseritur in celeberrima Coloniensi academia studiosis philosophiae proposita a Valentino Nabod amplissimi senatus Coloniensi mathematicarum ordinario.* Coloniae apud haeredes Arnoldi Birckmanni, MDLX. 472 pp.

Regiomontanus. Ptolemy is quoted a number of times in the original Greek. Guido Bonatti is cited, as is the speculation from aspects of Giovanni Bianchini. The disagreement between Campanus and Regiomontanus is noted, also that between the Arabs and Ptolemy, and between the Alfonsine and *Prutenic Tables.* Nabod corrects a previous slip of his own and thinks that his friend, Johann Stadius, in his *Ephemerides* of 1555 from the *Prutenic Tables* added three to the Alfonsine estimate when he should have subtracted that number. He rejects prediction of the year from the vernal equinox, preferring the Ptolemaic method of reckoning from the conjunction or opposition of sun and moon immediately preceding as easier to determine accurately.[53] Also, despite his frequent reference to the tables of Regiomontanus, he prefers the Ptolemaic method of directions. Many astrologers of his time follow the method of Regiomontanus, but Cardan finally abandoned it as too difficult and laborious and went back to the Ptolemaic method.[54] Nabod cites Cardan a number of times and approves his reduction of the four qualities to two, celestial heat and terrestrial humidity.[55] Nabod rejects a portion of the text of Alcabitius as superstitious and a matter of luck rather than founded on true and natural reasons.[56]

Nabod further displayed his attachment to Ptolemaic astrology by preparing a new Latin translation of the *Quadripartitum* with a full commentary. His introduction to this work is preserved in a manuscript of the Ambrosian library at Milan.[57] The chief point made is that science can teach universals only. Ap-

[53] *Ibid.*, pp. 358-59.

[54] *Ibid.*, p. 417.

[55] *Ibid.*, p. 167. Other places where Cardan is cited are: pp. 176-77, 328, 333, 347, 366, etc.

[56] *Ibid.*, p. 445: "Exposita sunt elementa astrologica autoris fere omnia quae ad veram artem nanciscendam pertinent. Reliqua vero que sequuntur excepto capite de planetarum supereminentia lunarique horoscopo seu parte fortunarum a natura dissentire et magis sortilegiis numerorumque fortuitis casibus et id genus nugis aliis quam veris et physicis rationibus consentanea"

[57] Milan, Ambros. A. 71. inf., (the volume consists of Pinelli's Collectanea), fols. 90r-94r: "Quoniam vero summam totius operis praecognovisse multum interest ideo attexam hic argumentum breve seu periodum horum quatuor Ptholoemei librorum de effectibus siderum . . . / . . . Sequuntur ergo libri primi capita."

plication to particulars is a matter of practice. Nabod further states that astrologers are excused from making any predictions concerning God or actions which He has reserved to Himself or which He performs supernaturally. Discussing the theory of the *magnus annus,* Nabod speaks unfavorably of the many persons who compose fabulous accounts of great changes in the world, especially at fixed periods. Those who adopt the doctrine of great conjunctions come closer to the truth, but Ptolemy laid the chief stress upon eclipses. Nabod also announces his intention of giving a brief summary of Ptolemy's four books, but the text of the Ambrosian manuscript breaks off just as he was beginning to deal with the first book.

A Sloane manuscript of the British Museum, however, preserves most of the rest of the work. It lacks the aforesaid introduction and a number of other chapters and passages of the first book but seems to contain the commentary on the last three books of the *Quadripartitum* in full, and even with the omissions mentioned runs to 377 leaves in length.[58] Nabod frequently alludes to the previous commentaries of Haly and Cardan and also often quotes the Greek text. Gaurico is much cited, and a number of horoscopes are borrowed from him. A geniture of the emperor Maximilian I is said to have been supplied by Schöner. Another is of baron Philip Edward Fugger, born at Augsburg on February 10, 1546, at 17.48 o'clock.

With this work of Nabod and his practice of astrological directions the tragic story of his death is closely connected. Campanella in his six books on astrology, published at Lyons in 1629, tells that "Valentin Vaiuodae," living at Padua, since from a direction of this sort he feared what might befall him from a sword, shut himself up with a supply of food. But robbers, seeing the house closed, concluded that there was no one at home

[58] BM Sloane 216, *Valentini Naibodae mathematici praeclarissimi in Claudii Ptolemaei Quadripartitae constructionis Apotelesmata Commentarius novus et eiusdem Conversio nova.* The first book, owing to the many omissions noted, covers only fols. 1r-13v, but the three remaining books occupy fols. 14r-91v, 92r-263v, and 246r-377v respectively. The MS is written in several different hands.

and broke in. They then killed Nabod lest he give the alarm.[59] Tomasini, in a work published at Padua in the same year, 1629, gives a much longer account which agrees essentially with that of Campanella but seems independent of it.[60] According to this narration, Valentinus Naiboda, after teaching at his birthplace, Cologne,[61] publishing commentaries on Alcabitius and the *Sphere* of Sacrobosco, and devising as a result of repeated experiences an easier method of astrological prediction of human events, came to Padua and set to work to outdo the commentary of Cardan on the *Quadripartitum* of Ptolemy. Fearing, however, death from steel, which had been indicated by astrological directions, he rented an undesirable house and locked himself up in it with a supply of food and utensils but no servants. When the landlord came to collect the rent and could not enter, he induced the town authorities to break down the door, and the body of Nabod was found, evidently murdered. Since his writings were missing, some attributed the crime to jealous rivals. The memory of the nefarious deed, concludes Tomasini, is still vivid among the learned men of our city.[62] As we have seen, however, the commentary on the *Quadripartitum* on which Nabod was working is still preserved in manuscript.[63] Moreover, at the close of the Sloane manuscript is a figure of his horoscope, indicating that he was born on February 13, 1527, at 18.32 P.M., and a note which describes him as from Erfurt and gives yet an-

[59] Tommaso Campanella, *Astrologicorum libri VI* [VII] *in quibus astrologia omni superstitione Arabum et Judaeorum eliminata physiologice tractatur,* Lugduni, 1629. Copy used: BM 718.e.19. The passage occurs in the supplementary seventh book, cap. 8, p. 23, this book having a new numbering of the pages of its own.

[60] Iac. Phil. Tomasinus, *Illustrium viroum elogia,* Padua, 1630, pp. 181-84. I have not had access to the original edition of 1629.

[61] Tomasini is mistaken on this point, since Nabod's own preface to the magistrates of Cologne in 1560 shows that he was not a native of the city.

[62] Papadopoli, in his history of the university of Padua, written in the eighteenth century, chiefly follows Tomasini's account of Nabod, and where he does not, is very likely untrustworthy, as is his general reputation.

[63] Nabod's commentary on two chapters of the *Quadripartitum* (III, 10-11) on the subject of directions was printed by Magini in 1607 at the close of his *De astrologica ratione. His additur de annui temporis mensura in directionibus et de directionibus ipsis ex Valentini Naibodae scriptis,* Venetiis, 1607.

other story of his death. It says that he was found in his own house at Padua transfixed by a sword and dead for three days. "And it is not known whether by his own hand or another's. Yet it is credible that he killed himself, since Saturn is the lord of the horoscope and of the eighth house, and Venus the other lord of the eighth house declining in Aries."

Sperone Speroni (1500-1588), one of the leading literary men of the century, according to Tiraboscni almost suffered the same fate as Nabod, since, when he returned to his native Padua to spend his declining years, he was attacked by burglars who entered his house at night, bound him in bed, and robbed him of what money he had.[64] Tomasini omits this incident but says that Speroni by his skill in the stars predicted many future happenings to his friends and fellow-citizens.[65]

Samuel Siderocrates (Eisenmenger) lived from 1534 to 1585. He began to study at Wittenberg under Melanchthon at the age of eleven.[66] As professor of mathematics at Tübingen from 1556 on he published in 1561 an astrological prediction in Latin[67] and in 1563 an oration on iatromathematics or astrological medicine.[68] He took the M.D. degree the following year and was physician to the bishop of Speyer, when Roeslin cited him in 1578 concerning the comet of May 17 of that year.[69] During the intervening years he had been physician to the margrave of Baden, archbishop of Cologne, and bishop of Strasburg successively.[70]

[64] *Storia della letteratura italiana,* Milan, 1824, VII, 1876. There are many MSS of works by Speroni at the Ambrosian library of Milan including an autograph copy of his *Trattato del principato:* Ambros. D. 260. inf.

[65] *Illustrium virorum elogia,* Padua, 1630, p. 86. There are other discrepancies between the accounts of Speroni in Tomasini and Tiraboschi.

[66] Melchior Adam, *Vitae Germanorum philosophorum.*

[67] Hellmann ((1924), p. 29.

[68] *Oratio de methodo iatromathematikon syntaxeon in qua eam semper medicis veteribus et recentibus usui necessario fuisse ipsorum testimonio ratione et experientia confirmatur et astrologiae fundamenta certissima indicantur,* 1563. Sudhoff (1902), 63-66, speaks of two long orations by him in favor of astrological medicine, delivered in 1562, and 1563, and printed in 1563 and 1564.

[69] Helisaeus Roeslin, *Theoria nova coelestium meteoron . . .,* Argentorati, 1578, Praefatio.

[70] Zedler, article "Eisenmenger (Samuel)."

The *Garden of Mathematicians, in which practically everything that can be desired in astronomy is treated most easily,* was published in 1563 at Venice by John Paduanius of Verona,[71] professor of liberal arts and once a pupil of Petrus Pitatus. After a calendar and tables there followed six tractates on time, computus, the sphere, arithmetic, all sorts of uses of the sphere, and instruments. Amidst all this there was considerable astrology or matter akin thereto: a table of the mansions of the moon with their qualities, significations and properties, for use in astrological elections; a discussion of Egyptian days; dignities of the planets, the decans, the properties of particular degrees; tables showing the relation of the signs of the zodiac to parts of the human body; an arrangement of cities under the same signs; an account of the threefold method of dividing the zodiac into astrological houses; how to draw up a horoscope and that of Paduanius himself, born on July 6, 1516, as an example.

Johannes Pratensis (1543-1576), a correspondent of Tycho Brahe whom we have mentioned in other chapters, published an annual astrological prediction for 1566[72] as well as a poem on chemistry and a work on the origin, progress, subjects and parts of the medical art. From 1571 until his death he was professor of medicine at Copenhagen.[73]

In 1565 there was published at Venice by Giordano Ziletti a *Discourse* in Italian of Domenico Scevolini, "in which by the authority alike of Gentiles and Catholics it is shown that judicial astrology is most true and most useful, condemning those who abuse it and impose necessity on human actions."[74] The author

[71] *Viridarium mathematicorum in quo omnia fere quae in rebus astronomicis desiderari possunt facillime pertractantur . . . ,* Venetiis apud Bologninum Zalterium, 1563. Copy used: BM 531.h.1.(3.).

[72] It is not noted by Hellmann (1924).

[73] Albertus Bartholinus, *De scriptis Danorum liber posthumus; anno MDCLXVI auctior editus a Thoma Bartholino. Nunc denuo recensitus passim emendatus et supplementis illustratus a Johanne Mollero,* Hamburg, 1699, in Moller's *Bibliotheca septentrionis eruditi,* 1699, pp. 86, 298.

[74] Domenico Scevolini, *Discorso di Domenico Scevolini nel quale con le autorità cosi de' Gentili come de' Catolici si dimostra l'astrologia giudiciaria esser verissima et utilissima, Damnando coloro che l'usano malamente e impongono necessità ne gli atti humani.* In Venetia appresso Giordano Ziletti al segno della Stella, MDLXV, 4to, 29 fols. Copy used: BM 8610.cc.13.

was then dead and had composed the *Discourse* a short time before. A preface signed "Giulio Fl." explains that, as a result of a discussion in Ziletti's bookshop during the past year, a friend of Ziletti afterwards presented him with this *Discourse,* which Scevolini had composed shortly before his death.

Scevolini contends that good astrologers do not subject mind and will to the stars. The fact that some astrologers have attributed religious diversities and miracles to the stars no more outlaws astrology in general than does Aristotle's asserting the eternity of the world and leaving in doubt the immortality of the soul prevent the study of philosophy. Scevolini is not interested in declaring true the astrology of any particular writer or practitioner but in defending the art and science of astrology at large. Scotus, Henry of Ghent, Alexander of Hales, Durand, Albertus Magnus and many other schoolmen in their volumes of theology confirm the dominion of the stars and heavens over us. But Scevolini is content to rest his case on the judgment of St. Thomas Aquinas alone.[75] He remarks that Francesco da Ferrara had interpreted the *Contra Gentiles* of Aquinas against Pico della Mirandola.[76]

Scevolini further notes that Cajetan in his *Summa,* under the title, "Observation of the Stars," declared judicial astrology wrong in three cases: 1) if the mysteries of our Faith are subordinated to the stars; 2) if contingent events are predicted as determined; 3) if one rules his entire life by the stars. But if one accepts the celestial influence as merely inclining one to things which depend on the body, one neither errs nor sins.[77] Antonino of Florence in his *Summa* (II, 12, 10) says it is proper to observe days for planting, bleeding and other corporeal actions. If the Council of Braga and pope Leo took action against the Priscillianists, it was because they subjected soul as well as body to the stars.[78] Paul IV included judicial astrology in the

[75] *Ibid.,* fol. 21r: "Scotto, Henrico de Gandavo, Alessandro d'Ales, Durando, Alberto Magno, et altri molti ne' suoi volumi di Theologia pur confermano il dominio delle stelle et de' cieli sopra di noi. Ma tutte le cose io son contento commettere al giudicio d'un San Tomaso solo."

[76] *Ibid.,* fol. 17v.

[77] *Ibid.,* fol. 24r-v.

[78] *Ibid.,* fols. 25v, 26v.

Index of prohibited books, but Scevolini adds that it does not ban *Ephemerides*.[79] Whether Scevolini realized it or not, however, the days of papal favor to astrologers were over, and the toils of the Counter-Reformation, Index and Inquisition were beginning to close in on the art.

Wolff or Wolfgang Geuss was a physician and astrologer of Nürnberg who in 1580 was sixty-one years old.[80] He made astrological predictions for one or more of the years, 1563-1565,[81] But his *Method of Curing Diseases in Mathematical* (i.e. astrological) *Fashion* seems not to have been printed until 1613,[82] when there were both Latin and German editions by a "Patrician ab Alto Saxo . . . in the college of truth," a pseudonym which Sudhoff describes as Rosicrucian.[83]

Levinus Battus, born at Ghent in April 11, 1519, began to teach mathematics and astronomy at the university of Rostock in 1560. At first he was appointed by the town council, but in 1567 the duke of Mecklenburg made him his physician and professor of medicine. In 1574 he became ducal professor of mathematics as well as medicine. Battus was a Paracelsist and believed both in astrology and astrological medicine. He wrote on eclipses and made prognostications from them.[84]

In 1571 Ioannes Baptista a Cerreto drew up a geniture of the oldest son of Philip II of Spain for the third of December at 13.57 P.M. in Madrid. Indeed, the time of birth is further specified as 39 seconds and 20 thirds. While the time of birth is thus given for Madrid, one infers from a letter to the grand-duke of Tuscany, dated February sixth, which precedes the horoscope,

[79] *Ibid.*, fols. 26r, 28v.

[80] It is so stated on a copperplate engraving of him cited by Will, *Nürnbergisches Gelehrten-Lexicon,* I (1755), 536.

[81] Hellmann (1924), p. 27, lists one in German for 1565 and adds, "wahrscheinlich auch für 1564." Will mentions a *Practica* for 1563, printed at Nürnberg.

[82] *Methodus curandorum morborum mathematica qua morborum depellendorum ex astrorum concordanti influxu ratio certa et evidens ostenditur. Cui et locorum hylegialium et thematum coelestium structura adiecta.* Francofurti excudebat W. Richterus, MDCXIII, 4to, 54 pp.

[83] Sudhoff (1902), pp. 73-74.

[84] Otto Carsten Krabbe, *Die Universität Rostock im fünfzehnten und sechzehnten Jahrhundert,* Rostock, 1854, p. 704.

that the nativity was drawn up at his request rather than at that of Philip II.[85] The same astrologer in 1581 and 1583 composed revolutions of the nativity of the next grand-duke, Francis, preserved like the other in a manuscript of the Laurentian library.[86]

Placido Foschi da Montefiore (1510-1574), physician to pope Pius V (1566-1572), left in manuscript a work, called by some a poem, on the use and abuse of astrology in medicine. In 1692 the Carmelite, Gaudentius Robertus, wrote to Mandosius from Parma that he thought the work might be found in the library of the Gambalunga family in Rimini,[87] but I do not know if if it is extant anywhere today.

The *Astrological Medicine* of Cornelius Schylander, a physician of Antwerp, was first printed at that city in 1570, while the dedication is dated there on June 28, 1569.[88] The opening pages are devoted to the finding of critical days from the constellations. Then comes prognostication as to safety or death. Together these compose the first part of the work. The second part is devoted to astrological diagnosis of the part affected without seeing the patient or inspecting his excrement. The third part deals with phlebotomy and purgations. The work ends with a peroration to the candidate in medicine in which Schylander expresses the hope that his manual has saved him time.

The earlier astrological compositions of Antoine Mizauld have been noticed in the chapter on Astrology at Paris. But since his prolific publication went on until his death in 1578, we may give one further illustration of it here.

The *Secrets de la lune* of Antoine Mizauld were published in

[85] FL Plut. 89 sup., cod. 35, pp. 83-(97).

[86] FL Plut. 89 sup., cod. 36, pp. 185-(93).

[87] Prospero Mandosio, *Theatron in quo maximorum Christiani orbis pontificum archiatros . . . spectandos exhibet,* Rome, 1784, pp. 125-27.

[88] I have used the 1570 edition in BM 718.f.29. Sudhoff (1902), pp. 69-70, who used the edition of 1577, was mistaken in stating, following *Lindenius renovatus,* p. 227, that the first edition was in 1575. The division into books or parts, judging from Sudhoff's account, is somewhat different in the editions of 1570 and 1577 although at bottom the same. Thus what I describe as the second and third parts in the edition of 1570 are the third and fourth books of Sudhoff's description.

French at Paris in 1571 with a dedicatory epistle to a noble master of requests dated August 15, 1570. Of the nine chapters which fill the twenty-four leaves of text proper the first deals with the accord of sun and moon, the second with the moon's feminine quality, the third with its sympathy with certain beasts, birds and fish, the fourth with its secret effects on rustic things like herbs and trees, the fifth with its relation to stones, the sixth with its influence on the tides and on the fluids of the human body, and the seventh with particular effects upon particular things. The two last chapters consider its effects on the human body according to the signs of the zodiac and upon diseases.[89]

Magini, writing in 1607, in a list of past adherents of astrological medicine included Ioannes Planerius Quintianus Brixiensis *De diebus decretoriis*.[90] The allusion is presumably to *Doubts and Solutions on the Third Book of Galen on Critical Days* and *Scholia* on the same by Giovanni Pianero of Brescia (c.1509-1584), printed at Venice in 1574 with account of his medical cases at Brescia and Vienna.[91] Pianero took his M.D. degree at Padua and served several emperors as physician. He also wrote a treatise on the comet of 1577.[92]

A Portuguese, Petrus de Peramato, physician to the duke of Medina, wrote a treatise on the subject whether astrology was necessary to a physician, which was published with his other works, first in 1576, and then in 1590 and 1596.[93] The same question was to be discussed by a Spanish physician, Juan de Carmona, and printed together with a pest tract at Seville in 1582 and again in 1590.[94] Baccius Baldinus of Florence, physi-

[89] Antoine Mizauld, *Secrets de la lune* . . . , Paris, 1571, 8vo. Copy used: BM 718.d.27.(1.).

[90] Maginus, *De legitimo astrologiae in medicina usu* etc., Venetiis, 1607, Preface to the reader.

[91] *J. Planerii . . . 1. Dubitationum et solutionum in III Galeni de diebus criticis liber unus . . . 2. In eundem tertium Galeni de diebus criticis scholia . . . 3. Consilium Viennae factum in curatione morbi gallici . . . 4. Consilium Brixiae factum in curatione difficultatis urinandi . . . 5. Collegia nonnulla ad varios morbos Viennae habita*, Venetiis, 1574, 4to. Copy: BM 543.b.6.(3.).

[92] Jöcher III, 1540, who nevertheless gives the dates of Pianero's life incorrectly as 1480-1570.

[93] Sudhoff (1902), p. 69.

[94] Sudhoff (1902), p. 70. Sudhoff had seen neither edition. From the fact that

cian to the grand-duke of Tuscany, and author of other works printed in 1578 and 1586, is another who, Magini says, proposed a disputation whether judicial astrology is useful to a physician.

Antonio Alvarez was an M.D. of Valladolid—in 1560—whose letters and consilia were printed at Naples in 1585. One of his correspondents, a Ioannes Bernardinus Longus, asserted that one element was often transformed into another, and that such alteration came not from the natures of the elements but from the fatal order of the universe and more particularly from the sun and planets which by their access and recess, motion and light, effected many permutations in the elements.[95] Another physician of Valladolid explained the *Metamorphoses* of Ovid according to moral and natural philosophy, astrology and history.[96]

Aloysius Lilius, or Ludovico Lilio, or Luigi Giglio, whose cycle of epacts was accepted after his death by Gregory XIII as the basis for the reform of the calendar,[97] is said by Corte[98] to have been a physician as well as astronomer at Rome,[99] but whether he accepted astrological medicine is not stated.

Francesco Giuntini or Iunctinus (1523-1590) supplies yet another example of a friar and a theologian who was or became not merely interested in but devoted to astrology. He himself tells us that he was born at Florence on March 7, 1523, but he spent most of his mature activity at Lyons. There he for four

the British Museum catalogue lists only a treatise on the pest and fevers, printed at Seville, 1582, while the Bibliothèque Nationale of Paris has the 1590 edition containing both a pest tract and the "An astrologia sit medicis necessaria." I suspect that previous bibliographers may have confused the two editions, and that the question as to astrology may not have been printed until 1590. It will be treated further in our chapter on Adversaries of Astrology.

[95] Antonio Alvarez, *Epistolarum et consiliorum medicinalium pars prima omnibus non medicis modo sed etiam philosophiae studiosis utilissima.* Naples, Horacio Silvano, 1585, 4to. Copy used: BN Td[34].39.

[96] Pedro Sánchez de Viana, *Las transformaciones de Ovidio en tercetos y octavas reales con el comentario y explicaciones de las fábulas reduciéndolas a filosofia moral natural astrologia e historia,* Valladolid, 1589.

[97] Tiraboschi, VII, 722.

[98] Bartolomeo Corte, *Notizie istoriche intorno à scrittori milanesi,* Milan, 1718, pp. 4-5, citing Peruchot or Purchot (Edemondo), *Instit. phil.,* III, 21, a work which I have not seen.

[99] Tiraboschi shows that he was born in Calabria, not Rome.

years preached to the Italians of that city, there he was almoner to Francis, duke of Anjou and brother of Henry IV, there he published his *Mirror of Astrology* and his *Commentary on the Sphere of Sacrobosco.* Giuntini became a Carmelite and was even provincial of the Order. On November 18, 1554, he attained the degree of doctor of theology. He left his Order and strayed from the Catholic Faith for a time but returned to it and made public recantation. His astronomical and astrological publication came in the latter years of his life. The story that he died from the fall of his books or ruin of his library, although he had predicted a different form of death for himself, is probably apocryphal, since we have heard the same tale told of Stoeffler earlier in the century, and repeated by Wolf.[100]

Giuntini's *Mirror of Astrology* will perhaps suffice to indicate his astrology in particular and his position towards magic and science in general. It was first issued at Lyons in 1573,[101] and again in 1583, but brought together treatises some of which at least had been previously printed separately. The volume opens with a preface of six pages to the queen mother, Catherine de' Medici. Then comes a list of authorities with dates covering two pages. Most of the names are familiar,[102] though some are badly misdated, like Witelo in 981, Campanus in 1030, and Thebit in 1198. Sacrobosco is placed over a century too late, and John de Lineriis was dead by 1365. The somewhat scanty representation of the thirteenth century in the list is increased by transferring the names of Campanus, Sacrobosco and Witelo to their proper

[100] For the biography of Giuntini see Zedler and Michaud and the works there cited.

[101] Franc. Junctinus, *Speculum astrologiae quod attinet ad judiciariam rationem nativitatum atque annuarum revolutionum cum nonnullis approbatis astrologorum sententiis,* Lugduni, Phil. Tinghi, 1573, 4to.

[102] I do not recognize Vuelius the astrologer of 250 A.D., unless Vettius Valens be meant, Egmund the astrologer of 846 A.D., or Almeon the mathematician of 1139. The Arabs, Bethen (910 A.D.) and Azophi (1062 A.D.), are also somewhat obscure, unless Bethen is meant for Henri Bate of the late thirteenth century. These names and dates, as well as those in the next note, are somewhat suggestive of Simon de Phares's *Recueil des plus celebres astrologues,* but are not from it.

places, but only two names from the fourteenth century are given.[103]

Next in the volume comes "A Defense of Good Astrologers against Their Calumniators," which is a welcome change of emphasis from the tendency to criticize vulgar or ignorant astrologers which we have often encountered. Giuntini says that this work was first published by him in Italian. Since then "a certain sycophant has arisen" and made, against the original Defense, twenty-two arguments which Giuntini lists and refutes one by one. He also notes that Calvin's arguments against astrology are inapplicable in the case of good astrologers.

The Defense is followed by a much longer treatise on judging human nativities, and this by another work on judging revolutions of nativities. Thus we have another instance of the attention given to nativities by astrologers of the later sixteenth century. Giuntini also, like Gaurico, Garcaeus and others, gives many examples of the genitures of noted persons from Savonarola to Henry II.

In considering the influence of the stars on mental traits, Giuntini introduces a discussion "of prohibited sciences" which seems largely indebted to Pomponazzi's *De incantationibus*. He holds that Aristotle denied the existence of demons as contrary to natural principles. But Giuntini admits their existence in agreement with Holy Mother Church. Nevertheless he says that according to the thought of the Peripatetics it is not incredible that a man may be born under such constellations that he can rule sea, winds and tempests, cure human bodies of many in-

[103] From 1200 on the list runs: 1200 Leopold of Austria, Omar Tiberinus; 1245 Alfonso, king of Spain; 1282 Guido Bonatus; 1317 Peter of Abano Conciliator; 1365 John de Lineriis; 1393 John of Sacrobosco; 1411 Jacobus Angelus of Florence; 1417, Pierre d'Ailly; 1438 Gazulus Ragusinus; 1458 Peurbach, Bianchini; 1484 Ficino, Pico della Mirandola, Regiomontanus; 1495 Pontano; 1506 Augustinus Niphus, Werner, Stoephlerinus (i.e. Stoeffler), Tricassus the chiromancer; 1522 John Schöner; 1531 Oronce Finé, Appian; 1540 Gaurico; 1550 Cardan, John Guido Villariensis; 1554 Cyprian Leowitz, John Ferrerius of Piedmont, John Stadius.

Gazulus of Ragusa is presumably the name usually coupled with Campanus as advocates of the method of directions rejected by Regiomontanus.

firmities, and work other marvels. This is not more remarkable than the power of the tiny remora to stop a ship two hundred feet long, or than the story of Albertus Magnus of two German boys before whom all doors opened—to the right for one of the boys and to the left for the other. Furthermore, if demons work their wonders by applying active to passive, and such feats can be naturally understood by men, then men too can perform them naturally. Therefore it well may be that many past persons who have been considered magicians and necromancers, like Peter of Abano and Cecco d'Ascoli, really had no commerce with evil spirits, perhaps even believed with Aristotle that they do not exist. Here we have again the germ of Gabriel Naudé's book on great men falsely suspected of magic, which was written and published in the next century.

Giuntini continues that there are men who have such potential energy that, when they exert their imagination and will, virtue goes forth from them and so affects their blood and spirits that these seek release by evaporation through the pores and produce great external effects. Also the stars warn men in dreams or give signs through the elements, animals and human beings. Giuntini therefore concludes that men work many marvels by the influence of the stars and not by the art of demons. He further questions whether magic and necromancy are not sciences like medicine and natural philosophy, and whether they are not subordinated to astrology, since in them the demons operate nothing except by natural application of active forces to the appropriate and proportionate passive objects, which is the work of nature, and this at determined times and under determined signs, which is astrology.[104]

Why then are magic and necromancy condemned by law? If they are acquired by study or from a good angel, Giuntini sees no objection to them. If they are worked by invoking impure spirits, they are still true science, in so far as they involve natural operations. But the mode of acquisition is not scientific but pestiferous and criminal, since it is manifest idolatry. And

[104] Giuntini, *op. cit.*, fols. 45v-47r.

so rarely are these arts properly exercised, that the law, which has regard to the great majority of cases, prohibits them. But the kings of France are not forbidden to cure scrofula. Giuntini censures faith in words and characters as superstitious, since the power of imagination cannot naturally produce the effects ascribed to them. He also concedes that the rare properties of certain individuals among men cannot be the basis of science, which is universal not particular knowledge. Giuntini has nevertheless cleverly and courageously indicated the essential kinship between magic and science, and the fact that demons have no more necessary connection with the one than with the other. On the other hand, experimentation with natural forces and a regular orderly procedure are characteristics of both. But Giuntini does not quite arrive at this last conclusion.[105]

As to the relation between religion and the stars, Giuntini has this to say. Although the stars possess no authority in matters of religion, yet from examples of many genitures it is evident that, if Saturn or Mars or the tail of the dragon is found in the ninth or the third house, the person concerned will not persevere in one religion but change about and care little for divine things.[106]

The treatise on the revolutions of nativities had already been published separately in 1570 with a preface to Pétrus Arnaldus Navalius and is largely a compilation from ancient and Arabic astrologers. The remaining constituents of the *Mirror of Astrology* are a brief introduction to judgments of the stars, a compendium of the fixed stars and judgment of them in nativities, an astrological and poetical calendar with many genitures, a treatise on solar and lunar eclipses, notes on comets, and *tabulae resolutae* for estimating the movements of all the planets according to the observation of Nicolaus Copernicus.

Nicolaus Eberhard[107] Winckler of Forchheim became physician and astrologer to the handsome medieval town of Schwä-

[105] *Ibid.*, fols. 47v-49r.

[106] *Ibid.*, fol. 49r, col. 2.

[107] I have seen this middle name, Eberhard, only in Hellmann (1924), p. 30, who presumably takes it from one or more of the annual predictions by Winckler.

bisch Hall. Hellmann found thirty-three annual prognostications[108] written in German by him extant for the period from 1563 to 1611, and he probably composed one every year. I have seen that for 1585, a brief *Practica* in three chapters addressed to the town council.[109] He also wrote concerning medicinal simples and when to collect them,[110] and on the comet of 1577.[111] In 1580 he published a more general work, of which we shall speak further presently, defending astrology and other arts of divination against those who contended that the stars were not causes.[112] Sometimes, as in a publication of 1582,[113] Winckler combined prediction from the Bible and church fathers as to the end of the world with astrological prognostication for several ensuing years.

The full title of Winckler's work of 1580 may be translated as, "The Principles of Astrology and of All the Arts and the Differences in Divinations, against Certain Anonymous Writers Who Contend That Nothing Is Caused by the Stars."[114] The learned character and humanistic pretensions of the work are suggested by the bits of Greek which it contains. Winckler dis-

[108] Hellmann (1924), p. 30.

[109] Nicolaus Winckler Forchemius, M.D., *Practica oder Bedencken . . . auff das Iar nach der Geburt Iesu Christi und der Regirung dess hochlöblichen römischen Käysers Rudolphi II im X Iar und im andern Iar dess VII grossen Iars MDLXXXV,* Nürnberg durch Nicolaum Knorrn, (1584). Copy used: BM 8610.bbb.8.(8.).

[110] *Chronica herbarum florum seminum fructuum radicum succorum animalium atque eorundem partium quo nimirum tempore singula eorum colligenda atque in usum adferenda sint medicum, res ut scitu pharmacopeis dignissima ita reipublicae maxime necessaria.* Augsburg, Mich. Manger, 1571, 4to, 92 fols. Copy used: BM 987.g.3. There is a German edition of 1577 in octavo.

[111] *Cometae Pogoniae qui anno labente 1577 apparuit demonstratio una cum parallaxi distantia a centro terrae et significatione eius,* Nürnberg, 1578.

[112] Jöcher IV, 2010, was mistaken in dating this publication as early as 1550.

[113] *Bedencken von künfftiger Veranderung weltlicher Polizei und Ende der Welt aus heyliger göttlichen Schrifft unnd patribus auch auss dem Lauf der Natur des 83 biss auff 88 unnd 89 Jars beschriben: durch Nicolaum VVinckLerum Forchemium.* Getrucht zu Augspurg durch Michael Manger, 1582, 4to. Copy used: Bern Stadtbibliothek E.B. v 194 (2).

[114] *De astrologiae et omnium artium principiis et differentiis divinationum contra anonymos quosdam qui nullas in astris causas esse contendunt, autore Nicolao Wincklero Forchemio doctore medico et physico Halae Suevorum ordinario,* Impressum Francofurti ad Moenum per Iohannem Feyerabendt Anno 1580.

tinguishes four ways in which truth may be found: by syllogisms, by induction, by example, and by questioning. The truth in theology rests on authority and faith alone. The principles of mathematics are absolute; in other subjects, concrete; in yet others such as astrology, mixed. Its principles are not absolute like those of mathematics, but probable with a varying latitude, yet no more unstable than those of medicine or jurisprudence. One should not lose faith in it because the effects expected do not always follow, and one should remember that superstition often intrudes into theology as well as astrology. Winckler still regards the celestial bodies as incorruptible, and believes that they affect inferiors by an occult influence as well as by their more manifest motion and light. That this influence is more subtle and penetrating than light is seen from the fact that the generation of metals in the bowels of the earth is regulated by the planets. Winckler further believes in various forms of divination of the future by omens, prodigies, dreams, oracles and the like, whose revelation or interpretation requires divinity of intelligence. God's love toward us is evidenced by these various signs by which He would lead us upward to things celestial. There are also, however, diabolical and fabulous forms of divination. Winckler then begins with necromancy which invokes demons and goes through the usual list of 'mancies, augury, lots, and so forth.

Henry Ranzovius or Rantzovius published in 1580 at Antwerp a Catalogue of Emperors, Kings and Princes who have Loved, Adorned and Practiced the Art of Astrology. The work is of interest chiefly for naming along with more familiar authors a number of astrologers concerning whom it is difficult to find notices elsewhere. Thus we are told that Guido Maltraversus, a count of Padua of the street Lucius had a son Niccolò by Constance the daughter of Obizzo, marquis of Este, whom the astrologer Iambonus Andreades said would be a dangerous citizen to the city. Guido would have disinherited him, unless friends had intervened. Niccolò, rendered powerful by his inheritance, conspired with Cane della Scala to the destruction of his fatherland, whence a war resulted in which more than one hundred thousand men were said to have been killed, and the event showed the truth of Iambonus's prediction. Or we are told that Manilius Antonius, chamberlain to Sixtus IV and Julius II, made many true prophecies and revelations to those pontiffs. John Crato, physician to the late emperor Ferdinand, states that the astrologer and physician Moiebanus predicted truly the time of death of himself and his wife, while Seraphinus, another physician and astrologer, though wasted by fever died most courageously at the day and hour he had predicted. Dethlevus Reventlovius, a noble of Holstein, promised Frederick I and Christian III the rule of Denmark and Norway, while Christian II, son-in-law of Philip I of Spain, still ruled. He also predicted the death of the bishop of Lübeck, Andrea de Barbi, as an autograph manuscript shows. To Charles V he foretold the outcome of his war against the Protestant elector of Saxony and landgrave of Hesse, and died on his way to join that emperor. Matthaeus Delius, a Dane, at Innsbruck in 1551 predicted to Philip II of Spain from his nativity that his father's empire would be divided and his own power diminished.[115]

That these recollections of Ranzovius are not very accurate may be inferred from the report of one hundred thousand slain, and from another passage in which John of Legnano is said to have foreseen by the stars in the time of pope Martin V (1417-1431) the execution of his son, whereas John died in 1383 and the son was hanged in 1391. When Ranzovius says that Franciscus Maria Ferrariensis predicted dignities, marriage and the year, day and hour of his death to Jacobus Piceninus who was killed by Ferdinand of Aragon, one suspects that Ranzovius has confused the names of the two founders of the friar orders and that Dominicus Maria Novara de Ferraria is meant.

Many passages such as those we have been recounting were repeated verbatim from Ranzovius in a volume by Rudolph

[115] These accounts of successful predictions all fall between pp. 48-53 of the 1580 edition of Ranzovius.

Goclenius published in 1618.[116] Meanwhile the work of Ranzovius was itself sufficiently in demand to have reached a third and enlarged edition in 1585.[117]

Giovanni Battista Benedetti of Venice (1530-1590) was a person of a critical, mathematical and original turn of mind. He wrote treatises on arithmetic, Euclid, perspective and mechanics. He professed to repeat nothing from others except in order to criticize and disagree with it, and to break away from the old method of compilation in his writings.[118] He ventured to criticize first-rate mathematicians like Pedro Nunes,[119] Tartaglia and Jordanus[120] as well as such second-rate writers as Stadius and Oronce Finé.[121] He attacked both the physics and astronomy of Aristotle,[122] and has been represented as a precursor of Galileo.

What was the attitude of this critical, analytical mind towards astrology? Asked by a correspondent, Volfardus Aisestain,

[116] Rodolphus Goclenius, *Acroteleution astrologicum triplex hominum genus circa divinationem ex astris in scenam producens falsamque astrologiam a vera rationibus exemplis et experimentis distinguens contra novas criminationes,* Marburg, 1618, 78 pp.

[117] Henr. Ranzovius, *Exempla quibus astrologicae scientiae certitudo astruitur. Item de annis climatericis et periodis imperiorum, cum pluribus aliis artem astrologicam illustrantibus,* Cologne, 1585, 8 fols., 401 pp.

[118] See the preface "Ad lectorem" in the front of his *Diversarum speculationum mathematicarum et physicarum liber,* Taurini, Apud haeredem Nicolai Bevilaquae, 1585, in folio.

[119] *Ibid.,* Epistolae, p. 214, "Per eundem parallelum absque correctione semper navigare non posse. Ubi notantur Petri Nonii lapsus in correctione erroris navis et alii Petri Medinae errores."

[120] *Ibid.,* pp. 148-51, De mechanicis, cap. 7, "De quibusdam erroribus Nicolai Tartaleae circa pondera corporum et eorum motus quorum aliqui desumpti fuerunt a Iordano scriptore quodam antiquo"; p. 271, Epistolae, "Quod male senserit Nicolaus Tartalea circa attractionem machinae tormentalis"; p. 258, Epistolae, "De ictu bombardae secundum diversas elevationes. Et de quibusdam erroribus Nicolai Tartaleae circa idem."

[121] *Ibid.,* Epistolae, p. 260, "De erroribus Ioannis Stadii"; p. 360, "Notabiles errores Orontii et Tartaleae."

[122] *Ibid.,* pp. 168-97, "Disputationes de quibusdam placitis Aristotelis."

Libri III (1840), 129, has rather overstated the case in asserting that Benedetti at p. 197 rejects the incorruptibility of the heavens and at p. 195 maintains the plurality of worlds. Both passages are brief, and all that Benedetti does in either is to question the Aristotelian arguments for the incorruptibility of the heavens and against the plurality of worlds. At p. 197 and again at p. 255 he suggests that the earth would look incorruptible to an observer in the eighth sphere. Similarly there may be particular alterations in the heavens which we cannot see at this distance.

whether he accepts as true all that is found in the books of judicial astrology, Benedetti replies that he thinks that much of their contents is false. He would reject their multiplicity of parts, except the *Pars fortunae,* also the facies, decans, termini and certain designations of degrees. But he believes that astrological houses, exaltations and triplicitates have been confirmed by experience, and that the influence of the planets can be inferred from their colors. True for the most part, too, are what such books say concerning conjunctions, aspects, annual revolutions, and the lord of the year. But of a lord of the orb and divisor he does not approve. He denies *novenaria, dodecathemoria, alfridaria,* and many similar refinements. But *antiscia* are true.[123] In another letter, to Adrian Panetius, Benedetti discussed the dignities of the planets.[124] He further referred Aisestain to a special treatise on such astrological matters, which he hoped to finish before he came to the direction of his horoscope with Mars, which would happen about 1592. His fatal year came quicker than his calculation, however, for he passed away in 1590. It is clear that his criticism of the literature of judicial astrology extended only to certain details of technique, and that he had no doubt as to the influence of the stars or the possibility of an art of prediction based thereon. Among the ridiculous errors, to Benedetti's mind, of Lucilio Maggi,[125] "most unskilled of all men in mathematical philosophy,"[126] in his commentary on *De coelo et mundo,*[127] was his denial of astrology. Benedetti listed it on a par with his assertions that the pyramid had six bases, that oil was heavier than water, that God was in the east, and that astrology was older than astronomy. Indeed, de Thou tells us that Benedetti, who first served the duke of Parma and then the duke of Savoy, predicted to the latter the restitution which was made the next year by Henry III.[128]

[123] *Ibid.,* Epistolae, pp. 425-26. It is the last letter and terminates the volume.

[124] *Ibid.,* Epistolae, p. 411.

[125] *Ibid.,* p. 268. Benedetti mentions Maggi under his pseudonym, Lucillus Philalthaeus.

[126] It is in a latter letter, *ibid.,* p. 291, that Benedetti says, "Desine igitur mihi citare Lucillum Philaltaeum qui in philosophia mathematica fuit omnium imperitissimus."

[127] Printed in folio in 1565.

[128] Thuanus, *Hist.,* lib. 99.

Benedetti also defended *Ephemerides* and their use by astrologers from *Animadversions* against them printed by Benedict Altavilla in 1581.[129] He charged Altavilla with having misinterpreted Ptolemy, with not knowing that the rule for change of triplicitas was for the mean motion and not the true places of the planets, and with having blindly followed the ancients in stating the period of the complete circuit of the conjunctions of Saturn and Jupiter as 960 years, since the time between conjunctions of these planets is not exactly twenty years but nineteen Egyptian years and about 314 days. Benedetti showed by elaborate calculations that Mars could spend seven months in one sign, which Altavilla had denied, and that Altavilla had been confused by and had made too much of a slight difference between the calculations of Leowitz and Stadius, of whom one had used the Alfonsine and the other the *Prutenic Tables*. Benedetti concedes that the latest observations and tables should be followed, when available, but he points out that reckoning from the *Prutenic Tables* is especially laborious, and that Copernican *Ephemerides* are not available for dates before 1554 and after 1576, those of Stadius covering only the years included between those dates.

The *Discourse* of Gioseppe de Rossi of Sulmona on climacteric years was addressed to cardinal Sirleto and printed at Rome in 1585,[130] the year preceding the bull of Sixtus V against astrology. Rossi notes that some are of the opinion that the number seven belongs to the body, and nine to the soul, and that 49 and 81 are most perilous years because squares are more potent than other numbers. He affirms the influence of the stars, citing Aristotle, Aquinas, Haly and the Conciliator.

[129] *Io. Bapt. Benedicti Diversarum speculationum . . .*, 1585, Epistolae, pp. 228-48, Defensio Ephemeridum ad illust. Bernardum Trottum. I have not found the work of Altavilla. Benedetti at p. 228 gives its title as *Animadversiones in Ephemerides* and the date of printing as August 11, 1581, while at p. 248 he names the author, "Benedicti Altaevillae."

[130] *Discorso sopra gli anni climaterici di Gioseppe de Rossi da Sulmona, dove si mostra la ragione perche siano cosi perigliosi alla vita dell' huomo.* Con licenza de' superiori, In Roma per Iacomo Bericchia & Iacomo Tornieri, MDLXXXV. 74 pp. At the end, "In Roma appresso Bartholomeo Bonfadino et Tito Diani Nel Pelegrino 1585." Copy used: BM 52.e.25.

The number seven is important in human generation and life which it divides into periods of seven or multiples thereof: infancy, boyhood, adolescence, youth (from 22 to 42 years), virility (from 43 to 56), old age (from 57 to 70), and decrepitude being the seven ages of man. The unfavorable planet Saturn rules the years from 43 to 49 in general and the 49th year in particular. At 56 the moon is lord in general, Saturn in particular; at 63, Mercury in general and Saturn once more in particular. The moon and Saturn in their passage through the zodiac measure by sevens, the one the days of infirmity, the other the years of life. As the accidents of the moon in illness correspond to the sixteen angles of its circuit, so those of Saturn in the course of the year correspond to 28 directions and retrogradations. Very melancholy persons rarely survive their forty-ninth or fifty-sixth year, since Saturn is especially fatal to them, while the sixty-third year is less fatal to *melancholici adusti*.

Thomas Finck, professor at Basel, then court physician to the duke of Schleswig-Holstein, is said to have been the first to employ the words tangent and secant,[131] which he did in his *Geometria rotundi* of 1583. He also issued an *Ephemeris* for the year 1582 calculated from the *Prutenic Tables*. His *Horoscopographia* of 1591,[132] dedicated to Henry Ranzovius, is primarily concerned with finding the positions of the stars and ends with the hope that astrologia may revive on physical foundations freed from superstition. Finck evidently uses this word, astrologia, to include astronomy in our sense. But that it also for him still included judicial astrology is indicated by the considerable attention he gives to the division of the zodiac into houses and the method of directions.

Henricus à Lindhout, a doctor of medicine of Brussels, gave proof of the continued association of medicine with astrology by publishing an introduction to judicial astrology at Hamburg in

[131] Dreyer, *Life of Tycho Brahe*, 1890, p. 240. A. von Braunmühl, *Vorlesungen über Geschichte d. Trigonometrie*, I(1900), 187.

[132] Thomas Finck, *Horoscopographia, sive de inveniendo stellarum situ . . . in qua tabulae declinationum ascensionum* etc., 1591. Copy used: BM 1480.aaa.11.

1598.[133] The dedication to queen Elizabeth of England is dated from Hamburg on September 9, 1597,[134] and is another indication of her interest in occult arts and sciences. Despite his own combination of medicine and astrology, Lindhout was opposed to the three principles and to the astrology of Paracelsus.[135] He further illustrates the tendency of which we have spoken to improve the method of astrology and purge it of the vanities and excesses of the Arabs. On the other hand, he cites such exponents of the occult as Zoroaster and Trismegistus. He has a chapter against theologians who oppose astrology. He asserts that there are the same laws of nature for the universe and for man the microcosm.

Henri de Monantheuil (1536-1606) was a pupil of Ramus who became royal professor of medicine at Paris in 1574. In the same year was printed there his *Oration for the Mathematical Arts*.[136] He seems to have lost his professorship for a time, as in 1585 he delivered an oration asking for reinstatement, supported by a petition to the king to the same effect which was signed by seven other scholars.[137] After 1585 he was professor of mathe-

[133] *Introductio in physicam iudiciariam in qua brevissime sed accurate vera astrologiae fundamenta. . . . Item in quo vera ac legitima praesagiendi methodus statuitur et quam multae lateant in Genethliacae Arabum doctrina vanitates involutae. Contra calumniatores artis Astrologiae . . . auctore Henrico à Lindhout Bruxellensi medicinae doctore ac philosopho* . . . Hamburgi Ex Officina Binderiana per Philippum de Ohr. Anno MDLXXXXIIX. Copy used: BN V. 8790. In-4°. This copy appears to be incomplete, since the text ends at p. 112 with the 17th chapter on nativities, whereas the preliminary table of contents lists 24 chapters, the last beginning at p. 187.

Valerius Andreas, *Bibl. Belg.*, 1643, p. 361, ascribes to Henricus à Lindhout a *Speculum astrologiae:* in quo vera astrologiae fundamenta et genethliacae Arabum doctrinae vanitates demonstrantur, Hamburgi, 1597, 4to, and a *Tractatus astrologicus, seu Introductio in physicam iudiciariam*, Lipsiae, 1618, 4to. Both would seem variations on the above title.

[134] "Hamburgi 6 Idus Septembris anno 1597."

[135] *Ibid.*, pp. 5, 14.

[136] David Eugene Smith, "Medicine and Mathematics in the Sixteenth Century," *Annals of Medical History*, 1917, p. 137.

[137] *Henrici Monantholii medici et mathematicarum artium professoris regii pro suo in regiam cathedram reditu oratio.—Coppie du placet présenté au Roy pour le rétablissement de Henry de Monantheuil . . . signé: Jean de Cinquarbres, Loys Duret, Nicolas Goulin, Jean Passerat, Jean Pelerin, Gilbert Genebrard, Jacques Helias*, Paris, 1585, 8vo, 24 pp. Copies in BN.

matics, and his *Ludus iatromathematicus,* printed at Paris in 1597,[138] was in the nature of an introductory oration to the two courses of lectures that he gave, the one royal in the morning, the other Ramian in the afternoon. The *Ludus* was addressed to Henry IV. In 1599 de Monantheuil edited in Latin translation with a commentary the *Mechanica* ascribed to Aristotle,[139] and in 1600 at Leyden published a treatise *On the Point, First Principle of Geometry.* In the same year he published at Paris a brief *Demonstration of a Problem the Noblest of All Those Which Have Been Invented for Twelve Hundred Years.*[140]

The *Ludus iatromathematicus* illustrates the continued interest in astrological medicine at the close of the century. After citing ancient and recent medical authors in favor of the union of medicine and mathematics, de Monantheuil takes up in turn arithmetic, music, geometry, optics, mechanics and finally astronomy, and shows the utility of each for medicine. He says that the two chief requisites in sidereal science are to know the positions of the planets and fixed stars at any given moment, and, in the second place, their properties.[141] Incidentally he alludes to horoscopes of all the kings of France from Francis I to Henry III, which had been drawn up by the Capellani, father and son, who were royal physicians, and which, when their library was broken up and scattered after the massacre of St. Bartholomew's day, he had received from their nephews.[142]

In Georg Henisch (1549-1618) we have a man of broad culture and learning, who taught logic and mathematics and practiced medicine at Augsburg, translated Hesiod and writers on the Trojan war, wrote a philological work on the German language, translated the *History of the Turkish War* by G. P. Contarini into German, published medical handbooks and works in

[138] *Ludus iatromathematicus musis factus ab Henrico Monantholio medico et mathematicarum artium professore regio ad averruncandum tres Academiae perniciosissimos hostes,* Paris, 1597, 136 pp. Copy used: BN T[21].334.

[139] Doppelmayr (1730), p. 17.

[140] *Problematis omnium quae a mille et ducentis annis inventa sunt nobilissimi demonstratio ab Henrico Monantholio,* Paris, 1600, 4to, 8 pp.

[141] *Ludus iatromathematicus,* 1597, p. 88.

[142] *Ibid.,* p. 10.

arithmetic and astronomy,[143] but also composed various astrological predictions of which the first extant was in 1577, the last in 1600.[144] Tycho Brahe described his treatment of the comet of 1577[145] as completely astrological and as still accepting the Aristotelian doctrine of comets.[146] I have seen two tracts by him in German on the year 1585, one a prediction,[147] the other a calendar,[148] which contained weather prediction and further prognostication from eclipses. He wrote upon the comets of 1580 and 1596 as well as that of 1577.

That annual astrological predictions were still in good odor among scientists north of the Alps at the close of the sixteenth century may be further illustrated by the case of Peter Ryff of Basel (1552-1629). He became a doctor of medicine of the university of Basel in 1584 and professor of mathematics there in 1586. He was the author of many works of mathematics, astronomy and astrology.[149] Among the last is a prognostication in German for 1594.[150] In 1617 his name appeared as promoter of a conferring of the doctorate in medicine upon candidates who were to discuss the harmony of macrocosm and microcosm.[151]

Wolfgang Satler of Basel in 1605 wrote from Montbéliard or Mömpelgard on true and false astrology.[152] He opened the dedi-

[143] For his various works thus far referred to, consult the catalogue of the British Museum.

[144] Hellmann (1924), p. 27.

[145] *Iudicium de Pogonia ad finem anni MDLXXVII conspecto Georgii Henischii medici,* Augustae, 1578, 4to.

[146] *Opera,* ed. Dreyer, IV (1922), 362.

[147] *Geo. Henischius der Artzney doctor und mathematicus, Practica oder Iudicium astrologicum . . . uber die mundanam revolutionem auff das Iar . . . MDLXXXV,* Augsburg, Michael Manger, dedicated to the magistrates of Augsburg. Copy used: BM 8610.-bbb.8.(12.).

[148] Georgius Henischius, *Alter und newer Schreybkalender auf das Jar MDXXXV,* Augsburg. Copy used: BM 8610.bbb.8.(1.).

[149] A. Burckhardt, *Geschichte der medizinischen Fakultät zu Basel 1460-1900,* Basel, 1917, p. 129; D. E. Smith, "Medicine and Mathematics in the Sixteenth Century," *Annals of Medical History,* 1917, p. 139.

[150] Hellmann (1924), p. 29.

[151] *Petri Ryff Promotor rite electus . . . I. Harbrechto . . . item C. Peckio . . . doctoratus medici titulum collaturus omnes bonarum artium cultores et amatores ut de harmonia macrocosmi cum microcosmo et de peregrinationum utilitate disserentes audiant officiose rogat,* Basel, 1617.

[152] *Dianoia astrologica quae omnium praedictionum astrologicarum veras causas inquirit, falsas vero examinat et damnat. Accessit . . . succincta exegesis astrologica,* Montisbelgardi, 1605, 8vo. Copy used: BM C.79.a.26.

cation of his work with the statement that so great is human infelicity and misery, that the more anything is wrapped in obscurity and difficulty, the more does man strive to attain perfect knowledge of it. Hence the search of the alchemist for the philosophers' stone, the effort of geometers to square the circle, of mechanics to obtain perpetual motion, of astrologers to solve the celestial forces. The principles of astrology are so hidden and recondite that they escape most men, and there has hardly ever been an astrologer who could always predict the weather correctly. All knowledge of the stars is *a posteriori*. Weather prediction depends upon the configuration of the eighth sphere, of which knowledge is impossible. Other reasons for defects in human astrological science are the shortness of man's life, the dullness of human genius, laziness, the superstition of some astrologers, and the difficulty and subtlety of the art. The true astrologer is he who gives a satisfactory explanation of astrological predictions, separating the futile foundations which are contrary to orthodox religion from true and genuine principles.

Magic and diabolical superstition are too often confused and intermingled with astrology. Satler further rejects nativities, *antiscia*, directions and such superstitious methods of divination as Egyptian days or from the calends. On the other hand, he holds that true astrology is not only to be tolerated in the Christian state but embraced. He instructs as to election of the lord or the year or season or lunation, as to the future significance of the two superior planets at the time of the sun's entry into Aries, as to critical days and astrological medicine. He believes that it is possible to predict wars and tumults from the positions of the stars, but criticizes the prognostication of the Peasants' Revolt from the conjunction of 1524. In the *Exegesis* he gives many maxims as to houses, triplicitates, termini, facies, aspects, elections, venesection and purging.

CHAPTER XXXIV

THE CATHOLIC REACTION: INDEX, INQUISITION AND PAPAL BULLS

At postquam summorum procerum iussu e catholicorum scientiis sublata est, quanto eam prius ardore conquisieram tanto postea toto animo exhorrui.

—GIOVANNI BATTISTA PORTA

This chapter will consider the effect of the Catholic or Counter Reformation upon scientific activity and the occult sciences. We shall see that the former was, before the decree of 1616 against the teaching of the Copernican theory as true, affected only indirectly, while the latter were proceeded against more directly but with varying vigor. The chief instruments in this were the *Index expurgatorius,* the revived papal inquisition, and the bull against judicial astrology of Sixtus V, reaffirmed in 1631 by Urban VIII. These measures against the occult arts and sciences operated chiefly in the Italian peninsula, so that we shall give some indication of the state of affairs in France and Spain for purposes of comparison. Even in Italy it is important to inquire to what extent these agencies against the publication and spread of superstition acted as deterrents or official expressions of policy, and to what extent they were actually operative against magic and divination in their various forms, most of which had long since been forbidden by canon law.

Such occult arts, and more especially sorcery and witchcraft, had come to be regarded as varieties of heresy. In countries, therefore, where the Inquisition functioned such as Spain and Italy, persons who were reputed to be witches fell under its jurisdiction, whereas in France, Germany, Switzerland and England they were now commonly dealt with by the secular courts. But, as Nikolaus Paulus has pointed out,[1] this meant that there

[1] Nikolaus Paulus, *Hexenwahn und Hexenprozess vornehmlich im 16. Jahrhundert,* 1910, Chapter 13, "Rom und die Blütezeit der Hexenprozesse."

was no such wholesale execution of supposed witches in the Italian and Spanish peninsulas as in the northern countries. For only relapsed and stubborn heretics were burned at the stake. Those who recanted and were penitent were assigned some lesser penance or at most condemned to perpetual or life imprisonment, a sentence which was often commuted later. Even though they confessed to having caused the death of other persons, if penitent, they were not handed over to the secular arm in the sixteenth century. Another factor tending greatly to reduce the number of trials and condemnations in Italy and Spain, according to Paulus, was that the Inquisition did not encourage and elicit by torture, as the secular judges did—and as the Inquisition often did in cases of heresy proper—testimony inculpating others as present at sabbats. The secular judges also often put to death even penitent first offenders who renounced their supposed pact with the devil. We shall see, however, that they sometimes dismissed such cases with a whipping. Secular courts were perhaps more apt to be swayed by popular feeling against reputed witches, but the chorus of bloodthirsty writers demanding that witches be not allowed to live is in itself an indication that they often were not or had not been put to death by the secular judges.

Judging from the lists of forbidden books published by Reusch[2] for the sixteenth century, these were at first devoted chiefly to the attempt to prevent the spread of the doctrines of the religious reformers and did not begin to list works in the occult and illicit arts until just after the middle of the century. The Indices of Venice and Milan of 1554 condemn generically works of geomancy, hydromancy, pyromancy, nigromancy or necromancy, and the notory art, while among their condemned authors are Bartholomaeus Cocles the chiromancer, Joseph Grumpeck (i.e. Grünpeck) the astrologer, Nicolaus Perazonus on the notory art and memory, and Henry Cornelius Agrippa on occult philosophy.

[2] *Indices librorum prohibitorum des sechzehnten Jahrhunderts, gesammelt und herausgegeben von Franz Heinrich Reusch,* Tübingen, 1886.

In the *Index* issued by Paul IV at Rome in 1559, to the five arts condemned generically in 1554 in their alphabetical order, is added the magic art, while under the letter L and "Libri omnes . . ." are listed all books and writings of chiromancy, physiognomy, aeromancy, geomancy, hydromancy, onomancy, pyromancy and necromancy. Also those in which are found sortilege, veneficia, auguries, aruspicia, incantations of magic art, or divinations of judicial astrology concerning contingent future events or the succession of events or fortuitous happenings, exempting only those natural observations which are written to aid navigation, agriculture and medicine. Here we have already in brief form the substance of the later bull of Sixtus V in 1586. It will be noted that alchemy is not mentioned. No particular work of alchemy was forbidden in this or the Spanish list of the same year.

Various books of magic are specifically condemned such as the *Clavicula* of Solomon, the book of Hermes the magician to Aristotle, and works on rings, magic mirrors and images. Of chiromancers and physiognomists besides Cocles are now named Corvus, Tricasso and Indagine: of writers on the arts of nomandia and geomancy, Annibale Raimondo of Verona, Gaudentius Tervisinus, Joachim Ringelberg, and Peter of Abano. Among authors whose entire literary output is condemned without distinction are Conrad Lycosthenes, author of the chronicle of portents and prodigies, Caspar Peucer and Joachim Camerarius who wrote on divination, Cornelius Agrippa, the astrologers Grünpeck, Leowitz, Gaurico and Gaspar Brusch to whom Hellmann ascribes a *Prognostication* for 1548. It is probable that some of these authors are forbidden for their Protestant affiliations rather than their writings on the occult. Both Peucer and Camerarius, for example, condemned the arts of divination, and the work of the latter on this theme was not yet printed. Milich is presumably listed as a professor at Wittenberg rather than for his *Oration* in behalf of astrology. And such men as Rheticus, Leonard Fuchs, and Otho Brunfels are hardly prohibited for their scientific writings. However, the work on inventions of

Polydore Vergil is specified, as is that of Pompeius Barba on the secrets of nature,[3] and also the fourteenth century book of judgments of the stars of John of Saxony, which is surprising since he was careful to make no statements to which religious objection might be taken. The *Ars cabalistica* and *De verbo mirifico* of Reuchlin are also particularly mentioned.

The Spanish *Index* of 1559 is very similar, with a few additional items of interest, such as Arcandam on nativities, Johann Schöner on the same theme, and Paul Riccio's cabalistic *De caelesti agricultura*. Cardan's *De subtilitate* and *De rerum varietate* are listed as well as his work on genitures and commentary on the *Quadripartitum* of Ptolemy. Yet Roman Catholic writers on nature, at least outside of Spain, continued to cite *De subtilitate* and *De rerum varietate* freely.

The decrees of the Council of Trent rather incidentally censure some minor observances which might be regarded as bordering on magical procedure, such as laying any stress on the number of candles used in the celebration of masses.[4] Similarly the Jesuit Delrio held that it was superstitious to attach any importance to the number of a Psalm.[5]

Already in the first half of the century Julius II and Adrian VI had renewed the power of the inquisitors to proceed against magicians.[6] In a bull of October 14, 1562, Pius IV, confirming powers which had been granted to inquisitors by Paul III, authorized them to take action against those committing sortilege as well as against Lutherans, Zwinglians, Calvinists, Anabaptists, and other heretics and apostates.[7] Gregory XIII on July 1, 1581, authorized inquisitors to act against Jews, if they invoked or consulted demons, received responses from them, directed

[3] I have not found this work by Pompeo della Barba but only his *Discorsi filosofici*, Venice, 1553; *Espositione d'un sonetto platonico*, Florence, 1549; and editions of Cicero's *Topics*, Venice, 1556, and Pico della Mirandola's *Heptaplus*, in Italian, 1555.

[4] Session 22, *Decret. de observ. et evitand. in celebr. missae*, ed. A. L. Richter, 1853.

[5] *Disquisitionum magicarum*, I, 4.

[6] Antonio Battistella, *Il S. Officio e la riforma religiosa in Bologna*, Bologna, 1905, p. 167.

[7] *Bullarum diplomatum et privilegiorum sanctorum romanorum pontificum Taurinensis editio*, called on the cover *Magnum Bullarium Romanum*, VII, 237.

prayers and sacrifices to demons for purposes of divination, or if they instructed Christians in such nefarious practices.[8]

The history of the papal inquisition in the sixteenth century has remained obscure because of the refusal to open the archives of the Holy Office even to a Catholic historian of the papacy like Pastor. He wrote in 1912 that, despite the publications of Vito La Mantia, Battistella, Luigi Fumi and G. Buschbell concerning the operations of the Inquisition in Sicily, Bologna, Friuli, Milan and Venice, "The development and activity of the central Roman administration remains as before enshrouded in deep gloom."[9] From documents in the Roman state archives, however, and from Barberini manuscripts Pastor was able to publish a number of decrees of the Roman inquisition in the years 1555-1597, and these throw some light upon the attitude of that institution to the occult arts.[10]

In two out of three manuscripts astrology was one of the captions under which Pastor found the decrees of the Inquisition alphabetically arranged. But with one exception and that not from these manuscripts, astrologers are not mentioned in any of the decrees between 1555 and 1597 which he published, even the bull of Sixtus V being described as "against diviners."[11] The single exception is a statement which he reprinted from a seventeenth century inquisitor's manual of cardinal Francesco Albizzi, that the most frequent form of divination is by astrology, and that by a decree of November 19, 1556, astrologers were punished by assignment of penance and exile from the States of the Church.[12] In a Bologna manuscript of decrees of the Holy Office Battistella found an order from Rome of November, 1556, expelling astrologers from the States of the Church, "under penalty of the galleys with salutary penance enjoined."[13] He re-

[8] *Ibid.*, VIII, 378-80.

[9] Ludwig von Pastor, "Allgemeine Dekrete der römischen Inquisition aus den Jahren 1555-1597. Nach dem Notariatsprotokoll des S. Uffizio zum erstenmale veröffentlicht," *Historisches Jahrbuch*, 33 (1912), 480.

[10] *Ibid.*, pp. 479-549.

[11] *Ibid.*, p. 518, "Die 17 Octobris 1585. Sanctissimus D.N.D. Sixtus papa quintus praelibatus mandavit expediri bullam contra celebrantes non habentes ordines sacros et contra divinatores."

[12] *Ibid.*, p. 541.

[13] Antonio Battistella, *Il S. Officio e la riforma religiosa in Bologna*, Bologna, 1905, p. 148. He described the

marked the inconsistency of this order with the action of Julius II in seeking a favorable astrological moment for the foundation of the castle of Galliera and the erection of his own statue at Bologna.

Several of the decrees published by Pastor direct that superstitious books containing incantations and sortilege found in the possession of persons brought before the Inquisition or existing in the Holy Office itself shall be burned and a record made of the fact.[14] From these decrees one rather gets the impression that occult arts were regarded by the Inquisition as a side issue and secondary matter which should not be allowed to clog its procedure. In 1580 the Congregation of Cardinals ordered a letter to be written to the inquisitor at Bologna directing him not to interfere in cases of geomancy but to leave them to the Ordinary.[15] On July 6, 1588, they decreed that where there was more than one charge against a person, for example, heresy and necromancy, the heads concerning heresy should be first expedited.[16]

Among prohibited books specified in the processes of the Holy Office at Friuli were Agrippa's *Occult Philosophy* and *On the Vanity and Uncertainty of the Sciences*, Porta's works on physiognomy and chiromancy, and "the writings of Pietro d'Abano." Probably the last words have reference only to the spurious books of magic and geomancy ascribed to him.[17] Battistella was of the opinion that the Inquisition punished persons for the offense of possessing or reading such books merely with spiritual penalties.[18]

As in previous centuries, the clergy figure prominently as offenders in connection with the occult arts. In the last decade of the century the Friars Minor of the Observance appear to have caused scandal in this respect. On September 19, 1591, the Con-

---

MS of Decreta s. Congreg. S. Off. at p. 33, n.1, as in the Biblioteca Comunale of Bologna but gave no shelfmark for it.

[14] Pastor, *op. cit.*, pp. 510, 525, Decrees of Feb. 11 and Nov. 25, 1573, and July 25, 1590.

[15] *Ibid.*, p. 514.

[16] *Ibid.*, p. 521.

[17] Antonio Battistella, *Il S. Officio e la riforma religiosa in Friuli*, Udine, 1895, pp. 91-92.

[18] *Ibid.*, p. 94.

gregation approve the monitory letters of the Commissary General of that Order that no friar shall dare to retain in his possession books or writings of necromancy, geomancy, chiromancy and the like. They further direct that for the present year these letters shall be read and published before witnesses three times each month and in general and provincial chapters. After that they shall be read once a month and on the chief feast days. Returning to the same matter on May 25, 1593, the Congregation explain that the penalty of ten years in the galleys for those found culpable in this affair is to be interpreted as a maximum which may be varied in amount according to the nature of the offense, person, place and time, consequent scandal and other circumstances. Finally, on August 26, 1594, the Congregation announced that henceforth it would be sufficient to publish once each month the general decree issued against lot-casters or necromancers and those retaining their writings in the Order of the Friars Minor of the Observance.[19]

On March 1, 1595, the Congregation recalled all permits to read prohibited books which had been issued by bishops, local inquisitors, and any other authority than themselves and the pope.[20] The next year Clement VIII ordered that the General of the Society of Jesus be informed that he could not permit at will the fathers of the said Society to use prohibited books corrected by themselves.[21]

On the question of Hebrew books two slightly conflicting decrees were published by Pastor.[22] When in 1592 Clement VIII heard the petition of the Jews that certain of their books be expurgated, and that then they be allowed to retain them, he was advised that such expurgation would be useless, ordained that the Jews might possess only the Bible, and so informed all inquisitors. The next year, nevertheless, Jews of Ancona petitioned the Congregation that they depute someone to expurgate their books. They were informed that the Congregation were not accustomed and had no intention of expurgating or deputing anyone to expurgate Hebraic books, but that it was for the Jews

[19] Pastor, *op. cit.*, pp. 526, 531, 532.
[20] *Ibid.*, p. 533.
[21] *Ibid.*, p. 537.
[22] *Ibid.*, pp. 528, 530-31.

themselves to expurgate them satisfactorily or suffer severe punishment.

We turn to the experiences with the Inquisition of two or three men of learning and science of whose works and ideas we have treated or shall treat in other chapters.

Cardan began to lecture in the medical faculty of the university of Bologna in October, 1562, and was admitted to citizenship there in 1563. He continued to teach there until 1570,[23] when on Friday, October 27, his name was erased from the faculty roll by the order of the legate and senate, since the local inquisitor had informed them that letters from the Holy Office at Rome directed the appointment of another lecturer, Cardan being under arrest.[24] Cardan says in his autobiography that he was arrested on October 6, kept a prisoner for 77 days, and then confined in his house for 86 days more.[25] On February 18, 1571, the Holy Congregation ordered the inquisitor at Bologna to force Cardan to abjure and to prohibit his books, especially *De*

[23] U. Dallari, *I rotuli*, II, 155-79. In 1562-1563 the name of Cardan headed the list of those giving ordinary lectures on the theory of medicine in the morning with the further specification in his case that he should lecture "after the bell of St. Peter's had struck and after the other lecturing." This divergence between his hour and those of the other ordinary lecturers is probably what he grumbles about in *De propria vita*, ed. of 1643, cap. xvii, p. 78, when he complains that there was scarcely time for his lecture between the preceding one and dinner time. During the remaining years his name appears separately and later in the roll as lecturing on the theory of medicine "after tierce" (*post tertiam*), although this last statement of the hour is not always made. At this time the four main lecture periods were *mane* or *matutina, ad tertiam, ad nonam* and *vespertina,* the early morning hour being the most dignified, while "post tertiam" was somewhat exceptional. These periods had replaced the *de mane, in tertiis, in nonis,* and *de sero* of the rolls of the fifteenth and early sixteenth centuries, but Dallari does not state just what hours of the day they covered at Bologna. Bilfinger, *Die mittelalterlichen Horen,* 1892, has shown that the tendency was to advance these canonical hours so that the *nones* became noon and so on. It also was the custom at this time to dine as early as ten A.M. The attempt to insert three lectures before dinner or two between *tierce* and *nones* would inevitably tend to crowd so prolix and garrulous a writer and lecturer as Cardan.

[24] Dallari, *I rotuli,* II, 179. In the roll for 1571-1572 the name of Fabritius Gargionius appears in Cardan's place: *ibid.*, p. 182.

[25] *Hieronymi Cardani Mediolanensis de propria vita liber ex bibliotheca Gab. Naudaei,* Paris, 1643, pp. 22-23. His arrest was therefore not on October 13, as stated by Henry Morley, *Jerome Cardan,* 1854, I, 290.

rerum varietate, since errors in matters of faith were found therein. Another letter of March 10 permitted the abjuration to be made privately. It requested that Cardan henceforth abstain from lecturing and publication, but this was not to be inserted in the sentence.[26] This would appear to be slow work on the part of the Inquisition and to have amounted to locking the barn door after the horse had been stolen, since *De rerum varietate* had been in print since 1557, while Cardan had taught unmolested in the university of Bologna for eight years, and was now seventy years old and to live for only five years more. He had friends and patients in the college of cardinals and says in his autobiography that at the end of the following September he left for Rome, arriving there October 7 and living there in retirement with a papal pension.[27]

The life and scientific activity of the naturalist Aldrovandi were not free from the shadow of the Inquisition which more than once fell across his path and interrupted his labors. Already in 1549 he had been summoned to Rome with other nobles of Bologna to undergo a process but was acquitted. In 1571 he was examined as to the views of a friend, Giovanni Grisostomo, prior of the monastery of S. Salvatore, and was warned to tell the whole truth or risk imprisonment as furthering heresy. His depositions were forwarded to Rome, but the matter seems to have been allowed to rest there. In 1615, after Aldrovandi's death, the government of Bologna petitioned the Holy Congregation at Rome to be permitted to retain in Aldrovandi's library, which had been housed in six rooms of the palazzo pubblico, certain prohibited books. The answer was that the books should be kept at the Holy Office but labelled as belonging to the municipality.[28]

[26] Antonio Battistella, *Il S. Officio e la riforma religiosa in Bologna,* Bologna, 1905, pp. 156-57.

[27] *De propria vita,* 1643, p. 23. On July 13, 1571, before leaving Bologna, Cardan made a will in which he named four cardinals to look after the revision of *De rerum varietate* to suit the pope, to reprint 113 treatises already in print by him and 44 others as yet unpublished which he lists. Enrico Rivari, "Un testamento inedito del Cardano," *Studi e Memorie per la Storia dell'Università di Bologna,* IV (1929), pp. 3-25.

[28] Antonio Battistella, *Il S. Officio e la riforma religiosa in Bologna,* Bologna, 1905, pp. 119-20, 162.

Francesco Barozzi, a Venetian noble, studied and maybe taught at Padua, travelled in Asia as well as Europe, collected manuscripts, corresponded with the learned, and was praised by his contemporaries. He wrote four books of cosmography, a *Rithmomachia,* a demonstration in thirteen ways of how to draw two lines in the same plane that will never meet, and translations into Latin of Hero on military engines and the commentary of Proclus upon the first book of Euclid's *Elements.*[29] In 1587 Barozzi was condemned by the Inquisition for magic and sortilege, not however for what he had himself composed and published but for magic books found in his possession. He had strenuously objected to the inquisitors visiting his study and, instead of destroying his books of magic, had hid them away and continued unrepentant. The Inquisition then, after ten months of further investigation, resumed proceedings against him in earnest. He now confessed that while in Crete he had collected books and manuscripts in Greek and Latin on sortilege, necromancy and the magic art, and had performed experiments in the conjuration of spirits such as Peter of Abano and Cornelius Agrippa teach.[30] By these means he had checked a drought in Crete. For this Barozzi was assigned various penances, was to pay for silver crosses in churches, and was condemned to imprisonment, if and for so long as the Inquisition willed. The last part of the sentence was probably merely held over his head, since it was further decreed that he must keep holy water in his room as a defense against infernal spirits. According to Tiraboschi, this was the last heard of Barozzi, but Mazzuchelli, whom Tiraboschi cites, says that he died well along in life and, since his son had passed away before him, left his library, marvelous mirrors, and many other instruments to a nephew. Mazzuchelli says further that this nephew, Jacopo Barozzi, printed

[29] Tiraboschi, Milan, 1824, VII, ii, 775. Libri IV (1841), 85-86.

For the full titles of Barozzi's books see the British Museum Catalogue of printed books.

[30] The reference is presumably to the spurious books of magic which passed under their names. Pierre Belon was entertained and shown about in Crete by "Ioan Francesco Baroczo" and speaks enthusiastically of the Venetian noble's gardens there: *Les observations de plusieurs singularitez,* 1553, I, 5 and 17, fols. 7v-8r, 18r.

a catalogue of his uncle's books and manuscripts which afterwards passed to England.[31] Libri said that the name of Barozzi would today be forgotten but for his trial.[32]

In his *Cosmographia,*[33] one of the numerous sixteenth century efforts to improve upon the *Sphere* of Sacrobosco—which he admitted was the best treatment of the sort thus far and on which he had lectured at Padua 26 years since—Barozzi noted 84 "errors" of Sacrobosco. They were largely, however, matters of definition and order of treatment rather than astronomical mistakes or cosmographical sins. In this work Barozzi divided astrology or astronomy into cosmography and judicial or divinatory. Cosmography in turn divided into astronomy and geography, while judicial or divinatory astrology divided into weather prediction and genitures. It is impossible even to suggest in the case of Barozzi, as some have done in the case of Giordano Bruno, that advocacy of the Copernican theory was a reason for his plight with the Inquisition. The astronomy of his *Cosmographia* remains Ptolemaic throughout, and its single allusion to the new doctrine appears to be a brief history of arguments why the earth is to be considered immobile, while the opinion of those who would transfer the movement of the *primum mobile* to the earth is indicated in the margin as the "false opinion of Aristarchus and Copernicus."[34]

Of Bruno's experience with the Inquisition, more tragic than any of the foregoing but perhaps less related to magic and science, we shall treat in connection with his views on nature and magic in a subsequent chapter.

The inclination towards the occult of another Neapolitan,

[31] Gianmaria Mazzuchelli, *Scrittori d'Italia,* Brescia, 1753-1763, II, i, 412-13.

[32] Libri IV (1841), 86-87.

[33] Some notion of its excessively long title page may be given thus: *Cosmographia in quatuor libros distributa . . . Francisco Barocio . . . cum praefatione . . . in qua perfecta quidem astrologiae divisio . . . Ioannis de Sacrobosco vero 84 errores . . . Praecesserunt etiam quaedam communia mathematica,* Venetiis ex officina Gratiosi Perchacini, 1585. Copy used: BM 533.b.10.

Houzeau et Lancaster, I (1887), 597, list earlier Italian *Commentarii sopra la sfera* and *Trattati astronomici* by Barozzi, both printed at Venice, 1573, in quarto.

[34] *Cosmographia* pp. 33-35, with the marginal entry at p. 35.

Giovanni Battista della Porta, seems to have brought him more than once to the verge of difficulties with the ecclesiastical authorities, but he always escaped serious molestation or punishment by submission or by influence in high places. Thus the Accademia de' Secreti which met at his house and to which it is said no one was admitted who had not discovered something new in nature—it must have had a small membership—was forbidden by the papal court because its members were given to illicit arts.[35] Porta was denounced to the Inquisition for using demon aid but successfully defended himself against this charge,[36] although it was repeated in 1581 by Bodin. After the bull of Sixtus V, Porta, as we shall see, altered his attitude towards astrology.

A sharp reaction from the favorable attitude, at least personally, towards astrology of previous popes like Paul III and Pius IV or even Gregory XIII,[37] immediate predecessor of Sixtus V, was marked by the bull of Sixtus V of January 5, 1586, against those practicing the art of judicial astrology and other forms of divination or reading and possessing books on such subjects.[38] This bull may be regarded as a manifestation of the stricter moral and intellectual attitude which characterized the Counter or Catholic Reformation, the revived papal inquisition, and the period following the Council of Trent. It declares that God alone knows the future, which not only the weakness of the human mind ignores but not even demons can forecast. It excepts from censure, however, the prediction of future events which occur necessarily or frequently from natural causes. Thus the way is left open for natural astrology. But there are no true arts or disciplines of predicting contingent and fortuitous events, only false and vain ones introduced by the craftiness of wicked men

[35] See the article on Porta in Zedler.

[36] *Vita di Gia Battista della Porta Napolitano scritta da Pompeo Sarnelli,* in the 1677 edition of Porta, *Della chirofisonomia . . . libri due . . . tradotti da un manuscritto latino dal signor P. Sarnelli.*

[37] A figure of his nativity by Alfonso Ceccarelli is found in MS Vatic. lat. 6253, fol. 26. Other horoscopes by the same astrologer are preserved in another Vatican MS of which I neglected to note the shelfmark.

[38] *Bullarium Romanum,* Turin, VIII, 646-50: Contra exercentes artem astrologiae iudiciariae et alia quaecumque divinationum genera librosque legentes vel tenentes, opening, "Sixtus episcopus servus servorum Dei, ad perpetuam rei memoriam. Coeli et terrae Creator Deus quem. . . ."

and the deceits of demons. In this familiar distinction between naturally necessary and contingent happenings the bull might seem merely to repeat the medieval attitude of both Christian theologians and Christian astrologers. But then it definitely specifies the casting of nativities as illicit. It further affirms that each human soul has a guardian angel to aid it against the stars, which seems a tacit admission that the force of the stars is difficult to resist. Gregory the Great is cited against the Priscillianists. Other forbidden arts of magic and divination like catoptromancy are again condemned. It is stated that the *Index* has already forbidden the reading of certain works of judicial astrology. Astrological prediction in connection with agriculture, navigation and medicine is pronounced permissible. But inquisitors and other ecclesiastical officials are to prosecute those who deal in contingent or fortuitous events or with events dependent on human free will, even if the astrologers protest that they do not affirm such matters certainly and absolutely. In these last words is another indication of a tightening of the restrictions upon astrologers, who are not to predict or even conjecture such events at all.

How far this bull of Sixtus V was observed and executed may be to some extent judged by a survey of subsequent publication, especially in Italy, in the fields of astrology, physiognomy and chiromancy. Pèrcopo probably goes too far in calling Luca Gaurico the last of the astrologers, even if we alter this to read, "the last of the Italian astrologers." Hellmann in his elaborate census of extant annual predictions during the course of the sixteenth century notes a gradual increase in the number of authors in Germany, Austria and Switzerland from 17 in the opening decade to 62 in either of the closing decades, while the Italian peninsula shows a falling off from 17 in the first decade to only two in the closing decade of the century.[39] This suggests a fairly thorough enforcement of the bull, although *Index* and Inquisi-

[39] G. Hellmann, "Versuch einer Geschichte der Wettervorhersage im XVI Jahrhundert," *Abhandlungen der preussischen Akademie der Wissenschaften,* Jahrgang 1924 physikalisch-mathematische Klasse, Berlin, 1924, Nr. 1, 54 pp., of which pp. 1-40 review and classify the annual predictions.

tion had doubtless prepared the way and already discouraged many from issuing such predictions. We have traced the cessation of the teaching of astrology at the university of Bologna in an earlier chapter. It might, however, be argued that annual *Almanachs* and *Ephemerides,* which limited themselves to predicting the weather and telling what days were favorable for planting and bleeding, were predicting only in connection with agriculture, navigation and medicine and so did not contravert the bull. Therefore it would seem that other factors than ecclesiastical prohibition must have contributed to the great falling off in such literature in Italy, or that fewer specimens have survived there, or that Hellmann's search was less thorough for that region than for Germany.

Ioannes Paulus Gallucius of Salò in 1584 at the request of the bishop of Modena published at Venice a volume comprising various works of astrological medicine: that of 1532 of Johann Virdung von Hassfurt, the *Iatromathematica* of Hermes Trismegistus in the translation of Stadius, the pseudo-Galenic *Prognostica ex egroti decubitu* in the translation of Jacobus Antonius Mariscottus of Florence, Ficino on the pest and triple life. Finally, brief chapters of his own on erecting the celestial figure, finding the part of fortune and of the liver, dividing the zodiac, essential and accidental dignities of the planets, and the times appropriate for taking medicine.[40]

After the bull of Sixtus V Gallucius continued to manifest the same interest in astrological technique. In fact in his *Theater of the Universe* in six books, dedicated to Sixtus V, whom he urges to endow an astronomical observatory, he discussed the nature and qualities of the planets, their radiation, the influence which they exerted by reason of their particular positions in the zodiac, and the distinguishing of the signs of the zodiac as masculine or

[40] *Ioannis Hasfurti . . . de cognoscendis et medendis morbis ex corporum coelestium positione libri IIII cum argumentis et expositionibus Ioannis Paulli Gallucii Saloensis . . . quibus accesserunt in eandem sententiam auctores alii . . . ,* Venetiis, ex officina Damiani Zenarii, 1584, 4to. Copy used: BM 718.f.22. The final tracts by Gallucius occupy fols. 222-28. See also Sudhoff (1902), p. 71.

feminine, commanding, obedient or hostile.[41] Gallucius believed that it had been found by long observation of most prudent men that different effects were produced in these inferiors by the planets when a certain distance apart than when at another interval.[42] He explained how the planets are lords of unequal hours and the relation of the signs of the zodiac to the members of the human body.[43] He repeated the opinion of the astrologers as to critical days, noted that the figure of sixteen angles from the *Centiloquium* was approved by Nifo and rejected by Chrisogonus, and held that the natures of the fixed stars could be inferred from their colors.[44] He maintained that it was essential to draw up an astrological diagram or figure of the constellations in medical practice, also to consider the patient's geniture, and that this was contrary neither to the decree of the Council of Trent nor to the bull of Sixtus V. But he warned physicians who employ astrology not to attribute too much to it.[45] This work of Gallucius was printed three times at Granada in the Spanish translation of Perez in rapid succession in 1606, 1612, and 1617.[46]

In his *Speculum Uranicum* of 1593,[47] dedicated to cardinal Mauroceno of Venice, Gallucius distinguished the different senses in which the planets were called *combusti* in the theory of

[41] The work seems to have been first published in 1588, BM 536.e.34. (1.), *Theatrum mundi et temporis in quo . . . precipuae horum partes describuntur et ratio metiendi eas traditur . . . astrologiae principia cernuntur ad medicinam accomodata, geographica ad navigationem,* etc., but this copy is incomplete, having only the first book, or in 1589, BN V. 7650, *Theatrum mundi et temporis . . . ubi astrologiae principia cernuntur . . . nunc primum in lucem editum,* Venetiis apud J. B. Somascum, 4to, 478 pp.

I have used the edition of 1603 which the catalogue of the Bibliothèque Nationale says is the same work as the foregoing but which has the further title: *Coelestium corporum et rerum ab ipsis pendentium accurata expositio per instrumenta rotulas et figuras,* Venetiis apud Rubertum Meietum, 1603. Copy used: BM C.79.b.11. The passages cited are II, 1, 5, 9, 4; pp. 87, 98, 108, 97.

[42] *Ibid.,* II, 5; p. 98.

[43] *Ibid.,* III, 2, 8; pp. 129, 220.

[44] *Ibid.,* III, 9, pp. 222 and 224; VI, 1, p. 401.

[45] *Ibid.,* III, 2; p. 123.

[46] *Theatro del Mundo y de el Tiempo . . . traducido . . . por M. Perez,* Granada, 1606, folio: BM 531.m.9. For the editions of 1612 and 1617 consult the printed catalogue of the Bibliothèque Nationale.

[47] Giov. Paolo Gallucci, *Speculum Uranicum in quo vera loca tum octavae sphaerae tum septem planetarum . . . ad quodlibet datum tempus ex Prutenicarum ratione colliguntur, una cum*

the planets and by astrologers,[48] and gave the method of dividing the zodiac into twelve houses and of directing *significatores* to the following *promissores* not only according to Regiomontanus but Alcabitius whom, he said, not a few skilled men still followed.[49] All of which suggests that, whatever effect the bull of Sixtus V may have had in checking prediction of contingent events, the attack of Pico della Mirandola upon astrological rules and technique had not had much effect after the lapse of a century.

Two works on physiognomy were published in Italy by Italian authors with ecclesiastical permission in the years 1588 and 1589 soon after the bull of Sixtus V. The author of the former work, Giorgio Rizza Casa, states that he had made many observations in chiromancy in years past and that he had had difficulty in persuading the inquisitor to allow him to publish the work in Italy. This seems to have been owing to the fact that he not merely dedicated his volume to queen Elizabeth of England but wished to make favorable prognostications as to her emprise against the king of Spain. The work is in two parts, of which the first deals chiefly with the outward signs of different types of human character, while the second is principally devoted to the significations from each member of the human body. Despite the author's professed experience in chiromancy, less than two pages are given to the hand. The work is in Italian.[50]

Rizza Casa was also the author of astrological predictions covering the years 1586-1590, and of a treatise on natural judicial astrology with some discussion of nativities. But he published both these works at Lyons, the predictions in French,[51] the nat-

---

regulis fabricandi duodecim caeli domici'ia ex Regiomontano et Alcabitio et dirigendi significatores, Venetiis, 1593, folio.

[48] *Ibid.*, III, 6; fol. 23r, col. 2.

[49] *Ibid.*, III, 9, 10; fols. 24v, col. 1, 26r, col. 1.

[50] Rizza Casa, *La fisionomia*, Carmagnola, 1588, small quarto, dated Nov. 10, 1588, while the accompanying ecclesiastical permit is dated August 10, 1588. Copy used: BM 1141.c.4.(2.).

[51] Rizzacasa, *Prédictions ou discours de Rizzacasa sur les merveilleux effets que les influxions célestes montrent devoir advenir par l'Europe, les années 1586, 1587, 1588, 1589, et 1590*. Lyon. Athanase Petit-Jean. Cited by J. Baudrier, *Bibliographie lyonnaise*, I, 336.

ural astrology in Italian,[52] probably because he would not have been allowed to print either in Italy. The work on natural astrology was dedicated to the viscount of Turenne from Basel on July 25, 1591. It is primarily concerned with nativities and gives the horoscopes of Henry IV, Turenne, Signor di Biron baron of Salignac, and the king of Spain.[53] The usual Ptolemaic topics as to the person's destiny are considered, including whether the stars promise him a natural or violent death, and whether by iron, fire, hanging, a fall or sickness.[54] Later the author says that he does not wish to speak of the length of life, which is in the hands of God rather than of the stars, but then he does so in order to satisfy the curious.[55] He also, however, states that by virtue, good customs and free will we can evade the malign influences of the heavens.[56]

The other work on physiognomy of which we were to speak is on the significations of single parts of the human body.[57] It is in Latin, arranged in tabular form, and published "with the license of the holy Inquisition." The author, Ioannes Padovanius of Verona, is identical with the John Paduanius of Verona whose *Garden of Mathematicians* was published in 1563.[58] Since he is of Verona, he can scarcely be connected with John of Padua, the alchemical writer.[59] He cites a number of authors from whom his particular significations are drawn, but they include no recent names, being all either ancient, Arabic, or medieval Latin.

Bound together with these tracts on physiognomy of Rizza Casa and Padovanius in the volume which I examined at the

[52] Georgio del Rizza Casa, *Breve Trattato di naturale Astrologia giudiciaria intorno a giudicii o discorsi sopra le nativita in tre parte diviso. . . .* A Lyone (15)91, 4to: BM 8610.d.9.

[53] After the text proper ends at page 79, these are added as an appendix at pp. 81, 89, 91 and 95.

[54] *Ibid.*, p. 60.

[55] *Ibid.*, p. 88.

[56] *Ibid.*, p. 63.

[57] Ioannes Padovanius Veronensis, *De singularum humani corporis partium significationibus*, Verona, 1589, 88 pp. It is bound with the work of Rizza Casa in BM 1141.c.41.(3.).

[58] *Jo. Paduanii Viridarium mathematicorum*, Venice, 1563.

[59] Mentioned by Ludwig Combach in his preface to the 1649 edition of the works of George Ripley, printed at Cassel, and by whom there is an alchemical treatise in a manuscript at Cassel: Kassel Landesbibl. Chem. 8vo (2), Johannes de Padua, *Philosophia sacra, Praxis de lapide minerali.*

British Museum is a *Natural Physiognomy* attributed to Giovanni Ingegneri, bishop of Capo d'Istria, an office which he held from 1576 to his death in 1600.[60] This edition appeared at Vicenza in 1615,[61] but there had been earlier printings there and at Milan in 1607,[62] with the imprimatur of the inquisitor, archbishop and senate. The Milan printers in their address to count Girolamo Morone say that the treatise had been recently printed in Naples, and that a copy had been despatched thence to Angelo Ingegneri, a nephew of the dead bishop, who had given it to them to issue in Lombardy. Apparently this Naples edition was the first but, like the others, posthumous. There were further printings at Viterbo in 1619 and so on to 1652. In the prohemium the author says that physiognomy is not an art, as some suppose, of judging what may happen to men in the future. He decries the attempt to predict contingent events, in which astrologers, chiromancers, and other like impostors go too far. But he holds that physiognomy is useful in revealing natural inclinations. The treatise takes up the parts of the human body in top to toe order with no special stress upon the hand.

One of the most impressive illustrations of the effect of the bull of Sixtus V against astrology is offered by Giovanni Baptista Porta, who had written on natural magic, physiognomy and other subjects bordering upon the occult. In 1603 he published at Naples six books of *Celestial Physiognomy,* in which the future could be easily conjectured from inspection of the human countenance, but in which also astrology was refuted and shown to be inane and imaginary.[63] In the prooemium Porta stated that among all peoples in all ages the arts of divination had received much attention. He from boyhood had been devoted to astrology,

[60] Eubel, III, 233.

[61] Giovanni Ingegneri, vescovo di Capo d'Istria, *Fisionomia naturale,* Vicenza, appresso Pietropaolo Tozzi, 1615, 60 pp. Copy used: BM 1141.c.4. (4.). The printed catalogue by error gives the date of printing as 1595.

[62] I have examined both at the British Museum: 1143.b.13 and c.77.a.18. (2.).

[63] *Coelestis physiognomoniae libri sex Ioan. Baptistae Portae Neapolitani, Unde quis facile ex humani vultus extima inspectione poterit ex coniectura futura praesagire, In quibus etiam astrologia refellitur et inanis et imaginaria demonstratur.* Neapoli, Ex typographia Io. Baptistae Subtilis, MDCIII, 191 pp.

until by order of the supreme pontiffs it had been forbidden to Catholics. Thereafter he abhorred it as much as he once had pursued it, and upon further examination found it to be a pretended and imaginary science, in which the basis of truth was physiognomy rather than the influence of the stars. In short he now contends that what the astrologers state as the effects of the planets, signs and constellations are rather to be attributed to the qualities, humors and other peculiarities of the human body. This does not deter him from repeating what such astrologers as Ptolemy, Firmicus Maternus and Dorotheus, Haly, Alcabitius and Messahala, Leopold and Bonatus ascribe to the planets and signs of the zodiac. He keeps explaining, it is true, that the effects on bodily form and health or disease and upon human character are really produced rather by the physical forces which the planets and signs merely represent. But under this guise of reinterpretation he appears to be offering the reader a series of systematic extracts from astrological authors, reading of whom might otherwise be taboo. This device, however, sufficed to satisfy the ecclesiastical censor, who grants permission to print the volume anywhere except in the city of Rome itself.[64]

A like attitude is seen in the posthumous publication in Italian of what professes at least to be a translation of a Latin manuscript by Porta on the subject of *chirofisonomia,*[65] a new name to distinguish it from the superstitious chiromancy of Cocles, Corvo and Tricasso, who are dismissed as ignorant impostors and mountebanks. In the proemio the translator, Pompeo Sarnelli, alludes to Delrio's distinction between physical chiromancy as a licit part of physiognomy and astrological chiromancy which is utterly vain and illicit and does not deserve the name of science. Sarnelli also refers to the bull of Sixtus V, which he contends

[64] *Ibid.*, p. 191.

[65] G. B. della Porta, *Della chirofisonomia . . . libri due . . . tradotti da un manuscritto latino dal signor Pompeo Sarnelli,* 1677. Copy used: BM 1141.b.32. At p. 9 the MS is said to have been preserved in the library of Lorenzo Crasso. It did not contain the figures which Porta promised in the text. At Montreal, McGill Univ., Osler 7618, a paper MS of 34 fols., J. B. Porta, De manuum lineis, is said to be the author's autograph of the Latin original of which the printed *Della chirofisonomia* is the Italian translation.

was directed only against astrological chiromancy and such writers as John ab Indagine, Taisnier, Cocles, Michael Savonarola, Michael Scot, Tricasso, Antonio Germisone, Marcello Saya, and Giva Teukesberg. A disciple of Porta, Giovanni Battista Longo, warns that the names of the planets employed in the Latin manuscript do not denote that the signification of the parts of the hand are infallibly directed by the stars but are merely indications of a jovial or saturnine *complexio*. One cannot predict such an event as violent death from the lines of the hand but only that the person has an irate temper which makes such an end probable.

Similarly in the text Porta states that he was ready to drop the art, disgusted by the errors of previous writers upon it, until he read a passage favorable to it in Aristotle's *History of Animals* and further reflected that the Supreme Artificer and Creator always followed a certain order in all His works. Porta has therefore developed the present work upon the same basis as his treatises on human physiognomy, celestial physiognomy, and signatures in plants, and has laid a foundation of detailed data for it by examining the hands, feet and foreheads of executed criminals and persons who suffered a violent death or died without confession. He then proceeds to distinguish seven mountains in the hand named after the seven planets. He keeps disagreeing, however, with those writers whom he calls charlatan empirics and taking a different view based on the physiognomy of Aristotle and Polemon. More particular parts of the hand and their significance are added, and it is suggested that one should also observe the soles of the feet. At the close the translator adds some chapters from Porta's *Human Physiognomy*. Then follow five pages of imprimaturs.

Magini was bolder or more open than Porta in his defense of astrological medicine in his work of 1607 on critical days and the legitimate use of astrology in medicine.[66] Despite the fact that the bull of Sixtus V had expressly permitted the use of

[66] Jo. Ant. Magini, *De astrologica ratione et usu dierum criticorum*, Venice, 1607. Copy used: BM 718.e.16.

astrology in medicine, there seems to have been some hesitancy about publishing a work in that field. As we have seen in our chapter on Astrology at Bologna, Magini printed his book after consultation with the inquisitor and university of Padua, and with the approval of the Council of Ten. Perhaps he was not encouraged to print it at Bologna in the papal territory. He stated his intention of not exceeding the limits set by the Roman Catholic church. He held that the church condemned only superstitious Arabic astrology and nativities which impinge on human free will, but not the use of nativities in medicine to determine the patient's temperament, to what diseases he is naturally prone, and how long he can live. He further affirmed the control of the stars over the world of nature and advised study of the annual recurrence or revolutions of the nativity and the election of favorable times .He regarded it as essential to observe the moment when the patient fell ill, the critical days of his illness, and the best times for administering drugs. He lamented, however, that astrology was now utterly neglected by physicians.

Astrology continued to be taught at the university of Salamanca long after the bull of Sixtus V. Gabriel Serrano was teaching it there on March 21, 1592. On September 7 and November 8 of the same year he took the necessary oaths to receive the degrees of licentiate and master of arts.[67] In a manuscript at the Escorial are still preserved his lectures introductory to judgments in his chair of astrology in 1593.[68] In the same manuscript is another treatise on judicial astrology, comments of Jacobus Perez de Messa on a book of astrological aphorisms, and a discussion of the constitution of the new-born child which is probably also astrological (*De nati complexione*) by the licentiate Balthazar de Mendoza.[69] With Serrano's death on June 26, 1598, the chair became vacant but did not permanently remain so, since Bartolomé de Valle was professor of astrology from 1612 to 1615, and in 1619 published an *Explica-*

[67] E. E. Arteaga, *Historia pragmatica e interna de la Universidad de Salamanca,* II (1917), 399.

[68] Escorial O.III.30, 16th century, fol. 2.

[69] *Ibid.*, fols. 18, 52 and 103 respectively.

ción y pronósticos de los dos cometas. From 1615 to 1624 Francisco Reales, a priest, was professor of astrology, then Núñez de Zamora, 1624-1640, Sánchez de Mendoza, 1647-1673, and others. The chair was again vacant from 1706 to 1726, but then Diego de Torres Villarroel held it from 1726 to 1770.[70]

That not much attention was paid to the bull of Sixtus V in Spain, and that the Spanish inquisition was less strict than the Roman with regard to subjects bordering upon the field of divination, is further indicated by a volume by Gerónimo Cortés printed at Cordova in 1601, Zaragoza in 1603, and, in an enlarged edition which I have examined, at Tarragona in 1609. It bears an Approbacion by the Dominican and master of theology, Iusepe Lerquian, prior and lector of the see of Tarragona, and a Licencia to print by the official and vicar general, Francisco de Torme. The Approbacion declares that the volume contains nothing contrary to the Christian faith and doctrine of the Catholic church or to good morals, that the author has followed the infallible rule, *Deus super omnia,* and has always saved freedom of the will with reference to the stars and their movements and influence. Cortés was born in Valencia. He had published a *Lunario y prognostico perpetuo* there in 1598 and at Barcelona in 1599. In 1604 he printed an *Arithmetic* and in 1615 a treatise on animals, terrestrial and flying. He died prematurely.[71]

The little volume in question of some 120 leaves is entitled *Physiognomy and Varied Secrets of Nature*[72] and is composed of five treatises: on physiognomy, rosemary, *aqua ardens,* a collection of natural secrets, and a treatise on the elementary and celestial regions. The *Physiognomy* does not predict matters of fortune from the parts of the body but does indicate the mental and moral characteristics corresponding to various physical fea-

[70] Arteaga, *op. cit.,* pp. 508-9, 502-3, 491-92, 601-2, 586, 582, 650, and 668-71, respectively.

[71] See Zedler, and Nicolas Antonio, *Bibl. Hisp. Nova,* for his life and works.

[72] *Phisonomia y varios secretos de naturaleza: contiene cinco tratados de materias diferentes todos revistos y majorados en esta tercera impression a la qual se han añadido muchas cosas notables y de mucho provecho. Compuesto por Hieronymo Cortes natural de la Ciudad de Valencia con licencia.* En Tarragona por Felippe Roberto, Año 1609.

tures. The three authorities on physiognomy cited in the preliminary bibliography to the volume are "Isnerio, Escoto, y Pedro de Ribas." The first two names seem to refer to Taisnier and Michael Scot, while Pedro de Ribas, who was vicar of the church of St. Nicholas at Zaragoza, had recently addressed to the archbishop of that city a volume translated from the Italian on medicine, botany and physiognomy.[73]

In the fifth treatise of the volume Cortés has a chapter on each planet and its sphere and the physiognomy and characteristics of those born under it. He cites "Cardan, skilled astronomer,"[74] apparently oblivious to the fact that some of Cardan's works were on the Spanish *Index* of 1559. In discussing the element air, he notes that Pliny and Ptolemy say that comets in the upper region of air usually denote evil. For a fuller discussion of their effects he refers the reader to his *Repertorio perpetuo de los tiempos,*[75] that is, his very popular *Lunario y prognostico,* which reached its eighth impression in 1614. Astrological interest is also displayed in the fourth treatise on natural secrets where, to keep one's nails and hair from growing too fast, it is recommended to cut them when the moon is waning in the sign of Cancer, Pisces or Scorpio. To attain perfection in studies easily and rapidly one should begin them when the moon and Mercury are in friendly aspect, best of all when both planets are in Gemini or Virgo.[76]

To the fifth treatise Cortés added a supplementary tract, "brief and very curious," on the significations and causes of the black and white marks which appear on the finger nails,[77] thus adding a further refinement to both physiognomy and chiromancy. Stating that the spots are produced by the four humors under the influence of the celestial bodies, Cortés proceeds to tell what part of the body and hand each planet rules. He assures

[73] *El Porque: sive librum huius nuncupationis,* Madriti apud Petrum de Madrigal 1598 in 8. Cf. Antonio, *Bibl. Hisp. Nova.*

[74] *Phisonomia,* 1609, fol. 87r.

[75] *Ibid.,* fol. 83v.

[76] *Ibid.,* fol. 48v.

[77] *Ibid.,* fols. 107v-112r: "Tratado breve y muy curioso de las significaciones y causas de los señales blancos y negros que aparacen en las uñas."

us, however, that all that he has said and will say is subject to obedience to and correction by the holy Roman Catholic church. Yet now the things signified by the spots on the nails are matters of fortune and not merely of health, character and ability, as in his *Physiognomy*. For example, when a white spot appears in the middle of the thumb nail, it denotes some undertaking or important business of great profit, usually through the agency of women, while if a black spot appears there, it indicates expenditure and loss of money by reason of women.

In discussing the air and its meteorological phenomena, Cortés introduces an account of the *Agnus Dei*,[78] which constitutes an instructive bit of ecclesiastical magic to set over against the ecclesiastical prohibitions of occult arts. The *Agnus Dei,* Cortés says, has virtue not only against meteors but every kind of storm and many other perils, visible and invisible. The pope does not bless these wax images of lambs annually, as some think, but only in the year of his election and every seventh year thereafter. The forms, large or small, of very pure wax are prepared by the sacristan of the pope and his chaplains and clerks who impress on them the figure of the lamb in token of Jesus Christ, the Lamb without spot or blemish. Then they take them to the chapel of the pope, who blesses a quantity of water with many prayers and supplications, then takes a bit of balsam and shapes it into the form of a cross and casts it into the holy water, saying, "Lord, deem good to consecrate and bless this water with this unction of balsam of our benediction. In the name of the Father and of the Son and of the Holy Ghost." Next he takes the oil of chrism and pours it upon the water in the form of a cross, uttering the appropriate words. Then, girt with a white towel, he takes the wax lambs, immerses them in the holy water and baptizes them. Other prelates dip them out with silver ladles and put them aside to dry off, after which the pope repeats over them many prayers and supplications, that they may bestow blessings and avert all evils from all the faithful who employ them with purity and devotion.

[78] *Ibid.*, fols. 80r-81r. It is in substantial agreement with the article, Agnus Dei, in the *Catholic Encyclopedia.*

Cortés then enumerates the virtues of the *Agnus Dei*. These include to those who bear them with devotion and confidence immunity from enemies visible or invisible, from many perils corporal and spiritual, pardon from venial sins and even from mortal sins, if worn with great devotion. Also against bad weather, hail and lightning, pestilence, epilepsy and sudden death, fire, phantasms, goblins, visions, possession by demons. The *Agnus Dei* also has great virtue in relieving women in childbirth, especially if they take three tiny bits of it in water and repeat with great devotion, "Lamb of God, pity me! Thou who suffered for us, pity me!"

The following interpretation of the bull of Sixtus V was given in his treatise on sortileges[79] by Johannes Franciscus Leo of Ivrea, doctor of both laws and bishop of Telesia from December 15, 1608, to his death on April 14, 1613. The bull brought astrologers as well as diviners under the jurisdiction of ecclesiastical judges. It prohibited all books of judicial astrology, geomancy, hydromancy, pyromancy, onomancy, chiromancy, necromancy and magic art. Inquisitors were to proceed against those who knowingly read and retained books or writings of this sort.

A different interpretation was given by Jean Taxil, doctor of medicine, who in 1602 had published a treatise on epilepsy at Tournon on the Rhone,[80] and who in 1614 issued there a work on astrology and physiognomy.[81] In part at least this work was composed earlier at Arles in 1608.[82] The volume really consists of three distinct works. Of the first, on comets, we treat in another chapter. The second, on astrology, is divided between revolutions, nativities and elections. It justifies the casting of nativities at length and says that Pico della Mirandola wrote against

[79] *Libellus de sortilegiis*, published in the *Malleus maleficarum* of 1669.

[80] Jean Taxil, *Traicte de l'epilepsie maladie vulgairement appellée au pays de Provence la gouttete aux petits enfans*, Tournon, Claude Michel, 1602, 8vo.

[81] *L'astrologie et physiognomie en leur splendeur*, Tournon, R. Reynaud, 1614, 8vo.

[82] At pp. 161-90, a Judgment of the new star of 1605—Iudicium Ioannis Taxilli D. medici de nova illa stella quae colluxit in Sagittario anno . . . 1605—which is in Latin, not French like the preceding text, is dated at its close, "Arles 5 cal. Maii 1608."

astrology because his own early death at the age of thirty-four had been correctly predicted thereby. Then with a new pagination begins the part on physiognomy which again divides between metoposcopy, physiognomy and chiromancy. Taxil justifies all three arts. In the section on astrology there seems to be no allusion to the bull of Sixtus V, but in connection with chiromancy Taxil says that if pope Sixtus has made a bull against chiromancers, its purpose is to excommunicate sorcerers and magicians, not true and natural chiromancers. Otherwise one would be forced to believe that this bull excommunicated physicians, "who ordinarily derive many indications of diseases of the body by contemplating the hand" of the patient.[83] Like the astrological publications of Rizza Casa at Lyons, this of Taxil suggests that it was possible to print books in France which would have hardly been allowed in Italy after 1586.

Some light on the legal standing of astrology in France in the early seventeenth century is supplied by the 1615 edition of Laurent Bouchel's *Library or Treasury of French Law.* Under the topic of Almanacs[84] we are told that prognostications exceeding the limits of astrology are forbidden by the Ordinance of Orléans, article 26, and that they may not be printed without having first been inspected by the archbishop, bishop or episcopal representative, under pain of prison and arbitrary fine for the printer and bookseller and of corporal punishment for the author. Bouchel goes on to say that astrology, otherwise called astronomy, is wholly deceitful, more so than the fables of the poets. Its practitioners disagree among themselves, while the more subtle of them, like Nostradamus, purposely cultivate obscurity. Bouchel adds, however, that he does not wish to forbid judicial astrology, if it remains within its due limits and common rules. But too often it is found mixed with magic. A similar blowing hot and cold alternately characterizes the article, Astrologie. First the writer of the article represents even such authors as Aquinas, Cirvelo, George of Trebizond, and Corne-

[83] *Ibid.*, II, 128.

[84] Laurent Bouchel, *La bibliothèque ou thresor du droit français*, 1615, I, 220, col. 2-221, col. 2.

lius Agrippa as opponents of astrology, which would certainly seem to be stretching a point. But then follows an "Advertissement sur les iugemens d'astrologie," addressed to "Mademoiselle," which is in general favorable to astrology and urges men not to cut down so fine a tree because it has a single rotten branch.[85] This Advertissement was omitted in the later edition of 1671,[86] which may have been a sign that astrology lost ground as the century proceeded. However, the article on Almanacs remained the same in the edition of 1671 including its final qualification in favor of judicial astrology.

That astrology did not entirely disappear even from the papal court after the bull of Sixtus V, is indicated by an astrological discourse on the year 1618 addressed by Gioanni Bartolini to one of the cardinals.[87]

In 1631 Urban VIII approved and reaffirmed the bull of Sixtus V with emphatic language that no one, whatsoever his rank, was immune from its prohibitions, and with threats of severe penalties even to death and confiscation. From this one is inclined to infer that the decree against astrologers had not been well enforced in the interim. Moreover, the fact that Urban VIII in particular forbids predictions concerning political and ecclesiastical matters, especially the life of the pope or of relations of the present pope to the third degree, makes one suspect that it was the boldness of the astrologers in forecasting such matters which elicited the bull, and that it was such predictions which would actually be most likely to be punished.[88]

Petrus Antonius de Magistris Galathei, who perhaps may be identified with Antonio Pedro (1614-1675), composed a treatise distinguishing permitted from superstitious astrology and declaring "the true sense of the bull of Sixtus V, which Urban VIII confirmed and strengthened."[89] He says that the majority of the-

[85] Whereas the article, Astrologie, occupies only about a column on p. 363, this supplementary Advertissement runs on to p. 370.

[86] L. Bouchel, *Bibliothèque du droit français,* 3 vols., 1671.

[87] Vatic. lat. 6304, Gioanni Bartolini, Discorso astrologico sopra l'anno 1618 al Card. Sta. Susanna.

[88] *Bullarium Romanum,* Turin, XIV (1868), 211-14.

[89] Vatic. Barberini lat. 921 (XVII, 24), 17th century, 73 fols. Petri Antonii de Magistris Galathei de astrolo-

ologians regard the bull as not binding in the forum of conscience. Furthermore, the bull applies to fictitious, not physical, astrology. It is aimed at particular predictions, "concerning which science is not possible." It forbids attempts to predict voluntary acts. Antonius argues further that the bull should be interpreted to agree with the decrees of the Council of Trent and with the doctrine of Aquinas. He declares that astrology is one of the seven liberal arts and that Hippocrates considered it necessary for a physician. He intends to show by an examination of the writings of leading theologians what part of it is permitted and what interdicted. Augustine and Aquinas may be cited both for and against astrology, the explanation being that it is twofold, physical and fictitious. Antonius will follow the authority of Cartagena, Alexander de Angelis, Michael Zanardus of Bergamo, and Magini. He contends that the physical part of astrology is that of which Ptolemy treated, and that the Chaldeans and Arabs introduced the superstitious variety. A proof of this is that the Ptolemaic astrology has never been placed on any index of prohibited books. The *Quadripartitum* deals chiefly with the effects of the stars on the weather and upon human genitures, in no way transcending natural limits. Elections, however, pertain to the superstitious side of astrology. Jacobus Sprenger in the *Malleus maleficarum* calls it false and heretical to say that the stars affect human character necessarily and efficaciously but true to say that they so dispose contingently. The attacks of Pico della Mirandola and Savonarola do not apply to the true variety of astrology. The bulls of Sixtus V and Urban VIII also are directed only against the fictitious and superstitious side of astrology, in support of which interpretation Antonius cites Kepler and various theologians.

The attitude of Campanella to the two papal bulls is also in-

gia narratiuncula in qua permissa a superstitiosa distinguitur. Ex diversis auctoribus nuper collecta ubi verus sensus bullae Sixti V declaratur quam postea Urbanus VIII confirmavit atque roboravit. Incipit, "Ut de astrologiae antiquitate nihil dicam cum ab Adamo ducat originem . . ." Explicit, ". . . ex quibus omnibus adductis nullus remanebit amplius dubitandi locus. Finis." This treatise appears to have remained unprinted.

structive, but first we must give some idea of his long previous devotion to astrology.

Campanella's letters during his long captivity repeatedly testify to his belief in and practice of astrology. In 1606, writing to pope Paul V and asserting that the prince is prejudiced against him, he states that he has a great constellation against him, and that where sense rules and not reason, the stars will without doubt conquer, for which dictum he cites Aquinas *Contra Gentiles*. Or on August 30 of the same year he writes to a cardinal that he had seen the nativity of an unknown man who would probably become a prophet. The next year he writes to Rudolph II that the stars indicate changes of sciences and the culmination of monarchies. "But, alas, your imperial Majesty will not deign to look at my predictions, and I write in fear and trembling lest, if my keepers find it out, they add to my fetters." Or he asks a later correspondent to send him the date and place of his birth and also a statement of his physical condition so that he may advise him from the stars as to journeys and diseases. Or writing to Galileo in 1611 he assures him that he predicted the recent advances in astronomy from the conjunction of 1603. He again defends the influence of the stars in a letter of March 8, 1614, to Galileo.[90]

In his six or seven books on astrology, published in 1629 at Lyons[91] and in 1630 at Frankfurt,[92] Campanella professes to eliminate all superstition of the Arabs and Jews, to treat the

[90] For the passages cited in this paragraph see Tommaso Campanella, *Lettere,* 1927, pp. 11, 36-37, 87, 137, 169, 177.

[91] Tommaso Campanella, *Astrologicorum libri VI (VII) in quibus Astrologia omni superstitione Arabum et Judaeorum eliminata physiologice tractatur secundum sacras scripturas et doctrinam S. Thomae et Alberti et summorum theologorum,* Lyons, J. A. & M. Prost, 1629, 4to. Copy used: BM 718.e.19.(1.).

[92] I have also examined a MS of the work in which the author is alluded to only by the initials, F.T.C. (Frater Thomas Campanella) and the text opens in the middle of the first book just before article 8 of chapter 5: Vatic. lat. 7180, fols. 29r-223v (now numbered 1r-195v). This MS has only the six books and not the additional seventh book.

Luigi Firpo, "Il Campanella astrologo ed i suoi persecutòri romani," *Rivista di filosofia,* 30(1939), 200-15, is chiefly concerning the differences between the two editions of 1629 and 1630.

subject naturally and according to holy Scripture and the doctrine of Aquinas, Albertus and the leading theologians. He does not, however, invariably interpret their views correctly. Thus he represents Aquinas as a supporter of astrological images and accepts *De fato* as a genuine work of Aquinas.[93] He affirms that the stars act upon inferiors by their heat, light, motion and aspect, and that it is not superstitious to observe their situation. "Neither are our affairs changed without the action of the stars, nor, when these are unchanged, do those change."[94] Primarily Campanella follows Ptolemy who compiled all the rules of the Chaldeans, Egyptians, Indians, Greeks and Latins, based upon observations made through many centuries. It would be foolish for Campanella, who has been examining genitures hardly ten years, to try to formulate a new procedure and neglect the old.[95] But he opposes the Ptolemaic doctrine that great alterations and beginnings are caused by eclipses, which are of brief duration, whereas empires, sects and customs last for many years. He prefers with Cardan the Arabic doctrine of conjunctions, especially of change of triplicitates.[96] He thinks that the planets each rule a millennium in turn and he gives four astrological causes for the passing of empires, arts and religions.[97] He has distinct books on nativities and elections. Cajetan is cited for the view that astrologers can judge and predict marvelously even concerning arbitrary matters involving exercises of the will, although in such cases their predictions are not infallible,[98] and Campanella agrees with Aquinas and Albertus that the will is not subject to the stars directly.[99] He believes that his own imprisonment was caused by a constellation of 1599,[100] and he notes that Tuesday and Friday have always been unlucky days for him. All seven times that he was tortured fell on these days. He even accepts the Egyptian days as derived from experience and evades the apostolic censure of those observing days and years and the pas-

[93] Edition of 1629, p. 21.
[94] Vatic. lat. 7180, fol. 66r (38r).
[95] Edition of 1629, pp. 9-10.
[96] Vatic. lat. 7180, fol. 66r-v.
[97] Edition of 1629, p. 229.
[98] *Ibid.*, p. 6: "Et Caietanus super secunda secundae in tractatu de religione et superstitione."
[99] *Ibid.*, p. 4.
[100] *Ibid.*, p. 206.

sage in the *Decretum* of Gratian against Egyptian days by contending that these strictures apply only to those who observe them superstitiously and not to those who observe them scientifically.[101]

To these six books on astrology was added a seventh, *On Avoiding Sidereal Fate,* with separate pagination. The printer explained that it arrived too late to incorporate with the others. Its sixth chapter deals with the "peculiar times of applying remedies to catch or avoid" specific influences of the stars. Its seventh chapter on more secret remedies says that there are stones, metals, plants, colors, savors and other things peculiarly endowed with the forces of the planets which, if applied under certain constellations, guard us from evil events, and that natural magic has to do with these.

In a review of his own works[102] Campanella tells us that he composed this seventh book in 1626, and that a treacherous friar, to whom he had lent it and the six books which he had written earlier, gave it to a printer in Lyons to publish in order to make Campanella lose favor with Urban VIII who detested astrology. At the same time he accused Campanella of both disobedience and superstition. Campanella therefore refused to recognize the work as his and wrote an *Apologia* which two censors approved. Judging from Campanella's letters, the publication of his seven books on astrology was one of the causes of his flight from Rome to France in 1634.[103] But since the books on astrology were printed in 1629, presumably the *Apologia* also came before Urban VIII's bull of 1631, and therefore was not identical with the treatise to which we next turn and in which Campanella again eats his earlier favoring words concerning that art.

This was a treatise printed at Paris in 1636 with the approbation of the Sorbonne in which the bulls of Sixtus V and Urban VIII were discussed at some length.[104] First are listed arguments

[101] *Ibid.*, p. 227.

[102] *Syntagma de libris propriis,* Artic. iv, *Opuscoli filosofici,* II (1927), 37-38.

[103] *Lettere,* 1927, p. 258.

[104] It forms a part of the volume entitled, *Atheismus triumphatus,* Paris, 1636, pp. 254-73, "An bullae SS pontificum Sixti V et Urbani VIII contra iudiciaros calumniam in aliquo patiantur?" Copy used: BM 480.b.2.

against or criticisms of these bulls. One is that astrology is a science, and that he who overthrows astrology destroys all philosophy and classes scientists with haruspices and diviners. The same complaint applies for chiromancy, hydromancy, geomancy, pyromancy, metoposcopy and physiognomy in so far as they seem to be founded on astrology. Another objection is that by these bulls astrologers are treated more harshly than heretics and schismatics. The precedent of the Magi and star of Bethlehem is adduced, and it is affirmed that not only did Albumasar, Cecco d'Ascoli, Pierre d'Ailly and Cardan put Christ under the stars, but that even Albertus Magnus drew up a scheme of Christ's nativity. This is going farther than Campanella cared to in his six books on astrology, where he refused to place the life of Christ on earth under the stars or to attribute to melancholy and astral influence the gift of tongues and other manifestations of angels or devil.[105] A fifth objection is that the bulls of Sixtus V and Urban VIII not merely prohibit prognostications pronounced with certainty but even those advanced tentatively (*per incertitudinem et suspicionem*), and that this contradicts the schoolmen who all allowed conjectures as to the future even in moral matters. Aquinas granted that some were well born and some ill-fated, Cajetan took up a like position, and the Council of Trent in its ninth rule condemned only those who dared affirm certainty for future contingents and voluntary acts. Moreover, the bull of Urban VIII even forbids making or repeating prognostications in order to disprove them, and so binds the hands of the soldiers of the church of Christ and arms the hands of the soldiers of the devil. Which is not only impious and contrary to natural and divine law but even ridiculous.

Despite these specious arguments—and his own private penchant for astrology, of which, however, he is now careful to say nothing—Campanella accepts the bulls as a papal command which must be obeyed. Moreover, he grants that astrology in all its extreme claims is not a science, while he interprets the bulls as admitting the physical action and influence of the stars.

[105] *Astrologicorum libri VI,* Lyons, 1629, p. 157.

Turning for a moment to other arts of divination, he says: "Nor are men given to chiromancy, metoposcopy and divination of dreams, like Tricasso, Corvus, Gesner, Cardan and Artemidorus to be excused, because, as they say, they observe signs established by God and nature. For in this they do not sin. But they do sin because they extend those signs through astrology to effects of which they are not signs."[106] The star at Christ's birth was not natural, nor were His conception and nativity. When in 1630 most astrologers announced the pope's death, Campanella ever contradicted this prediction because he knew the vanity of the art and of their practice of it. "For in this art he who knows more believes less and he who knows less believes more."[107] The work cited as Albert's by opponents of the bulls is of dubious authenticity, while Cecco, Cardan, Albumasar and d'Ailly disagree in their horoscopes for Christ. Sixtus V was wise to condemn all predicting as to future contingents, chance happenings, and voluntary actions, even if they say that they do not affirm certainly. Such predictions, though not false, are perilous, since men often adapt their course of action to them and are deceived thereby. Finally, Campanella denies that the bulls forbid the reproving or disproving of prognostications and divinations. They merely forbid prediction under a pretense of rebuttal. Especially is it illicit to repeat prognostications concerning the pope and the state of the church. "For it is of these that the bull speaks, and on account of them it was promulgated."[108] From which it might seem that Campanella, while professing complete adherence to the bulls, is trying to restrict their scope and force as much as possible. It also appears that he had totally ignored the bull of 1586 until that of 1631 brought it to his attention.

Antonio Merenda, writing against astrology in 1640, recognized that the papal bulls did not forbid all parts of astrology and that he was arguing against some phases which had not yet been forbidden.[109]

[106] *Atheismus triumphatus*, 1636, p. 266.

[107] *Ibid.*, p. 269.

[108] *Ibid.*, p. 272.

[109] Antonio Merenda, *La destrutione de' fondamenti dell' astrologia giudici-*

Jean Baptiste Morin (1583-1656), royal professor of mathematics at the university of Paris, in his *Astrologica Gallica* discussed the action of the Council of Trent as to the index of forbidden books and the bull of Sixtus V against astrology and nativities. His interpretation of the bull was that it did not condemn prediction of future events contingent upon natural causes but merely those concerning fortuitous events.[110] Incidentally it may be noted that Morin states that he owed to astrology his appointment by queen Marie de' Medici to the royal professorship of mathematics, which has enabled him to support two nieces in the best monasteries and to marry off a third.[111]

---

aria, a gl' huomini particolari predicente dignità, ricchezze, sanità ouero malattie del corpo & altri successi accidentali, Pavia, 1640, 68 pp., p. 63. Copy used: Col 156.4 M54.

[110] Johannes Baptista Morinus, *Astrologica gallica principiis et rationibus propriis stabilita . . .*, Hagae-Comitis, 1661, pp. xxxii-xxxiii. Copy used: Col 156.4 M82.

[111] *Ibid.*, p. xxxi.

CHAPTER XXXV

ADVERSARIES OF ASTROLOGY

Auguria naturalia non contemnenda;
Auguria artificiosa penitus explodenda
—George of Ragusa

Abundant illustration has been supplied in previous chapters of the gamut of degrees and gradations in men's attitude towards astrology and of the wide latitude of variation between the opposite extremes of excessive devotion to the art and of absolute denial that there was any truth in it. How dangerous it is to infer a person's attitude towards astrology from a single passage in his works may be shown by the case of the geographer Mercator who died in 1594. In one place he declares that the luminaries were not created to serve the vanity of the astrologers.[1] But in the preface to his *Atlas* he promises that he will presently treat celestial astromantics which pertain to divinations from the stars.[2] Death prevented his doing so, but it would seem that he was not opposed to divination from the stars or astrological prediction *per se,* but either only to certain aspects of it or to certain astrologers who went to superstitious extremes. In the closing decades of the sixteenth and early decades of the seventeenth century a number of treatises were written and published against astrology. As we shall see, this does not always mean that their authors rejected the influence of the stars. But it does suggest an increasing opposition to astrological prediction.

Maurolycus (1494-1575), writing from Messina in August 1556, expressed his aversion from regarding uncertain judicial astrology as the end of most noble astronomy and pleasing speculation. In order not to be at odds with everyone else, however, and to please his friends he descended into judgments and com-

[1] Van Raemdonck, *Gérard Mercator, sa vie et ses oeuvres,* 1869, p. 99.

[2] *Ibid.,* p. 100.

piled an introduction to astrology "from Ptolemy, Hermes, Dorotheus, Alkindi, Saphar (Albumasar), Messahalla, Aomar, both Halies, Albumasar, Zael, Jergis, Abraham, Alfraganus, Albubater, Alcabitius, Bonatti, Leopold, Campanus, Gazulus, Firmicus, Manilius, Abano, John of Saxony, Regiomontanus, Bellantius, Gaurico, Cardan, Schöner and others."[3] At least he showed no prejudice against Arabic astrology.

In 1558, in the Proemio to his work on the theory of the planets, Alessandro Piccolomini, while recognizing that it would be useful to forecast floods and the course of diseases, contended that at present judicial astrology was so difficult and imperfect, and its predictions so ridiculous and idle, that it was better not to waste time over it. Therefore, although granting that astrology was not illicit and without cause or reasoning, as were geomancy, necromancy, augury and auspices, he confined himself to the speculative, astronomical side of the science of the stars.[4]

William Fulke published at London in 1560 an *Antiprognosticon* against the useless astrological predictions of Nostradamus, Cunningham, Lowe, Hill, Vaughn, "and all the rest."[5] Since the names mentioned are mainly those of popular and sensational rather than learned and would-be scientific astrologers, perhaps his objection was more to such practitioners than to the art.

Lucillus Philalthaeus, whose real name was Lucilio Maggi, in his commentary on *De coelo et mundo,* published in 1565[6] after he had been teaching philosophy for twenty years at Pavia,[7] admired the genius of Ptolemy except as an astrologer. He further declared that the details of astrological technique nauseated him, and that the arguments of the astrologers to prove the moist nature of the moon were of no weight.

[3] *Scritti inediti di Francesco Maurolico,* BB IX(1876), 35, 37.

[4] Alessandro Piccolomini, *La prima parte de le theoriche ó vero speculationi dei pianeti,* Venice, Giordano Ziletti, 1558, Proemio (unnumbered pages). Copy used: BM 718.e.8.(2.).

[5] *Antiprognosticon contra inutiles astrologorum praedictiones Nostrodami Cunninghami Lovi Hilli Vaghami et reliquorum omnium authore G. Fulcone,* London, 1560, 8vo. BM 718.c.6.

[6] *In quatuor libros Aristotelis de coelo et mundo commentarii,* 1565, in folio, 680 pp., pp. 74-75, 80. Copy used: BM 520.l.15.

[7] *Ibid.,* p. 680, "Haec faciebat Lucillus Philalthaeus publice annos 20 professus philosophiam in gymnasio Ticinensi."

Reference has already been made to the discussion which Adam ab Invidia of Bayonne, a notary of the papal court, had with a doctor in the pontificate of Paul III but which he did not develop into the form of a treatise until 1572 and which has therefore been reserved for consideration here. The contention of Adam is that the human will is not subject to the stars,[8] but the very fact that he deems it important to establish this position suggests that opposition to astrology has not yet succeeded in advancing far. Adam admits the physical influence of the stars, and his adversary grants that the wise man can rule the stars. So it might seem that there is little room for disagreement between them. But the adversary asks, "Who is wise?" and argues that each man is governed by the constellation at his birth, as Jesus was by the star of Bethlehem. Adam for his part asserts that almost all the ills suffered by true religion have come from devotees of the stars, and questions whether the stars even endow men with qualities at birth. Asked if he will not concede that the stars incline us to act, though they do not compel us, he objects that inanimate bodies cannot act in any way upon the human soul. If the stars do not compel plants and animals to do anything unnatural, why should they incline man to sin? Finally, however, Adam does admit that indirectly and *per accidens* through universal natures and qualities which depend on the aspects of the stars man may be incited and inclined to evil. He also grants that the stars act upon human as upon other bodies.

Aside from this indecisive conclusion, discredit is cast upon Adam's intellectual capacity by a second tract in the same manuscript which is also ascribed to him. It is likewise in the form of a dialogue between him and the doctor, and is dated in

[8] MS BN 6689, 16th century, fol. 1r, "Voluntatem hominis non esse astris suppositam." After 3 blank pages the dedication begins on fol. 3r, "Magnifico et excellenti viro Horatio Arrigonio nobili romano iurium peritissimo Adam ab Invidia Baionensis salutem." It ends on fol. 3v and then on fol. 4r or 1r, since a new numbering begins for the text, "Liber primus. De hominis voluntate quod nullis agatur syderibus nec ad ea spectare homini qualitates ullas ad malum dare(?)", opening, "Omnes fere clades . . ." Subsequently the numbering of the leaves becomes confused but liber secundus begins on one numbered fol. 15r and ends at fol. 35r.

1574. But it advocates the extraordinary thesis that the sun does not pass beneath the earth and illuminate the other hemisphere, while it is night with us.[9] The argument by which this contention is maintained is so puerile, and any serious discussion of such matter at so late a date as 1574 seems so inconceivable, that it is difficult to believe that Adam ab Invidia is really its author. It is still insisted, for example, that the sun is too hot in the equatorial regions to permit access to the southern hemisphere. Or it is held that, if the sun were shining on the other side of the earth, some of its rays would reach this side. This is illustrated by an absurd little diagram in which the sun almost touches the earth.[10] The climax of nonsense is reached, when it is affirmed that, if the sun is always in the other hemisphere at night, the moon should always be there while we have day, but that actually we often see it while the sun is shining. Despite this observation, the text goes on to say that sun and moon divide day and night between them by divine command alone, that when the moon appears, it has to be night, and that the sun hides or loses its light in order that the moon may take its turn.[11] The handwriting of this second tract seems distinctly more modern, and probably the work is a hoax by some later writer. One wonders if he was trying to satirize and parody Adam's arguments against astrology, which perhaps seemed equally nonsensical and antiquated to him. Since neither tract appears to have been printed, their circulation and influence was presumably limited. However, Adam's dedication to a noble Roman jurist, Arrigoni, and the marginal comments on the manuscript indicate that it found some readers.

Quenay of Evreux, in a work against fate published at Paris in 1575, devoted two out of thirteen chapters to an attack on astrological fate and predictions.[12]

[9] BN 6689, fols. 36r-49r: "De sole quod noctu non transeat per partes terre inferiores quo nobis noctem conficiat. Adam ab Invidia de anno 1574 apud Valerame dum molles legerentur castaneae." On fol. 1r the title was given as, "De sole quod non transeat per loca nobis subterranea."

[10] A marginal note well comments, "Ista figura nihil convincit."

[11] *Ibid.*, fols. 41r-42v.

[12] *Quenaei Ebroicensis De fati expugnatione libellus*, Paris, 1575. Cap. 10, "Astrologicum fatum variis exagita-

Among the works elicited by the comet of 1577 were two which took that event as an occasion for hostile criticism of astrologers and astrology. Their authors were Marcellus Squarcialupus[13] and Andreas Dudith.[14] Squarcialupus addressed his treatise to Dudith, and, as has been stated in our chapter on Erastus, their tracts were printed together with his on the same subject of comets. Squarcialupus was an Italian physician and philosopher who became a religious exile and apparently was a Socinian.[15] Dudith, who had earlier been a Roman Catholic bishop of Fünfkirchen and had attended the Council of Trent, seems to have been a Lutheran at the time of writing on the comet of 1577, but eventually turned Socinian, thereby forfeiting the friendship of Erastus, who ceased to correspond with him.[16] In the present treatises Dudith cites Erastus as showing that the comet years of 1556 and 1558 were both salubrious, while Squarcialupus rejects the Aristotelian theory of comets which Erastus maintained and contests the statement of Erastus that the earth possesses great internal heat which produces exhalations. Squarcialupus writes in a tiresome oratorical style

---

tur rationibus aut potius evertitur"; cap. 11, "Ex Nigidii Figuli responso praedictionum astrologicarum falsitas aperitur." Copy used: BN Rés. R.885.

[13] *De cometa in universum atque de illo qui anno 1577 visus est opinio Marcelli Squarcialupi Plumbinensis . . . / . . .* Datum Pascovii anno salutis 1578. Printed in *De cometis dissertationes novae,* 1580, pp. 27-97: copy used, BM 532.e.12.(3.).

[14] Andreas Dudith, *De cometarum significatione commentariolus in quo non minus eleganter quam docte et vere mathematicorum quorundam in ea re vanitas refutatur. Addidimus D. Thomae Erasti eadem de re sententiam.* Basileae, ex officina Petri Pernę, anno 1579. Copy used: BM 532.e.12.(2.).

Tycho Brahe, *De mundi aetherei recentioribus phaenomenis,* 1588, although enumerating many tracts on the comet of 1577, fails to mention that by Dudith. Yet in a letter of August 17, 1588, to Scultetus Tycho states that he has sent Dudith a copy of his book and is eager to learn Dudith's opinion of it. *Opera,* VII, 124.

Dreyer in his notes (*Ibid.,* IV, 509) seems acquainted only with the later edition of 1580 which we have mentioned in the previous note: *De cometis dissertationes novae clarissimorum virorum Thomae Erasti, Andreae Dudithii, Marcelli Squarcialupi, Symonis Grynaei,* s.l., 1580, 4to.

[15] Gisbertus Voetius, *Exercitatio de prognosticis cometarum,* 1665, p. 20.

[16] *Ibid.,* pp. 21-22. More recent and fuller treatments of Dudith are: Pierre Costil, *André Dudith, humaniste hongrois, 1533-1589, sa vie, son oeuvre et ses mss. grecs,* Paris, 1935, 8vo. 482 pp. C. Juhasz, "Andreas Dudich, ein Beitrag z. Gesch. des Humanismus und der Gegenreformation," *Hist. Jahrbuch,* 1937, pp. 55-74.

with many rhetorical questions. Dudith too is a trifle too rhetorical and adds quotations from classical poetry.

Squarcialupus criticizes Ptolemy as the leading representative of ancient astrology and Mizaldus as representative of more recent astrologers. "If they are so inept," he asks, "how much faith can be put in the others?" He goes on, however, to attack Camerarius and Peucer, and to ridicule Agostino Nifo, although he calls him "no mean philosopher," for continuing the effects of a comet to the eighth year after, and Gemma Belga (Frisius?) for prolonging such effects for forty years. He calls attention to recent disagreement among Cornelius Gemma, the imperial astrologer Paul Fabricius,[17] and a third astrologer. Cornelius Gemma, Fabricius, Dasypodius, Valentin Steinmetz and others also differed as to the form or shape of the recent comet. Almost no one was in a position to observe its entire course, and hence the astrologers differed as to when it first appeared and when it finally disappeared. Four authors who discussed the comet in German all disagreed, namely, Valentinus Nolthius, Philomathesius, Samuel Muller, and "R.P." Such disagreement Squarcialupus regards as fatal to the claims made for astrology. He also contends that if the Aristotelian theory of comets as generated from terrestrial vapor is abandoned, as it had been by astrologers like Gemma and Praetorius as well as by himself, "all the doctrine and glory of the astrologers perishes." Yet, if the comet is a celestial and superior body, as he contends, is would seem that it should influence inferiors all the more potently.

Other arguments which Squarcialupus advances against comets as heralds of disaster are that ills and wars befall equally in years and periods when there are no comets, and that pestilence does not come from dryness which is a characteristic of comets (according, however, to the Aristotelian theory which he rejects). On the other hand, the new star of 1572 was hailed as a good omen, and Cornelius Gemma interpreted it as a sign of the tri-

[17] Paul Fabricius, who was a physician as well as a mathematician, wrote on the comets of 1556 and 1558 and new star of 1572, and composed a catalogue of plants growing about Vienna as well as astronomical tables and astrological predictions.

umph of Christianity. But there has been little but wars since it, whether in the Low Countries or in Italy. Of writers on the recent comet Squarcialupus speaks especially harshly of Raimundus Vennensis, by whom Annibale Raimondo of Verona is probably meant. He was also castigated by Tycho Brahe. The critical attitude of Squarcialupus towards the doctrines of Aristotle and Ptolemy does not extend to Pliny. Rather he expresses amazement that anyone should "deny this and spurn Pliny, a most serious and honest writer . . . Pliny, a man of so great authority."

Tycho Brahe, while approving the stand of Squarcialupus against the Aristotelian doctrine of comets, criticized him for not supporting his own position by either mathematical demonstrations or astronomical observations. This was a trenchant criticism and shows not only that it was easier to find fault with astrologers than to make a constructive contribution to astronomy, but that opponents of astrology might be less scientific in other respects than many of its practitioners.

Dudith in his work on the significance of comets aimed to refute the vanity of certain astrologers. Against their appeal to experience he retorted that innumerable instances could be recalled in which none of their predictions were fulfilled or quite the contrary took place. He quoted Julius Caesar Scaliger that many comets had occurred without any princes dying, while many princes had died without any comet to announce this. He pointed out that of late there had been many pestilences in Poland, Turkey, Hungary and Germany unpreceded by any comet, and that before the recent comet appeared over a hundred thousand persons were said to have died in a plague at Venice, not to mention other cities of central and southeastern Europe. Repeating such an exaggerated figure gives us an unfavorable impression of Dudith's scientific capacity. He also, like Squarcialupus, made capital of the disagreement among the astrologers themselves and sneered at Annibale Raimondo of Verona in particular. He declared that prediction from comets was based on superstition and childish fear, not on the nature of comets themselves, nor on any discipline, sacred or profane, which had firm and true foundations. He would admit only a natural astrology which would confine itself to prediction of eclipses, the future positions of the stars, and sometimes the appearance of comets. Such a natural astrology would not seem to differ from astronomy. Finally Dudith rather weakened his case by arguing that portents must be events contrary to the course and order of nature, a view which the astrologers, with such theories as that of great conjunctions of the planets which occur at regular intervals, would hardly accept.

The *Quaestiones physicae* of Freige, published in 1579,[18] at the age of thirty-six, are perhaps more significant for the opposition shown to astrology than for anything else. Otherwise the volume is a summary in 36 books and 1296 small pages of traditional theory and beliefs as to nature with about the usual modicum of scepticism as to some of these. The author says that he has contributed nothing but the order and method of presentation.[19] He covers the usual round of Aristotelian and astronomical topics, and such matters of more recent interest as cinnabar and cinnamon, or the horn of unicorn and the rhinoceros. The opposition to astrology stands out the more, because in other respects Freige has remained attached to customary beliefs in marvels and occult relationships. He still accepts the concept of sympathy and antipathy and believes that snakes will not tolerate even the shadow of the ashtree and will flee into flames kindled about the tree in preference.[20] He still retails the traditional statements concerning the basilisk and viper, the echeneis and the dolphin, the emerald and jasper, and states that the diamond is softened by the blood of a goat.[21] But this cheerful

[18] Jo. Thomas Freigius, *Quaestiones physicae in quibus methodus doctrinam physicam legitime docendi describendique rudi Minerva descripta est libris xxxvi*, Basileae, Seb. Henricpetri, anno 1579 mense Martio.

[19] *Ibid.*, p. 1294, Ad lectorem.

[20] *Ibid.*, pp. 165, 172, 800.

[21] *Ibid.*, pp. 1141, 1146, 1036, 759, 756. He ascribes to the jasper the property which other of our authors assign to the turquoise of saving its bearer from injury in a fall by itself breaking in pieces. But he then adds that Isidore says that it is superstitious to believe this.

credulity is no longer extended by him to astrological predictions.

Freige would limit astrology to weather prediction and perhaps selection of favorable times in agriculture, medicine and the like. He inveighs against nativities and, while he explains interrogations, elections and astrological images, disapproves of them. He holds that the changed position of the signs of the zodiac vitiates astrological judgment from conjunctions of the planets. Thus a conjunction in Scorpio in 630 announced the conquests of the Arabs. But Ptolemy put southern Asia under the signs Taurus, Virgo and Capricorn. The conjunction of 1484, also in Scorpio, heralded the French and Spanish invasions of Italy and the unheard-of disease, syphilis. But Ptolemy subjected Europe to Aries, Leo and Sagittarius, Africa to Scorpio. Or the conjunction of 1344 (*sic*) in Aquarius brought the Black Death to Europe, which has nothing in common with Aquarius. Pisces according to Ptolemy is a sign governing Africa. But the events which followed the conjunctions of 1464 and 1524 in Pisces had nothing to do with Africa.[22]

Another sign of opposition to astrology was the publication in 1581 of a Latin translation of the work of the reformer Savonarola against the art. A German translation by Erastus had already appeared in 1569. The Latin translator was Tommaso Buoninsegni, a rich money-lender who became a Dominican and then was professor of theology at Florence for twenty-five years. He also wrote on economic subjects and at his death in 1609 left in manuscript a discussion whether the celestial bodies were moved directly by God without the mediation of other intelligences and movers.[23] That he could not find any heavier ammunition to offer learned readers of Latin against astrology than the popular, religious and insufficient work of Savonarola goes to show that foes of astrology were often not animated by any more critical and scientific intelligence than the astrologers themselves.

[22] Freige's criticism of astrology occupies pp. 388-412 of his *Quaestiones physicae*. The criticism of conjunctions in particular occurs at pp. 397-99.

[23] Jöcher, I, 1485.

Jacques Fontaine of St. Maximin in Provence, a doctor of medicine, wrote two works against astrology which are separated by a space of forty years. The first, printed at Paris in 1581, was a *Discourse on the Power of the Sky over Inferior Bodies and Chiefly of Influence against the Astrologers.*[24] While it is thus entitled, *Against the Astrologers,* the work rather affirms the influence of the stars, although Fontaine subjects this to considerable discussion and some qualification and limitation. The old problem whether fire would still burn tow, if the motion of the sky ceased, is thrashed out once more, with citation of Duns Scotus and "Claude Celestin in the book of influences." Averroes and Albertus Magnus are cited on the more general question of celestial influence. It is noted that Albertus believed that actions of which the causes are unknown to us depend on celestial influences. Fontaine then turns to the particular question of generation without seed than which, he says, there is none more difficult in all natural science. Its obscurity has constrained many to attribute to the heavens marvelous powers of generation, surpassing those exercised by the elements in the generation of qualities. For himself Fontaine comes to a typical scholastic conclusion, that the stars cannot be a univocal cause of animals engendered without seed but are an equivocal cause of them. He goes on to argue that nature, not the moon, is the principal cause of crises and critical days in disease. In his separate treatise on the crisis and critical days he omitted the Pythagorean and astrological explanations of them as already sufficiently refuted by Fracastoro.[25] He now piously suggests that God has ordained the sun to show that, as man is sole master of all inferior animals, and as the sun is the paragon of all the stars, so in the supreme and intelligible world there is but one God.

But this does not mean that Fontaine denies that sun and stars influence inferiors. Their light is visible: their influence

[24] *Discours de la puissance du ciel sur les corps inferieurs et principalement de l'influence contre les astrologues indiciaires* (sic) *avec Une dispute des elements contre les Paracelsistes,* Paris, 1581. Copy used: BM 718.d.27.(4.).

[25] *De diebus criticis et de crisi: Opera,* Cologne, 1613, new pagination follow-

is not, but nevertheless exists and, like that of the magnet, is not cut off by the interposition of other bodies. "The influence is a natural power of the stars to produce in these inferior bodies, without any intermediary, qualities similar to those of the elements for their maintenance and conservation." For the view that the stars incline the reason indirectly through the body Fontaine cites authors as favorable to occult science as Cocles and Bellantius. He suggests that both the stars and inferior elements are causes of good and ill fortune. But the stars communicate their effects in a different way than the elements—a concession not only to astrology in particular but to occult influence and science in general.

So far Fontaine would seem to have made very little headway against the astrologers. In his six books of pharmacy, however, as published in the 1613 edition of his works, he declared that the astrological explanation of the occult properties of compound bodies as caused by the constellations "had been long since exploded," since such occult properties were neither forms nor faculties dependent on form alone.[26] Also less favorable to the influence of the stars was Fontaine's latest pronouncement on the subject, a work on and against astrological medicine which appeared posthumously in 1622 and 1625,[27] although the permits to publish at its close are dated in 1620, the year before Fontaine's death. The full title may be translated: "A Book on Astrological Medicine, in which from natural principles and ones implanted in the human body it is proved most evidently that all those things are vain which judicial astrologers have asserted concerning human morals, institutions, diseases, crises and cures." That the air is affected by the stars, Fontaine admits,

ing Pars IV, p. 98, col. 1, "Neque in refutandis Pythagoreorum et astrologorum sententiis immorabimur, cum a Fracastoro lib. de crisibus fuerint confutatae."

[26] *Opera*, Cologne, 1613, p. 645, col. 2: *Pharmacia medica generalis*, I, 29, De occulta facultate corporum mixtorum, "Astrologi referunt illam ad constellationes, quorum opinio iam diu explosa est.".

[27] Sudhoff (1902), p. 77, lists an octavo edition of Lyons, apud Thomam Soubron, of 1622, while I have read the book in a Lyons duodecimo edition of 1625: BM 718.b.18.

but he contends that it is sufficient if the physician takes into consideration the state of the air. He need not go behind this and inquire as to the constellations. Similarly knowledge of the temperament of the human body does not depend on knowledge of the stars but on effects existing in the body. The temperament of the foetus does not follow that of the parents, since the semen of a bilious person may be phlegmatic or melancholic. Fontaine further denies that there are any astral diseases, as the Hermetics and Paracelsists have supposed. In administering medicines astrological rules must often give way to considerations of necessity.

Fontaine admits that many general predictions can be made from the stars but not particular predictions. He will not agree with Bellantius that most men follow their senses rather than their will and reason. For he holds that the senses are more affected by the individual's temperament and constitution than by the stars. Astrologers would insist that the individual's temperament and constitution were fixed by his nativity, but Fontaine has already denied this. He therefore affirms that most true predictions are the work of demons and that astrology is confused with magic.

In his closing pages Fontaine discusses comets. He agrees that they are not generated in the sphere of fire but in the celestial spheres, which are not solid but rarefied. Fontaine speaks well of the researches of Tycho Brahe and Galileo, and had seen the latter's four satellites of Jupiter through the telescope. But comets, he still believes, may be signs to men of God's will and judgment, and of future events.

Nicodemus Frischlin (1547-1590) was a person of some consequence in the history of education and letters as well as of astronomy and astrology. He wrote against the logic of Ramus[28] and became involved in a grammatical controversy with Martin Crusius.[29] Morhof reproduced his curriculum for the six forms

[28] Nicodemus Frischlinus, *Dialogus logicus contra P. Rami sophisticam pro Aristotele. Addita eiusdem refutatione scripta a Conrado Neubecker,* Francofurti, 1590.

[29] Will I, 226 gives titles of three works published by Martin Krauss or Crusius against Frischlin in 1586, 1587 and 1588.

of a grammar school.[30] His oration on schools was first printed some thirty-seven years after his death.[31] De Thou called him a poet as well as astronomer but a man of dissolute life and unable to keep his mouth shut. He studied at Tübingen with Nicolaus Taurellus and Helisaeus Roeslin as fellow students, taught there for years and then in Styria and Carniola, at Freiburg-im-Breisgau and Brunswick. He also visited Frankfurt, Wittenberg, Marburg, Speyer and Mainz. His unbridled tongue caused his imprisonment, and his death resulted from injuries sustained in an attempt to escape from jail in Wurtemberg.[32]

The work by Frischlin which especially concerns us, on the congruence of the astronomical art with celestial doctrine and with natural philosophy, was printed already in his lifetime in 1586,[33] but had been composed some years before, as a Vatican manuscript of it shows.[34] It is there dated at its close April 1, 1581.[35] But since it refers to the Gregorian reform of the calendar,[36] authorized by the bull, "Inter gravissimas," of February 24, 1581-1582, and since Easter did not occur until April 15 in the year 1582, it is probable that the manuscript reckons the year as beginning with Easter rather than January first, and that in our reckoning the date of completing the work should

[30] Morhof, *Polyhistor,* I, 450. I presume it is taken from his *De ratione instituendi puerum ab anno aetatis sexto et septimo ad annum usque decimum quartum,* edited by Albertus von Molnar, *Syllecta scholastica,* Heidelbergae, 1621, 4to. BN X.9066.(3.) and 16496.(2.).

[31] *Oratio de scholis et gymnasiis aperiendis et simul tempestatibus quibus affliguntur avertendis . . . nunc in lucem protracta a Friderico Hermanno Flaydero,* Tubingae, 1627, 12mo, 106 pp. BN R.20871.

[32] J. A. Thuanus, *Historiarum lib. XCIX,* Francofurti, 1628. Melchior Adam, *Vitae Germanorum philosophorum.*

[33] *De astronomicae artis cum doctrina caelesti et naturali philosophia congruentia ex optimis quibusque Graecis Latinisque scriptoribus theologis medicis mathematicis philosophis et poetis collecta libri V. Passim inserta est huic operi solida divinationum astrologicarum confutatio repetita ex optimis quibusque auctoribus tam recentibus quam veteribus quorum nomina post praefationem invenies,* Francofurti, Excudebat Ioannes Spies, 1586. Copies used: BN V.29248, BM 529.a.26.

[34] Vatic. 5397, Nicodemi Frischlini Alemanni congruentia artis astronomicae cum doctrina coelesti et naturali in quinque libros distributa, opening, "Astronomia ut Plato. . . ."

[35] *Ibid.,* fol. 199v, "Absolutum hoc opus fuit ab authore 1581 Calendis Aprilis."

[36] *Ibid.,* fol. 189r, "De novissima anni Romani correctione." In the printed edition of 1586 at p. 429 (V, 10).

be 1582. The manuscript version has a prologue to archduke Charles of Austria, but the printed edition is dedicated to the elector Christian, duke of Saxony.

The first of Frischlin's five books bears no particular title; the second deals with circles, zones and climates; the third treats of the eighth sphere of the fixed stars; the fourth discusses the seven planets and the sun in especial; the last book is devoted to the moon in especial. Biblical authors are cited a good deal. At the close Frischlin apologizes for not adding "theories of the superior planets." He would have done so unless the same calamity had prevented which has most cruelly frustrated all his previous intellectual undertakings.[37]

Along with this astronomical exposition goes what the title of the printed edition describes as "solid confutation of astrological divinations." That the argument is not always impeccable is shown however by the assertion in the dedication to the duke of Saxony that king Alphonse of Aragon (*sic*), after whom the astronomical tables are named, would not tolerate the presence of an astrologer at his court.[38] In his first chapter Frischlin asks whether God lit those heavenly torches as signs of future events and answers, "By no means." Later he returns the same reply to the question whether eclipses do not threaten us with wars, famine and disease. Such disasters happen continually regardless of eclipses. Nicias suffered defeat not because of the moon but because of his superstition with regard to it. God instituted eclipses not as signs of the future but to manifest His power and to show men that sun and moon are not gods. When Christ spoke of coming signs in sun and moon, He did not refer to ordinary eclipses but to such signs as had never been seen before.[39] Frischlin will not even admit weather prediction from stars and planets[40] but he grants the influence of the moon on humors, and that to act differently at the time of the new moon than when it is full is not superstition. His opposition to astrology seems to

[37] Edition of 1586, p. 469.

[38] The same assertion is made at p. 467. Really of course Alfonso the Wise was a patron of astrology.

[39] The denial of astrological influence to eclipses begins in Vatic. 5397 at fol. 198r, in the edition of 1586 about p. 453 It occurs in the fifth book, chapter 12

[40] Edition of 1586, p. 455 (V, 13).

proceed mainly from religious motives.

Much more novel was the method of attack adopted by Sixtus ab Hemminga of Frisia (1533-1586) in his *Astrologia ratione et experientia refutata (Astrology Refuted by Reason and Experience)*, published at Antwerp in 1583. He had the bright idea of putting astrology's own procedure to a practical test. After declaring astrology the chief among such false arts as geomancy, hydromancy, pyromancy, chiromancy, aruspicina, metoposcopia, goetia, theurgy, necromancy, praestigiae, "and that noble alchemy," Sixtus remarks that Pico della Mirandola's criticism of the art, although elaborate and formidable, had been limited to general and theoretical arguments. This had likewise been true of Bellantius's reply to Pico and of the work of Cornelius Scepper. And it was because Pico did not touch on the actual exercise of the art, that defenders of astrology like Bellantius, Gaurico and Cardan, had not hesitated to take issue with him. Therefore Sixtus, who has had the advantage which Pico lacked of long practical experience in astrology, proposes to demonstrate from the nativities of a number of well-known personages that their destinies have not corresponded to what an astrologer should have predicted from their horoscopes, and that consequently the casting of nativities is an error and delusion. In this specific testing Sixtus takes Cyprian Leowitz, whom he regards as the best of recent astrologers, as the particular object of his examination and criticism rather than Cardan and Gaurico whom he regards as inferior to Leowitz in casting nativities and prognostication. This does not mean, however, that he does not occasionally direct a shaft of caustic criticism at the other two astrologers. For example, he notes that Cardan, who during the lifetime of Edward VI of England drew up according to the method of Ptolemy a future for him which was quite incorrect, after his death at the age of only sixteen issued an *Epignosticon* in which he rejected the Ptolemaic method but which Sixtus finds equally deserving of censure.[41]

[41] *Astrologiae ratione et experientia refutatae liber . . . nunc primum . . . editus contra C. Leovitium, H. Cardanum et L. Gauricum,* Antverpiae, 1583, p. 121. Copy used: BM 718.e.10.

Various recent writers are adduced for or against astrology by Hemminga. In defining the word he cites Milich, Erasmus, Flock, and Hieronymus Wolf.[42] Petreius Tyara, professor of Greek at Louvain, Douai and Leyden, trained also in medicine and philosophy, despised astrology.[43] On the other hand, Francis Monk (Monachus) by name as well as profession, a Minorite of Mechlin and well known among recent astrologers, went so far as to infer from the stars that some friend would present him with a new pair of shoes.[44] Conrad Dasypodius, the very learned astrologer of Strasburg, nevertheless showed in his nativity of Henry Ranzovius "how frigidly and negligently not merely common astrologers but even the more celebrated pronounce in such matters. For in it he says nothing that is not seen to be drawn from obsolete collections of the Arabs, and that does not fall apart the moment it is put to the test."[45]

When astrologers are ignorant as to the exact moment of a person's birth and the precise position of the stars then, they often determine the degree of the horoscope by inspecting the position of Mars or Saturn at the time of some accident, disease, danger or mishap during the individual's later life. If either or both of the two before mentioned evil planets are then found near the degree which had been tentatively taken as the horoscope, they accept that position of the evil planet or planets as the true horoscope and abandon the other. Leowitz extended this mode of operating to any planet whose signification corresponded to the accident in question, and held that, if such a planet either crossed the degree of the tentative horoscope or was in aspect with it, the planet's position gave the degree and minute of the true nativity. Sixtus attacks this doctrine of Leowitz.[46]

Among the historical personages whose nativities are reviewed by Sixtus ab Hemminga is Alessandro de' Medici who was strangled in bed at night by his relative, Lorenzo, in 1537 at the age of twenty-five. Yet from his horoscope one would infer that

[42] *Ibid.*, p. 8.

[43] *Ibid.*, p. 272.

[44] Or perhaps hose: *Ibid.*, p. 142.

[45] *Ibid.*, pp. 195-96.

[46] *Ibid.*, p. 211.

he would die either in infancy of some such disease as epilepsy, "or surely in his eighth year, 1519 A.D. in the month of March or the beginning of April, by drowning or poison." Of the actual time of his death there is no hint either in his own horoscope or in that of his murderer.[47]

At the time of the death of the duke of Parma and Piacenza and natural son of pope Paul III there were found among his papers questions which had been put to an astrologer of Mantua shortly after the death of Leo X and had been answered by him on the basis of Paul's geniture. To the first query, whether there was hope of Farnese's succeeding Leo as pope immediately, the astrologer replied in the negative. To the second question, when he might expect to become pope, the astrologer gave the exact year, 1534. In answer to the third interrogation, what would happen to him in the interim, the astrologer predicted danger in waters during his sixty-first year. To the fourth and final question as to the duration of his life, he was warned of peril of death in 1549 sixty-eight days after his eighty-first birthday. Cardan had regarded these predictions as evidence of astrological skill, but Sixtus tries to find other explanations. He attributes the papal election of 1534 to a concourse of causes: the death of Clement VII, Farnese's seniority and authority among the cardinals, his ability and his own faith in the astrologer's prediction. Sixtus further objects that in the space of twenty-six years with so many cardinals the same favoring constellation would have occurred in the geniture of other cardinals.[48] As for the assassination by conspirators of the pope's natural son, Petrus Aloisius, on September 10, 1547, Sixtus affirms that there was nothing in his nativity to suggest it. But he fails to explain a statement which he repeats from the historian Sleidan that the duke had received letters from his father to beware of that day, "for the stars threatened him with some marked disaster."[49] Sixtus admits that from the geniture of Don Juan of Austria Leowitz correctly calculated his remaining term of life.[50]

[47] *Ibid.*, pp. 105, 112, 114.

[48] *Ibid.*, pp. 85-91.

[49] *Ibid.*, p. 96 *et seq.*

[50] *Ibid.*, pp. 48-50.

Other genitures expounded by Sixtus ab Hemminga include those of Henry VIII, Mary Tudor, and Elizabeth of England; Louis, son of Ladislaus, king of Hungary, born in 1506; the emperor Ferdinand; John Frederick, duke of Saxony; Maurice of Saxony; Philip, landgrave of Hesse; Bernard de Merode, Adrian Iunius Hornanus, Gemma Frisius, Docon ab Hemminga who died in 1570 of inflammation of the brain, and Sixtus ab Hemminga himself.

Although made up chiefly of an exposition of the unreliability of the nativities of well-known persons, the work of Sixtus is not entirely void of more theoretical argument against astrology. For instance, he draws the analogy that, just as stars of huge size seem mere specks to our eyes, so we can measure only a tiny portion of their influence.[51] This influence, however, I believe he does not dispute.

In 1586, as has already been noted in another chapter, was issued the papal bull of Sixtus V against astrology and other arts of divination. It probably had some influence upon such of the following works against astrology as were by Roman Catholic authors.

Gabriel Naudé in a work published in 1647, listed among writers against astrology Alexander de Angelis, Sixtus ab Hemminga, Sixtus the pope, and Sixtus Senensis, presumably the author of the *Bibliotheca Sancta,* printed in 1574-1575.[52] If he wrote some separate treatise against astrology, I have not seen it. Naudé represented pope Sixtus V as assailing the art of astrology with dire execrations as if he wished to cast it down to hell, which would seem something of an exaggeration.

Juan de Carmona, a physician and philosopher of Seville who was born in 1534, was for a time physician for the Spanish inquisition at Llerena in Estramadura. In a discussion whether astrology is necessary to physicians, he decided the question in the negative.[53] In the first chapter he gave the arguments

[51] *Ibid.,* p. 8.

[52] Gabrielis Naudaei . . . Πεντὰς *questionum iatro-philologicarum,* Genevae, 1647, 8vo, 322 pp. Our passage occurs in the fifth opuscule, De fato et fatali vitae termino, at p. 264.

[53] *Ioannis de Carmona medici atque philosophi Hispalensis (quondam Lle-*

for astrology, in the second proved that it was not necessary in medicine, and in the third chapter answered the astrologers' arguments. He cites a large number of past astrological and other authors. Towards the end of the treatise he discusses the more particular question whether in bleeding, purgation and the like it is necessary to observe the conjunction and opposition of sun and moon or other aspects. He ends condemning Peter of Abano for defending the use of incantations in the 156th Differentia of the *Conciliator* and for his astrological errors—already designated by Symphorien Champier. A number of past writings favorable to occult arts current under the names of Aristotle, Plato and other famous writers are rejected as spurious, while Hermes and Ptolemy are said by Juan to rave in their respective *Centiloquiums*.

Frischlin was often quoted approvingly against astrology by Otto Casmann in a work printed in 1599.[54] Sixtus ab Hemminga also was cited, while such supporters of astrology as Albumasar and Peter of Abano were severely criticized. Arguments against genethlialogy by Favorinus and the church fathers were repeated, but acquaintance was shown with recent writers—some astrological—like Pontano, Ficino, Agrippa, Cardan and Hieronymus Wolf. Casmann declared that no flood had followed the conjunction of 1524, questioned the powers, qualities and aspects attributed to the planets by astrologers, inquired whether Chris-

renae perpetui decurionis eiusdemque sanctae Inquisitionis Medici iurati Regiaque mercede conducti) Tractatus an Astrologia sit medicis necessaria. Ad illustrissimum Dominum Dominum Rodericum de Castro Archiepiscopum Hispalensem necnon Cardinalem sanctae Romanae AEcclesiae duodecim Apostolorum. Accessit insuper praxis subtilissima ac Ad curandam cognoscendamque pestilentiam apprime necessaria eiusdem Authoris. Hispali. Apud Franciscum Perez Typographum. Anno 1590.

I have used a photostat of the 1590 edition in BN Te[130].18. The work runs to a hundred leaves. "Cap. 2 in quo astrologiam non esse medicis necessariam probatur," begins at fol. 17v; "cap. 3 in quo Rationes astrologorum dissolvuntur," at fol. 45r.

[54] *Othonis Casmanni Astrologia chronographia et astromanteia, seu Commentationum disceptationumque physicarum syndromus methodicus et problematicus,* Francofurti, ex officina M. Z. Palthenii, 1599, 8vo. Copy used: BN V.21784. Astrology is opposed at pp. 437-584 of the first part, and then, in Pars altera astrologiae de astropraxia, with a new pagination, at pp. 110-247, caps. 7-9.

tians should use the names and images of the stars, and denied that the star of Bethlehem and the eclipse at the crucifixion were natural phenomena. Most Christian astrologers, however, had also done the last. In general, Casmann's arguments against astrology seem neither novel nor effective.

Scipione Mercurio in his work on the popular errors of Italy opposed the consultation of astrologers by the sick and proclaimed the vanity of astrology in particular predictions, citing approvingly the work of Pico against astrology and alluding more than once to the bull of Sixtus V. He also denied that the influence of the sky could produce human beings. But he admitted that the physician should consider the influence of the stars and critical days. This for him was not judicial astrology but scientific, natural and praiseworthy.[55]

George of Ragusa presents one of those combinations of attitudes which might at first sight seem curious or inconsistent but which numerous cases in our preceding chapters have prepared us to expect. In his case the combination is of traditional Peripateticism and scholastic philosophy with a considerable opposition to astrology. His *Peripatetic Disputations* of 1613 were still occupied with questions and topics which had been discussed in the thirteenth and fourteenth centuries: the subject of natural philosophy, the existence and potency of matter, the eternity of the universe, the free action and infinity of the First Mover, the motion of heavy and light, the virtues of numbers, the substance and animation of the sky, the forms of the elements, the origin and the plurality of forms, accidents, how the elements remain in the compound, that the rational soul according to Aristotle is *forma informans*, of the immortality of the soul, of the active intellect, of knowledge of the particular, and of individuation.

The letters concerning divination of George of Ragusa devote a large fraction of their space to astrology. The various letters are dated in such years as 1602, 1610, 1615 and 1618, while

[55] Scipione Mercurio, *De gli errori popolari d'Italia*, Venice, 1603, IV, 9-12. Copy used: BM 1039.h.25.

the entire collection was printed in 1623.[56] Morhof, writing a century later, represented these letters as opposed to all divinatory astrology as well as to such other occult arts as chiromancy, physiognomy and geomancy.[57] It is to be noted, however, that Ragusaeus doubted neither the rule of superiors over inferiors, nor the influence of the stars, nor that it was exercised through occult virtue in addition to their motion and light. He accepted the existence of occult virtues, although he recognized that Aristotle never taught this, and that nothing seemed more foreign to Peripateticism. But he felt that such hidden forces were needed to explain the formation of metals in the earth, the relation of the tides to the moon, the prevalence of wind and rain at the time of great conjunctions of the planets, the marvelous powers of herbs and stones—which came not from their constituent ingredients but from the stars—and the spontaneous generation of animals, in which also he believed. He even granted that the stars influenced man at birth, that the humors and diseases of the body were moved by them, and that God after having created the world left the subsequent operation of nature to the heavens and first matter.[58]

But the will and reason remain free, and the action of the stars is universal and not singular. The rules and technique of the art of astrology consequently have no validity. As a youth Ragusaeus had been strongly attracted by that art and had spent six years at Venice under Octavianus of Ghent and the Venetian patrician, Barocius, studying the *Quadripartitum* and *Centiloquium* of Ptolemy and the minute observations of the Arabs, and had drawn up many nativities and revolutions of years, and had observed elections. Later he discovered that Cicero, Tacitus, Seneca and the church fathers had criticized astrology, while Aristotle and Plato were silent on the subject. Thereupon his former allegiance waned, and he became a hostile critic of the art to which

[56] Georgius Ragusaeus, *Epistolarum mathematicarum seu de divinatione libri duo*, Paris, 1623, 8vo. Copy used: BM 719.c.13. The letters dealing with astrology occupy roughly the first 250 pages of the volume.

[57] Morhof, *Polyhistor,* II (1732), 452-53.

[58] Ragusaeus, *Epistolarum,* 1623, pp. 3, 5, 8, 16, 150-52.

he had once attached himself as an enthusiastic tyro.[59] But his motive was classical reaction, not scientific advance.

Ragusaeus repeated the old contention that the technique of astrology was neither learned by experience nor imparted by divine revelation, and that astrologers were sometimes aided by demons to make what seemed true predictions. He rejected the dignities and aspects of the planets, denied that their retrogradation or combustion had any ill effect, pronounced the place of fortune a pure figment, and asserted that there was no active force in the head or tail of the dragon, and that length of life was not foretellable from *Hyleg* and *Alcochoden.* He opposed elections and interrogations.[60] He had no objection to a natural and orderly weather prediction, since in his opinion the weather depended on the sky as its efficient cause and was affected by the three superior planets and the fixed stars. But he held that Albumasar and others put forth false rules and doctrines of weather prediction.[61] Ragusaeus granted that a knowledge of the heavens was of some use in medicine, but he rejected the prohibition of bleeding or operating when the moon was in certain signs, and the notion that each planet and sign of the zodiac governs a certain part of the human body. Nor would he connect critical days with the moon. He concluded that on the whole it was better to attend to immediate causes especially in disease rather than to remote influences. He affirmed that many celebrated physicians had been and were ignorant of astrology or made little use of it.[62] Astrological chiromancy he regarded as deservedly condemned by the Apostolic See.[63] Luck in gaming he attributed to the demons rather than to the stars. Demons could move the dice or reveal the cards in one player's hand to his opponent. They favored some players in order to induce them to enter upon pacts with themselves, and brought bad luck to others in hope of inducing them to curse God for it.[64]

Several of Ragusaeus's correspondents were more favorable to astrology than he was. Vincentius Blancus, a Venetian knight,

[59] *Ibid.,* p. 26 *et seq.*
[60] *Ibid.,* Letters iv-x, xiv-xv.
[61] *Ibid.,* Ep. xvi, p. 218.
[62] *Ibid.,* Ep. xvii, pp. 225-35.
[63] *Ibid.,* pp. 237, 253.
[64] *Ibid.,* Ep. xiii, pp. 189-91.

consulted an astrologer on setting out for Lyons.[65] Ernest à Skendorf of Belgium, when his brother fell ill, feared that he had been poisoned or bewitched because in his nativity Mercury and the tail of the dragon were in the eighth house.[66] Writing a second time to another Venetian and member of its secret council, Ragusaeus explains that he did not flatter himself that a single letter would recall a learned man and one long versed in astrology from an inveterate opinion and one so fixed in his mind.[67] To yet another Venetian who was engaged in chemical operations Ragusaeus wrote that it was important, while experimenting, to have the moon in the common signs and the sun in the fiery signs. But he explained to yet another correspondent, Erastus Savona, a physician of Venice, that he had been importuned for this information by the aforesaid chemist, and had merely stated the views of the astrologers, not his own.[68] He further recommended the reading of a number of writers against astrology, including Pico della Mirandola, Savonarola and Possevin, while he spoke unfavorably of such defenders of the art as Iunctinus, Bellantius and Pirovano, and of writers like Cardan and Taisnier who had presumed to draw up horoscopes for Christ.[69] Finally, it is to be noted that Ragusaeus's astronomy remained Ptolemaic, at least in a letter of 1610,[70] while Copernicus and Galileo also passed unrecognized in his *Peripatetic Disputations* of 1613.

George of Ragusa died in 1622 at the age of only forty-three. Tomasini writing shortly afterwards in 1629, says that he was in clerical orders and endowed with rich benefices and came to Padua in 1601 as second ordinary professor of philosophy. He first cultivated eloquence, then philosophy and theology, then devoted himself entirely to medicine and mathematics. Nor did he stop there but became a devotee of the Lullian art—a fact which tends to devaluate somewhat his opposition to astrology. Tomasini says that he left manuscripts on the Lullian art as well

[65] *Ibid.*, pp. 119, 127.

[66] *Ibid.*, p. 128.

[67] *Ibid.*, Ep. viii, p. 104, referring back to Ep. vii.

[68] *Ibid.*, Ep. xiv, p. 195.

[69] *Ibid.*, Ep. iii, pp. 49-50.

[70] *Ibid.*, p. 120.

as on the philosophy of Aristotle. His treatise against Cremonini's work on the forms of the elements was printed with his *Peripatetic Disputations*. He owned a celebrated library which unfortunately was auctioned off after his death. Tomasini, who was himself favorable to astrology, compares George of Ragusa as a critic of the art to Pico della Mirandola and adds that the disease to which he succumbed in 1622 at forty-three had been foreseen by astrological conjecture.[71]

Guy Coquille, seigneur de Romenay, in his history of the Nivernois, published in 1612, combined somewhat Pythagorean reflections on the climacteric year and fall of ancient Rome in the year 1176 *ab urbe condita* and that of Constantinople after 1120 years (333-1453 A.D.) with others on the time-worn theme of the sad fate of kings and potentates who had relied on the predictions of astrologers and diviners.[72]

Alexander de Angelis of Spoleto, head of the Jesuit college at Rome, published in 1615 five books against astrologers with a preface to one of the cardinals.[73] Despite the relatively late date at which de Angelis wrote, he appears to be especially incensed against Cardan and to devote particular attention to answering the arguments of Bellantius for astrology. He also pays his respects to Fernel, affirming that no one has found more occult virtues of the heavens or more unlikely and absurd ones than the author of *De abditis rerum causis*.[74] On the other hand, he cites more than once as having recently refuted astrology Sixtus ab Hemminga whom he calls "astrologorum facile princeps," and who, he says, maintained that Ptolemy had composed the *Quadripartitum* not as a believer in astrology but to show the nullity of that art.[75] He also cites such exponents of astrology as Wolf, Iunctinus and Leowitz,[76] who, although they died at about

[71] Tomasini, *Illustrium virorum elogia*, Patavii, 1630, pp. 338-41. Giuseppe Vedova, *Biografia degli scrittori Padovani*, Padua, 1832-1836, II, 335, mentions a tract on the revolution of the year 1614 and also 1616 by Tomasini.

[72] *Histoire du pays et duché de Nivernois*, Paris, 1612, 4to, pp. 35-37.

[73] Alexander de Angelis (S.J.), *In astrologos conjectores libri quinque*, Rome, B. Zannetti, 1615, 4to, 304 pp. I have used the Lyons edition of the same year with 351 pp.: BN Inventaire V.8830.

[74] *Ibid.*, p. 37.

[75] *Ibid.*, pp. 256, 281, 319.

[76] *Ibid.*, p. 281.

the same time as Cardan, were somewhat younger men and later writers.

In his five books de Angelis gives an elaborate rehearsal of past arguments against astrology, but there is little or nothing new said. In the first book on the general action of the sky upon inferiors he admits that it has great and even occult power over the sublunar world. It affects the four first qualities by its light alone, for its motion is felt only so far as the upper air. In his opinion, however, inferiors are not entirely dependent on superiors, and he doubts whether the elements would destroy one another but for the stars. Matter is not prepared for forms by the sky alone, nor are the specific natures of effects dependent on it. In the procreation of things the heavens play no part. If the seed is weak, the offspring will be weak, no matter how strong a star it may be born under. The sky is not animate, not all sublunar causes are its instruments, and substantial forms do not come from it. Astrologers improperly refer marvelous effects to the stars.

The second book treats of conception and the foetus. If the stars exert influence, they affect not the mind but the body, and in such matters one should trust philosophers and medical men more than astrologers. De Angelis asserts that no conclusion can be drawn as to the foetus from the position of the stars at conception, that astrologers do not observe and cannot observe all the causes of its formation. He criticizes their investigating the genitures of the parents in this connection. The foetus depends more on food than on the stars and is affected by what happens to the mother. Monstrous births may not be attributed to the stars. De Angelis ridicules the theory of Peter of Abano and others that Saturn always presides over the first month of the formation of the foetus regardless of that planet's location in the sky, on the ground that this nullifies other astrological doctrines of aspects, ascensions, houses and the like. The distribution of the parts of the human body under the twelve signs he dismisses as a mere fable.

In the third book on birth and delivery de Angelis argues that the human mind and will are free as well as divine providence, that astrologers cannot mark the exact constellations at conception or birth, that education and nutrition affect the child's temperament more than the stars do. Yet other factors are work, environment, custom and usage, medical treatment, chance, nationality, force of example, law and conscience.

In the forty-seven chapters of the fourth book astrology is attacked through its own tenets. It is impracticable. It cannot measure or test by experience the force of the stars. Elections and the doctrine of great revolutions are condemned. The division of the zodiac into signs and houses, and the doctrine of aspects are arbitrary and of no significance. To observe the genitures of cities is ridiculous. Then follow such arguments as that of Augustine from twins, the query why horoscopes are not cast for plants and brutes as well as for men, or the contention that true predictions are either clever conjectures or the suggestion of demons and not from the stars. De Angelis is indignant that astrologers predict concerning the pope and that Christians listen to them. Indeed, they can deduce nothing from the stars concerning future honors, prosperity and adversity, or life and death. De Angelis condemns the practice of rectifying genitures by examining subsequent accidents of the individual.

The fifth book is in the nature of a closing exhortation. De Angelis contends that wise men have put no faith in astrology, cites various church fathers against it, and recalls the expulsion of its practitioners from ancient Rome. He holds it responsible for the death of many princes and the unhappy end of Cardan's son. Finally he notes the dissensions among the astrologers themselves.

It is well to remark before leaving de Angelis that his criticism did not extend from astrology to occult virtues. Not only did he admit that the stars exerted an occult influence. He also accepted the statement that a child weaned on goat's milk, after it had grown up, would leap like a goat and eat such plants as goats are wont to crop.[77]

In the same volume in which he devoted 41 chapters and 182

[77] *Ibid.*, p. 113.

quarto pages to discussing the nature and substance of the heavens, Tommaso Giannini, professor of philosophy at Ferrara, added 45 chapters and 201 pages on the effects of sky and stars.[78] His main position may, however, be indicated quite briefly. He denies that the heavens exert any influence upon inferiors other than by their motion,[79] and holds that in this they are a common and universal cause of motion and generation in this elementary world. But no particular event or dissimilitude of species is caused by the stars, and no part of the sky or constellation has peculiar virtue of its own. The sky is a simple body and all its parts have the same properties. Therefore there is no place for astrology of no matter how limited a sort, since Giannini denies that even physical peculiarities and the marvelous occult virtues of stones, herbs and animals are produced by the stars. He even denies that the tides, as well as critical days, are due to the moon. He asserts that in past controversy on these points more learned men have taken the negative than the positive side of the argument—an assertion which may be doubted.

It cannot be said that Giannini is always either convincing or consistent in maintaining his position. He rejects the occult influence of the stars but often falls back on occult virtue to explain inferior phenomena. For this he apologizes in one passage, telling his students that he hopes none of them will think that he wishes to refer everything to causes hidden from sense, but that, when an event is proved by experience and the cause is unknown, he prefers this course to suggesting highly improbable solutions based on manifest qualities and virtues.[80] He doubts very much the statement that the tiny fish echeneis can stop a ship, although this is asserted by such reputable authors as Aristotle, Pliny and Aelian. But if it is true, all other attempted explanations than

[78] Thomas Gianninius, *De substantia caeli et stellarum efficientia,* Venetiis, 1618. Owing to numbering the page after 275 as 376, the volume appears to have 483 pp. when it has only 383.

[79] He recognizes (*ibid.,* p. 232) that Scotus (II Sent., Dist. 14, Quaest. 3), Durandus (II Sent., Dist. 15, Quaest. 3), and the commentators of Coimbra (Comm. de caelo, lib. 2) held that many things are caused by influxes of the heavens which are in no way dependent on their motion, so that, if the motion ceased, generation might still continue in many cases.

[80] *Ibid.,* II, 6; p. 210.

that of occult virtue fail, as is likewise the case for the shock received from the torpedo fish.

This confession and avoidance by Giannini may be all very well, but the fact remains that, to avoid recognizing any particular influence of the stars, he is forced to adopt explanations which seem equally or more unsatisfactory. Thus he accounts for the tides by winds and spirits within the ocean. He affirms that indigestion, not the influence of the planets Saturn and Mercury, is the cause of melancholy in men of letters. He ascribes the death of the eighth month's child to the womb's being more susceptible to disease then instead of to Saturn. He accounts for the sixty-third year of life being climacteric by the supposition that the innate heat then weakens and no longer throws off the excrements as it should. Yet he denies any force or power to numbers as well as to the stars. But he does not explain why the womb should be more susceptible to disease in the eighth month than in the ninth, or why innate heat should be weaker in the sixty-third year than in the sixty-second or sixty-fourth. He also weakens the force of his main position against the influence of the stars by piling up other arguments from authors like Favorinus and Sextus Empiricus, which are superfluous and irrelevant, if his fundamental contention is correct. Nor does he increase our faith in his perspicacity by a long digression in which he contends that iron seeks the magnet rather than is attracted by it.

For the most part the arguments against astrology noted in this chapter repeat those already worn threadbare in previous centuries. Sixtus ab Hemminga, George of Ragusa, and Alexander de Angelis, however, show something of an advance, and their attitude holds out hope for the future.

CHAPTER XXXVI

MEDICINE AFTER 1550

Idque facimus ut uno in loco suos medici medicos videant.
—TIRAQUELLUS

In this chapter we shall consider various aspects of the medical literature of the second half of the sixteenth century, which have not been covered in our discussion of the Paracelsan revival, the chapters on such topics as pharmacy, poisons and hydrophobia, anatomy, and on such men as Cardan and Erastus, or the many allusions to astrological medicine contained in the chapters on astronomy and astrology. Moreover, we shall leave until a later chapter the attitude of a number of members of the medical profession towards possession by demons and the witchcraft delusion. This may result in a somewhat discursive and scattering presentation and of course means that the present single chapter does not stand by itself as a unified and complete picture of medical theory and practice at the time. Rather it offers a series of glimpses of certain aspects of medical thought and writing then, but they may prove to be instructive for the general history of medicine as well as for their bearing upon our particular investigation and the relations of later sixteenth century medicine to occult science.

Rapard, whose controversy with Haschard as to astrological almanachs has been already noticed, also has a markworthy passage on bathing. He states that his contemporaries do not bathe much and, when they do, bathe more for pleasure than for health. Dry baths are in his opinion better suited than moist baths to men of his region, i.e. Flanders, especially in winter time, but their use is rare. He believes that in a cold and damp climate where men eat and drink a great deal—and that of cold and moist food and beverages like cheese, milk and fish—damp baths are to be eschewed except by the rich whose diet is more refined and includes hot and dry things like good wines, strong spices, hares, partridges and pheasants. Even such persons should not bathe without first consulting a physician or at least should take purgatives the day before bathing. "And this in summer only, for in winter I would advise them to abstain from ordinary baths entirely." For Rapard foresees danger that the heat of the bath may stir up the noxious humors which were before quiescent in the body and carry them to the vitals or spread them throughout the entire system. He affirms that diseases such as the scab, colic, fevers, vertigo, headache and toothache often follow such bathing.[1] Against this pessimistic picture of bathing and discouraging attitude towards it, it may be well to remember that a large collection of past and recent treatises on mineral and medicinal baths was printed soon after at Venice.[2]

Falloppia, noted in the history of anatomy, began to lecture on medicated waters at Padua in 1556 on feast days. His lectures were published posthumously by a disciple in 1569 together with the lectures on fossils or metals which he delivered the following year, 1557.[3] Falloppia had died in 1562, and in a preface dated Jan. 1, 1564, and addressed to cardinal Bernardus Naugerius, the disciple explains that he had not published his notes on Falloppia's lectures sooner for fear that he might not do him justice, since he was a rapid lecturer. But when he saw the recent editions of *Secreti,* which were falsely attributed to Falloppia, and of *De ulceribus et tumoribus,* which gave a faulty text full of barbarisms, whereas Falloppia was facile and elegant

[1] F. Rapardus, *Magnum et perpetuum Almanach . . . de phlebotomia de balneis de purgationibus certiora precepta continens,* Antwerp, 1551, signature c 5 r-v.

[2] *De balneis omnia quae extant apud graecos latinos et arabes . . . ,* Venet. apud Iuntas, 1553.

[3] *Gabrielis Falloppii Mutinensis medici ac philosophi praestantissimi De medicatis aquis atque de fossilibus . . . ab Andrea Marcolino Fanestri medico ipsius discipulo amantissimo collectus . . . ,* Venetiis, Ex officina Ludovici Avantii, MDLXIX. At fol. 1r is given the different form of title, "Excellentissimi Gabrielis Falloppii Mutinensis De thermalibus aquis atque metallis tractatus." I used the copy contained in the Rare Book room of the New York Academy of Medicine.

in style, as his *Anatomical Observations* show, his hesitation vanished.

Falloppia criticized previous writers on mineral springs such as Michael Savonarola, Bartholomaeus Montagnana, and Giovanni de' Dondi, especially for their assertions as to the minerals found in these springs. He had distilled the water from one spring said to contain copper and found none, and he denies that various other baths contain iron.[4] He also disagreed with the three authorities just named—who had further disagreed among themselves—as to the constituents of the baths of Abano.[5] Some say that a bath near Reggio contains camphor and smells of it, but it is almost odorless. Savonarola said it contained alum, salt or nitre, while Menghus of Faenza, who wrote more learnedly than others on this subject of baths, said it contained salt and alum. Falloppia found in it salt and nitre in about equal quantities and a little marble or chalk. The waters keep their properties so long that they are exported to Spain, Gaul, Naples and other distant places, and there are always porters waiting at the baths for this purpose.[6]

Falloppia rejected the notion that thermal waters should not be drunk in leapyears, that all things altered their nature then, and that it was dangerous for domestic animals and women to conceive then. He tells his students that they look the same to him as last year and that he does not believe any one of them has changed from male to female. Leapyears are not the work of nature but of calendar-makers, and cannot be connected with Saturn which goes from fifth to fifth, although it is true that melancholy moves from fourth to fourth.[7] Aleardus of Verona said that the baths of Abano were sometimes poisoned by an occult influence of the stars and killed those who drank them. Falloppia does not question the influence of the stars or the existence of occult virtues, but holds that in this case the changed character of the water should manifest itself in some outward

[4] *Ibid.*, fols. 28v-29r.

[5] *Ibid.*, fols. 68r-71r.

[6] *Ibid.*, cap. 25, "De balneo Aquariano in agro Regiensi," fols. 80v-81r.

[7] *Ibid.*, fols. 47v-49v.

manner such as its color. However, it may not be safe to drink it in a pest year when the air is infected.[8]

In the second half of the sixteenth century various treatises on the pest continued to attribute that affliction to the influence of the constellations. Oddus de Oddis (1478-1558), professor of philosophy and medicine at Padua, maintained this view against Pico della Mirandola and held that it was supported by Galen, Avicenna and personal observation. Like most of Oddus' medical works, his four books on the pest and all pestiferous diseases were published posthumously, being printed at Venice by his son in 1570.[9]

Michele Mercati of San Miniato of whose work on minerals we treat in the chapter on Cesalpino, is said by Rossi and Magini to have repeated in his work on the pest and avoiding poisons the caution to princes, already made in the fifteenth century by Antonio Guaineri, that they keep their genitures concealed from their enemies lest they suffer bodily harm thereby. The work referred to seems to be one which was published in Italian at Rome in 1576.[10]

Johann Bokel, in a tract printed in 1577 on the pest which had afflicted the city of Hamburg in 1565,[11] noted that it had followed the conjunction of the three superior planets in the sign Leo in 1564. Progressing from the east with the movement of the *primum mobile*, it had afflicted all Europe most severely in many places, and finally spread to Hamburg from Lübeck. On that occasion a medical colleague remarked, "This pest laughs at us and our drugs. Like all epidemics, it has some singular property." Bokel explains further that bleeding and purgation are ineffective when the very air is infected, because then the

[8] *Ibid.*, fol. 50r.

[9] Jöcher, III, 1019; Io. Ant. Magini, *De astrologica ratione ac usu dierum criticorum*, Venice, 1607, fol. (b 3); Tomasini (1630), p. 47; Papadopoli, I, 313.

[10] *Instruttione sopra la peste nella quale si contengono i piu eletti . . . rimedii . . . Aggiuntevi tre altre instruttioni sopra i veleni occultamente ministrati, podagra e paralisi*, etc., Roma, 1576: copy noted, BM 1167.i.1.(1.).

[11] Iohannes Bokelius, *De peste quae Hamburgum civitatem anno LXV gravissime adflixit*, Henricopoli ex officina typographica Conradi Cornei, 1577. Copy used: BM 1167.c.30.(2.).

disease is not in the humors but in the spirits. In his preface to the consuls and senators of Hamburg, Bokel states that he was not born in that town but had been educated there with all his brothers and sisters from his early years, when his parents came thither as religious fugitives.

Petrus Salius Diversus of Faenza, in a work on pestilential fever first printed at Bologna in 1584,[12] defended the thesis that pestilence was sometimes produced by the stars without any contributory inferior causes. He also drew no line between Greek and Arabic medical writers, commenting on both Hippocrates[13] and Avicenna.[14]

In a pest tract dated from Bologna on February 20, 1592, Georgius Rivettus discussed conjunctions and eclipses as well as inferior causes of pestilence but was rather more inclined to stress divine punishment for sin than either. It may further be remarked that his work, like that of Bokel and a pest tract of 1568 by Pistorius, which is bound with them in one volume at the British Museum,[15] displays no medical advance over the pest tracts of the fourteenth century. In his thirty-third chapter Rivettus describes a bag, "which they call an amulet," containing a compound medicine and worn over the heart. Unprogressive and lacking in distinction as his work may seem, it was translated from Italian into Latin by Thomas Aubel, mathematician and medical man, for the use of the town of Cologne during the plague there in 1597.

Although Rivettus was inclined to attribute the plague to divine wrath rather than to the stars, a more pronounced turning away from astrology was manifested in a pest tract by Horatius Augenius which was first printed in Italian at Fermo, then in Latin translation by Lebzelter at Leipzig in 1598. Augenius came from Mons in the low countries but taught natural philosophy

[12] *De febre pestilenti tractatus et curationes quorundam particularium morborum*, Bononiae, 1584, 4to. Also Frankfurt, 1586, octavo, and Hardevici, 1656.

[13] *Commentaria in Hippocratis libros quattuor de morbis*, 1602, folio.

[14] *In Avicennae librum tertium de morbis particularibus . . . opus posthumum nunc primum in lucem editum*, Patavii, 1673, folio.

[15] BM 1167.c.30.(3.): Georgius Rivettus, *De peste ex anthematibus et anthracibus*, Cologne, 1597.

and medicine at Turin and Padua. His various medical works also include a treatise on bleeding. In the pest tract he says that, although astrologers claim to be able to predict the pest, he notes such diversity in their doctrine and such inaccuracy in their prognostications that he puts little faith in them. A person who has been thoroughly trained in the science of astrology may be able to foresee the future, but it is very difficult. Augenius therefore turns "to the signs of other causes" of the pest.[16]

With these pest tracts may be associated a treatise by Francesco Campi on another epidemic,[17] which he says first became known in 1580 in Italy, France, Spain and the world generally, called the disease of the ram, or *galantinum* or *Mazuccum*. Among reasons given why it is named after the ram are that rams suffer from it, and that, as a ram butts with its head, so this sickness hits the head. Nothing is said by Campi of its being associated with the sign of the ram in the zodiac. But later its origin is connected with cold winds in 1580 and these are attributed to the influence of the planets, and such astrological authors as Ptolemy and Ficino are cited. First of the many symptoms listed are fever, headache and a dry cough. Perhaps the epidemic was akin to la grippe, or influenza.

Oswald Croll in a work published in 1609[18] enumerated the following past controversies between medical men: that between Scheck and Fuchs as to the cause of disease; that between Argenterius and Fernel as to fevers; that of Rondelet against Galen concerning paralysis, epilepsy and stone; that between Rondelet and Falloppia concerning syphilis, and that between Altomarus and Fernel as to gout. Croll appears to have overlooked the lively controversy in 1544-1545 between Fuchs and Hermann Ryff. When Fuchs sent copies of his first reply to "the malicious charges of that inveterate liar, H. Ryff" to the Frankfurt fair,

[16] *De vera ratione qua quisque vitae suae amans periculosissimo pestis tempore sese praeservare possit . . . tractatus. Primum Italico conscriptus nunc vero ex illo conversus in Latinum a J. Lebzeltero,* Lipsiae, 1598, p. 74 (I, 16).

[17] Francesco Campi, *De morbo arietis libellus,* Lucca, 1586, 48 fols. 20 caps. Copy used: BN Td[87].18.

[18] Oswald Croll, *Basilica chemica,* Frankfurt, 1609, 4to., p. 76.

Egenolph, Ryff's printer, bought them all up and suppressed them. Thereupon Fuchs included Egenolph in his second reply. Ianus Cornarius, professor at Marburg, then entered the fray with three successive publications against Fuchs, in which he made plays upon his name such as *Vulpes excoriata* (Skinning the Fox) and Fuchseides the Third. Fuchs replied with a *Cornarius furens.*[19]

A few further examples may be given of medical controversy in the second half of the sixteenth century. In 1562 Giovanni Andrea Nola of Croton, doctor of arts and medicine and a disciple of Johannes Altimarus, published at Venice a treatise of 82 pages in small italics in which he contended that the sediments of healthy and sick bodies were not of the same species. This treatise was directed against Ferdinand Cassanus and others who thought the contrary.[20] Nola further held that the sediment in the sick was not always part of putrid humor, nor were all the humors contained in it. Also that in intermittent fevers the humor did not putrefy within the vessels (of the body); that the Arabs, especially Avicenna, argued rashly as to the cause involved; that they with Galen thought wrongly concerning the containing or contentive cause. Nola's work is dedicated to Altimarus and contains a reply from him.

Our next example is an *Examination* by Gabriel Cuneus of Milan of the *Defense of Galenic Anatomy* by Franciscus Puteus. It is dated at Milan on March 26, 1563, and was printed at Venice in 1564.[21] Cuneus professes to write at the urging not only of those who attend his lectures on anatomy at Milan and Pavia but also in response to letters from many physicians of the subalpine school, in order to point out to Puteus how foully he has directed his defense of Galen against Vesalius. Cuneus

[19] For the full bibliography of the controversy see W. L. Schreiber (1924), pp. xxxvii-xxxviii.

[20] *Quod sedimentum sanorum aegrorumque corporum non sit eiusdem speciei adversus Ferdinandum Cassanum et alios contrarium sentientes Ioanne Andrea Nola Crotoniata Art. et Med. doctore clariss. Altimari discipulo auctore,* Venetiis, 1562.

[21] *Gabrielis Cunei Mediolanensis Apologiae Francisci Putei pro Galeno in anatome examen,* Venet. apud Franciscum de Franciscis Senensem, 1564.

especially objects because Puteus claims support for his position from the dissections of Falloppia, recently deceased, John Cenanus, Peter Martyr and himself, all of whom are really supporters of Vesalius. The work of Cuneus covers 125 pages.

The third work we have to note is by a Eudoxus Philalethes *Against the Calumnies and Sophistries of a Certain Person Who Named Himself Euandrophilaetes*. This work, printed at Verona in 1573, is all in italic type. It opens with a defense of Donzellini of which the pages are unnumbered, and then fills 83 leaves with eleven disputations, all concerned with the pest. They begin with the use of theriac during a recent outbreak of the pest at Brescia.[22]

Altimarus figures again in our last example but this time the author is his opponent, not his disciple. Salvus Sclanus Prochitanus addressed to John Altimarus, a medical man of Naples, an *Apologia* to the effect that what he had said in his commentaries on the *Aphorisms* against the father of Altimarus was quite true, while the latter's rebuttal was entirely beside the point. This *Apologia* I have read in an edition at Venice in 1584 printed at the expense of a bookseller of Naples. It covers 55 leaves in small roman type.[23] Sclanus had once taught medicine in the university of Naples. His *Apologia* is divided into five chapters. In the first he insists that the art of medicine, contrary to the opinion of all recent writers, divides into significative, salubrious, and curative, and that the division of Altimarus into curing, diagnosis and prognostic (*praenotio*) cannot be accepted. In the second chapter he holds against Altimarus that in an indication taken from virtue there is something harmful on the part of the indicating just as in an indication taken from disease. In the third chapter he contends that the causes of particular circuits

[22] *Eudoxi Philalethis Adversus calumnias et sophismata cuiusdam personati qui se Euandrophilaetem nominavit Apologia,* Veronae apud Sebastianum a Donnis, 1573.

[23] *Apologia Salvi Sclani ad Ioannem Altimarum medicum Neapolitanum quod ea quae dixit in Commentariis Aphorismorum contra Altimarum sint verissima et adducta ab eo in oppositum nihil penitus concludant.* Venetiis apud Gratiosum Perchacinum MDLXXXIV. Sumptibus Anielli S. Viti Bibliopolae Neapolitani.

cannot be referred to thickness and thinness of the humors, in this defending Fernel against Altimarus. Chapter four argues that to assert that Hippocrates delayed bleeding in the pleurisy of Anaxion till the eighth day because he hoped to cure the affection by fomentations alone, is to accuse him of ignorance. In the fifth chapter he defends Manardus against Altimarus and others on the question whether medicines should be taken crude or concocted. Sclanus cites the Arabic medical authorities as well as Hippocrates and Galen and various recent writers. He protested against the assertion that the work ascribed to Galen on the parts of the art was regarded as spurious by everyone, pointing out that it was accepted as genuine by such Galenists as Leonicenus and Manardus, while Franciscus Valeriola had expressed surprise that anyone should doubt its authenticity.

The reaction against classical medicine was seen not only in the Paracelsan revival but in such a work as the *New and True Medicine Proved by Experiments and Evident Reasons* of Gómez Pereira, published in 1558, in which he combatted Galen in regard to fevers.[24]

Publication of the literature of secrets, medicinal and otherwise, received a great impulse from the appearance in 1555 or 1557[25] of the *Secrets* of Alessio of Piedmont—whether this or Girolamo Ruscelli of Viterbo was the real name of the author.[26] They were followed in 1558 by the *Natural Magic* of Porta, were translated into Latin by Wecker (1528-1586) in 1559, and had already in 1558 been translated into English from the French translation of them.[27] Ferguson listed fifty-six editions of the

[24] Gómez Pereira, *Nova veraque medicina experimentis et evidentibus rationibus comprobata,* 1558. I have been unable to see a copy of the book and it does not seem to be in the catalogues of the British Museum and Bibliothèque Nationale, but perhaps I do not have the form of the author's name accurately.

[25] Graesse, *Trésor,* lists an edition of "Venezia per Sigism. Bordogna, 1555, 8vo," but 1557 was the earliest edition Ferguson had seen.

[26] Jeronimo Ruscelli, *Secreti nuovi di maravigliosa virtu I quali continouando a quelli di Donno Alessio cognome finto del detto Ruscelli,* Venice, 1567.

[27] *The Secretes of . . . A. of Piedmont . . . translated out of Frenche into Eng. by Wyllyam Warde,* London, 1558, 4to.

Secrets of Alexis during the remaining years of the sixteenth century and thirteen more up to 1691.[28] Wecker's Latin version in the edition of 1588 is a chunky little volume of over eight hundred pages divided into seventeen books.[29] The reader may turn to Ferguson's article for further details as to the *Secrets* of Alexis, such as an "Oil of a red-haired dog," to make which the dog is to be seethed in oil until it disintegrates and then combined with scorpions, worms, herbs, marrow of hog and ass, and other ingredients in a prescribed order. Like Porta's *Natural Magic,* the *Secrets* are in large measure a printing, continuation and further development of the medieval manuscripts of secrets and experiments, containing medical recipes, waters, oils and colors.[30] Here we may further illustrate this type of literature and the impetus given to it by the book of Alessio, by noting a few other specimens of such compositions from the years immediately following its appearance.

Antoine Mizauld had already published in 1555 his *Little Forest of Arcana of Nature.*[31] In the edition of 1558 it was enlarged by two books.[32] In 1566 appeared the first edition of his *Nine Centuries of Arcana,*[33] of which there were other editions, beginning with that of 1567.[34] Mizauld's *Medicinal Garden* also contained various remedies and secrets.[35] In the *Musaeum metallicum* of Aldrovandi, edited long after his death by Bartholomaeus Ambrosinus, Mizauld is cited for such data as that mix-

[28] John Ferguson, "The secrets of Alexis. A sixteenth century collection of medical and technical receipts." *Proceedings of the Royal Society of Medicine,* 24 (1930), 225-46.

[29] *De secretis libri xvii. Ex variis authoribus collecti methodiceque digesti et aucti per Ioan. Iacobum Vveckerum Basiliensem medicum Colmariensem,* Basileae, Ex officina Pernea, 1588. I own a copy.

[30] *De secreti del Alessio Piemontese,* 1557. Copy used: BM 42.f.19.

[31] *Arcanorum naturae sylvula.*

[32] Ant. Mizaldus, *De arcanis naturae libelli quatuor.* Editio 3a libellis duobus pulcherrimis aucta et locupletata, Paris, 1558, 16mo, 158 fols.

[33] *Centuriae novem rerum memorabilium utilium et iucundorum,* Paris, Morellus, 1566. This is the wording of the title as given in the catalogue of Mizauld's published and forthcoming works, appended to his *Opusculum de sena planta,* Paris, 1574.

[34] *Memorabilium utilium ac iucundorum centuriae novem in aphorismos arcanorum omnis generis locupletes perpulchre digestae,* Paris, Morellus, 1567, 8vo.

[35] *Le Jardin Medicinal enrichi de plusieurs et divers Remèdes et Secrets,* 1578, 8vo, 462 pp.

ing in the hoofs of horses accelerates the fusion of copper, or that oil of tartar removes spots from iron or the human countenance.[36]

The *Capprici medicinali* of Lionardo Fioravanti were published at Venice in 1561, and his *Mirror of Universal Science* (*Dello specchio di scientia universale*) at the same place three years later. He is described in the latter title as a physician and surgeon but in the posthumous *Musaeum metallicum* of Aldrovandi is called "Empyricus Venetus,"[37] and later is cited for the notion that the sapphire stimulates gaiety, since it is jovial, and for this reason is a wonderful remedy for all affections of the heart.[38] Woodcuts of distilling apparatus accompany the *Capprici medicinali,* and Fioravanti is called by Hirsch one of the few Paracelsists in Italy,[39] while Ferguson states that he had "unbounded trust in specifics," and that a balsam named after him and containing many ingredients "was in use till a comparatively recent period."[40] His *Mirror of Universal Nature* is in three books, of which the first treats of all the more important secrets of the liberal and mechanical arts, the second of divers sciences and many fine thoughts of the ancient philosophers, the third of notable inventions. Some of Fioravanti's works were reprinted in the next century, the *Capprici* in 1647.

Also printed at Venice in 1561 were the *Medicinal Secrets* of Pietro Bairo or Bayro of Turin, formerly physician to Charles II, duke of Savoy.[41] In a note to the reader a Giovanni Tatti assures us that Bairo was an excellent doctor in Turin and that the work is rare and the secrets not feigned but true and drawn from Galen, Avicenna, Mesue, Hippocrates, and other great men. He therefore publishes it for the public utility. It is arranged in forty-one chapters in top to toe order. Bairo had died

[36] Aldrovandi, *Musaeum metallicum,* Bologna, 1648, pp. 107, 817.

[37] *Ibid.,* p. 871.

[38] *Ibid.,* p. 973.

[39] *Biographisches Lexikon d. hervorragenden Aerzte,* II, 368.

[40] John Ferguson, *Bibliotheca Chemica,* Glasgow, 1906, II, 178.

[41] *Secreti medicinali di M. Pietro Bairo da Turino gia medico di Carlo Secondo duce di Savoia.* In Venetia appresso F. Sansovino, MDLXI. Copy used: BM 1038.c.4.(1.).

Medical and philosophical writings by Petrus de Bayro are found in a Latin MS of the 16th century and partly of the year 1556: Milan Ambros. D.461.Inf.

in 1558. He had published a pest tract back in 1507 and a work on the comparative merits of medicine and law in 1512. He is said to have advised whispering an incantation in the patient's ear to facilitate childbirth. There were further editions of his *Secreti* in 1585 and 1592.

It was a not infrequent practice of lords and ladies in the early modern centuries to collect recipes and secrets for their own use and satisfaction.[42] Signora Isabella Cortese compiled such a collection, mineral, medicinal, artificial, alchemical and cosmetical, which was printed at Venice in 1561[43] and several times thereafter.[44] In the dedication to an archdeacon of Ragusa Isabella says that man not only investigates the occult secrets of nature but tries to surpass them and to do what is impossible for nature unaided. Among the medical recipes are an oil of scorpions and potable gold. A Particolare of Chirico, an abbot of Cologne, advises one who wishes to succeed in alchemy not to read the works of Geber, Raymond and Arnald but to follow ten precepts which ensue.

Secrets, Divers and Miraculous, were published under the name of the anatomist, Falloppia, after his death but were said in 1564 by Andreas Marcolinus Fanestris, in his edition of the lectures of Falloppia on baths and minerals, to be falsely attributed to him. The work was divided into three books dealing with various oils, unguents, pills, electuaries and other medicaments, with wines and medicinal waters, and with secrets of alchemy. There were many subsequent editions.[45]

[42] See T II, 806 for some examples. "Lady Seldey's Receipt Books of 1686 and Other XVIIth Century Receipt Books," are discussed in the Proceedings of the Royal Society of Medicine, London, 1913, VI, 150-69.

[43] *I secreti de la Signora Isabella Cortese ne' quali si contegnono cose minerali, medicinali, artificiose et alchimiche et molte dell' arte profumatoria appartenenti a ogni gran signora,* In Venetia appresso Giovanni Barilatto, MDLXI, 8 fols. and 207 pp. Copy used: BM 1038.c.4.(2.).

[44] The British Museum also has editions of Venice, 1588, 1595 and 1655.

[45] The first edition is said to have appeared in 1563. There was also an edition of Venice, 1565, by B. Borgarucci: BM 1038.d.8. I have examined that of Venice, 1582, "Appresso Camillo Franceschini," at the Academy of Medicine, New York, and that of 1588 at Paris: BN 8° Te^{18}.22. The Columbia University library has an edition of Venice, 1650. A German translation appeared in 1616.

The huge volume *On Medicine Old and New*[46] that Guinther of Andernach, otherwise known as a translator of works of classical medicine, dedicated to the emperor Maximilian II, consists of 867 large pages of dialogues, of which, however, three or four hundred pages are made up largely of recipes. Besides castor oil, oils from foxes, vipers and scorpions are recommended. The work is chiefly notable for its recognition of chemical remedies and Paracelsan medicine. Guinther knows that Paracelsus was not the first inventor of such chemical remedies, as his disciples suppose, but thinks that he none the less deserves credit as the first "in our time" to recall the chemical art to medical use and to amplify it. Guinther also alludes to remedies sought from cabala, demons and idle superstitions, and notes that some say that so long as a cure is effected, it makes no difference whether God or the devil is responsible for it.[47] Guinther of Andernach had been royal professor at Paris for a while, but with the Wars of Religion retired to Metz and Strasburg, and died in 1574.

Quacks and empirics flourished in medical practice of the second half of the sixteenth century, albeit contrary to the wishes of medical faculties. Queen Elizabeth of England was always taking up with superstitious charlatans, as was her secretary Walsingham, whom the London College of Physicians thrice defied, says Robert Steele, in restraining from practice an herbalist named Margaret Kenwix who was "a quack pure and simple."[48] Simon Forman, physician and astrologer, in his diary from 1552 to 1602, has recorded his questionable practices, dabblings in alchemy and magic, and the troubles into which these got him.[49] At Avignon there was complaint of many empirics and impostors "wandering about in this city with impunity," until in 1577 the medical faculty of the university prohibited the following per-

[46] *De medicina veteri et nova*, 1571: BM 773.m.20.

[47] *Ibid.*, Preface to Maximilian II, "Argentorati Calendis Ianuarii."

[48] Robert Steele, article on Alchemy in *Shakespeare's England*, Oxford, 1917, I, 432.

[49] *The Autobiography and Personal Diary of Dr. Simon Forman from* A.D. *1552 to* A.D. *1602*. From the unpublished MSS in the Ashmolean Museum, Oxford, ed. J. O. Halliwell, London, 1849.

sons from practicing medicine: pharmacists, surgeons, barbers, masseurs, mid-wives and empirics.[50]

Works on the subject of popular errors call for some mention in discussing the medical literature of the later sixteenth century. Laurent Joubert (1521-1583), chancellor of the university of Montpellier, gained a great name, the historian de Thou says, by his book on this theme addressed to Marguerite of France, queen of Navarre, and was called to court by her.[51] Before publishing this volume in French in 1578[52] Joubert had issued two decades of paradoxes in Latin[53] in which, while denying that menstrual blood was harmful or that poisons could be administered to take effect at a fixed future time, he had credulously discussed living without food for years and how an ostrich could digest iron. In the former case he held that copious phlegm could take the place of food. In the latter he explained that the ostrich did not digest the iron by its heat, for the lion was of much hotter temperament yet could not do so, but by its entire substance, peculiar temperament and a certain property of its stomach. These instances warn us that Joubert's treatment of popular errors was not likely to result in much scientific advance or diminution of interest in the occult and marvelous. Similarly in a pest tract of 1567, while rejecting as very superstitious a remedy which Ficino had taken from the magi of Persia, Joubert recognized as a cause of pest a sinister influence of the stars which could not be avoided or turned aside, although human bodies might be so fortified that they would be less susceptible to this impression made upon the air by the celestial bodies.[54]

In the work on popular errors Joubert completed only five books, dealing with the topics of medicine and physicians, con-

[50] L. Bardinet, *Universitatis Avenionensis historica adumbratio*, 1880, 8vo, p. 42. Copy used: BN 8° R.3257.

[51] Thuanus, *Hist.*, Bk. 76.

[52] *Erreurs populaires au fait de la médecine et régime de santé*, Bordeaux, 1578. Copy used: BM 1482.a.1. The preface to Marguerite is dated January 1, 1578.

[53] *Paradoxorum decas prima atque altera*, Lugduni, 1566, 8vo, 532 pp. Copy at Paris, BN 8° T^{21}.36. I have consulted it in the 1582 edition of Joubert's *Opera*.

[54] *De peste liber unus*, Lyons, Frellonius, 1567. I have consulted the work in the 1582 edition of his *Opera*, where its 19 chapters fill pp. 133-68.

ception and generation, pregnancy, birth, and the nourishment of infants. In these, while complaining that everyone dabbled in medicine and of the incorrectness of popular notions, he maintained such a belief as that nine children might be delivered at one birth. Joubert outlined the chapter headings of twenty-five books more on such subjects of general interest as the *complexio,* air and clothing, appetite and thirst, meals and embonpoint, digestion, food, sleep, disease, bleeding and purgation. Sometimes the phrasing of the caption makes it evident what opinion or practice is condemned, as in that directed against those who complain of the hot nights in summer, yet sleep in feather-beds with the windows shut, or that on the error of those who think they will die of the same disease and at the same age as their parents. In other cases the wording leaves it an open question which side the author intended to take. Some of the more superstitious notions are that in months whose names contain no letter R one should drink deep but embrace little, that one's ears burn when others are speaking of one, that one should not pare one's nails on days in whose names there is an R, that it is possible to replace a dislocation without seeing or touching the patient, whether herbs plucked on St. John's eve have more virtue, amulets of spider's web against the colic in infants, the German assertion that one should be sober on the day of bleeding and drunk the third day after, and the belief that marriages made in May turn out unhappily.

There were many subsequent editions of Joubert's work, including Italian[55] and Latin translations.[56] Gaspard Bachot, a royal physician and counselor, and municipal physician of Thiers, undertook to complete the chapters which Joubert had only outlined. He obtained a royal privilege for his book at Lyons in 1600, but publication was deferred until 1626.[57] The opinion of a woman that one should spend March and Septem-

[55] Lorenzo Gioberti, *La prima parte degli errori popolari . . . ,* Florence, Giunti, 1592.

[56] *De vulgi erroribus,* Antwerp, 1600.

[57] Gaspard Bachot, *Erreurs populaires touchant la médecine et régime de santé,* Lyon, 1626. Copy used: BN T^{21}.47.

ber in bed to escape illness during the rest of the year, which Joubert may have meant to list as a popular error, was upheld by Bachot.[58]

Meanwhile at Venice in 1603 had been printed a book by Scipio Mercurio[59] in which he endeavored to do for Italy what Joubert had done for popular errors in France. His attitude towards astrology has been noticed in the preceding chapter. An earlier Italian work was concerned with popular errors in general rather than in the special field of medicine. This *Discorso contro il Volgo* by Cosimo Aldana, "in which are reproved many false opinions," was published at Florence in Italian in 1578[60] and at Madrid in Spanish in 1591.[61] It is less, however, a rebuttal of particular popular errors and superstitions, than it is a general invective against the stupidity and wrong-headedness of the crowd, populace and Philistines, and a vague defense of letters, learning and astrology. Auguries, however, it condemns.

Finally, we may note that the idea of Joubert was also taken up by James Primrose in a book first printed at London in 1638 and then at Amsterdam in 1639, after which many other editions followed,[62] and an English translation.

In the medical schools much the same questions were being put and debated as in the days of Peter of Abano, as the following theses of 1574 at Montpellier will illustrate. From the seventh to the ninth of October Jean Blazin, who was a candidate for a professorial chair, discussed the questions: whether rest or motion was more healthful after meals, whether barley bread should

[58] VII, 10 in Joubert's work; II, 10 in Bachot's.

[59] *De gli errori popolari d'Italia.* Copy used: BM 1039.h.25.

[60] Cosimo Aldana, *Discorso contro il Volgo, in cui con buone ragioni si reprovano molte sue false opinioni,* Florence, 1578, 442 small pp. in coarse italic type without any division into chapters or paragraphs but with marginal headings and a full index. Copy used: BM 714.a.7.

[61] Cosme de Aldana, *Invectiva contra el vulgo y su maledicencia,* Madrid, 1591: BM 11451.aa.5. Reprinted in *Biblioteca de autores españoles,* 1848-1886, XXXVI, 495-514.

[62] *De vulgi erroribus in medicina libri IV.* Copy used: BN T[21].91. Previously had appeared John Cotta, *A Short Discoverie of the Unobserved Dangers of Severall Sorts of Ignorant and Unconsiderate Practisers of Physicke in England,* 1612: BM 551.a.2. (1.). Bound with it is the 1617 edition with the different title, *A true discovery of the empericke with the fugitive physition and quacksalver . . .* etc.

be eaten with fruit, whether the flesh of animals killed by poison was poisonous, whether it was safe for persons with kidney trouble or fever to eat eggs, whether a contusion should be treated with agglutinating medicaments, whether purging and bleeding were good for virulent stings and bites, whether suppuration was produced by unnatural heat, whether distillations of the head were more frequent in winter than in summer, whether salacious persons were more liable to consumption than the continent, whether stinks relieved suffocation. Blazin was repeatedly rejected as a candidate for an academic chair, but it was hardly because of the questions selected for discussion. For two months before, from August 2 to 4, Francisco Sanchez, later celebrated for his *Quod nihil scitur,* had been examined on such questions as these: whether dinner or supper should be the more frugal meal, is man hotter than woman, is the vital faculty diverse from the natural, is respiration necessary for all animals? Sanchez answered No to the last two questions. He further held that water was more healthful than wine, that purging was better than bleeding for children, and better than vomiting in cases of dysentery.[63]

Among questions disputed for the licentiate and doctorate at Montpellier and printed at Paris in 1607-1608[64] were these: whether lovers are to be cured with the same remedies as the insane (with a play in the Latin upon the words *amantes* and *amentes*), whether there is such a thing as intermittent pestilential fever, whether a certain plant (althaia or wild mallow) has the virtues ascribed to it by Dioscorides and Galen, whether water drinking is more useful to the young than to the old, whether the life of kings, princes and magnates is more healthy and long than that of plebeians and rustics, whether remedies for the bladder are good for arthritis, whether a poison can be prepared which will kill at a certain time.

[63] For these theses and the candidates' answers see the *Cartulaire de l'Université de Montpellier,* Vol. II, 1912.

[64] *Quaestiones medicae iiii agitatae pro licentiae gradu consequendo; Quaestiones iiii principales pro doctorali laurea triduo agitatae,* Paris, 1608. Copy seen: BM 1160.b.1.(3.).

Pierandrea Mattioli or Petrus Andreas Matthiolus (1500-1577) is especially known for his commentaries on Dioscorides, first printed in Latin at Venice in 1554.[65] His five books of medicinal epistles, first printed at Prag in 1561, further illuminate the state of medicine at that time.[66] They include letters between other persons such as a reply of Conrad Gesner to Melchior Guilandinus, keeper of the botanical garden at Padua who engaged in a controversy concerning plants with Mattioli. Gesner states that Mattioli has made mistakes in his edition of Dioscorides, but that to err is human and that he will perhaps correct them in a new edition. Although most of the component epistles were written and even the collection published before the Paracelsan revival can be said really to have gotten under way, Mattioli, despite the fact that we might expect him as a commentator upon Dioscorides to take a narrow and conservative classical stand, approves of the use of chemical remedies, which, he says, Montanus employed.[67] Mattioli included in his *Epistolae* a letter from a young physician of Prag, Andreas de Blavven, on varied ways of preparing potable gold, in which it is stated that gold can be dissolved by *aqua fortis* or by salt of human skull, that human hairs are very useful in rendering metals ductible, and that potable gold is probably to be identified with the elixir. De Blavven also cited the medieval alchemist, Geber.[68] Mattioli himself had distilled salt from two human skulls. He further affirms that quicksilver can safely be taken internally against worms and in cases of childbirth.[69]

[65] Schreiber (1924), xliv-xlv. S. Savage, "A Little-known Bohemian Herbal," *The Library, Transactions of the Bibliographical Society*, 2nd series, XI (1922), 117-31, appears to he mistaken in stating that it "appeared first in Italian in 1544."

[66] *Epistolarum medicinalium libri quinque,* Prag, 1561, folio, 395 pp. I have used the edition of 1598, "Francofurti ex officina typographica Nicolai Bassaei," through the kindness of the John Crerar library which sent the volume from Chicago to New York for my use.

[67] *Ibid.,* lib. IV, 180. The Montanus referred to is presumably Johannes Baptista of Verona, author of numerous medical works, extracts from which were printed in *Verae alchemiae,* 1561, II, 35, rather than Joh. Scultetus of Silesia, to whom we owe the preservation of Paracelsan works in manuscript and who was the teacher of Huser, their editor in 1589.

[68] *Ibid.,* IV, 175-79.

[69] *Ibid.,* IV, 158.

Mattioli's letters include instructions to pharmacists as to the preparation of the ancient antidotes, theriac and Mithridatic. For the former he gives a great many ingredients but rejects some suggested by Fuchs, complains that Ruellius knew only French herbs, and laments that not so good theriac can be made now as in Galen's time, because not all the herbs which Galen employed are now available. One should use only female vipers.[70] The pharmacist whom Mattioli instructed as to the preparation of Mithridatic further asked him if an unguent of alabaster described by Jacobus Manlius in his *Luminary* was the same as that used by Mary Magdalene to anoint the feet of the Saviour.[71] The physician of the queen of Bohemia, Ioannes Odoricus Melchiorius, informed Mattioli of a Spanish herb which cured the bite of the viper and had been discovered by a slave from Africa who had known a similar herb there.[72] Mattioli himself writes from Prag to Caspar Peucer that, while he had often read in Aristotle's *History of Animals* of the he-goat of Lemnos giving milk and its male offspring doing the same, he had thought this a prodigy peculiar to the goats of that Greek island. But recently a billy goat which gave milk had been brought to the local archduke. Moreover, its milk cured epileptics, especially infants, which Mattioli thought very strange, because its liver gave them fits. Yet another specimen gave less milk and had its tits in a different place. It remained to be seen whether their young males would likewise give milk.[73] Such were some of the marvels and foibles of Mattioli's medical science in the middle of the sixteenth century. We have seen him on the one hand open-minded enough to admit chemical remedies, although himself a commentator on Dioscorides, but on the other hand narrowly enough attached to classical pharmacology to deplore the lack in his day of herbs mentioned by Galen, in seeming blindness to the new flora of America and increasing materia medica from the Far East.

The conception of spirits in the sense, not of demons and im-

[70] *Ibid.*, V, 185-96.
[71] *Ibid.*, V, 215-16.
[72] *Ibid.*, V, 210.
[73] *Ibid.*, III, 141.

material substances, but of refined matter and motive force existing in human and other bodies was, as we have already had occasion to observe, in great vogue in the sixteenth century as an explanation for almost any natural phenomena. Even in the seventeenth century Francis Bacon had frequent recourse to it and asserted that such spirits "govern nature principally." This conception, while itself hardly a superstition or part of occult science, was often substituted for or associated with those of celestial influence and of occult virtue in terrestrial substances, or was used to supply a natural explanation for what would otherwise have had to be regarded as magical or at least marvelous. We shall now examine this notion of spirits in works by two physicians, Argenterius and Bertacchi.

In 1556 there was printed at Florence a work by Ioannes Argenterius entitled, *Two Books on Sleep and Waking* in which are contained two disquisitions on native heat and on spirits.[74] The book does not deal with divination from dreams but otherwise largely follows Aristotle and Galen as to sleep and waking and ends with the conclusion that heat by its presence or absence is the cause of sleep or waking. In the dedication to Philippus Meliorius, a patrician of Florence, Argenterius states that he formed the plan of writing on sleep and waking some years ago when he first published his medical work on diseases.[75] Later when he had more leisure at Rome he read up on the subject and then developed it further in his teaching at Pisa and at Naples. He also seems to have published in 1553 a work on the errors of ancient medical writers which I have not seen.[76] In the same

[74] Ioannes Argenterius, *De somno et vigilia libri duo in quibus continentur duae tractationes de calido nativo et de spiritibus,* Florence, 1556, L. Torrentinus, 4to, 336 pp. Copy used: BM 1039.1.33.

[75] "Cum aederem iam ante aliquot annos opus meum de re medica quod nunc de morbis aptiore titulo inscribere placuit." The allusion appears to be to his *De consultationibus medicis sive ut vulgus vocat de collegiandi ratione liber,* Cum privilegio cudebat Laurentius Torrentinus ducalis typographus, Florentiae, MDLI. This was reissued in 1556 at Florence as *De morbis libri XIIII:* BM 544.h.12.

[76] Gio. Argentero, *De erroribus veterum medicorum,* Florence, 1553, in fol. Probably Constantinus (1555), p. 150, had this work in mind when he said that Bartholomaeus Argenterius composed a medical work in which he often criticized Galen.

year Remigius Melioratus issued against him a *Disputation Concerning Putridity.*[77]

Argenterius was a medical writer and teacher of high repute. He was born at Castelnuovo in Piedmont and died at Turin in 1572 aged fifty-eight.[78] He was persuaded to publish his volume of *Medical Consultations* in 1551 by Joannes Baptista Susius and dedicated it to cardinal Grimani. In the preface, written at Pisa, he states that cardinal Gaddi had brought him "to Italy" —in which he apparently did not include Piedmont or perhaps even Cisalpine Gaul—to teach seven years before. In the same volume is a foreword by Laurentius Gryllus, who was born at Landshut, Bavaria, but had been enabled to visit the Italian schools of medicine through the generosity of Johann Jakob Fugger, the merchant prince. Gryllus, who was something of a botanist, became a professor at Ingolstadt, where he died in 1561 before he could complete commentaries for a projected edition of Dioscorides.[79] Some minor medical works by him were printed posthumously at Prag in 1566.[80] Whereas de Thou looked back on Argenterius as an Aristotelian, Gryllus praised him as neither an Arabist nor too conservative a classicist in medicine, and as one who had ventured to strike out for himself. Tiraqueau included Argenterius in his alphabetical list of famous physicians and spoke well of his medical writings but regarded them as primarily directed against Galen.[81]

Returning to the work on sleep and waking, we may note particularly what Argenterius has to say of the spirits in the human body. He denies that one principle can be constituted in the body of animals as Aristotle thought. Incidentally he still accepts the *Problems* as a genuine work of Aristotle. He follows Galen for the views on the spirits of the Stoics, since their own

[77] *De putredine adversus Joannem Argenterium disputatio,* Florentiae, 1553, 8vo, 53 pp. Migliorati died in 1554 after teaching the Peripatetic philosophy seven years at Padua and eleven at Pisa. See Ugo Viviani, *Medici fisici e cerusici della provincia Aretina vissuti dal V al XVII secolo,* 1923.

[78] Thuanus, *Hist.,* lib. LIV.

[79] Jöcher, *Gelehrten Lexicon.*

[80] *De sapore dulci et amaro libri II,* etc.: BN 4° Tb[56].4.

[81] Andrea Tiraquellus, *Commentarii de nobilitate,* Venice, 1574, fol. 136r, col. 1.

books are not extant, but censures Galen for having adhered too closely to their fantastic ideas in this regard. Argenterius holds that men breathe in air and breathe out spirit, which is crasser than air and is produced from matter composed of all the elements. He disagrees with the doctrine of Fernel, which some attribute also to Aristotle, that spirit is an ethereal substance serving as a mean between the divine soul and elemental body. Nor does he approve the opinion of Montanus of Verona that it is a transparent, lucid, resplendent substance. Rather he defines spirit as a vaporous substance essential to the performance of bodily functions, but all of one kind and not differentiated as animal, vital and natural.

Domenico Bertacchi dedicated his four books on spirits to Alfonso II of Ferrara of the Este family and seems to have been his physician. The work was printed in 1584.[82] In a preface to the general reader Bertacchi states that he has spent most of his life in practicing and teaching medicine. But this treatise and a discussion of the vital faculty which accompanies it seem the only extant publications by him. He died on September 23, 1596. He complains that Hippocrates was brief and obscure on the subject of spirits, Galen copious but confusing. Only Actuarius had composed a book especially on spirits. Bertacchi has tried to collect, order, reconcile and correct the statements of Hippocrates and Galen, adding thereto the views of Aristotle, Plato and other philosophers and physicians. He criticizes the opinions of certain recent writers: Donatus Altomari, Argenterius, Manard and Fernel. He defines the spirits as bodies, not a soul, and denies that they are the seat of the soul. The members of the Old Academy held that the spirits of the rational soul were ethereal, those of the irrational soul elementary—a distinction which Actuarius seems to follow. Fernel held that the spirits were ethereal and from the sky, but Bertacchi objects that this would diminish the incorruptible celestial bodies. He grants, however, that the spirits are quasi-ethereal, approaching the per-

[82] Dominicus Bertacchius, *De spiritibus libri quattuor; necnon de facultate vitali libri tres,* Venetiis, 1584.

fection of the heavenly bodies, generated of the best matter, of long enduring concoction, refined and splendid. Unlike Argenterius again, he accepts the Galenic classification of animal, vital and natural spirits, associated respectively with the brain, heart and liver. How to conserve and restore them is the topic of many of his chapters. In the companion treatise on the vital faculty Bertacchi cites medieval authors more than in his work on spirits, examining the opinions of Aquinas, Plusquam Commentator, Averroes and Gentile da Foligno.

Limits, however, were sometimes set to the extent to which the spirits could be offered as an explanation for otherwise inexplicable phenomena. Joachim Cureus reports a discussion at Padua concerning a case of suffusion in both eyes.[83] There were certain corpuscles like grains of millet in both eyes. That in the right eye was the more concrete and dense, yet the patient saw fairly well with that eye, whereas he could see neither distant nor near objects with the other eye, in which the obstacle was more tenuous. Trincavelli (1496-1568), who taught at Padua after 1551 and whom Cureus called *facile princeps* of Italian philosophers and medical men of that time, gave the best explanation offered, which was that this could not be referred to the spirits, since the same spirits were conveyed to both eyes, but was to be accounted for rather by the medium, that is, the intrinsic medium or organ of sight. Possibly, however, this explanation may seem less satisfactory to the modern reader than it did to Cureus.

Salomo Alberti, who took his M.D. degree in 1574 with a dissertation on contagious diseases addressed to Caspar Peucer, died in 1600. In the intervening years he first taught at Wittenberg, where he was dean of the philosophical faculty, thrice dean of the medical faculty, and also thrice rector of the university. Later he went to Dresden and became physician to the elector. Will calls him a great anatomist, the discoverer of the valves in

[83] Joachim Cureus, *Libellus physicus continens doctrinam de natura et differentiis colorum sonorum odorum saporum et qualitatum tangibilium*, Wittenberg, 1572, I, 35, p. 141.

the colon and of the ostiola venarum.[84] This, however, represented but one of his many interests. He was still sufficiently attached to Galen to edit one work ascribed to him and to write a preface to another. The Arabic medical writer, Rasis, also still claimed his attention. He discussed the study and science of medicine and its professors. He recorded medical cases or *consilia,* as had been the custom in the fourteenth and fifteenth centuries. He composed an *Antidotarium* and wrote on compound medicines including theriac and Mithridatic. He also discussed such questions as why boys should not be forbidden to cry, why sobbing generally goes with tears, and whether metals and minerals burned on coals help asthma by their vapor or odor. He wrote treatises on some particular diseases or complaints. He delivered orations on the knowledge of herbs and the nature and efficacy of musk. Despite this breadth of interest, he seems not to have entered the fields of astrology, alchemy or demonology, although his compound medicines border upon magic. He thus serves to remind us that there were physicians who did not concern themselves with occult sciences.

On the other hand, Giovanni Francesco Olmo, a physician of Brescia,[85] treated twice of the theme of occult virtue. Over twenty years elapsed between the two publications. The former, addressed in 1576 to Ferdinand, archduke of Austria, was an outgrowth of annotations on the thirteenth book of Galen's *De methodo medendi,* which dealt with those things which act from a property of their whole substance, and bore a like title.[86] It was a short treatise of 52 small leaves in coarse type without any division into chapters or even paragraphs, written during a time of misfortune to relieve its author's mind and, as it seemed to him later, rude and without form.[87] In 1597 he addressed to

[84] Will, *Nürnbergisches Gelehrten-Lexicon,* 1755, I, 9-11, where will also be found a list of his works.

[85] Franciscus Ulmus Pictaviensis, doctor med., author of *De liene libellus,* Lutetiae, Rob. Stephanus for M. Patisson, 1578, 8vo, 28 fols., was perhaps a different person.

[86] *Ioannis Francisci Ulmi medici Brixiani De iis quae in medicina agunt ex totius substantiae proprietate . . . ,* Augustae, Anno MDLXXVI. Copy used: BM 547.d.27.(1.). I shall henceforth cite this as Ulmus (1576).

[87] So he says in the dedicatory preface to his work of 1597.

Rainutio Farnese, duke of Parma and Piacenza, a revised and greatly enlarged edition, divided into books and chapters, with the new title, *Of Occult Properties in Medicine.*[88] Roughly speaking, the underlying plan and purpose remained the same, and many sentences were unchanged, but upon at least one important point Olmo had altered his opinion in the interim.

Olmo held that the subject of occult virtues had not yet received adequate treatment. Those since Galen who had discussed it had done so very briefly or had put forth various unordered and contrary statements, while others had derided the conception and attempted to dispense with it.[89] I cannot say, however, that I found any ideas concerning occult virtues in the treatises of Olmo which I had not repeatedly encountered before in the works of other authors. Indeed, he stresses the thought that it would be idle to attempt to determine their nature from the very fact that they are occult.[90] He therefore largely contents himself with adducing numerous particular examples of them in foods, medicaments, poisons and antidotes, and with rebuttal of such attempted explanations of them as Avicenna's identification of occult virtues with nature and others' identification of them with form. Olmo also regards them as a function of the total substance rather than of the temperament, as Alexandrinus, Montanus and others had held.[91] Olmo further closely associates them with the relations of sympathy and antipathy between things, while the heading of the opening chapter of the treatise of 1597 affirms that the universe consists of contraries, and that thence is deduced the occult property of things. But how it is deduced the ensuing text fails to elucidate.

It should further be noticed that in both treatises or versions is found the statement that, whatever occult virtue is, almost all authorities are agreed that it is nought else than a certain celes-

[88] *Io. Francisci Ulmi medici Brixiani De occultis in re medica proprietatibus libri quatuor* . . . , Brixiae, Ex typographia Comini Praesenii, MDXCVII, 164 pp. Each page contains more words than a leaf of the 1576 treatise. Copy used: BM 543.b.6.(1.). This will be cited as Ulmus (1597).

[89] Ulmus (1576), fol. lv; (1597), p. 4.

[90] Ulmus (1576), fols. 2-3, 21r; (1597), p. 5, I, 3.

[91] Ulmus (1597), p. 8, I, 4.

tial faculty entering into particular things from superior causes after the first admixture of the four elements.[92] But in the 1597 text Olmo presently attacks those who ascribe such virtues to the stars. He says that nothing more absurd can be conceived than that such constant virtues should be joined to the varying aspects of the stars. The stars indeed act upon these inferiors but only by their motion, light and heat. Hippocrates and Galen never referred occult virtues to the stars. Olmo also cites such writers against astrology as Pico della Mirandola, Augustine, Favorinus, and Benedictus Pererius. He quotes Fracastoro that no contagions are produced from the sky *per se,* although nothing prevents their being so produced *per accidens* and even predicted by astrologers. This would seem to hint that occult virtues too may be accidentally produced by the sky. Olmo, however, does not draw this conclusion but attacks Marsilio Ficino for subjecting the most noble art of medicine to the stars. "We indeed," says Olmo, "gladly recognize a certain connection and harmony of superiors with inferiors, but we reject all necessity of rule." This rather strange outburst of Olmo may perhaps be accounted for by the fact that the bull of Sixtus V against astrology had appeared since the treatise of 1576 and by the further fact that the text of 1597 was printed at Brescia, "superiorum permissu," and not at Augsburg as was that of 1576.

Already in 1575 Olmo professed to omit superstitious and uncertain remedies.[93] Such beliefs as that a unicorn's horn or serpent's tongue would sweat in the presence of poison, that the gem Prasinus would lose its gleam, and the toadstone, if worn in one's ring, would burn one's finger, repeated by Mattioli on the author-

[92] Ulmus (1576), fols. A 5 verso—(A 6) recto, "Quicquid sit certe in hoc omnes fere conveniunt quod proprietas haec nil aliud sit quam facultas quaedam coelestis post primam quatuor simplicium corporum commixtionem a superioribus causis in singulis adveniens." Ulmus (1597), p. 5, I, 3: "Conveniunt tamen in hoc fere omnes quod proprietas haec nil aliud sit quam facultas quaedam coelestis post primam simplicium quatuor corporum mixtionem a superioribus causis in signis adveniens."

Ulmus (1576), fols. E 3 verso—E 4 recto (33v-34r), further states that certain things which are naturally most wholesome acquire a noxious or lethal character from some occult reason, whether of the air, earth or constitution of the stars.

[93] Ulmus (1576), fol. D 2 (24r).

ity of others, Olmo characterized as "very similar to the figments of the magi and not necessary to the present treatise."[94] But he accepted as certain that the excrement of a wolf produces marvelous effects in colic, and as proved by the experience of many that human and canine dung are beneficial for angina. A little powdered human skull, "they say, has wonderful efficacy in routing epilepsy, which too Savonarola used in quartan fever as a great secret." All such remedies are explainable for Olmo in terms of antipathy, "for nothing is so contrary to anything as a dead or corrupt body or excrement of its own species."[95] Some persons put no faith in suspensions, but Olmo believes that experience is to the contrary and he gives many instances of cures wrought by the use of amulets. Others, although conceding that witches fascinate children and that a wolf renders a man mute, if it sees him first, denied such action at a distance in the case of inanimate objects. But again Olmo piles up examples against them.[96]

As to the power of words and characters, knots and signs, a somewhat different position is taken in 1597 than in 1576. In the earlier text there is a single brief passage in which Olmo says that he has seen certain persons who cured even the absent by words alone or characters or knots or signs. It seemed impossible, but the fact was undeniable. These cures were not natural, however, but by a power to be considered elsewhere. They raise the question whether the physician is justified in employing such methods, which some medical writers have noted in their books. For his part, Olmo would not venture to answer in the affirmative, since such things seem alien to the majesty of medicine nor suitable to human modesty, wherefore they are rightly disapproved by many.[97] In the revision of 1597 Olmo says that he has purposely omitted knots, signs and characters, because it is clear that many of these are superstitious.[98] But he has previously de-

[94] Ulmus (1576), fols. G 5 verso—(G 6) recto, or fols. 51v-52r.

[95] Ulmus (1576), fols. D-D 2 (23v-24r).

[96] Ulmus (1576), fol. D 5 or 27r; (1597), p. 79 *et seq.*

[97] Ulmus (1576), fol. D 6 or 28r.

[98] Ulmus (1597), p. 81, close of book II.

bated the power of words at greater length, recognizing that most recent writers like Cardan, Fernel and Bodin agree with Galen in attributing little effect to words, but stating himself that many things argue the excellence of words, and that it can scarcely be doubted that they receive from the spirit, "informed and animated by notions of the divine part," a superior power over diseases of mind and body. Words themselves, speech itself, and poetry, by the varied occult numerical proportion of their numbers and consonance affect our bodies as music does, so that it should not be deemed absurd that marvels are sometimes effected by their means. But after he has adduced various examples, Olmo suddenly shifts his attitude, saying that these are what deceive many into thinking that there are natural powers in words against all diseases. Christian truth has dissipated these shadows from the mind and has "finally determined" that in all these cases (except certain sacred names and prayers) they are not free from superstition, especially if unknown and apparently meaningless words are employed, beneath which deception and pacts of demons often lurk. It has therefore established that the physician should abstain from these entirely, both as profane and as alien from the majesty of medicine, nor suitable to human modesty. Wherefore they are rightly condemned by law.[99] The language here employed by Olmo suggests that there had been some recent ecclesiastical pronouncement or definition of policy akin to the bull of Sixtus V with reference to divination and astrology.

Olmo differentiated ordinary poisons (*venena*) from veneficia or secret drugs and sorceries by which injury could be done to human bodies or to air and water. Again he distinguished between veneficia wrought by natural means and veneficia of demons. The latter were considered the more difficult to remedy, for it seemed improbable that spiritual powers could be affected in any way by sensible things. But Olmo inclines to believe that sulphur or musical harmony, as in the playing of David before Saul, may disturb them by antipathy. He cites the case of the

[99] Ulmus (1597), pp. 72-73.

angel and Tobias and the opinion of some theologians that demons for their sins have been divinely subjected to corporal things. This discussion seems to occur only in the treatise of 1597.[100]

It may be of some service to note a few comments by Olmo upon other medical or scientific writers of the time. Manard, who derided an occult property in the works of Avicenna, in his own *Letters* (XV, 4) recommended to cure suffusion the head of a swallow cooked to a crisp in a bronze vessel, reduced to a powder, and rubbed on alone or with honey.[101] All were at sea as to the origin and nature of the bezoar stone until Garcia da Orta and Monardes demonstrated that it was found in the intestines of certain wild goats.[102] Vesalius, as well as Mesue, is accused of error by Olmo for arguing in his work on surgery (VII, 3) that the humors were attracted by purgatives in a violent manner, like the action of the magnet on iron or of horses drawing a car,[103] whereas Olmo holds that all purgatives act by occult property. Olmo thought the pest, to which he devoted several chapters in the treatise of 1597, worse than all other poisons combined. No cure was known, and the plague-stricken were abandoned by all their friends. Against Altomarus Olmo argued that the causes of the pest were occult.[104]

We close our chapter with a treatise on the powers of the imagination. Thomas Fienus or Fyens (1567-1631), a native of Antwerp, who had studied in Italy under Mercurialis and Aldrovandi, was professor of medicine in the university of Louvain at the time that he dedicated his work on the powers of the imagination to Ernest, archbishop of Cologne, chancellor of the Holy Roman Empire, bishop of Liège, count palatine, duke of Bavaria, etc.[105] He had formerly been private physician to Maximilian, duke of Bavaria and to archduke Albert at Brussels. He

[100] Ulmus (1597), pp. 158-61.

[101] Ulmus (1576), fols. (A 7) verso—(A 8) recto, or 5v-6r.

[102] Ulmus (1597), p. 141; IV, 5.

[103] Ulmus (1576), fols. C 3 verso, (C 7) recto, or 17 and 21; Ulmus (1597), p. 44, II, 3.

[104] Ulmus (1597), III, 8-12.

[105] Thomas Fienus, *De viribus imaginationis tractatus*, Lovanii, 1608, 8vo. Copy used: BM 784.c.9. Another edition was printed in 1635.

wrote other medical and surgical works and upon the comet of 1618. The present treatise is scholastic in form, containing 57 conclusions grouped under 24 questions. The main thesis is that imagination cannot affect an external body but can potently influence to the extent of marking for life the child in its mother's womb.

Phantasy has some power over the humors and spirits within one's own body, but "phantastic species is not productive of real quality nor can it formally alter." Avicenna in *Sextus Naturalium* says that souls at the instant of their creation acquire peculiar powers from the constellations then prevailing. "Many other vain and superstitious men," like Paracelsus, have said the same. But Fienus denies that phantasy receives any operative power from the stars, or that demons and characters are affected by the stars. Nor will he admit a relation of sympathy between the human soul and the heavens as a consequence of which the sky acts in accord with human imagination. He further declares that the notion of a world soul is false and damned. He also condemns the explanation given by Pomponazzi that relics of the saints work miracles only by virtue of the imagination and confidence of the patient who is cured.

The influence of the mother's imagination—during pregnancy or at the moment of conception—on the formation of the foetus is quite another matter. From previous writers Fienus collects thirty-two illustrative cases and, while he grants that some of these are probably false, and that women often ascribe to their own imaginings what was really mere chance or invent such stories to cover up cases of illegitimate birth, still he insists that enough true instances remain to prove his point. He regards as possible, for example, the case which he repeats at second or third hand,[106] of a girl who was born near Pisa covered with hair, because her mother at the time of conception had gazed at an image of Saint John the Baptist which hung by the bed. On the other hand, he does not believe that looking at a beautiful pic-

[106] *Ibid.*, p. 115, "Marcus Damascenus, ut testatur Petrus Messias libro variarum let. c. 7. . . ."

ture will produce a beautiful child. But he does believe that the imagination of the father as well as that of the mother may mark the offspring. He rejects, however the common opinion of old wives, which Levinus Lemnius had accepted[107] but which Hercules Saxonia had already ridiculed,[108] that such anticipated marks may be transferred to another part of the child's body by such dumb show as, for example, wiping one's face with one's hands and then applying them to other portions of one's anatomy. The index to the treatise of Fienus contains the question whether fascination can be worked by mere touch or look or word, but his text has little or nothing concerning fascination in the strict sense of the word. He cites many authors: ancient, patristic, Arabic, medieval, but especially those of the sixteenth century.

[107] *Ibid.*, p. 197, "Dicit Levinus Lemnius, lib. I, cap. 4, de occult. nat. mir. . . ."

[108] *Idem,* "Hercules Saxonia 4 cap. 30 sui Panthei." The work referred to is: *Pantheum medicinae selectum . . . nunc primum editum ab eius discipulo Petro Uffenbachio,* 1603, 1063 pp.: BM 545.i.13.

CHAPTER XXXVII

LIBAVIUS AND CHEMICAL CONTROVERSY

Certain devotees of chemistry differ little from magicians.
—LIBAVIUS

Andreas Libavius was born at Halle in Saxony in 1550 and died in 1616 in Franconia. He was a doctor of medicine but in 1588 became professor of history and poetry at Jena, and in 1605 rector of a gymnasium at Coburg. Meanwhile he had become so embroiled in the controversial literature of that age that before the end of the sixteenth century he published a volume "of varied controversies."[1] One of the controversies in which he engaged was that between the Peripatetics and Ramists.[2] Libavius complained that the Ramist faction tried to overthrow the natural truth explained by Hippocrates, Galen, Aristotle and others. He regarded as unattainable their ideal of limiting each art to deduction from a set of homogeneous, self-evident and germane axioms, since he held that God alone knew all the details of art and nature well enough to lay down as a starting-point such impeccable axioms and scientific rules for constituting arts. The *Questions* of Libavius were especially directed against two British Ramists, Temple of Cambridge and a Scot, James Martin, of Oxford. He did not agree with Temple that physics should include the science of the stars. He further complained that Temple and Martin needlessly charged Aristotle with errors of which others were already aware and able to detect for themselves, while they offered nothing constructive of their own in the way of science to take the place of these errors.

[1] Libavius, *Variarum controversiarum . . .*, 1600. Copy used: BM 775.b.8.

[2] Libavius, *Quaest. physicarum controversarum inter Peripateticos et Rameos tract. in quo . . . octo quaest. ex illis quae de elementis nuper ut inaudita protulit contra Aristotelem J. Martinus*, 1591. Copy used: BM 519.c.20. (2.).

He felt that too much time was now spent on method, that real learning and science had fallen off in consequence, and that there were no great geniuses as of yore. Both factions aimed at the same goal, and the Ramian method had its merits, but the dissent and hatreds to which it had given rise were a deplorable handicap to scientific progress.

In 1594 Libavius published together two treatises which well illustrate the attention given in his time to occult matters.[3] In the first he dealt with the cure of wounds by use of weapon ointment, a practice which he attributed to the Paracelsists. In the second he discussed the bleeding of a corpse in the presence of the murderer. His ideas on these subjects had first been ventilated at the university of Jena in the form of lists of theses for disputation: 315 on weapon ointment, and 314 on the bleeding corpse. These were now published with notes and scholia, making in all a volume of nearly four hundred pages, of which the theses alone occupy about sixty-seven.[4] Libavius complains that men consult theologians concerning physical and medical questions, but he himself is guilty of importing a great deal of theology into his physics. For example, he affirms that God hates magic, he asserts the immortality of the soul, he goes for scientific information to the first chapter of The Book of Genesis, he declares that it is absurd not to posit God as present in everything.[5]

Towards the twin superstitions, as they would appear to the modern reader, which were the themes of his theses, Libavius took up two different, and what again to the modern reader must seem inconsistent, attitudes. The asserted cure of wounds by anointing the weapon with which the wound had been inflicted he pilloried as an imposture of the Paracelsists. He would merely have laughed at such nonsense rather than argue against it at

[3] Andreas Libavius, *Tractatus duo physici: prior de imposturia vulnerum per unguentum armarium sanatione Paracelsicis usitata, . . . posterior de cruentatione cadaverum iniusta caede factorum praesente qui occidisse creditur,* Frankfurt, 1594. Copy used: BM 780.a.29.

[4] *Ibid.,* pp. 8-34, 100-39.

[5] *Ibid.,* theses 141, 172 and 185 of the first part, also p. 93.

length, were it not for the fact that it found defenders among great men, theologians, physicians and professors in universities. Libavius contends that the wound heals naturally, while the ceremonies of weapon ointment are either diabolical magic, mere imposture, or a pretense to keep the patient's courage up. Healing by weapon ointment can be explained neither by the influences of the stars, nor by magnetism, "that sheet anchor of Paracelsic stupidity," nor by recourse to the Cabala such as Johannes Pistorius Niddanus made. Libavius repeats several recipes for weapon ointment. One combines two ounces of scrapings from a human skull with the same weight of human liver and half an ounce of human blood, pounded together in a mortar. The weapon is to be left for a time in the ointment and afterwards applied by the patient to his wound. A second method is to thrust the weapon into bread, earth, lard or other fat, and the wound, if only it is not exposed to the air, will heal without suppuration or pain. A third recipe employs pork fat, old bear fat, earthworms and two drams of human skull, if obtainable.

Incidentally Libavius opposes magic, which he will not grant a natural basis but regards as superstitious and worked by demon aid. He frequently cites Bodin's *Démonomanie* but often disagrees with it. Against astrology he objects that, since the earth is a mere point compared to the vast extent of the heavens, it is impossible that a given constellation should affect a certain individual rather than the Indians or Antipodes. He alludes somewhat sceptically to the power of royal touch claimed for the kings of France and England. The practice of boys foretelling from the salt on Christmas eve the lives and deaths of the ensuing year he declares a ridiculous procedure yet sometimes true to the event.[6]

To such tales of human superstition in his first treatise Libavius adds his own beliefs in the second part, where he is no longer attacking but defending a doctrine which borders on the occult. That the corpse does resume bleeding in the presence of the murderer he accepts as an indisputable fact certified by various

[6] *Ibid.*, pp. 11, 118-19, 68, 37, 51.

jurisconsults and other authorities.[7] His task is therefore merely to offer a satisfactory natural explanation of the phenomenon. So he argues that the blood, even after death, is a very sensitive part or fluid of the body. The blood of a goat breaks the stone, and the blood of a fascinated person even after his death is pestiferous. Indeed, Langius goes so far as to assert that some powers of the sensitive soul, namely of cupidity and revenge, subsist in the corpse before it putrefies. The guilty conscience of the murderer and his perturbation at the sight of the dead body of his victim raise his temperature, agitate his spirits and humors. These in turn, whether by radiation, evaporation or antipathy, affect the blood of the corpse and cause it to flow. This seemingly occult action Libavius supports by various analogous cases: the effect of fear and imagination in producing disease, the discord between drums of wolfskin and of sheepskin, the occult virtues of herbs and stones—some are magical, but not all are to be so rejected—the detection by the bezoar of the presence of poison, the perception by a sleeper of an enemy's propinquity, an African animal called Catoplepa which kills by its glance like the basilisk, and the devil's inability to endure the sign of the cross.

The objection is entertained that the blood of a dog ought to flow in the same way in the presence of the beast's killer, but Libavius thinks that canine gore is less susceptible to receiving alteration. He says that no one has ever tested by experiment whether a dog killed by another dog would so bleed in its presence. He admits the force of another objection, namely that the corpse might also bleed at the approach of an innocent person, say an intimate friend between whom and the deceased there was close sympathy. To avoid thus indicating the wrong person as guilty, Libavius suggests that any close friends be removed when the test is made. He also recommends other precautions to avoid disturbing factors. But if these are duly observed, he thinks that the criminal should be revealed as certainly as when

[7] On the general subject, especially for the seventeenth century, consult W. G. Aitchison Robertson, "Bier Right." *Ve Cong. Internat. d'Hist. de la Médecine* (Genève, 1925), Geneva, 1926, pp. 192-98.

we infer from light the presence of the sun. He would not, it is true, put a man to death on this evidence alone, but he seems to hold it sufficient to justify the judge in proceeding to the application of torture to elicit further evidence or a confession of guilt. Thus it is not merely occult doctrine which Libavius defends but a life and death matter of legal practice and criminal procedure. Bad beliefs seldom remain isolated in some purely intellectual domain, they almost inevitably foment evil customs.

Libavius has been called "the first chemist of note in Germany who stood up manfully against the excesses of Paracelsus and who vigorously combatted the defects in his doctrine, the obscurities in his writings, his phantasies and sophisms, and the employment of 'secret remedies.' "[8] This does not mean that he was opposed to alchemy or to iatrochemistry. His position was rather about half way between that of Paracelsus and his opponents. Indeed, he has sometimes been called a follower of Paracelsus. In 1594 he published *Neo-Paracelsica*. In his textbook on *Alchymia* or *Alchemia,* published at Frankfurt in 1597 and again in 1606[9] and 1615, he defined alchemy as the art of accomplishing masteries and extracting pure essences from compounds by separating the body, while Chymia or chemistry was the second part of Alchemia and concerned with making chemical species. Libavius still held to the doctrine of a fifth essence and quoted liberally from the alchemical works attributed to Arnald of Villanova and Raymond Lull. He defended the art of alchemy against the censure of the Parisian medical faculty.

Among the topics treated in Libavius's textbook are distillation, co-liquefaction, exaltation, digestion, circulation, fermentation, projection, gradation, cementation, fulmination, coloring, the mastery of changed consistency while preserving the substance as in potable metals, the mastery of increased weight, of touch, color, heightened odor, taste. Other topics are the altera-

[8] Ernst von Meyer, *Geschichte der Chemie,* 4th edition, 1914, pp. 70-71.

[9] Libavius, *Alchymia . . . recognita emendata et aucta tum dogmatibus et experimentis nonnullis tum commentario medico-physico-chemico . . . praemissa defensione artis opposita censurae Parisianae,* 1606. Copy used: BM 535.k.5.

tion of the sound of metals by chemistry, the vitrification of metals, lithosis, reduction to ashes, pyrotechnics, the azoth of the philosophers, mineral waters, tinctures, oils, spirits, alkali, crystals, vitriol, flowers and chemical compounds.

In his professed opposition to Paracelsus it is doubtful how far Libavius correctly represents the ideas of Paracelsus. He calls him impious, whereas he was actually devout. He keeps imputing fantastic and magical notions to him, giving at best an extreme and one-sided picture of his doctrine. Thus he ascribes to him a prescription of electrum and mixture of metals compounded under a certain constellation and inscribed with certain characters. He tells of a follower of Paracelsus who tried to cure the daughter of a friend of his of pain in the side by applying a certain herb which had been boiled and then burying the herb to putrefy, with the idea that the complaint would simultaneously disappear. But the pain remained. Anent the belief that incense made of alcohol and human blood will not cease to burn so long as the man whose blood it contains lives, Libavius remarks that Paracelsus describes a remedy against gout in which human blood is thrice distilled and taken by the patient without his knowing for what it is administered. Libavius rejects this remedy as a most impudent lie.[10] "We know," he says again, "that certain devotees of chemistry differ little from magicians and, like that impious Paracelsus, construct from the motion of the stars and from the constellations magic mirrors, gems, globes, and many similar devices for exploring the future and predicting the occurrence of disease."[11] In his work on mineral waters Libavius enlarges on "the stolidity of Paracelsus,"[12] and says that "Paracelsus, as in many other matters he is stupid and uncertain, so also here writes like a madman."[13] Yet in the same volume Libavius cites approvingly such medieval alchemical au-

[10] *Tract. duo physici*, 1594, pp. 36-37, 39, 49.

[11] *Alchymia . . . recognita*, 1606, p. 181.

[12] Libavius, *De natura metallorum et cognatorum mineralium*, Frankfurt, 1597. Copy used: BM 1033.h.i.(3.). De iudicio aquarum mineralium occupies pp. 275-392. For the quotation see II, 68, p. 363.

[13] *Ibid.*, II, 44, p. 337.

thors and works as the pseudo-Aquinas and the *Emerald Tablet,* or discusses such topics as azoth, *aqua permanens,* and the philosophers' stone.[14]

Nicolas Guibert was the author of two works against alchemy in the early years of the seventeenth century. First in 1603 he published at Strasburg his *Alchemy Impugned by Reason and Experience.*[15] He says that he has spent forty years in chemical experiments, both applying manual industry and reading everything for and against alchemy that he could lay hands on. He has come to the conclusion that metals are species and that species cannot be transmuted. "From privation to possession [*habitus*] there is no regress, and generation is not circular." Iron cannot be changed into copper. Guibert rejects all such arguments from analogy for the transmutation of metals as the change from worm to butterfly, hatching eggs by heat, or alterations in plants. Books of alchemy are of no authority and were not composed by their pretended authors but by the most sordid and abject impostors. The *Emerald Tablet* is not by Hermes, and the alchemical writings attributed to Avicenna, Albertus Magnus, and Aquinas are all spurious. That Arnald of Villanova and Raymond Lull wrote alchemical treatises Guibert does not deny, but he discredits them as quacks, deluded by demons, and heretics. His ignorance concerning them is shown by his making Lull flourish about 1254. Although Albertus is acquitted of alchemical writing, Guibert says that he was over-curious and sometimes made idle statements. Guibert's ignorance of the true history of the alchemical literature of the fourteenth century is further displayed in his representing Rupescissa's work on the fifth essence as "transcribed from Raymond" Lull. Roger Bacon is stigmatized as an ignoble, stupid and impious author of no weight,

[14] Book II of *De natura metallorum* is De mercurio philosophorum in dialogue form; book III is De azoth et aqua permanente philosophorum; book IV at pp. 97-160 is De lapide philosophorum.

[15] Nicolaus Guibertus, *Alchymia ratione et experientia ita demum viriliter impugnata et expugnata una cum suis fallaciis et deliramentis quibus homines imbubinarat ut numquam in posterum se erigere valeat,* Argentorati, Impensis Lazari Zetzneri Bibliopolae, MDCIII, 104 pp. Copy used: BM 1033.f.8.(1.2.).

given to every kind of superstition and vanity, including astrology and magic as well as alchemy. Paracelsus is cursed even more violently as a limb of Satan and the world's worst liar—which is, however, repaying him in his own coin. Agrippa is not dealt with much more mildly, nor do Ficino and Fernel escape censure. Some recent impostors in alchemy are also mentioned. Marcus Bragadinus, after deceiving many eminent men at Venice, came to the duke of Bavaria but in 1591 confessed to fraud in order to escape torture.[16] Angelus Siculus by sleight of hand feigned transmutation before the very eyes of Gregory XIII. Later he went to Spain, where Philip II would have nothing to do with him, and to Naples, where he died in extreme poverty.[17] Both these impostors are again mentioned in Guibert's *De interitu alchemiae* of 1614.[18] In his earlier work he also refers to a goldsmith, Leonard Turnifer, who played the Paracelsus for a while and deceived many princes, magnates and learned men.[19] Probably Thurneisser is meant.[20]

In 1604 Libavius composed a *Defense of Transmutatory Alchemy* against Guibert's attack of 1603. The latter replied with an *Apology against the Sophist Libavius, Raging Calumniator of Alchymia Refutata,* which was printed with his *De interitu alchemiae* of 1614. In this work Guibert says that he was told, both by Battista Porta at Naples and by Domenico Pizzimenti at Rome under Gregory XIII that they had once succeeded in converting quicksilver into silver by heating a toad with it in an earthen pot over a slow fire, until the parched toad absorbed a good part of the mercury and finally was consumed by the fire. But they never could attain the same result again. Pizzimenti was Porta's teacher in the classics and claimed to be the actual author of his pupil's work on *Natural Magic* as first pub-

[16] His career is fully treated by Ivo Striedinger, "Der Goldmacher Marco Bragadino, Archivkundliche Studie zur Kulturgeschichte des 16. Jahrhunderts," Munich, 1928, in *Archivalische Zeitschrift herausg. vom Bayerischen Hauptstaatsarchiv,* II, Beiheft, 379 pp.

[17] Guibertus, *Alchymia,* 1603, pp. 88-90.

[18] At pp. 99-100.

[19] *Alchymia,* 1603, p. 92.

[20] His career is treated at length by J. C. W. Moehsen, *Beiträge zur Geschichte der Wissenschaften in der Mark Brandenburg,* 1783.

lished. Guibert recognizes that Porta had greatly altered it in subsequent editions, "but it still requires expurgation." Guibert had heard recently from Rome that Porta, now a very old man, still pretended to know the secret of making gold, but never actually made any.[21]

Guibert was also sharply criticized by Hoghelande in a note to the reader at the close of his life of Raymond Lull.[22] Hoghelande accused Guibert of repeating Eymeric's false statements concerning Lull, and further objected to Guibert's strictures against Arnald of Villanova and Roger Bacon. He asserted that, although Guibert had spent some forty years studying chemistry with all his might and main, he had failed to grasp even its elements.

The *De interitu alchemiae* or *Destruction of Alchemy* of Guibert consists of three parts. The chief purpose of the first section is to show that there is no support for alchemy in the Bible. It is proved from the Book of Genesis that no procreating or seminal force was implanted in stones and metals at creation, and that they differ in species as well as accidents. Other passages of Scripture are cited against alchemy, while those which the alchemists adduce from Scripture in their favor are refuted. So is their interpretation of the Sibylline books, and it is denied that alchemy is to be accepted as divinely revealed.

In the next section it is asserted that there is no evidence for the existence of alchemy in classical antiquity. The Argonautic expedition and garden of the Hesperides should not be so interpreted. Pliny and other authors are examined and held to give no indication of the existence of alchemy in their own or more remote times. A passage mentioning the art in the astrological work of Julius Firmicus Maternus is declared to be a later interpolation, and Hermolaus Barbarus in the fifteenth century is said to have been the first to tell of a chest found near Padua in which was an earthen vessel containing one of silver, within

[21] *De interitu alchemiae,* 1614, pp. 134-35. Copy used: BM 1033.g.10.

[22] Ewaldus de Hoghelande, *Historiae aliquot transmutationis . . . pro defensione alchymiae . . . Adiecta est . . . R. Lullii vita,* Cologne, 1604, pp. 49-50.

which was yet another of gold, and in it a lamp still burning after many centuries.

The third section on the detection of the legerdemain and impostures of the alchemists (*chymicorum*) attributes their occasional seeming successes to demon aid and repeats, chiefly at third hand, a number of stories which suggest that it was no lack of credulity that led Guibert to attack alchemy.

In the first years of the seventeenth century a complicated controversy developed at Paris between certain Paracelsists, or rather advocates of chemical remedies, and the medical faculty. In 1603 Joseph Duchesne or Quesne[23] or Quercetanus published *De materia verae medicinae philosophorum priscorum*, in which he maintained the truth of the three principles, salt, sulphur and mercury, and, according to his opponents, opposed the fundamental doctrines and accustomed remedies of Hippocratic medicine. Duchesne (c.1544-1609), although born in Armagnac, had studied in Switzerland, receiving his M.D. degree at Basel in 1573, where he had probably become acquainted with the theories of Paracelsus, and serving at Geneva on the council of two hundred. In 1575 he became involved in a controversy with Jacques Aubert who had attacked the Paracelsans in his *De metallorum ortu et causis*.[24] In 1593 he returned to Paris and became physician to Henry IV. His vanity and his scorn for other physicians are said to have made him hated by them, although Riolan affirmed in 1606 that he was formerly on good terms with the physicians of Paris. But his book of 1603 was condemned by the medical faculty.

Thereupon another royal physician published an attack upon the faculty. This was Theodore Turquet de Mayerne (1573-1655), whose previous career had somewhat resembled that of Duchesne. The son of a Protestant historian who at the time of the massacre of St. Bartholomew's in 1572 had fled to Geneva, Turquet attended school there and then studied medicine at

[23] The article on him in Moreri's *Dictionary* occurs under this form of his name.

[24] See Paul Delaunay, "Les médecins manceaux en Suisse au seizième siècle," *Ve Cong. Internat. d'Hist. de la Méd.*, Geneva, 1926, pp. 55-56.

Heidelberg and Montpellier, receiving his M.D. in 1597. He then came to Paris and began to lecture in 1602, chiefly, however, to the young surgeons and apothecaries. The faculty of medicine now condemned his attack upon them and he ceased to lecture. Some years later he left France for England, becoming in 1611 first physician to James I, whose court seems to have been a haven for fugitive fakirs or storm-tossed scientists from the continent. Mayerne treated many of the English nobility, concocted cosmetics for the queen, composed in 1612 a good account of the attack of typhoid fever of which prince Henry died, and in 1616 became a fellow of the London College of Physicians. His works were much read through the rest of the century and a collected edition of them appeared at London in 1703. Besides these, twenty-three volumes of manuscripts in the Sloane collection at the British Museum are filled with records of his cases, while others contain his chemical and physical experiments.

To return to Paris and Duchesne. Despite the condemnation of his first book, Duchesne wrote another affirming that salt, mercury and sulphur were not only in all inferior elements and compounds but also in the heavens. The faculty condemned it likewise, although Riolan states that their censure was directed not against Duchesne but the doctrine which he defended. Duchesne then sought the aid of two physicians of Orléans, Guillaume Bauchinet and Israel Harvet. The former contributed *Scholia in apologiam et censuram medicorum Parisiensium*. According to Riolan, however, who of course, speaks for the medical faculty, Bauchinet withdrew from the controversy when he learned that the faculty had not condemned chemical remedies or new preparations but a fourth sect which conflicted with their dogmas, employed mineral rather than plant or animal remedies, and tried to cure like by like. Harvetus, on the other hand, clung to the fray, nor did he and Riolan desist until each had replied thrice, the final publication by Harvet in that particular series of duels apparently being his *Demonstration of the Truth of Chemical Doctrine against Jean Riolan's Comparison of the Old Medicine with the New*.

Libavius was now drawn into the conflict. Thereupon Riolan in yet another publication of 1606 expressed his amazement that Libavius should dare to resist the opinions of so many select doctors, adding that the school of Paris out of fifty doctors could select at least ten any one of whom could completely overwhelm Libavius in debate. But since Libavius had challenged him in particular, he replied.[25] Libavius thereupon in 1607 in a book of nine hundred pages[26] took up this work of Riolan sentence by sentence, after an opening chapter of one hundred pages in which he rehearsed the previous history of the controversy. Nor was Duchesne himself silenced, for in 1607 he published at Paris a *Restored Pharmacopeia of the Dogmatics Illustrated with Precious and Select Flowers of the Hermetics.*

It might prove too tedious to attempt to outline all the arguments of these various works, but some further indication of their general drift may be given. The full title of Duchesne's first book was *De materia verae medicinae philosophorum priscorum deque modo praeparationis et in curandis morbis praestantia—Of the Matter of the True Medicine of the Ancient Philosophers and the Method of Preparation and Superiority in Curing Diseases.* With it he published two tractates on signatures and one book on the legitimate preparation of the medicaments of dogmatic medicine. In his preface he added to the three sects of Empirics, Methodics and Dogmatics a fourth called Spagiric, which he said was new to some persons but to followers of the Hermetic art was most ancient. He further dilated upon a medicinal fifth essence present in all things. Although it was a spiritual, celestial, invisible and occult substance, more subject to reason than to the senses, he promised in a book on the recondite nature of things and mysteries of art to show that it existed and could be obtained by a true philosopher.

An anonymous *Apology for the Medicine of Hippocrates and Galen against Duchesne* is ascribed by Libavius to Riolan. First

[25] *Ad Libavii maniam J. Riolani responsio pro censura Scholae Parisiensis contra Alchymiam lata,* Paris, 1606. Copy used: BM 1032.b.4.

[26] Libavius, *Alchymia triumphans de iniusta in se Collegii Galenici Spurii in Acad. Paris. censura . . . ,* 1607. Copy used: BM 1032.a.18.

in it comes a petition of the College of Medicine to the Parlement of Paris to prosecute the Chymiatri or Iatrochemists, with the assertion that not one physician in sixty agrees with Duchesne. The *Apology* then denies that Hermes or Democritus was an alchemist, while it asserts that Paracelsus admitted that alchemy was an invention of the devil, that Duchesne's fourth sect is really just a branch of the Empirics, and that Chymia is not an independent art or science but subordinate to pharmacy as pharmacy is to medicine. Chemists can amplify pharmacopias by many formulae of distillations but such new preparations alone do not constitute a new art or science. Objection is made to the Spagirists' practice of preparing their remedies at home on the grounds that the professions of physician and pharmacist should be kept distinct. The *Apology* further argues that the world could get along without chemical remedies as it did in the good old days of Hippocrates and Galen, that the old tested remedies are safer than such new drugs as antimony, and that the chemists take the old remedies themselves while prescribing the new for others. Extracts and essences are inferior to the old simple and compound medicines, and distillations to the old decoctions. Salt is not a principle of natural things, and the atoms of Democritus were quite different from salt, mercury and sulphur. Gold or potable gold as a medicine is opposed, and nitre is declared an ingredient of that diabolical invention, gunpowder. Gold-making and the transmutation of metals are denied and condemned. Each metal is perfect in its species and not a crude imperfect form of gold. The art of the fifth essence and of the philosophers' stone are not the same, and there is no fifth essence in this sublunar world.

To this *Apologia* Duchesne replied in a treatise divided into two books. In the former he held that he had never departed from the dogmatic school of Hippocrates, that he condemned the Paracelsists, but had imitated such good old authors as Raymond Lull, Roger Bacon, Ripley, Rupescissa and Christopher of Paris. He further contended that the physicians of old used to prepare medicaments with their own hands and knew of the extraction of salts and of metallic medicines. He further pointed out that some of the old medicines were dangerous, while some chemical prescriptions were quite salubrious. His second book was then devoted to the tenet derived from John of Rupescissa that, as the philosophers' stone transmutes metals, so the fifth essence transmutes the diseased human body to a healthy condition.

Riolan and Duchesne answered each other once more, but we pass on to the work of Israel Harvet. He ignored the transmutation of metals but praised the careful methods and elaborate processes of chemical laboratories. He complained that other universities had not been consulted, at which alchemy was no less flourishing than at Paris. He argued that the old medicines no longer sufficed for the many new diseases prevalent today, that in the past medicine had taken new ideas from the Arabs and others, and should not hesitate to expand now. Diagnosis was not the sum total of medicine, and the safer remedy was not always the better one. It was silly to say that distillation destroyed the force of purgatives, since these were seldom prepared by that method. It was false to hold that there was no acute disease without fever, or that drugs acted materially, not formally. Finally, contending that Riolan did not understand the dispute as to cure by like or contraries, Harvet affirmed that one should use like remedies if one wished to preserve the nature of a part of the body, but contrary medicines to expel a disease which one was fighting.

Petrus Palmarius (Pierre Le Paulmier?) in two treatises which were printed in 1609[27] took up a position against both

[27] Petrus Palmarius, *Lapis philosophicus dogmaticorum quo Paracelsista librarius restituitur, scholae medicae Parisiensis iudicium de chymicis declaratur, censura in adulteria et fraudes Parachymicorum deffenditur asserto verae alchemiae honore . . . Adiecta est historia laeprosae mulieris persanatae*, Paris, 1609, 8vo. Copy used: BM 1033.e.43.

Laurus Palmaria fugans ventaneum fulmen cyclopum aliquot falso scholae Parisiensis nomine evulgatum in librum P. Palmarii, Paris, 1609, 8vo. Copy used: BM 1180.b.1.(5.).

According to Ferguson II, 163, "Paulmier or Palmarius was the nephew of Julien Le Paulmier who wrote on gunshot wounds. He was born in 1568, studied at Paris, graduated M.D. and was physician in the Hôtel-Dieu. He died 15 Jan. 1610."

Paracelsan sophistry and Libavius, posing as a supporter of the old medicine and pharmacy, of the school of Paris, and of such writers as Riolan and Sylvius, Mesue and Avicenna, Rasis and Geber. But he favored chemical preparations and the fifth essence. He believed that the superior world rules the inferior by motion, influence and light.[28] He asserted that not all minerals were poisons, and that not all vegetables and animals were salutary.[29] The simple remedies and regimen of Hippocrates he believed no longer adequate in these degenerate days when human nature is weakened by luxury and intemperance. Art, especially that of the chemist, was helpful in remedying this defect of nature.[30] But he preferred to the drugs of Paracelsus or of Libavius the medicines of the Parisians. If Paracelsus's remedies were so efficacious, why did he himself fail to reach old age? Palmarius cited the case of a leprous woman whom three years' treatment by Hermetic and Libavian drugs failed to benefit and whom he cured by giving her potable gold on the first day and antimony, but not the vulgar variety, on the second day.[31]

Some opponents of Palmarius issued objections against him under the name of the medical school of Paris, charging that he really condemned Parisian pharmacy and medicine, that he made alchemy as old or older than medicine, that he usurped the name of Galenochymicus, and that, while he reproved common alchemists for their obscurity, he was in reality even obscurer himself. Such charges excited the ire of Palmarius and he replied with abusive names.[32]

Libavius was also one of the many authors who wrote on the comet of 1604, but his *Declamation* concerning it seems not to have been published until 1641 or 1665 by Voetius. It covers about a dozen pages. Libavius attempted to reconcile the Aristotelian doctrine of comets with recent astronomical observations and calculations by suggesting that the recent new but not last-

[28] *Laurus*, p. 57.
[29] *Ibid.*, p. 71.
[30] *Lapis*, cap. 22, pp. 117-18.
[31] *Ibid.*, cap. 33, p. 161.
[32] *Laurus*, p. 23 and thereabouts. Ferguson II, 163, accepts the censure of the *Lapis* of Palmarius by the medical faculty on January 28, 1609, as genuine and signed by the dean, George Cornuty.

ing stars beyond the sphere of the moon be called celestial comets, but that the terrestrial exhalations of the Peripatetics be also accepted as comets of another category. Toward prediction from comets Libavius showed himself rather luke-warm. It grieved him that men should pay more attention to a new comet than to the marvelous everlasting stars and heavens. He contended that, if the star of 1604 was not a comet, astrologers should not predict from it as they would from a comet. He also noted disagreement between past astrologers. Roeslin thought that the effects of the new star of 1572 would not be felt until after thirty years. He predicted happy events from that of 1604, while others foretold nothing but evil from it. Cardan listed comets among a half dozen great occurrences in the sky. These included also conjunctions of Saturn and Jupiter, but later Libavius states that Cardan did not think much of them because the beginning of the conjunction is unobservable. On the other hand, Thobias Mollerus—who had regarded the new star of 1572 as favorable—and others prognosticated from such conjunctions above all, especially that of 1583 whose events he set for 1588 or 1590. "And indeed the Spanish Armada was then overcome by the English." The geometer of Wolfenbüttel, Johannes Crabbe, predicted all dire events from the comet, Eliseus Roeslin—as Libavius has said before—all favorable. Libavius objects to astrologers pretending to read in the stars what "we have already read in the prophecy of Carion." He then turns to the Bible for the last two pages of his *Declamation*.[33]

Jacques Fontaine in his medical works printed in 1613 quoted Libavius extensively against the Paracelsists, although he thought that Libavius was at times too favorable towards alchemy.[34]

[33] And. Libavius, *Declamatio de cometa anno 1604,* Amsterdam, 1665. Copy used: BM 532.e.16.(3.). The catalogue lists another edition of Amsterdam, 1641.

[34] Jacobus Fontanus, *Opera omnia medica,* Cologne, 1613, pp. 750-61.

CHAPTER XXXVIII

THE SIXTEENTH CENTURY NATURALISTS

Buffon, qui a signalé les défauts de l'Histoire naturelle d'Aldrovandi, dit cependant que l'auteur 'a été le plus laborieux et le plus savant des naturalistes'; et il ajoute que 'ses livres doivent être regardés comme ce qu'il y a de mieux sur la totalité de l'histoire naturelle.'

—LIBRI

Interest in natural history appeared in the first part of the sixteenth century chiefly in connection with herbals and with commentaries on Dioscorides which also dealt mainly with plants. On the linguistic and literary side the attack by Leonicenus in the closing decade of the previous century upon Pliny's pharmaceutical and botanical nomenclature and Latin rendering of Greek names seems to have set something of a fashion. Dryander in an oration of 1536 at Marburg remarked on the amazing fact that today the schools were at swords' points concerning any little herb whose name had been incorrectly rendered by this or that author.[1] In the way of practical fieldwork such botanizing excursions as those into the Alps by Simon de Phares in the second half of the fifteenth century now come increasingly to our notice—for instance, in the case of Gesner as a boy[2] and the *Botanologicon* of Euricius Cordus—and result ultimately in

[1] Edition of 1537, fol. c iii verso: "Mirum quantum hodie de herbula quapiam perperam apud hunc vel illum autorem pronuntiata digladientur scholae."

[2] Gesner continued to make such botanical excursions in later life, for Caspar Wolf, writing in 1587, reminded Peter Hafner, a surgeon of Zurich, of Gesner's delight in collecting herbs and that Hafner had often accompanied him upon mountain excursions or longer travels. See Wolf's dedication of the posthumous edition of Gesner's *Historiae insectorum libellus.*

Belon travelled with Valerius Cordus and other students through Saxony, Thuringia, Pomerania and Bohemia and later gathered botanical specimens with Cordus near Leghorn. See Paul Delaunay, "L'aventureuse existence de Pierre Belon du Mans," *Revue du seizième siècle,* IX (1922), 251-68.

the appearance of works which display an intimate acquaintance with the plants themselves, such as those by Brasavola, Hieronymus Bock (Tragus) and Valerius Cordus. Ioannes Hessus of Nürnberg, who wrote to Mattioli in 1559, had travelled extensively in Italy, Germany and France in compiling his catalogue of plants.[3]

Few new works on animals, and those of a slight character, were printed during the first half of the sixteenth century. Paolo Giovio wrote on Roman fish;[4] Petrus Gillius, on those of Marseilles.[5] Gesner was searching in 1555 for a treatise on fish in the Baltic by a Thuringian doctor of laws, named Nicolaus Marescallus, which he said had been printed at Rostock thirty years before.[6] During the summer of 1540 the intolerable heat[7] forced Carolus Figulus to postpone his journey to Paris and pause at Cologne. He published there a brief dialogue on fish in the Moselle with citation of Ausonius.[8] Among the friends he made at Cologne was Gybertus Longolius of Utrecht (1507-1543), a doctor of arts and medicine who taught at Deventer, then Latin and Greek at Cologne, where he also practiced medicine. Figulus complained that the senate of Cologne paid Longolius only forty gold pieces annually, and that he was too occupied with care of the sick to finish a work on herbs which would obscure all those of his predecessors. Longolius was presently called to the university of Rostock but, when he returned to Cologne to get his

[3] *Petri Andr. Matthioli Epistolarum lib. III*, Francofurti, 1598, pp. 112-15.

[4] Gesner (1545), fol. 538v, mentions an edition of Basel, Froben, 1531, 8vo. I have not seen the work.

[5] Printed with his translation of Aelian, Lyons, 1533, 4to: Gesner (1545), fol. 549v.

[6] Georgius Fabricius, *Epistolae ad W. Meurer et alios . . .*, nunc primum edidit Baumgarten-Crusius, 1845, p. 105. Gesner (1604), and the British Museum catalogue date the edition more precisely in 1520, with a third volume of illustrations dated 1517. Another work which Gesner was seeking in this letter of 1555 was Dubravius on fishpools or *piscinae*.

[7] According to Stadius, *Ephemerides novae*, Cologne, 1556, fol. A 3 verso, this hot summer had been forecast by conjunctions of the planets in hot signs: "sic in calidis signis maximos aestus anno 1540."

[8] *Ichthyologia seu dialogus de piscibus autore Carolo Figulo*, Coloniae ex officina Eucharii (Cervicorni) anno 1540 mense Iulio, 4to minori. Copy used: BM 1257.d.20.

Gesner (1545), fol. 162r, speaks of Figulus as "recently of Coblentz" and further ascribes to him a treatise *De mustellis*, also printed at Cologne.

library, fell ill and was buried at Bonn.[9] A dialogue on birds and their Greek, Latin and German names, which he had nearly finished and which imitates Brasavola, was published in 1544,[10] the year after his death, with a dedicatory letter by William Turner.[11] Turner said that recently Ruelle, Fuchs, Brasavola, Cordus and Gesner had written on herbs, while Paolo Giovio, Massarius of Venice,[12] and Pierre Gilles had aided one in comprehending what Aristotle and Pliny had to say of fish. But concerning birds, so far as Turner knew, no modern except Pierre Gilles had written anything until Longolius. Longolius himself complained that Aristotle and Aelian among the Greeks, Pliny and Nemesius of the Romans, had described birds more meagerly than any other phase of nature. Since Nemesius was a Christian writing in Greek about 400 A.D., and the sole extant work by him is on human physiology and psychology (*peri physeos anthropou*), this allusion to him by Longolius seems more pretentious than accurate. He praised Raphael Volaterranus (Maffeius) for having done what he could—presumably in annotations on some of these ancient authors—but rejected "Albertus monachus" as a barbarian who wrote much which neither he nor anyone else had seen. "Aside from these you will hardly find anyone worth reading." Surprise is expressed by the other participant in the dialogue that Longolius did not mention Ioannes Carus who, "navigating with his Spaniards, depicted some prodigious forms of birds." Longolius replies that Carus indulged in travellers' yarns. When asked point-blank if he deems him not worth reading, he says that many who seek after novelty would approve of him, if he did not along with his barbarian birds speak a barbarous tongue.[13]

[9] Gesner (1545), fol. 295r-v, Zedler, and Figulus, *Botanomethodus,* Cologne, 1540, fol. B iii recto.

[10] *Dialogus de avibus et earum nominibus Graecis Latinis et Germanicis per Dn. Gybertum Longolium artium et medicinae doctorem clarissimum paulo ante mortem conscriptus. Epitaphium authoris ad libelli finem adiecimus.* Coloniae excudebat Io. Gymnicus anno MDXLIIII.

[11] It is dated "Coloniae decimo calend. Februarii anno MDXLIIII."

[12] The allusion is to Francesco Massari's commentary on the ninth book of Pliny's *Natural History,* printed at Basel in 1537 and Paris in 1542. It was the sole work by him known to Gesner who states (1545), fol. 251v, that he died prematurely.

[13] *Dialogus de avibus,* fol. B r-v. "Carus" is apparently a misprint for

Other works on animals were of a literary and poetical rather than scientific character. Paul Belmisserus, a doctor and professor of Bologna, where he taught between 1512 and 1519,[14] turned the first two books of Aristotle's *History of Animals* into Latin elegiacs, which were printed at Rome in 1534.[15] Ursinus in his *Prosopoeia animalium* made a number of familiar animals, about the same group as were included in the bestiaries, speak of themselves in the first person in verse recounting especially their medicinal virtues. These little poems, sometimes hardly more than a couplet, were embroidered by Jacobus Olivarius with a marginal prose commentary,[16] in which he added anything that he happened to know and that the poet had left out, such as the old story of the viper's conception and delivery which had been denied in 1499 by Franciscus Caballus of Brescia.[17]

Only towards the middle of the century, when were composed and published the works on birds of Turner and Belon, that of Rondelet on fish,[18] and the general history of animals of Gesner,

---

Canus, the person meant being probably Juan Sebastian del Cano.

[14] Dallari, *I rotuli,* consult the Index.

[15] Gesner (1545), fol. 536v.

[16] Io. Ursinus, *Prosopoeia animalium aliquot in qua multa de eorum viribus natura proprietatibus praecipue ad rem medicam pertinentibus continentur versibus elegiacis,* Apud Mathiam Bonhomme, Vienne, 1541, 4to, 55 pp. Copy used: BM 954.f.27. See also Gesner (1545), fol. 462r. The *Prosopoeia* was printed again in four books with a commentary by J. M. Simoneta, Papiae, 1552, 8vo: BM 727.b.1.(1.).

[17] T IV, 597, n.9.

[18] Scaliger accused Rondelet, Scévola de Sainte Marthe accused Belon, and the historian de Thou charged both Belon and Rondelet with having attached their names to the work of others. In de Thou's account of Petrus Gillius, who died in 1555 after travelling for Francis I in the Levant, Belon is said to have been his amanuensis, to have absconded with some of his manuscripts, and to have published them under his own name: Iac. Aug. Thuanus, *Historiarum sui temporis ab a.d. 1543 usque ad annum 1607 libri CXXXVIII,* close of Bk. XVI. Sc. de Sainte-Marthe, *Gallorum doctrina illustrium Elogia,* 1598, 1602, 1606. Concerning these charges against Belon see further Paul Delaunay, "L'aventureuse existence de Pierre Belon (7e article)," *Revue du seizième siècle,* XII (1925), 259-63.

Rondelet is said to have plagiarized a commentary in manuscript on Pliny's *Natural History* by Guillaume Pellicier, bishop of Montpellier: see Robert Hamilton, Memoir of Rondelet, prefixed to his *History of British Fishes,* 1876, I, 44. Aldrovandi praised the learning of Pellicier and gave him credit for having taught Rondelet the difference between the *sturio* and *galeum Rhodeum: De piscibus,* 1613, p. 532. The charges against Rondelet and Belon do not appear to have ever been substantiated, and for our present purpose the question of authorship between them and Gillius and Pellicier is of slight importance.

could there be said to be any extensive publication in the field of zoology. Such publication culminated in the series of heavy tomes by Aldrovandi which followed one another at the very end of the century and during many years of the seventeenth century. Meanwhile the study of botany continued, although to a large extent in connection with pharmacy, until at the beginning of the last quarter of the century it was represented by such works as those of Dodoens and Lobel.[19]

In the preface to the reader of his first volume on birds Aldrovandi listed leading authors on natural history of the sixteenth century: among Frenchmen Ruellius, Pierre Belon, Jacobus Sylvius, Fernel, Rondelet, and Dalechamps, the editor of Pliny. Of Germans, Valerius Cordus, Hieronymus Tragus, Joachim Camerarius the son, the two Bauhin brothers, John and Gaspar, Dodoens, Lobel, Clusius, and Melchior Guilandinus. Among Italians, Julius Caesar Scaliger, Petrus Andreas Matthiolus, Bartholomaeus Maranta,[20] Antonius Brasavolus, Andrea Cesalpino, Andrea Bacci, Giovanni Battista Porta, Hieronymus Mercurialis, Iohannes Costaeus Laudensis,[21] Fabius Columna, Massarius of Venice, Luca Ghini (once his teacher), and two former prefects of the botanical garden at Padua, Aloysius Anguillara[22] and Iacobus Antonius Cortusus.[23] Of Spaniards, Amatus Lusitanus,[24] Andreas Lacuna,[25] Garcia da Orta, and Franciscus Valesius. He does not here list the Englishmen Turner, Wotton and

[19] The important work of Cesalpino, printed in 1583, will be considered in our separate chapter upon him. I have not seen the following treatises which appeared later in the closing years of the century: Castore Durante, *Herbario nuovo,* Romae, 1585, folio; Joannes Gerhardus, *Historia plantarum,* London, 1597, folio.

[20] Author of *Metodo de' semplici medicamenti,* 1558; Latin edition, 1559; and *Della theriaca et del Mithridato,* Venice, Olmo, 1572.

[21] Giovanni Costeo of Lodi taught medicine at Turin and Bologna and published various works including *De universali stirpium natura,* Turin, 1578.

[22] Luigi Anguillara, *Semplici li quali in più pareri ecc.,* Venice, 1561.

[23] Jacopo Antonio Cortuso, *L'horto dei semplici di Padova,* Venice, 1591.

[24] Harry Friedenwald, "Amatus Lusitanus," *Bulletin* of the Institute of the History of Medicine, V (1937), 603-53.

[25] Joaquin Olmedilla y Puig, *Estudio Historico de la Vida y Escritos del sabio Español Andrea Laguna,* Madrid, 1887. His reactionary anatomy has been mentioned in our chapter on that subject.

Eliot, although they are elsewhere cited in his works, but the most notable omission is the name of Conrad Gesner, whose work on animals bore the closest resemblance to Aldrovandi's and was most used by him.

During his summer at Cologne Figulus not only published the brief dialogue on fish but a more pretentious dialogue on method in the study of herbs.[26] He said that, while many had written on herbs, no one had told how they were to be sought and recognized. His own essay towards a botanical method must be regarded as extremely elementary, not to say puerile, but he asserts that the matter is difficult, new and "recently born at our house."[27] Herbs are distinguished as wild or found in gardens, in swamps or on mountains, annual or perennial, as flowering at different seasons, as named after their inventors or other persons, by their size, figure, color, odor, taste, and virtue or degree of hot, cold, dry and moist. The botany of Figulus remained markedly Christian. He declared Christ the author of the world and of herbs. Nor is He like a ship-builder who gives the vessel over to sailors and the mercy of the waves. He preserves and sustains the things created by him and still daily creates. Grains of wheat and herbs are manifest signs of our future resurrection. The phyllitis of Dioscorides lacks flower and seed, and so must be propagated directly by Christ. Nor are those to be heeded who ascribe the origin of things to secondary causes and assert that species are propagated only by their kind. Herbs were created before the stars. Hence they grow from earth not by the influence of the stars but by the power of the divine Word. We should pray to Him to grant us knowledge of all herbs such as He gave to Adam, who "undoubtedly could call each herb by its proper name," whereas today you will scarcely find any man who can name three hundred correctly. A Jewish physician who came from Italy to Saxony knew the Hebrew names of all the

[26] *Dialogus qui inscribitur Botanomethodus autore Carolo Figulo, opus nunc recens natum et in lucem editum,* Coloniae apud Iohannem Schoenstenium prope divi Pauli, anno MDXL. Copy used: BM 968.k.1.(1.). Across the top of the title page is written, "Bibliothecae Colbertinae."

[27] *Ibid.,* fol. A ii recto.

herbs and *ipso facto* knew their virtues too, although he had never read Hippocrates, Galen or Avicenna.[28] Many old wives know herbs better than many members of the medical profession do.[29] Which is perhaps enough of the figments of Figulus, except to note that he affirmed that he cured a man who was nearly blind from cataract by use of swallow-wort (chelidonia) with which the birds were supposed to restore the sight of their young.[30]

Another and somewhat more advanced effort at botanical method was made by Bartolomeo Maranta of Venosa in his *Method of Knowing Simples,* which was published in Italian in 1558 and in Latin in 1559.[31] His three standards for classification were nomenclature, delineation and properties, to which his division into three books corresponds. The work was undertaken at the suggestion of his teacher, Luca Ghini, now dead, and was submitted for approval to Falloppia who encouraged Maranta to publish it.[32] Maranta thought that no one could compare with Dioscorides in correct description of plants, but he recognized that many unknown to Dioscorides had been found since. He felt that ignorance concerning simples was largely due to lack of perseverance and iteration in their employment as medicaments, and that preparing medicaments was the best way to become acquainted with simples. This suggests that in his case the medical outran the botanical interest. He included such magical lore as that, if men ate the greater root of the plant testiculus,

[28] *Ibid.,* fols. B recto—B ii verso, C verso, C ii verso.

[29] *Ibid.,* fol. B iv verso.

[30] *Ibid.,* fol. C recto. Bound with the dialogue of Figulus in this volume is the abusive *Apology* of Melchior Guilandinus against Petrus Andreas Matthiolus, Patavii apud Gratiosum Perchacinum, 1558; then *De stirpibus aliquot epistolae V,* also by Guilandinus and of the same place, date and printer; then two works by Fabio Colonna, *Phytobasanos sive plantarum aliquot historia,* Ex officina Horatii Salviani, Neapoli, MDXCII, and *Piscium aliquot plantarumque novarum historia.*

[31] *Bartholomei Marantaę Venusini medici Methodi cognoscendorum simplicium libri tres cum indice copioso,* Venetiis ex officina Erasmiana Vincentii Valgrisii, MDLIX, 4to, 296 pp. Copy used: BM 431.a.18. For the Italian version see note 20 above.

[32] Their interchange of letters, Maranta's from Naples on July 1, 1558, and Falloppia's from Padua on August 7, is given at the beginning of the volume.

they would beget males, while if women ate its smaller root, they would give birth to females.[33] As to what might happen, if they did so simultaneously, or if men ate the smaller root and women, the larger, Maranta betrayed no curiosity, though there might seem to be a fruitful field for speculation and experimentation in these directions.

While botany seems to have made advances during the sixteenth century in respects which have been illustrated in detail by E. L. Greene,[34] It must be kept in mind that the medieval background has not yet been sufficiently studied or compared with the later works. For example, not only was the book of Rufinus of the later thirteenth century apparently quite unknown to writers of the sixteenth century, but the very plants for which he added his own descriptions to those of past authorities remained in large part unnoticed by them. Compare, for example, the names noted in my article on Rufinus[35] with the indices of Ruellius, *De natura stirpium,* 1536; Turner, *The Names of Herbs,* 1548; Lobelius, *Plantarum Observationes et Adversaria,* 1576; Dodonaeus,[36] *Stirpium Historia,* 1583; the *Commentaries* of Mattioli on Dioscorides, edition of 1598; and Greene's *Landmarks* which mentions many of the herbs included in the works of Brunfels, Fuchs, Tragus and Cordus. *Aristologia* or *Aristolochia* is of course found in them all, but of the names, *terrumalium* (or *terrae malum*) and *mellumcelli,* for its fruit given by Rufinus, only Dodoens mentions either and he only the former. The other five plants whose names began with the first letter of the alphabet for which I quoted Rufinus's descriptions from life, namely, *auricula leporis, aurigea duplex, aucheta, aucha* and *athanasia,* are all absent from the indices for the sixteenth century works, except that Ruellius notes that *athanasia* is the common name for his third species of artemisia. Nor do

[33] *Ibid.,* III, 9, p. 231.

[34] *Landmarks of Botanical History,* 1909.

[35] Lynn Thorndike, "Rufinus: a Forgotten Botanist of the Thirteenth Century," *Isis,* 18 (1932), 63-76. I hope to edit the work of Rufinus.

[36] Incidentally may be mentioned the work of P. J. van Meerbeeck, *Recherches historiques et critiques sur la vie et les ouvrages de R. Dodoens,* 1841, 8vo. Copy used: BM 551.d.21.

these indices mention most of the plants with which Rufinus compared *aurigea duplex* and other varieties of *aurigea,* namely, *paradella* or *paratella, cauliculus agrestis, cottula foetida,* and *tursulum,* although *tanavete* or *cavanete* is probably the same as their *tanacetum.* It must be admitted, however, that the indices of these sixteenth century works with the exception of Ruellius *De natura stirpium,* which has an excellent index are often faulty. For instance, *cottula foetida* at least is mentioned in Dodoens.[37] Ruellius notes that *paradelos* is the common name for the flower of *bellis,* that what the apothecaries call *cotula foetida* is probably Pliny's *buphthalmos,* and makes *tanacetum* another name for *athanasia* or the third variety of artemisia. Of the names of other herbs which Rufinus gave in connection with *aucheta,* the indices of Turner, Lobel, Mattioli and Dodoens have *polium* and *betonica* but neither *sticados* nor *canusula,* while Ruellius has all but the last, stating that unskilled persons call *stoechas, sticados citrinum.* They have, however, *fraxinus* (i.e., the ash tree), with which he compared the leaves of *aucha,* and of the other names for *athanasia* Ruellius, Lobel, Dodoens and Mattioli give *tanacetum* and *matricaria.* Ruellius, however, associates *matricaria* with *parthenium.*

Of three herbs described by Rufinus whose names begin with the letter B, namely, *bismalva, bruscus* and *bursa pastoris,* Turner and Dodoens give none, while Lobel, Mattioli and Greene have only the last. In the 1560 German edition of the work of Bock or Tragus, however, all three are found, while Ruellius had already identified the *bismalva* of the apothecary shops with *althaea* and their *bruscum* as a corruption of *ruscum*: The sole approach to *caput galli* is a *caput gallinaceum Belgarum* in the pages of Lobel. *Centaurea media* is not distinguished from *centaurea maior* and *centaurea minor* by these sixteenth century authors as it was by Rufinus. *Coclearia* appears in Mattioli,

[37] *Historia stirpium,* II, iii, 16. Similarly it does not appear in Bock's index, but in his text, German edition of 1560, fol. 54v, we read, "Die ander stinckende Chamill ist ein Cotula oder Caula oder Chamomilla foetida." It is, however, in the index of Matthiolus.

Dodoens and Lobel, but their description is worded differently from that of Rufinus.

So it goes. The sixteenth century indices do not include *centumgumma, cinoglossa,* or *cicer imperatoris.* They have *daucus* but not the *daucus asininus* of Rufinus, except Ruellius who after distinguishing three kinds of *daucus* says that he hears both the second and third called *daucus asininus* by the herbalists (*herbarii*). He also informs us that *helenium* is called *enula* in the apothecary shops and *campana* by rustics. Otherwise only Dodoens and Mattioli have an *enula,* and it is called *enula campana. Esula, eupatoria* and *filipendula*[38] are duplicated in the sixteenth century works, but not *gita* or *genuissa,* except that Dodoens and Mattioli note that some persons call *melanthium gith* while Ruellius so uses it regularly, and unless the *genista* of Ruellius, Turner and Mattioli or Bock's *genistae* and *genista humilis* may be identified with *genuissa.* The sixteenth century works have *lunaria* but neither *Turonensis grossa* nor *Turonensis parva.* They give various kinds of plantain, but only Turner[39] precisely parallels the *plantago lanceolata* of Rufinus, although it is the modern scientific appellation for it. Ruellius, Bock and Dodoens virtually name it, since they make *lanceola* or *lanceolata* another name for *plantago minor,* while Lobel lists a *plantago lanceola,* but as with the others it appears in his index only as *Lanceola,* not under *Plantago.*

Thus the botanical researches of Rufinus in the thirteenth century seem to have extended to a number of plants which remained unknown to the naturalists of the sixteenth century. On the other hand, the descriptions of plants by Tragus and Valerius Cordus, for instance, are fuller and sometimes show more minute examination of detail than did those of Rufinus, indicating that botanical research was becoming more intensive, if not extensive, than in the thirteenth century.

It is to be feared that other medieval botanical knowledge than that peculiar to the forgotten work of Rufinus escaped the atten-

[38] Ruellius does not have it.

[39] Edition of 1881, p. 63: ". . . the other is called Rybwurte or Rybgrasse and of some Herbaries Lancea lata."

tion of our sixteenth century herbalists. This may be demonstrated as follows. The manuscript of Rufinus was as little known to Hermann Fischer, when he published his *Mittelalterliche Pflanzenkunde* in 1929, as it was to the naturalists of the sixteenth century. Fischer too omits in his index three of the five names of plants above mentioned which began with the letter A, giving only *athanasia* and *auriculus leporis*. But of the herbs with which Rufinus compared *aurigea*, Fischer has *paratella* and *cottula foetida*, though not *tursulum*, while his *colliculus* perhaps corresponds to *cauliculus agrestis*. He has *sticados*, *bismalva*, *bruscus*, *cinoglossa*, *daucus asininus*, *gith* and *genuissa*. In general, while Fischer does not include all the plants named by Rufinus, he has a larger percentage of them than our books from or on the sixteenth century. The evidence of Ruellius suggests that the men who gathered and sold herbs retained the medieval names and terminology more than did learned writers. One also wonders if the works of Lobelius and Dodoens really improved upon Ruellius.

It would be instructive to turn the comparison the other way round and see how many of the herbs listed by the sixteenth century authors were unknown to Rufinus, but this would require a critical edition and exhaustive index of his work, or at least a collation of the manuscript with these sixteenth century authors which I am not now in a position to make. We may, however, in a rough way compare Fischer's index of plant names with that of Dodoens, remembering that allowance should be made for the fact that Fischer includes more variant spellings of the same name, and that his index appears in other respects to be the more exhaustive. But as things stand Fischer has some 3,800 entries against about 2,000 by Dodoens. Under the letter A, Fischer lists some 400 names of plants; Dodoens, about 200. Of these at least seventy are common to both. Thus where the sixteenth century seems to add about 130 herbs to those known to medieval botanists, it fails to include some 330 names with which previous herbalists were familiar.

The divergence may be illustrated in another way. Of varieties of *absinthium* Fischer has seven, Dodoens, nine, while of *apium* Fischer lists about a dozen kinds[40] and Dodoens, half a dozen. They have in common *absinthium marinum, ponticum* and *sandonicum,* and four varieties of *apium, aquatile* or *aquaticum, montanum, risus* and *silvestre.* Under *absinthium* Dodoens does not have *absinthium dulce, murinum, romanum* or *subalbidum,* while he adds *absinthium angustifolium, Aegyptium, absinthia externa, absinthium inodorum, latifolium* and *tenuifolium.* Under *apium* he lacks *cerfolium, emoroidarum, fluviale, ranarum, raninum, regale* and *rusticum,* while he adds *hortense* and *palustre.*

It should further be stated that some of the herbs which Greene represented as new discoveries of Valerius Cordus had really been previously known. For example Greene wrote: "The first four types described are, in modern nomenclature, Drosera, Gratiola, Sagittaria, and Bistorta. Every one of them, at the time when Cordus here described them, was new to science."[41] Yet *gratiola* and *bistorta* appear in Fischer's *Glossar.* Again of a list of fifteen supposedly new names for plants devised by Cordus,[42] Fischer gives *millegrana,* while his *balsamillo* is the same as the *balsamella* of Cordus.

On the other hand, there is this to be said for the sixteenth century. If the work of Rufinus remained in manuscript and was lost sight of for centuries, this was similarly the case with some of the best and most advanced botanical compositions of the sixteenth century. Fuchs' *Historia stirpium,* as printed in 1542, had 500 plates against the 135 of Brunfels' *Herbarum vivae icones.* But before his death Fuchs had prepared an enlarged work treating of 1,500 plants which remained in manuscript.[43] In like manner the magnum opus of Gesner on herbs was not printed until the eighteenth century,[44] whereas his work on secret remedies within a decade after its first appearance at Zurich in 1552 had

[40] I assume that *apium aquae* is probably identical with *apium aquaticum, apium emoroidarum* with *apium hemoroidarum,* and *apium silvaticum* with *apium silvestre.* This reduces Fischer's fourteen entries to eleven.

[41] *Landmarks,* p. 274.

[42] *Ibid.,* p. 304.

[43] *Ibid.,* p. 195.

[44] I have not had access to it. It was published at Nürnberg in 1754 by C. C. Schmiedel.

been reprinted in Latin there, at Lyons, and at Venice, and had further been published in French, English and Italian translations. Caspar Ratzenberger in 1598 completed "with incredible labor" an *Herbarium vivum* in four volumes which seem not to have been printed.[45] It is therefore probable that some naturalists of the sixteenth century knew of more plants than were listed even in the works of Lobel and Dodoens in the last quarter of the century.[46]

That botanical studies did not rank very high at the universities in the sixteenth century or even in the opinion of men who have been considered most interested in natural and experimental science is shown by a letter to Aldrovandi written by Falloppia on January 23, 1561. The name of Falloppia occupies a high place in the history of anatomy. He also lectured and published on minerals and metals. Yet we find him chiding Aldrovandi for preferring a chair on medicinal simples to one in philosophy. In the former field he asserts that there is nothing to be done but to print figures of plants and to write a commentary on Theophrastus—which Scaliger has already done. He really does not know who has bewitched Aldrovandi into abandoning the other field of lofty speculation.[47] Similarly Cesalpino, albeit famed as a botanist, did not long remain a teacher of medicinal simples but advanced to the chair of the theory of medicine.[48]

In a manuscript written in 1573 is found an attempt to divide herbs into thirteen classes according to such distinctions as whether they have one or many petals and of what shape, whether the pistil or calyx goes into the fruit or seed, and whether the fruit are capsular or siliquose, or unicapsular or multicapsular.[49]

[45] Gotha chart. in folio 152-155.

[46] Johann Schwimmer, "Hieronymus Harder [c.1523-1607] und seine Herbare," *Süddeutsch. Apoth.-Ztg.*, 75 (1935), 434-36, describes eight herbals by him, the oldest of 1562 now in private hands at Heidelberg, the next of 1574 in the Deutsches Museum at Munich, the third and largest of 1576 in the Bayer. Staatsbibliothek, Munich.

[47] Quoted by Francesco Fiorentino, *Studi e ritratti della Rinascenza*, 1911, pp. 201-202: "Non so veramente chi vi habbia fascinato . . . tutto sublimato delle speculationi."

[48] *Ibid.*, p. 203.

[49] BMsl 3169, ff. 1r-50v. The writing is not neat and hard to read. The

Under each Classis there may be further division and classification by chapters but three chapters is the largest number under any Classis.

A feature of natural studies which seems to become more prominent in the sixteenth than in preceding centuries is cooperation between different individuals. They send one another specimens or at least drawings or written descriptions of strange animals and unfamiliar herbs which they have run across. Gesner maintained a correspondence with Turner, whom he had met at Zurich as Turner returned from Italy with the doctoral degree,[50] and many other persons on such matters. He learned about salmon from Uldrich Huguald, professor of moral philosophy at Basel, and from Adam à Bodenstein, a physician of the same city.[51] In his *History of Animals*[52] Gesner lists famous men who had aided him with it, including Achilles Gasser (as Gesner spells it), Fracastoro, Froben, Cardan, Massarius, John Caius of London, Belon, Theodore Beza, physicians of Cracow, Schaffhausen and Verona, pharmacists of Ulm and Strasburg, theologians, poets, etc. This cooperation in science by men of diverse nationalities, professions, religions and even philosophies is indeed impressive.

George Fabricius wrote Wolfgang Meurer on June 26, 1553 that he was sending Gesner twenty kinds of ducks of which he had learned from fowlers, and some further specimens.[53] To another letter Fabricius appends a postscript that there had been twenty-four rainbows in a single week of April at Strasburg.[54] A physician of Lyons, Carolus Paludanus, sent to Jacobus Sylvius a sample of *costus subamarus*.[55] Friends at Montpellier forwarded to Hieronymus Bock or Tragus a picture of wild rue.[56]

MS once belonged to Dr. Robert Gray and was bought in his auction of the year 1730. On the verso of the fly-leaf is written, "For my own use superfluities cut off and the method altered a little."

[50] Gesner (1545), fol. 294r-v.

[51] Gesner, *Hist. animalium lib. IV qui est de piscium et aquatilium animantium natura*, Frankfurt, 1604, p. 829 (incorrectly numbered 809).

[52] *Ibid.*, fol. (b 5 verso).

[53] *Epistolae*, ed. Baumgarten-Crusius, Leipzig, 1845, p. 90.

[54] *Ibid.*, p. 118.

[55] Ryff's edition of Dioscorides, 1549, p. 13 (I, 15).

[56] *Ibid.*, p. 222 (III, 44).

Pennius received a beetle from Joachim Camerarius, while others came from Quickelberg in Antwerp and from Edward Elmer in Russia.[57] Quickelberg supplied other specimens, while Edmund Knivet, knight, forwarded pictures of the first species of *proscarabeus* seen by him in England and of a vermiform *staphylinus*.[58] Rondelet added to the ancient authors what he had observed and learned from experience and what learned friends had communicated.[59] Brother Gregory the Capuchin of Reggio, when he came to Mount Padernus near Bologna to inspect the herbs there, brought Aldrovandi some wild bees and their honeycomb.[60] Two of Aldrovandi's seven examples of the zoophyte, *Tethya,* were presented to him by an erudite pharmacist of Modena, Antonia Maria Lombardi.[61] Gesner praised Henry Billing and others who with great zeal and at great expense imported plants for their gardens from all over the world and thus rendered a great service to mankind.[62] Dodoens prefaced his book not only with a bibliography of ancient and modern writers whom he had used but a list of owners of gardens to which he had had access and of persons who had sent him dried herbs from Italy, Germany and other places. William Quacelbenus sent Matthiolus plants, minerals and other drugs from Constantinople.[63]

Such correspondence concerning plants and animals, which perhaps was to some extent an offshoot from the letter-writing of the humanists, and such transmission of specimens or sketches

[57] Moufetus, *Insectorum . . . theatrum,* London, 1634, p. 150 (incorrectly numbered 134). Samuel Quickelberg, a physician of Antwerp, was at Ingolstadt in 1553 and printed medical tables there, and biblical apothegms at Cologne, 1571. He planned a vast work on all nature but published only a tentative analysis: Andreas, *Bibl. Belgica,* 1643, p. 806.

[58] *Ibid.,* pp. 162, 174, 197.

[59] *Liber de piscibus marinis,* Lugdunii Apud Matthiam Bonhomme, 1554, V, 1, p. 114.

[60] Aldrovandi, *De animalibus insectis,* Bologna, 1602, p. 190 (I, 4).

[61] Aldrovandi, *De exanguibus,* Bologna, 1606, p. 583, (IV, 5).

[62] Conrad Gesner, *Historia plantarum et vires ex Dioscoride Paulo Aegineta Theophrasto Plinio et recentioribus Graecis iuxta elementorum ordinem,* Basel, 1541; dedication to Henry Billing.

[63] See his letter of July 26, 1557 listing them in *Petri Andr. Matthioli Epistolarum lib. III,* Francofurti, 1598, pp. 100-102. Various other correspondents sent Matthiolus specimens.

for another to utilize in his impending volume, seem a step towards the formation of scientific societies and academies with their corresponding fellows and cooperative undertakings. At the same time it is well to remember that the specimens collected and sent, like those stored in the museums of that day,[64] were often intended to confirm faith in the strange and marvelous. Thus Crato sent Gesner a description and picture of a bezoar stone. Kentman sent him an account of stones found in human bodies.[65] Kentman,[66] however, had sent Gesner a full catalogue of his collection or cabinet of minerals in 1559, and again six years later a fuller list which Gesner published in 1565.[67] In an accompanying letter Kentman praised Gesner for his enthusiasm in investigating nature and professed to have been inspired by his example to devote no little time and expense to mineralogy and the collection of specimens.

Observation was apt to be somewhat cognately occasional and sporadic, not to say exceptional, rather than systematic and protracted, though a work like that of Dodoens on plants approached more closely to the latter scientific method. The extent to which Aldrovandi observed nature may be illustrated by the case of an eagle which he watched for eight days in captivity, then killed and dissected.[68] After Aldrovandi's death, if not be-

[64] As late as 1696 in the catalogue of the royal museum at Copenhagen there were listed a dried liver, the ear of an elephant measuring three and a half by two and a half feet, sandals made of human skin, hairs with skin torn out by an irate hand, monstrous fingernails grown by a youth of Copenhagen; the shaggy hand of a wild man from India, two hands of a siren, a stone from a human bladder which (i.e. the stone) weighed twelve and a half ounces, a foetus turned to stone which a woman in France had borne for the space of twenty-eight years, embryoes of one and seven thumbs length, a salamander, and various bezoardic stones, oriental as well as occidental. From L. Neocoro, *Bibliotheca librorum novorum,* I (1697).

[65] Willy Ley, *Konrad Gesner,* 1929, p. 120.

[66] He is called John Kentman of Dresden, doctor of arts and medicine (Iohannes Kentmanus Dresdensis artium et medicinae Doctor), but his dedicatory letter to Gesner is dated at Torgau, November 8, 1565.

[67] Gesner, *De omni rerum fossilium genere,* Zurich, 1565. The catalogue is preceded by a picture and scheme of contents of the cabinet, in which Kentman's specimens were stored under 26 groups, with two of these in each of 13 drawers. In the subsequent text is a slight amplification of this classification under 30 headings.

[68] Compare with this the painstak-

fore, his Museum and collection of materials, written and pictorial, gained much fame and were the treasury exploited, sometimes none too wisely, by the successive posthumous editions of works in the field of natural history under his name.

It is a trifle misleading and something of a misnomer to speak of sixteenth century naturalists, since natural science in general or botany or zoology in particular was often not their sole or even primary aim, but was subsidiary to other interests: the grammatical, literary and antiquarian; or medical, practical and encyclopedic; even moral and religious, or marvel-mongering and magical. Gesner, for example, was a polyhistor and encyclopedist rather than a scientific specialist. Aside from varied editorial activities, his energies were devoted largely to compilation. Both of the two chief works published during his lifetime partook of that character, namely, his *Universal Library* and his *History of Animals*. On the other hand, the field in which he had been personally interested since boyhood and in which he had made careful detailed observations approaching a truly scientific character, botany, profited by only one or two minor publications during his lifetime, his main botanical work, as has been stated, being printed only two centuries after his death. This suggests that specific scientific research was then even less an interest of the reading public than it was of men of learning like Gesner.

In the volume of his *History of Animals* which dealt with fish and aquatic animals Gesner justified the employment of an alphabetical order rather than some attempt at a more scientific classification of species on the ground that his work was "grammatical rather than philosophical." That is to say, it was primarily concerned with names and words, and with information and allusions connected with them, for the use and enjoyment of the classical scholar and literary reader rather than with the collection and presentation of facts for scientific purposes. It is true that his explanation implies that there were readers who might have preferred and writers who practiced a "philosoph-

---

ing and continuous observation of an eagle's eyrie recorded by Francis H. Herrick, *The American Eagle*, 1934.

ical" arrangement. Most of our sixteenth century naturalists attempted to group or at least to juxtapose things that seemed related. Aldrovandi objected to an alphabetical order as separating related objects and bringing together dissimilar things.[69] In such efforts at arrangement the sixteenth century writers sometimes merely repeated groupings of the ancients but sometimes were guided by their own observations and powers of association. Gesner himself in 1565 in his work on fossils or minerals abandoned the alphabetical order as "too popular and elementary."[70] Rondelet tried to distinguish fish by differences in habitat, food, parts, taste, odor, and so on.

The works on plants and animals printed during the sixteenth century may be regarded on the one hand as a continuation and outgrowth of previous medieval herbals and encyclopedias, and on the other hand as a product of further humanistic study of Aristotle, Theophrastus, Galen, Dioscorides, Pliny, and other classical authors. In the latter case it was liable to be largely limited to a discussion of names and to the identification of those plants and animals mentioned in the classics. For instance, William Turner's first botanical publication in 1538[71] was little more than a brief alphabetical list with the Greek, Latin and English names, while his first zoological writing was upon the principal birds mentioned by Pliny and Aristotle.[72] If it be true, as we are told, that when Turner wrote in 1538, he "had no instructor in his study beyond the classical writers," this means that he had failed to profit by the work of his medieval predecessors. This was true in some degree of other writers whose outlook and reading were too concentrated in and confined by the ancients. Usually, however, medieval as well as classical authorities were quoted by sixteenth century writers on plants and animals.

As has been said, much time and space were devoted to the

[69] Preface to his work on birds, edition of 1599.

[70] Epist. dedic., "utpote nimis vulgatam et trivialem."

[71] William Turner, *Libellus de re herbaria novus in quo herbarum aliquot nomina graeca latina et anglica habes una cum nominibus officinarum,* London, 1538; facsimile reprint, London, 1877.

[72] *Avium praecipuarum quarum apud Plinium et Aristotelem mentio est brevis et succincta historia,* Cologne, 1544; edited with English translation etc. by A. H. Evans as *Turner on Birds,* Cambridge, 1903.

attempted identification of the plants and animals named in classical works. This may be illustrated first from Walther Herman Ryff's comments upon the translation of Dioscorides by Ruellius. Ryff's edition first appeared at Marburg in 1543[73] and then at Frankfurt with additional material in 1549. Ryff informs us that Jacobus Sylvius contends that the herb *cardamomum* of the medieval author, Serapion, has nothing in common with that of Galen and Dioscorides, while Valerius Cordus thinks that it has. Ruellius identified the *aspalathus* of the ancients with wood of Rhodes, while Ryff would identify the *lignum guaiacum* of the New World with the ebony of Dioscorides. Valerius Cordus identified *acanthius* with *carduus benedictus*, but Ruellius thought that it was *atractylis*. Ryff criticized other suggested identifications without naming their authors, asserting vaguely, "Those are mistaken who . . ." or, "Those are hallucinated who . . ." or, "Certain persons today think in shameful error. . . ." Of Rondelet's work on fish published in 1554 Robert Hamilton wrote in 1876: "It is true that no small degree of what we are now prone to regard as useless labour and erudition are employed in tracing out the old names of species, and making us acquainted with all that "those ancients" have said and sung about them: but when released from this prolixity, we find a good deal of accurate observation and description, and what may be called legitimate natural history."[74]

Doubtless such efforts at identification and disagreement over them led in some cases to closer observation, but the moot point also was apt to be a textual problem or a matter of opinion, and sometimes led nowhere. Later in the century there was something of a reaction against spending so much time on the identification of classical names, so that we find Dodoens writing in

[73] W. L. Schreiber, *Die Kräuterbücher des XV und XVI Jahrhunderts*, Munich, 1924, p. xxxvii, who fails to note the 1549 edition, although it was by the same printer, Egenolphus. There is a copy of the 1549 edition at the Columbia University library, but its title page and a number of other pages are missing and some illustrations have been torn out. Ruellius' translation of Dioscorides appeared first in 1516 and frequently thereafter.

[74] Robert Hamilton, Memoir of Rondelet, p. 35: prefixed to his *History of British Fishes*, I, 1876.

1583, "We have preferred to describe herbs under their common names rather than rashly to ascribe ancient appellations to them."[75]

Yet a decade later the *Phytobasanos* of Fabio Colonna was devoted to the identification of some twenty-six plants with those mentioned by Dioscorides and in a few instances by Theophrastus and Pliny.[76] Only in a sort of appendix to this publication did Colonna note eight new plants.[77]

However, it also should not be overlooked that there was an interest in the flora or fauna of one's own country and in the vernacular names for herbs, birds, and other animals, as the works of Turner, Belon, Rondelet, and Gesner illustrate. Some of the best works of the century, like the *Kreutterbuch* of Hieronymus Bock, appeared first in a vernacular language, and introduced something in the way of freshness of outlook and treatment lacking in Latin works dominated by the interest in classical authors, since the flora especially of central and northern Europe differed considerably from that of the Mediterranean world recorded by Dioscorides.

Otho Brunfels already in 1530, in his *Herbarum vivae icones*,[78] often turned from learned authors to herbalists of his own time, who were not trained by books but by experience of things, for the name and description of an herb.[79] When he found great dissension among medical authors as to the herb *Aron*, he rep-

[75] *Remberti Dodonaei . . . Stirpium Historiae Pemptades sex sive libri xxx*, Antwerp, 1583, I, ii, preface.

[76] *Phytobasanos sive plantarum aliquot historia in qua describuntur diversi generis plantae veriores ac magis facie viribusque respondentes antiquorum Theophrasti Dioscoridis Plinii Galeni aliorumque delineationibus ab aliis hucusque non animadversae Fabio Columna auctore. Accessit etiam piscium aliquot plantarumque novarum historia eodem auctore ad . . . cardinalem Antonium Columnam.* Ex officina Horatii Salviani, Neapoli, MDXCII. Apud Io. Iacobum Carlinum et Antonium Pacem. Copy used: BM 968.k.1.(4.). There are full page illustrations of each specimen.

[77] See previous note. This supplementary tract which has a new pagination covers 32 pp. against 120 pp. of the *Phytobasanos*.

[78] *Herbarum vivae icones ad naturae imitationem summa cum diligentia et artificio effigiatae una cum effectibus earundem in gratiam veteris illius et iamiam renascentis herbariae medicinae per Oth. Brunf. recens editae*, Argentorati apud Ioannem Schottum, 1530, folio. Copy used: BM 547.m.2.(1.).

[79] *Ibid.*, p. 133 (misnumbered 135).

resented it as it had been shown him "by our herbalists."[80] In another passage, while he cursed the herbalists of a former age for giving the vernacular instead of classical name of an herb, he warmly agreed with the opinion of vulgar herbalists who identified it with *solidago minor*.[81] Again he remarks that the herbalists of our time boast that they have found more kinds of a certain plant than are mentioned by Dioscorides.[82] Or he quotes in the same breath experimenters and herbalists,[83] and cites Bock or Tragus frequently as "the noble experimenter and herbalist, Hieronymus," "Hieronymus, noble empiric," "the noble herbalist, Hieronymus."[84] Or when Theobald Fettich showed him as a species of *solidago* a plant which he called *Masslieb* or *Zeitlösslin,* he preferred his evidence to that "of a hundred dreamers who pronounce concerning any herb without erudition or experience."[85]

Another source of fresh inspiration was supplied by the strange plants and animals found in the New World and other distant regions opened up by the voyages of discovery. These too were sometimes first described in works written in a vernacular, as was the case with the *Colloquies Concerning the Simples . . . of India* by Garcia da Orta, first published in the Portuguese tongue at Goa. Other books like that of Acosta had to be translated from Spanish into Latin. Such data, however, in part rested on unreliable tales of travelers or the narratives and specimens brought back by well-meaning but not especially scientific Jesuit fathers and missionaries. It is true that the study of these new phenomena was not overlaid and loaded down by a mass of classical and medieval citation, while the native lore associated with them was only in part transmitted to Europe. So the way might seem cleared for factual observation and description, free from magical accretions and survivals. But of course the natural tendency was to view the new phenomena from the same angle and with the same prepossessions that other flora and

[80] *Ibid.,* p. 58.

[81] *Ibid.,* p. 82.

[82] *Ibid.,* p. 78.

[83] *Ibid.,* p. 82, "Adiiciunt Experimentatores et herbarii. . . ."

[84] *Ibid.,* pp. 55, 79, 81, 110; also 87, 98, 102, 128, etc.

[85] *Ibid.,* p. 78.

fauna had hitherto been described; while in their case novelty and distance added to their charms. Acosta[86] and Monardes[87] did not fail to sing the praises of the bezoar stones of oriental India and of Peru in their respective works. Or the latter mentioned an herb in Peru by which one could divine whether a patient would live or die, according as he became more cheerful or sorrowful from holding it in his hand.[88]

The historical schoolbooks of our childhood used to give us the impression that the voyages of Columbus dispelled the fear of mythical sea-monsters which had hitherto kept sailors from venturing out of sight of land. As a matter of fact, such voyages rather confirmed the faith in and multiplied the number of such monsters. Now it was possible to believe Pliny's assertions concerning monstrous races of men, or the tales of Solinus and John de Mandeville. Gemma Frisius, although reckoned one of the earliest supporters of Copernicus, when writing in 1530 on astronomy and cosmography could still speak—with some qualification it is true—of "schiopodes" (i. e. skiapodes)[89] with a single foot so large that they used it as a sunshade, and who were swifter than a hare, or of men with the heads of dogs or with eight toes.[90] Indeed, some contemporaries would probably have said that the Copernican system was a greater absurdity than any of these. A meridian in the Azores was called the true west and diameter of the world. The magnetic needle of the compass was there believed to point directly to the poles and stand perpendicular to the equator. Iunctinus in 1577 further quoted Gonzales de Oviedo in the summary of voyages to the West Indies, chapter 82, as asserting that all vermin there disappeared from their clothing and heads, and that they were

[86] *N. Christophori Acosta medici et cheirurgi Aromatum et medicamentorum in Orientali India nascentium liber:* Latin epitome by Clusius, Antwerp, 1593, pp. 282-84.

[87] *Simplicium medicamentorum ex novo orbe delatorum quorum in medicina usus est historia . . . a Nicolao Monardis:* Latin version by Clusius, Tertia editio, Antwerp, 1593, pp. 394-402, 447-54.

[88] *Ibid.,* pp. 434-35.

[89] Gemma's spelling of this word suggests that his knowledge of Greek was somewhat faulty.

[90] Gemma Frisius, *De principiis astronomiae et cosmographiae,* Basel, 1530, Pars 3, cap. 26. He qualifies, "si credere fas est."

free from them until they returned eastward and recrossed the lice-line.[91] Aldrovandi, or his editor of the middle of the seventeenth century, could depict negroes with the lower lip hanging to the breast, could believe in Patagonian giants and in the prevalence of hermaphrodites in Virginia. Pigafeta had said that there were islanders near the Moluccas whose ears reached their shoulders, and the Jesuit Eusebius told of natives in the vicinity of California whose ears drooped almost to the ground.

Despite the inspiration to be derived from new flora and fauna, names and regions, the method employed was still largely that of compilation and citation from past authors. There seems to have been a feeling, habitual or instinctive, that nothing said by them must be omitted. Even if the present writer branded it as false or superstitious, he nevertheless included it all. It seemed not to occur to him that it would be better to omit it. Elimination of deadwood was therefore not a characteristic of sixteenth century works on nature. What little new they may have to offer is smothered under a great mass of traditional lore, partly irrelevant and partly incorrect. It therefore does not appear that they or their period had many new ideas or any very extensive intellectual development. Be it kept in mind, too, that it is not merely both ancients and medievals—so far as the latter were available in print—that our naturalists exhaust. Like the Glossators and Post-Glossators of the twelfth to fifteenth centuries, each successive writer on nature in the sixteenth century embodied the work of his immediate predecessors, until in the tomes of Aldrovandi an enormous bulk is attained, and his volumes are more or less all-inclusive and summarize the century's development in that field.

The retention of characteristics from medieval encyclopedias and accounts of herbs and animals may also be illustrated from the works of Aldrovandi. He not only made liberal use of such authorities as Albertus Magnus and an anonymous writer on the nature of things (perhaps Thomas of Cantimpré), but further

[91] *Francisci Iunctini Commentarium in Sphaeram Joannis de Sacro Bosco,* 1577, I, 457.

retained many medieval viewpoints and interests. Thus he thought of certain animals as being nobler than or superior to others. He opened his three volumes on birds with the eagle, on the ground that it was superior to either the cock or the peacock.[92] He also came very near the attribution of human qualities to animals, stating that each has its own *ingenium*. Some are gentle, slow, and not at all lively, like cattle. Some, like wild boars, are full of animosity and vivacity. Some are ingenious and timid, like deer, hares, and rabbits. Some are illiberal, perfidious, and treacherous, like serpents. Some are liberal, brave, and generous, like lions. Some are astute and malicious, like foxes. Some are bland and obsequious, like dogs. Some are modest and cautious, like geese. Some are envious and attentive to their decorativeness, like peacocks.[93] The use of remedies by animals is also still stated. Aelian is cited that even beasts guard against the glances of fascinators, the eagle employing the stone *aetites* for this purpose.[94] The crow eats laurel as an antidote to the virus of the chameleon and, as Ruellius attests, employs other remedies in diseases and fortifies its nest with *vitex* against fascination. This does not involve reasoning on its part but is the result of some occult natural sympathy.[95] I do not mean to imply that such views concerning animals are exclusively or even distinctively medieval. They were inherited or taken directly from ancient writers like Pliny, Aelian, and even Aristotle, but were also characteristic of medieval encyclopedias. Other medieval features—or what are usually so regarded—in Aldrovandi's treatment are his noting the mystical and symbolical significance of each animal and the moral lessons that may be drawn from it, as well as its use for food, in medicine, in hunting, and in heraldry.

Aldrovandi's account of a particular bird, however, is much longer than that in any medieval work. This may be illustrated from his treatment of the eagle. He quotes every passage in the

[92] *Ornithologiae hoc est de avibus historiae libri xii*, Bologna, 1599, I, 17.
[93] *Ibid.*, p. 30.
[94] *Ibid.*, p. 47.
[95] *Ibid.*, p. 704.

Greek and Latin poets and even a modern like Ariosto where an eagle is mentioned, every myth where it is concerned like that of Jupiter and Ganymede, every story, fable and anecdote about eagles that is known to him, their use in pagan rites and augury and auspices, their employment as hieroglyphs and emblems. Such sections on Hieroglyphica throughout Aldrovandi's works on animals are almost invariably simply excerpts from the books on that theme of Horapollo and Pierius Valerianus. Ruellius had set the example for Aldrovandi in this, quoting Horapollo as to the scarab, cynocephalus, and so forth.[96] Aldrovandi further lists synonyms and gives the etymology of the name of the bird; goes into things with similar names or names derived from it; and enumerates various men, rivers and towns that have been called Aquila, not to mention an eagle fish, eagle herb, eagle star, or the use by alchemists of the word for a chemical. Paracelsus applied it to sal ammoniac because of its volatility in sublimation, while Hortulanus used the name now for sulphur, now for arsenic, and now for gold. We have hardly indicated all the captions under which Aldrovandi ordered his eighty folio pages of miscellaneous matter upon eagles in general, before he took up particular kinds of eagles, but it must be evident that his account of their physical appearance and anatomy, generation, habits and ailments occupies a rather modest fraction of the space. Even when supposedly discussing the eagle's ailments, he drifts off to the theme of the love of the stork for its young.

The criteria of truth and standards of scientific credibility applied in the sixteenth century were often, if not generally, far from satisfactory. Not only was there too much indiscriminate respect for the printed page or written word, but hearsay was accepted because of the moral, social, academic, or religious standing of one's informant without taking into account the soundness or reliability of his organs of sense perception, his intellectual acumen, or his possession or lack of anything approaching scientific or historical training. Although Coelestinus's summary of the discussion of marvelous happenings by Nicolas

[96] *De natura stirpium,* 1536, p. 616.

Oresme had been printed in 1542,[97] the warning counsels of fourteenth century writers as to the deceptibility of the human senses and imagination, and that saintly persons were apt to be more easily deceived, passed unheeded by a Cardan who accepted the existence of mermaids on faith because he felt sure that Greek scholars like Theodore Gaza and George of Trebizond would not have lied about it,[98] or a William Turner who was convinced of the generation of barnacle geese from rotting ships by the affidavit of an Irish theologian that he had seen and touched them,[99] and who believed and induced others to believe in another variety of such geese which grew out of trees along the Scotch coast, "because so many men of so great integrity have affirmed it."[100] The notion of inextinguishable and ever burning lamps would have seemed utterly incredible to Melchior Guilandinus, prefect of the botanical garden at Padua, had not Ermolao Barbaro, a most illustrious man whose good faith no one could doubt, in his book of corollaries, and Franciscus Maturantius, a most erudite man, in a letter to a friend testified that they had found such lamps still burning in subterranean monuments of Italy. Moreover, Bernardino Scardeone, a man of singular learning and admirable probity, at the close of his first book of antiquities of Padua mentioned such a lamp as having burned for more than fifteen hundred years at a place near Padua which he carefully specified.[101] Some liquor prepared alchemically occurred to Guilandinus as the probable explanation of such prolonged combustion.

Seldom was any distinction drawn as to scientific value and reliability between past authors, who were cited indiscriminately,

[97] Lynn Thorndike, "Coelestinus's Summary of Nicolas Oresme on Marvels: a Fifteenth Century Work Printed in the Sixteenth Century," *Osiris*, I (1936), 629-35.

[98] *De rerum varietate*, VII, 38.

[99] *Turner on Birds*, edited by A. H. Evans, 1903, pp. 26-27.

[100] *Ibid.*, p. 107.

[101] *In C. Plinii maioris capita aliquot ut difficillima ita pulcherrima et utilissima commentarius varia et non vulgari eruditione refertus ubi Matheoli errores non pauci deteguntur authore Melchiore Guilandino philosopho et medico praestantissimo et in cognitione simplicium maxime versato.* Lausannae Excudebat Franciscus le Preux Illustris. Domin. Bernens. Typographus, MDLXXVI, p. 65. Copy used: BN Rés. S.512.

Aelian and Athenaeus being utilized as if of equal worth with Aristotle, or Isidore and John de Mandeville being put on the same plane with Albertus Magnus. It is true that particular errors of past writers were occasionally pointed out, but this was for some particular reason and might occur in the case of any author. Most often it was because things had not been properly identified under their ancient names. As Leonicenus had criticized Pliny, so his pupil, Euricius Cordus, in his *Botanologicon* of 1534 accused the apothecaries of his day of incorrectly labelling their drugs. And the first botanical publication of Leonard Fuchs, printed in 1531 as an appendix to the second volume of Otto Brunfels' *Herbarum vivae icones,* was *Notes on Herbs and Simples hitherto misrepresented by physicians,* chiefly because of incorrect application of classical names to them. Less often the error noticed was one of classification. When Valerius Cordus observed a relationship between the weed *Lithospermum arvense* and the anchusas and echiums, he added that it was "something which the ancients did not apprehend."

In the work on snakes and dragons edited in 1640 under the name of Aldrovandi by the professor of medicinal simples in the university of Bologna, Bartholomaeus Ambrosinus, such authorities were still cited as Solinus, the *Herbarium* of Apuleius, and Isidore, to say nothing of Olaus Magnus, Albertus Magnus, the anonymous author of the *Liber de natura rerum,* Bartholomaeus Anglicus and Arnald of Villanova. In many cases such post-classical and medieval authors were cited indirectly through the medium of Gesner writing a century earlier. For some snakes the work of 1640 still relied entirely upon the statements of Avicenna and Albertus Magnus, or Ambrose Paré would be the only modern writer cited. Thus is illustrated and demonstrated the prevalence of the old literary tradition and lore into the middle of the seventeenth century. Sometimes the old is rejected; more often it is accepted; in either case it is reiterated in detail and occupies a large share of the space in the series of stately tomes that imposingly house the works of nature of Aldrovandi and his continuators. The same characteristic is found two years later in the same editor's publication of the volume on monsters. For example, after asserting, "Faith nevertheless is to be placed in authors whom we have found trustworthy in many instances," the text proceeds to cite John de Mandeville, Solinus, Augustine and Isidore for the existence of men without mouths who live on odors alone, with an accompanying full-page picture of one sniffing at an apple.[102]

In those works which he himself lived to put through the press and which were not patched up from his and other materials after his death by later editors, Aldrovandi strove somewhat more manfully to draw a line between the results of observation and dissection, and the idle tales (*nugae*) of past writers.[103] Once he called Kiranides fabulous[104] but in another passage cited that work without disapproval.[105] While rejecting the fable of the phoenix, he accepted the notion that lions are afraid of a cock, and that the latter seems to know the stars from its discerning the hours by threes.[106] The anatomist, Gaspar Taliacotius, had shown by dissection that vipers, both male and female, possessed sexual organs and therefore did not conceive by the female's biting off the head of the male.[107] But the reason for thinking that Isidore was in error in stating that the cicada is born from the spittle of the cuckoo is that there is such an antipathy between the two animals that the cuckoo ceases to sing when the cicada begins to chirp, and further that cicadas get under the wings of the cuckoo and torment it to death, unfilial conduct which would be unthinkable ingratitude were they even indirectly its offspring.[108] Aldrovandi admitted that it was strange that the generation of bees from a dead ox had not been mentioned by Aristotle but only by Vergil and Pliny.[109] But this did not keep him from giving the proof of such generation adduced by Ber-

[102] *Monstrorum historia,* Bologna, 1642, pp. 5-6.

[103] See the preface to the reader in his first volume on birds, Bologna, 1599.

[104] *De avibus,* III (1603), 517.

[105] *De piscibus,* 1613, on medicinal use of the muraena: somewhere between pp. 343 and 371.

[106] *De avibus,* I (1599), 17: "ternas discernendo horas."

[107] *Ibid.,* p. 27.

[108] *De animalibus insectis,* 1602, p. 321.

[109] *Ibid.,* p. 58.

nardinus Gomesius Miedis of Saguntum, that he had squeezed out of no less than five drones a substance resembling the horned head of an ox.[110] Such were the arguments and "proofs" into which the assumption of relationships of sympathy and antipathy led one!

Aldrovandi asserted that flies would not enter a house where the head or the tail of a wolf had been suspended or buried.[111] He does not appear to have demonstrated this experimentally, but occasionally a sixteenth century naturalist tested such a statement. Caelius Rhodiginus had remarked that where Palladius seemed to say that raven-black pitch would keep ants off trees, the text should read "the fish coracinus" (*coracinum piscem* instead of *coracinam picem*). Rondelet tested whether this fish by some secret antipathy would keep ants from a tree as a suspended crab protects trees from cattle, found that it did not, and therefore concluded that pitch was the correct reading. But Aldrovandi objected that he might not have used a genuine coracinus fish.[112] The entire episode is instructive, since it was a textual problem rather than any tendency to question antipathies that induced Rondelet to make the experiment, and since even the failure of his test does not seem to have led him to doubt or to verify that a crab would protect trees from cattle.

To take another example of testing an assertion, Paracelsus had affirmed that the attractive power of the magnet would be increased by repeatedly igniting it and quenching it in an oil prepared from the best steel. Porta tried this out and found that the magnet rather lost its attractive power entirely. He further found false the statement that the magnet will not attract iron if anointed with garlic or in the presence of a diamond, unless the latter be counteracted by the blood of a goat.[113] Lest, however, we give Porta too much credit for verification, it may be added that where Hermolaus Barbarus had stated that a toad could be induced to void the gem from its head by placing the animal on purple cloth which it loves (but the gem must be quickly snatched

[110] *Ibid.*, p. 60.
[111] *Ibid.*, p. 358.
[112] *De piscibus*, Bologna, 1613, p. 76.
[113] Aldrovandi, *Musaeum metallicum*, 1648, pp. 557 and 948.

away or the toad itself will reabsorb it), Porta further stipulated that one must anger the toad by blows before it would void the gem.[114]

Aldrovandi found nothing in Aristotle or other classical writers to support the notion that the cock sometimes lays an egg, while Albertus Magnus had explicitly branded it as false. But so many very learned men, including Levinus Lemnius, not merely believed it but affirmed it from their own experience, that Aldrovandi, who had been shown eggs purporting to be those of cocks, was inclined to concede that in its old age a cock might void something resembling an egg. That, however, this substance had no shell, yet a skin so tough that it could not easily be broken by violence, or that a basilisk could be generated from it, he refused to believe.[115] Yet his editor in 1640 gave not merely a full-page picture of a cock with a serpent's tail but a half-page illustration showing a frog with a snake's tail which the text states was born of a woman in 1553.[116] Moreover, the same posthumous work devotes a chapter of fifteen pages to the basilisk, although doubts are again expressed whether it is hatched from an egg of a cock or hen.[117]

If in some respects the sixteenth century was less given to scientific scepticism than Albertus Magnus had been in the thirteenth century, yet some progress was being made in that direction. A wholesome effect was perhaps exercised by some of Scaliger's criticisms of Cardan. Cardan having argued that bees were spontaneously generated from honey because they were in too continual flight to carry eggs about with them, Scaliger replied that spontaneous generation required putrefaction, whereas honey, far from putrefying, was a preventive of putrefaction. Furthermore, that bees were not always on the wing, and that he had seen other flying insects have intercourse and generate. Scaliger, however, still accepted spontaneous generation, showers of frogs, and that the eel and purpura generated by their saliva, "non e coitu." And although Aldrovandi

[114] *Ibid.*, p. 810, cap. 60 de bufonite.

[115] *Ornithologiae tomus alter*, Bologna, 1600, p. 221, lib. XIV.

[116] *Serpentum et draconum historiae libri duo*, Bologna, 1640, pp. 61-63.

[117] *Ibid.*, pp. 361-75.

repeats Scaliger's aforesaid criticism of Cardan, he leaves it to the reader to accept or not.[118] Scaliger also criticized Cardan for holding that snakes shed their skins because of their dryness. He pointed out that the lizard which is not a dry animal at all also sheds its skin, while trees and cantharides, though both very dry, do not shed their bark or shell.[119]

Scaliger could, however, be quite wrong. After Cardan had correctly contended that usually rain was sufficient to account for rivers, Scaliger held that the pressure of the sea—which was raised above its natural place by the fact that mountains and highlands obtruded into this—upon small apertures at the bottom of the sea drove the water by subterranean channels up inside the mountains to a height above sea level, whence it descended in rivers. Cardan in reply argued that the water was rather raised underground by heat, a doctrine which he declared new but had been advanced long before by Albertus Magnus, Themo and Leonardo da Vinci.[120]

The pelican wounding itself to nourish its young with its blood, Aldrovandi distinguished as the pelican of painters and populace rather than the pelican of nature.[121] But he rather clung to the swan song legend.[122] After quoting Cesalpino against the notion that worms were generated or found alive within metals and rocks, Aldrovandi, although he had nothing new to contribute in favor of this belief, expressed his opinion that animals might be found in rocks and metals, although very rarely.[123] Similarly Thomas Moffett finally came to agree with Pennius that there were worms in stones. Felix Platter, dean of the physicians of Basel, had told him of finding a live toad in the center of a stone, and Zwinger narrated the same tale of a scorpion. Moffett,

[118] *De animalibus insectis,* Bologna, 1602, p. 57, lib. I. For Aldrovandi's own discussion of the spontaneous generation of the purpura see his posthumous *De reliquis animalibus exanguibus,* Bologna, 1606, pp. 299-301.

[119] Aldrovandi, *Serpentum et draconum historiae libri duo,* Bologna, 1640, p. 12.

[120] Duhem I (1906), 243-44.

[121] *Ornithologiae tomus tertius et postremus,* Bologna, 1603, p. 47.

[122] *Ibid.,* p. 21.

[123] *De animalibus insectis,* Bologna, 1602, p. 700 (VI, 8), citing lib. I de metal. cap. 2. I have verified the quotation from Andreas Caesalpinus, *De metallicis libri tres,* Rome, 1596, p. 5.

for his part, could not see why animals should not be generated in stones, since stones were generated in animals. And Bonus of Ferrara had not blushed to affirm that there had been showers of calves, blood and stones.[124] In Aldrovandi's posthumous work on bloodless animals it is asserted that a living frog was found in a block of marble at Antwerp, while at Ancona a score of living fish or mussels were released from one big rock.[125]

Cardan would have stigmatized as fabulous the statement that a goose lived sixty years, even though this was said by Albertus Magnus, had he not known of a goldfinch, a much smaller bird, which survived in a cage for thirteen years. Another consideration favorable to longevity of geese is the solidity and hardness of their flesh, so that even after a wild goose has been cooked for three days, its flesh does not soften and not even dogs will touch it.[126] All this was duly repeated by Aldrovandi with the supplementary statement from Gratarolus that a goose had been known to live for two hundred years, but this last assertion Aldrovandi said he would not accept even if it were made under oath.[127] As for Cardan, only two chapters later on he censured Albertus Magnus for sometimes repeating things said by others as if experienced by himself.[128] The posthumous edition of Aldrovandi's book on quadrupeds with cloven hoofs still cited Albertus, Hermolaus Barbarus and Georgius Agricola for the softening of adamant or the diamond by the blood of a goat, although it further stated that "our dealers in gems think this false and ridiculous."[129]

We have already sufficiently illustrated the point that Aldrovandi's posthumous editors of the seventeenth century, although likewise professors at Bologna and presumably having

[124] Moufetus, *Insectorum sive minimorum animalium theatrum, olim ab Edoardo Wottono, Conrado Gesnero, Thomaque Pennio inchoatum,* London, 1634, II, 18, pp. 247-48. Although the work was not printed until 1634, Moffett, who died in 1604, is said to have completed it in 1590.

[125] *De reliquis animalibus exanguibus,* Bologna, 1606, p. 241.

[126] *De rerum varietate,* VII, 34.

[127] *De avibus,* III, 118.

[128] *De rerum varietate,* VII, 36.

[129] *Quadrupedorum omnium bisulcorum historia,* Bologna, 1621, p. 701: "etiamsi hoc gemmarii nostri falsum et ridiculum existimant."

the advantage of more years of modern science behind them than he had had, seem to have been less cautious and sceptical and more credulous than he. Possibly, however, the circumstance that two of these posthumous volumes dealt with somewhat sensational subjects, namely, snakes and dragons and in the second case monsters, would have led to the inclusion of more questionable material even by Aldrovandi himself, had he lived to complete and publish them. Gesner at least had already depicted a sea-serpent coiling itself about a sailing vessel, and had cited those who averred that the serpent often raised its coils so high above the waves that a ship could pass under one of them.[130] Belon had seen embalmed bodies of winged serpents or of dragons with feet as well which flew from Arabia to Egypt. He further gave a picture of one.[131] Mattioli (1500-1577) in his commentaries on Dioscorides had denied that the basilisk could kill by its mere glance, but Aldrovandi or his editor of 1640 replied that the spirits from the eyes of old women could injure tender children.[132]

The interest of the late sixteenth and early seventeenth century in the subject of monsters and monstrous births is illustrated by the publication of works on that theme at Paris in 1570 by Sorbinus,[133] at Ursel in 1585 by Christopher Irenaeus,[134] at Frankfurt in 1609 by Schenck a Grafenberg,[135] and at Padua in 1616 by Fortunius Licetus,[136] professor of philosophy and

[130] *Conradi Gesneri . . . Historiae animalium lib. V qui est de serpentium natura*, Zurich, 1587, fol. 70v.

[131] *Les observations de plusieurs singularitez*, Paris, 1553, fol. 133r-v.

[132] *Serpentum et draconum hist. lib. II*, Bologna, 1640, p. 369.

[133] Arn. Sorbinus, *Tractatus de monstris*, Parisiis, H. de Marnet et G. Cavellat, 1570, 24mo.

[134] Christoph. Irenaeus, *De monstris: Von seltsamen Wundergeburten*, Ursel, Nic. Henricus, 1585, 4to.

[135] J. G. Schenck a Grafenberg, *Monstrorum historia memorabilis*, Francofurti, M. Becker et Th. de Bry, 1609.

[136] Fortunius Licetus, *De monstrorum causis natura et differentiis*, Patavii, 1616, 4to. A recent French translation is by Fr. Houssay, *De la nature des causes des différences des monstres d'après Fortunio Liceti traduit et résumé*, Paris, 1937, 8vo, 96 pp. 36 illus. G. Blasius added new monsters to those of Licetus in another Latin edition of Amsterdam, 1665, A. Frisius. An intervening edition of Padua, 1634 is also cited. Licetus had also published a work on spontaneous generation: *De spontaneo viventium ortu*, Vicenza, 1618.

medicine at that university. Indeed, works on the subject continued to appear in the eighteenth and nineteenth centuries. The authors of such works might better be called unnaturalists than naturalists, Broadsides printed at London in 1565, 1566 and 1568 show "The true fourme . . . of a monsterous chyld" by William Ellerton, "The discription of a . . . most monstrous fishe," and "A moste true and marveilous straunge wonder . . . of xvii monstrous fishes" by Thimothy Granger.[137]

Pierre de L'Ancre, in his *Tableau of the Inconstancy and Instability of All Things,* a jaunty work of over one thousand pages in octavo, published at Paris in 1607,[138] and again in 1610, was impressed by the bizarreness and extravagance of nature,[139] as manifested in such matters as mutation of sex, the discovery of a wild man in the forests of France in 1599, the antipathies between things, stones that seem to have sense, cruel animals that turn kind, the bizarre production of certain animals and plants, strange wounds and their marvelous cures, madness and dreams, and the fact that often our names bear some presage of prosperity or of a sinister event. With this estimate of the world of nature as odd and lawless went a belief in the action of spirits and witchcraft, so that we are not surprised to find de L'Ancre writing in 1612 a *Tableau of the Inconstancy of Evil Angels and Demons* with an ample discussion of sorcerers and sorcery.[140] This work too was republished, in 1613 and in 1622.

Modern historians, biographers and editors have too often failed to note all sides of the works of these sixteenth century naturalists, their weaknesses and superstition as well as their contribution towards future science. They have even sometimes carelessly or stupidly or wilfully misrepresented their views. Thus A. H. Evans, after affirming rather gratuitously that Turner's book on birds is the first "which treats them in any-

[137] Huntington Library Photostats, List 4, Items 54, 53 and 70. See too 121, "A true discription of two monsterous chyldren," London, 1565.

[138] P. de L'Ancre, *Tableau de l'inconstance et instabilité de toutes choses,* Paris, 1607, 8vo, 1067 pp. Copy used: BN R.40586.

[139] *Ibid.,* p. 320 *et seq.*

[140] *Tableau de l'inconstance des mauvais anges et démons ou il est amplement traicté des sorciers et de la sorcellerie,* Paris, 1612, 4to, 569 pp.: BN 4° R.2995.

thing like a modern scientific spirit," and that "almost every page bears witness to a personal knowledge of the subject which would be distinctly creditable even to a modern ornithologist,"[141] grants that it contains some errors, "as in the case of the very old story of the breeding of the Bernicle-Goose (which, however, he was most loth to credit even when assured of its truth by an Irish Divine.)"[142] But on turning to the text itself, we find that while Turner hesitated to accept the statement of the medieval historian, Giraldus Cambrensis, and the popular report along the coasts of England, Scotland and Ireland, he seems to have been convinced by an Irish theologian named Octavian who swore by the Gospel that he had seen and touched such barnacle birds while they were still growing out of rotten shipwood like fungi and gradually assuming the shape of birds. Indeed, Turner wrote to Gesner that so many men of great integrity affirmed such generation "that I venture to believe it and to persuade others to believe it." He was therefore hardly "most loth" to believe it. Evans even mistranslated Turner's very words. Thus in his English version we read, "No one has seen the Bernicle's nest or egg, nor is this wonderful, since Bernicles without a parent's aid are said to have spontaneous generation in this way."[143] But in the corresponding Latin text there is no justification for the words "are said to." The spontaneous generation of these geese is stated as a fact without any such qualifying words.[144] Or Evans translates, "This curious generation of the Bernicle . . ." where Turner speaks merely of "This generation of the Bernicle. . . ." Turner went on to say that this generation would not seem so very prodigious to those who had read what Aristotle wrote concerning the Ephemerus, a four-footed flying creature that lived for only a day and emerged from pouches a trifle larger than grapes on the surface of

[141] This is humbug in the same style as we heard from Richter concerning Leonardo da Vinci.

[142] *Turner on Birds*, ed. Evans, pp. ix-x.

[143] *Ibid.*, p. 27.

[144] *Ibid.*, p. 26: "Nidum berniclae aut ovum nemo vidit nec mirum quum sine parentis opera berniclae ad hunc modum spontaneam habeant generationem."

a river near the Cimmerian Bosphorus. If this was true and worthy of so great a philosopher, it did not a little to convince one of the possibility of barnacle birds.

Incidentally it may be noted that this fable of barnacle geese, which had already been discredited by Aeneas Sylvius in the fifteenth century,[145] continued to vex the pages of supposedly scientific works as late as 1668, when it appeared once more in the posthumous edition of the work of Aldrovandi on trees by Ovidius Montalbanus, professor emeritus at Bologna, where he had taught logic, the theory of medicine, mathematics and astronomy, and moral philosophy for nearly half a century. Already in 1592, however, Colonna decided that the story of geese or ducks growing out of shells which were the fruit of trees had developed from finding in the water or cast up on the shore branches of trees to which shellfish had attached themselves. His servant had collected some after a winter storm lasting ten days and they resembled almonds or Rondelet's *balani*.[146]

In the same year that the astronomers of Europe were filled with astonishment at the new star of 1572, quite a stir in local scientific circles had been caused by the discovery near Bologna of a creature such as had never been seen before in all Europe, namely, a dragon with two feet. It had been killed by a peasant who was driving an oxcart, had been depicted to the life in a painting by Aldrovandi, and had also been preserved dried in the museum at Bologna. It was about two cubits in length. It was considered a fortunate circumstance, which had probably prevented the dragon from attacking the oxen and teamster first, that the cart was made of ash, a wood well known for its antipathy to every variety of serpent. Where had this strange creature come from? Had it migrated from distant regions? Had it fallen from the sky? Was it the product of miscegenation between two different species? Or had it been generated from putrefaction like the barnacle geese? After citing the views of Avicenna, Scotus, and other past authors, and consulting with

[145] T IV, 393-94.
[146] Fabio Colonna, *Piscium aliquot plantarumque novarum historia*, Naples, 1592, p. 14.

his present colleagues at Bologna, namely Pompeius Bolognetus, ordinary professor of medicine, Ioannes Augustinus Cucchius, professor of surgery, and Sebastianus Regulus, ordinary professor of philosophy, Bartholomaeus Ambrosinus, the editor of Aldrovandi's posthumous publication on serpents and dragons, came to the conclusion that none of the above explanations was satisfactory, and that the two-footed dragon must be classed as a monstrosity.[147]

On the question of the spontaneous generation of lower forms of animal life Aldrovandi himself steered a somewhat middle course. He affirmed that wasps and flies were produced both from putrefaction and by sexual intercourse.[148] He had not yet observed butterflies in the act of intercourse but had watched the cohabitation of silkworms.[149] Worms without feet, on the other hand, he thought were generated from putridity rather than by sexual intercourse,[150] just as they were inferior to bees, wasps and hornets in having neither memory nor *ingenium*.[151] Rondelet had a chapter on fish that were spontaneously generated.[152] Writers on herbs were even more ready to believe in the spontaneous generation of plants. Greene writes of the work of Tragus: "One may doubt if any other book was ever printed, or even written in any age, in which there find expression so many whimsical and superstitious fancies about seeds.[153]

Interest in detailed demonstration of how marvelous are the works of God was still a leading motive in the study of natural phenomena, whether through the writings of the past and the more recent accounts of travelers to distant parts of the globe, or through more direct observation by dissection and botanical excursions. In this way religion stimulated the study of nature and vice versa, instead of the warfare of science and theology which some have supposed. Caspar Wolf, in dedicating to Peter

[147] *Serpentum et draconum historiae lib. II*, Bologna, 1640, pp. 401-16 (II, 5), De dracone bipede in agro Bononiensi.

[148] *De animalibus insectis*, Bologna, 1602, pp. 205, 354-55.

[149] *Ibid.*, p. 253.

[150] *Ibid.*, p. 638.

[151] *Ibid.*, p. 641.

[152] *Libri de piscibus marinis*, IV, 4: "De piscibus sponte nascentibus."

[153] E. L. Greene, *Landmarks of Botanical History*, 1909, p. 236.

Hafner, a surgeon of Zurich, his edition of Gesner's posthumous work on the scorpion and other serpents, pointed out that it contained not only marvels but even prodigies.[154] Gesner himself in 1558, in dedicating his *History of Fish and Aquatic Animals* to the emperor, dwelt upon the marvelous works of God in the vasty deep, such as the echeneis and the torpedo.

The belief in spontaneous generation, in the existence of worms in stones and of live frogs in rocks, in the formative influence of the stars, in monsters, freaks of nature, and marvelous works of God, logically disposed Aldrovandi to account for fossils as incomplete animals whose spontaneous generation had failed of full accomplishment, rather than as fossilized remains of once living creatures. He noted, however, the opinion of certain ancients that Egypt had once been covered by the sea because shells abound on its mountains, the attribution by Isidore of Seville of such remains to the flood, and the suggestion of Olympiodorus that vehement winds might have carried them far inland or to mountain tops. He agreed with Ioannes Goropius Becanus (1518-1572), who practiced medicine at Antwerp, that there is no region so high or so far from the sea that shells of creatures who live only in marine waters are not found there. But the very acceptance of this fact apparently made it the harder for him to believe that all such places could once have been near or under the sea. Instead he argued that, if the Giver of forms can produce fish and frogs in the air, mice and worms from mud, then shells may be produced on mountains and far inland. If a toad can be generated in the heart of a rock, why may not marine animals be similarly generated on mountains: as living beings, if the place and material are adequate; as lifeless bodies, if the force of nature is equal only to this much?[155] Thus Aldrovandi still adhered to the scholastic doctrine of Avicenna and Albertus Magnus, although, according to Ley,

[154] *Conradi Gesneri . . . Historiae insectorum libellus qui est de scorpione per Casparum Wolphium Tigurinum medicum ex relicto schedarum fasciculo methodice collectus et in lucem editus.* Tiguri in officina Froschoviana MDLXXXVII.

[155] *De reliquis animalibus exanguis libri quatuor,* 1606, pp. 238-41.

Fracastoro had already rejected the notion of the *vis plastica* of the stars in 1517.[156] Certainly Leonardo da Vinci had shown by close examination of shells that it could not be applied in their particular case. But his notes unfortunately remained unpublished.

It should be realized that there is no necessary correlation or variation in inverse ratio between an individual's positive scientific achievement on the one hand and his acceptance or rejection of superstition, occult notions and trust in magical procedure on the other hand. Cardan may have been a great mathematician and Falloppia a first-rate anatomist. Whatever their merit and standing in these respects, it did not keep the one from using human blood, seven times distilled to free it from all water, in resolution of the nerves, nor the other from advising the wearing of an umbilicus in a silver ring as an amulet against colic.[157]

The occult and magical still formed a considerable constituent in sixteenth century accounts of plants and animals, as it had done in the ancient and medieval writers from whom they quoted so extensively. There appears, however, to be more of it in the works on animals than in those on plants. Bock, for instance, showed commendable reticence in this regard, referring the reader to Pliny and Dioscorides for further details concerning the mandragora, and to the alchemists for their use of the herb lunaria, while he contented himself with remarking that vervain was still today employed more in magic than in medicine.[158] Aldrovandi regularly included under each animal treated a section on its antipathies and sympathies; less regularly, a section on presages from it other than through augury and auspices. He also included the last two, as we have already seen, but as a Christian he did not approve of them,[159] especially since they had recently been forbidden by the Council of Trent.[160] But he believed that

[156] Willy Ley, *Konrad Gesner,* 1929, p. 117. Unfortunately no reference is given to any work by Fracastoro to enable one to verify this statement.

[157] Ulysses Aldrovandus, *Monstrorum historia,* 1642, pp. 310-11.

[158] German edition of 1560, fols. 329v-330r, 337r-v, 78r.

[159] Aldrovandi, *De avibus,* I (1599), 15-16.

[160] He adds at the close of his first volume on birds (*ibid.,* p. 893):

when birds congregated in great numbers in unusual places that it was a sign of injury and wrath divine.[161] The interpretations from animals seen in dreams which he repeated from Cardan and Artemidorus he generally condemned as nonsense, yet intermingled them with his science. His use in medicine of plants and animals and their parts was also likely to include their occult virtues and employment of them as amulets. In view of the exhaustive manner in which he usually quoted the classics on any bird, it seems odd that he included nothing concerning the use of the iunx in Greek magic.[162]

Dodoens described the faculties or medicinal qualities of plants as of four orders. The first order were direct from the four elements and first qualities and their compounds. On these were based or from these were derived the second order of faculties which hardened and softened, rarefied and condensed, attracted and repelled, allayed and excited pain. Also the third order which maturated, suppurated, grew flesh, conglutinated, formed scars, evoked the bodily fluids, and allayed coughing. The fourth order of faculties, on the other hand, did not depend from the previous orders but were knowable only from experience. They were occult, specific and latent, following the property of the substance or essence itself.[163]

Scaliger in his *Exoteric Exercises on Cardan's De subtilitate,* in discussing the reputed property of the blood of a goat to soften diamonds, noted that recent writers, who detested occult properties and called them the asylum of ignorance, said that the blood acted on the diamond because of an analogy between them which existed in a common principle. Scaliger was unable to see that this was any improvement upon, or essentially different from, the conception of occult virtue.[164]

"Meantime if anything has been inconsiderately said or written contrary to the Holy Fathers and the decrees of the Synod of Trent, let it be infect and unsaid."

[161] *Ibid.,* p. 9.

[162] *Ibid.,* p. 863 (XII, 28).

[163] Dodonaeus, *Stirpium historia,* I, i, 3.

[164] *Exotericarum exercitationum liber quintus decimus de subtilitate ad Hieronymum Cardanum,* Paris, 1557, 344,8: cited Aldrovandi, *De quadrupedibus bisulcis,* Bologna, 1621, p. 701.

Anent the statement of Pliny and Aelian that stags extract snakes from their holes by the breath of their nostrils Gesner entered into a long discussion, which was quoted verbatim in the posthumous 1621 edition of Aldrovandi on cloven-hoofed quadrupeds. The question was whether this phenomenon was to be explained as the result of their breathing into the hole and thereby alluring the snakes to come out, which would seem contradictory to the antipathy commonly believed to exist between stags and snakes, or whether it should not be attributed to the stags' inhaling all the air from the hole and so forcing the snake to follow, as a liquid does in the operation of syphoning.[165]

The doctrine of signatures in plants, that their external appearance bore indications of their curative properties, especially of their occult virtues, had spread with the Paracelsan revival and continued in favor during the course of the seventeenth century. Dodoens spoke of it as a recent invention not mentioned by the ancients, and as so variable and uncertain that it could not be accepted as a part of science.[166] The editors of Aldrovandi's posthumous works in the middle of the seventeenth century were more favorable to signatures, Bartholomaeus Ambrosinus discussing those of parts of the human body in plants without citing authorities,[167] and Ovidius Montalbanus quoting Croll and Porta on the subject.[168] Or we are told of a stone with markings like those of small-pox which a Jesuit brought back from India (and another Jesuit from the West Indies) and which two pharmacists had found the year before in the territory of Lucca. Suspended from the neck so that it touched the region of the heart, it drew the poison of the disease to the surface and relieved the patient. Rubbed above the eyes, it protected them from the small-pox. The cowherds of India, so the Jesuit said, suspended it from the necks of their cattle to protect the animals

[165] *Ibid.*, p. 801.

[166] Dodonaeus, *Stirpium historia*, I, i, 11: "tam fluxa et incerta est ut pro scientia aut doctrina nullatenus habenda videatur."

[167] *Monstrorum historia*, Bologna, 1642, p. 306.

[168] *Dendrologiae naturalis s. arborum historiae libri duo*, Bologna, 1668, p. 84.

from the disease. Nature by the signature of this stone taught men that it was beneficial for small-pox.[169]

The relationship between the beginnings of scientific botany and the gathering of magic herbs by sorcerers may still be seen in the work of Tragus. Elsewhere I have mentioned the belief in medieval Lorraine that midsummer night was the best time for the gathering of herbs for magical purposes.[170] Similarly Tragus tells how for four years in succession he and three companions kept watch all through that night to see if ferns would shed seeds at that time. He collected the falling seeds by placing pieces of cloth or mullein leaves under the plants. He assures us that he employed no incantations or other superstitious observances, and in general magic procedure in the plucking of herbs is not found in the writings of sixteenth century naturalists. But, as Greene has remarked,[171] it does not seem to have occurred to him to collect the seeds, or that these would fall to the ground, at any other time than during midsummer night.

The belief in demons in human form in deep wells, mines, and elsewhere underground, which Agricola had set forth in his book concerning subterranean animals, continued to appear in learned and scientific works from Pierre Belon's discussion of a *demon metallicus* in 1553,[172] to the posthumous *Musaeum Metallicum* of Aldrovandi in 1648.[173]

The naturalists of the sixteenth century can in only a few cases be said to surpass a thirteenth century botanist like Rufinus in observation of nature and descriptive ability. None of them is the equal of an Albertus Magnus in intellectual range and grasp, critical and logical power. None of them could write as directly and lucidly, or develop a subject as he could. But there were more of them, or at least so it seems when we compare the

[169] *Musaeum metallicum,* Bologna, 1648, pp. 882-83, cap. 67, de lapide variolato.

[170] T IV, 277: probably instead of "noon" ('midi' in Digot) one should read "midnight" as the moment most favorable for plucking the herbs.

[171] *Landmarks of Botanical History,* 1909, p. 238, citing Tragus, *Stirp. comm.*, p. 544.

[172] *Les observations de plusieurs singularitez et choses memorables, trouvées en Grece, Asie, Indée, Egypte, Arabie, & autres pays estranges,* Paris, 1553, I, 53, fol. 51v.

[173] *Op. cit.*, p. 19.

number of authors of printed works with the fewer extant naturalists in manuscript. They had other advantages: that books and writings of the past were more accessible for them; that they understood the Greek language and texts somewhat better; that dissection and knowledge of anatomy had made strides since the thirteenth and especially during the sixteenth century; that new species of flora and fauna were brought to their notice from the American continents and the Far East. Also pictures were multiplied, although for some time those illuminated by hand were preferred. The habit of collecting and the institution of gardens and museums had apparently developed farther. Some of these advantages, however, seem at times to have been a little too much for them and to have constituted a load under which they staggered rather than a vehicle by which they progressed more rapidly. New data were presented in the old patterns and framework; in consequence were often lost sight of; and, as isolated or misplaced facts, failed to illuminate and to signify as they should have done and as they do when looked back upon from our vantage-point. One might jump to the conclusion that the invention of the microscope was essential for any real advance, but it cannot be said that it exerted any markedly beneficial influence on Aldrovandi's editors of the following century.

The works of Aldrovandi not only continued to satisfy the standards of natural history in the seventeenth century, as we have repeatedly illustrated from their posthumous continuations, but were fairly acceptable to Buffon in his equally voluminous natural history of the eighteenth century. He indicated some of Aldrovandi's failings it is true—his prolixity and excessive credulity—but then called him the most industrious and learned of naturalists, and said that his books should be considered among the best on the whole field of natural history.[174] Earlier in the eighteenth century le Gendre in his *Treatise on Opinion, or Memoirs to Serve the History of the Human Mind,* had treated

[174] Buffon, *Hist. nat.,* Paris, 1749-1789, I, 26. The passage has already been quoted by Libri, IV (1841), 105.

of Aldrovandi at considerable length.[175] He said that Aldrovandi had superseded all his predecessors and had spared neither pains nor expense nor travels, and had employed designers, painters, sculptors and engravers at high salaries to illustrate his volumes. Le Gendre confessed himself unable to discern the true from the fabulous in Aldrovandi's volumes, and so set forth the opinions of the naturalists in a topical order, treating first of sympathy, then of human beings, then of other animals, plants, stars, waters and minerals. He still included such monstrosities as men with ten to twelve feet and a patriarch seen by the Portuguese in the far east in 1535 who was then 335 years old and had a son aged ninety.[176] The father had had three new growths of teeth and beard, and in 1535 the third beard was still black. Its wearer finally died at the age of over four hundred. Later le Gendre concluded that "the researches of the naturalists, full of uncertainties, make it plain to us that while nature serves our needs, it equally balks our curiosity."[177]

[175] Gilbert-Charles le Gendre, *Traité de l'opinion ou memoires pour servir à l'histoire de l'esprit humain,* Paris, 1733, IV, 8 (tome IV, pp. 10-11).

[176] *Ibid.*, pp. 71, 83-84.

[177] *Ibid.*, p. 193.

CHAPTER XXXIX

THE LORE OF GEMS

He who speaks against common beliefs is detested.
—GARCIA DA ORTA

In our chapter on The Sixteenth Century Naturalists we were concerned chiefly with the treatment of herbs and animals. In the present chapter we consider the lore of gems as illustrated by a number of representative works on that subject from that published in 1502 by Camillo Lunardi to that of Anselm de Boodt which first appeared in 1609. Metals and other minerals than gems will also receive some attention.

Camillus Leonardus or de Leonardis or Camillo Lunardi of Pesaro seems to have been a man of considerable learning and even scientific proficiency. He was a doctor of arts and medicine, and already in 1480 had joined with Lorenzo Bonincontri in drawing up astronomical tables[1] and had himself verified the positions of certain fixed stars.[2] In 1496 he had published a work[3] which seems to have been in part a commentary on the treatise on the movements of the heavenly bodies,[4] issued two years before by William Aegidius or William Gilliszoon from Wissekerke in Zeeland, who was at that time a citizen of Carpentras. In addition to two astronomical sections, the work of Camillo included horoscopes and astrological rules for bleeding and administering drugs. The work of Aegidius too, however, had treated of the influences of the stars as well as of their movements. Lunardi's astronomical publications were continued into

[1] Tiraboschi stated that they were extant in an Este MS.

[2] In his work of 1496 at fols. 3-4 occur, "Stelle fixe verificate per me Camillum anno 1480."

[3] *Expositio canonum equatorii celestium motuum absque calculo,* Venetiis, Georgius de Arrivabenis, July 21, 1496. Dedication to Giovanni Sforza, lord of Pesaro. Hain 4283; Pellechet 3178.

[4] T IV, 558.

the sixteenth century by a *Theory of the Planets* which appeared at Pesaro in 1508.[5] In the meantime he had printed a book on the theme which concerns us in this chapter.

The *Speculum lapidum* or *Mirror of Stones* of 1502[6] was dedicated to Caesar Borgia. Camillo justified the writing of it by the assertion that he had not found the subject treated completely by any previous author, although it had been touched on by divers doctors, both ancient and modern. It does not seem, however, that his book represents any distinct advance over the treatment of gems and their sculpture in the *De mineralibus* of Albertus Magnus, from whom he has borrowed extensively. Neither in tone nor content does Camillo make any noteworthy departure from the traditional treatment of gems common to previous authors. Indeed, his book is merely a compilation with little trace of independent or scientific observation. A few such passages as an allusion to the invention of gunpowder in the midst of a discussion of nitrum or saltpeter are the sole indication of changing time. Brasavola, writing in 1534, said that he knew of no one who had written more ineptly on any subject than Lunardi on stones. He thought that *cyaneus* and *coeruleus* were two different stones yet had used the same words in describing both.[7] The *Speculum* is not a long treatise, running to about thirty thousand words. More than a third of the space is devoted to an alphabetical listing and description of particular stones, while another third is occupied with astrological and magic images carved on gems and is in large part made up of chapters drawn from various books of magic. In both cases it is the occult virtues of gems or of images engraved upon them that especially attract the author's attention.

[5] *Tehorice* (sic) *planetarum nuper aedite cum declarationibus additionibus ac figuris peroptime signatis quae sine aliquo commento intelligi possunt.* (fol. A ii) *Theoricae planetarum imitantes Gerardum cremonensem ac eas declarantes . . . a Camillo Leonardo Pisaurensi aedite.* Pisauri impressum per Hieronymum Soncinum imperante . . . Joanne Sfortia, calen. April. MCCCCC. VIII.

[6] Camillus Leonardus, *Speculum lapidum*, Venice, J B. Sessa, 1502, 4to.

[7] Ant. Musa Brasavola, *Examen omnium simplicium medicamentorum*, Lyons, 1537, p. 428.

Lunardi lists his authorities as Dioscorides, Aristotle, Hermes, Evax, Serapion, Avicenna, Mesue, Solomon, Physiologus, Pliny, Solinus, Lapidarius, Heliamandus (Helinandus?), Isidore, Arnald, Juba, Dionysius of Alexandria, Albertus Magnus, Vincentius historialis (i.e. Vincent of Beauvais), Thetel, Rabanus,[8] Bartholomaeus de Ripa Romea, Marbod, Ortulanus, the *Liber pandectarum* which was a work by Matthaeus Silvaticus of Mantua, dedicated to Robert of Naples in 1337 and printed as early as 1474, *Cornucopiae,*[9] Kiranus (i.e. Kiranides), and *Liber de natura rerum* (of Thomas of Cantimpré). It is evident that this list is not arranged in chronological order, and that some of the authors are known to Lunardi only indirectly through others. In the course of his work he cites yet other authors: for instance, Plato, Peter of Abano the Conciliator, the commentary by his own teacher, Cajetan de Thienis, on the *Meteorology* of Aristotle, Niccolò de Comitibus of Padua and his treatise on weather prediction, and Henry of Saxony as a commentator on the *De secretis mulierum* of Albertus Magnus, a work of which Henry has sometimes been incorrectly represented as the author.[10] To Albertus Magnus, Lunardi incorrectly ascribes a work on the magnet, perhaps that of Petrus Peregrinus. He accepts Solomon without question as the writer of a book on precious stones from which he quotes a number of times, once for their diverse and marvelous virtues. He even cites it against Albertus Magnus that sculptured stones do not as a rule lose their virtues with age. Lunardi also assigns to Solomon a book on the seals of stones

[8] "Thetel Rabanus" appears as if a single name in the printed edition and was so accepted by C. W. King, *The Natural History of Gems,* 1865, p. 10, where he speaks of "Thetal Rabanus, better known as Rabanus Maurus. This last, styled by Camillo 'a most ancient doctor,' was abbot of Fulda in 822." But Camillo obviously has reference to two authors: the Thetel concerning images carved on gems who is cited by Thomas of Cantimpré, and not improbably the Rabanus who is cited by Bartholomaeus Anglicus: T II, 389, 399, 415. Possibly "Bartholomaeus de Ripa Romea" is meant for Bartholomaeus Anglicus.

[9] *Cornu copiae. Thesaurus Cornu copiae et Horti Adonidis.* Venice, Aldus Manutius, 1496. (Reprinted, 1500).

[10] See E. Wickersheimer, *Henri de Saxe et le De secretis mulierum,* Communication faite au 3e Congrès de l'Histoire de L'Art de Guérir (Londres, 17-22 juillet 1922), Antwerp, 1923, pp. 3-8, for a refutation of this error.

which he found without name of author and from which he quotes for several solid pages. He further draws many images from "Chael, one of the sons of the sons of Israel," whom he makes a different personage from Thetel, but both names are probably corruptions for Zael or Zehel or Sahl ibn Bishr, a Jewish astrologer who wrote in Arabic. Lunardi also takes magic images from Raziel in the *Book of Wings.*

All these magical and necromantic images are quite superstitious, and, lest his account of them seem to conflict with the Catholic faith, Lunardi warns Caesar Borgia not to believe that their virtues operate necessarily upon man, since his will is free. "Nor when I say that the image makes the wearer of it an emperor, potent, victorious, and so on, do you understand that I say this absolutely, since that too would be false. For if a person of low rank or a woman should wear it, this would seem not to be true. But interpret what I say with common sense. For in whatever condition it finds a man, it extols him in that and in others makes him more powerful. So should my words be understood and not otherwise."

It goes without saying that Lunardi is a believer in astrology. He subjects stones completely to the influence of the heavens but grants that man by his free will may resist that influence. In the matter of fascination he asserts that he has personally experienced the power of Italian wolves by their glance to make a man hoarse and unable to shout for aid. Yet Camillo gives one or two signs of scepticism. He affirms that in his time there are many deceivers in every matter. In another passage he ridicules the idea that it is perilous for vessels with iron nails or parts to navigate in the vicinity of regions where the stone magnet abounds.

The *Speculum lapidum* was reprinted a number of times: at Venice in 1516, at Augsburg in 1533, at Paris in 1610 by Petrus Arlensis de Scudalupis together with that author's own work on the sympathy of the seven metals and seven select stones with the seven planets, and at Hamburg in 1717. This Petrus Arlensis, who is styled a priest of Jerusalem, while condemning the "false magic" of the Arabs, approves of natural magic and of "holy and divine wisdom." He admits that there are many evil characters employed in magic, and that the characters carved on stones have no power or significance, but he approves of Hebrew characters and of the sign of the cross.[11] Knowledge of natural magic, he says, is "the contemplation of secret things in their natures, properties, powers, qualities, substances and virtues." All these editions were in Latin. An Italian translation appeared in 1565 and was reprinted in 1617. There was an English version in 1750. It is a reasonably safe conjecture that the work owed its long continued popularity to its astrology, magic, and other superstition and not to its mineralogy. Yet according to Gaffarel who wrote in the next century Lunardi incurred the charge of atheism by his assertion of the efficacy of images.[12]

What seems to have been the first edition of the eleventh century work of Marbod upon gems, with its emphasis upon their occult and marvelous properties, was printed at Vienna in 1511.[13] It seems strange that it had not been published sooner. It was printed again in 1531, probably at Freiburg im Breisgau,[14] with the scholia of Georg Pictorius of Villingen, and at Cologne in 1539.

Erasmus Stella or Stueler of Zwickau (d. 1521), where he was a magistrate and historiographer as well as physician, composed a treatise on gems which is of little independent value or importance.[15] It was written in Prussia,[16] dedicated to the head of

[11] For the passages cited see pp. 479, 487, 492-94, of his *Sympathia septem metallorum ac septem selectorum lapidum ad planetas,* which occupies pp. 245-499 of his edition of Camillus Leonardus, *Speculum lapidum,* Paris, 1610.

[12] Jacques Gaffarel, *Curiosités inouies,* edition of Hamburg, 1676, p. 105, "atheismi nota iniusta est."

[13] Marbodaeus (*sic*), *Libellus de lapidibus preciosis,* Vienna, Hieronymus Victor, 1511, 4to.

[14] Marbodaeus, *De lapidibus preciosis encheiridion cum scholiis Pictorii Villingensis. Eiusdem Pictorii de lapide molari carmen,* 1531, 56 fols., 8vo.

[15] *Erasmi Stellae Libonothani Interpraetamenti Gemmarum libellus . . . Finit libellus de Gemmis doctoris Erasmi Stueler Zuickauiensis phisici & senatoris precipui quem Nuremberge imprimebat Federicus Peypus Mense sextili Anno partus virginei MDXVII.* George Fabricius in his life of Rivius, prefixed to the 1614 edition of the latter's *Opera,* calls Stella consul of Zwickau and says he wrote on amber as well as gems.

[16] "Ex aedibus nostris in Basiliavia Borusicorum."

the Teutonic Order,[17] and was printed at Nürnberg in 1517.[18] It was little more than a compilation from Greek and Latin writers, above all Pliny, although Stella professed to use Theophrastus also and cited Dioscorides, Solinus, Serapion and Marsilio Ficino. The chief new feature was an arrangement of gems in groups according to their colors. Stella was led to compose his work by hearing others call gems by more recent names instead of their classical appellations. He was complimented by Christopher Scheurl for purging his account of gems from superstitious and magical vanity, whereas about all that he has done is to repeat Pliny as to the lies and vanity of the magi. But also like Pliny he still ascribes many powers to gems and an occult force. He further makes the Plinian excuse that if he has repeated any too extreme powers of gems, he has done so merely in order to illustrate what former writers thought of them and not because he believes or asserts such himself.

In our chapter on pharmacy we have heard Brasavola and Mundella make serious restrictions upon the powers attributed to gems or their employment in pharmacy.

The work on gems of Franciscus Rueus or François de la Rue, first published in 1547,[19] continued the favorable attitude towards astrological images carved upon gems which we have seen in Lunardi. This attitude, however, led to the deletion by the censor of a passage in which de la Rue asserted that all those skilled in the lore of the stars, and many medical practitioners who had tested it, agreed that the image of a lion carved on gold when the sun occupied the first degree of the sign of Leo was an amulet against the stone.[20] This, it may be recalled, was a

[17] "Jobo ecclesie Pomesaniensis praesuli sacrosanctae militiae theutonicorum Primati."

[18] Melchior Adam, *Vitae Germanorum medicorum,* incorrectly represents it as a posthumous publication, thirty years after Stella's death.

[19] Franciscus Rueus, *De gemmis aliquot iis praesertim quarum divus Ioannes Apostolus in sua Apocalypsi meminit,* Parisiis, 1547, 8vo. I have not seen this original edition but have used the text included in Gesner's *De omni rerum fossilium genere gemmis lapidibus metallis et huiusmodi libri aliquot plerique nunc primum editi,* Tiguri, 1565. Here our work is entitled: "De gemmis aliquot iis praesertim quarum divus Ioannes meminit, De aliis quoque quarum usus hoc aevi apud omnes percrebuit libri duo. . . Editio secunda nam prima mutila et inscio authore edita fuerat."

[20] This deleted passage was restored in the 1565 edition, fol. 24v.

moot case which had the support of the great medical authority, Peter of Abano, in his *Conciliator,* but had been condemned by the French ecclesiastic, Jean Gerson, in the case of a doctor of Montpellier, and had subsequently been much debated in the treatise on astrological images published by the Spaniard, Jerome Torrella, at Valencia in 1496.[21] Rueus introduced the passage in question by saying that he would omit magic images, since many were terrified by the very name of magic, and would give this example of an astrological image. In the second edition of 1565 at Zurich, by Conrad Gesner, beyond the confines of France and Roman catholicism, he added the qualification that he would not have the reader interpret his remarks, as the censor of the first edition had, to mean that those philosophers or Rueus himself thought that there was such virtue in a mere image. The healing virtue resides in the gold thus carved, and the carving merely made the gold more ready to receive the influence of the stars.[22]

Rueus also wrote a longer defense of such astrological images and reply to his censor, most of which Gesner omitted in the Zurich edition[23] as too prolix, not in conformity with true religion, and magical. He reproduced certain passages, however, which consist chiefly of citations from Bonaventura, the *De fato* ascribed to Aquinas,[24] the *Speculum astronomiae* of Albertus Magnus, Peter of Abano, and the life of Apollonius of Tyana by Philostratus, which in de la Rue's opinion supported astrological images. Gesner pointed out that the citations from Bonaventura merely recognized the influence of the stars on nature, not on images. But Gesner did not contest the authenticity of *De fato.* His own attitude, however, was against such images. On the other hand, that the heavens and stars influenced all inferior bodies, even subterranean ones, he held that there was no need for de la Rue to demonstrate, since practically no one denied it.[25]

Gesner also once or twice qualified extreme virtues attributed

[21] T IV, 122, 576, 578, 580ff.

[22] *De gemmis,* 1565, fol. 25r.

[23] In an "Ad lectorem" at the close of de la Rue's text, fol. 73r.

[24] Fr. Pelster, *Philosophisches Jahrbuch,* 36 (1923), 150-54, has shown grounds for attributing the work to Albertus Magnus.

[25] *De gemmis,* 1565, fols. 73v-74r.

to gems by Rueus with marginal comments such as "Believed superstitiously" and "Ridiculous and not to be taken seriously."[26] The former comment had reference to intellectual and emotional effects ascribed in the text to sapphires. The latter applied to the statement that a certain stone would detect a thief, if offered to him in bread, or even if the bread had merely been cooked with it. De la Rue himself had said that he would not have included this property of the gem, had it not been confirmed by grave and trustworthy authors—the old excuse. It must be added that other equally incredible virtues attributed to gems in the text escaped without any such criticism by Gesner in the margin. And the further question may well be asked why Gesner republished such a work at all.

It is true that Rueus repeatedly states that he omits or passes over the properties ascribed to the gem under consideration by the superstitious vanity of magicians. In this respect, like Stella, he repeats the words and attitude of his highly esteemed authority, Pliny, who had similarly censured such lore of the magi and had less often included it in the case of gems than in that of herbs and parts of animals. Or Rueus mentions other properties asserted of a gem only to reject them. Thus he denies that a diamond will reveal a wife's unfaithfulness or that it will attract the virtues of other gems to itself as it attracts iron.[27] Or he declares false the attribution to Dioscorides of the statement that swinging a sapphire over a box containing a spider will kill the insect.[28] But he repeats without criticism many of the marvelous virtues assigned to gems by such past writers as Thetel,[29] Marbod and Albert, nor are these confined to medical and physical properties. To charchedon is ascribed force against evil demons as well as against atrabile. Nor are authorities wanting "who dare to promise victory to its wearer."[30]

As this last indicates, Rueus is inclined to shun personal re-

[26] *Ibid.*, fol. 33v, "Superstitiosa credita"; fol. 65r, "Ridicula et non digna fide gravitas."

[27] *Ibid.*, fols. 52v-53r.

[28] *Ibid.*, fol. 34v.

[29] Once Thetel is censured: fol. 40v, "Quanquam et id suam abunde redolet vanitatem."

[30] *Ibid.*, fol. 36r.

sponsibility for much of his text. Yet he confirms the belief that a turquoise loses its beauty when its owner dies but recovers it when worn by the new owner, by telling his personal experience in failing to buy a turquoise which had belonged to a fellow townsman because of its poor appearance when put up at auction after its owner's death, only to find to his chagrin that it cleared up when worn by another man who purchased it.[31] Or he once states boldly in his own name, "I find too that this gem is potent against injuries from enemies and against sloth, sharpens one's natural talent, and conciliates married pairs."[32]

It may further be noted that Rueus attempted to recommend his work to Christian readers by emphasizing the gems mentioned in the Apocalypse, by affirming that marvelous occult virtues turn our minds Godward,[33] and by professing to reject anything that a Christian should not believe.[34] It is evident that his chief interest is in the virtues of gems and that he adds nothing of scientific importance to previous works. For the most part he reproduces the statements in the *De mineralibus* of Albertus Magnus as to the causes of their generation and occult properties. His few personal contributions are restricted to small details, such as questioning whether the stone of Lorraine described by Symphorien Champier was a true charchedon,[35] or describing a topaz that was shown to him the previous summer.[36] In the main his work is a compendium of past lore with little or nothing in the way of personal observation or classification. It nonetheless found readers, being reprinted as late as 1591-1596 and 1626, both times at Frankfurt with the work of Levinus Lemnius on herbs and trees of the Bible. It further was published in 1622 and 1652 with Vallesius on natural science in the Bible and on sacred philosophy, and in 1629 with the *Corona gemmata* of Thylesius. Thus its appeal appears to have been especially to religious and marvel-loving readers.

[31] *Ibid.*, fol. 55r, cap. 18.

[32] *Ibid.*, fol. 41r, cap. 8.

[33] *Ibid.*, fol. 28r-v.

[34] *Ibid.*, cap. 11, fol. 44v, "Magiam plus redolere cernebantur quam Christianam eruditionem deceret admittere"; cap. 15, fol. 53r, "Absit non ab hoc tantum uno sed a quovis alio vere docto et pie Christiano."

[35] *Ibid.*, cap. 3, fol. 35r.

[36] *Ibid.*, cap. 9, fol. 41v.

A different note is struck by two other tracts among those published by Gesner in 1565, namely, the account or catalogue by John Kentmann of his collection of minerals,[37] and Gesner's own work on the figures and resemblances of fossils, stones and gems.[38] These writings are purely descriptive and classificatory. They do not deal with the virtues of stones at all, whether occult or manifest, medical or more marvelous. Kentmann groups his specimens as earths including salts, alums and atramenta, succi nativi, afflorescentes, pingues, stones, stones found in animals, fluores, silices, gems, marbles, rocks, petrified woods, sands, gold, silver, quicksilver, copper, cadmia et plumbago, pyrites, black lead, cinereum, candidum, stibi, iron, stomoma, and marina varia. He describes under each head a number of particular specimens and tells where each came from. Altogether his catalogue covers 95 leaves and is said by him to be much fuller than that which he had sent to Gesner six years ago.

Gesner states that his treatise was composed hastily and offhand for diversion and recreation after he had been long at work on his *History of Plants*. It had the more serious purpose of inciting persons interested in mineralogy to send him specimens or drawings of those species which he still lacks, as they have communicated such to him in the past. Gesner classifies stones according as they are marked on their surfaces by lines, points and figures; as they have something in common with the sun, moon, stars and elements; as they resemble meteors, or inanimate terrestrial objects; as they resemble artificial objects by nature, or by art; and as they are like herbs, fruit or trees. He then has two chapters on coral and other stony marine or maritime plants. Next are considered stones that resemble, or are found in, man or quadrupeds; those that come from birds or take their names from birds; and those which are similarly related to aquatic animals or to serpents and insects. This arrangement seems quaint, superficial and extraneous, relating stones in appearance

[37] *Io. Kentmanni Dresdensis medici Nomenclaturae rerum fossilium que in Misnia praecipue et in aliis quoque regionibus inveniuntur.*

[38] *Conradi Gesneri De rerum fossilium lapidum et gemmarum maxime figuris et similitudinibus liber cum iconibus plurimis.*

or otherwise to alien things, rather than attending to the structure of the stones as such. It may be partly accounted for by the fact that fossilized remains of plants and animals were not then distinguished from stones, while stony growths in living beings had a greater medical interest than now.

A work on minerals and metals by an author less known than Agricola or Gesner or even Camillo Lunardi, was the *De re metallica* of Christophorus Encelius or Entzelt of Saalfeld, printed at Frankfurt in 1557.[39] It had been recommended to the printer by Melanchthon as offering new material on the subject. That this work was not very widely read is suggested not only by the rarity of the volume but by the fact that in the summer of 1935, almost four centuries after it was first published, I found some of the pages still uncut in the copy at the National Library in Munich. However, that it was read is indicated by its citation in the posthumous *Theater of Insects* of Thomas Moffett in 1634 and in the posthumous *Musaeum metallicum* of Aldrovandi in 1648. On the other hand, in the long chapter on the magnet in this publication of 1648 the work of Gilbert was not cited.

Encelius acknowledges his debt to Agricola whom he ranks above Pliny or Dioscorides as an authority on metals.[40] Actually, however, he cites Pliny, Dioscorides and Serapion much oftener than he cites Agricola. The reason perhaps is that he is not primarily interested in metallurgy but in the medicinal use of metals, stones, gems, and other minerals. He generally gives their German names and alludes to mines and other localities in Germany. But in the main he repeats ancient traditions and beliefs. He recognizes, however, that the methods which Dioscorides gives for making ink are entirely obsolete today, when very different procedures are employed.[41]

[39] Christophorus Encelius Salvedensis, *De re metallica hoc est de origine varietate et natura corporum metallicorum lapidum gemmarum atque aliarum quae ex fodinis eruuntur rerum ad medicinae usum deservientium libri III*. Franc. Apud Haered. Christiani Egenolphi, 1557, 271 pp. (all in italics).

[40] *Ibid.*, I, 7, p. 18.

[41] *Ibid.*, II, 38, De atramento librario, pp. 144-45. The different subject of shoe-blacking was treated at the beginning of book II: p. 73, "Incipiam ergo et nunc dicam de atramento sutorio id est vitriolo."

Encelius makes some mention of medieval Latin as well as Arabic writers. Albertus Magnus is criticized for saying that pyrites or marchasite is consumed by fire, since Avicenna, Dioscorides and Serapion state that metals are smelted from it, and Encelius has seen this done in many parts of Germany. He suggests that Albert gave too ready ear to chemists (*chimisti*) and was not diligent enough in scrutiny of mines and ores.[42] In another passage, after exclaiming at the stupidity of the Germans at Meissen in using a species of jasper found there instead of flint to strike fire, when the jasper is valuable for certain medical purposes, Encelius adds that the property of conferring grace and love which Albert and others ascribe to jasper "is, I believe, magic, which you can read for yourself."[43]

On the whole, however, it cannot be said that Encelius manifests any real advance over the work of Lunardi a half century before, either in accretion of new information, facts and correct scientific detail, or in the rejection of superstitious tradition and occult notions. Only six pages after the slur on Albert as magical, he says that the same property of gaining love and grace and that of making girls comely and curing their diseases is attributed to the stone, Umbilicus Veneris or Meerbonen, and that "our matrons" attach it to their children as an amulet and think highly of it. This is, in fact, the concluding statement of his last chapter and the note upon which his work ends.[44] Similarly he repeats from Pliny that the impudence of the magi ascribes to the gem heliotrope the property of rendering men invisible,[45] but he also resembles Pliny in repeating kindred beliefs without censure or mention of the magi. He does not dwell on astrological or other images engraved on gems as Lunardi did. But he regards all seven species of jasper as amulets[46] and believes that a diamond can be broken by the blood of a goat, especially if the goat has previously drunk wine or eaten parsley and siler montanus.[47]

It is on the marvelous properties of stones found in animals

[42] *Ibid.*, I, 20, pp. 30-31.
[43] *Ibid.*, III, 71, pp. 264-65.
[44] *Ibid.*, III, 80, p. 271.
[45] *Ibid.*, III, 67, p. 260.
[46] *Ibid.*, III, 71, p. 263.
[47] *Ibid.*, III, 10, p. 179.

that Encelius especially dilates. He still believes in the formation of a stone from the urine of the lynx, in a bezoar stone from the tears in a deer's eyes, in chelidonia red and black found in swallows' gizzards, in the toad stone which changes color in the presence of poison.[48]

Encelius was equally interested in the marvelous ways of animals and proposed to write books on fish and birds.[49] Meanwhile in the *De re metallica* he shows faith in the old story of the viper conceiving through the mouth and the young gnawing their way out of its womb,[50] although this had been rejected back in 1499 by Franciscus Caballus. Encelius mentions the use in occult arts of the hoopoe and a stone which is found in its nest. "But we will not treat of magic: let us proceed."[51] He affirms that there are halcyon birds in lower Germany,[52] and that he had seen a dead basilisk which had been killed by a shepherd in a forest near the town of Luckenwald.[53] As for the question of the relation of cinnabar to the death struggle of dragon and elephant, he merely states the views of various past authorities without committing himself.[54]

In the field of alchemy and metallurgy Encelius holds to the old view that all metals are generated from sulphur as their father and mercury as their mother. In addition to the seven metals he discusses such minerals as chalcitis, misy, sory, orpiment, sandarac, alum, pumice, and native and manufactured salt. The limitations to his chemical knowledge are indicated in his chapter on gypsum, where he says nothing of sulphur and its other chemical constitutents, but merely repeats what Pliny and others have said concerning it.[55] A like reproach may be levelled a century later at the posthumous *Musaeum metallicum* of Aldrovandi.

That the bezoar stone continued to command credence and admiration through the sixteenth century is indicated by a work on bezoardic medicaments published at Antwerp in 1587 by

[48] *Ibid.*, III, 27, 49, 44, 37; pp. 210-11, 235-36, 229-30, 221.
[49] *Ibid.*, II, 43, p. 149.
[50] *Ibid.*, III, 38, p. 222.
[51] *Ibid.*, III, 46, p. 230.
[52] *Ibid.*, II, 43, p. 149.
[53] *Ibid.*, III, 54, p. 243.
[54] *Ibid.*, II, 24, p. 127.
[55] *Ibid.*, II, 41, pp. 147-48.

Ioannes Iuvenis or de Ionghe, a physician of Ypres,[56] and by annotations of Apollonius Menabenus, a physician of Milan, towards the close of the century, upon the tract on the bezoar stone of Claudius Ricardus, a physician and surgeon of Franche-Comté.[57] It was the opinion of Menabenus that Ricardus had not praised the bezoar enough. Menabenus cites recent authors favorable to occult influences like Cardan and Mizaldus, and older medieval writers like Arnald of Villanova and Peter of Abano. He makes such affirmations as that it is attested by experience that emeralds comfort the stomach, that they relieve apoplexy, if suspended about the neck, and, if held in the mouth, soothe the teeth. He further discusses these topics and questions: deer's tears; the true contrary to poison; whether the disease of the stone is always caused by immoderate heat; and whether qualities or specific forms or occult properties come from the whole substance.[58] Menabenus was for a time physician to king John III of Sweden. In 1581 he printed treatises on the stag and on the causes of the tides at Stockholm.[59]

That during the seventeenth century faith in the medical virtues, especially against poisons, of marvelous stones produced within animals gradually waned, is suggested by a treatise in French in a manuscript of the later part of that century on the deceits practiced with the bezoar.[60] Nevertheless the royal museum at Copenhagen as late as 1696 had a collection of bezoardic stones, both oriental and occidental.[61]

The lectures of Falloppia at Padua in the summer of 1557 on metals or fossils were printed posthumously from the notes of

[56] In the same volume with Aegidius Gerardus, *De herba panacea:* Valerius Andreas, *Bibl. Belgica,* 1643, p. 522.

[57] Milan Ambros. H.40.inf., fols. 61r-93r: "Claudii Ricardi Sequani medici chirurgi de lapide Bezoari libellus cum annotationibus Apollonii Menabeni." It appeared to me, however, that this MS gave only the annotations: the work of Ricardus or an extract from it appears to have been published in 1603.

[58] These supplementary discussions begin at fols. 93r, 96v, 103v, 117v and 118r. Earlier in the same MS is the work of Menabenus on peach-trees.

[59] Argellati, *Bibl. SS. Mediolanensium,* II, i, 921-23; also Tiraboschi.

[60] BM Sloane 1009, late 17th century, fol. 284: Discours du Bézoart et des tromperies qu'on pratique avec cette pierre.

[61] From the account of the catalogue of the museum published in 1696 given by L. Neocoro, *Bibliotheca librorum novorum,* I (1697).

one of his students[62] and bear evident marks of their origin. Falloppia begins by stating that last year he commenced the explanation of the last part of the fifth book of Dioscorides and dealt with things that spring from the earth spontaneously such as vapors, fumes, fires, waters. Now he comes to those dug from earth by man. After a long general discussion and rather too much allusion to Aristotle, Plato and other ancients, the lecturer suddenly says, "But since—listen, please—there were some of you who said that I was dwelling too much on universals, therefore, if it please you, I will omit what remains concerning universals to another time and I will take up particulars. Do you want me to or not?" The class having evidently voted in the affirmative, Falloppia announces that in tomorrow's lecture he will turn to particulars and take up cadmia with Dioscorides, and finish concerning universals later, if there is time. The editor and disciple adds that so far as he knows Falloppia never went farther with universals and that that year he did not even finish with particular minerals because of the shortness of time and the very great heat.[63] To this last Falloppia also alludes in closing, stating that it is time to put an end to the labors of this year, since not only the holidays but the intense heat invite us to rest. "Farewell and love me as you have done hitherto. In the university of Padua, the twentieth day of July, 1557."

In his general discussion Falloppia follows the *De mineralibus* of Albertus Magnus a great deal although he at times disagrees with Albertus. He affirms, for example, that earth, not water, predominates in the composition of gems.[64] He holds that mountains are formed and kept in repair—which is too gradual for us to notice—by exhalations from earth. An indication of this is the pyramidical shape of mountains like that of a flame.[65] He does not believe that the fossilized sea shells found on mountains were left by the deluge or by the water of the sea, since a mountain is very high and far removed from the sea. Those found in the mid-

[62] *Excellentissimi Gabrielis Falloppii de metallis seu fossilibus tractatus,* fols. 85v-176v (following his lectures on mineral waters), Venice, 1569.

[63] *Ibid.,* fol. 124r-v.

[64] *Ibid.,* fols. 99v-100r.

[65] *Ibid.,* fol. 102r.

dle of rocks must be produced by spontaneous generation there.[66] His discussion of this matter is vastly inferior to Leonardo da Vinci's.

The particular metals and minerals which he treats hardly include any gems. He charges his teacher Brasavola with having confused antimony and lead, but acquits Galen of calling lapis lazuli a purgative. He states that "our drug stores" have pills of lapiz lazuli and that it is an excellent medicament. He rejects as a fable the story that cinnabar is a by-product of the struggle between the dragon and the elephant. Against Conciliator, Avicenna and Mattioli, he contends that mercury can be taken through the mouth in small doses. Shepherds administer it inside a nut to calves suffering from worms, and he has administered it and seen it given to boys for worms. Dioscorides says that it corrodes the intestines, but Falloppia has not observed this. He advises, however, those who are anointed with it for syphilis to suck a gold ring so that the mercury will collect on it and not penetrate too far and corrupt the bones.[67]

Three books on gems published in Italian by Lodovico Dolce in 1565[68] or 1566[69] were stated by Apostolo Zeno[70] two centuries ago to be largely a repetition of the work of Camillo Lunardi, and are described in the British Museum catalogue as a translation of it. Dolce also published a treatise on colors,[71] full of poetry and allegory. His dialogue on painting is of more practical importance.[72]

A refreshing scepticism as to the past lore of gems was manifested by Garcia da Orta in his work of 1563 *On the Simples and Drugs of India,* and was partially transmitted, albeit in abbre-

[66] *Ibid.,* fol. 109r-v.

[67] *Ibid.,* fols. 154v, 161r-v, 164r, 169v-170r, for the passages cited in this paragraph.

[68] This date is given by Tiraboschi, VII, 2 (Milan, 1824), p. 898, and is that of BM 972.e.2. *Libri tre di Lodovico Dolce* [translated from the Latin of C. Leonardus] *nei quali si tratta delle diversi sorti delle gemme che produce la natura,* Venezia, 1565.

[69] Lud. Dolce, *De diversis generibus gemmarum e terra provenientium,* Italice, Venetiis, 1566, 8vo. I have not seen this edition.

[70] *Lettere,* III, 165, cited by Tiraboschi.

[71] *Dialogo di M. Lodovico Dolce nel quale si ragione delle qualità diversità e proprietà de i colori,* Venetia, 1565, 86 fols. BM 232.k.32.

[72] *Dialogo sulla pittura,* Venezia, 1557.

viated form, through the Latin epitome of the same by Clusius and the Spanish work of Fragoso in 1572 and its Latin translation by Spachius in 1600. Garcia recognized that "he who speaks against common beliefs is detested," but uttered his criticisms nevertheless. He held that diamonds were neither poisonous nor medicinal. This did not mean that he denied medicinal virtues to all gems, since he admitted that the carnelian staunched the flow of blood, and apparently had no objection to the use of pearls as an ingredient in cordials or of turquoises in electuaries. As for the diamond, he further denied that it could not be broken by hammer and anvil, or that it could be softened by goat's blood. He held that the last was effective only against the stone in the human body. He also rejected as an absurd fiction the notion that the magnet would not attract iron in the presence of a diamond, or that putting a diamond under a wife's pillow would test her fidelity. Coming to the magnet, he denied that it was poisonous or would make a man a lunatic, or that Indian ships had wooden nails because of magnetic mountains near Calicut, or that a magnet supporting several pieces of iron would weigh no more than one with a single bit attached. He affirmed, however, that diamonds were marvelously generated within two or three years' time only a cubit beneath the surface of the soil. And of the gem called cat's eye, which brought a greater price in Ceylon than in Portugal and was believed by the people of India to preserve and increase one's wealth, he asserted that, if it is placed on top of an open cloth, no fire will make it burn, as he had convinced himself by applying a candle to it—which might seem a not sufficiently intense heat.[73]

Fragoso repeated much of this, but still maintained that the diamond counteracted the force of the magnet, and that the diamond could be dissolved only by fresh hot goat's blood, preferably that of a goat which has drunk wine and eaten diuretic herbs. He also said that the philosophers attribute to the diamond such divine powers as to avert bad dreams, fear, phantasms, and

[73] For the foregoing statements see Markham's translation, pp. 299, 342, 346-47, 349, 351, 355, 357-58, 360, 482; Clusius (1579), pp. 171-72 *et seq.*

the evil eye. It is called the gem of reconciliation because it mitigates wrath and discord. Fragoso repeated Albertus Magnus's story of the king of Hungary whose emerald broke into three pieces while he was with the queen. He quoted Mundella against those imitators of Arabic doctrine who advocated its use in cases of putrid and malignant fevers. But then he quoted the Arabic physician, Zoar, for its validity against poison. After eating a poisonous herb, Zoar put one emerald in his mouth and another on his stomach and made a quick recovery. As an annex to the chapter on the emerald Fragoso mentioned some quite large and bellicose fish, found on the coasts of "our Indies," in whose heads are found stones, of which the fragments and powder, taken internally, produce the same effects as the stone nephritis. He also tells in his chapter on the bezoar of a stone which congeals from the humor distilled from the eyes of deer when they stand in water up to their lips in order to suffer no ill effects from the poison of the snakes which they have eaten in order to renew their youth or to free themselves from worms.[74]

Andrea Bacci, physician to Sixtus V, besides works on baths, poisons, simples and other medical topics, published in 1581 or 1587 in Italian a treatise on the twelve precious stones in the breastplate of the highpriest after the similar work of Epiphanius, together with other gems and a discussion of the unicorn and its most singular virtue, with a dedication to cardinal Alessandro Peretti.[75] This book contained such assertions as that chrysolite would preserve one from fascination, especially if worn on the left arm, that gold was marvelous both in its substance and its every quality, that bezoar stones from the New World were more surely derived from animals, although not so great virtues were claimed for them as were asserted of oriental bezoars by Arabic authors.[76] Bacci upheld the existence of the unicorn, to whose horn great virtues were attributed, and refused to identify it with

[74] Ioannes Fragosus, *Aromatum fructuum et simplicium . . . historia,* 1600, I, 1, de adamante; I, 2, de smaragdo, fols. 4r-6v; I, 10, de lapide bezaar, ff. 11v-15v.

[75] Andrea Bacci, *Le xii pietre pretiose . . .*, Roma appresso Bartolomeo Grassi, 1587. Copy used: BM 956.g.2. Vecchietti, *Biblioteca Picena,* lists an edition of 1581 which I have not seen.

[76] *Ibid.*, pp. 15, 28, 33.

the rhinoceros. To the argument against its existence that it was unknown, he replied that so were spices. To the argument that accounts of it were confused and conflicting, he responded that its nature was marvelous in very varied ways. To the objection that excessive virtues were ascribed to it, he retorted that occult virtues could not be denied. To the objection that unicorns were never seen in the Roman amphitheaters, his answer was that the Romans had not penetrated to its habitat.[77]

Bacci's book appeared in Latin translation in 1603 at Frankfurt, with additional annotations by Wolfgang Gabelchover, M.D., who dedicated his translation to the duke of Wurtemberg and cited various sixteenth century authors.[78] His notes contain such statements as that it has been shown by frequent experience that the stone allectory held under the tongue checks thirst and heartburn.[79] A ten page description of the bezoar stone to the archbishop of Gran is signed Claudius Richardus,[80] whom we have already mentioned. In a letter of Johann Lang, physician to the elector Palatine, on the question whether gold and silver should be employed medically, Lang declares against the magic virtues of gems but affirms their medicinal properties which he attributes to occult virtues or the influence of the stars.[81]

Since the attraction of iron by the magnet had long served as the stock example and unassailable argument of believers in occult virtue, and various other marvelous properties, medical or magical, had been ascribed to it in lapidaries from the time of Marbod, it may be well to note the attitude in such matters of William Gilbert (1544-1603) in his great work on the magnet, published in the last year of the century.[82] Gilbert is said to have expended five thousand pounds in experimentation, and his book is an important landmark in the history of experimental science

[77] *Ibid.*, pp. 61-62.

[78] *Andreae Bacci liber de gemmis . . . in latinum sermonem conversus a Wolfgango Gabelchovero,* Francofurti impensis N. Steinii, 1603, 8vo. Copy used: BM 987.b.30.

[79] *Ibid.*, p. 173.

[80] *Ibid.*, pp. 187-96.

[81] *Ibid.*, pp. 220-31.

[82] William Gilbert, *De magnete magneticisque corporibus et de magno magnete tellure: physiologia nova plurimis et argumentis et experimentis demonstrata,* London, 1600, 240 pp.

as well as of electricity. Many of the medicinal properties attributed to the magnet by past writers Gilbert rejected as figments and absurdities, together with such assertions of the ancients as that a magnet rubbed with garlic would not attract iron. He declared that it had no medical efficacy powdered in plasters and would no more cure headache than would a steel helmet. Nor would it move the bowels. But it would correct overhumid and putrescent viscera.[83]

Gilbert had more faith in the medical properties of iron. Falloppia was wrong, it was true, in recommending iron for scirrhosis of the spleen, since its effect is to dry and harden that organ the more. But for lax livers and excessively damp spleen it is beneficial. So Gilbert affirms that "in some diseases of the human body it is very helpful by its innate virtues and those acquired by proper artificial preparation, and works wonderful changes in the human body, so that we may learn its nature more certainly through its medicinal force and certain manifest experiments."[84] He would prepare iron for medicinal use by first pulverizing it, then soaking it in vinegar, drying it and washing. Past writers have disagreed as to its manifest qualities: Galen, Piso and Montagnana calling it hot, while Manard, Curtius and Falloppia call it cold.

Gilbert denied the doctrine of the chemists and alchemists that the metals are composed of quicksilver and sulphur, which he regarded as substances of a different order. He preferred Aristotle's explanation that metals were composed of an exhalation which hardened in the veins of earth, where some are found in a pure state, others mixed with ore. Gilbert also held that within the earth were hid germs (*primordia*) of metals and stones, just as on its periphery were the seeds of herbs and plants. He denied that earth was a simple substance, "as the Peripatetics dream," yet presently affirmed that especially in the best iron earth was in its true nature and genuine, while in other metals there was not so much earth as fixed salts which were efflorescences of earth.[85] He contemptuously rejected the astrological

[83] *Ibid.*, I, 14.
[84] *Ibid.*, I, 15.
[85] *Ibid.*, I, 7.

association of seven metals with the planets, asserting that they corresponded neither in number nor in properties.[86] In another passage he criticized Ptolemy for making a distinction, in which he had been followed by most philosophers and superstitious astrologers, between eastern and western regions, whereas east and west are purely relative directions and bear no relation to the planets.[87] He also was unfavorable to the notion of antipathy between bodies,[88] but retained the time honored hypothesis of form and matter. He was aware that "from fables and lies false and idle conjectures arise in philosophy."[89]

If we closed this chapter here, it might seem that scepticism as to the lore of gems was at last in the ascendent. A glance at two works of the early seventeenth century will alter this impression.

Anselm Boetius, Boèce, de Boodt or de Boot was born at Bruges about the middle of the sixteenth century and died there in 1632. At the time of the first edition of his work on stones in 1609[90] he was physician to the emperor Rudolph II. Hoghelande, writing in 1604, asserted that Boot made gold at Prag.[91] After this first printing at Hanover there were other editions at Leyden in 1636 and 1647, and a French translation at Lyons in 1644.

The catalogue of authorities which de Boodt prefixed to his text is free from the names of supposititious and superstitious writers, particularly on astrological and magical images, which were noticeable in Lunardi's list a century earlier, such as Hermes, Evax, Solomon, Kiranus and Thetel. Names of writers in Arabic such as Avicenna, Mesue and Serapion have also disappeared. Of medieval Latin writers only Albertus Magnus and Bartholomaeus Anglicus remain. Isidore, Rabanus, Marbod, Thomas of Cantimpré, Arnald of Villanova, Ortulanus and Sil-

[86] *Idem.*

[87] *Ibid.*, III, 9.

[88] *Ibid.*, II, 39.

[89] *Ibid.*, I, 14.

[90] *Anselmi Boetii de Boodt Prugensis Belgae Rudolphi secundi imperatoris Romanorum personae medici Gemmarum et lapidum historia,* Hanoviae, 1609. Joh. Erich Hiller, "Boèce de Boodt, précurseur de la mineralogie moderne," *Annales Guébhard-Séverine,* XI (1935), 74-81, is based on a longer monograph completed in 1933 but as yet unpublished. D. C. Allen, "Drayton's Lapidaries," *Modern Language Notes,* 53 (1938), 93-96, points out the English poet's debt to de Boodt.

[91] Hoghelande, *Historiae aliquot transmutationis,* 1604, p. 27.

vaticus, who were in Lunardi's bibliography, are omitted. It should be remembered, however, that some of these authors were known to and cited by Lunardi only indirectly through the pages of others. Of the ancients de Boodt omits Aristotle, by whom no genuine work on stones is extant, but lists Dioscorides, Pliny, Galen and Epiphanius. The missing medieval authors are replaced by a number of more recent writers: Agricola, Gesner, Cardan, Mattioli, Libavius, Quercetanus, Ioannes Kentmannus, Andreas Baccius, Franciscus Rueus, Ludovicus Dulcis, Prosper Alpinus, and the less known names of Jacobus Mockius and Matthias Mairhofer.

While the choice of authors in this preliminary bibliography is illuminating in the way which we have indicated, it is true that de Boodt cites others in the course of his text: for example, Garcia da Orta, Christophorus à Costa, Nicolaus Monardes, Giovanni Battista Porta, Caesalpinus *De metallicis,* Falloppia *De metallis et fossilibus,* Aelian of the ancients, and an occasional medieval like Paul of Venice or Antonius Guainerius. Even Marbod is cited but in order to reject the magical and psychological effects which he ascribed to the magnet. Like Lunardi, de Boodt denies that a magnetic mountain can extract nails from passing ships. But while he discusses the magnet at length, he makes no reference to the recent work of Gilbert upon it, nor is any mention made of it by the commentator in the edition of 1647.

The work of de Boodt shows a marked advance in several respects, especially if compared with that of Lunardi a century earlier. It completely omits all matter concerning marvel-working images carved on gems. It profits by the discovery of the new world and knowledge of other distant lands. De Boodt says that Peruvian emeralds have brought down the price of that stone and are preferred by most dealers to those from the orient. The autograph papers of Jacobus Bontius, physician in ordinary and afterwards treasurer of New Batavia, had been put at de Boodt's disposal by William Bontius, his brother. De Boodt also embodies the experience in mineralogy of Germany and central Europe, and gives German as well as Latin names. He had observed and studied stones for himself, although he repeats a good deal that he has been told by other persons or has read in books. He makes an attempt, although not a very satisfactory one, at more exact description and more methodical classification of gems than those found in previous writers.[92] He complains that all previous works on the subject have admitted foreign, magical, superstitious and false matter, and even intentional fictions. Nor does he himself entirely omit such. Of galactites, lac lunare, or Moon milch he tells us not merely that it is used to increase the flow of milk and to dry up ulcers, but also that the superstitious believe that it benefits a patient in whose name it is taken from the mountain caves where it is found.[93]

Before considering stones individually in his second book, de Boodt devotes the two closing chapters of the first book to a rather long general discussion of the virtues attributed to gems. Some would reject them entirely; others would limit them to elemental powers; others, influenced by the example of the magnet, would concede them more occult powers from their form and essence; others would grant them supernatural force. De Boodt denies the first and last of these four positions, and accepts the second and third. He will not admit virtues and effects such as rendering one invisible[94] which cannot be attributed to the matter, form or accidents of the stones, or which he believes cannot be produced by inanimate bodies but require the consent of animate beings. Such are riches, eloquence, favor with kings, detection of adultery, and divination of the future. Supernatural effects are to be ascribed to divine or demonic influence, not to stones. Nor can gems receive such virtues from the stars, whose influence is a constant force and never contrary to nature. He further decries any employment of superstitious ceremonial, figures and characters in connection with gems as approaching di-

[92] On these points see his prefaces to the emperor Rudolph II and to the reader.

[93] *Gemmarum et lapidum historia*, II, 229.

[94] Yet his preface to Rudolph II makes much of the dazzling light of gems, and states that kings wear them to impede the vision of beholders and to keep their own faces and bodies somewhat inconspicuous.

abolical magic. Not only supernatural but many natural effects cannot be produced by stones. The normal conditions of physical action, expressed by de Boodt still in Aristotelian terms, must be observed. He further lays down various rules to determine whether an apparent cause is the true cause of a phenomenon. In general he affirms the physical and medical properties of gems but denies them influence on the human intellect or morals except indirectly and to a slight degree. This distinction seems neither to have been drawn theoretically nor observed in practice in the posthumous *Musaeum metallicum* of Aldrovandi in 1648. Yet it cited de Boodt in other respects frequently.

De Boodt still believed, however, that the physical and medical virtues of gems were very great. They have all the force of light, and in their tiny bodies God seems to have concentrated the beauty of the universe and all the virtues of other things. These last words are scarcely consistent with his previous statement that many natural effects cannot be produced by stones. Bones that would otherwise take forty days to heal, with the aid of the stone ossifrage knit in three or four.[95] The crucifix stone, worn touching the flesh, is said to stay the flow of blood, enrich the milk, and ward off ills coming from demons. Suspended from the neck, it is said to cure all fevers.[96] Nor does de Boodt merely state such properties on hearsay; in some cases he has himself observed and tested them. He had experimented with a marvelous jasper which checked a flow of the menses from which a maid had suffered for days, also prevented a foot from bleeding, and cured a virgin of Prag of haemorrhages from which she had suffered weekly for six years. As soon as the gem was removed, the haemorrhages recurred. So de Boodt kept repeating the experiment. After a while the haemorrhage did not recur until some time after the jasper was left off, while it stopped at once when the gem was again applied. Finally he was able to dispense with the applications of the jasper entirely: the patient was cured![97]

[95] *Gemmarum et lapidum historia*, II, 235. In the edition of 1647 it is added that William Fabricius Hildanus (1560-1634) questions this in his work in surgery, centuria 3, observat. 90.

[96] *Ibid.*, II, 245.

[97] *Ibid.*, II, 102.

The turquoise was believed to strengthen the eyes and spirits, and, in the case of a fall, to relieve its wearer of injury by receiving this itself. De Boodt grants that this property exceeds reason, but has a supporting experience to relate concerning a turquoise which he has long worn in a gold ring. The first part of his relation bears a suspicious resemblance to what we have already heard from Rueus. The stone had previously belonged to a Spaniard who had worn it for thirty years. When it was put up for sale at auction after his death, it had so lost color that no one wanted to buy it and many doubted if it was the same stone as that which the Spaniard had worn. De Boodt's father bought it cheap and gave it to Anselm with the remark, "Since, my son, 'tis the common belief that for the turquoise to exercise its power it must be received as a gift." De Boodt had his arms carved on it, and as he wore it, it recovered much of its pristine color, which he thinks may have been a natural effect of exhalations and warmth from his body. As he was returning to Bohemia from Padua where he had received the doctorate, he fell at least ten feet from his horse which was on a raised path. De Boodt was uninjured, but the turquoise broke in two. He then wore the larger fragment and when he nearly strained himself in lifting a large load from a stream, it was the stone instead that was fractured again, and again he continued to wear the larger bit. He recognizes that a gem cannot naturally transfer the injury from a fall to itself, and that this must be the work of angels or demons, God willing or permitting. But he did not cease wearing the stone lest he become the debtor of demons and thereby imperil his soul. He is more sceptical as to a turquoise which is suspended by a thread held between the thumb and finger having the property of indicating the hour by its oscillations. Hours were instituted by man, not by nature, and de Boodt is sure that the hand of the holder regulates the number of swings, whether consciously or not.[98]

[98] *Ibid.*, II, 116. In the posthumous *Musaeum metallicaum* of Aldrovandi, Bologna, 1648, this property is ascribed to the jasper rather than to the turquoise.

De Boodt devotes five of his three hundred pages to the bezoar stone and discusses at some length from what sort of animal it comes. There was now added to the oriental bezoar from Egypt, Persia, India, China and Cathay, a western bezoar from America and Peru. Rudolph II owned a bezoar stone the size of a goose egg. When he ordered a cup to be fashioned from it, redolent herbs were found inside. De Boodt treats of various other medicinal uses of the bezoar besides as an antidote for poisons. He advises against giving the patient anything else before or after administering it, lest some occult antipathy between them impair the action of the bezoar.[99]

De Boodt notes various other stones generated in animals such as that found about the eyes of crabs in hemispherical form, when their skins are changed. It was believed to reduce the stone to powder and void it through the urine, and to purge ulcers and wounds. Chemists reduced it to an essence or liquor.[100] The toad-stone, another produced by lightning, and a third generated by the hissing of snakes, were all alike thought to protect their bearer from being poisoned or struck by lightning. As for these and the further virtue of bringing sleep and victory which was asserted of the toad-stone, de Boodt mildly remarks, "Virtues indeed not to be contemned, if they possess them, but faith often exceeds the truth."[101]

A few further examples of the extent of de Boodt's credulity and scepticism may be given with regard to other things than stones. With regard to the salamander he expressed disbelief that any animal could live in fire.[102] He also doubted the existence of horn of the monoceros or unicorn, to which such vast powers against poison had been ascribed that it was worth its weight in gold. The reason for his scepticism in this case was not that he doubted the vast powers but because he was convinced that no such animal had yet been found. The rhinoceros was not it, while such reputed specimens of the monoceros's horn as had been of-

[99] *Ibid.*, II, 191-94; pp. 181-86 in edition of 1609.

[100] *Ibid.*, II, 176, De oculis cancri.

[101] *Ibid.*, II, 265.

[102] *Ibid.*, II, 204.

fered to de Boodt were really stones or fossilized woods.[103] In general the mixture of scepticism and credulity in de Boodt's pages suggests the reflection that, while mankind has always had on tap a certain amount of unbelief as well as faith, these have not always been respectively applied where it would have been most advantageous.

In 1611 P. Constantius Albinius published under the title, *Magia astrologica,* a key to the work of 1610 of Petrus Arlensis de Scudalupis *On the Sympathy of the Seven Metals and Seven Stones with the Planets,* for the greater elucidation of that work, which we have already mentioned. Albinius published his with the same printers or booksellers.[104] Despite the other work's rejection of them, Albinius gave various rings of the planets, seals of the twelve signs, and other images, which he assured the reader were strictly astrological, not magical.[105] He also associated hierarchies of angels with different stones and colors for magical purposes.[106] Yet the work was printed with a royal privilege. Thus gems retained their magical associations into the seventeenth century.

[103] *Ibid.,* II, 242-44.

[104] *Magia astrologica hoc est P. Constantii Albinii Villanovensis Clavis sympathiae septem metallorum et septem selectorum lapidum ad planetas pro maiori illius elucidatione. Opus tam astrologis quam chymicis perutile et iocundum.* Parisiis apud Carolum Sevestre et Davidem Gillium via Iacobea et Ioannem Petit-pas via D. Ioannis Lateranensis in collegio Cameracensi, MDCXI. Copy used: BM 718.b.15.(2.), where it is bound with the aforesaid work of Petrus Arlensis de Scudalupis.

[105] *Ibid.,* fol. 28v.

[106] *Ibid.,* fol. 42v, "Qui hos lapides colores et angelos attrectare sciverit vel intellexerit totum secretum in magia absconditum possidebit. . . ."

CHAPTER XL

CESALPINO'S VIEW OF NATURE

Caesalpin ist der erste Botaniker der Neuzeit, der das Pflanzenstudium auf wissenschaftlichen Grundlagen erbaut hat.

—RADL

Cesalpino has been made the subject of a chapter apart from our more general survey of sixteenth century naturalists because it was primarily concerned with botany and zoology, while works on stones and metals were discussed in a separate chapter. But Cesalpino wrote on both plants and minerals, touched on vexed astronomical and biological problems in his *Peripatetic Questions* and furthermore composed *A Peripatetic Investigation of Demons,* which, so far as its subject-matter is concerned, would come under yet another chapter. To avoid this scattering, to show how the same man might display a varying attitude in different fields, and to provide something approaching a complete picture in miniature of a particular sixteenth century naturalist in his strength and weakness is the object of this chapter.

Andreas Caesalpinus or Andrea Cesalpino (1519-1603) seems to have been esteemed in his own day more as an Aristotelian philosopher and medical man than as a botanist. De Thou in his history calls Caesalpinus a Peripatetic who, after he had long taught at Pisa and spread the fame of his name, died at Rome.[1] He was in point of fact, as he himself states in 1596, also professor of medicine there. Prominent among his writings were his five books of *Peripatetic Questions,* which seem to have been the first considerable work published by him, appearing at Venice in 1571,[2] although dedicated to Francesco de' Medici on June 1,

[1] *Thuanus,* Bk. 129.

[2] Caesalpinus, *Quaestionum Peripateticarum libri V,* Venetiis, 1571, 4to: BN R.2862. I have mostly used the edition of Venice, 1593: BM 461.b.2, but have sometimes referred to that of 1588.

G. Ceradini, *La scoperta della circolazione del sangue,* Nuova edizione, Milano, 1876, p. 221, n. 2, re-

1565. Other works by Cesalpino were two books of medical questions, a *Medical Art,* and a *Practice of the Whole Art of Medicine,* printed respectively in 1593, 1601-1603, and posthumously in 1606.

The *Peripatetic Questions* of Cesalpino differ from the ordinary commentary upon Aristotle in that they try to bring out something new rather than to follow in the beaten track. These unusual and sometimes seemingly paradoxical positions are supported by citation from the works of Aristotle, but such other sources as astronomical theory and anatomical dissections are also drawn upon. The questions themselves or the fundamental ideas underlying their solution are sometimes apparently Cesalpino's own.

In the field of astronomy, instead of the system of homocentric spheres commonly attributed to Aristotle, Cesalpino rejects the notion of separate moving spheres, contending that Aristotle meant that the whole sky moved as one continuum about the earth as center. He even goes the Ptolemaic system one better by not merely accepting the demonstration of the "astrologi" that six planets have epicycles, but by affirming that the sun and all the fixed stars are borne by epicycles too. He keeps the earth at the center of the universe and asserts that it can have only one elementary motion of its own, i.e. downward towards its center. But while he does not mention Copernicus by name and denies his theory by implication, he takes a leaf out of his book by referring to the earth all apparent inequalities of motion of the heavens, such as have led men to suppose a ninth sphere, a tenth sphere, and an anomaly of the equinoxes. These are reduced to a very slight, irregular and accidental movement of rotation on the axis of the heavens, which the earth, like the spheres of fire and air but to a much less extent, receives from the revolution of the heavens about them and it. This movement is irregular because

---

jects the supposed edition of Florence, 1569, and others at Florence, 1580, and Geneva, 1588, and regards that of 1593 as the second. The work, however, as just stated, was also published in 1588 in *Tractationum philosophicarum tomus unus,* excudebat Eustathius Vignon Atrebat., cols. 361-552. Copy used: BM 526.n.6.

of the unevenness of the earth's surface and the consequent varying resistance offered by it. Cesalpino also accounted for the tides by this slight movement of the earth rather than by the attraction of the moon.[3]

In supplementary Peripatetic questions of 1603 Cesalpino distinguished two parts of the sky, one more solid and earth-like whose motion produced friction and heat in inferior bodies, the other spirituous and nobler like air and fire which constituted the *primum mobile* by whose most rapid motion all the inferior spheres were revolved westward. So were the spheres of fire and air, and to some extent the earth, as one inferred from the altered position of certain fixed stars over a very long period of time.[4] Thus Cesalpino to the end maintained, on supposedly Peripatetic principles, a slight accidental revolving of the earth.

Cesalpino had original astrological as well as astronomical opinions. He held that heat was produced on earth by the motion westward of the entire heavens, while the movement of the planets in the opposite direction tempered this heat by a refrigerating influence. The heat from the motion of the heavens penetrated to the earth's center, while the frigidity extended only to the limit of the sphere of fire.[5]

In biology Cesalpino not only admitted spontaneous generation but contended that whatever species were generated from seed could also be produced without it. According to Aristotelian principles even man, he maintained, might be born from putrid matter, although it would be foolish to think that the rational soul could be so produced.[6] Furthermore, despite his familiarity with dissection, he still argued that the heart was the source not only of the arteries and of the veins, which Galen had associated with the liver, but also of the nerves, a word which he seems to have used to include both nerves and muscles.[7] He further held

[3] *Quaest. Peripat.*, III, 3, 4, 6.

[4] Caesalpinus, *Appendix ad libros de plantis et quaestiones peripateticas*, Rome, 1603, 4to, p. 32.

[5] *Quaest. Peripat.*, III, 7 and 9.

[6] *Ibid.*, V, 1, fols. 104v-109v in the 1593 edition.

[7] *Ibid.*, V, 3, fol. 121r: denying that all the nerves descend from the brain and spinal medulla, he says, "tendines enim et ligamenti nervi quidam sunt non tamen inde ortum ducunt."

with Aristotle that the heart was the seat of the soul and the center of sensory and motor activity.[8]

Yet it is in the midst of this partially reactionary argument that Cesalpino has been thought by some to have displayed an acquaintance with the circulation of the blood almost sixty years before its much fuller and clearer enunciation by Harvey. Were this true, it would furnish a striking instance of a scientific discovery of first importance blossoming forth in a work not only based upon Aristotle and full of errors but not free from magical notions. Cesalpino, for instance, held that the imagination could be affected by external objects without movement of the senses, and that future events were often thus revealed.[9] But I fear that the close association of science and magic in the past cannot be demonstrated from this particular point of the discovery of the circulation of the blood.

Concerning the question of priority between Cesalpino and Harvey there has been repeated controversy between Italian and English writers,[10] which I have been unable fully to follow because some of the Italian material has been inaccessible to me.[11] I can therefore only say that from my own reading of the *Peripatetic Questions*[12] I am not convinced that Cesalpino clearly

[8] *Ibid.*, V, 7.

[9] *Ibid.*, V, 9.

[10] For bibliography see U. Viviani, *Vita ed opere di A. Cesalpino,* 1922, pp. 231-37. Unfortunately he gives no precise references to the source material, quoting instead a "splendido discorso" of Scalzi on October 30, 1876, with brief Latin, quotations which I have failed to find in Cesalpino.

Others than Italians have associated the name of Cesalpino with the discovery of the circulation. Thus M. J. P. Flourens, *Histoire de la découverte de la circulation du sang.* 1857, quoted two or three passages from Cesalpino.

[11] What I have found has not always impressed me as strictly accurate in its citation or interpretation of Cesalpino's text. Luciani, *Fisiologia dell' uomo,* Terza editione, I (1908), 173-74, gives the title of Cesalpino's work as "Peripateticarum questiones libri quinque," and garbles the text of *De plantis,* 1583, I, ii, 3, "In animalibus videmus alimentum per venas duci ad cor tanquam ad officinam caloris insiti et adepta inibi ultima perfectione per arterias in universum corpus distribui agente spiritu qui ex eodem alimento in corde gignitur," to read as follows, ". . . Cesalpino afferma che il sangue 'per venas duci ad cor et per arterias in universum corpus distribui.'" Ceradini, *op. cit.,* p. 291, in quoting *Ars medica,* VI, 19 (1606), p. 503, speaks of "continus quidam motus" instead of continuus.

[12] *Quaest. Peripat.,* V, 3-4, fols. 116r-126r in the 1593 edition; cols. 514-29 in the edition of 1588.

stated or even clearly understood the general circulation of the blood. He knew and clearly stated as "this circulation" the lesser or pulmonary circulation, but it had already been noted by Servetus and by Colombo (1559), while Cesalpino still believed that some blood passed through the septum,[13] although Vesalius had denied this in 1543. Cesalpino asserted the unity of the vascular system,[14] understood probably that the veins opened only into the heart and towards the heart,[15] and stated that they brought it aliment which was there converted into spirit and diffused by the arteries from the heart through the body.[16] As to passage from arteries to veins he is less explicit, employing such ancient Greek terminology as anastomosis, which may mean inosculations between veins and arteries at any point in their course and in either direction,[17] or using the term, capillamenta,[18] which the Italians in the controversy interpret as capillaries, while the English insist that it still meant for Cesalpino the Aristotelian

[13] *Ibid.*, V, 4, fol. 126r, ". . . deinde autem in sinistro ubi syncerior iam sanguis est partim per medium septum partim per medios pulmones refrigerationis gratia ex dextro in sinistrum transmittitur."

[14] *Ibid.*, V, 3, fol. 116r; ed. of 1588, col. 515: "Quod si cor principium est sanguinis, venarum quoque et arteriarum principium esse necesse est; vasa enim haec sanguini sunt destinata. Ut igitur rivuli ex fonte aquam hauriunt, sic venae et arteriae ex corde."

[15] *Ibid.*, V, 4, fol. 122r; ed. of 1588: col. 523: ". . . omnibus autem membranulae sint appositae ei officio delegatae ut oscula intromittentia non educant et educentia non intromittant." But the last sentence quoted in the previous note shows that Cesalpino sometimes spoke as if blood flowed from the heart into the veins. Other passages might be cited on either side.

[16] *De plantis,* 1583, I, ii, 3. Latin quoted in note 11.

[17] *Quaest. Peripat.*, V, 3, fol. 121; ed. of 1588, col. 522: ". . . cum osculorum sit communio non solum in corde sed etiam per totum venarum atque arteriarum ductum." V, 4, fol. 123r; ed. of 1588, col. 525: "Motus igitur continuus a corde in omnes partes agitur. . . . Simul autem alimentum nutritivum fert et auctivum ex venis elicit per osculorum communionem quam Graeci Anastomosim vocant."

[18] In arguing that the vena cava and arteria aorta do not terminate in any other internal organ than the heart but merely pass through the others, Cesalpino says—V, 3, fol. 116r; ed. of 1588, col. 515— ". . . aut si quae desinunt in capillamenta resolvuntur," and "fines autem earundem in capillamenta tenuissime scissa desinunt." But he says nothing explicitly that I have found as to intercommunication of the capillamenta into which the veins and arteries peter out.

Viviani (1922), p. 203, quotes this passage from Scalzi without a reference: ". . . in ductibus autem parvorum osculorum etiam communicatio apparet sed imbecillis." I have failed to find such a passage. See also ed. of 1593, fol. 120v, "Nam venulae in fibras rectas desinunt nervos constituentes."

"filamentous terminations of the arteries in nerves."[19] It is also possible, however, that he may have read a new meaning into the old terms in his anxiety to support his novel position by the authority of Aristotle. Thus he uses the term "anastomosis" of the pulmonary circulation.[20]

In further support of the claim made for Cesalpino that he discovered the circulation of the blood a passage is cited from his later *Medical Questions,*[21] in which he states as a fact "deserving speculation" that when a ligature is made in a vein, it swells up with blood on the side of the ligature away from the heart. "For this ought to happen in opposite wise, if the movement of blood and spirit is made from the vitals to the entire body." That he should still, twenty-four years after the dedication of his *Peripatetic Questions,* regard this fact, readily observable in the blood-letting of medical practice as well as in surgical operations, as a matter for speculation would seem to indicate that he still had no very decided or definite views on the subject rather than that he had already promulgated the general circulation in unmistakable terms.

The circulation of the spirits through the body had long since been stated and may perhaps be regarded as by this time a generally accepted doctrine. But the spirits were thought of as so rarefied that they could penetrate almost anywhere and did not need to follow a defined path or orbit in their rapid diffusion and circulation. Cesalpino was endeavoring to prove that the heart was the source of the spirits as well as the seat of the soul. He

[19] Sir George Johnson, *A Defence of Harvey as the Discoverer of the Circulation of the Blood in Reply to Prof. Scalzi,* 1884, pp. 14-15, says of Cesalpino: "The only kind of communication between the arteries and the veins of which he had any conception was that taught by the ancient anatomists—namely by means of inosculations which, as he repeatedly says, the Greeks call 'anastomosis'" and, "He believed in a direct lateral communication between the arteries and the veins throughout their whole course." See also Johnson's *Harveian Oration* of 1882, and D. Fraser Harris in the *Edinburgh Medical Journal,* VII (1911), 140 *et seq.*

[20] *Quaest. Peripat.,* 1593, fol. 125v: "Idcirco pulmo per venam arteriis similem ex dextro cordis ventriculo fervidum hauriens sanguinem per anastomosim arteriae venali reddens que in sinistrum cordis ventriculum tendit."

[21] II, 17 (1593), fol. 234r.

still believed that the arteries contained spirit as well as blood. As we have seen or shall see in other chapters, it was more common in this period to explain physiological and psychological phenomena in terms of the spirits than it was from the blood. Cesalpino does not seem to have been particularly interested in the blood. He failed to grasp the true character of the heart or satisfactorily to describe its action. Had he possessed this interest and understanding, he might have worked out the general circulation more thoroughly and have foreshadowed or even enunciated it more clearly and unmistakably.[22]

The *Peripatetic Questions* were given a thorough overhauling and criticism by Nicolaus Taurellus of Montbéliard (1547-1606), doctor of philosophy and medicine and professor at the university of Altdorf, in a work of over a thousand pages published at Frankfurt in 1597 with the derisive title, *Alpes caesae*.[23]

[22] I find that the question as to Cesalpino's share in the discovery of the circulation of the blood had already been discussed with considerable acumen and acquaintance with his writings in the eighteenth century. Astrucius, *De morbis venereis,* Venice, 1748, II, 304, already asserted that Cesalpino was the inventor and Harvey only the developer and exploiter of the circulation. Haller, *Adnotationes ad Methodum Studii medici Boerhaave,* thereupon pointed out that while Cesalpino—like Servetus, Colombo and Pigafetta—was acquainted with the lesser pulmonary circulation, as his *Peripatetic Questions,* V, 4 showed, as for the greater circulation, "De ea Caesalpinus cogitata aliqua reliquit, in systematis vero speciem numquam constituit." In *De plantis,* I, 2, "ubi alimentum a venis ad cor duci, inde per arterias in totum corpus adduci ait; non satis tamen manifesto addit, ab arteriis sanguinem in venas reddi." As for the passage in the *Medical Questions* on the swelling of the vein between the ligature and the extremities, Cesalpino explained this "by the native heat which passes from the arteries to the veins by anastomosis."

Calvi, who has quoted these interesting passages from Haller in his history of the botanical garden at Pisa, written in 1777, himself says that Cesalpino "discovered the valves of the larger vessels and observed the pulmonary circulation and inosculations of the arteries into the veins, so that firmer foundations were laid upon which Harvey based the discovery of the general circulation." Giovanni Calvi, *Commentarium inserviturum historiae Pisani Vireti botanici academici,* Pisis, 1777, p. 44 *et seq.:* "maiorum vasorum valvulas adinvenisse atque arteriarum inosculationes in venas et sanguinis circuitum per pulmones animadvertisse ita ut firmiora iacerentur fundamenta quibus Harvaeus universum, sanguinis eundem circuitum detegerit."

[23] *Alpes Caesae, hoc est, Andr. Caesalpini Itali monstrosa et superba dogmata discussa et excussa a Nicolao Taurello Montbelgardiensi . . . ,* Francofurti apud M. Zachariam Paltheniium typographum, anno MDXCVII.

What interests us here is the comment of Taurellus on the passage in which Cesalpino says: "Therefore continual movement is produced from the heart in all parts of the body, because there is continual generation of spirits. Moreover, it simultaneously brings nutritive aliment and elicits auctive from the veins by communion of openings which the Greeks call anastomosis."[24] To this among other criticisms Taurellus, who does not always seem to have penetrated Cesalpino's meaning, objects that not venous but arterial blood made in the heart ought to be transmitted to the arteries, that the most manifest and convenient explanation of this transmission is the heart itself, interjected between the vena cava and the great artery, and that there is no need "of this false and impossible reception of the blood from the veins into the arteries through the conjunction of openings at their extremities."[25] What a proof this would have been, not only that Cesalpino understood the general circulation long before Harvey, but that his explanation had been recognized by a contemporary and a hostile critic at that, and hence should have been known to Harvey too:—what a proof, I say, this would have been, had Taurellus only written "from the arteries to the veins" instead of "from the veins into the arteries"!

Cesalpino's sixteen books on plants came out in 1583[26] in the interval between the first appearance of the *Peripatetic Questions* and his subsequent medical works. They were in part the result of many years of personal observation of plants as a traveller and as a teacher and head of the botanical garden at Pisa. They were dedicated to Francis, grand-duke of Tuscany. The difficulty of identifying the old Greek, Arabic and Latin names for plants and the need of classifying the new flora since the voyages of discovery further served to convince Cesalpino of the crying need for some arrangement other than the alphabetical. He therefore attempted something approaching to a scientific classification by genera, which he felt would have the additional

[24] *Ibid.*, p. 892, quoting *Quaest. Peripat.*, V, 4, fol. 123r in ed. of 1593; col. 525 in ed. of 1588.

[25] *Alpes caesae*, p. 893.

[26] Andreas Caesalpinus, *De plantis*, Florentiae, 1583, 4to. Copy used: BM 447.b.2.(1.).

advantage of brevity, since it would not be necessary to repeat common characteristics of each plant. He also thought that a verbal description might be more complete and accurate than a picture. His classification, which is somewhat obscured by absence of any chapter headings or other captions within each book, consists of such distinctions as that between trees whose seeds are external and trees whose seeds are in the heart of the fruit. Or he distinguishes plants which bear solitary seeds under single flowers or seed pods from those with two seeds under the same flower or seed receptacle.[27] Finally the sixteenth and last book is given over to apparently seedless plants. This scheme is buttressed by personal observation and generalization, as the following passage will indicate.

> Those which carry four seeds in the common seat, in all cases that I have observed to date, include the seeds in a sort of low leaflet covering the flower, nor is any vessel suitable for this given them within the flower. Therefore the seeds can be seen from outside after the flower has fallen off unless the leaflet again closes up. And in all cases the flower grows from the seat of the seed. They differ however in that some seeds have the heart on top like Buglossa and Ancusaeum, while other kinds on the contrary have the genital force at the base of the seed as in sage and marshmallow and many others related to them. Moreover, the leaflet in those is divided as in Buglossa and the genital power more integral, so that the seeds lie more deeply. In all, the flowers are formed of a single concave leaf.[28]

Cesalpino nevertheless recognized the contributions to botany of other recent writers: Ruelle, Ermolao Barbaro, Brasavola, Mattioli of Siena, Luca Ghini his own preceptor at Pisa, Aloysius Anguillara, Garcia da Orta on simples of India, and Monardes on the flora of the New World. Besides the positive interest in botanical classification and description which largely absorbs the author's energy and attention, another negative feature of his method which works against the introduction of magic and occult virtues is his abstention, except in the case of new plants, from retailing their properties, for which in the case of most species he

[27] *De plantis,* libri XVI, 1583, p. 146. [28] *Ibid.,* p. 432, lib. XI, cap. 1.

refers the reader to Dioscorides and Galen. In these books on plants, then, the science of Cesalpino shows to the best advantage. Rádl, although classifying him under "Neue Aristoteliker," called him the first modern botanist to establish the study of plants on scientific foundations.[29]

The situation changes somewhat in *De metallicis,* a work dedicated to Clement VIII and printed at Rome in 1596. In the preface Cesalpino informs the pope that he had intended to supplement his work on plants by one on minerals, observing the same method of treatment. But on coming to Rome he found that his former pupil at Pisa, Michael Mercatus, had undertaken a like task in his *Metallotheca Vaticana.* He had, however, finished only those portions dealing with earths, salts, alums, sulphur, bitumen and certain stones when he died early of the stone. Cesalpino has therefore undertaken to supply the missing sections on marbles, gems and metals. But while this supplement appeared in 1596, the original work of Mercatus seems to have been printed only in 1717. Actually the two works would seem to have overlapped a good deal. The ecclesiastical censor, Frater Vincentius Guerra magister, approved the book on September 2, 1596, not only because it contained nothing against "our faith" or good morals, but because its author as a most diligent Peripatetic had clearly explained difficult passages of Aristotle and showed wide and varied reading of other authors.

Cesalpino claimed no originality for his *De metallicis,* which he represented as a useful compendium especially for those not in a position to do wide reading. He uses such authors as Pliny, Dioscorides, Galen, Theophrastus, Marbod, and Albertus Mag-

[29] Em. Rádl, *Geschichte d. biologischen Theorien in der Neuzeit,* 1913, p. 125. Rádl's further characterization (at p. 126) of Cesalpino as "ein hartnäckiger Aristoteliker, sogar als ein Anhänger der Feinde Galileis!" seems to me questionable in view of the original tendencies which we have noted in the *Peripatetic Questions.* Therefore Rádl's inference from this supposed contrast that the triumph of the science of Galileo meant the decline of biology, that Cesalpino was forgotten, and that Linnaeus had to found it afresh, also seems hardly justified. Botany was generally regarded as a subject less advanced and less important than physics or astronomy. Cesalpino, who was no Darwin anyway, did not devote his whole time and heart to it. He passed on to medicine and Peripatetic questions. Linnaeus specialized much more in biology and wrote not one but several works to reinforce his views.

nus a great deal but does not seem to cite Conrad Gesner. An Arabic author like Mesue is quoted with the same respect as an ancient Greek or Latin writer. Cesalpino's attempt at a generic classification is vitiated by being based upon the theory of four elements and four qualities. All subterranean minerals are a mixture of earth and water and the first genus considered is of those which are formed from a dry exhalation. Also there seems to be more magic lore than in *De plantis*. Not only do we hear of a lynx-stone near Naples that bears mushrooms, which Cesalpino regards as a great marvel but which may be a fact, but we have the gem jasper suspended as an amulet or are regaled with the virtues of bezaar or bezoar stones. One from Persia that grows in goats is tested in this wise. They smear a thread with poison such as the juice of white hellebore and draw it with a needle through the foot of a dog or other part of an animal, leaving the thread in the wound. When symptoms of poisoning aggravate, they bring the stone near, and if it is genuine, the animal feels relief from that remedy. If not, they consider the stone adulterine. "But to-day merchants refuse this test, apparently because few specimens come up to the promised effects." The variety from the New World is less efficacious than that from Persia. In treating of metals proper Cesalpino sets forth the views of the alchemists but does not have much sympathy with them. He is rather brief as to the medicinal properties and uses of metals. To Paracelsus and his followers in particular Cesalpino does not seem to refer.

If Cesalpino was somewhat more inclined to the marvelous and magical when treating of gems than when classifying herbs, he was vastly more so when he had to treat of demons. In point of time, however, his *Peripatetic Investigation of Demons* anteceded the publication of the other two works, since it was printed in 1580.[30] The occasion of writing this treatise was as follows. The archbishop of Pisa called together the theologians, philosophers and medical professors of the university to decide concerning certain nuns, who seemed to be vexed by demons, whether

[30] There is a Bonn dissertation by Ernst Breit on *Die Engel- und Dämonen-lehre des Pomponatius und des Çäsalpinus*, 1912.

the disease depended on natural or supernatural causes. Cesalpino, like the others, decided that the infliction was supernatural and his *Daemonum investigatio peripatetica* instead of being, as one might have inferred from the mere title, a work after the order of Pomponazzi's *De incantationibus,* giving a natural explanation of the phenomena and denying, implicitly if not explicitly, the existence of demons, is a credulous acceptation of demoniac possession and of the testimony extorted at witch trials which would put many a primarily theological writer on such subjects to blush.

"What ever was more marvelous in all nature," says Cesalpino in his preface to Ioannes de Tonsis, a patrician of Milan, "than the invention of the magic arts?" This question has puzzled and even now perplexes the greatest philosophers, how at a mere nod divers kind of witchcraft are brought on or dissolved, or how human bodies are transported in a twinkling to most distant regions without any visible carrier. Avicenna ascribed such phenomena to the divinity of the human mind; the theologians, to demons; while Peripatetic philosophers, persuaded that Aristotle did not admit demons in the realm of nature, have devised various explanations, some ascribing these arts and other miracles to vehement fixed imagination, some to occult virtues, some to the celestial influence of the stars. Others, finding no probable explanation, have not feared to deny miracles and to condemn as fabulous anything exceeding the natural order. Since Cesalpino has always held that the truth revealed in holy theology never is contrary to the truth based on scientific principles, he proposes in the present work to give a natural explanation of demons, something which no one, so far as he knows, has done before.

Cesalpino therefore tries to make out that Aristotle did not deny but even conceded the existence of demons (in nature), and that Galen misinterpreted the Hippocratic saying that there was something divine in disease as having reference merely to the influence of the stars on disease. Cesalpino, on the contrary, asserts that there are nine orders of angels and nine orders of demons. He then adverts to shocking superstitions and sacrilegious actions of witches as revealed by their confessions when examined under torture. "From which," he continues, "no mediocre knowledge is had towards certification of those things which we are now investigating." He then embarks upon a terrible sea of utterly foul and incredible stories. A youth in Germany found his genitals gone but induced the witch who had removed them to restore them. The following tale was doubtless suggested by *The Golden Ass* of Apuleius. A youth in Cyprus who ate eggs purchased of a woman turned into an ass and was restored to human form only when visiting Genoese merchants noticed the ass standing on its hind legs to venerate the host, and so suspected foul play. A young husband in San Gimignano, infatuated by a witch, left his wife and children. His spouse discovered a toad with its eyes sewn up in the pot under the bed. When this was removed, the toad's eyes freed, and the toad cremated, the husband came back to her. Witches condemned to be burned alive continue to deny their guilt until the instrument of their sorcery is found under the skin. It has been found by experience that witches cannot weep before the judge, no matter what torture is applied. Such are a few milder instances of the painful and revolting picture invoked by Cesalpino's "Peripatetic investigation."

The powers of demons are discussed at length by Cesalpino and how they employ divers bodies, although their substance is separated from all corporeity. But since he takes up the usual theological positions, we need not repeat his views on this point. It may be noted, however, that he now attributes to a book of divination the idea which we have already met in his *Peripatetic Questions,* that the imagination may be moved by external objects directly without any intercession of the senses.[31]

Natural signs of demoniac possession are the speaking of unknown tongues, a movement under the skin to another part of the body, and abstention from divine worship. Some trustworthy priests say that persons possessed by demons cannot endure the smell of roses—another survival from *The Golden Ass* of Apuleius. Natural remedies against demons are also considered, for

[31] See cap. 12, fol. 19v, "Si autem vera sunt quae ex libro de divinatione collegimus imaginationem a rebus externis moveri posse non intercedente sensu, nulla erit difficultas."

inasmuch as demons use natural forces, it seems reasonable to employ nature against them. A negative measure is to burn the instruments of witchcraft. As positive procedure Cesalpino puts faith in amulets and alexipharmaca, aromas and suffumigations. A wreath of rue defends a child from fascination, as is known today to the populace, especially to those dwelling in the woods. Cesalpino also approves Galen's recommendation of a peony suspended about a boy's neck as a preventive of epilepsy.

Fiorentino,[32] while admitting that the *Peripatetic Investigation of Demons* is the Achilles' heel of Cesalpino, sees in it the influence of his trips to Germany, where the witchcraft delusion was in full swing. He asserts "In Italy fortunately there was more good sense," and represents Cesalpino as saying that cases there were rare, while in Germany and in England they were quite frequent. But Cesalpino continued, "and much more so in the islands to the north of Britain," which Fiorentino omits and which suggests that the marvels increased, as Aeneas Sylvius had said, with distance. Fiorentino further states that Cesalpino's Italian examples are confined to Tuscany and more particularly to San Gimignano and Pisa. But this omits the incident of the Genoese merchants in Cyprus. Again Fiorentino remarks that Cesalpino extracts practically all the cases of witchcraft which he adduces in his last chapter from the records of the German inquisitors. But it is not in the last chapter but several earlier ones that his terrible stories occur. Moreover, the German inquisitors had received their authorization from an Italian pope, and Cesalpino was not the only Italian to write credulously on witchcraft in the sixteenth century. He was, however, the most distinguished Italian scientist to do so, and his entitling his deluded mixture of theology and gross superstition a Peripatetic investigation must be regarded as a blot upon the escutcheon of Aristotelianism.

[32] F. Fiorentino, *Vita ed opere di A. Cesalpino,* in *Nuova Antologia,* Seconde serie, Florence, vol. XVI (1879), fasc. 16. Reprinted in *Studi e ritratti della Rinascenza,* Bari, 1911, pp. 195-231: see especially pp. 213-16. U. Viviani, *Vita ed opere di A. Cesalpino,* 1922, pp. 209-211, reproduces Fiorentino's argument.

The passage in Cesalpino (1580), cap. 8, fol. 13r-v, reads: "Sed exempla in Italia quidem rara sunt, extant tamen nonnulla. At in Germania et Britannia frequentissima ac multo magis in insulis ad aquilonem spectantibus."

CHAPTER XLI

EFFORTS TOWARDS A CHRISTIAN PHILOSOPHY OF NATURE

Now first in our age God's creatures, set forth by Moses in his Physics, seem to have been sufficiently illuminated.
—SCRIBONIUS

In this and the chapters immediately following we bring together a number of works or discussions of nature which are primarily of a general character. Some offer a Christian philosophy or physics; some are Aristotelian, while others oppose Aristotle; still others emphasize natural magic or the occult in nature. Although these writings may seem more marked by a Christian bias and an interest in the occult, especially astrology and natural magic, than by any close approach to a modern scientific character, nevertheless by their very number and the many editions through which some of them ran, they testify to a widespread concern with the world of nature which prepared the ground for the development of modern science. They are not specialized works and do not go into such detailed discussion of particulars as the treatises on plants or animals, on stones or minerals, on human anatomy and medicine, of which other chapters have treated. They offer a desirable elementary modicum or minimum of knowledge concerning the universe rather than the maximum of natural philosophy which an educated person might then acquire. At the same time one suspects that they express about all that their several authors knew concerning the vast subject with which they attempted to grapple.

On the verge of the second half of the sixteenth century we encounter the *Prelude to Christian Philosophy* of Guillaume Bigot of Laval, which was printed at Toulouse in 1549.[1] It hardly

[1] *Christianae philosophiae Praeludii libri iv, opus cum aliorum tum hominis substantiam luculentis expromens exemplis et rationibus, Gulielmo Bigo-*

attains the scope of a general work on nature, since its four books are devoted to the physiology of the human body and to the vegetative, sentient, and rational soul respectively. These limits also partially serve to explain why the work contains no astrology or alchemy and seems free from occult science. The work is noteworthy for its Christian title, for reflecting the progress in anatomical knowledge by stressing that subject, for criticizing Aristotle, than whom Bigot thinks Galen would be a better introduction for beginning students.[2] Bigot opens his own work with a discussion of chyle. This may seem a promising start for a materialistic philosophy on a purely physical basis, but before he finishes we find Bigot expressing his belief in varying degrees of intelligence among the orders of the angelic hierarchy and among demons.[3] And while he makes some criticisms of Aristotle or claims to have treated the nature of visual species more clearly than his predecessors,[4] his discussion seems to follow traditional channels and to show little progress towards modern science.

Bigot's text is preceded by a long and involved preface,[5] addressed to cardinal Jean du Bellay, in which he seeks to vindicate his innocence against his calumniators and enters into a detailed narrative of his relations with the university of Nîmes and Baduel. In his earlier *Somnium* he had been similarly concerned to defend himself and Budé from calumnies.[6] I have failed to discover whether these "calumnies" against Bigot resulted in the subsequent use of his name in the sense of a bigot, or whether the resemblance is purely accidental and the word

---

tio Lavalensi autore. Eiusdem et ad Iesum Christum Carmen supplex et Antilogica dedicatrixque Epistola perapte tam Praeludio quam reliquis ipsius Christianis scriptis praelegenda . . . , Tolosae Ex Praelo Guidonis Bondevillai typographi Academiae, MDXXXXVIIII. Copy used: BN Rés. R.210, of which the early pages are much damaged with portions missing.

[2] *Ibid.*, p. 84. He says that Ioannes Durantus, a physician of Nîmes, and Honoratus Castellanus, professor of medicine at Montpellier, agree with him in this.

[3] *Ibid.*, p. 442.

[4] *Ibid.*, p. 382.

[5] It runs to p. 51, other preliminary matter follows, and only at p. 83 does the text proper begin. It ends at p. 531, the volume at p. 540.

[6] *G. Bigotii Lavallensis Somnium . . . in quo cum alia tum Imperatoris Carolis describitur ab regno Gallie depulsio. Eiusdem explanatrix somnii epistola qua se item G. Budaeum a quorundam defendit calumniis,* Paris, 1537. Copy used: BM 11405.b.1.

has some other derivation. Gesner, writing in 1545, said that he had seen Bigot at Basel seven years before, and that he had promised a work on some books of Aristotle but had not yet published it so far as Gesner knew.[7] Bigot had first studied at Angers, where he was wounded in a fight with the young seigneur de la Tour Landry. He then fled the realm and studied successively in Liège, Louvain, Marburg and Frankfurt an der Oder. He lectured on the *Physics* of Aristotle at Tübingen in 1535 but soon quarreled with Camerarius and passed on to Basel. It was in 1536, according to Delaunay, that he met Gesner and composed a poetical apology to la Tour Landry which procured permission for him to return to France.[8]

Guillaume Postel died in 1581 after a life of almost a century, spent partly in travel in the orient and elsewhere, partly as professor of mathematics and philosophy at Paris, where he was now forbidden to lecture and now allowed to proceed again.[9] He also taught at Vienna, where he received the same salary of 200 aurei nummi that he had had from Francis I, although most professors at Vienna then were receiving only eighty.[10] Most of the works by Postel with which we are here concerned were published soon after the middle of the century.

Postel's conception of the world of nature, as of everything else, was much affected by the Bible, religion and a mystical and fantastic turn of mind. He held that all things are made mobile in Christ, but are immobile in God; that the power of the Father unites at the center, while the wisdom of the Son tends towards the circumference, with the Holy Spirit in between; and that first matter correspondingly originates from a central atom.[11] Or

[7] Gesner (1545), fol. 287r.

[8] Paul Delaunay, "L'es médecins manceaux en Suisse au XVIe siècle," *Ve Cong. Int. d'Hist. de la Médecine,* Geneva, 1926, pp. 53-54.

[9] Thuanus, *Historia,* Bk. 74. See Chas. Muteau, *Les écoles et collèges en province,* Dijon, 1882, pp. 193-95, for manuscript evidence as to his teaching and writing at Dijon about the middle of the century.

[10] *Compendium cosmographiae,* 1561, preface to the emperor Ferdinand. Copy used: Bern Stadtbibliothek. Geogr. VIII. 20.

[11] *De nativitate mediatoris ultima nunc futura et toti orbi terrarum in singulis ratione praeditis manifestanda opus in quo totius naturae obscuritas origo et creatio ita cum sua causa illustratur . . . autore Spiritu Christi et scriptore Gulielmo Postello,* no place

he explained springs on mountain tops and salt water ascending rivers as "done by the will of the Lord Jesus."[12] That there were waters above the firmament, or at least above the first region of the air, he regarded as proved not only by the Bible but by experience. For example, heavy snows fell in the polar regions during the night of six months, although there was no sunshine then and hence no evaporation to supply the clouds to account for such precipitation.

Postel thought that there were four regions of air rather than three and that in one of these, the penultimate, many living creatures were generated, like calves, and ferruginous rocks of great weight, all which were put together by force of intelligence and not instantaneously. He also distinguished four fires, but these were simply the different colors appearing in the process of combustion. Water had its miracles, and Postel affirmed that two hundred miles away from the coast the sea attained a higher level than the highest mountains, and that he with many sailors had measured this with an astrolabe.[13] He also held that, inasmuch as the length of the Nile is equal to one-seventh of the earth's circumference, either it flows uphill for a part of its course, or the earth is not round. Postel appears dimly to sense geologic processes in saying that places have receded from the sea with the passage of time, that antiquity located high mountains in regions which are now swamps under the rule of the Muscovites and Tartars, that there are veins of heavy metals such as gold and silver on the highest mountain ridges, or that mountains are suspended out of place and sometimes rest on water. But he explains all such phenomena as miracles of Jesus Christ.[14]

Beyond the four elements were ten celestial spheres, each with its moving Intelligence by whose will the influence of the heavens was made varied, thus accounting for the diversity between regions of the globe situated on the same parallel. The eighth

---

or date of publication, 4to, 187 pp., p. 123. Copy used: Bern Stadtbibliothek b. 148.

[12] *Ibid.*, p. 50.

[13] *Ibid.*, pp. 42-50, for everything since the last note. For the waters above the firmament see also his *De universitate*, Reims, 1552, fol. 7r.

[14] *De nativitate*, pp. 52-53.

sphere moved one degree in 106 years. The ninth sphere completed its movement on poles placed in the first and seventh signs in seven thousand years. The four colors seen in combustion were also those of the four elements: black for earth, red for water, blue for air, and white for fire. Unless the natural order by which the earth was enclosed by a sphere of water had been altered by divine wisdom, "man would either never have been or would be a fish." But the densest part of the earth, full of rocks and metals, was raised from its original location near the center of the globe and formed into mountains, while the covering waters were divinely removed from a portion of the earth's surface by the movement of the moon. Despite what we have heard Postel say about the sea reaching a higher level than the land, he believed that the spheres of earth and water had a common center, or nearly so. For both on journeys and during lunar eclipses the surface of the earth seemed uniformly round.[15]

In his treatise on causes or principles and origins Postel was concerned to vindicate natural philosophy from the charge of impiety and to show that, although Aristotle had neglected the supreme scope of truth which is the glory and love of the First Cause, nevertheless from his words rightly understood the providence of God and immortality of the soul could be demonstrated.[16]

Postel sometimes set forth his peculiar views as to nature and

[15] The contents of this paragraph are based on Postel's *De universitate,* as those of the two preceding paragraphs were upon his *De nativitate.* The full title of the former work is: *De universitate liber in quo astronomiae doctrinaeve coelestis Compendium terrae aptatum et secundum coelestis influxus ordinem praecipuarumque Originum rationem totus orbis Terrae quatenus innotuit cum Regnorum temporibus exponitur. Sed ante omneis alias orbis parteis TERRA SANCTA summo hoc est amplissimo compendio describitur cui Gallia ob primarium orbis nomen et Ius substituitur eo quod ambae toti orbi legem sunt daturae. Guilielmo Postello restituto in regni evangelici assertionem authore.* E typographia Ioannis Gueullartii ad Phoenicem e regione collegii Remensis MDLII. 58 fols.

[16] G. Postel, *Liber de causis seu de principiis et originibus nature utriusque in quo ita de eterna rerum veritate agitur ut et auctoritate et ratione non tantum ubivis particularis Dei providentia sed et animorum et corporum immortalitas ex ipsius Aristotelis verbis recte intellectis et non distortis demonstretur clarissime . . . ,* Parisiis, Apud Sebastianum Nivellium sub ciconiis in vico Iacobaeo, MDLII.

God, and his political propaganda, in the form of single broadside sheets or charts. In 1552 he published one for arithmetic, one for music, and one for astronomy.[17] In 1553 there followed two double-page charts of the heavens,[18] a table of eternal ordination, an eternal resolution destined to the king and most Christian people which embodies a series of pro-Gallic propositions, a Table of the Restitution of All Natural and Supernatural Constitutions,[19] and a Petition to Parlement that the king of Gaul should be supreme.[20]

Probably Guillaume Postel had never read Pierre du Bois, of whose *De recuperatione terrae sanctae* there is only a single manuscript extant. But his mind was equally obsessed by the thought of the Holy Land and of universal monarchy for the king of France. He urged the latter in the preface to cardinal Lorraine of his translation of the work of Justin Martyr on the overthrow of the false dogmas of Aristotle.[21] In his work on monarchy printed the year previous he had argued that the Holy Land and Gaul were both under the influence of the sign Aries, and hence were respectively destined to religious empire and temporal monarchy.[22] It may be added that other of his arguments for universal French monarchy were even more far-fetched than this astrological reason. On the very title page of his *De universitate* he placed the Holy Land above all other parts of the world, adding that Gaul was substituted for it "because of the primary name of the world and right" and because they were both to give law to the whole world.[23] And even in his *Compen-*

[17] At Paris, Apud Gulielmum Cavellat in pingui Gallina ex adverso Collegii Cameracensis, 1552.

[18] Parisiis, Apud Hieronymum Gourmontium sub insigni trium coronarum e regione Collegii Cameracensis, 1553.

[19] Exemplaria venalia sunt apud Ioannem Gueullart ad Phoenicem e regione Collegii Remensis.

[20] All these charts and broadsides are bound in one volume at the British Museum: 17.h.1.(7.).

[21] *Eversio falsorum Aristotelis dogmatum authore D. Iustino martyre . . . Guilielmo Postello in tenebrarum Babylonicarum dispulsionem interprete,* Parisiis Apud Sebastianum Nivellium sub Ciconiis in vico Iacobaeo, 1552, 16mo, 76 fols. Copy seen at Bern, Stadtbibliothek, m. 89, bound with *Liber de causis seu de principiis et originibus naturae utriusque . . .*, 1552.

[22] *Les raisons de la monarchie,* Tours, 1551, 16mo, pp. xx-xxi. Copy used: Bern, Stadtbibliothek, W. 146.

[23] See note 15.

dium cosmographiae addressed to the emperor Ferdinand he stated among other absurd names and etymologies that the Gauls were named from Gal which means a flood that they alone of all the world might preserve an undying memory of the great miracle of the deluge.[24]

As one who had traveled widely, Postel should illustrate to what extent the Spanish and Portuguese discoveries were known outside of those countries among the learned of Europe about the middle of the century. Besides Europe, Asia and Africa, he recognized an American continent reaching south to the Straits of Magellan but unknown beyond that. He also once speaks of an extensive fifth continent about the south pole which is as yet little known. This does not agree very well with his statements elsewhere that the southern hemisphere is in large part covered by water and that most of the inhabited land is in the northern hemisphere. Against the old view that the polar zones were uninhabitable because of cold and the torrid zone because of heat, however, he asserts that all land everywhere is inhabitable, as there is nothing that men do not become used to, although at the poles a night of six months is followed by a day of the same length. Near the equator, on the other hand, the fact that days and nights are always of equal length makes the heat tolerable—an argument which it is well to remember could be found in medieval writings since at least the thirteenth century. Postel therefore argues that there should be twelve climes rather than seven. He describes the Portuguese route to the East as 38 degrees this side of the equator and 35 beyond to the west, then 43 degrees eastward in the southern hemisphere and 90 degrees from the Arabian Gulf to the Moluccas. This would seem to make 206 degrees each way but Postel states that in going and returning they cover 416 degrees whereas the earth's circumference is only 360 degrees. He saw that canals at Panama and Suez would greatly shorten the circumnavigation of the globe.[25] He speaks

[24] *Compendium cosmographiae,* 1561, pp. 19-20.

[25] *De universitate,* 1552, fol. 56r, "Angustiae sive Isthmus Parias et Arabicus facerent circuitum orbis brevissimum si semel scinderentur perfoderenturve . . ." It is difficult to interpret the words which immediately

of the promontory of Good Hope. He states that the term, Fortunate Islands, is today applied to the West Indies—Isabella and Hispaniola and many others discovered by Columbus. In both works he seems ignorant of the existence of Madagascar, since he speaks of Zanzibar—"as it was once named but now the Portuguese call it St. Lawrence"—as the only island of any size adjoining the African continent. Although Postel was a believer in astrological influence, he fails to inform us what signs and planets the newly discovered lands are under or to attempt any extension of Ptolemaic astrology to them. Apparently the problem did not occur to him.

The *Christian Physics* of Lambert Daneau offers an example how science and Calvinism comported themselves when in close proximity. Daneau was born at Beaugency in 1530, studied law at Orléans, became a counselor of the Parlement of Paris, then went to Geneva to study theology, became a Protestant minister, and was professor of theology at Geneva and for a brief spell at Leyden. He died at Castres in 1595.[26] The dedication of the *Christian Physics* is dated in December, 1575, but I have used the third edition in two parts respectively dated at Geneva in 1580[27] and 1589.[28] Other books by Daneau also appeared at Geneva and were mainly theological: *Elenchi hereticorum,* 1573; *De antichristo,* 1576; *Opuscula omnia theologica,* 1583; *Symboli apostolici explicatio,* 1592; *La vie de St. Paul,* s.l., 1595. He also composed a work on witchcraft, of which we treat in another chapter, but his combination of interest in witchcraft and Christian physics should be noted now. Daneau seems to have possessed no particular qualifications for writing on science and the world of nature. His book is not much above the level of Basil's *Hexaemeron* and the early medieval bestiaries. But that he

follow, "Terra Aulonis Florida Francesca et Britannorum sequitur littora ubivis auro copiosa praeterquam inter cannibales in America."

[26] P. de Félice, *Lambert Daneau. . . Sa vie, ses ouvrages, ses lettres inédites,* 1881.

[27] *Physice Christiana sive De rerum creatarum origine et usu disputatio e sacrae scripturae fontibus hausta et decerpta.* It is in 45 chapters and ends at p. 182 of the volume.

[28] *Physices Christianae pars altera sive de rerum creatarum natura.* It is in six tracts following the six days of creation.

should treat of nature at all, and that this book should so soon reach a third edition, indicates that it reflects an interest and attitude of the time. It was put in the popular form of a dialogue.

Daneau's chief concern is to show the Bible and science in agreement. He asserts that the world was divinely created but maintains that visible creatures are subject to scientific knowledge.[29] Like many clerical writers of previous centuries, he is much interested to explain what the waters above the firmament were and are,[30] even to the point of offering the gratuitous hypothesis that birds have an especial affinity to those celestial waters.[31] He repeats the patristic argument that the celestial bodies were created later than plants in order to demonstrate that they were not their cause. But then, he holds, "lest they should be thought to have been produced by God in vain," they were put by divine providence and ordination in charge of producing and conserving all inferior creatures including plants.[32] Daneau also feels it incumbent upon him to tell why poisonous and harmful things exist in nature, why the Mosiac account of creation says nothing of the creation of metals, how all the terrestrial animals could get into the ark.[33] Sin is his answer to the first question. His explanation in the second case is that metals do not appear on the earth's surface. Yet he would hardly admit that the Mosaic account of creation was superficial. As for the third problem, he repeats the explanation of Buteo that the ark was very large, and that all terrestrial animals can be reduced to about thirty genera. But it is doubtful if this can be taken as indicative of a tendency on his part to accept the possibility of the evolution of new species. Whenever Daneau cannot find a satisfactory explanation on natural grounds of a phenomenon, he usually says that God did it that way in order to display His wonderful power, as for example in the creation of both fish and birds from water. Or when asked why the waters above

[29] Pars I, cap. 7, "Physicae cognitionis subiectum est creatura visibilis et aspectabilis."

[30] Pars I, cap. 23; Pars II, ii, 2.

[31] *Ibid.*, II, v, 28. However, there is the reason that fish go with terrestrial waters, and perhaps the further thought that some birds are aquatic.

[32] *Ibid.*, II, iv, 3.

[33] *Ibid.*, I, 42; II, iii, 30; II, vi, 9.

the firmament do not fall to their natural place (i.e. next to earth), he replies that their natural place is where God put them.[34]

That Daneau's ideas concerning nature were often far removed from modern science is to be explained not merely by his adherence to the biblical story of creation and to religious dogma, but by his following, half unconsciously perhaps, the long established doctrines of ancient and medieval natural philosophy. When he says that the heavenly bodies do not generate others from themselves,[35] he is in accord with the Aristotelian theory of the eternity and incorruptibility of the heavens, and the nebular hypothesis was still far in the future for all his contemporaries. Once an approach is made to modern knowledge of plant fertilization. The disciple in the dialogue, noting that *physiologi* distinguish male and female varieties of certain plants, asks if there is not some secret conjunction of male and female even in plants for the propagation of new offshoots. But the master terms the belief in sexual intercourse between plants an error and says that not all species of plants can be separated into males and females. Moreover, many of those which are called males emit no seed. This function in many cases is limited to the female plants, and the males are so called merely because more robust.[36] In some respects Daneau is either unaware of or not in sympathy with recent developments and changing viewpoints in the scientific thought of his time. He discusses "the sun and its movement" without any reference to the Copernican theory.[37] He says that the female viper kills the male in the act of conception by biting off its head, and that the resultant brood avenge their genitor by gnawing their way out of the womb and so killing their dam.[38] Yet this myth had been denied at least as early as 1499 by Franciscus Cabalus.[39] Daneau also still believes in the existence of many viviparous flying dragons in Egypt with breasts to nourish their

[34] *Ibid.*, II, ii, 14.
[35] *Ibid.*, II, iv, 8.
[36] *Ibid.*, II, iii, 63.
[37] *Ibid.*, II, iv, 23.
[38] *Ibid.*, II, v, 24.
[39] T IV, 597, n. 9.

young, in the basilisk which kills men by its mere glance, in the power of human saliva to poison a snake because of the serpent's frigidity, and that old snakes restore their vision by touching their eyes with the herb *marathrum*. He holds that while some frogs are procreated from seed, others fall from the sky.

One recent author whom Daneau had read was Conrad Gesner. He notes the different orders of marine fish distinguished by Gesner[40] and seems to have been influenced by him further in the direction of biological classification, which is about the most scientific feature of Daneau's volume.

Daneau recognizes the influence of the heavenly bodies over inferior nature and the processes of generation and corruption, but holds that the stars have no influence on the human mind and will. Moreover, their present positions signify only the immediate future, not remote events. He opposes judicial astrologers, charging them with making dependent upon the stars things done privately or publicly either by human deliberation or the sole will of God. He asserts that the subsequent course of events has always proved the science of the astrologers to be most false. He tries to explain away the biblical passages which were commonly cited in favor of astrology. When Christ spoke of signs in sun, moon and stars, He had in mind the end of the world, not ordinary astrological significations. The star of Bethlehem was neither an ordinary star nor the sole inspiration of the three Magi, who were also moved by the Spirit. The signs in the sky mentioned by Isaiah and Ezekiel as portending the overthrow of the Medes and Egyptians were not ordinary constellations but miraculous apparitions.[41]

In 1576 was printed in six books the work of Nicolaus Contarenus, son of John Gabriel, patrician of Venice, on the perfection of things.[42] The author alludes to cardinal Contareni as his kinsman.[43] The first book treats of God; the second, of the

[40] *Physice Christiana*, II, v, 17.

[41] *Ibid.*, II, iv, 31-36.

[42] *Nicolai Contareni Ioannis Gabrielis filii patritii Veneti De perfectione rerum libri sex ad virum amplissimum Leonardum Donatum*, Venetiis Ioan. Baptista Somaschus excudebat, MDLXXVI. I own a copy.

[43] *Ibid.*, V, 6, p. 265.

universe, providence, fate, fortune, and sympathy and antipathy. The third book on angels discusses their production and nature, multitude, place, motion, intellect, will and love, bliss or fall, and hierarchies. Our author rebuts the views of the Peripatetics as to angels and adheres to the usual orthodox Christian point of view. The brief fourth book, on the principles and affections of natural things, treats of matter and form, causes, motion and quiet, place and time. The fifth book deals chiefly with the heavens, its sixth and last chapter on the inferior elements being largely based on the treatise of cardinal Contareni on that subject. The sixth book on man discusses the immortality of the soul, the intellect and will, and predestination. Thus only a small fraction of the work is concerned either with what we would call things or natural science.

The work is for the most part cast along traditional lines. The opinions of the Academy and Peripatetics, of Plato, Aristotle and other ancient philosophers, are reviewed. Averroes and Avicenna also receive attention, more so than medieval Latin writers who are seldom cited except in the margins of the final chapter on predestination. Recent writers are seldom mentioned by name.

A mystic attitude and one favorable to occult science is at times apparent. The perfection of the universe is demonstrated by the perfect numbers, six and nine. As six, for example, is three plus or times two, plus or times one, so the universe proceeds from the Trinity, consists of matter designated by duality, and tends towards the divine unity, the *Summum bonum*. Contareni also believes in relations of sympathy and antipathy between things, but regards these terms as inapplicable to such relationships as that of attraction between the magnet and iron, or the fear of a lion at the sight of a cock.[44]

If the work seems in many ways more theological and philosophical than scientific, it is none the less not without a considerable admixture of astrology. Whatever may be the explanation of the action of the magnet on iron, or of the terror inspired in

[44] *Ibid.*, II, 4, 8; pp. 114-15, 138.

the lion by the cock, Contareni feels certain that sympathy and antipathy between human beings are produced by the stars. Often at the mere mention of a name we fall in love and frequently we hate persons whom we have never seen. "For there is between the sky and mortal affairs a certain assent of nature in many parts sublimer than is seen between mortals themselves."[45] In a chapter of the fifth book devoted to the efficiency of the sky, after enumerating various effects of sun and moon, Contareni asserts that the risings and settings of other stars also have manifest effects. With the dog star come intense heat, stormy seas, growth of plants, rabies. With Arcturus come clouds and rain. From which examples Contareni jumps to the conclusion that no person of sense can deny that all the stars exert influence on earth. He rejects the argument of Plotinus that the stars are merely signs and insists that the motion of the heavens is the source and cause of all other motion. He appears to be blissfully ignorant of the article of Paris to the contrary. After a long discussion of the relation between heat and light, Contareni also attributes other occult influences to the stars. But he denies that they coerce intellect and will, or that divine providence acts by no other medium. Even angels cannot penetrate the counsels of God as to such turning aside of causes from their courses. But angels know openly what will happen of necessity, since even men with inferior faculties can foresee the future positions and effects of the stars.[46]

Of much the same order as the work of Daneau was that of his contemporary, Guilielmus Adolphus Scribonius, a physician of Marburg, entitled *A Methodical Doctrine of Nature*.[47] Moreover, as Daneau combined interest in witchcraft with that in Christian physics, so Scribonius went even so far as to de-

[45] *Ibid.*, II, 9, pp. 140-41.

[46] *Ibid.*, V, 5, pp. 244-64; III, 5, p. 178. Concerning the article of Paris see T III, 470.

[47] I have used the enlarged edition of 1583: Guil. Adolphus Scribonius, *Rerum naturalium doctrina methodica, post secundam editionem denuo copiosissime adaucta et in iii libros distincta*, Basileae, ex officina haeredum Petri Pernae, 1583. Scribonius had outlined the plan of his projected work in a letter of Sept. 10, 1578, to Freige, which is printed at the close (p. 1290) of the latter's *Quaestiones physicae*, 1579.

fend the superstitious test of persons suspected of being witches by casting them bound into cold water and seeing whether they floated or sank. He tried to find a natural explanation of this in the loss by the witches of their human form and their assumption of the aerial or ethereal nature of evil demons, which made them very light and buoyed them up in the water so that their bodies did not sink like those of other human beings. This lightness would also serve to explain their flights through the air to attend sabbats.[48]

The enlarged edition of 1583 of Scribonius's *A Methodical Doctrine of Nature* is accompanied by laudatory poems by Johann Stechmann, by Rodolphus Goclenius, professor of physics at Marburg, and by Thomas Freige, author of *Paedagogus,* a book which might be called the first children's encyclopedia, and of *Physical Questions* printed in 1579. Freige, who writes from Basel on October 24, 1582, calls Scribonius a master of the physical art such as has not been seen for nine centuries. Let us see how far this praise is justified.

These poems are preceded by a short preface of four pages by Scribonius to Bernhard Cop, professor of law at Marburg, and the preface by a longer letter of twenty-seven pages to William, landgrave of Hesse, dated October 27, 1583. In it Scribonius declares that God did not create the world indirectly through angels, virtues or other secondary causes infinite ages ago, but created it directly just 5544 years since. He also quotes biblical passages to prove that the earth does not move. After these religious restrictions upon science, Scribonius essays to distinguish four past schools of physics, a word by which he denotes the study of nature (*physica est rerum naturalium scientia*) rather than the science of physics in the modern sense. These four schools are very likely an imitation of the theory of four monarchies then current in historiography. The first of these schools, that of the Assyrians, was founded by Adam, who had sufficient science to name the animals and who was

[48] *De examine et purgatione sagarum per aquam frigidam Epistola Guilielmi Scribonii Marpurgensis,* Lemgoviae apud Conradum Grothenium, 1583.

followed by such distinguished men as Noah, Abraham, Moses, David and Solomon. Josephus states that the last-named vanquished the king of Tyre in a discussion of the natures of things. No writings in this field by Solomon are extant, except that some assert that in the Turkish library there are two books on plants by him written in Hebrew. This Assyrian school of physics was given to astronomy, augury, interpretation of dreams, and astrology.

The second school was of the Egyptians whom Abraham first instructed. Hermes of that school flourished before the days of the pharaohs but apparently Scribonius regards them both as later than Abraham. This school excelled in natural magic, and discovered the twelve hours from the urinating of the sacred animals. Scribonius annexes the Persian magi to this second school. Similarly he lumps together in the third school of the Greeks both the Druids and the Brahmans or gymnosophists of the Indies, who were sons of Abraham by concubines and were sent away to the east by him with gifts. They were fine astrologers and magicians who still today, if we believe Portuguese travelers, communicate at will with separate intelligences.

Of the fourth and last school of the Romans or Latins Cicero was the king-pin. But Scribonius also includes in it recent medical men who, beginning with the greatest things have progressed through medium ones to the lowest and smallest, "so that now first in our age God's creatures set forth by Moses in his Physics seem to have been sufficiently illuminated." Scribonius ranks Mattioli first in study of plants above Dioscorides, Galen, Fuchs or Bock;[49] for him Gesner excels the ancients in the history of animals, while in anatomy Vesalius far outranks Hippocrates, Galen, Alessandro Benedetti, and the rest.

Next in his letter to the elector Scribonius praises the devotion shown by certain kings of the past in different fields of science. The emperor Frederick III surpassed the physicians of his time in his knowledge of herbs and gardens.

[49] Cesalpino's work on plants had not yet appeared when Scribonius wrote.

Finally in his letter Scribonius comes to criticism of Aristotle's eight books of physics. He quotes Ramus's criticism of them, in his controversy with Scheck, as too dialectical, and praises Melanchthon for having alone included the stars in his physics. Scribonius will attempt a better arrangement and method than Aristotle's. Rejecting universals he will first treat of the heavenly bodies and their properties, then of elemental bodies, then of imperfect compounds such as all meteoric phenomena are, then of those mixed more perfectly and solidly such as metals, plants and animals. To explain all these is the task of physical scientists rather than of medical men, to whom Scribonius would leave only the cure of the body. He has been called to teach natural physical philosophy at the school of Korbach recently opened by the Waldeck assemblies.

Actually Scribonius does not begin with the celestial bodies but with spiritual and formal things such as genii and souls. Turning to material things, he considers first and second qualities, colors, tastes and odors, and then occult qualities which are known only by daily experience. They proceed from the form and whole essence of the thing and so are called specific qualities. Plainly they are celestial and ruled by the positions of the stars and are found more efficacious in matter which has been subjected to certain times and duly prepared in certain ways. When other examples of their powers are considered, it is not surprising if they can rout demons. Scribonius next asserts the existence of sympathy and antipathy in nature, and ascribes thereto the bleeding of a corpse in the presence of the murderer.

Scribonius holds that the sky is made of water, thus saving the biblical waters above the firmament. The outermost heaven, where the angels and souls of the blest see the face of God, is immovable. Scribonius omits the ninth and tenth spheres as figments but spends a long time on the eighth sphere of the fixed stars. The planets exert the greatest influence when in their own houses and when in conjunction. Such conjunctions may portend the destruction of certain kingdoms and climes or the rise of new sects. Comets also announce various ills and are discussed by Scribonius with the stars rather than with meteors and inferior exhalations. He states, however, that the comet attracts many earthly exhalations. Thus he seems much more favorable to astrology than was Daneau.

More of a tendency to abandon old views and to attempt something like a scientific advance is displayed by Scribonius in his discussion of the elements. Like Cardan and other writers of the sixteenth century he criticizes and alters the old doctrine of four elements. He rejects fire as an element, holding that the upper air has been wrongly regarded as a region of elemental fire, that fire is merely a state of heat and extreme dryness in combustible bodies, and that its flame is only kindled air. Of the three other elements which he retains, air is the most pellucid, earth the most opaque. Air is cold and very humid, water is humid and very cold, earth is cold and very dry, and "is perpetually immobile." Thus Scribonius retains the long-established doctrine of four qualities, hot, cold, moist and dry. And, like Daneau, he ignores or denies the Copernican hypothesis.

After concluding his first book with a discussion of meteors and winds, Scribonius in the second book turns to living natures. He defines the vegetative soul as the faculty which gives bodies life, and then takes up such processes or natural faculties as nutrition, concoction, boiling, baking, putrefaction, attraction, retention, expulsion, increase and generation. Under the head of living natures he includes metals, gems, salts and earths as well as plants, trees, fruits, grains, and vegetables. The third and last book on animated beings briefly discusses the senses, sleep and ecstacy, other faculties, the humors and spirits. Christ's sweating blood is adduced as a physical phenomenon, due in His case to sadness over the sins of mortals but found in others suffering from some disease affecting the blood. Tears, earwax and the mucus of the nostrils are all explained by Scribonius as excrements of the brain. After twenty-five such pages on parts of the body, "common to all animate beings," Scribonius devoted only four more to certain species, notably fish.

Franciscus Vallesius or Valles de Covarrubias was physician

to king Philip II of Spain. His work on those passages in Scripture which concern nature or on sacred philosophy,[50] takes up such passages one after the other, devoting all but forty of the 656 pages to the Old Testament and Apocrypha, only the last eight of the ninety-one chapters having to do with the New Testament. Vallesius recognizes that the Bible was not written to teach us natural science. But he contends that when it does speak of nature, it does not mean to deceive us and, as the inspired word of God, may be confidently relied upon. Now that he has finished commenting upon Aristotle, Hippocrates and Galen, he intends to devote the rest of his life to study of the Bible from this standpoint. He thinks that by no other method can sure conclusions be reached as to things of nature, while the soul experiences a pious satisfaction even from the historical or physical reading of Scripture. His previous philosophical works have been matters of opinion: what he now writes—with the assistance of the natural sciences—will be true.[51] He exercises a considerable latitude, however, in his scientific interpretation of Scripture. He does not always accept the literal sense, taking some things as parables[52] or explaining that "to eternity" in many places merely means a long time.[53] At times he prefers a natural to a miraculous explanation, as that the boy resuscitated by Elisha probably was an epileptic.[54] Apparently his work was first printed in 1587, but in one passage he refers to 1573 or 1574 as the current year.[55]

Among the passages taken up by Vallesius are the story of creation, whether the names given by Adam to the animals had any secret significance or power, whether Adam would have lived forever, had he eaten of the tree of life, the rainbow of promise after the flood, Jacob's showing the rods to the ewes, Naaman's washing seven times in the Jordan, and Nebuchad-

[50] Franciscus Vallesius Covarrubianus, *De iis quae scripta sunt physice in libris sacris sive de sacra philosophia*, Turin, 1587. Copy in the Columbia University library.

[51] *Ibid.*, Proemium.

[52] *Ibid.*, cap. 3, anent the asp's stopping up its ear. See also p. 514.

[53] *Ibid.*, cap. 6, p. 107.

[54] *Ibid.*, cap. 35, p. 295.

[55] *Ibid.*, cap. 1, p. 40.

nezzar's seven years of grass-eating. It may be guessed from these examples that the work of Vallesius is far from being a connected system of philosophy or orderly presentation of natural phenomena. His survey of the story of creation encounters the stock difficulties of the waters above the firmament, why light was created three days before the sun, whether the words, "for signs and seasons and for days and years," are to be taken astrologically or chronologically, how the statement in the eighteenth chapter of Ecclesiastes that God created all things simultaneously can be reconciled with the six day duration of creation found in Genesis, and so on. He does not contribute much that is new towards their solution. As we look over his text, we find that he accepts the spontaneous generation of certain forms of animal life from putrefaction, that he believes in the perfection of certain numbers, like seven and one hundred and twenty, in climacteric years, in the activity of demons as incubi and succubi. For although he more than once states that his concern is merely with the natural, philosophical and scientific interpretation of the Bible and not with the theological, he does not confine his consideration to physical bodies. A propos of the angel Raphael in the Book of Tobias he argues that if a moving body would pass instantaneously through a vacuum, there is no reason why an immaterial being should not so pass through a plenum.[56] But in discussing whether fascination is naturally possible, he states that if it is explained as the action of demons, this does not concern him or his book, since such a cause is not physical.[57]

Vallesius maintained that the heavens were solid in conformity with Job, 37. 18, "Tu forsitan cum eo fabricatus es coelos qui solidissimi quasi aere fusi sunt?" He further suggested that both sky and stars were composed of elements, not those of the inferior world but corresponding celestial elements, the stars differing from the rest of the heavens in having more celestial fire and air in their composition.[58] When Tycho Brahe wrote

[56] *Ibid.*, cap. 41, p. 314.

[57] *Ibid.*, cap. 68, p. 514.

[58] *Ibid.*, cap. 51, pp. 380-84.

to Caspar Peucer in September, 1588, concerning these views of Vallesius, whom he characterized as a man of varied erudition, Peucer replied that he had never heard of him before. Both Tycho and Peucer regarded the notion of four celestial elements as absurd.[59]

Vallesius admitted that the star of 1572 was of first magnitude and had no parallax but he was unwilling to call it either a new star or a comet in celestial regions, lest he violate the doctrines of the incorruptibility of the heavens—not to mention their solidity—and of the completion of the work of creation in six days. He therefore held that this star had all along been in existence but by some change of intervening media now became visible for a time.[60]

That the father of Tobias was blinded by the droppings of swallows Vallesius attributed to the manifest quality of heat rather than to any operation of occult virtue. Nothing was better known experimentally than that the parts of venomous animals were beneficial applications for their bites or stings, so that he would expect the excrement of the birds to cure rather than cause blindness by its specific property. As for the fish whose gall Tobias applied to restore the old man's eyesight, Vallesius found the like mentioned in Galen, Pliny, Aelian, and more recently by Edward Wotton,[61] so that this cure was by natural causes, God nonetheless permitting.[62]

While Vallesius attributed force to numbers,[63] he denied power or secret significance to words and names.[64] Fascination he regarded as a superstitious fear without physical basis. That the basilisk kills by its glance he termed a fable, and he asserted that we associate daily with menstruating women without suffering any harm.[65] He rejected Avicenna's contention in explanation of magic, that the human soul possesses the power

[59] For their allusions to the work of Vallesius see Tycho's *Opera* in Dreyer's edition, VII (1924), 133-34, 190.

[60] *Sacra philosophia*, cap. 1, pp. 40-41.

[61] "Odoardus Oxoniensis."

[62] *Ibid.*, cap. 42, p. 316.

[63] *Ibid.*, cap. 80, p. 606, "Quod tempus multis morborum longissimorum est fatale et decretorium ob vim septenarii." See also cap. 70 on the Pythagorean philosophy and numerology.

[64] Cap. 3.

[65] *Ibid.*, cap. 68, pp. 504, 513.

of moving external objects.[66] On the other hand, he agreed that Samuel really appeared before the witch of Endor. But this was by divine provision and not by the witch's own power.[67] It remains to notice the attitude of Vallesius towards astrology and other forms of divination.[68]

Vallesius noted the biblical passages against astrology but also expressed the opinion that the statement in the fifth chapter of The Book of Judges on the stars fighting against Sifaras was more favorable to astrology than the representation of the stars as signs in The Book of Genesis or the verse in the eighteenth Psalm that the firmament sheweth forth His handiwork. Vallesius thought well in general of Pico della Mirandola's attack upon astrology but believed that Pico gained nothing by reducing the effects of the sky to motion and light, since these contain or give rise to other virtues. Vallesius further conceded that even the smallest star conferred some peculiar commodity on the whole universe, and that there were many marvelous virtues in the celestial bodies. Nevertheless he declared judicial astrology not a science or art but imposture or sortilege, since it dealt with chance matters. All its predictions, whether of good or evil, had a bad effect on their hearers in his opinion. It was derided by learned men as inane, he affirmed, was exploded as useless, and was forbidden by divine legislators and prophets, by pontiffs and emperors. By judicial astrology he meant the current annual predictions of the weather, health, good or bad harvests, war and politics; also elections, interrogations and nativities. Despite these observations of Vallesius, the work of Rueus on gems, with its favorable attitude towards astrological images, was reprinted with editions of the *Sacra Philosophia* four times—in 1588, 1595, 1622 and 1652.

Of other forms of divination Vallesius distinguished three chief varieties: vain, natural and divine.[69] He denied, however, that certain persons were especially gifted by nature in divination, or that the mind, when freed from corporal concerns,

[66] *Ibid.*, p. 251.

[67] *Ibid.*, cap. 33, pp. 287-90.

[68] *De sacra philosophia*, 1587, cap. 31, pp. 261-75, on astrology.

[69] *Ibid.*, p. 254.

could know the future, since he held, a century before Locke, that the mind received ideas and knowledge only through the senses.[70] He admitted the existence of a certain natural divination in brutes and uneducated men "by compassion with causes or by the preludes of future events." But this was quite a different matter from true divination or prophecy.[71] He also granted that the mind during sleep was more conscious of very slight sensations or suffering, and so might help to predict imminent diseases or sometimes changes in the weather.[72] But the ancient oracles were false or ambiguous and most other divination was the deceptive work of demons.[73] Chiromancy he was inclined to recognize as natural in so far as it was a part of physiognomy, but he rejected the division of the palm of the hand according to astrological diagrams. He noted that passages from The Book of Job and from Aristotle's *History of Animals* were adduced in support of chiromancy.[74]

Most of the works of Jean Belot, curé of Mèl-Monts, in the early seventeenth century either dealt directly with occult arts or bordered on that field. It is true that the title of the treatise with which we are now chiefly concerned, *Flowers of Christian and Moral Philosophy,* published at Paris in 1603, continues, "or Refutations of Henry Cornelius Agrippa and of Peter of Abano in their Occult Philosophy."[75] But Belot's censure has reference only to the spurious and extremely necromantic fourth book which was sometimes attached to Agrippa's work on occult philosophy and to a similar extremely superstitious treatise ascribed only at a late date to Peter of Abano. In 1619 Belot published at Paris a book in French on chiromancy and physiognomy with an astrological discourse on the comet of 1618. In 1622 he followed the lead of the *Steganographia* of Trithemius by issuing at Paris *L'Œuvre des œuvres ou le plus parfaict des*

[70] *Ibid.,* pp. 239-40. I do not mean to imply that others had not held this view even earlier.

[71] *Ibid.,* p. 257.

[72] *Ibid.,* p. 249.

[73] *Ibid.,* pp. 241-42.

[74] *Ibid.,* cap. 32, pp. 278-85.

[75] *Les fleurs de la philosophie chrestienne et morale ou Refutations de Henry Corn. Agrippa et de P. d'Albano en leur philosophie occulte,* Paris, 1603, 153 fols. not including the dedicatory preface to the bishop of Evreux. The pages are very small.

sciences steganographiques paulines armadelles et lullistes.[76] This duodecimo edition was followed the next year by an enlarged second edition in octavo, while in 1624 appeared another edition of the work on physiognomy and chiromancy augmented by a treatise on divination, auguries and dreams. Belot also printed at Paris in 1624, with a dedication "to his majesty," *Centuries prophetiques revelees par la sacree Theologie et secrette Astrologie a M. Jean Belot curé de Mél-monts Maistre és sciences Divines et Celestes.* In this publication he refers to like previous works: "our Centuriateur . . . in his Almanach of the year 1621," his predictions on the comet of 1618, and "our Centuriateur which in the year 1621 predicted the loss of the Palatinate."

In the *Flowers of Christian and Moral Philosophy* Belot manifests acquaintance with a wide range of authors. That he cites the classics and the church fathers is to be expected. But he also cites such diverse groups as the anatomists, the Jewish rabbis and cabalists, and the Protestants Marot, Calvin, de Bèze, Sleidan and Melanchthon, the last-named with approval. A theory of Servetus even is mentioned, although declared erroneous. Of medieval writers Isidore, Thebit, Serapion, Marbod, Bartholomaeus Anglicus, Albertus Magnus, Thomas Aquinas, Nicholas of Lyra, and Dionysius the Carthusian are used. From the sixteenth century are cited Camillo Lunardi, Agrippa, Cardan, Fernel, Bodin, Launay, Postel, the historians Bourgoing and Carion, the geographers Thevet and Sieur de Lery "in his Cosmography of the Americans," and the Spaniard "Antoine de la Turque in his Garden of Flowers."

In the preface to Jacques Davy, bishop of Evreux, Belot alludes incidentally but rather favorably to the Copernican theory, stating that, if his own arguments seem paradoxical, he will offer as a pertinent excuse no other example than that of Copernicus, "which will be agreeable to you," and thereby "you may

[76] The second and third adjectives have reference to the Pauline art, for which see T II, 282, and to Almadel, concerning whom see Lynn Thorndike, "Alfodhol and Almadel: Hitherto Unnoted Medieval Books of Magic in Florentine Manuscripts," *Speculum* II (1927), 326-31.

The work includes Lullian rhetoric and dialectic, while Belot's treatise on artificial memory is also Lullian.

know the end of my intentions and the desire I have to sap the edifice of some ignorant persons of this time who have for architect only a pompous arrogance."

Among the notions harbored by Belot in this work were some which were to continue through the seventeenth and eighteenth centuries, such as that the sea is the source of fountains and streams, that there are caverns in the earth, that Hebrew is the oldest language. He already held that Italian and a dozen other languages were derived from Latin. He repeats many long accepted views as that the angels fell through pride or the arguments against sexual intercourse by spirits. Other opinions voiced by him seem less common: that fire is the only element suited to man, that our souls which are ideas of this divine fire act with the same velocity, that fire encircles the human brain and resides there, and that some philosophers, including Agrippa, have called the pia mater the soul. The brain, liver and heart are the first parts of the body to be formed and the principal seats of the soul and represent the Trinity. Angels are sent by God to reside in certain virtuous men. "Now this is not merely my opinion but that of many learned persons." A Jesuit said as much of Ignatius Loyola, and many modern doctors affirm that St. Francis of Assisi was an angel who was "alembicated into the human viscera." This last phrase illustrates the somewhat disrespectful tone in which Belot now and then alludes to divine mysteries or the orthodox faith, despite his title, *The Flowers of Christian Philosophy*. He notes that there are religious deceivers who lead exemplary lives, and that an image of the Virgin was made to weep by a scheming priest.

Although Belot's later writings show his interest in the occult, he denies in the *Flowers* of 1603 that the numerical value of the letters in a Greek name has any significance.[77]

[77] A use of the word tourbillon by Belot before Descartes may be worth noting. After stating that form separate from its two parts is useless for operation, he continues, "sa matiere et substance n'est qu'un petit tourbillon de matiere Meteorique qui n'occupe aucun lieu." *Op. cit.* (1603), fol. 83r.

To those interested in pursuing the subject of Christian philosophy of nature further into the seventeenth and eighteenth centuries may be recommended the work of Katharine Brownell Collier, *Cosmogonies of Our Fathers*, New York, 1934.

CHAPTER XLII

FOR AND AGAINST ARISTOTLE

The ancient philosophers, and especially Aristotle, were, with all their errors and defects, far more genuine high-priests of nature than any moderns of the sixteenth century.

—HALLAM

The works to be considered in this chapter center about the name of Aristotle. The old armor of the stalwart Stagirite was still very much in the thick of the fight, whether one encased oneself in it for protection or broke spears against it. Some works of natural philosophy, such as that of Alessandro Piccolomini,[1] were so closely cast along traditional lines that we shall not take further cognizance of them here. Others, while largely based upon and favorable to Aristotle, offer some variations which may be noted. Yet others, written professedly in revolt from Peripateticism and opposition to Aristotle, nevertheless are apt to attest his abiding influence, whether positive or negative, more than they do the originality of their authors. These look like Lilliputians standing on the body of a fallen giant.

In 1543, the same year that had seen appear the great works of Copernicus and Vesalius, Ramus had assailed the logic of Aristotle in his *Dialecticae partitiones ad academiam Parisiensem* and his *Aristotelicae animadversiones*, while Ortensio Landi had devoted certain chapters of his *Paradossi* to an attack on Aristotle. In one he questioned the authenticity of the works now current under the name of Aristotle. In another he accused Aristotle of being the most wicked man of his age, having shown ingratitude to Plato, been driven from Athens for his wrong doings, and poisoned Alexander. Landi also charged Aristotle

[1] Alessandro Piccolomini, *La prima parte della filosofia naturale,* 1551. Copy used: BM 534.c.32.

with various erroneous opinions: that the semen gave only the motive principle to the menstrual blood, that children resemble the mother, that the testicles were useless in the generation of semen, that the origin of spontaneous movement and of sense were in the heart, whereas the most certain demonstrations show that they originate in the brain. Others errors of Aristotle according to Landi were concerned with the proportion of the elements, Milky Way, rainbow, and the number of bodies filling space. Landi further complained of those who thought the works of Aristotle essential in theology. He said that Luther, armed only with the Bible, put all the Aristotelian theologians of Leipzig, Louvain and Cologne to rout. Why then should we endure the yoke of Aristotle longer?[2]

We have spoken of Joachim Cureus as a pupil and admirer of Melanchthon but have postponed consideration of his *Libellus physicus* to the present chapter for reasons which will now become apparent. In the preface he says that he follows especially the old and most approved Peripatetics, and of recent Aristotelians Antonius Passerus of Genoa, Victor Trincavelli of Venice, Bassianus Landus of Piacenza, and Gabriel Falloppia of Modena—all four of whom were teaching at Padua while he was a student there in 1557. Trincavelli he once calls *facile princeps* among Italian philosophers and physicians of his time. But in another passage he gives "Antonius Passerus of Genoa, my teacher," first place among "the leading philosophers of our age," and in a third place states that all Italy was convinced that Aristotle spoke through the mouth of Passerus.[3]

Cureus thus in the main follows the thought of Aristotle and his recent Italian interpreters, although he occasionally notes the views of the Arabs in general or of Averroes and Avicenna

[2] Ortensio Landi, *Paradossi cioè sententie fuori del comun parere novellamente venute in luce,* a Lione per Gioanni Pullon da Trino, 1543. Copy used: BM 8408.aaa.6. Other editions followed in 1544, Venice 1545, 1563, 1594, and 1602. See Paradossi 28 and 29.

[3] For the three passages *Libellus physicus,* edition of Wittenberg, 1572, I, 35, p. 141; II, 25, p. 249; and Praefatio. As stated above, the work seems to have been first printed in 1567.

in particular, and does not entirely neglect either medieval Latin writers or recent non-Italian authors like Fernel and Zwinger. He also takes some account of medical opinion, as in a "dispute of the Peripatetics and medical men whether odors are nutritious."[4] He decides with Galen for the brain against Aristotle for the heart as the seat of the sensitive soul,[5] and is offended with Gentile da Foligno for having criticized Galen sharply.[6] He accepts a new definition of color as clearer than the Aristotelian.[7] But he thinks that Occam is "not to be listened to, who rashly departed from Aristotle and from his own master, John (Duns?) Scotus and would have it that bodies appear to our sight without any emission of species."[8] He adheres to the Aristotelian doctrines of natural place and that the air propels a body moving in it, although he is aware that Montanus has explained the acceleration of a falling body by an acquisition of momentum from its own weight.[9]

Towards novel views and revolutionary doctrines, like those of Paracelsus, Cureus was apt to be suspicious or hostile. He characterized as superstitious the attempt of certain recent writers to distinguish alimentary, aqueous and radical humor in each animal.[10] Fernel's opinion that innate heat was an ethereal radiation from the sky with no relationship to the four elements Cureus rejected as contrary to Peripatetic doctrine. Fernel had cited in his favor a passage from the *History of Animals* (II,3), but Cureus felt that he had misinterpreted Aristotle's meaning.[11]

This rejection of Fernel's derivation of innate heat directly from the sky does not mean that Cureus excludes celestial influence from the Peripatetic view of nature. He asserts that "all the mass of the inferior world would lie inert, opaque and cold," were it not illuminated, heated and vivified by the celestial bodies.[12] In the dispute between Greeks and Arabs whether first

[4] *Ibid.*, II, 6, p. 187.
[5] *Ibid.*, I, 6.
[6] *Ibid.*, II, 16, p. 221.
[7] *Ibid.*, I, 19: "Traduntur definitiones coloris primum quidem Aristotelicae deinde etiam nova et magis perspicua."
[8] *Ibid.*, I, 33, p. 134.
[9] *Ibid.*, II, 37-38, pp. 289, 293-97.
[10] *Ibid.*, II, 35, p. 287.
[11] *Ibid.*, II, 29, pp. 260-64.
[12] *Ibid.*, II, 34, p. 280.

qualities are the substantial forms of the elements or instruments of the same substances, the Averroists, including Passerus, said that the heavens imprinted these qualities on matter, and that from this interaction the peculiar form of each element was educed. Cureus preferred their view to the teaching of Alexander of Aphrodisias that the qualities of each element constitute its substantial form.[13] That the horoscope of Cureus himself had indicated that he would become a scholar of distinction was affirmed in 1601 by his biographer Ferinarius, who reproduced in detail the positions of the planets at the moment of his birth and the inferences to be drawn from them.[14] The influence exerted by the book of Cureus is suggested by four editions in rapid succession in 1567, 1572, 1577 and 1584.[15]

Love of the marvelous in general and an inclination towards astrology in particular were apt to characterize works based upon the *Meteorology* of Aristotle, as may be illustrated by that of Wolfgang Meurer (1513-1585),[16] the educator of Leipzig and the correspondent of George Fabricius. There are found tales of the freak action of lightning, fourteen prodigious kinds of rain which include stones, iron and flesh as well as fish, worms and frogs, and an account from Cardan of men who one after another descended a ladder into a subterranean furnace and died there. Many thought that the furnace contained a basilisk, but corrupt air inside is accepted as a sufficient explanation by Meurer.[17] He repeats the excessive estimates of the distance of the clouds and the height of mountains which we have had occasion to specify elsewhere. He explains why snow chills more than water and suggests that the reason why marvelous images,

[13] *Ibid.*, II, 25, pp. 249-52.

[14] Ferinarius, *Narratio historica*, 1601, fol. B 2 recto: C. F. Heusinger, *Commentatio de J. Cureo*, 1853, p. 44.

[15] Heusinger, *op. cit.*, p. 56. All were presumably issued at Wittenberg, although Heusinger gives no place of publication for the edition of 1577 and I have not seen it.

[16] *Wolfgangi Meureri medici et philosophi Meteorologia quaestionibus informata et explicationibus dilucidis illustrata, olim in celeberrima Academia Lipsensi publice tradita, nunc vero primum in lucem edita a M. Christophoro Meurero filio mathematum professore publico. Huic praefixa est narratio de curriculo vitae eiusdem autoris studio M. Barthlolomaei Waltheri*, Lipsiae, 1587. Copy used: BM 717.g.11.

[17] *Ibid.*, pp. 138-46, 296-98, 242, for these three passages.

such as a monk's head or pig's snout, are sometimes impressed on hailstones may be to warn men against living like swine.[18] Among thirty signs of rain Meurer lists pigs with straws sticking out of their mouths and dogs eating grass. The explanation of these phenomena is that dogs eat grass to refresh themselves against excessive drought, and that excessive drought is usually followed by rain, while the pigs hurry home from pasture to avoid getting wet and do not stop to finish their last mouthful.[19]

Meurer gives four reasons why nature produces meteors: to declare the majesty of God, to adorn and variegate the world, to purify the air, and to announce and give warnings of future events.[20] He cites such astrological authorities as Pontano and the *Centiloquium* ascribed to Ptolemy.[21] He represents comets as of infrequent occurrence, because they are generated by certain rare constellations, and because a great exhalation has to be collected to excite and to feed so great a fire.[22] He goes on to explain why comets announce war, turbulence, drought, death of fish, sterility, pest, and death of kings, and to list past examples of comets and their effects.[23] The human microcosm, too, has its meteors. Fevers and inflammations correspond to fiery apparitions; ructions, wind and flatulence correspond to winds and earthquakes; coughs and sneezes, to thunder; catarrh and fluxes, to rain, snow, hail, dew, fountains and rivers.[24] Meurer refused to agree with Albertus Magnus that the Milky Way is part of the sky. He argued that it was not always visible and so must be an occasional apparition produced by the light of the stars.[25]

Meurer's book possesses a religious as well as astrological flavor and is interlarded with biblical quotations. Speaking of the rainbow, he says that we who are church members know that it is the bow of promise that there shall not be another universal flood. At the same time it signifies that the world will be consumed by fire at the last judgment, since its two chief colors

[18] *Ibid.*, pp. 303, 312-13.
[19] *Ibid.*, p. 273.
[20] *Ibid.*, pp. 25-26.
[21] *Ibid.*, pp. 111, 115-16.
[22] *Ibid.*, p. 159.
[23] *Ibid.*, pp. 160-70.
[24] *Ibid.*, p. 16.
[25] *Ibid.*, p. 58.

are purple, signifying the perishing of mankind in the deluge, and red, which is indicative of the final conflagration.[26]

The three books by Francesco Vimercati of Milan, who died in 1570, on the principles of natural things,[27] seem to have been written in mid century.[28] Guinther of Andernach dedicated a translation to Vimercati as physician of queen Leonora of France in 1533,[29] and he was made a royal professor by Francis I in 1540.[30] According to Corte,[31] Vimercati dedicated his commentary on the *Physics* to Henry II in 1550, and published commentaries on the *Meteorology* and *De anima* in 1556 and 1574. The last would be posthumous, like the work in which we are interested and which was not printed until almost the end of the century. Since its first book is devoted to matter, the second to form, and the third to nature, it hardly emerges from the domain of metaphysics into that of either magic or science. First matter is identified with *potentia* and its eternity insisted upon. However, the discussion advances far enough to touch on astrology. Vimercati contends that Aristotle thought that forms were educed from matter, and that those are mistaken who ascribe to him the view that forms come from the sky and are sent into matter which has been prepared extrinsically. He includes the sky among natural things as consisting of form and matter. But he regards the sky and earth as the two extreme bodies of the universe, and believes that the heavens perpetually revolve in a most constant order to bring into being sublunar things.

[26] *Ibid.*, p. 71.

[27] *Francisci Vicomercati Mediolanensis De principiis rerum naturalium libri III cum praefatione Rodolphi Goclenii Logicae prof. in Acad. Marpurg.*, Marpurgi, 1598, 382 pp. Copy used: BN R.12611. The *editio princeps* was at Venice, 1596: copy at BM 536.e.7.(1.); BN Rés. R.885.

[28] Francesco Bolzeta, in a preface of 1596 to Alessandro Massaria, professor of the practice of medicine in the university of Padua, remarks: "Nam tametsi eiusdem argumenti commentationes a claris philosophis postea sunt editae quam harum fuerat annis ab hinc quadraginta aut eo amplius concitata expectatio."

[29] Argellati, *Bibliotheca scriptorum Mediolanensium,* Milan, 1745, cols. 1661-63.

[30] Tiraboschi, 1824, VII, ii, 638, citing Bulaeus, VI, 934, and Gaillard, *Hist. de François I,* VII, 348.

[31] Bartolomeo Corte, *Notizie istoriche intorno a scrittori milanesi,* Milan, 1718, pp. 70-71.

In the dedication of his thirty books on nature[32] to pope Sixtus V on September 30, 1589, Iacopo Zabarella states that he had spent his whole life of fifty-six years in the study of philosophy and had lectured publicly on the books of Aristotle for twenty-six years at the university of Padua. He died that same year. His book, an outgrowth of this classroom instruction, treats of these topics: the constitution of natural science, first matter, nature, the invention of the eternal mover, the nature of the heavens, the movement of fire in its sphere, the movement of heavy and light objects, the constitution of the individual, generation and death, reaction, mixture, elementary qualities, the regions of the air, celestial heat, the generation and corruption of compounds, faculties and divisions of the soul, accretion and nutrition, active sense, vision, the human mind, intelligible species, the active mind, and the order of understanding. Zabarella thinks that no one doubts that the heavens are animated and consist of a moving mind and moved body.[33] Furthermore all concede that this moving soul is not the form of the sky and does not give it being but only motion. He approves the view of Averroes that the sky is a simple body,[34] against Aquinas and Aegidius Romanus who held that it consists of matter and form. He accepts the opinion of many that precedent motion is the cause of the greater velocity of subsequent motion.[35] In holding that specific form is the determining factor in the constitution of the individual, he adopts a position favorable to belief in occult and marvelous virtues.[36]

Tomasini tells us that Zabarella delighted in optics and astrology, that many predictions by him were extant, that he foretold the lives of all his nine children from the stars, and that

[32] Iacopo Zabarella, *De rebus naturalibus libri XXX,* 1594, 4to, over a thousand pages: copy used BN R.1831. Editions are also sometimes listed for Padua, 1589; Venice, 1590; and Cologne, 1590 as well as 1594, but I have not seen them. I have also used the folio edition of 1617: BN R.1834.

[33] *Ibid.,* p. 273.

[34] *Ibid.,* p. 282, "corpus simplex." Duhem II (1909), 255-59, says that Averroes, *De substantia orbis,* held that the sky was pure form, and adds the varying views of Aquinas, Bonaventura, Aegidius Romanus, Duns Scotus, William of Ockham, Jean de Jandun, and Albert of Saxony.

[35] *Ibid.,* p. 343.

[36] *Ibid.,* p. 387.

he himself was born under the favoring planet, Mercury.[37] If this be true, he showed a certain boldness in dedicating his thirty books on nature to Sixtus V only three years after that pope's bull against astrologers.

In 1574 Archangelus Mercenarius, professor of philosophy at Padua, in commentaries on Aristotle and Averroes had dealt with the vexed question whether intelligence was united to a heavenly body as form or as mover. Achillini, Nifo and many other moderns had held that the meaning of Aristotle and Averroes was that intelligence is form giving being formally to the heavens, but Mercenarius denies that this was their opinion. He grants that no other form except intelligence is found in a heavenly body, but it is there only as mover or *forma assistens*.[38]

Bernardino Telesio of Cosenza (1508-1588) attacked the natural philosophy of Aristotle and influenced later writers like Campanella by his work on nature according to his and its own principles, published first at Rome in two books in 1565,[39] then at Naples in 1570 with other tracts on natural themes,[40] and at Naples in 1586 in an enlarged edition of nine books. This book was for the most part a theorizing about nature rather than the outcome of observation and experiment. Following Parmenides Telesio made heat and cold the two fundamental principles of nature. For him they were immaterial until joined with the third factor, matter. Heat preceded motion in time, nature and dignity. Motion was merely an operation of heat, and no new heat was produced by motion but only pre-existing heat excited.[41] The antithesis, so favorable to astrology, of heavens and earth was still fundamental in Telesio's thought. He associated heat with the sky and cold with the earth. Although professing belief in

[37] Jac. Phil. Tomasini, *Illustrium virorum elogia iconibus exornata,* Padua, 1630, pp. 136-38.

[38] Archangelus Mercenarius a Monte Sancto, *Dilucidationes . . . in plurima Aristotelis perobscura et nonnulla Averrois loca,* Venetiis, Apud Paulum et Antonium Meietos fratres bibliop., Patav., 1574, pp. 65-73.

[39] *Bernardini Telesii Consentini De natura iuxta propria principia liber primus et secundus,* Romae, Apud Antonium Bladum, anno MDLXV.

[40] *De rerum natura iuxta propria principia liber primus et secundus* denuo editi Neapoli apud Josephum Cacchium, MDLXX.

[41] *Ibid.*, I, 8.

an immortal soul from God, Telesio rejected the Aristotelian distinction between rational, sensitive and vegetative soul, holding that all faculties of the soul were equally rational and opposing the arguments by which Aristotle maintained the motive soul to be incorporeal and unmoved.[42] The soul informed the spirits in the brain and body. These spirits were Telesio's great reliance in explaining bodily functions. He assigned to them an even greater part than they had had in medieval thought, in which he was to be followed by Francis Bacon. Although we have just heard him reject Aristotle's distinction between the rational and irrational soul, he represented plants as having crasser spirits than animals.[43] He even explained intellectual and moral qualities by the difference between the spirits in heat, tenuousness and purity.[44] Telesio still believed that certain animals were generated spontaneously[45] and in the existence of occult qualities.[46] For him each ens was endowed with a nature and disposition and species of its own, with its own faculties and aptitude of acting and operating and suffering.[47] It would therefore seem that his view of nature would hardly have much effect, at least immediate, in hastening the discovery and application of broad general laws of nature, but would rather produce a confused and *ad hoc* outlook favorable to empiricism and occult science. I have to agree with Radl that he was "no biologist" rather than with Zavattari.[48]

Honoratus de Robertis, an Augustinian canon of the Lateran, held against Aristotle in a brief treatise published in 1585 that the sky was fire and not a fifth essence or element.[49]

[42] *Ibid.*, V, 17.

[43] *Ibid.*, VI, 24.

[44] *Ibid.*, VIII, 36: "Non intelligentia modo spiritus inter se differre quod calore tenuitateque et puritate differant sed moribus etiam et bonitate pravitateque virtutibusque nimirum vitiisque."

[45] *Ibid.*, VI, 21.

[46] *Ibid.*, VIII, 3.

[47] *Idem.*

[48] Edoardo Zavattari, *La visione della vita nel Rinascimento e Bernardino Telesio,* Torino, 1923, xii, 302 pp., with chapters on Telesio's general physiology, special physiology and anatomy, and embryology.

[49] *R. P. domini Honorati de Robertis Iuvenatiensis Cong. Lateranensis Canonicorum reg. S.Aug. Unica quaestio de elemento ignis utrum detur in concavo orbis lunae,* Venetiis Apud Ioannem Baptistam Somaschum, 1585, small quarto, 23 pp. Copy used: BM 538.e.27.(4.).

According to Severinus, writing fourteen years earlier, this was a Paracelsan tenet.[50]

Of Giovanni Battista Benedetti (1530-1590) and his original and critical attitude we have already spoken in other chapters. In his *Diverse Mathematical and Physical Speculations* of 1585[51] he criticized the *Physics* of Aristotle in a number of respects, although he professed to be a great admirer of the Stagirite and to believe it very difficult and perilous to write anything against him. Some of the points that he made against Aristotle were as follows. Heavy or light bodies, of the same shape and material but of unequal size, in their natural movement of velocity in the same medium will maintain a far different proportion than Aristotle thought. Two unequal bodies of the same material in different media will retain the same proportion of velocity. It is not so easy to assign the proportion of velocities of two natural bodies as Aristotle thought in the last chapter of the seventh book of the *Physics*. Direct motion or that in a straight line is continuous despite the dissent of Aristotle.

Benedetti's *Diverse Speculations*, as the title suggests, are not a unified work but comprise arithmetical problems, a tract on perspective, a third on mechanics, criticisms of Aristotle, a commentary on the fifth book of Euclid, and letters replying to physical and mathematical inquiries. The last make up over half the volume. Of Benedetti's attitude to the Copernican theory, to judicial astrology, and to mechanical devices we treat in other chapters. He seldom or never uses the expression, "natural magic," or shows an interest in animate nature and occult virtues—much less occult philosophy. But "even Homer nods," and Benedetti gives the following explanation why a very cold winter follows a hot summer. The heat comes from the sun and is not natural to earth, water or air. Therefore when it goes, the earth returns to its natural cold quality with the greater impetus, just as objects do in natural local motion which have exceeded

[50] Petrus Severinus, *Idea medicinae philosophicae,* Basel, 1571, cap. 5, pp. 40-41.

[51] *Iohannis Baptistae Benedicti Diversarum speculationum mathematicarum et physicarum liber,* Taurini, 1585. Copy used: BM 531.n.14.(1.).

the limits set for them. Similarly heated water freezes faster and is harder and colder afterwards than other ice.[52]

The historian de Thou denied that Benedetti was a Venetian noble and held that his father was really a physician of Valencia. Benedetti was an excellent mathematician, who first served the duke of Parma and then the duke of Savoy, but he hardly knew Latin and was helped in it by Franciscus Maria Vialardus. De Thou said that Benedetti wrote *Gnomica* and on proportion against Silvius Pellus, and left in manuscript much on optics, music and machines.[53]

Another to essay a new philosophy of nature in opposition to Aristotle was Francesco Patrizi, Patrizio or Patricius (1529-1597). Born in the island of Cherso off the Dalmatian coast, he went to Padua to study at the early age of nine and finished the curriculum in 1554. Subsequently he is found at Rome, Bologna, Venice and Modena with trips to Cyprus, France and Spain in between. From 1578 to 1592 he taught philosophy at Ferrara,[54] but left for Rome in April of the last named year to take the chair of Platonic philosophy at the Sapienza with a salary of 600 scudi.[55] Already in 1571 Patrizi began to publish four volumes of *Peripatetic Discussions,* which may be described as in large part a historical study of Aristotle and his philosophy, a comparison of it with previous thinkers, and a confutation of some of his criticisms of his predecessors.[56] In 1587 he issued a *New Geometry;* in 1591 he dedicated his *New Philosophy*[57]

[52] *Ibid.,* p. 271.

[53] Thuanus, *Hist.* lib. 99.

[54] For Patrizi's life I chiefly follow Tiraboschi, VII, ii (1824), 664-71, where citations from Patrizi's own writings will be found for most of the facts.

[55] P. Donazzolo, "Francesco Patrizio di Cherso," *Atti e memorie della Società Istriana,* 28 (1912), 37. Much of the bibliography is reproduced from Guerrini (see note 57 below).

[56] The first volume appeared at Venice in 1571; all four volumes at Basel in 1581.

[57] Olindo Guerrini, "Di Francesco Patrizio e della rarissima edizione delle sua Nova Philosophia," *Il Propugnatore,* Bologna, 12 (1879), 172-230, held that the Venetian edition of 1593, which I shall cite, was a reprint of that of Ferrara, 1591, except that it had a new title page and omitted the dedications of various parts of the work to members of the college of cardinals. In the copy of the 1593 edition which I used (BM 536.1.10) the Zoroaster was still misplaced between the Panaugia and Panarchia as in the *editio princeps.*

to pope Gregory XIV and in consequence received the call to Rome from Clement VIII.

In his *New Philosophy* Patrizi was more favorable to Platonism than to the philosophy of Aristotle, which he urged Gregory XIV in the dedicatory epistle to oust from its position of supremacy in the schools. He also cited Zoroaster and the Chaldean Oracles a good deal. For example, even with regard to the position of the sun he preferred the authority of Plato or the Chaldean Oracles to that of recent astronomers.[58] Donazzolo has criticized the *New Philosophy* as bizarre and leaving the mind of the reader confused, and, aside from its Alexandrian, Chaldean, Egyptian and Neoplatonic sources, drawing what little new it contained from Telesio.[59] Tiraboschi called it a composite of useless subtleties and of dreams, although he recognized the vast erudition of the author.[60] Patrizi in opening the work promised to prove his contentions by "divine oracles, geometric proofs, philosophical reasons, and the clearest experiments," thus paying lip service at least both to mathematical and experimental method. Both Tiraboschi and Donazzolo were impressed by his many observations as to nature. My own impression of the *New Philosophy* is that, while Patrizi was too prone to extravagant and mystical views, he was an ingenious theorist and especially acute in refuting an opposing argument. Although Patrizi was the friend of popes and taught in the Roman university, his work was soon put on the *Index,* subject to correction by him with the approbation of the Master of the Sacred Palace. The *Index* was approved by a Bull of Clement VIII of October 17, 1597, but Patrizi had then been dead over eight months.[61] His regarding the universe as infinite was probably one of the passages objected to.[62] By inclining to the opinion that each star was a separate world[63] he approached the belief in a plurality of worlds. His entitling the four component parts of the *New Philosophy* by the rather fantastic titles, "Panaugia," "Panarchia," "Pam-

[58] *Pancosmia,* ed. of 1593, fol. 109r, col. 2.

[59] Donazzolo (1912), 96-97, 103.

[60] Tiraboschi (1824), VII, ii, 670-71.

[61] Donazzolo (1912), 109-15.

[62] *Pancosmia,* 1593, fol. 150v, col. 2.

[63] *Ibid.,* fol. 116v, col. 1.

psychia" and "Pancosmia," may also have savored a little too much of pantheism. He spoke of light as the image equally of incorporeals and bodies and as a medium between divine incorporeal beings and the nature of bodies, which he distinguished as lucid, opaque and transparent. For the four traditional elements he substituted space, light, heat and humor.[64]

Although Patrizi noted the arguments of Plotinus, Ficino and Pico against astrology, he felt that such huge bodies as the stars must have some effect and would not have been created by God in vain or for man alone. For himself he would believe that seeds of life are scattered all through the stars and sky. The light and heat of the stars does not directly touch the earth, for which the sun seems the sole generator of all things by its light and heat and seeds. The stars act on themselves and on other stars and from the empyrean receive humor, heat, light, life, soul, mind and ideas. From the stars light, heat and seeds go to our sun, while the moon receives a fluid or ether from them and passes it on to us. Patrizi held with some reason that it was preferable to have the sun receive light from the stars than to assert that the stars received their light from it.[65]

In discussing the properties of space in 1587 Francesco Patrizi made the earth immovable about the center of the universe.[66] In a letter of November 13, 1577, he had somewhat similarly treated of space and fourteen spherical bodies existent in it, with earth at the center surrounded by successive spheres of water, air, fire, the moon, Mercury, Venus, the sun, Mars, Jupiter, Saturn, the fixed stars and the crystalline and empyrean heavens. A second letter treated of the moon to which he ascribed seven movements. A third dealt with the motion of the sun and the eccentrics and epicycles of the other planets.[67]

[64] Donazzolo (1912), 99-102.

[65] *Pancosmias* XXI, 1593, fols. 115r, col. 2—117r, col. 2.

[66] *De rerum natura libri ii priores. Alter de spacio physico, alter de spacio mathematico,* Ferrara, Victor Baldinus, 1587, 4to, 26 fols., fol. 17v. Copy used: BM 233.f.41.

[67] Concerning these autograph letters, twelve in number, of Patrizi in the Bibliotheca Estense of Modena see P. Donazzolo," Francesco Patrizio di Cherso," *Atti e memorie della Società Istriana,* 28 (1912), pp. 108-9.

Thus he then adhered to the conventional Aristotelian physics and Ptolemaic astronomy.

In his *New Philosophy* of 1593 the attitude of Patrizi had become unfavorable to Aristotle and to the astronomers, and his thinking is affected both by the Copernican theory and the new star of 1572. To say, however, as Donazzolo does, that he defends Copernicus or teaches the Copernican system is to give a false impression.[68] He still kept the earth at the center of the universe and took over from Copernicus, whom he called "the greatest astronomer of our age," the idea of its revolving about its axis, carrying the air and water about with it. This, he argued, was far more likely than that the firmament or fixed stars should move 42,398,437 miles in a day. And since he, unlike Copernicus, assigned only one motion to the earth, the argument that it as a simple body could have only one motion had less force against him. If, however, its pressure towards the center were admitted to be another movement in a straight line, he argued that it was not a simple but a complex body, and that the stars, which were considered simple bodies, had more than one motion. For, like Tycho, he held that the stars were not moved by spheres in which they were fixed but themselves moved. He also held that the planets like flames, moved up and down as well as circularly, approaching and receding from our earth like the new star of 1572.[69] But for him the universe was still geocentric and the sun revolved about the earth. Moreover, in an onslaught upon the astronomers, after setting forth the hypotheses of Fracastoro, Copernicus and Tycho Brahe, he characterized them as deliriums of the astronomers and presently added concerning those of Tycho and Copernicus that none of the positions of older astronomers were so monstrous as these two. He called Aristotle the champion and Achilles of the astronomers and concluded that with so great a protector, so great a number of heavens, so great contradictions, so great an inversion and perversion of the universe, all this so great

[68] *Ibid.*, p. 98.

[69] *Nova de universis philosophia*, Venice, 1593, *Pancosmias* XVII, fols. 103r-104v, 150v-151r.

observation and science of astronomy is ridiculed and derided.[70]

Launoy in his work on the varied fortune of Aristotle at the university of Paris, first published in 1662,[71] quoted the opinion of Ionsius,[72] with which Morhof was in agreement, that Patrizi was a man of bold genius who, in the endeavor to make a name for himself, undertook to refute the philosophy of Aristotle. Ionsius praised his diligence but thought that he lacked judgment and was too audacious. Janus Nicius Erythraeus in his *Pinacotheca*[73] felt that Patrizi was merely dashing his head against a wall, and that the authority of Aristotle would last so long as thought and philosophy should endure.

Vitale Zuccolo, a theologian of Padua and Camaldulensian monk, published in 1590 a dialogue in Italian on meteorological phenomena and marvelous properties of fountains, rivers and seas based primarily upon Aristotle.[74]

The five books on nature of Francesco Piccolomini, published first in 1596,[75] conform to the general plan and divisions of the Aristotelian books on natural philosophy, although also taking note occasionally of the views of Plato and other ancient phi-

[70] *Ibid., Pancosmias* XII, fols. 89v-92r.

[71] *Joannis Launoii de varia Aristotelis in academia parisiensi fortuna liber.* I have used the edition of 1720, where the passage begins at p. 279. Launoy cites Io. Ionsius, *De script. hist.*, III, 20; Morhoffius, *Polyhist.*, II, i, 8; and Ianus Nicius Erythraeus, *Pinacoth.*, I, 204.

[72] Joannes Jonsius of Rendsburg in Holstein was pro-rector of the university of Frankfurt an der Oder, where his *De scriptoribus historiae philosophicae* appeared in 1659.

[73] *Pinacotheca imaginum illustrium doctrinae vel ingenii laude virorum qui auctore superstite diem suum obierunt,* Cologne, 1642, 8vo.

[74] *Dialogo delle cose meteorologiche di D. Vitale Zuccolo Padoano theologo e monaco Camaldolense in cui si dichiarano tutte le cose maravigliose che si generano nell' aere et alcune mirabili proprietà de' fonti fiumi e mari secondo la dottrina d'Aristotele con le opinoni d'altri illustri scrittori.* Con privilegio. In Venetia MDXC Appresso Paolo Megietti, 4to, 165 pp. Copy used: BM 538.e.27.(6.).

The works of Zuccolo formerly filled over a hundred volums (MSS 401 to 521) in the library of S. Michael de Muriano and included sermons, biblical commentaries, theology, commentaries on Plato's dialogues, Euclid, astronomy and the various subjects covered by Aristotle. See Mittarelli, *Bibl. cod. mss. monasterii S. Michaelis Venetiarum,* 1779. Zuccolo is not mentioned in Tiraboschi's *Storia della letteratura italiana.*

[75] I have consulted both the edition of 1596, Franciscus Piccolomineus, *Librorum ad scientiam de natura,* BM c.78.c.15, and that of 1628, *Naturae totius universi scientia,* BM 537.d.2.

losophers or even of medieval schoolmen. Thus of various opinions as to the subject of philosophy which Piccolomini gives, the first is that of Aquinas and John of Ghent, the second of Albertus Magnus and Aegidius Romanus, the third of John Canonicus, Antonius Andreas Trompeta and the Scotists, the fourth that of certain recent thinkers, and the sixth that of the Greek interpreters.[76]

Of magic Piccolomini distinguishes four varieties: divine, mathematical, physical and demonaical. The last is to be regarded as absolutely diabolical illusion, although Aristotle who did not recognize demons reduced it to the physical variety, stating that nature is demoniacal. Of physical magic Piccolomini approves as applied science, including medicine, agriculture, distilling and the like. Mathematical magic considers varied aspects and properties of the stars and forms varied characters and images under them. It is in large part superstitious and false. What truth there is in it is from astronomy.[77] Such a notion as that of a *magnus annus* Piccolomini would likewise reject except in so far as it is conceded concerning the motion of the eighth sphere by recent astronomers.[78] Whether there is any virtue in number is another question discussed by Piccolomini, a problem suggested by Aristotle's allusions to the perfection of the number three. Plato and Pythagoras answered it affirmatively, and Aristotle seems to do so in certain passages. The Hebrews attribute great virtue to numbers, resolve names and letters into them, and base the Cabala largely upon them. Physicians observe the number of days of illness and reckon certain numbers critical. Theologians seem to observe numbers in prayers and fasts. But Aristotle, *Metaphysics*, XIV,5, denies that number is ever a cause. It is formed by human reason; virtue is from nature. The Academics distinguished five kinds of

[76] *Ibid.*, Introd. cap. 25, p. 58 in 1628 edition.

[77] *Ibid.*, Introd. caps. 6, 9, pp. 17, 23-24 in edition of 1628.

[78] *Ibid.*, Pars I, De communibus affectibus, cap. 18, pp. 442-43 in the 1628 edition. In this connection he says that Ficino's estimate of 36,000 years for the revolution of the eighth sphere agrees neither with Plato nor Aristotle, and cites Nicolas Oresme, *De proportionibus proportionum*.

numbers: divine, ideal, rational, physical and mathematical. They held that all except the last variety had virtue. But Piccolomini finds the solution of the problem in the Peripatetic distinction between *numerus, numeratus* and *numerans*.[79]

As to the influence of the stars Piccolomini rejects the extreme opinion of the Assyrians, Egyptians, Arabs and many astronomers on the one hand, and that of Pico della Mirandola on the other, and further the midway view of the Academics which endows the stars with souls and is rejected by the Peripatetics. Instead he advances a fourth view that the celestial bodies act only by motion and light but in such a way that each has an influence peculiar to itself. Such influence is natural and does not violate human free will and may be legitimately utilized in physical and astronomical magic.[80] He makes the four first qualities depend on the sky.[81] Piccolomini still preferred the Aristotelian doctrine of comets.[82] He held that only low, small and imperfect animals were generated from putrefaction; higher animals from seed; and mediocre forms of life from dew and the like. Those born from putrefaction were not of the same species as those born from seed.[83] He still maintained with Aristotle that the heart was the seat of the soul.[84] He would admit only three internal senses: *sensus communis,* phantasy and memory. He agreed with the theologians that the sky would come to rest in due time and would not on that account be destroyed but preserved with a better disposition. The elements too, purged by fire, would be preserved and no longer subject to alteration, since their changing depends on the motion of the sky. Man too would be preserved, since he is the end of other bodies and has an immortal rational soul.[85]

Although the *New Philosophy Concerning our Sublunar World* of William Gilbert was not published until 1651 long after his

[79] *Ibid.,* Pars II, De mundo, cap. 41, p. 664 in edition of 1628.

[80] *Ibid.,* Pars II, De caelo, cap. 38, pp. 765-72 in 1628 edition.

[81] *Ibid.,* p. 1043.

[82] *Ibid.,* Pars IV, Meteororum, cap. 8, pp. 1287-88.

[83] *Ibid.,* Pars IV, De ortis ex putri, caps. 1 and 11, pp. 1433, 1438.

[84] *Ibid.,* Pars V, De sede animae, cap. 17.

[85] *Ibid.,* Pars II, De caelo, cap. 43, pp. 779-80.

death,[86] we may include it in our survey of the sixteenth century, since it seems in the main to reflect his views and not to have been seriously altered in the process of transmission and editing. It essays especially a new "Physiology" and a new meteorology against Aristotle. It is to be borne in mind that Gilbert himself never saw fit to publish it and that he apparently left it in an incomplete and unfinished state.

Gilbert called the belief in four elements a fable.[87] Fire cannot be an element since it requires fuel.[88] Sea, rivers and air are mere effluvia of the earth and rise only a few miles above its surface.[89] Experienced sailors, he said, rejected as false the statement that the peak of Teneriffe was seventy-two miles high.[90] Mariners also assured him that the sea was shallow in most places.[91] Gilbert estimated the amount of earth as five thousand times that of water in place of the old view that the sphere of water was ten times that of the earth.[92] He further rejected the conception of celestial spheres, holding that the heavenly bodies moved themselves[93] and that aside from their effluvia there were vacant spaces between them rather than either air or ether.[94] All things placed in a vacuum are at rest, and this is the state of most of the stars, but the planets move about the sun or about the earth, the earth about its axis to (around?) the sun, the moon about the earth and so about the sun.[95] Elsewhere Gilbert states that the earth is moved circularly which also seems to imply that it revolves about the sun.[96] Light shining through a vacuum arrives instantaneously. If the world were filled, the light of the fixed stars would reach us after they

[86] William Gilbert, *De mundo nostro sublunari philosophia nova.* Opus posthumum ab authoris fratre collectum . . . nunc ex duobus codicibus editum ex Museio Guilelmi Boswelli. Amsterdam, Ludwig Elzevir, 1651, 4to. Cornelius van Beughem, *Bibl. math.,* Amsterdam, 1688, p. 52, would seem in error in giving Leyden (Lugd. Bat.) as the place of printing.

[87] *Philosophia nova,* 1651, I, 3, 5, 6; pp. 4-12.

[88] *Ibid.,* p. 19.

[89] *Ibid.,* pp. 29, 37, 43.

[90] *Ibid.,* p. 132.

[91] *Ibid.,* I, 17; p. 45.

[92] *Idem.*

[93] *Ibid.,* I, 4; II, 9; pp. 8-9, 147, 157.

[94] *Ibid.,* I, 10; p. 30.

[95] *Ibid.,* I, 20; p. 49, "tellus circa axem suum ad solem."

[96] *Ibid.,* II, 7.

were below the horizon.[97] Which shows that even as keen a mind as Gilbert's had little notion of the transmission of light or the immense distance of some of the stars. Although Gilbert rejected spheres, he still spoke of poles, at least of the equinoctial circle.[98] Comets have a motion peculiar to themselves, but it is in large part caused by the sun, that center of the motive world which everywhere exercises its power.[99] Tycho, Maestlin, Dee, Digges, Hagecius and others have demonstrated that recent comets were far above the moon,[100] but Gilbert also cites Vogelinus and Cruserus on the earlier comets of 1532 and 1517 to prove that sometimes they exist below the moon.[101]

Gilbert seems to point towards Newton when he contends that there is no force in a place or places but only in bodies and that it is ridiculous to think that the globe of earth has gravity but that the other globes do not.[102] He further held that celestial and elementary heat were the same.[103] He regarded cold as mere privation or lack of heat, and so reduced the primary qualities to three,[104] while he denied that secondary qualities were derived from the primary.[105] He asserted that flame was the vehement action of sulphur dissolved and fused together with water, that there was no heat without humor, and that all fire was the action of attenuating humor.[106] He said that the spirit in the arteries was attenuated humor seeking an exit with violence. When it found none, it was reflected back to the heart, ventilated in the lungs, received aliment, and then again surged forth, "which reciprocal movement is called the pulse."[107] As in his work on the magnet, Gilbert held that the earth was a great magnet, magnetic in form, and probably in color inside, and that the magnetic core of the earth remained unaltered, while land and water changed on its surface like skin and hair.[108] As if internal organs did not change too!

[97] *Ibid.*, I, 20; p. 52.
[98] *Ibid.*, II, 22; p. 199.
[99] *Ibid.*, pp. 157-58.
[100] *Ibid.*, II, 10; p. 155.
[101] *Ibid.*, III, 7; p. 242.
[102] *Ibid.*, I, 21; p. 63.
[103] *Ibid.*, I, 27.
[104] *Ibid.*, II, 30; p. 215.
[105] *Ibid.*, I, 25.
[106] *Ibid.*, II, 29-30; pp. 215-16.
[107] *Ibid.*, II, 32; p. 218.
[108] *Ibid.*, II, 1, 3; pp. 107, 120, 133.

Gilbert alluded to the Chaldeans and to the Magi, "who were closely related to them," as the first of all in the disciplines.[109] Primitive man, he held, lived a simple life in ignorance of science and mechanical arts. The savages of the West Indies now lived the same life as early man.[110] He did not, however, believe in steady human progress and development, since he represented the medieval period as Dark Ages[111] and the schools as filled with most absurd doctrines, vanities and errors, and as holding Aristotle and Galen in veneration as if gods.[112] On the other hand, he at least professed to accept the Mosaic account of creation and to find in it nothing contrary to his scientific beliefs.[113] He cited, not always with approval, many recent writers: Cardan, Apian, Cornelius Gemma, Squarcialupus, Munzius, Erastus, Maurolycus, Franciscus Patritius, Benedetti. He criticized adversely the explanations of the tides given by Delphinus, Taisnier, Levinus Lemnius, and Scaliger.[114]

The work of Chassinus on nature or the world[115] reminds one of the writings of Descartes in a number of respects and may be regarded as anticipating some features of Cartesianism and preparing the way for it. Like Descartes he had studied under the Jesuits, pursuing the humanities at their schools at Lyons and Tournon. He then, however, heard Legerius lecture on Aristotle at Paris but was not satisfied by what he heard. After spending three years on the study of the law at Padua, he himself read the works of Aristotle and of his chief followers, the Portuguese commentators of the university of Coimbra. He also read Plato and the Platonists. But he found everywhere sophisms and false arguments. After this schooling, more prolonged and varied than that of Descartes, he spent seven years in observa-

[109] *Ibid.*, I, 3; p. 4.

[110] *Ibid.*, I, 1-2.

[111] *Ibid.*, I, 3; p. 7: "a Gothorum illuvie . . . usque ad avos nostros cum rursus emergere literae et ingenia coepere nihil inventum observatum fere nihil cuncta caligine et tenebris obscurata delitescebant."

[112] *Ibid.*, I, 3, 17; pp. 6, 45.

[113] *Ibid.*, p. 39.

[114] *Ibid.*, V, 10; p. 298.

[115] Godefridus Chassinus, *De natura sive de mundo libri octo quibus recta notio veraque scientia rerum humanarum et divinarum hactenus ignota demonstratur et simul in illis Aristotelem omnino male sensisse,* Lugduni e typ. S. Rigaud, 1614, 8vo, 378 pp. Copy used: BN R.9711. There was a second edition in 1619: BN R.54593.

tion of and meditation upon nature, and then wrote up his findings without reference to Aristotle or other philosophers. He then, however, decided that he ought at the same time to demonstrate how far and in what way Aristotle had deviated from the right path, a task which occupied him for four years more. Like Descartes, he believed that his own philosophy was simple, clear and expedite, and that it did not require great learning in languages and arts as Aristotle did but only effort and judgment.

Chassinus's philosophy is not quite so much of a new departure as these preliminary remarks of his might lead one to expect. Although he often contradicts Aristotle, he is limited to much the same round of conceptions and topics. The scope and pattern of his ideas of nature and the world are still strongly determined by Aristotle and other preceding writing and thought. His entire method and arrangement are still very scholastic, with numbered Ratio's and Solutio's, Nota's, Admonitions, Preoccupations and Objections. Indeed, his pages give evidence of far more meditation and internal reasoning than they do of observation of the external facts of nature. Although the Jesuits taught the Aristotelian philosophy of nature, Chassinus ventured to submit his new findings to them.

We may now run rapidly through Chassinus's volume, indicating some of his disagreements with Aristotle and some of his own characteristic tenets. He rejects the Aristotelian argument against a plurality of worlds that one would fall into another. He holds that the world lives and has a soul. All the forms of sublunar things are contained in the form of the world. Aristotle set the order and series of things from superiors to inferiors, but Chassinus would have it proceed from the center and he still regards the earth as the center of the universe. He grants, however, that the earth moves, revolving very slowly and thus explaining the difficulty which astrologers past and present have experienced in measuring accurately the solar year. He denies that the tides are caused by the moon and ascribes them to the vital motion of the world soul which moves the ocean in as close an approach to circular motion as it can. Chassinus discards other explanations why the sea is salt and contents himself with the sole reason that such is its nature. He believes that there is no sphere of fire, and that the sky is not composed of a fifth essence but of form and matter like earth, water and air. The sympathy existent between superiors and inferiors shows that they are alike. The heavens used to be thought as solid as marble,[116] but really are an aerial fluid in which the bodies we call stars move. Chassinus still maintains with Aristotle the spherical figure and circular motion of the stars, all of which he makes move from east to west. But to uphold circular motion he has to distinguish ten varieties thereof, of which a number are about a point in various spirals, remotely suggesting Descartes' vortices. He rejects the moving intelligences of Aristotle, however, and states that the stars are moved by themselves. "The world therefore is the first and last and greatest and most perfect of living beings, the immediate work of an infinite cause," and itself the cause of all things which are born and die.

Chassinus states that Copernicus in the endeavor to avoid old errors fell into new aberrations, making some parts of the universe immobile contrary to the highest reason of living nature which suffers nothing immobile, and having the earth move too rapidly. For when he realized that truth could not be attained, he preferred "to invent his own errors which he thought easier rather than follow more difficult and alien" hypotheses.[117]

Chassinus still has three principles, adheres to the conception of final cause, and prefers the dictum that nature abhors a vacuum to more circumstantial and particular explanations.[118] He makes water the matter of things and heat the instrumental cause, while the *causa agens* is the form of the world or world-soul. His natural order or *Scala naturae* is: the supreme cause, God; nothing; first matter; a positive degree of life; potentiality; the motive function of minerals; the vegetative function of

[116] I think that this is not a correct statement of the view of the majority of medieval writers.

[117] Chassinus (1614), p. 138: IV, 8.

[118] *Ibid.*, p. 242, VI, 3: "Digressio de fuga vacui contra Cardanum."

plants; the sensitive, of fish, animals and birds; the rational, of man; the intellective and intuitive, of demons; world-soul; universe; and again the supreme cause God. Even demons probably have to have some sustenance, but exhalations and vapors suffice for some of them, thin air for others.

No sublunar thing moves itself as the stars do. Discussing whether motion is free or necessary or from fate, Chassinus decides that two kinds of motion are necessary, a third free. He discusses whether motion can occur in an instant. He regards perpetual motion by art as possible, since the natural motion of the ocean, rivers and stars is perpetual. He rejects the view of Albertus Magnus that heat is from motion and the conception of latent heat in Durandus and others. He asserts that natural death is an evil but painless, while violent death is the greatest evil and extremely painful. Discussing whether the dead can be revived, he agrees with Aristotle that there is no return from privation *ad habitum*.

With his seventh book Chassinus comes to the discussion of qualities, "exterior and interior," i.e. manifest and occult, to sympathy and antipathy, and to place and time. The fact that the qualities and virtues of things are not immediately destroyed at death makes possible the accomplishment in medicine and other subjects of many things contrary to the usual course of nature which excite the wonder even of the learned. Sympathy was implanted in things by the First Cause when He made the world, and exists between genera, species, and according to the occult qualities of individual things. Chassinus distinguishes twenty kinds of sympathy up and down his Ladder of Nature and affirms that those who know the forms and qualities of things can by means of sympathy and antipathy achieve operations and effects, the sight of which will arouse wonder and the hearing thereof, incredulity.

In an epilogue to his brief eighth and last book Chassinus states that he has been investigating insects and other minutiae of leaves, herbs and minerals for the last three years, being dissatisfied with what the ancients have said thereon, especially concerning what goes on underground and in the air. But these latest investigations he does not here publish.

Although we have indicated certain points which Descartes may have surreptitiously borrowed from Chassinus, it is evident that the leading feature of the latter's view of nature, his animism and vitalism and theory of a world-soul, sharply differentiates it from Descartes' mechanical interpretation and associates Chassinus with the school of thought represented by Bruno and Campanella.

Tommaso Giannini, whose work of 1618 on the heavens and influence of the stars we have had occasion to cite in several previous chapters, in an earlier treatise of 1615, addressed to cardinal Bonifacio Bevilacqua, discussed what was the proper Aristotelian attitude towards the state of the human mind after death and the character of demon knowledge. He cited Peter of Abano, Pomponazzi and various schoolmen but added little or nothing to previous discussion of these matters.[119]

The publication at Geneva in 1621 by Sebastian Basso of twelve books of natural philosophy against Aristotle[120] testifies as much to the abiding influence and even dominance of the Stagirite as it does to the existence or success of opposition to his teachings. In the preface Basso justifies his criticism of Aristotle by the fact that Aristotle himself sharply attacked all previous philosophers, not sparing even his master Plato, and the further circumstance that there are so many contradictory passages in the traditional text of Aristotle that there is great dissent among his followers. He explains the great ascendancy of Aristotle by the loss of other books of the ancients on natural philosophy, a gap which the works of Aristotle served to fill. Professedly at least Basso's own treatise is not a step forward towards modern science but a step backward to the natural science of Aristotle's predecessors. Actually he deals with roughly the

[119] T. Giannini, *De lumine, et speciebus spiritalibus, de mente effectrice et speciebus intelligibilibus, de daemonibus et mentibus a materia separatis disputationes,* Padua, 1588. I used the edition of Ferrara, 1615: BM 525.e.13.(3.). There was another at Venice in 1616.

[120] Sébastien Basso, *Philosophiae naturalis adversus Aristotelem libri XII, in quibus abstrusa veterum physiologia restauratur et Aristotelis errores solidis rationibus refalluntur,* Geneva, 1621, 8vo, xl, 700 pp. Copy used: BN R.25548.

same set of topics and problems as do the Aristotelian works of natural philosophy and their subsequent commentators. And while professing to "restore the abstruse natural science of the ancients," Basso cites and depends upon his immediate predecessors like Zabarella and Piccolomini a great deal. Or he finds it advisable to refute and attack Scaliger, Toletus and the Conimbricenses.[121] In other words his book, like several others of which we have treated, is more in the nature of a critical commentary upon the Aristotelian philosophy as developed during the medieval and sixteenth centuries than it is a new departure in the direction of modern science.

It does not appear that Basso's explanations of natural phenomena are markedly more correct than those of Aristotle and his later adherents. He recognizes the existence of air pressure but ascribes the acceleration of falling bodies entirely to increasing pressure of the air above them and diminishing resistance of the air beneath them. He tends to attribute the ecliptic to the movement of the earth, and asserts that the planets can move or be moved by God without containing spheres. But he still believes that the planets exert most diverse effects on mortals through the very varied spirits which they have. Surely the most wise Creator of nature would give these noblest parts of the universal animal even more subtle and fine spirits than those with which He has endowed the human body or which appear in the art of distillation. The body of the mother protects the foetus from the action of these celestial spirits, but the moment the tender body is exposed to them at birth, they take effect. Basso affirms that snow flakes are not formed in the clouds but by the chill of the air as the moisture falls, while he explains hail as formed from hot vapors, for he agrees with Aristotle that hot water freezes faster than cold. He also believes that a manure heap retains its heat longer in winter than in summer, and that vision is performed by emission of rays from the eye. He makes a striking comparison of the sea to a

[121] The Jesuit commentators on Aristotle at the Portuguese university of Coimbra.

vast tree trunk with its branches in the clouds and its roots extending through the whole earth. But he dislikes to explain either critical days or the tides by the influence of the moon, and compares the tides to accessions of fever or the pulse. That heat which ascends from the bowels of the earth could not be from the earth, because its nature is most cold. It must originate from spirits intromitted from the sea underground.

Basso adopted the atomic philosophy and, as has been already implied, tried to explain natural phenomena in terms of actual physical contact—in which he may be regarded as anticipating Descartes. But just as very fine spirits took the place for him of the occult influence of the stars, so he spoke of Democritus as most experienced in secrets of nature and poisons. He agreed with Scaliger and Pliny that the flesh of a fowl was the poison of gold and that, thrown into liquefied gold, it dissolved the gold.[122] He further stated that the worst poisons made the best cures for other poisons. Dried toads applied to the region of the heart would draw out all the poison. Or he exclaims, "What shall I say of that powder made from worms which kills worms marvelously?" In short, criticism of Aristotle's natural philosophy did not make Basso any more scientific or any less magical. He explained astrology and marvelous cures a little differently but he still clung to them both.

The abiding influence of Aristotle to which we referred was shown further three years later in 1624, when fourteen theses in opposition alike to the Paracelsists, cabalists, and dogmatic Peripatetic physicists, which had been issued by Iohannes Bitaudus, Antonius de Villon, and Stephanus de Claues, were censured by the Sorbonne and suppressed by the Parlement of Paris.[123] The three authors of the propositions were expelled from Paris and forbidden to teach or print them in the realm. Their theses

[122] This interpretation corresponds more closely to the usual Latin text of Pliny (*Naturalis historia*, edition of 1518, 29, 4, 90: "Si auro liquescenti gallinarum membra misceantur, consumunt illud in se") than that of Portaleone (T V, 645).

[123] Jakob Brucker, *Historia critica philosophiae*, 1742-1744, IV, 468. For a fuller account of the affair see *Joannis Launoii . . . de varia Aristotelis in academia parisiensi fortuna liber*, Paris, 1720, p. 310 *et seq.*

were of a paradoxical and sensational character, including the assertion that fire was not dry in the highest degree but of all bodies the wettest—possibly in the sense of being the most fluid. In the same year Gassendi published his *Exercitationes paradoxicae adversus Aristoteleos,* in which he criticized especially the Aristotelian dialectic and philosophy. He had intended to follow this up with a further onslaught upon the Physics, Metaphysics and Ethics, but abandoned his plan, according to Bayle because of the outburst of formidable indignation from the Peripatetic party, but if we believe Jonsius[124] because he was ashamed of his insolent attempt, and condemned the remaining books to eternal darkness.

[124] Author of *De scriptoribus historiae philosophiae,* 1659 (BN Z.9152) and *De historia Peripatetica,* 1720 (BN R.25980).

CHAPTER XLIII

NATURAL PHILOSOPHY AND NATURAL MAGIC

Esse autem Magiam quandam naturalem quae est secretior quaedam et abstrusior sapientiae pars et quae occulta quadam cognitione et usu quarundam rerum naturalium mira perficit, nullo modo viris doctis dubitandum est.

—PERERIUS, *De magia*, I, 3.

While some were guided in their interpretation of natural phenomena and problems by the account of the creation of the world in the first chapter of the Book of Genesis and by other passages in the Bible, while others were primarily motivated, whether positively or negatively, whether in accord or in revolt, by the Aristotelian books of natural philosophy, there were yet others to whom the boundless possibilities of the physical universe itself appealed, who felt that nature had secrets to disclose and wonders to work surpassing those of necromancers and demons. These men not only fared forth, so to speak, on foot, where modern science, aided by telescope and microscope and a thousand other inventions, has built the double track railroad of experimental and mathematical method. They even failed to take advantage of trails which the science of the later middle ages had blazed for a way at least into the forest.

Interest in natural philosophy was sufficiently widespread for dialogues on it to be composed in Spanish by Alonso de Fuentes and then translated into Italian.[1] In this work the influences of the stars and of demons receive much attention. It is stated that a physician should not only be a good philosopher but also an

[1] Alfonso di Fonte, *Somma della natural filosofia di . . . divisa in dialoghi sei ne' quali oltra le cose fisiche s'ha piena cognitione delle scienze astronomia et astrologia dell' anima et della notomia del corpo humano. Novellamente tradotta di spagnuolo in volgare da Alfonso di Ulloa,* Venetia per Plinio Pietrasanta, 1557.

astronomer,[2] and that the stars were the cause of the creation of terrestrial animals.[3] For when the stars were created and began to move, they thereby heated the air, which in turn scalded the water and made it boil and throw off vapors, from which different kinds of animals were created. Spirits and demons are located in the regions midway between heaven and earth, and tempests are produced by bad demons who dwell in the humid regions. The demons do not know the future or our thoughts, but work miracles by applying seminal virtues and impeding motion. But they cannot impede the regular processes of nature such as the courses of the heavenly bodies. The soul of Adam possessed universal knowledge as did the angels, but this faculty was lost after the fall of man. Maddalena della Croce of Cordova performed miracles by the aid of demons, but Pharaoh's magicians generated serpents naturally by the application of seminal virtue and not by force of demons.[4]

Despite its astrology and demonology, the work constantly professes to seek a physical explanation (*Ragione fisica*) of the phenomena discussed. The author says that in matters touching the Catholic Faith a sinner like himself has no license to dispute the conclusion of the Venerable Bede or of any other holy doctor, but that concerning natural phenomena he ventures to disagree with Bede—in which he repeats without acknowledgement the attitude of Alexander Neckam in the twelfth century.[5] The author is represented as a Platonist, but the atoms of Epicurus are discussed.[6] Such questions are raised as why early men lived so long, why the human head was created round, why most women have no beards and why some women have, why the sea is salt, and why fountains are warm in the spring but cold in summer.[7] Evaporation by the sun is given as the cause of the saltness of the sea, while fountains are said to grow colder in summer, because the pores of the earth open then and allow the hot vapors within to escape. Fuentes still divides the world into only three

[2] *Ibid.*, p. 79.
[3] *Ibid.*, p. 56.
[4] *Ibid.*, pp. 9-12, except on Adam, p. 160.
[5] *Ibid.*, p. 51.
[6] *Ibid.*, pp. 151, 15.
[7] *Ibid.*, pp. 58, 141-42, 105-7.

parts, Asia, Europe and Africa, but he states that all the zones are habitable contrary to the opinion of the ancients.[8] On the whole his sprightly little book displays a certain boldness of utterance and will not suffer much by comparison with the Latin tomes of his contemporaries.

For John Dee the world was a lyre from which a skilful player could draw new harmonies.[9] Every thing and place in the world radiated force to all the other parts and received rays from them. There were also relations of sympathy and antipathy between things. Species, both spiritual and natural, flowed off from objects with light or without it, impressing themselves not only on the sight but the other senses, and especially coalescing in our imaginative spirit and working marvels in us. Moreover, the human soul and the specific form of every thing has many more and more excellent virtues and operations than has the human body or the matter of the thing in question. Similarly the invisible rays of the planets or their secret influence surpass their sensible rays or light. Dee stressed the influence of the stars in various other passages and believed that each star had its own nature. He affirmed that a person skilled in catoptric could by art impress the rays of each star more strongly than nature can, and that this was the main feature of the natural magic of the ancient sages. His attempted experiments with angels were in accord with his attributing greater operations to soul than body and with his semi-spiritual view of nature.[10]

[8] *Ibid.*, pp. 118, 115.

[9] *Propaedeumata Aphoristica de praestantioribus quibusdam naturae virtutibus,* Londini, Excudebat Henricus Suttonus, 1558 mense Iulio. Copy used: BM 717.g.13.(1.). Another edition, with a letter from Dee of Dec. 24, 1567, immediately follows in the same volume. This second edition was printed at London on January 9, 1568, by Reginald Wolf. BM 8630.dd.9 is another copy of it.

[10] See *A True and Faithful Relation of What Passed for Many Years between Dr. John Dee and Some Spirits,* edited by Meric Casaubon from Bibl. Cottoniana, London, 1659, in folio. Also the following MSS: BM Sloane 3189, 16th century paper folio, 65 leaves, Liber mysteriorum sextus et sanctus, in the hand of Edward Kelley, Dee's coadjutor. Sloane 3188, 16th century paper folio, 169 leaves, Dr. John Dee's conference with angels from Dec. 22, 1581, to May 30, 1583, being what precedes the other conferences printed by Dr. Meric Casaubon, London, 1659, with a preface by Elias Ashmole in 1672, fols. 5-168, is the original in Dee's hand. Ashmole's

In 1559 appeared the first edition of the work of Levinus Lemnius on the occult miracles of nature.[11] The title is the most significant feature of the book, which is a disorderly miscellany of little value, with entertainment rather than instruction the author's aim. Bits of medical and natural lore are thrown together hit-or-miss. Anything may be the theme of the next chapter. All that one can be sure of is that there will be frequent quotation from the Latin poets. A few of the things discussed are *aqua vitae* or brandywine, the effects of human saliva, whether it is better to sleep with the mouth closed or open, whether measles can be cured with red wine. It will not do, however, to dismiss this farrago too cavalierly, since it was often cited by subsequent learned authors, and since the numerous editions and translations of it show that it well suited the taste of the century. There were Latin editions at Antwerp in 1561, in 1564 when two new books were added to the original two, in 1567, 1574, and 1581; at Ghent in 1570; at Cologne in 1573 and 1581; at Jena in 1588; at Frankfurt in 1590, 1593, 1598, 1604, 1611, 1628, 1640 and 1655; at Amsterdam in 1650 and at Leyden in 1666. An Italian translation was printed at Venice in 1560, 1563 and 1567; French at Lyons in 1566 and Paris in 1567 and 1575; German in 1586, 1592, 1593 and 1601. There seems to have been no English version until 1650.

Lemnius, who is said to have been a pupil of Vesalius, Gesner and Dodoens, had already in 1554 published at Antwerp three brief tracts dealing respectively with astrology, length of life, and care of one's health. He issued a longer work in two books on the *complexio* of the human body in 1587. Another much read book by him was an explanation of the similitudes and

---

copy is Sloane 3677. Sloane 3190 seems a copy of 3188 and the 1659 edition. Sloane 3191, 16th century paper folio, 80 leaves, fols. 1-3, Claves angelicae a. 1584 Cracoviae ab Aprilis 13 ad Iulii 13 . . . receptae, in English. More of the same sort follows.

See also C. Kiesewetter, *John Dee, ein Spiritist des 16. Jahrhunderts,* 1893; René Johannet, "La vie mouvementée d'un astrologue," *Revue de Paris,* V (1932), 909-29.

[11] Levinus Lemnius, *Occulta naturae miracula ac varia documenta probabili ratione atque artifici conjectura duobus libris explicata,* Antwerpiae apud G. Simonem, 1559, 8vo, 192 fols.

parables which are found in the herbs and trees of the Bible. It appeared at Antwerp in 1566 and 1569; at Lyons in 1588, 1594, 1622 and 1654; and was printed at Frankfurt in 1591, 1596 and 1626 together with the aforesaid tract on astrology and the work of Franciscus Rueus on gems. It was not entirely limited to herbs mentioned in the Bible but gives some from the New World. It also displays the same interest in the occult that characterized the author's work on the occult miracles of nature.

In the preface to his tract on astrology, dated from Zierikzee on March 7, 1553, Lemnius says that he has been practicing medicine for twenty-one years. In the text he notes that the astrologers had failed to predict either an epidemic of a cardiac sweating sickness in 1529 or the more recent bursting of the dykes and inundation by the ocean of a large part of the Low Countries. He nonetheless affirms that no one is more studious of the art and more addicted to it than himself. He had made verbal predictions to his fellow citizens of Zierikzee. He sets forth the influence of the heavens and of the moon in especial upon the human body, disease and medicine, but holds that food, exercise, medicines and education have a greater immediate influence than the stars. Consequently a physician should not let an unfavorable aspect of the constellations cause him to delay the application of a medical treatment that seems urgently called for. Lemnius also maintains the freedom of the will.

Valerius Andreas, who lists some further works by Lemnius, says that he was an affable practitioner who cheered his patients up by jokes and funny stories, that he was of medium stature, stocky, erect bearing, well chiselled features, and serene countenance.[12]

Nicolaus Biesius (1516-1572) of Ghent studied medicine at Louvain and then visited Spain and Italy, finally taking the M.D. degree at Siena. He returned to Louvain to teach medicine and was academic orator to the duke of Alva. Afterwards he became physician to the emperor Maximilian II at Vienna and died

[12] Valerius Andreas, *Bibliotheca Belgica,* 1643, pp. 608-9.

there.[13] Besides works on medical themes,[14] Biesius published volumes on the Republic or universal philosophy of morals,[15] on the variety of opinions,[16] and on the art of speaking.[17] The *De varietate opinionum* of Biesius does not present him in an attitude favorable to intellectual development, since it takes the position that variety of opinions and liberty against the general consensus of the good, at least in religious matters such as the Eucharist, is harmful to the state and the cause of many evils, and that the state should enforce uniformity.[18]

Yet in his *De universitate* or three books in verse and prose on natural philosophy, published a decade before in 1556 and dedicated to Philip II,[19] Biesius had closed with the assertion that knowledge of nature was essential for the well-being of the republic.[20] Earlier in the same work he had raised the question whether the truth of the mind was always consonant with the truth of nature. He had warned against being deceived by mathematical conceptions and had emphasized the need of always understanding natural things.[21] He had showed a certain tendency towards uniformity in natural science too, however, assuring Philip II that unless the fundamental principles of nature were well constituted, one could be certain of nothing further.[22] He

[13] For the facts of Biesius's life and lists of his works see Valerius Andreas, *Bibl. Belgica,* 1643, p. 679; Melchior Adam, *Vitae Germanorum medicorum;* Johann Hallevoord, *Bibliotheca curiosa,* 1676, p. 285. Adam dates his death in 1573.

[14] *Theoreticae medicinae libri sex,* Antwerp, 1558, 4to; *In artem medicam Galeni commentarii,* 1560; *De methodo medicinae liber unus,* Louvain, 1564, 8vo.

[15] *De republica sive de universa morum philosophia libri vi ad rev. Anton. Perrenotum episcopum Atrebatensem,* Antwerp, 1556.

[16] See note 18.

[17] *De arte dicendi seu Rhetorica,* Antwerp, 1573; *ibid.,* typis Nutii, 1577.

[18] Nicolaus Biesius Gandavenses, *De varietate opinionum liber unus,* Louvanii, 1567, small octavo: copy used, BN R.29086. It is a little book in twenty chapters.

[19] Nicolaus Biesius, *De universitate libri tres quibus universa de natura philosophia continetur,* Antwerp, 1556, 4to, viii, 224 pp. and index. Copy used: BN Ye.2009.

[20] *Ibid.,* pp. 223-24.

[21] *Ibid.,* p. 26, "Sed dubium esse nequit quin veritas mentis semper consentanea sit veritati naturae"; p. 27, "Sed cavendum est ne rebus mathematicis quae priores cadunt in phantasiam decipiamur, sed oportet ut naturalia semper intelligamus."

[22] *Ibid.,* preface, "quae nisi bene constituta sint reliqua constare nullo modo possunt."

also declared that there was "one infinite cause of all things, one finite ens in our souls, and one summum genus." He had indeed not a little to say concerning the monad and monads.

In *De universitate* Biesius deals with such usual topics as matter, the elements and their mixture in compounds, the celestial bodies, the human body, spirits and soul. He holds that springs, rivers, swamps are not generated by rainfall, but from vapor which is condensed within the earth and bursts forth in springs, and that even the ocean similarly flows from the bowels of earth, whose sweat and excrement it is, as Aristotle has written, and from which it gets its saltiness.[23] Likewise the lower air in which we live is a sort of terrestrial vapor, the element air filling a much larger space between the spheres of water and fire.[24] As these passages might suggest, Biesius is not adverse to a sweeping conception of geological change and historical development. He states that we see a certain perpetual vicissitude of all things, that in many regions there is now deep sea where there once was cultivated land, that areas now desert were once fertile and densely populated. "How many celebrated emporia we might list which are now completely abandoned by merchants!" Empires also wax and wane. Biesius would trace their course first in the south and north, then in the east and now westward. Indeed, nothing in nature can be constant, for the celestial bodies themselves continually slip and draw these inferiors into unceasing vicissitudes.[25]

The last sentence shows the favorable attitude of Biesius towards astrology. He is as certain that the rule of the ethereal region extends to the innermost parts of the earth as he is that all things are full of divine providence. The convergence of all the celestial rays at the earth's center explains the vehement heat there.[26] Yet Biesius speaks with respect of the calculations of Copernicus.[27] But God would have made man prone like the

[23] *Ibid.*, p. 49.

[24] *Ibid.*, p. 50.

[25] *Ibid.*, p. 143, the closing passage of the second book.

[26] *Ibid.*, p. 52.

[27] *Ibid.*, p. 73: "Sive per epicyclos sive per eccentricos sive partim hoc partim illo motu planetas ferri dicamus, eadem ferme positionis et virtutis ratio manet, sed non si per concen-

other animals, had He wished him to consider only inferior phenomena and not to regulate his life by observation of the stars.[28]

Alchemy also is regarded with favor by Biesius. The chemists, he says, strive to render matter apt to the form of a better metal by subjecting it to suitable fires, places and celestial influence, and now reducing it to vapor, now to a powder.[29] In another passage he states that they separate not merely the elements but a fifth celestial nature.[30]

Biesius further lists various kinds of divination and occult arts, and observes that they all seem to have originated in the idea that all things, even the least, are bound in an inevitable series of causes, and that all bodies are governed by incorporeal forces. He himself, however, would draw a line between natural and voluntary causes. But he thinks that brute animals are more sensitive to movement in nature than is man, who is occupied with his voluntary affairs, and that therefore many signs of the weather may be had from the behavior of brutes. And he is further convinced of the great sympathy and antipathy between things, which are all connected in marvelous ways.[31]

This viewpoint, with its close combination of the natural and occult, continues characteristic of another work on nature by Biesius in five books which was printed at Antwerp in 1573.[32] In it he accepts the "incredible sympathy of all things, especially those which are most closely joined by Nature." He also admits astrological influence but is more doubtful whether magic has natural force and associates astrological images with magic. Magic at best is mixed with inane superstitions, illusion, and the activity of evil spirits. Biesius finally concludes that, if there be any natural virtue in magic, it is too obscure for the human mind to discover and reduce to an art. It is true that such natural properties as attraction of iron by the magnet or drawing of bile by scammony are likewise discoverable only by experiment. But

tricos. Exactam autem supputationem et rationem motuum tradit Copernicus. . . ."

[28] *Ibid.*, p. 79.

[29] *Ibid.*, p. 52.

[30] *Ibid.*, pp. 191-92.

[31] For the contents of this paragraph, *ibid.*, pp. 58-63.

[32] *De natura libri v*, Antwerp, 1573. There was another edition in 1613.

these properties are generally constant: the experiments of magic are inconstant and of no avail unless one puts faith in them.

The question whether magic has natural force involves another whether words, characters and figures possess natural virtue. Many arguments tend to destroy all faith in their efficacy. Artificial figures of the constellations do not really depict the stars as they are naturally. Substance, property and virtue communicate themselves to natural objects but not to artificial figures. Sympathy exists between substances, not between figures. All action is due not to matter or dimension or position or figure but to forms, whether of the four elements or composite bodies or of celestial bodies and incorporeal beings. By figure neither the temperament nor form of a substance is altered. Therefore by artificial figures no natural force either of celestial or inferior bodies is set in motion. Even less is this the case with characters and words, which must owe to demons any virtue that they may seem to possess. But the demons are not compelled by them. In other words, Biesius, with most of the men of his century, affirms the existence of potent sympathy and antipathy or occult influence between things of nature and earth and sky, but, like Thomas Aquinas and other schoolmen of the medieval past, denies such virtue to artificial figures, words, images and characters.

In 1563-1564, when its dedicatory letters are dated, was first published at Venice in Italian *The Ladder of Nature or Sweetest Fantasy Concerning all Things Occult and Desired in Philosophy* of Giovanni Camillo Maffei da Solofra, a place near Naples. The most recent event referred to in the text is the earthquake of 1561. I have had access only to a later edition of 1600, a volume of 140 small leaves, a tenth of which are occupied by a full table of contents.[33] The style of the work reminds one of that by Ristoro d'Arezzo on the composition of the world, but Maffei seems less original in his thought and content than his thirteenth century predecessor. He cites authorities a great deal, including

[33] *Scala naturale overo fantasia dolcissima intorno alle cose occulte e desiderate nella filosofia*, Venetia, Appresso Marco Guarischo, 1600. Copy used: Col 156.4 M269.

ancients like Aristotle, Theophrastus, Pliny, Galen, Plutarch, and Ptolemy, church fathers like Augustine, Arabic writers like Avicenna, Avempace, Alpetragius, Albumasar and Averroes, medieval schoolmen such as Peter of Abano, Aquinas, Albertus Magnus, Robert Grosseteste and Aegidius, or the more recent works of Ficino, Pico della Mirandola, Giacomo Sannazaro and Andrea Mattioli.

The rungs in Maffei's natural ladder are the successive spheres of the four elements and ten heavens. Thus "Il XIII Grado della Scala" is the starless ninth heaven, while the book ends with the fourteenth step or empyrean heaven. Evidently Maffei remains unaffected by the Copernican theory. He further contends that the world is not eternal according to the thought of Aristotle. He still accepts the Aristotelian explanation of comets as earthly exhalations. He takes up the somewhat peculiar position of granting the evil significance of comets, which he illustrates by the history of various past comets, and the dominion of the stars, to which the specific forms or occult virtues of matter are due and to which even man is in part subject, but of agreeing with Pico della Mirandola in assailing the art of astrology as false and at present impossible. He also agrees with Aquinas and Augustine that the stars are only secondary causes. He further has a chapter on fortune and chance. He does not always accept the statements of Pico, citing him as having claimed to have seen a rainbow in full circle, which Maffei asserts could not have been a true iris which is only semicircular.[34]

Georg Pictorius von Villingen (c.1500-1569) provides a good example of the continuance in the sixteenth century of interest in medieval works of science and medicine, and of the taste for the curious and marvelous, the occult and superstitious, which marked that century. At first a schoolmaster at Freiburg-im-Breisgau, Pictorius became an M.D. and professor of medicine there, then physician at the archducal court at Ensisheim in upper Alsace. His publications began in 1530 with a treatise on the preservation of health, which also appeared in later editions.

[34] Edition of 1600, fol. 105r.

They comprised commentaries, scholia and tabulations upon or of such characteristically medieval authors in natural science and medicine as Macer on herbs, Marbod on gems, and Mesue, or such ancients as Hippocrates, Galen, and Oppian on fishes. In 1557 Pictorius published in German a medical work for travellers which was praised and utilized by Gratarolo in his Latin treatise on the same theme four years later.[35]

We shall be here concerned, however, with works by Pictorius which appeared in print in the seventh decade of the century in the years 1563,[36] 1568[37] and 1569.[38] These include an encyclopedic poem or set of poems treating of man and his physical constitution, of quadrupeds, birds, and fish, of herbs, metals, gems and their marvelous powers. Also a dialogue between Castor and Pollux as interlocutors on the subject of demons, an epitome on different varieties of ceremonial magic or *goetia,* and a discussion whether witches should be burned. The fact that Pictorius combined such matters in one volume with a treatment of animals, herbs, minerals and other natural phenomena is in itself of significance in the history of magic and science. Then there are three centuries of questions on nature and an account of errors in past authorities. Finally may be noted a *Phylologia* which is devoted to marvels of nature and to other miscellaneous matters.

[35] Gratarolus, *Profiscentium seu magnis itineribus diversas terras obeuntium,* or, *De regimine iter agentium. . . ,* Cologne, 1571 (the edition I have used rather than the *editio princeps* of 1561), dedicatory preface, pages unnumbered, ". . . in lingua Germanica edidit Georgius Pictorius medicus in Hensisheim praeclarus a quo nonnihil hac in re adiutum me esse non diffiteor."

[36] Georg Pictorius, Παντοπώλιον, *continens omnium ferme quadrupedum . . . naturas carmine elegiaco . . . de apibus methodo . . . de daemonum . . . ortu . . . Isagoge . . . de speciebus magiae ceremonialis quam goetiam vocant epitome et an sagae . . . cremari debeant resolutio,* Basel, 1563. It would take too long to quote the full wording of the title. This volume will henceforth be cited as Pictorius (1563). A MS in Paris, Arsenal 824, ff. 3v-59r, reproduces at least portions of it.

[37] Georg Pictorius, *Physicarum quaestionum centuriae tres. . . His accedunt quorundam magnorum autorum errores . . . contra quorundam philosophorum opiniones quis verus Deus unde Gentiles Dii ex quibus humani corporis fabrica . . . ,* Basel, 1568. This volume will be cited as Pictorius (1568). Copy used, BM 1169.c.3.

[38] Georg Pictorius, *Opera nova in quibus mirifica,* Basel, 1569. This will be cited as Pictorius (1569).

Most, if not all, of what Pictorius writes is taken second-hand from other works, either those of earlier authors or such a contemporary composition as that of Porta on natural magic. Even when he seems to recount something of his own, as when he tells of a friend who was at death's door being saved by voiding through the left nostril a worm a palm in length, we find that the same tale was told in the previous century by Antonio Benivieni of a friend of his.[39] Indeed, the writings of Pictorius are chiefly important as illustrating the long survival and slow disappearance of such traditional and legendary lore. In his pages we still meet the barnacle geese and such incredible stories as the bearing in the year 1314 by Margarita, countess of Holland, at the age of forty-two, of 364 infants at one birth.[40] The bishop of Utrecht baptized all the males as John and all the females as Elizabeth. Shortly after this christening the mother and all her brood died. This absurd story, impossible even according to the medical and scientific knowledge of that time, might seem to rule Pictorius out of court as quite unworthy of our consideration. But his own medical compositions and his editing of past authors of note indicate that he had his place in the learning and thought of the sixteenth century and is in certain respects representative of it. For the aforesaid story he professes to have the authority of Campifulgosus in the sixth chapter of his *Memorable Deeds and Sayings,* and also that of a funeral monument and epitaph of the mother and children in question. This latter agrees with Campifulgosus except as to the precise number of the children, which it gives as 360 rather than 364. Against such an agreement of historical and epigraphic evidence Pictorius seems to have found it impossible to maintain such scanty scientific criteria and medical scepticism as he ordinarily possessed and exercised.

In view of such credulity and marvel-mongering on the part of Pictorius, his presumption in pointing out errors in other authors is rather ridiculous. Nevertheless we find him asserting that Avicenna, Albertus Magnus and Theophrastus "have impudently

[39] Pictorius (1569), p. 41; for the like passage in Benivieni see T IV, 587.

[40] Pictorius (1569), p. 10.

erred in the description of the root mandragora."[41] But again it should be noted that his correction of past errors is almost entirely taken from previous authors. Thus we have detection of Avicenna's errors from Marcus Gattinaria, professor of the university of Pavia, from Giovanni Arcolani of Verona, Ferrari da Grado, Bartholomew de Montagnana, Michael Savonarola, Manardus of Ferrara, Nicolaus Leonicenus, and Matthaeus Silvaticus. Or Cornelius Agrippa is used to correct Hippocrates, Philip Beroaldus of Bologna to amend Cornelius Celsus, Manard to correct Mesue, Nicolaus Beraldus to correct Pliny, Hermolaus Barbarus and Beroaldus to rectify Albertus Magnus, George Merula to correct Galeotto Marzio da Narni, and so on.[42] Some of the errors, like those which Leonicenus found in Pliny, are purely verbal.

The natural questions of Pictorius remind one more of those of Adelard of Bath in the twelfth century than one might expect in the age following Vesalius and Copernicus. Among the chief authorities used in his first century are Aristotle, Pliny, Hippocrates and Galen. The questions start in top to toe order with the subject of baldness. Soon we come to eyesight and the old query why the glance of a menstruating woman spots a clean mirror, or why eunuchs have weak sight. Presently it is asked why man lacks wings and has very large feet, and the answer is based on Galen's work on the utility of parts of the body. There are several queries as to monstrous births. The question why a man thinking of past matters inclines his head towards the earth especially reminds us of Adelard of Bath, while that why one's fingers are bigger before eating than after is solved by Albertus Magnus's explanation that a fasting man is distended by bad humors.

Astrology enters into the explanation why the child born in the eighth month rarely lives, but we are informed that there are those who reject the dominance of cold, slow Saturn over that month as the cause. They suggest instead that the embryo, if it

[41] Pictorius (1569), V, 16.

[42] Pictorius (1569), II, 19; Pictorius (1568), pp. 119-136, "Quorundam optimorum autorum errores."

fails to emerge in the seventh month, becomes exhausted from its efforts and does not recover sufficient strength both to emerge and to live until the ninth month. The saturnine explanation would seem preferable to this. Another question involves blood-letting according to the moon's phases, while Peter of Abano's astrological explanation of greater human longevity before the flood is, like the discussion of the eighth month's child, given in both 1568 and 1569. Indeed Pictorius states that he had treated it more fully in yet another work.[43]

In the second century of physical questions Avicenna is much cited, so that Pictorius cannot be said to show a classical bias against Arabic medicine. Among various questions as to food and drinking, sleep and air, it is asked if Avicenna was right in recommending one to get drunk once a month. And the explanation why worms are generated when, immediately after eating, the hands are washed in hot water is taken from Avicenna. It is that this draws off the natural heat essential for digestion. In connection with sleep it is asked why dreams towards morning are called truer than others. We are afraid of the dark not because of the darkness itself but because our eyes seem powerless and exposed to injury.

In the third century it is explained that diseases are sometimes cured by incantations through strong mental application and imagination on the part of both the enchanter and the enchanted —a suggestion of cure through hypnotism. Why the lion fears the cock is solved from Marsilio Ficino, why water-clocks flow slower in winter than summer from Plutarch "in Physiologico suo." One is struck by fear and trembling when crossing ground where a man has been slain or a corpse recently buried, because one's spirits are affected by the air there, which is filled with horrible species of homicide. A corpse weighs more than a living body, because its celestial heat has exhaled with the soul, just as lead gains weight when turned into ceruse. Chemical interest

[43] Pictorius (1568), p. 98: "De hac re abundantissime scriptum habes apud Georgium Pictorium Succisivarum lectionum dialogo primo." Perhaps the reference is to *Les sept dialogues de Pictorius*, Paris, 1557, or to *Tuendae sanitatis ratio vii dialogis*, Basel, 1544.

rather than knowledge is shown in the question why gold smeared with quicksilver becomes more fragile than an egg shell.

Many kinds of divination which are enumerated by Pictorius as species of ceremonial magic will be noted in our chapter on Divination. Here we may notice the plucking or digging of magic herbs at a given time with certain ceremonies, or the curing of toothache by saying "Anasageus" thrice, touching the aching tooth with a spear and driving the spear into the pavement of the baptistery. When he was a boy, Pictorius saw on St. John the Baptist's day before dawn a root of chicory dug from the ground on bended knee with a sword of gold, silver and iron, and exorcized with many ceremonies. Nor do the rites always terminate with the magic cure. In one case the patient after his cure must give silver to the poor every Tuesday for a year and say the Lord's prayer thrice. Or a woman who has been freed by an old wife of pain in the womb must taste no eggs for three years and for two years every Sabbath evening near the cemetery with arms outstretched in the form of a cross and facing the east must say: "Happy souls, just as that good N. has freed me from the pain of my womb by her aid, so may our lord Jesus Christ free you from eternal damnation," and must sprinkle their bones three times three with holy water in the name of the indivisible Trinity. Pictorius also mentions magical measures to protect domestic animals and such popular superstitions as that miscarriage will result if a tripod is left standing idle in the fire, that the infant will sicken if its cradle is moved often while empty, that one will be defeated who receives his arms from a woman, and will be killed if one descends into the arena to fight in woman's clothing. Such precautions against witchcraft are mentioned as not throwing away any of one's hair that has been combed out without first spitting on it, and breaking eggshells with a knife thrice after eating eggs.

Concerning demons like everything else Pictorius in his *Isagoge* does little but collate previous authorities. He deserves some credit for conscientiously specifying them: Apuleius, Augustine and Iamblichus, Pliny, Saxo Grammaticus, Psellus whom he calls a necromancer, Peter Lombard, Trithemius and Marcus Cherrhonesus (for Chersonesus?), "a distinguished devotee of demons." Pictorius distinguishes northern and southern sublunar demons, also "criminatores et exploratores" and "tentatores vel insidiatores" who accompany individual men as evil geniuses. He believes that they have flexible bodies of fire, air or water. Augustine and Peter of Abano deny that they possess the power of generation but Pictorius prefers to follow the aforesaid Marcus Cherrhonesus who avers that they have genitals and are fecund in seed. Pictorius treats in two of his works[44] of remedies against demons and means of routing them. He approves the use against them of the name of Jesus, of the element fire, swords, contumelies, suffumigations with various herbs or red coral, the shaking of keys, sounding of bells, or clash of arms. But he does not approve of the Pentagon ascribed to Solomon being used against them. He twice quotes Averroes against Algazel to the effect that magic characters and signs are of no avail except in conjunction with pacts with demons. It may be doubted whether this citation correctly reflects Averroes' attitude. He merely says that the "science of images," which Algazel had listed among branches of natural science, is false and impossible, and mentions neither demons nor pacts in connection with it.[45]

As for witches, Pictorius would put them to death not only as non-Christian and as injuring others but as guilty of the worst form of bestiality in having carnal intercourse with the devil. If his readers do not accept this last, he still argues that the rapidly growing number of these furies needs to be checked by burning them, if anyone is to remain free from their incantations.[46]

The *Isagoge* of Pictorius may be said to have been put in its proper place when in 1665 it was printed at London in English translation bound with the spurious and highly magical fourth

[44] Pictorius (1563), pp. 35-38, 70; (1569), pp. 64-66.

[45] *Subtilissimus liber Averois qui dicitur Destructio destructionum philosophie Algazelis nuperrime traductus...* Venetiis in edibus Io. Baptiste pederzani Brixiensis Bibliopole Anno Domini MDxxvii, fols. q i verso—ii recto.

[46] Pictorius (1563), pp. 78-80.

book of *Occult Philosophy* attributed to Henry Cornelius Agrippa. Wier, who had once been Agrippa's disciple and amanuensis, in a controversial writing against Leo Suavius accused him of having used "a jejune writing of Georgius Pictorius concerning sublunar matters."[47]

Cornelius Gemma (1535-1579), son of Gemma Frisius and professor of medicine at Louvain, made desperate but ineffectual efforts to concoct a method and synthesis which should unify past teachings in one universal philosophy, combine inferiors and celestials, nature, soul and intellect, numbers, ideas and external objects. His three tomes of the art cyclognomic,[48] which was somewhat on the order of the Lullian art, so attempted to fuse the doctrine of Hippocrates, Plato, Galen and Aristotle by one circular and catholic method. It indulged in many charts and groups of three—a sacred number upon which it laid great stress—in diagrams of the sky, and spherical triangles. It emphasized the analogy of the external senses to the internal faculties, the ascent and descent of the soul. It sought suggestions as to method from the philosophy of Plato and Zoroaster, which it recognized was "utterly confused and hitherto undigested."[49] So far as this first work is concerned, Cornelius Gemma might seem to belong in our next chapter on Mystic Philosophy, but he wrote another work which seems to justify treating him here, although it might be taken up separately in our chapter on Divination.

A few years later Cornelius somewhat narrowed his field and scope to divine characters, marks or features of nature,[50] and to a cosmocritical art which was to scrutinize not only the occult virtues and causes of bodies and singular affections, but also the critical mutations of things which occur in the triple world, and

[47] *Adversus Leonis Suavii calumnias*, 1583, p. 892: bound with Wier's *De lamiis*, BM 719.i.3.(2.).

[48] Cornelius Gemma, *De arte cyclognomica tomi III doctrinam ordinum universam unaque philosophiam Hippocratis Platonis Galeni et Aristotelis in unius communissimae ac circularis methodi speciem referentes*, Antwerp, 1569. Copy used: BM 8532.e.18.

[49] *Ibid.*, p. 155.

[50] Cornelius Gemma, *De naturae divinis characterismis seu raris et admirandis spectaculis causis indiciis proprietatibus rerum in partibus singulis universi libri II*, Antwerpiae, 1575. Copy used: BM 1135.b.3.

The dedication is dated at Louvain, August 9, 1574.

more especially was to forecast from those events which are divinely proffered contrary to the usual run of nature, such as prodigies, monsters and dreams.[51] Cornelius felt that he was the first to develop this particular field, although he recognized that his treatise belonged in the same general category as that of Fracastoro on the sympathy and antipathy of things, that of Fernel on the hidden causes of things, that of Levinus Lemnius on occult miracles of nature, that of Pomponazzi on incantations, and that of Peucer on divinations. It was true that there had been previous collections of monsters or prodigies, but they lacked system and set forth no regular method of predicting from these. The new star of 1572 had inspired Cornelius to undertake this task and he thanks his God for letting him live in an age to see that dazzling phenomenon.[52]

Cornelius treats of the species of divinity diffused throughout the world, of ideas and celestial rays, of the intricate form of mixture and proportions which produces occult virtues, of microcosm and macrocosm, of the sacred science of true magic, and of the order of relationship and similitude which is the bond of the universe. He cites such authorities as Mercurius Trismegistus and Proclus *De magia et sacrificio*. He concludes that there is one art of curing bodies, souls and the entire state, that meteors in the universe are like diseases in man, and that a single method applies to signs in the air of storm or tranquillity, to signs in the body of health or illness, to signs of war and peace in the state. The significance of numbers is stressed. Charts are employed for ten pages to show the differences between prodigies. But God is said often to act beyond the order of inferior nature, and the vanity of astrology and other arts of divination is proclaimed. As from some defect in the blood of the mother the spirits of her body paint some enormous appetites in the foetus, or it is affected by the mother's imaginative faculty, so vicious concepts pass from human lust to the spirit of the universe, which imprints corresponding characters upon the elements and through them on the state and politics.

[51] See the Operis argumenta on the verso of the title page.

[52] *Ibid.*, pp. 26-28.

Although Cornelius has attacked the vanity of astrology, he defends astrological medicine and hints that the disappearance of ancient diseases and coming of new maladies are caused by the stars and especially by their conjunctions.[53]

From the universal cataclysm and confusion after the tower of Babel were born such beings as fauns, satyrs, androgyni, "sciopodes" (i.e. skiapodes), cyclopes, centaurs, pygmies, giants, headless men, dog-headed men and cannibals. Such freaks are found not merely in the newly discovered islands but in Europe. Physicians attribute them to the influence of the stars and to illicit intercourse or an abnormal quality or proportion of the semen. But Gemma would adduce more potent causes in our sins and the harmony of nature with the sky and the divine.[54] He gives many pictures of monstrous births.[55] Incidentally he accepts the notion that the corpse of the victim bleeds in the presence of the murderer, but denies operative force to words and characters.[56]

The work of Cornelius flounders about without evincing a clear plan or seeming to make any marked progress. He discusses prodigies of dreams, affirms that the new star of 1572 was not a comet but a new divine creation, discusses comets a while and suggests that they be located in a third ethereal orb which is neither wholly celestial nor elementary, below the moon but above the meteors of the air. He would put the Milky Way in the same place. Presently, influenced perhaps by Pomponazzi's *De incantationibus,* he asserts that seers and workers of incredible things and rulers of the elements are produced naturally by certain genitures, although they may be unjustly suspected of necromancy and pacts with demons. After further discussion of astrology and interpretation of dreams, and the importance of the relation of active to passive, he questions how prodigies of the first degree which proceed from the occult force in matter are to be distinguished from others. He also treats of the marks of demons and of divine miracles.

[53] *Ibid.,* pp. 72-74.
[54] *Ibid.,* pp. 75-76.
[55] *Ibid.,* pp. 84-96. At pp. 98-102 are figures of stones, worms and other objects found inside human beings.
[56] *Ibid.,* pp. 78-79.

We then turn to historical examples of the cosmocritical art.[57] Before the German war in 1546 they say that a child was born in Franconia with a knife stuck in its belly, a clear sign of intestinal wars. In a town of the Norican Alps was born a child with horns whose cries had been heard for fourteen days before. Civil wars and countless deaths followed. In Saxony in the time of Luther a child was born with bovine feet, four eyes, the mouth and nose of a calf, a monk's hood, a priest's tonsure, and its arms and legs full of fissures.[58] At the end of the first book is a letter to the pious reader of eight unnumbered pages in which Gemma warns him to accept Platonism with caution, protests his own attachment to the Catholic church, and explains away his citations of Proclus, Iamblichus and Hermes Trismegistus. An approval of the work by the censor follows.

A second book with a fresh pagination is in part repetitious. Again the defects and merits of astrology are aired; again the star of 1572 is discussed; again rare portents and divine prodigies are given, which in this case preceded late events in France and Belgium. Medical matter is added concerning epidemics and pestilential fevers and a girl of Louvain with an abscess who excreted a live eel. We must say in conclusion that Cornelius completely failed to attain the system and regular method at which he aimed. His book is a confused hodge podge, put together from many sources. Some of the odd big words, like *characterismus*[59] and *cyclognomic,* may be of his devising, but cosmocritical was very likely suggested by the earlier *Cosmotheoria* of Fernel.

Benedictus Pererius (Benito Pereyra or Bento Pereira), a Jesuit of Valencia (1535-1610), produced two works in the fields of magic and science which had great currency. His book on the common principles of all natural things, with especial refer-

[57] *Ibid.,* I, 8, p. 166, "Quo totius artis cosmocriticae praxia et ratio per exempla perque epilogismos historicos confirmatur."

[58] *Ibid.,* pp. 174-75.

[59] Gemma continued to use this word in his work on the comet of 1577, printed at Antwerp, 1578, Plantin, *De prodigiosa specie naturaque cometae.* . . . The opening chapter is, "De praesentis aetatis characterismo. . . ." Copy used: BN V.21081.

ence to the *Physics* of Aristotle, was first issued at Rome in 1562,[60] then in 1576, at Paris in 1579, at Lyons, Paris, and Rome in 1585, at Venice in 1586, at Lyons in 1588, at Paris in 1589, at Ingolstadt in 1590, at Venice in 1591, at Cologne in 1595, 1601, 1603 and 1609, and at Venice in 1609. Presumably it was used as a text in Jesuit schools in teaching the *Physics* and natural philosophy of Aristotle. Its fifteen books deal with philosophy, natural philosophy, physics, the varying opinions of the ancient philosophers concerning natural principles, matter and privation, form, nature, causes, fortune, chance and contingency, quantity, place, time, eternity and *aevum,* the nature of motion, the variety and chief divisions of motion, and of the eternity of motion and the universe. The other work was in three books dealing respectively with magic, observance of dreams, and divination by astrology.[61] It was dedicated to Camillus Gaetanus, patriarch of Alexandria, and was printed at Ingolstadt and Venice in 1591, at Lyons and Venice in 1592, at Cologne in 1598, Lyons in 1602 and 1603, Cologne in 1612 and Paris in 1616. It was being read as late as 1661 and 1674 when there were editions of an English translation.

Pererius admits the existence of natural magic, which is the noblest part of physical science, medicine and mathematics. Men skilled in knowledge of nature can work great wonders by it. But

[60] Benedictus Pererius, *De communibus omnium rerum naturalium principiis et affectionibus libri quindecim qui plurimum conferunt ad eos octo libros Aristotelis qui de Physico auditu inscribuntur intelligendos,* Romae, Fran. Zanettus et Barthol. Tosius, 1562. I have used an edition of Cologne 1595 in the Columbia University library. In it the title is a little longer, inserting the words, "non tantum" after "conferunt" and "sed etiam multos alios difficilimos Aristotelis locos" between "inscribuntur" and "intelligendos," but omitting "Aristotelis" after "libros."

[61] The order of wording the title varies in different editions. For example, Col 156.4 P414 is: *Benedicti Pererii Valentini e societate Iesu Adversus fallaces & superstitiosas artes, id est, De magia, de observatione somniorum, et de divinatione astrologica.* Libri tres. Venetiis, MDXCII. Apud Ioan. Baptistam Ciottum, Senensem. Sub signo Minervae. But Col 156. 4 R2831 is: *De magia, de observatione somniorum, et de divinatione astrologica libri tres Adversus fallaces et superstitiosas artes. Auctore Benedicto Pererio Valentino societatis Iesu. . .* 1598, Coloniae Agrippinae, Apud Ioannem Gymnicum sub Monocerote. . . .

wicked or ignorant men learn even natural magic only from demons. "For scarcely any mortal or certainly very few indeed, and those men of the keenest genius who have employed diligent observation for a long time, can attain to such natural magic."[62] On the other hand, Pererius rejects the attempt of Peter of Abano, Cardan, and Pomponazzi in his book *De incantationibus* to reduce all works of magic to natural causes and to exclude any influence of demons. While Pererius admits the validity of natural magic, he denies any validity to either astronomical magic which employs astronomical images or to cabalistical magic. He also denies that souls of the dead can really be raised by necromancy.

One of his longest chapters is that on alchemy.[63] After quoting such authorities against and in favor of transmutation as Avicenna, Averroes, Aquinas, Aegidius, Peter of Abano, Cardan, and as Albertus Magnus, Janus Lacinius, and Antonius Mirandulanus, he states his own opinion. It is that there is no philosophical argument which is decisive against transmutation, since animals are produced by incubators, while drugs and many other things are made artificially. But the failure of the alchemists to succeed is against them and leads to such evils as poverty, counterfeiting, and harmful medicines. Even natural magic may with some reason be forbidden in the state, since its occult character readily lends it to abuse.

In his second book on dreams Pererius holds that many are vain and idle, but many also true. Otherwise the most famous medical men would not observe the dreams of their patients so subtly and curiously. Nor would physiologists labor at determining their causes, force and significations. And history and holy Scripture would be mendacious, which have given so many instances of dreams fulfilled. Similarly it is licit for a Christian to observe certain dreams but not others. Those signifying ills of body or mind are usefully examined by physicians. In the case of dreams which repeatedly trouble us, it is well to seek the

[62] *Ibid.*, I, 3, closing sentence.

[63] *Ibid.*, I, 12.

cause and try to remove it. Holy men have done this in times past, for we read in Cassian (*Collatio* 22) that the old masters and rectors of the monks were skilled in investigating the causes of certain dreams. From some dreams one may get inspiration or glean information towards taking future action or acquiring the speculative sciences. In the case of other dreams we should sedulously consider whether they are from God or the demon. Those which incite to lust are probably from the evil one, while those which instigate to alms, celibacy and taking religious vows should be carefully weighed as possible divine messages. But Pererius would reject as superstitious and worse than astrology any art of interpreting dreams in which all were included without distinction and interpreted by fixed rules.

Yet his third book seems more uncompromisingly hostile to astrology than the second was to the interpretation of dreams. Noting that many readers are deterred by the prolixity of Pico della Mirandola's disputations against astrology, Pererius aims to state the case more briefly. He argues that the art is contrary to the Christian religion, that astrologers do not understand the heavens, that their rules are unreasonable, that the stars are neither signs nor causes of future events, and that the realization of certain predictions is to be assigned rather to demon aid, human shrewdness and other causes. This sweeping indictment is doubtless framed primarily against the casting of nativities and other prediction of human affairs, but it would seem not to leave much room for astrological medicine or for weather prediction. The argumentation is largely a repetition from the classics, church fathers and Pico, without hardly entering the field of natural science proper, much less attempting to meet the astrologers on their own ground or to win them over by a sympathetic comprehension and rebuttal of their positions. Writers like Albumasar and Peter of Abano are openly censured, but the favoring attitude to prediction from the stars of Aquinas and Albertus Magnus is veiled in a discreet silence. Pierre d'Ailly, however, is roundly condemned for his too friendly attitude towards astrology. The same passage from Cajetan that Scevolini cited in arguing for astrology is interpreted by Pererius as an unqualified prohibition of the art. Pererius seems not to allude to the recent bull of Sixtus V of January 5, 1586, against judicial astrology, although his own attitude is similar and he has a chapter against astrologers' predicting who will be the next pope.

The earlier work of Pererius on nature had been more noncommital, or even by implication tacitly favorable, towards astrology. It said that Aristotle proved that the matter of the sky differed from the matter of sublunar things, and, at least on philosophical grounds, seemed not averse to his doctrine of the eternity of the universe. As one cause of monsters it listed the aspect or constellation. It represented St. Thomas as affirming in many places that something can happen in nature by accident and chance with respect to the sky, the implication of course being that ordinarily things happen of necessity from the stars as causes.[64] But the earlier work was composed before the bull of Sixtus V.

Bearing some relation to the science of physiognomy but marked by an original turn of mind was the *Examination of Human Aptitudes for the Sciences* of Juan de Dios Huarte Navarro. It was addressed to Philip II and published at Pamplona in 1578 in Spanish.[65] It was thereafter often reprinted and was translated into other languages including Latin. The author maintained that much reading and the best masters would not make a person proficient in a study for which he had no natural aptitude. He traced all variations of human genius to the three primary qualities, hot, moist and dry. He contended that eloquence and elegance in speaking could not exist in men of great understanding, and that the theory of theology pertained to the intelligence but preaching to the imaginative faculty. Legal theory, on the other hand, he associated with memory, advocacy and judging with intelligence, and governing a state with imagination. The theory of medicine was partly a matter of memory and partly of intelligence, the practice of medicine a matter of imag-

[64] *De communibus omnium rerum naturalium principiis,* Cologne, 1595, pp. 300, 849, 529, 512.

[65] Huarte Navarro, *Examen de ingenios para las sciencias . . . ,* Pamplona, 1578. Copy used: BM 528.e.27.

ination. Huarte Navarro further discussed how fathers could generate and rear intelligent and talented children.

The brief treatise of Caesar Aevolus or Cesare Evoli of Naples on the causes of antipathy and sympathy between things in nature[66] is of an elementary character and adds little or nothing to previous discussions of the subject. After reviewing the opinions of the ancients as to the cause of antipathy and sympathy—they having variously suggested God, ideas, the intelligences, the stars, matter, form, composition and qualities—and adducing arguments against these suggestions, Aevolus declares them due to contrary qualities in natural bodies which may be both from the stars and from the qualities of the elements. He chiefly stresses celestial influence, however, and distinguishes causes of sympathy and antipathy for each planet. Again it may be noted that this treatise was printed in 1580 before the bull of Sixtus V, which, however, it would not seem to infringe.

In 1581 the question of magic and science was up again for debate at the Catholic university of Ingolstadt. One of the professors, Matthias Mairhofer, who was also a member of the Society of Jesus, proposed some 273 theses, and the respondents were two "most learned bachelors of philosophy," brother Michael Mayer of the imperial monastery and Philip Baumgartner. These theses were printed under the title, "A philosophical disputation concerning the principles of discerning true and more recondite philosophy from infamous and superstitious magic."[67] The theses were divided under the following captions:

1-25 Concerning natural magic
26-81 Of causes and their conditions
82-131 Natural causes are distributed under certain heads
132-158 Of the imagination
159-187 Of figure, words, and local motion
188-202 Of the antipathy and sympathy of things
203-273 Of intentional causes and effects.

[66] Caesar Aevolus Neapolitanus, *De causis antipathiae et sympathiae rerum naturalium,* Venice, 1580, 4to minori, 25 fols. Copy used: BM 8705.b.10.

[67] *De principiis discernendi philosophiam veram reconditioremque a magia infami ac superstitiosa disputatio philosophica,* Ingolstadt, 1581, 4to. Copy used: BM 719.g.23.

Natural magic is the application of true and natural causes to produce rare and unusual effects by methods neither superstitious nor diabolical. It is subordinate to natural philosophy but is not the same thing. Although all natural science might be called magic, the name natural magic is in fact applied only to what resembles diabolical magic in the effects produced and which is more highly regarded by the common run of men than other sciences. Originally the Persian word for wisdom, as men fell off into judicial astrology and worse superstitions, it became confused with sorcery, *goetia* and infamous magic worked by invocation of demons.

After this rather conventional, yet fairly acceptable, delineation of natural magic, our theses turn to the topic of causation. Mairhofer accepts only the four Aristotelian causes, material, formal, efficient and final, and maintains the old categories of form and matter, substance and accident. Beyond a certain distance an efficient cause cannot affect its material, and within that distance its effect is not equal but greatest at that particular distance which best conforms to the nature of both. The intervening space must be full and aptly disposed to receive the virtue of the agent.

Having set up this standard for physical action, Mairhofer discusses criteria of credibility. When anything is accepted as a certain or probable cause by prudent and circumspect men who are not misled by their emotions or by devotion to suspect arts but have knowledge and experience in natural science, the same should be accepted by less prudent and expert persons, or at least they should not deny that it is a cause. On the other hand, a thing should not be accepted as a cause, if, when compared with other known causes, it involves a mode of application too discrepant from them or suggestive of voluntary rather than physical action. Nor should it be accepted as a cause if it fails to work at another time with like conditions prevalent. Nor if it lacks that affinity with its supposed effect which other causes commonly have. Nor when it never produces the effect by itself but only in conjunction with other factors which might be the true cause.

Miracles are effects which the doctors of the church regard as beyond the powers of natural causes. Some of the ancient philosophers and more recently Pomponazzi have tried to explain them naturally as the outcome of occult virtue impressed on things and men by the action of the stars. But Mairhofer rejects this explanation and also that of Avicenna that the human imagination by the influence of the stars acquires the power to work wonders such as Catholic doctors deem miraculous. Indeed Mairhofer denies any operative force to imagination or figure and characters or voices and words. He censures Peter of Abano for favoring the use of characters in the 156th Differentia of his *Conciliator*. The wonders seemingly effected by such methods are really the work of demons, of diabolical rather than natural magic. Certain alchemists who employ astrological images are guilty of such evil magic.

Mairhofer admits that there is great virtue in the stars and in many inferior objects. But he holds that not all the occult virtues attributed to plants and stones are true. As examples he mentions the herb at whose touch, according to Pliny, wedges fly out of trees, doors open, swamps and rivers dry up, and the assertion of Albertus Magnus that certain stones have power to fascinate, divine the future, insure chastity, and transform one thing into another. Similarly he grants that no one can deny entirely the existence of sympathy and antipathy between things. He accepts such antipathies for the lion and cock, elephant and mouse, bull and fig, snake and ash-tree, man and the hyena, the lamb and wolf, eagle and other birds, and such sympathies between man and the dolphin, the viper and murena, snake and eel, crocodile and golden-crested wren, naphtha and fire, heliotrope and sun, elm and poplar, myrrh and pumice stone. But some supposed sympathies and antipathies are false, such as that men by antipathy with the stars can calm storms, tame wild beasts, produce gold from the vilest substances in short order, or find hidden treasure. This wholesome scepticism is extended to a practice generally accepted at that time, namely, weapon ointment which Mairhofer holds operates at too great a distance to be a natural cause. So do suspensions in hidden places to cure remote patients.

There are three modes of magical illusion. The spectators may be deceived by "indisposition of the object according to place and site," or by "indisposition of the medium, especially by interruption of its continuity, condensation, figuration, mixture of exhalations, or undue illumination." Human art can induce error by these two methods. But the third method, where a phantastic body is formed, is possible only for demons. Mairhofer seems to overlook the action of drugs. Even the powers of the demons are restricted to the virtue of moving and applying active to passive; they cannot produce anything immediately (i.e. create).

Turning from magical operations and illusions to divination of the future, Mairhofer allows weather prediction, medical prognostication, astronomical forecast of the future positions of the heavenly bodies, and any inference from previous experience. In such a practice as lot-casting God does not give signs of the future at human seeking unless the question is legitimate, not soiled with sin or superstition, and neither absurd nor idle. Of natural divination the two chief types are from dreams and from the stars. Joseph and Daniel interpreted dreams by special gift of God and may not be adduced as proving an art of divination from dreams. Mairhofer's discussion of dreams is weak and concludes that divination from dreams is never valid except when dreams can be judged to proceed from the *complexio* natural or contingent. Mairhofer has no doubt that the stars exert influence both on the rise of anything—and he raises no difficulty as between birth and conception—and during all its subsequent existence. But admission of this influence does not insure certain divination. However, he grants that,

> if the quality of the seed and parents is known beforehand, and their mode of life on which the quality of the seed depends not a little, one can predict something with some degree of probability, especially when the constellation is noteworthy according to the temperament of the quality, from the position of the stars at the moment of origin.

Human will is free, but even a man's voluntary acts may be

probably predicted, if one knows his natural inclination, because he ordinarily follows it. But one cannot predict what may happen to him from the application of another's will, on which his nativity and natural inclination have no influence.

As Mairhofer's science is still Aristotelian, so his attitude towards astrology and other occult arts varies little from that of Thomas Aquinas.

Giambatista Porta was born at Naples about 1535 or 1540 and, according to his own statement, first composed his book on natural magic at the early age of fifteen.[68] Pizzimenti who taught young Porta the classics claimed that he was really responsible for the work. It seems to have been first printed at Naples in 1558,[69] a year after the *Secrets* of Alessio of Piedmont, and then, with a royal privilege dated October 25, 1559 at Brussels and a brief undated dedication to Philip II, at Antwerp in 1561.[70] These early editions contained only four books which were increased to twenty in the expurgated and amplified edition of Naples, 1589.[71] Although Porta makes much use of the words magic and magician, his book is rather strictly limited to the natural variety and is more prosaic and less sensational than might be expected. This may have been partly because of deletions by the censors of which he complains in the preface to the edition of 1561.

The original edition in four books is quite evidently a continuation and almost entirely a mere repetition and compilation of the medieval books of secrets and experiments described in

[68] See his "Ad lectores praefatio" in the 1589 and subsequent editions. In the corresponding "Praefatio auctoris ad lectores" in the 1561 edition Porta says nothing of his age but talks of his "long labors."

[69] *Magiae naturalis sive de miraculis rerum naturalium libri iiii. Io. Baptista Porta Neapolitano auctore.* Neapoli apud Matthiam Cancer, MDLVIII, folio. Copy used: BM 7003.ee.17.

[70] *Magiae naturalis sive de miraculis rerum naturalium libri iiii. Io. Baptista Porta Neapolitano auctore,* Antverpiae ex officina Christophori Plantini, xxi Februarii, MDLXI. Copy used: BM 8560.aa.4.(2.). A small octavo of 98 unnumbered and 135 numbered leaves. The index merely reproduces that of the 1558 edition without altering the numbers of the pages.

[71] *Io. Bapt. Portae Neapolitani Magiae Naturalis libri xx ab ipso authore expurgati et superaucti,* Neapoli apud Horatium Salvianum, 1589. Copy used: BM 719.l.3.(2.).

chapters 63-65 of my second volume.[72] After the introductory first book, the second is devoted to various marvelous experiments and tricks from the transmutation of plants to secret modes of writing, from cosmetics to soporifics, from magic lamps to love philters and fascination. The third book deals with chemical experiments, and the fourth with optical experiments and mirrors, closing with the time-honored themes of physical ligatures, the virtues of stones and of images carved on gems. The first book, which remained essentially the same in all editions, discussed the chief causes, manifest and occult, of natural marvels and marvelous artificial operations: the elements and their qualities, forms, celestial influence, sympathy and antipathy, likeness and occult virtue, with some attention to time and place, to methods of preparing and mixing compounds, and to the properties of fountains.

In the later enlarged edition some chapters were increased to books, recipes and processes were multiplied, while others were omitted or reduced in length. The original plan, which was fairly well knit together, now became less perceptible. More attention was given to agriculture, applied science and useful arts such as breeding hybrid animals, crossing plants, and preserving fruits. The resemblance becomes closer to Cardan's *De subtilitate* and *De rerum varietate*. This enlarged version is somewhat more sober and less magical and probably a fairer picture of Porta's mature attitude. Such items in the index of the original edition in four books as that "the stone aetites suspended retains and accelerates birth," that an amethyst worn about the neck frees from drunkenness, while a spider similarly suspended checks the rounds of quartan fever, are sought for in vain in the index of the 1589 edition in twenty books. How far these omissions are the result of more scientific experience on Porta's part or of the repressive policy of the Catholic reformation towards occult arts is difficult to distinguish. In the preface of 1589 Porta complains that some had called him a sorcerer (*magum veneficum*). A Frenchman who was, however, not a good Catholic but a Protes-

[72] T II, pp. 720-812.

tant heretic in his own book on *Oenomancia* had declared Porta's book fit to be burned, because he had included an unguent of witches. Porta asserts that he had taken it from the writings of praiseworthy theologians.

Porta further insists that he has never treated anything here or elsewhere, unless a natural explanation could be given for it. He has not merely exploited past writings and personally tested those statements which seemed incredible, but has also collected much new material by travel and correspondence. He appears to cite classical authors by preference, although such medievals as Avicenna and Albertus Magnus are also used. His scepticism exercises itself chiefly at the expense of the marvelous virtues attributed to the magnet by Marbod. Porta proved experimentally to his satisfaction that the presence of adamant did not counteract the attractive force of the magnet. He denies the remedies ascribed to it, that anointing it with garlic nullifies its power, or that goat's blood increases it.[73] This criticism is not found in the discussion of the magnet in the original version.[74]

Porta's credulity far outran his scepticism. He lists herbs and drugs which will make a man think himself a bird or fish. He tells how to induce different kinds of dreams by varying one's diet. He assures us that his sight was restored within a day by an empiric by means of a marvelous water, and this after the regular doctors had given him up. He believes in fascination and the use of amulets against it. He would wear a bezoar stone from the West Indies over the heart as a safeguard against the pest. He mentions potions that cure wounds and accepts the weapon ointment of Paracelsus. He credits the pseudo-Aristotle's tale of the poisoned maiden sent to Alexander.[75] He tells without a qualm a horrible story of a goose being cooked alive and eaten at the table of the Aragonese dynasty.[76] He does not doubt that

[73] *Magia naturalis*, Naples, 1589 or Leyden, 1651, VII, 48, 53, 54, 56.

[74] *Magia naturalis*, II, 21: pp. 89-90 in the edition of 1558, fols. 74r-75r in that of 1561.

[75] Edition of 1589, VIII, 2, 3, 4, 10, 12, 14.

[76] *Ibid.*, XIV, 9. In the edition of 1561, II, 13, fol. 56r-v, he gives equally repellent directions for its preparation, ending: ". . . ubi vero insania ferri et cespitare conspexeris antequam deficit cordi humidum remove convivis appone evulsis semper parti-

mountebanks and necromancers force women to remove their clothing and dance naked so long as a magic lamp burns. But he attributes the effect to the fat of hares burned in the lamp rather than to the magic characters with which the lamp is engraved.[77] He repeats without criticism the legend that Ptolemy had a mirror or lens in which he could see ships six hundred miles distant.[78] He believes in the generation of animals from putrefaction and in the barnacle geese.[79]

Porta makes a close connection between experiments and natural magic: indeed, the two expressions are almost synonymous for him. He still employs the word *experimentum* as it was used in Pliny's *Natural History* and during the middle ages. There are medical experiments in the sense of recipes.[80] The eighteenth book is given over to static experiments like those of Nicholas of Cusa; the nineteenth book, to pneumatic experiments like those of Hero of Alexandria. Elsewhere there are "experiments of hunting," and such as to change the color of a dog or to prevent a dog from barking.[81] Or we are offered mechanical experiments, of which the chief is a flying dragon.[82] The last book is described as "A Chaos in which are contained experiments which do not fall under any of the previous classes," and is partly the result of Porta's finding it necessary, as he explains in the Prooemium to this particular book, to finish his work sooner than he had expected and not describe all experiments contained in the natural sciences, as he had at first intended.

It would seem probable that Francis Bacon owed something to Porta's work on *Natural Magic*. The recommendation which

---

bus vociferantem ut fere prius commestatus quam mortuus videatur." Reading such details inclines one to regret that the Inquisition did not substitute Porta for Bruno at the stake.

A much humaner suggestion how to preserve the fat humidity in cooking geese is offered in a medieval manuscript in a work ascribed to Alfarabi, namely, to cook them with green wood, never with dry. BN 7156, 13-14th century, fol. 47v, col. 1-2.

[77] Edition of 1651, XX, 8.

[78] *Ibid.* XVII, 11.

[79] *Ibid.*, II, 3.

[80] The title of Book VIII is given in the preliminary table of contents as "De portentosis medelis," in the text itself as "Experimenta continet medica."

[81] *Ibid.*, XV, 11.

[82] *Ibid.*, XX, 10. It corresponds to the first part only of II, 14, "De mechanicis quibusdam experimentis," in the editions of 1558 and 1561.

Porta makes in planning an instrument for hearing at a distance, to consider carefully the ears of all animals with keen hearing on the one hand and of those with defective hearing on the other, is quite in the Baconian manner.[83]

In his *Phytognomonica*[84] of 1588 Porta especially developed the doctrine of signatures by which the occult virtues of plants—and other things—could be recognized from their external appearance. He also was concerned to emphasize various secrets and similitudes in nature. First pointing out the resemblance between a plant and its parts and man and the human members, he presently affirmed that the science of nativities and the art of interpreting dreams were based on likeness. Plants which resemble parts of animals have similar virtues. By their likeness to human members they indicate what diseases they will heal. The difference of sex in plants was also important to note. In their movement, color and figure, plants are associated with different stars, metals and gems, and share their respective virtues. Each part of the world produces flora and fauna according to the qualities of its sky and earth. Plants and animals therefore alter their character when moved to another place. Porta distinguishes the virtues of aquatic and amphibious plants and animals, of those found in different zones, in mountains and plains, in hollows and hills, wild and cultivated. Plants with similar leaves possess like virtues, as do plants with similar odors. Plants of yellow color purge of bile. Those of black color and likewise black animals generate melancholy and the worst diseases and are harbingers of death. Milky plants are good for the milk; bony plants heal the bones; animals with big ears are remedial for deafness; digitated and articulated herbs are good for the fingers and gout. Parts of plants shaped like a scorpion heal its bite. Plants re-

[83] *Ibid.*, XX, 5.

[84] *Phytognomonica Io. Baptistae Portae Neap. octo libris contenta in quibus nova facillimaque affertur methodus qua plantarum animalium metallorum rerum denique omnium ex prima extimae faciei inspectione quivis abditas vires assequatur. Accedunt ad haec confirmanda infinita propemodum selectiora secreta summo labore temporis dispendio et impensarum iactura vestigata explorataque.* Cum privilegio Neapoli apud Horatium Salvianum, 1588, folio. Copy used: BM 719.l.3.(1.).

sembling flies and butterflies aid fecundity. Long-lived trees promote longevity. Parasitic plants help one to keep thin. Plants and animals that readily shed their skins cure skin diseases. Perforated plants are good for fistula and loquacious animals cure colic. The most beautiful plants and animals aid in the generating of beautiful offspring. Herbs growing in the clefts of rocks are suited to break the stone in human bodies. Plants that grow in the summer are beneficial for summer complaints. Those that flower often or long cure recurrent diseases. Vigilant animals make man wakeful, and eating sleepy animals is a soporific. Animals that dream make men dream, and plants also have influence on dreams. Beasts who eat poisonous herbs are antidotes for those poisons. Plants that rise against the sky protect from thunderbolts. Besides many more dicta of this sort, Porta notes remedies employed by animals, antipathies between plants and animals, and assures us that wherever there is any ill, in that place there also grows a remedy for it.

Giordano Bruno, although much belauded by recent historians as a martyr of science and free thought, in his earlier career, before the shades of the prison house of the Inquisition closed upon him, appears as an indiscreet intellectual vagabond and *mauvais enfant* who, like Servetus, had a faculty for getting into trouble wherever he went. An excommunicated member of the clergy and a religious fugitive from Italy, he came to Geneva, where he was soon imprisoned and forced to apologize for having printed an attack upon La Faye, the lecturer in philosophy there and an M.D. from Padua, in which Bruno had pointed out twenty errors perpetrated by him in a single lecture.[85] Later report exaggerated these to one hundred.[86] At Paris on May 28-29, 1586, he was said to have orated publicly against the errors of Aristotle, to have challenged anyone to answer, and then to have cried even louder that the victory was won. But when a young lawyer answered him and dared Bruno in turn to reply, he remained silent. The students present, however, would not let him leave until he had

[85] Vincenzo Spampanato, *Documenti della vita di Giordano Bruno*, Firenze, 1933, pp. 33-35.

[86] *Ibid.*, p. 44.

promised to answer on the morrow, but he failed to appear.[87] While the report of this encounter should perhaps be discounted as from a hostile source, it must be said that such writings and orations by Bruno as have been preserved from this period give the impression that he was superficial, boastful and too inclined to criticize others.[88]

Bruno's works fall partly within the scope of the present chapter and partly within that of the succeeding chapter. He continued the tradition of interest and belief in alchemy, astrology, magic and the cabala already manifested by men like Pico della Mirandola—although Pico had ended by attacking astrology—Trithemius, Paracelsus, Agrippa of Nettesheim, and Cardan. Bruno was familiar with and much influenced by their writings. He especially esteemed the works attributed to Raymond Lull, for he accepted the alchemical and other spurious works ascribed to Lull as genuine.[89] For Bruno's attitude towards natural magic we may turn especially to his treatises upon magic and upon the principles of things or of nature.[90] He was impressed by natural marvels and believed in the existence of occult qualities and more profound impressions in nature. Moreover, he held that the least thing in nature may work the greatest operations.[91] Like his medieval predecessors, he was convinced of the continuity of nature. That is to say, the external world is really all one continuous body in which no vacuum is possible. But mere body would be insensible, and according to Bruno body does not act directly on body, but all action is produced by quality, by form, and finally by soul.[92] He goes farther and affirms the existence of one spirit or sense diffused through the universe and found even

[87] *Ibid.*, p. 45.

[88] In his Valedictory Oration at Wittenberg he went to the opposite extreme, praising alike Albertus Magnus, Nicholas of Cusa, Copernicus, Paul III and Luther, and declaring Wittenberg superior to all other centers of learning.

[89] Felice Tocco, "Le Fonti Più Recenti della Filosofia del Bruno," *Rendiconti della Reale Accademia dei Lincei, Classe di scienze morali, storiche e filologiche,* Serie 5a, Vol. I, Roma, 1892, pp. 503-38, 584-622.

[90] These works remained in MSS until printed by Tocco and Vitelli in vol. III, Florence, 1891, of the modern edition of Bruno's Latin works: *Iordani Bruni Nolani Opera latine conscripta.*

[91] *Ibid.*, III, 407.

[92] *Ibid.*, III, 413-14.

in inanimate objects or in particles which are not animals in the sense of having particular or individual souls but are nevertheless animated by this world soul. It is this continuity and common sense of the universe which explains his statement—or repetition of Agrippa's statement—that the least thing in the world may work the greatest operations. Moreover, every soul and spirit has a certain continuity with this spirit of the universe, which explains why we can see distant objects without anything going out from the eye to them.[93] In his valedictory at Wittenberg Bruno spoke of each cause, principle and element contemplating itself in the universe and the universe in itself.[94]

Bruno would vary somewhat the familiar four elements. In addition to water, which he also called the abyss or styx, and earth, to which he gave the other names of atis and atom, he enumerated as the third, spirit or air or soul, and light rather than fire as the fourth and last. These elements are distinct and one cannot be transformed into the nature of another, but they readily concur and associate with one another.[95]

Bruno believed not only in a world soul but in various orders of invisible spiritual beings in the sense of demons. Besides the higher orders there are those which inhabit the bodies of men or of other animals, or plants, stones and minerals, including the spirits in mines.[96] He cites the Neo-Platonists Porphyry and Plotinus on the subject of spirits and holds it very probable that all diseases are evil demons.[97] Certain men have the gift of dominating over certain spirits of disease, as we see in the cure of scrofula by royal touch or the healing virtue of the spittle of a seventh son.[98] Presently Bruno enumerates eighteen bonds of demons and then five additional bonds.[99] Just as men ignorant of each other's language must communicate by signs, so we are able to communicate with demons only by figures, characters, seals, ceremonies and the like devices.[100] Bruno had printed an

[93] *Ibid.*, III, 408-9.
[94] *Opera*, Naples, 1879: I, i, 15.
[95] *Opera*, III, 417.
[96] *Ibid.*, III, 429, 431.
[97] *Ibid.*, III, 430, 432.
[98] *Ibid.*, III, 437-38.
[99] *Ibid.*, III, 435-54.
[100] *Ibid.*, III, 412.

Exposition of Thirty Seals,[101] which were mnemonic, but also an obscure work on the composition of images, signs, and ideas,[102] in which, however, he affirmed that images, seals and characters contributed to action as well as perception and signifying, and did so physically as well as mathematically and logically.[103] He professed to eschew magic images[104] but included some of the planets.

In magic Bruno expounds the following scale or ladder of interaction and influence between God and the inferior world. God acts upon the gods—who are presumably roughly equivalent to the Intelligences of Aristotle and medieval philosophy, although we may perhaps detect here Neo-Platonic influence—the gods upon the celestial bodies or stars, the stars on the demons, who are inhabitants of the stars—of which the earth is one—the demons act upon the elements, the elements act on compounds, compounds act upon sense, sense on soul, the soul on the whole animal. By magic the attempt is made to ascend this ladder in the opposite direction from animal to God.[105] This rather spiritual and transcendental characterization of magic does not agree any too well with a passage in the valedictory oration at Wittenberg in which agriculture, medicine, chemistry and "magic in all its species" are subordinated to "Physics" or natural science.[106]

Like Cardan, Bruno lists ten different meanings or varieties of magic,[107] but they are not the same ten as Cardan's. First is magic in the sense of wisdom; second, natural magic caused by active and passive qualities; third, sleight-of-hand and deceit; fourth, the relationship of sympathy and antipathy resulting from the soul or spirit in things; fifth, mathematical magic employing figures, characters, words, numbers, etc.; sixth, theurgy or invocation of demons; seventh, necromancy or invocation of

[101] G. Bruno, *Explicatio triginta sigillorum,* 1583 (?): copy used, BM c.37.c.17.(2.).

[102] *J. B. de imaginum signorum et idearum compositione ad omnia inventionum dispositionum et memoriae genera libri tres,* Francofurti, 1591. Copy used: BM c.37.c.14.(3.).

[103] *Ibid.,* I, 5, p. 7.

[104] *Ibid.,* III, p. 172.

[105] *Opera,* III, 401-2.

[106] *Opera,* Naples, 1879: I, i, 15.

[107] *Opera,* III (1891), 397 *et seq.*

the dead; eighth, maleficia or use of the parts of things to bind; ninth, divination; and last, vulgar witchcraft, of which Bruno had a very poor opinion. Bruno believed in the virtue of names and gestures.[108] He thought that the virtues of the seven planets had been noted by the ancient Chaldaeans[109] and that it had been experimentally verified that persons born under the influence of Venus were disposed to oratory, love and peace; those under Mercury, to deception, fraud and theft; those under Mars, to strife and hate.[110] Nor would he fail to note the mansions of the moon and like details of astrological technique.

It does not appear that the ecclesiastical authorities objected to those statements of Bruno which we have just reviewed or that will be mentioned in the next chapter. It was not for such beliefs as these that he had fled from Naples and Rome, been denounced at Venice, and finally was burned at Rome.[111] The reports that he owned a book full of conjurations, and had attributed the miracles of Christ to magic, were a different matter and were denied by him. Nor is it clear that advocacy of the Copernican system was charged against him. It is not mentioned in connection with the process of the inquisition against him in 1576, nor in the denunciation of him by Mocenigo at Venice in 1592. Except that on March 24, 1597, he was admonished to give up such idle notions of his as that of a plurality or infinity of worlds,[112] what counted most against him was his apostasy from his Order, his long association with heretics, and his questionable attitude as to the Incarnation and Trinity.[113] Of the eight propositions culled from his books which he was finally asked to abjure and which he refused to the end to recognize as heretical, only two are specified at all in the record as it has reached us, namely, the first, which is said to bear on the Novatian (*sic*) heresy, and the seventh, that the soul is in the body as a sailor is in a boat.[114] But his stubborn adherence to his positions and his

[108] *Ibid.*, pp. 560, 563.
[109] *Ibid.*, pp. 539-40.
[110] *Ibid.*, p. 542.
[111] For the latest and fullest information on these points see V. Spampanato, *Vita di Giordano Bruno con documenti editi e inediti*, Messina, 1921, and *Documenti della vita di Giordano Bruno*, Firenze, 1933.
[112] *Documenti*, p. 169.
[113] *Vita*, p. 242.
[114] *Documenti*, p. 182.

death at the stake in 1600 after eight long years of imprisonment glorified his thought and perpetuated his works and name to an extent that would be scarcely conceivable without the persecution and punishment to which he was subjected. And the Catholic church might never have been accused of putting Bruno to death for adherence to the Copernican theory, had it not in 1616 condemned that theory and later forced Galileo to disavow it.

A Tommaso da Ravenna[115] in 1593 dedicated and printed at Venice in Italian an *Idea del Giardino del Mondo,* containing "many marvelous secrets of nature."[116] Among the topics and questions discussed in the fifty-two chapters of this popularization of science and occult science were the virtues of stones and herbs, how to tell if the child will be male or female and how many children there will be, why women and children do not have beards, demons of the air, comets and their marvelous effects, the salamander's living in fire, the secret of holding one's hand in the fire without injury, a recipe for infernal fire revealed to Paracelsus by a demon who lived in the sphere of fire, remedies for the bewitched and impotent, signs of human complexions, and accounts of animals, diseases, the earth, planets, signs, and crystalline and empyrean heavens.

A Spanish example of the interest in such secrets and experiments is seen in the fourth treatise of the *Phisonomia y varios secretos de naturaleza* of Gerónimo Cortés of Valencia, first published in 1601, then in 1603, 1609, 1610, 1614, etc.[117] This fourth treatise, devoted to "secrets of nature and their marvelous effects," opens with the virtues of gems and stones, then turns to those of fountains, which are so wonderful that they could not be believed, had not such celebrated authors stated them. We then come to recipes: a secret to make seawater drinkable,

[115] He writes too late to attempt to identify him with Thomas Philologus or Gianotti Rangoni of Ravenna who flourished in the first half of the century, although works by the latter were printed in 1565, 1575 and 1577.

[116] Thomai (Thomaso) da Ravenna, fisico et academico innominato, *Idea del Giardino del Mondo ove oltre molti secreti maravigliosi di natura* . . ., Venetia, 1593, small 4to. Copy used: BM 43.d.31.(2.).

[117] The fourth treatise occupies fols. 29r-61v in the edition of Tarragona, 1609. Copy used: BM 7383.f.8.

others to preserve chastity, others against fleas, flies and mosquitoes, to shine shoes, prepare vinegar, squeeze an egg into a bottle, improve the memory, keep the hair black, make faces appear dead at night, kindle fire with water, write letters which are visible only when the paper is wet with water, and tell whether a woman is chaste. The resemblance to the medieval collections of marvelous experiments and secrets is evident. Astrology comes in, when, to keep nails and hair from growing too fast, it is recommended to cut them when the moon is waning and in the sign of Cancer, Pisces or Scorpio. Or to attain perfection in studies easily, they should be initiated while the moon is in friendly aspect with Mercury, and best of all when both planets are in the sign of Gemini or Virgo. Intermingled with these recipes are such other bits as Basil's and Ambrose's account of the halcyon birds. Many of the recipes are drawn from such previous writers as Albertus Magnus, Mizauld, Porta and Alessio of Piedmont.

In the second section of his *Dialogus Tripartitus,* first published at Venice in 1605,[118] Hyppolitus Obicius undertook to treat of all the sciences and arts thus far known including magic. The main interest of his survey covering over 150 pages is that, while some recent authors are mentioned, the division into departments of the field of knowledge and superstition remains, at the opening of the seventeenth century, almost the same as in the thirteenth. There are theology and metaphysics, arithmetic speculative and practical, geometry speculative and operative, optics or perspective with Alhazen and Witelo still the leading

[118] The British Museum has a copy of this edition. I have seen the work at Munich in the Staatsbibliothek in an edition of Mainz, 1619: *De nobilitate medici contra illius obtrectatores dialogus tripartitus in quo . . . comprobatur medicum iurisprudente esse nobilior. Postea de omnibus scientiis artibusque hactenus cognitis etiam magicis autore Hyppolito Obicio medico et philosopho Ferrariensi olim in patrio gymnasio simplicium medicamentorum publico lectore nunc Venetiis medicinam faciente.* Moguntiae. Ex officina typographica Ioannis Albini MDCXIX. The first section covers pages 1-130; the second, pp. 131-287. The third part, not specified on the title page, covers pp. 288-389 and is there entitled, Dialogus tertius in quo totius naturalis moralis ac rationalis philosophiae medicinae legumque summula traditur. A considerable part of it is devoted to a summary of the works of Aristotle.

authorities, although the explanations of Alhazen's text by Federicus Reinerius are noticed, while the contribution of Giovanni Baptista Porta to catoptric is mentioned. Next are listed scenographica, cosmography, geography, chorographia, topography, and hydrography, gnomics, architecture, astronomy, and astrology. The last is divided as of yore into nativities, interrogations, revolutions of years of the world, revolutions of nativities, and elections. The *Almagest* of Ptolemy is still considered the basis of all astronomy, although the *Sphere* of Sacrobosco and Peurbach's *Theory of the Planets* are easier to understand. Either the *Alfonsine Tables* or those of Copernicus called Prutenic and enlarged by Magini are recommended. Thus works of the thirteenth century still hold their own with those of the fifteenth and sixteenth. The same is true of astrology.

Of magic Obicius distinguishes three varieties: evil (*malefica*), superstitious, and natural. Under the first category come pyromancy, aeromancy, geomancy, hydromancy, captromancy, aruspicium, lecanomancy, capnomancy, necromancy, and praestigium. Under the seond are chiromancy, physiognomy, such geomancy as is not evil, augury, auspices, horospicium, sortilegium, nomantia, *ars notoria, ars Almadel,* the Pauline art, and the Cabala. All these are names of long standing. Of natural magic, chemistry (*Chimica ars*) is given as an example. Obicius believes that the magnet attracts iron by sympathy, and that poison kills by antipathy. For natural magic he cites Fracastoro's work on sympathy and antipathy, Fernel's *De abditis rerum causis,* Levinus *De occultis naturae miraculis,* and Wecker's *Secrets.* On the Cabala he cites Pico della Mirandola and Archangelus de Burgo Novo. Of recent astrological writers he uses Henricus Ranzovius and Franciscus Iunctinus. As a whole his survey seems drawn entirely from previous writers and to offer nothing new of his own. But that such a treatment could be written and enjoy a reprinting after a few years is not without significance. Indeed, its author was cited as late as 1688, when Mastrius de Meldula and Bonaventura Bellutus of the Minorite order, in the third volume of their review of the philosophy of Duns Scotus, noted that Hyppolitus Obicius in his defense of the truth of astrology held that the lines in the hand were caused by the stars and varied with the heavenly aspects, nay that by inspecting the palm one could determine a person's horoscope and nativity. If this were true, continue our authors, chiromancy would be a natural science and above suspicion, but it had been condemned outright by the bull of Sixtus V.[119] Indeed, we have just heard Obicius himself classify it as superstitious rather than natural.

A brief work in Italian by Pietro Passi in 1614 is largely devoted to rebuttal of the three arguments against natural magic put forward by Pedro Garcia in the fifteenth century in his refutation of the theses of Pico della Mirandola.[120] Furthermore the treatise of Passi is mainly a mass of citations and quotations. William of Auvergne from the thirteenth century is used a great deal, and Erastus from the sixteenth. The *De esse et essentia,* wrongly ascribed to Aquinas, is cited for the forced growth of a cucumber; Rasis and Giulio Camillo[121] for the artificial production of human beings; Albertus Magnus, Roger Bacon, Cardan, Porta, Alessio of Piedmont, and Girolamo Ruscelli for "secreti ludificatori," such as to make men appear headless or with the heads of asses. From the fourteenth century Henry of Hesse is cited as to whether the magnet receives its attractive virtue from the sky. Pietro Gregorio or Pierre Gregoire of Toulouse is authority that Gerardus Baccolidianius, imperial physician, had written concerning a girl born near Speyer in 1530 who was taken with a pain in the abdomen on Michaelmas in 1539 and

[119] *Philosophia ad mentem Scoti,* III, 535. The work by Obicius here referred to appears to be not the *Dialogus Tripartitus* but his *Iatroastronomicon,* printed at Vicenza in 1618, which contained an appendix in which writings of Julius Caesar Claudinus (who taught at Bologna from 1578 to 1618) against astrologers were refuted. See Karl Sudhoff, *Iatromathematiker vornehmlich im 15. und 16. Jahrhundert,* 1902, p. 75, and *Lindenius renovatus* which he cites.

[120] Pietro Passi, *Della magic' arte, overo della magia naturale, discorso nel quale si mostra che le meraviglie che si dicono di essa possono succedere in via naturale e che il Magho può lecitamente usarla,* Venetia, Violati, 1614, 16mo, 114 pp. Copy used: BM 719.e.39.(3.).

[121] *Ibid.,* p. 106, "Giulio Camillo nel suo Theatro delle materie": see Giulio Camillo (called Delmineo), *Tutte le opere,* Vinegia, 1552, 12mo.

went without food until 1540, after which she ate and drank again for three years.[122] The power of the kings of France to cure scrofula by their royal touch is affirmed, Passi informs us, by Bartolomeo Cassaneo,[123] Giovanni Feraldo,[124] and Giovanni de Selva,[125] but is denied by Antonio Bernardo Mirandolano in the twentieth book of his disputations, where he holds that not ten persons are cured out of ten thousand who are touched.

Bernardo further said that if Aristotle had seen kings cure diseases of this sort, he would have said that it happened in men's estimation but not in reality. This leads Passi to meet the argument against the existence of occult virtues that Aristotle does not mention them. One might reply that Aristotle limited himself to natural philosophy and did not go into natural magic. But Passi prefers to carry the war into the enemy's camp and charge that Aristotle did not even treat all parts of natural philosophy completely and that he made mistakes. Maimonides, the Academics, and cardinals d'Ailly, Bessarion and Nicholas of Cusa all made strictures upon him. He listed only eight heavenly spheres, whereas the ten curtains of the Tabernacle in the Bible show that there are ten. Regiomontanus discovered the truth (really of course medieval authors before him had maintained a ninth or a tenth sphere). Ptolemy corrected Aristotle as to the order of the planets. To Aristotle's explanation of springs as originating from air which putrefies in the caverns of the earth Passi prefers the view, which he attributes to Hebrew philosophers, that they come from the sea like veins from the liver. Aristotle held that there were no rainbows at night, but

[122] *Ibid.*, pp. 19-20. Passi first says that she was born in 1539, then that she was taken with the pain in the same year, 1530. Evidently one or the other is a misprint, while the whole story seems to require reconstruction as I have indicated. The work cited is Gerardus Bucoldianus, *De puella quae sine cibo et potu vitam transigit brevis narratio*, Paris, Stephanus, 1542.

[123] *Catalogo della Gloria del mondo*, V, 30: i.e. Barth. de Chasseneux, *Catalogus gloriae mundi* etc., first published at Lyons in 1526 by G. Regnault.

[124] *De iuribus et privilegiis regni Francorum:* i.e. Jean Ferrault, *Tractatus jura seu privilegia aliqua regni Franciae continens*, Paris, 1545. He also wrote *Insignia peculiaria christianissimi Francorum regni numero viginti*, Paris, 1521.

[125] *De beneficio*, II, qu. 22, col. 2. It was printed in *Tractatuum ex variis iuris interpretibus collectorum*, Lugduni, 1549, vol. 15.

Albertus Magnus, and later Pico and Amerigo Vespucci, corrected this. The notion of the eternity of the world was opposed by various ancients and refuted by Maimonides and Aquinas, while Scotus pointed out the incompatible contrariety of the reasoning employed in Aristotle's *De anima*.

The encyclopedia of John Henry Alsted, professor at the Protestant university of Herborn in Nassau, seems first to have appeared in 1620 in a briefer version in twenty-seven books[126] which I have not seen and which is not listed in the manuals of Brunet and Graesse or the catalogues of the British Museum and Bibliothèque Nationale. I have used the later and fuller editions of 1630[127] and 1649.[128] Alsted had laid the foundations for his encyclopedia by such earlier works as that in 1610 on the *Method of Forming Studies,*[129] or his four books of *Physical Harmony* in 1616 which included Mosaic Physics, the physics of the Hebrews, Peripatetic Physics, and Chemical Physics.[130]

Already too in a letter written in 1618[131] Alsted had described four columns of physical science, which much resembled those of Paracelsus. First was true chemistry, whose principle and the mother of all sublunar things was that water which contains in itself fire, these together sufficing for the generation of all things. "Avoid therefore in your travels," said Alsted to his

[126] *Cursus philosophici encyclopedia libris xxvii complectens universae philosophiae methodum serie praeceptorum regularum*, etc. 32 pp., 552 fols. 2210 cols, with maps, plates, cuts and diagrams, large 4to, Herborn, 1620. Listed in a sales catalogue of L'Art Ancien sometime in the 1920's with the number 3265. The books are divided as follows: 4 praecognita philosophica, 11 scientiae philosophie theorice, 5 prudentiae philosophie practice, and 7 artes philosophiae poetice.

[127] *Encyclopedia septem tomis distincta*, Herbornae Nassoviorum, 1630, folio, 2404 pp. and some 35 books. Copies used: BN Z.313-314 and BM 742.g.21.

[128] *Scientiarum omnium encyclopedia*, I-IV, Lugduni, Sumptibus I.A. Huguetan et M. A. Rauaud, 1649.

[129] *Joannis Henrici Alstedii Consiliarius academicus et scholasticus, id est Methodus formandorum studiorum . . . Accessit Consilium de copia rerum et verborum, id est, methodo disputandi de omni scibili*, Argentorati, sumptibus L. Zetzneri, 1610, 4to, 165 pp.

[130] *Physica harmonica quatuor libellis methodice proponens: I Physicam Mosaicam, II Physicam Hebraeorum, III Physicam Peripateticam, IV Physicam Chemicam*. Tertia cura J. H. Alstedii Herbornae Nassoviorum, 1616, 12mo.

[131] *Epistola iii Joannis Henrici Alstedii . . . ad nobiliss. et literatiss. iuvenem Josuam von der Tann.*

youthful correspondent, "impostors—I mean those who macerate and lacerate salt, vitriol, gold, vulgar mercury, and the like." The second pillar was the astrological concord of inferiors and superiors. Laying down the axiom that the seven planets were rulers of all bodies, Alsted argued that all fixed stars, herbs and animals should be reduced to seven classes, or no progress worth while could be made in philosophy. The third column was experience and that by hand and fire. The fourth was the physiognomy of all things and involved the doctrine of signatures in plants and animals. Thus for Alsted physical science seems largely a combination of magic—or at least, of alchemy, astrology and physiognomy—and experimental science.

Similarly in the *Encyclopedia* among thirty-seven disciplines are included magic, cabala, enigmatic writing, paradoxes, hieroglyphics, the Lullian art, polygraphy, sacred physics, theosophy and the philosophy of Solomon.[132] Or among twenty-four marvels of natural and mathematical magic are enumerated medical and metallic tinctures, perpetual motion, accelerating the growth of vegetables, arcane virtues in stones, plants and animals, gathering various animals in one place or dispelling them, long preservation or sudden corruption, marvelous fires and candles, marvelous waters, optical illusions and fallacies of colors, sympathies and antipathies, removal of fascination, polygraphy, steganography, tricks with mirrors, automata moved by the spirit of the world included in them, and magnetic operations.[133] The dependence of this classification on Porta and indirectly on medieval books of magic, secrets and experiments is evident.

Magic, in Alsted's definition, produces marvels by a secret method unknown to the vulgar and is either divining or operative, licit and philosophical or illicit and diabolical. Against diabolical magic lawful remedies are prophylactics or analeptics, while exorcisms and the use of the name of Jesus or sign of the cross are forbidden. Miracles are distinguished as of God, nature, art or the devil. Divination may be divine, diabolical, physical, vulgar or political, the last being Alsted's own addi-

[132] *Encyclopedia,* 1630, Book 35, pp. 2209-2394.

[133] *Ibid.,* pp. 2266-70.

tion to the four varieties of Peucer whom he cites. To work philosophical magic the operator must be pious and acquainted with nature, especially with the influences of the stars.

The sky is a body first in place, perfection and efficacy. Its matter is a fifth essence, distinct from the matter of sublunar bodies. The external form of the sky is a good angel. The internal form, which Scaliger, Zabarella and Piccolomini vainly deny, is the principle from which flow its qualities and operations. The heavens act on these inferiors by light, by motion, and by occult influence. They act immediately on all sublunar bodies, indirectly upon the soul of man. Thus Alsted maintains all the old hypotheses underlying astrology.[134] Later on he again discusses the way in which the stars act upon inferior objects, treating more particularly of the powers of the planets, fixed stars and signs of the zodiac, the essential and accidental dignities of the planets, the twelve houses, and how to draw up a horoscope.[135] He repeats the theory found in Peucer's work on divination that every five hundredth or seven hundredth year is fatal to states, or at least that they do not commonly endure longer. From Moses to Saul and from Ezra to Vespasian was about five centuries in either case. This was also the approximate duration of the power of Athens and Sparta, while Carthage and the Roman republic each lasted seven centuries. More than seven hundred years have elapsed since Charlemagne, and seven centuries since Otto III's institution of the electoral college will soon be run, so that it is no wonder that the Holy Roman Empire is hastening to its doom.[136]

Alsted accepts the possibility of the transmutation of metals and attributes great virtues to gems, though no greater than those of gold. As the sun is the chief planet, man the highest animal, wine the best product of vegetation, so gold holds first place in the mineral kingdom. Gems exert their virtues worn in rings, suspended about the neck, taken in drink, or reduced to shavings and filings, or resolved into their fifth essence. When they are said to produce moral effects, it should be understood,

[134] *Ibid.,* XIII, ii, 1-2; pp. 689-90.
[135] *Ibid.,* XVII, iv; pp. 1073-85.
[136] *Ibid.,* XXIII, 12.

just as in the case of the stars, that they merely incline the soul of man by their action on the humors and spirits of his body.[137]

Even the barnacle geese are still credited by Alsted and he repeats from the *Genial Days* the story of plants with leaves of pure gold. He treats of sensitive plants under the name zoophytes, classing them as animals on the ground that they possess the sensitive and not merely the vegetative soul. In such respects Alsted shows little or no advance on the calibre, scientific, superstitious or magical, of earlier writers. His chief additions to knowledge have to do with the New World, and even they are apt to be quaint and hazy. He repeats Ptolemy's seven climes, but affirms that recent navigation has demonstrated the existence of the Antipodes against the church fathers, in which connection he repeats the dubious story of the condemnation of Virgilius for believing in the Antipodes.[138] Asking whether the new world is larger than the old, he answers in the affirmative, if the formerly unknown Arctic and Antarctic continents are added to the new world. In North America he names twelve chief islands, five peninsulas, and fifteen continents. These last comprise Virginia, Nova Francia, Canada, Estotilandia in the northeast opposite Frisia (Iceland) under the auspices of whose king it was discovered in 1390 by Antonio Zeno, a patrician of Venice and was thus the first of all the lands of this new world to be discovered. Yet Alsted has earlier given Columbus credit for the first voyage to America. Other "continents" of North America are Fondura (Honduras), Nicaragua, New Spain or Mexico, New Granada, home of the seven cities, the kingdom of Quivira or what Drake called New England, Alaska or the kingdom of Anian, Florida, Canibas and Tolm, the fifteenth continent not being named.[139]

[137] *Ibid.*, p. 721.

[138] It was to be repeated in the French encyclopedia, and I have treated of it at some length in my article, "L'Encyclopédie and the History of Science," *Isis*, VI (1924), pp. 361-86; see note 30 at pp. 369-70.

[139] Geography occupies Book XVII at pp. 1106-69, the divisions of North America being listed at p. 1144.

CHAPTER XLIV

MYSTIC PHILOSOPHY: WORDS AND NUMBERS

Nostra philosophia coelestis est non terrena.
—TRITHEMIUS

It is doubtful if works of theosophy, occult philosophy and mystical knowledge, such as the *Pimander* of Hermes Trismegistus, the so-called *Theology* of Aristotle, the *Chaldean Oracles*, and the Hebrew Cabala bear so close a relation to the history of magic as the latter does to the history of experimental science. Certainly few persons would regard them as closely connected with the latter. Yet the name of Hermes cannot be disassociated from the history of chemistry, nor that of Aristotle from the course of biological science and natural philosophy, while Chaldea was the scene of the childhood of astronomy as well as of astrology. We have therefore paid some attention to such works and topics in our previous volumes and may here give a brief account of their continued influence in the sixteenth century, when their grandiose, oracular and enigmatic style was not infrequently carried over into books on other subjects such as Paracelsan treatises of alchemy and medicine. To this we add some notice of treatises on the mystic power of words and the mystic significance of numbers, cognate themes which seem to bear somewhat more closely upon the history of magic and science. If our account seems cursory, this is partly because such works are so mystical and cloudy that a definite exposition of their contents is difficult, and that one does not care to stand for long on the quicksands of their reveries.

The activity of Jacques Lefèvre d'Étaples, of Reuchlin, and of Trithemius continued from the fifteenth into the sixteenth century. In 1505 the first-named edited at Paris a recent work entitled, *The Basin of Hermes,* by Lodovico Lazzarelli[1] together with the *Pimander* and *Asclepius* of Hermes Trismegistus. Lazzarelli was also the author of a work on alchemy, thus illustrating the fact that theosophy and chemistry have been historically associated. The *Crater Hermetis* was reprinted at Paris in 1522, and in 1557 in French translation, attesting the popularity then of such mystical philosophy. Kristeller[2] has recently shown that Lazzarelli became a disciple of the wandering magician or prophet, Giovanni Mercurio, whose sensational appearance at Lyons is recorded by Trithemius and Surius.[3] To him Lazzarelli addressed three prefaces, hitherto unpublished, to Hermetic writings. In these he spoke of himself as "Lodovicus Enoch Lazarellus Septempedanus, once a poet but now by new rebirth the son of true wisdom." He therefore appears to be the author of a *Letter of Enoch* describing how Giovanni Mercurio rode through the streets of Rome on April 11, 1484, on horseback wearing a crown of thorns, and his appearance on another occasion before the college of cardinals.

Germain de Ganay, to whom in 1493 or thereabouts Lefèvre had dedicated his work on natural magic, is found corresponding in the first decade of the sixteenth century with Trithemius and with Charles de Bouelles, who since his eighteenth year in 1495 had been a disciple and collaborator of Lefèvre d'Étaples.[4] On July 30, 1505, Ganay wrote to Trithemius craving an interpretation of some enigmatic utterances as to numbers and the elements which Trithemius had made in a letter to a third person.[5] In reply Trithemius quoted at length the *Emerald Tablet of Hermes* and expounded alchemy mystically in terms of unity and the numbers two and three. He further asserted that his philosophy was celestial, not earthly, and required an ascent.

[1] A MS copy is Milan Ambros. D.389.Inf., *Lodovici Lazareli poete christiani ad Ferdinandum regem Dialogus cui Titulus Crater Hermetis,* opening, "Cum mecum diu ipse hesitans . . . ."

[2] Paul Oskar Kristeller, "Marsilio Ficino e Lodovico Lazzarelli," *Annali della R. Scuola Normale Superiore di Pisa,* Serie II, Vol. VII (1938), pp. 237-62.

[3] T IV, 557.

[4] On the life and works of Bouelles consult the index of Renaudet (1916).

[5] "Ex Parisio III Calend. Augusti Anno MDV": printed in Trithemius, *De septem secundadeis: adjecta sunt aliquot epistolae,* 1567, pp. 62-65.

"Study generates knowledge; knowledge bears love; love, likeness; likeness, communion; communion, virtue; virtue, dignity; dignity, power; and power performs the miracle. This is the unique path to the goal of magic perfection, divine as well as natural, from which all superstitious and diabolical wizardry is totally separated and confounded."

Trithemius continues that by magic he understands nothing else than wisdom. He further adds a few wise words concerning the stars, stating that they rule only bodies and not our minds.[6] Whether all this mystical persiflage served to enlighten Ganay any more than Trithemius's previous enigmatical utterances had done may be doubted. In a work on his own studies and writings which breaks off in the year 1507[7] Trithemius defended himself against the charge of practicing evil magic and necromancy but made such exaggerated assertions as that he had written a book giving an occult method by which a person totally ignorant of Latin could learn in an hour's time to write anything he wished in that language.[8]

Ganay in his letter to Trithemius said that Charles Bouelles, who had visited Germany in years past, had praised Trithemius to him. But there is also a later letter from Bouelles to Ganay, written from St. Quentin on March 8, 1509, in which he describes a recent visit[9] to Trithemius and forms an unfavorable opinion of him. Bouelles found Trithemius to be not a philosopher but a magician. When the abbot proudly showed him his *Steganographia,* Bouelles was shocked at the barbarous and strange names of spirits, not to say demons, which met his eye and at the innumerable characters and adjurations.[10] These

[6] For Trithemius's reply of August 24, 1505, *ibid.*, pp. 67-75, or *Epistolarum familiarum libri duo,* Haganoae, 1536, pp. 89-94.

[7] *Johannis Trithemii Nepiachus id est Libellus de studiis et scriptis propriis a pueritia repetitis,* J. G. Eccardus, *Corpus historiae medii aevi,* Lipsiae, 1723, cols. 1825-44.

[8] *Ibid.*, cols. 1842-43.

[9] Renaudet (1916), p. 419, however, makes this letter refer back to a trip in 1503.

[10] Wier, *De praestigiis daemonum,* Basel, 1564, p. 130 confirmed this unfavorable opinion of the *Steganographia,* saying that despite Trithemius's denial that he engaged in illicit magic, "res tamen ipsa secus docebit si quis Steganographiae libros accurate legerit quorum partem scriptam cum figuris et spirituum nominibus apud Henricum Cornelium Agrippam foelicis memoriae ego ipse olim legi atque eo inscio exscripsi."

names of spirits were arranged in hierarchies under twelve emperors who were related to the chief winds and points of the compass. Bouelles states that when Trithemius wishes to communicate with a distant friend, he will send him a prayer and a character instead of an epistle. Using this clue the friend will turn in his copy of the *Steganographia* to the designated point of the compass and invoke a spirit who will inform him as to all Trithemius's secret doings and thoughts. More likely, as in books of divination, the key word or character led one to an answer given in the text itself. Bouelles further noticed love incantations in the volume, and asserts that it teaches so many other shameful things that in his judgment it deserves to be burned.

Trithemius also told Bouelles' Swiss companion all about his family, although the man was unknown to him, and predicted the coming soon of a reforming pope named Urban. He offered to make a thief who had robbed Bouelles during the journey return everything he had stolen, if Bouelles had faith, but Bouelles did not have enough. The abbot boasted that he had once taught an illiterate German prince Latin in an hour,[11] and then, before the prince departed, took all his recently acquired knowledge away. Trithemius expressed annoyance at the publication of his letter to Arnold Bosch,[12] which had brought a crowd of seekers after magic down upon him. But Bouelles is convinced that such feats as Trithemius boasts of having performed can be accomplished only through demon assistance. He adds that Trithemius solaces himself with musical instruments, while his monks are much given to alchemy.[13]

[11] We have heard him make a like boast above in his *Nepiachus*.

[12] T IV, 524.

[13] The letter to Ganay occurs in the volume of Bouelles' works published in 1510 at fols. 172r-173v, but there are other leaves in it with the same numbers, the whole volume being badly mispaginated.

Carolus Bovillus (the name of the author does not appear on the title page but in the dedication on the verso thereof), *Liber de intellectu, Liber de sensu, Liber de nichilo, Ars oppositorum, Liber de generatione, Liber de sapiente, Liber de duodecim numeris, Epistole complures. Insuper mathematicum opus quadripartitum: De numeris perfectis, De mathematicis rosis, De geometricis corporibus, De geometricis supplementis.*

The colophon reads: "Editum est universum hoc volumen Ambianis in edibus reverendi in Christo Patris Francisci de Hallevvin eiusdem loci pontificis et emissum ex officina Hen-

The work of Trithemius (who died in 1516) on the seven secondary gods or intelligences or spirits moving the orbs assumes to be addressed to the emperor Maximilian in 1508 but was perhaps first printed at Nürnberg in 1522,[14] and subsequently in 1567[15] and 1600.[16] It traces the history of the world from creation to the year 1879 A.D.[17] by relating successive periods of 354 Arabic or 343 Christian years to the spirits of the seven planets in this order: Orifiel and Saturn, Anael and Venus, Zachariel and Jupiter, Raphael and Mercury, Samael and Mars, Gabriel and the moon, Michael and the sun. For example, "Gabriel in our time will preside over the moon. Hence it comes about that under his government the sciences of the liberal arts revive again, heresies pullulate, unjust wars and robberies are carried on, women dominate, magic arts, sorceries and other crimes everywhere reign with impunity."

Bouelles also corresponded with Ganay on the subject of numbers in connection with the proposal of Lefèvre d'Étaples to publish the treatise of Nicholas of Cusa on divine numbers.[18] Bouelles had talked about the number six with Ganay and on June 2, 1508, wrote further concerning it and also seven.[19] A year later, in a letter of August 5, 1509, he took up the number five.[20] Hitherto he had regarded five as alone "without mystery" of all the numbers from one to ten. But recently it had occurred to him that it signified the union of form—represented by unity—with matter—represented by the four elements. He further sug-

rici Stephani impensis eiusdem et Ioannis Parvi in chalcotypa arte sociorum Anno Christi Salvatoris omnium 1510 Primo Cal. Februarii Parisiis."

[14] *De septem secunda deis idest intelligentiis sive spiritibus moventibus orbes libellus sane preciosissimus.* Ed. Jo. Marquard. Nürnberg, impensis Jo. Haselberg, 1522, 4to. I have seen this edition offered for sale in second hand catalogues but have not examined it.

[15] *De septem secundadeis. Adjecta sunt aliquot epistolae,* 1567: copy used, BM 719.e.30.(1.).

[16] *De septem secundeis,* added to the Strasburg, 1600 edition of his *Libri sex polygraphiae.* There are two MSS of the work in Munich, but CLM 5043 is copied from the printed edition of 1522, while CLM 24606 is of the seventeenth century.

[17] At least this is the case in the 1600 edition. According to the aforesaid sales catalogues in the edition of 1522, "prophecies for the twentieth cycle, the third reign of Gabriel, to begin in 1525, are withheld."

[18] Renaudet (1916), p. 506.

[19] Edition of 1510, fol. 171v.

[20] *Ibid.*, fol. 173r.

gested that it was at the basis of alchemy, which strives to separate the four elements and to reach the quintessence. Ganay thanked Bouelles politely for these brilliant ideas of his but added that Plotinus too had touched on the subject. Nothing daunted by this reply, Bouelles continued in September, 1510, with letters to Ganay on the numbers six and twelve. He had made the great discovery that six circles exactly enclose one circle of like diameter, and that twelve spheres completely surround one sphere of equal size with them. "By this experiment," says he, "I have learned that the number twelve is the measure of all corporeal plenitude." He adverts to the part played by this number in astronomy and to the veneration which the Magi have for it in their arcana and mysteries.[21] His censure of Trithemius's arrangement of the names of spirits under twelve emperors must have therefore been entirely due to the use of spirits and not to the employment of the number twelve.

Besides these letters Bouelles addressed to Ganay in May, 1510, a *Book of Twelve Numbers,* written in a similar vein.[22] In it he avers that the number one differs from other numbers as much as God differs from the multitude of creatures.[23] His work of the previous year on perfect numbers, addressed to Lefèvre, seems on the other hand purely arithmetical,[24] and his work on the seven ages of the world is biblical, chronological and historical.[25] He again discussed the occult significance of numbers in a letter to Budé of October 8, 1511.[26] Erasmus regarded the works of Bouelles as unreadable[27] and, at least so far as those about mystical numbers are concerned, was quite right. In fact, practically all of his works are filled with charts, geometrical diagrams, and figures like those of the Lullian art intended to depict relationships between angels and men, man and the world, heavens and earth, the intellectual and physical worlds, or between almost anything and anything else. The

[21] *Ibid.,* fols. 173v-174v.

[22] *Ibid.,* fols. 148v-171r: "Liber de duodecim numeris ad inclytum virum Ganaiensem praesulem Cadurcensem."

[23] *Ibid.,* fol. 148v.

[24] *Ibid.,* fols. 171v-180r, but following the Epistolae.

[25] *Aetatum mundi septem supputatio,* 1521: BM 9004.h.23.

[26] Renaudet (1916), p. 620.

[27] *Ibid.,* p. 610.

angelic intellect which is like the sun makes a right angle with the human intellect which resembles the moon and which extends horizontally while the other mounts vertically. The triangle is the figure suited to the intellect; the circle, to memory. Bouelles made much of the conception of macrocosm and microcosm. The soul has its five zones. The heart is at the center of the body, as the orbit of the sun is in the middle of the universe. The brain corresponds to the firmament; the belly, to the elements. There are two hemispheres, vegetative and sensitive respectively, of sleep and waking. As the sun in the zodiac visits both hemispheres of our globe, so the heart at night turns to the inferior organs and produces sleep.[28] Man as a rational being is superior to the sensible world and penetrates the firmament and transcends it. There are two rational heavens: of the intellect and angels, of the mind and God. The soul is invested and walled about by three orbs: its own, that of the body, and that of the world.[29]

Bouelles was described by Conrad Gesner as "a man polished with the liquor of rhetoric, poetic variety, and most sparkling splendor of all philosophy, and an outstanding geometer." He was so given to contemplative philosophy and geometrical abstractions that he would often lean against the trunk of a tree for nine hours without moving an eye-lash. By the keenness of his genius he had discovered many things hid from previous ages such as the squaring of the circle, while his treatise, *On Nothing*, was greatly admired by all.[30]

Josse Clichtowe was another disciple of Lefèvre d'Étaples who showed an interest in mysticism and in the significance of numbers. As the century opened he reprinted Lefèvre's *Paraphrases on the Physics and Metaphysics of Aristotle* and in the preface spoke of the visible and sensible world as a mirror for the contemplation of God and the celestial universe.[31] On Decem-

[28] For these reveries see in the edition of 1510 (BM 528.m.1), De intellectu, fols. 2v, 15r, 18v; De sensu, fols. 22r, 25v, 30r, 39r-v, 40r.

[29] *Ibid.*, De sensu, fols. 42r, 47r.

[30] Gesner (1545), fol. 161v. The *Liber de nichilo*, completed on November 26, 1509, is the third tract in the volume of Boulles' works of 1510.

[31] *Philosophiae naturalis paraphrases*, printed March 25, 1501 (1502); see Renaudet (1916), p. 412.

ber 16, 1513, he published a work on the mystic significance of numbers.[32]

Lorenz Beheim, in a letter of July 20, 1515, reminded Reuchlin that they had searched together at Rome in 1498 for Jewish books and the secrets of the Cabala.[33] The power of words had already been ventilated by Reuchlin in his *De verbo mirifico,* first printed in 1494[34] and now reprinted in 1514. Three years later in 1517 appeared his work on the cabalistic art.[35] In it we find discussed the *Tetragrammaton* and the name of forty-two letters, numbers, seals, characters and voices, the pronunciation of the names of seventy-two angels and their distribution in the nine choruses, the fifty gates of Intelligence, and the ten steps by which we ascend to the knowledge of things. Also such topics and propositions as that there is a terrestrial and a celestial Adam, that the Cabala is loftier than the Talmud, that Pythagoras was the father of cabalistic philosophy, that there is naught better for the soul than symbolic theology, that divine things are not learned by demonstration, that barbaric names are to receive honor in sacred rites, and that that cabalist is stupid who attributes miracles to figures or words alone. Yet there is a multiplex distinction and virtue in the letters of the alphabet, a multiple diversity in the heavens, and all inferiors tend towards superior perfection.

Petrus Galatinus, a converted Jew of Apulia who became a Franciscan and papal penitentiary, undertook the defence of Reuchlin for his interest in the Cabala and Jewish books in his *Opus de arcanis Catholicae veritatis,* which was dedicated to the emperor Maximilian in September, 1516, and seems to have first been printed at Ortona in 1518.[36] Galatinus has been accused

[32] *De mystica numerorum significatione.* I have not seen the treatise but follow Renaudet (1916), p. 644. Much information concerning Clichtowe and his interest in the mystics is given by Renaudet, *passim.*

[33] E. Reicke, "Der Bamberger Kanonikus Lorenz Beheim, Pirckheimers Freund," *Forschungen zur Geschichte Bayerns,* XIV (1906), 8.

[34] T IV, 517-24.

[35] Johann Reuchlin, *De arte cabalistica libri tres Leoni X dicati,* Hagenau apud Thomam Anshelmum mense Martio 1517. Copy used: BM 719.l.4. For a fuller summary of the work than I shall give here see L. Geiger, *Johann Reuchlin,* 1871, pp. 185-95.

[36] I have used an edition of Basel, 1550, in which the *Opus de arcanis*

of copying wholesale in this work from the thirteenth century *Pugio fidei* of Raymond Martini or the somewhat later *Victoria adversus Judaeos* of Porchetus Silvaticensis. Gesner said that Pico, Galatinus and Justinianus, who edited the work of Porchetus in 1520, seemed to have derived most of what they said concerning the cabala from a work which Paul de Haeredia, a converted Spanish Jew, had printed in Italy about 1485.[37] In the passages which concern us Hogostratus or Hochstraten, the inquisitor and opponent of Reuchlin, is represented as arguing that the word Cabala is not found in the works of the church fathers or schoolmen and so is rendered very suspect. Galatinus explains that in times past it was secretly and orally transmitted, but that recent Jews such as rabbi Simeon have written more about it, lest it be lost entirely, but still in veiled terms.[38] Capnio or Reuchlin himself is also introduced as an interlocutor, and it is held that the Talmudic traditions sometimes enable one to piece out gaps or corrupt passages in the text of Holy Scripture.[39] Also considerable is said about the *Tetragrammaton* and other divine names in book two, but the rest of the twelve books into which the work divides are chiefly concerned with the Messiah and the time of His coming. Wadding seems to have seen a work on theology by Galatinus in five parts which he left unfinished and which had books on demons and the stars and their power with some criticism of astrological predictions. But Wadding did not specify any particular manuscript of it.[40]

Hochstraten[41] for his part printed in 1519 and dedicated to Leo X a work[42] of which the first three books were devoted to refuting "the venomous and utterly futile fables and sheer im-

---

Catholicae veritatis occupies the first 718 pp. and is followed at pp. 719-891 by the *De arte cabalistica* of Reuchlin, with a common index for the two works. Copy used: BM 6.f.3.

[37] Gesner (1545), fol. 538v.

[38] *Opus de arcanis,* I, 6.

[39] *Ibid.,* I, 8.

[40] Wadding, *Scriptores ordinis minorum,* Rome, 1906, pp. 187-89.

[41] Gesner (1545), fol. 426r, gives an unfavorable estimate of Hochstraten, stating that he hears that he was an uneducated and unprincipled rival of Reuchlin.

[42] *Destructio Cabale seu Cabalistice perfidie ab Ioanne Reuchlin Capnione iampridem in lucem edite . . .,* Cologne, 1519 in Aprili.

postures which had been published by Capnio under the name of Simon, a perfidious Jew."[43] The fourth book was largely devoted to a defense of Aristotelian dialectic, syllogistic reasoning and scholastic theology against the attacks of the cabalists.

Besides works on the Cabala and Talmud Paul Riccio in 1519 published a *Compendium Concerning the Soul of the Sky.*[44] In the preface he says that Eck both verbally at a meeting of learned men at Ingolstadt and in writing in his work on predestination declared it execrable and contrary to the Faith to hold that the celestial bodies were animated. By way of rebuttal Riccio advances three conclusions. First, that to call the celestial bodies animated or inanimate is a matter of indifference so far as orthodoxy is concerned. Second, that the affirmative position seems more in accord with the utterances of saints and prophets than the negative. Third, that reason and the sensible order of things show that the celestial bodies are animated by a soul which informs the sky itself. Riccio admits that some church fathers like Damascenus can be cited against him but he prefers to follow others like Aquinas and Scotus, Albertus and Jerome.

Printed with this brief treatise is a still shorter Response to a Question concerning the name *Tetragrammaton.*[45] In it Riccio says that by meditation, figure, number and position of letters and adapting these to nature and the ideas which exist in the Divine mind we grasp the *Tetragrammaton* by reason or sincere faith. The operation of imagination fixes in a stable concept the characters of the *Tetragrammaton* with their points. The external operation of the body proceeds with a certain moderation of the voice and gesticulation of head and hands. But there are multiform varieties of these operations according to the particular objects for which we ask and pray.

[43] Prologus libri quarti: "Postquam absolvimus tres libros precedentes quibus venenosas ac plene futiles iudaice perfidie fabellas merasque imposturas sub nomine Simonis perfidi Iudei a Capnione in lucem editae."

[44] *Pauli Ricii De Anima Coeli Compendium.* Excusum Auguste Vindelicorum Impensis Sigismundi Grimm medici et Marci Vuyrsung Anno salutifero MDXIX secunda die Martii. Copy used: BN Rés. p. V. 154.

[45] It occupies only fols. (c v)—(c vi) recto.

The hieroglyphic characters of ancient Egypt, whose true meaning had yet to be deciphered, inevitably mystified and fascinated a generation as enamored of cabalistic names and numbers as was that of Bouelles, Reuchlin and Trithemius. The ancient, if fanciful, work of Horapollo[46] on Egyptian hieroglyphics became well known in the first half of the sixteenth century. Its Greek text was first printed at Venice in 1505, while it appeared in the Latin version of Bernardinus Trebatius of Vicenza at Paris in 1515, 1521 and 1530; in 1534 at Basel with *Niphus de auguriis;* in 1538 at Venice; in 1542 at Lyons;[47] in 1551 at Paris with a new version by John Mercer of Utica; and at Rome in 1597.

Another popular work on hieroglyphics was by Giovanni Piero Valeriano, also called Bolzani, a native of Belluno, and further author of a compendium on the *Sphere,* printed at Rome in 1537, a book on the unhappiness of men of letters, and other works. He died in 1550, but I have not found an edition of the *Hieroglyphics* during his lifetime. It was printed in 1556 both at Basel[48] and Florence, then in 1567, 1575, 1576 in French translation, 1579, 1595, 1602 at Lyons in Latin and at Venice in Italian, and in yet other editions. Its first four sections are on the lion, elephant, bull and horse, and their moral and allegorical significance, and all its pictures are of animals not of hieroglyphs or characters. In its later sections plants and trees receive some attention.

Since the appearance at Rome in 1469 of the *editio princeps* of the Latin *Asclepius* and at Treviso in 1471 of Ficino's translation of the *Pimander* and much of the Hermetic corpus, a steady interest had been shown in such publications. Seven or eight incunabula of the latter are said to have been issued[49] and four-

[46] T I, 331-34.

[47] Gesner (1545), fol. 144v.

[48] *Hieroglyphica sive de sacris Aegyptiorum literis commentarii Ioannis Pierii Valeriani Bolzanii Bellunensis* . . . , Basileae, 1556, 424 fols. Copy used BM 704.k.1.

[49] Hain 8456-62 lists only seven. Klebs (1938) rejects one of these and adds another. V. Scholderer, "Der Buchdruck Italiens im fünfzehnten Jahrhundert," *Beiträge z. Inkunabelkunde,* II (1938), 33, says, "dieses Werk erlebte seit seiner Erstausgabe in Treviso 1471 mindestens ein halbes Dutzend Ausgaben."

teen more editions to 1641.[50] The astrological *Centiloquium* ascribed to Hermes had been printed at Venice in 1492, again in 1493, and at Leipzig in 1495,[51] in the medieval Latin translation for Manfred by Stephen of Messina. Hermetic alchemy issued more tardily from the press, the *Emerald Tablet* being embodied in an alchemical volume printed first at Nürnberg in 1541, then again at Berne in 1545.[52] Meanwhile the *Centiloquium* had been published again,[53] while in mid century were printed Latin translations of a work of astrological medicine attributed to Hermes[54] and two books on the revolutions of nativities.[55]

Walter Scott in his edition of *Hermetica* attempted to restrict that appellation to "those Greek and Latin writings which contain religious or philosophic teachings ascribed to Hermes Trismegistus," and to ignore as "masses of rubbish" and "of very different mental calibre" those "writings concerning astrology, magic, alchemy, and kindred forms of pseudo-science," which are also ascribed to Hermes. It is very doubtful if any such distinction can be drawn. Both sets of works involve much the same view of nature and astrological cosmology, while to a person interested in experimental and practical science and not in Platonic reveries and moonings, the works called *Hermetica* by Scott, at least in the corrupt state of the extant texts, seem more nonsensical and removed from reality than those he chose to ignore. However, in the present chapter it is with *Hermetica* in

[50] Walter Scott, *Hermetica,* I (1924), 33, citing G. R. S. Mead, *Thrice Greatest Hermes,* 1906, I, 8-16.

[51] Klebs (1938), 173, 266. The 1493 edition, fols. 118r-119r, also contained the "liber Hermetis . . . de iudiciis et significatione stellarum beibeniarum in nativitatibus."

[52] *In hoc volumine De Alchemia continentur* . . ., Norimbergae apud Ioh. Petreium, Anno MDXLI; *Alchemiae libri,* Bernae, Math. Apiarius sumptu Joan. Petrei, 1545; at pp. 363 and 294-95 respectively, opening and closing: "Verba Secretorum Hermetis que scripta erant in tabula Smaragdi . . . . . . completum est quod dixi de operatione solis."

[53] With Albubather at Venice, 1501. Copy used: BM 719.k.29. Also in 1551 with Firmicus, pp. 85-89.

[54] *Hermes Trismegistus de decubitu infirmorum,* Paris, Wechel, 1555. *Iatromathematica Hermetis Trismegistri,* Cologne, 1556, with *Ephemerides Ioannis Stadii.*

[55] *Hermetis philosophi de revolutionibus nativitatum libri duo incerto interprete:* in the volume edited by Hieronymus Wolf, Basel, 1559, containing introductions to the *Tetrabiblos* of Ptolemy ascribed to Proclus and Porphyry.

the sense of such mystical and theosophical works as the *Pimander* and *Asclepius* that we are especially concerned.

The *editio princeps* of the Greek text of the Hermetic corpus in this restricted sense was in 1554, while Stobaeus, who offers further excerpts from Hermetic literature, was partially edited (books III-IV) by Trincavelli at Venice in 1535-1536 and again by Gesner in 1543, 1549 and 1559, and completed (books I-II) by Canter at Antwerp in 1575. The Corpus was re-edited by Flussas or François Foix de Candalle at Bordeaux in 1574 without the Latin *Asclepius,* was commented upon at great length in six volumes published in 1585-1590 by Hannibal Rosselius, a Franciscan from Calabria who taught theology at Cracow, and was included by Patrizi with other mystical texts which accompanied his *Nova de universis philosophia.*[56] The commentary of Rosselius was reprinted with the Greek text and translation of Flussas at Cologne in 1630.

In 1519 was printed the Latin translation by Pietro Niccolò de Castellani of Faenza of the "Theology of Aristotle," also called "according to the Egyptians," a late Neo-Platonic work largely excerpted from Plotinus.[57] In a preface to Leo X, Franciscus Roseus of Ravenna says that, when he was in Damascus (in 1516), he found the work there in Arabic and had an Italian rendering made by a Jew of Cyprus, Moses Arovas or Rova or Rouas, from which Pietro Niccolò made his Latin version. There was perhaps an earlier medieval Latin translation. As I have indicated in the second volume,[58] this work includes a discussion of the influence of the stars on the world of nature and the working of magic by utilizing this celestial force and the natural attraction which things have for one another. While such natural

[56] For further details as to these editions see Scott, *Hermetica,* I (1924), 33-37. He supposes a first edition of Patrizi's work at Ferrara, 1591 but had not seen it.

[57] Petrus Nicolaus Faventinus, *Sapientissimi Aristotelis Stagiritae theologia sive mistica phylosophia secundum Aegyptios noviter reperta et in latinum castigatissime redacta,* Rome, 1519.

See F. Dieterici, *Die sogenannte Theologie des Aristoteles aus arabischen Handschriften,* Leipzig, 1882, 1883, 2 vols.; T II, 248, n. 2; GS I, 406-7; Duhem I (1913), 271-75, II (1914), 335-41, IV (1916), 364-76, 398-401.

[58] T II, 254.

magic is accepted, artificial magic is rejected. With Plotinus the influence of the stars is limited to the animal soul. The rational soul can resist them.

In 1572, the same year in which he has been said to have directed the cutthroats of Saint Bartholomew's to assassinate his university rival, Ramus,[59] Jacques Charpentier issued another Latin version of this lofty and soul-purifying *Theology* of Aristotle. He gave his paraphrase the slightly different title, *Fourteen Books on the More Secret Part of Divine Wisdom According to the Egyptians.*[60] In the preface Charpentier cited a treatise by Stephanus Conventius of Bologna on the ascent of the mind to God from Platonic and Peripatetic doctrine.[61]

Francesco Giorgio or Zorzi, or Franciscus Georgius, or George of Venice, was a Franciscan who has been represented as a disciple of Pico della Mirandola and John Reuchlin. In 1525 he published a tome the size of a large dictionary on the harmony of the universe[62] with a preface of six pages addressed to pope Clement VII (1523-1534) and a table of contents covering twenty pages. The harmony divided into three cantica and these subdivided into tones, carrying out a scheme of musical designation. The work is of a mystical, occult and theosophical nature. The author tells how through created things and their consonance with the archetype we can "come to knowledge of His fecundity," defends God and creation against the Peripatetics, and points out that, while philosophers disagree, Catholics are in agreement. He investigates why the number six was associated with the process of creation, and seven with the day of rest, how one is distended by twenty-seven, and that it is clear to all sages that the monad is diffused into multitude. Or, as God descended to

[59] Thuanus, *Hist.*, pp. 1078-79.

[60] Pseudo-Aristotle, *Libri xiv de secretiore parte divinae sapientiae secundum Aegyptios. Opus . . . illustratum scholiis per J. Carpentarium,* Parisiis, 1572, 4to.

[61] *De ascensu mentis in deum ex platonica et peripatetica doctrina libri sex,* Venetiis, Ex officina Ioannis Baptistae Somaschi, 1563, 123 fols. There is a copy of this rare book at the Staatsbibliothek, Munich, which I have looked over, but it seemed to call for only a mention here.

[62] *De harmonia mundi totius cantica tria,* Venice, 1525. Copy used: BM 526.m.5.

us by a tripartite order of angels, so we through them may ascend to God.

The influence of the stars is accepted, but it is denied that Saturn and Mars are evil planets. The cherubim are associated with the eighth sphere of the fixed stars, the Thrones with Saturn, Dominions with Jupiter, and so on. Man is represented as a microcosm, and Moses by sacred artifice describes in the ark of Noah that all things are contained in man. Another chapter deals with the consonance of the limbs of God and of man. The metals correspond to Ezekiel's supreme waters and to God the Son. In general a great network of harmonies and relationships, of emanations from and to God, is set forth.

Nicolas Guibert, writing against alchemy in 1603, called Giorgio's theory of a spirit of metals delirious but more against transmutation than for it, since Giorgio said that this spirit could never or only with great difficulty be separated from the metals.[63]

The second Cantica of Giorgio's work is more exclusively concerned with Christ, but the third, on the soul and the body, continues the occult interest of the first. We are told that Thomas Aquinas, while deep in thought on sublime subjects, was levitated above the ground a cubit. Man's possibilities as a prophet and lord of nature are enlarged upon, and his relations with spirits. The text then turns to the more religious topics of man's relation to God, the resurrection, and the heavenly city, the Tone on which divides into twenty modulations. The *Harmony of the Universe* was printed again in Latin at Paris in 1545 by Andrea Berthelin,[64] and in French translation there in 1579.

Giorgio also wrote eight books of problems concerned with sacred Scripture, first published at Venice in 1536 and later at Paris in 1574 and 1621 or 1622. It has been described as too given to Platonism and the doctrines of the Talmud. It was dedi-

[63] Nicolaus Guibertus, *Alchymia ratione et experientia impugnata et expugnata*, 1603, p. 84.

[64] A copy is BN A.1369. Brucker would seem to be mistaken in speaking of an edition of 1543.

cated to Paul III, but later certain passages in it were censured by the *Index,* while Mersenne confuted those relating to the Book of Genesis in his commentary thereon.

On December 28, 1532, the majordomo of cardinal Campeggio wrote to Henry Cornelius Agrippa that he had seen Franciscus Georgius Venetus at Padua, but for only a quarter of an hour, since he was embarking. There was therefore not enough time to go into mystic secrets, but Giorgio promised to see the majordomo later at Venice, where he had cabalistic works in which Agrippa and his correspondent were interested.[65] Of Agrippa's own *Occult Philosophy* and interest in the Cabala we have treated in our chapter on him.

Brucker two centuries ago gave a much fuller analysis than mine of the views set forth in Giorgio's *De harmonia mundi,* and noted that in his *Problems* he treated of certain occult operations of art and nature.[66] Hallam, on the other hand, a century ago dismissed our author with the caustic sentence, "A Venetian monk, Francis Georgius, published a scheme of blended Cabalistic and Platonic or Neo-Platonic philosophy in 1525; but, having no collateral pretensions to fame, like some other worshippers of the same phantom, he can only be found in the historians of obsolete paradoxes."[67] As a matter of fact, Giorgio exerted a wider and longer influence than one might think. The Jesuit Pererius and later Guibert described him as more intent on new and marvelous opinions than on true philosophy and theology.[68] He was further cited, under the appellation Georgius Venetus, in the posthumous edition of Aldrovandi's work on monsters for illustrations of the doctrine that from a man's physiognomy one can determine under what planet he was born.[69] Thus Giorgio's fancies still found a place in the literature of modern science over a century after they were composed. In-

[65] Agrippa, *Epistolae,* VII, 22.

[66] Jacob Brucker, *Historia critica philosophiae,* IV (1744), 374-86.

[67] Henry Hallam, *Introduction to the Literature of Europe during the Fifteenth, Sixteenth and Seventeenth Centuries,* I, 208.

[68] Nicolaus Guibertus, *Alchymia . . . impugnata et expugnata,* Argentorati, 1603, pp. 83-84, "ut ante me etiam annotavit Perrerius."

[69] Ulyssis Aldrovandi . . . *Monstrorum Historia,* Bologna, 1642, p. 92.

deed, they were no more illusive phantoms than were most of Aldrovandi's monsters and freaks of nature. So with all due reverence to Hallam, we may question if there are any such things in history as "obsolete paradoxes." Giorgio's mysticism was as true to the age as was Aldrovandi's science.

In 1536 the Abbé Tenaud or Thenaud of Mellynays, wrote in French on the Cabala at the request of king Francis I, who had previously conversed with him on the subject. The work is preserved in a manuscript at Geneva[70] but seems not to have been printed. The royal interest in the subject which it attests is none the less noteworthy. The author more than once alludes to his extreme poverty which he begs the king to relieve. Tenaud himself expresses scepticism as to the Cabala[71] and is careful to put his account of it in the mouth of a Jew. The Cabala is defined as science and knowledge of God and of the separate substances of the spiritual world and its secrets which cannot be known by the external senses, experience, reason, demonstration, syllogism, study or other human and rational method but only by faith, illumination and celestial revelation which moves the free will to believe that which is inspired and to know the aforesaid secrets by the holy written law of God and also by figures, names, numbers, symbols and other ways revealed to the patriarchs, prophets and doctors of the Hebrews.[72] There are set forth the three worlds, elemental, celestial and spiritual, and their union in man; the power of soul over body; the goddess of necessity and the three fates and three infernal judges; the question whether souls separated from their bodies can re-

[70] University of Geneva, MS Français 167. Jean Senebier, *Catalogue raisonné des manuscrits . . . de Genève*, 1779, p. 420, seems to have been mistaken in saying, "On voit dans une note que ce Manuscrit a été copié par Reverend Pere en Dieu F. J. Tenaud, Abbé de Mellynays, le 16 Mai 1536," since the note actually runs, "Ce livre a escript francoys gryuel demon. a Angiers Pour Reverend pere en Dieu F. I. Tenaud Abbé de Mellynays 1536 Le 19ᵉ de May." Also in the introductory verses to Francis I the author speaks of himself as "Treshumble serf Thenaud a vous enclin."

[71] In his introduction in verse addressed to the king he alludes to the cabala as

". . . la sacre mistere des hebreux
Par laquelle ils foulz supersticieux
Se osent iacter dacquerir tout scavoir"

(fol. ii verso) and later refers to "telles fantasies" (fol. v recto).

[72] Bk. VI, chap. 24.

turn to them; the triangle of triumph and the quadrilateral of love and alliance; the Seraphim, Cherubim and Thrones; the names of God; the ceremonies in the book of Aaron and in theomancy—with illuminated figures showing the robes and vessels to be used.

Another cabalistic treatise is found in a manuscript of the sixteenth century at the British Museum. It discusses the first inventors of the Cabala, explains its content, gives Psalms "to obtain our desires," an invocation to God for victory, an account of the sign Tau and its marvels, an invocation of five angels for the four points of the compass and upward, seven candelabra, and so on.[73]

In his *Nomenclator insignium scriptorum,* published at Paris in 1555, Robert Constantinus devoted ten out of 189 pages to an account of the Cabala and a brief list of works on it. He regarded the original Cabala as divine and holy and transmitted by God to Moses by word of mouth only but the recent Cabala as corrupted by impostors and so worthless.[74]

Constantinus also ascribed to Guillaume Postel a book on Platonic and Pythagorean numbers which I have not seen.[75] In his *De orbis terrae concordia* Postel offers proof of the Trinity from Cabala and Talmud as well as from the Old Testament.[76] In the same work he asserts that the harmony of the universe and of particular things is placed in the number four, whence the greatest light of knowledge of the Trinity arises.[77] It is also stated in this work that exorcists in the primitive church were different from those today when they are scamps.[78] The existence of

[73] Sloane 2879, fols. 15r-30, "Compilatoris prolegomena pro cognitione cabalae," and other headings, opening, "Multa sunt et sane diversa . . ." Our treatise is preceded at fols. 2-13 by an alchemical tract and is followed at fols. 31-41 by "Alberti parvi tractatus scientiarum" sive "Occultorum thesaurus ou le petit paysant reformé," dated Franc. 1544, but this may be a later copy of a work printed then.

[74] *Op. cit.*, pp. 138-47. Copy used: BM 619.a.1. Constantinus gave 3 pages to judicial astrology, 3 to divination, and 5 to alchemy.

[75] *Ibid.*, p. 103. It is not in the catalogues of the British Museum or Bibliothèque Nationale.

[76] *De orbis terrae concordia libri quatuor,* 1544, p. 23. Copy used: BM C. 76.d.12.

[77] *Ibid.*, p. 259.

[78] *Ibid.*, p. 61, in the margin. On the title page it was explained that cer-

separate substances or demons and angels is said by Postel to be proved by daily "experiments" as well as by laws and histories.[79]

The juvenile pretensions to omniscience of Fernando of Cordova and Pico della Mirandola in the previous century were resumed by the adventurer and impostor, Paul Skalich or Paolo de la Scala, prince of Scala and count of Hun, margrave of Verona and lord of Kreutzburg in Prussia, who was more successful in imposing upon the princes and prelates than upon the learned world of his day.[80] In the year 1553 he proposed 1553 theses for public discussion in the church of San Petronio, Bologna, on the first of April, which was an appropriate enough day for the purpose. These 1553 conclusions he characterized as "divine, angelic, celestial, elemental, human, Christian, philosophical, metaphysical, physical, moral, rational, doctrinal, secret and infernal." Two hundred and sixty of them deal with the archetype world, 210 with the intellectual world, 146 with the celestial world, and 104 with the elemental world. There are 67 about Christ, 27 about dreams, 31 concerning oracles, and 49 on secret philosophy. Paul proposed to dispute 12,000 theses at Rome, but the Jesuits refused to countenance this after a preliminary hearing before a commission of five had convinced them that he was deficient in the fundamentals of theology, philosophy and even grammar.[81] Loyola described him in a letter of June 26, 1554, as having "little learning, less judgment, but plenty of vanity."[82]

The 1553 conclusions were printed as a supplement to an encyclopedic work which at the age of twenty Paul dedicated to the emperor Ferdinand. The first edition at Basel in 1559[83]

tain annotations had been added in the margin by a pious and erudite man (Postel himself?) lest anyone of more delicate palate or evil judgment, as many are today, be offended.

[79] *Ibid.*, p. 9.

[80] Gerta Krabbel, *Paul Skalich: Ein Lebensbild aus dem 16. Jahrhundert*, Münster, 1915, 211 pp., with a bibliography listing the earlier literature on him.

[81] *Ibid.*, pp. 12-18.

[82] *Ibid.*, p. 18.

[83] *Encyclopediae seu orbis disciplinarum tam sacrarum quam prophanarum epistemon*, Basileae ex officina Ioannis Oporini anno 1559 mense Februario.

was full of errors which Paul blamed upon his amanuensis, and he published a revision which I have used in the edition of 1570.[84] After a brief summary of all science and philosophy—Orphic, Pythagorean, Platonic and Peripatetic—of medicine, law and theology, whether symbolic or Hebraic, Paul passes on to the arcana of mystic thought, to the separate soul and its passion, the sympathy and antipathy of things, barbarism, and the *praestigiae* of Johann Wier.

Wier did not like these comments upon his work and in 1583 published *An Apology against a Certain Paul Schalichius Who Calls Himself Prince de la Scala*. In it he accused Paul of copying Pico della Mirandola for nearly eight pages and Agrippa verbatim for ten pages.

Further books of Paul's volume deal with eternal justice, Christ, antichrist, Luther, and the mass. The eleventh discusses the Essenes, Argonauts, therapeuts and gymnosophists. The twelfth and last book is on alphabetical revolution or the most perfect method to acquire every science and attempts to improve upon the Lullian art. There is further an effort to improve upon the book of pictures accompanied with prophecies which circulated under the name of Paracelsus. Paul offered a new interpretation of the pictures.[85]

As one tries to read some of these pages, one is rather impelled to the conclusion that either much study had made Paul

[84] *Pauli principis de la Scala et Hun marchionis Veronae etc. domini Creutzburgi Prussiae primi tomi Miscellaneorum de rerum causis et successibus atque secretiori methodo ibidem expressa effigies ac exemplar nimirum vaticiniorum et imaginum Ioachimi abbatis Florensis Calabriae et Anselmi episcopi Marsichani super statu summorum pontificum Rhomanae ecclesiae contra falsam iniquam vanam confictam et seditiosam cuiusdam Pseudomagi quae nuper nomine Theophrasti Paracelsi in lucem prodiit pseudomagicam expositionem vera certa et indubitata explanatio*. Coloniae Agrippinae, Theod. Graminaeus, 1570.

[85] In the edition of 1570 this revision of the prophecies of Paracelsus immediately follows the general title page which has been quoted in the preceding note. The thirtieth and last picture occurs and the prophecy relating to it begins at p. 142, and the paging of this section of the volume ends at p. 152. Then comes a new title page for the *Miscellanea de rerum causis et successibus*, with the same date, place and printer as on the general title page, after which ensues a new pagination. The 1553 theses conclude the volume, the twelfth and last book of the *Miscellanea* terminating at p. 665, while the theses end at p. 760.

stark mad, or that, in the words of Pope, "a little learning" had intoxicated his brain. At least he was much inclined to the mystical and cabalistic, and belonged to that class of men whom we have characterized as intellectual vagabonds and religious turncoats. He was at Bologna, Rome, Vienna, Augsburg, Tübingen, Zurich, Heidelberg, Brandenburg, Wittenberg, Weimar, Erfurt, Gotha, Frankfurt, Mainz, Nancy, Paris and Münster. He passed from Catholicism to Protestantism and back again.

Almost all the mystical interests covered in this chapter are combined in the treatise by John Dee entitled *Hieroglyphic Monad Explained Mathematically, Cabalistically and Anagogically.*[86] Taking the character which stands for the planet Mercury, Dee strives to show that it is a mystical representation of all truth, combining the symbols of direct and circular motion, sun and moon, the cross—denoting the four elements—and so on. The text includes such dicta as that the letters of the alphabet embody great mysteries, that medicine is contained in our monad, and that we should raise cabalistic eyes to the sky. The monad assures us of what no professor or practitioner of hydraulics could prove, that the element earth can rise through water to fire without any machine to assist its ascent. Dee of course indulges in much number mysticism and depiction of characters. After declaiming about mysteries which are not for the vulgar, he closes with a request to the printer not to offer the work for sale promiscuously. It is dedicated to Maximilian, king of the Romans and of Hungary, on January 29, 1564.

The little book on the magic of the ancients issued under the name of Arbatel at Basel in 1575 in Latin[87] appears to have been a modern fabrication. Its opening line is made up of Hebrew characters, and it pretends to be properly Christian and directed against evil magicians. Nine kinds of magic are listed: Isagogic, Microcosmic, Olympic, Hesiodic and Homeric, Roman or sibylline, Pythagorean, Apollonian, Hermetic, and

[86] I have used the text as contained in Zetzner II (1659), 178-215, *Monas Hieroglyphica Ioannis Dee Londiniensis mathematice cabalistice anagogiceque explicata.*

[87] A German translation may be found in J. Schieble, *Kleiner Wunder-Schauplatz,* Stuttgart, 1855-1859.

prophetic. But all that the little volume of 1575 includes is forty-nine aphorisms forming the introduction or Isagoge.

Pietro Bongo or Petrus Bungus of Bergamo in 1585 published a treatise on the mystic significance of the number four, with a dedicatory letter from Achilles Mucius to Jacobus Contarenus.[88] This discussion of the number four was also printed as a section of his longer work on the mysteries of numbers.[89] Indeed, in it he treated of every number up to thirty except 26 and 29, while between 30 and 50 he omitted 31, 37, 39, 41, 43, 44, 45, 46, 47, 48, 49. Why he omitted some of these is hard to say, since the products of 4 and 7, or 6 and 8, and the square of 7 should hold their own with most perfect numbers. For two decades after fifty, he noted only sixty and seventy, but then discussed 72, 75, 77, 80, 81, 86, 90, 99, 100, 112, 120, 150, 153, 200 and others. He mentioned 1095 because the Egyptians signified taciturnity by it, while 5040 was highly commended by Plato in the partition of houses, fields and offices.

This work of Bungus is largely a network of quotations, especially from the Bible and poets. It does not stick very closely to numerical matters, under unity, for example, discussing the relative merits of marriage and single blessedness. Although many pages are often devoted to a number, they are neither divided into paragraphs nor characterized by any other perceptible arrangement. A list of authors used includes Conrad a Liechthenau, abbot of Ursperg and author of a chronicle, who died in 1240, Franciscus Cataneus Diacetus, Guido Bonatti and many Arabic astrologers, Hermes the astronomer and Hermes Tris-

[88] Petrus Bongus, *De mystica quaternarii numeri significatione*, Venetiis, 1585. Copy used: BM 528.b.2.

[89] I have used the edition of 1591: *P. Bungi Numerorum mysteria . . . opus . . . hac secunda editione ab auctore ipso diligentissime recognitum et tertia parte locupletatum*, Bergamo, 1591. Copy used: BM 529.c.8.

Graesse says that the work first appeared at Bergamo in 1583 (1584) under the title, *De mystica numerorum significatione*, and again in 1585 both at Bergamo in folio and Venice in octavo. This seems contrary to the implication of the 1591 edition that there had been but one edition before it, but perhaps the others were regarded as mere reprintings of the first edition.

The catalogue of the Bibliothèque Nationale, Paris, lists an edition of Bergamo, 1584-1585, folio, with which one of those mentioned by Graesse may presumably be identified.

megistus, Hugo Eterianus, Jacques Lefèvre d'Étaples, Jacobus Geauschelius Vitoduranus—probably the fourteenth century chronicler—John Dee, Johannes Ravisius-Textor (1480-1524) professor of rhetoric in the Collège de Navarre, Laurentius Surius the Carthusian and historian, Ludovicus Vivaldus of Mont Royal,[90] Michael Stiphelius, Nicholas of Cusa, Raymond Lull, Richard of St. Victor, Simon Lemnius, a German humanist who died in 1550, Simon Portius, and Tichonius Affer. Thus a wide range of reading is indicated, but it might very possibly have been better employed. The work of Bungus was approved by a representative of the Holy Office at Bergamo in 1591 and is more concerned with the sacred than the magical significance of numbers. The existence of several editions of it indicate that it was considerably read.[91]

In the same year, 1585, that Bungus published in Latin his discussion of the number four, there appeared at Paris in French a work by Georges l'Apostre in praise of the number seven, in which chapters were devoted to such topics as that number's power in human generation and its relation to the seven ages of man.[92] No doubt there were works of the same sort published in other vernacular languages.

Giordano Bruno discussed at length the numbers from one to ten and the circle and other polygons up to the decagon in his *De monade numero et figura*.[93] With the pentad, for example, he associated the shield of the magi, the key of Zoroaster, a figure of the hand with five lines and five *montes*, a sign to protect the theurgist from violent spirits, and various groups of five, with citation of Paracelsus, Talmudists and cabalists.[94] Other works by Bruno on the art of memory and on the Lullian art are redo-

[90] Concerning Vivaldus who flourished at the opening of the sixteenth century consult Jöcher and the British Museum catalogue.

[91] Besides those mentioned in the previous note, Graesse and Mittag-Leffler (*Bibl. math.*, 1914) list a quarto edition of 1599 at Bergamo, "revised by the author and augmented by a huge appendix," and another with appendix at Paris in 1617 (1618).

[92] Georges l'Apostre, *Le Septenaire ou Louange du Nombre sept. A très vertueux et docte personnage, George de Maubuisson, son Mécène*, Paris, G. Pinocier, 1585, small octavo, viii and 63 fols.

[93] *Jordani Bruni Nolani Opera latine conscripta recensebat F. Fiorentino*, 1884, I, ii, 319-484.

[94] *Ibid.*, cap. vi, pp. 402-19.

lent of mythological, astrological and magical names, figures and characters.[95]

At Paris in 1586 were printed *Prognostica of Orpheus or Hermes Thrice Greatest* from earthquakes, translated by I. Antonius Baifius.[96]

Under the title, Philosophical Magic (*Magia philosophica*), there were printed at Hamburg in 1593 three hundred and twenty Chaldean Oracles, the dialogue of Asclepius, and the great philosophy of Hermes Trismegistus including the *Poemander*.[97] These texts were accompanied by essays on Zoroaster and Hermes Trismegistus by Franciscus Patritius or Francesco Patrizi. He accepts all past reports concerning Zoroaster as of equal validity and so distinguishes different bearers of that name: including a Persian, a Bactrian, an Armenian or Pamphilian, and a Medo-Persian. He ventures to suggest that Zoroaster, the chief of the Magi, whom Diogenes Laertius called a Persian, was really a Chaldean—a case in which he would have done better to stick to his authority. He also affirms that Aristotle translated the Chaldean astronomy and philosophy into Greek. He much regrets that by his time many of the *Chaldean Oracles* which Pico discovered have been lost, and that Pico's commentaries on them are not extant. Fifty years ago at Paris Lodoicus Tiletanus published the *Oracles* in Greek. Patrizi has made additions from other authors and translated them into Latin. He argues at length that they are true magic in the sense of the divine cult. A second part of magic is knowledge of the movements of the heavens and the influence they exert upon inferiors. A third division of magic is knowledge of natural forces, not slavishly following Aristotle as present Peripatetics do, but bringing to light the virtues scattered in hiding throughout the world and noting the sympathy between the parts of the universe. Goetia and divination are not true magic at all. Patrizi is in-

[95] *Ibid.*, II, i (1886), 56-178, Ars memoriae; II, ii (1890), *passim;* II, iii (1889), 87-332, De imaginum signorum et idearum compositione (from the edition of Frankfurt, 1591); III (1891), 1-258, Lampas triginta statuarum.

[96] This text corresponds to Abel's edition of *Orphica*, p. 141 *et seq.*

[97] This edition is not noted by Walter Scott in his *Hermetica.*

censed because Jan Van Gorp (1518-1572) has denied the existence of Zoroaster, Hermes Trismegistus and Orpheus. Patrizi further disagrees with Van Gorp that hieroglyphs were not the sole letters and form of writing possessed by the ancient Egyptians. Finally Patrizi expresses the opinion that it would be much better for Christians to study Hermes than Aristotle, whose works reek with impiety. The work of Van Gorp was published in 1580. He and Sisto da Siena, whose *Bibliotheca Sancta* appeared in 1574-1575, are about the latest authors cited by Patrizi.

In the same year, 1593, that Patrizi published his essay on Zoroaster, Jessenius or Jessensky, who was born at Breslau in 1566 and in 1596 became professor of medicine at Wittenberg, printed there a book entitled *Zoroaster: a New Brief and True Philosophy of the Universe.*[98]

The possible relations between the study of the Cabala and the practice of medicine are well illustrated by the case of Johann Pistorius of Nidde (1546-1608). In the preface to a pest tract of 1568[99] he had attacked the blind worship of Hippocrates, Galen and antiquity which, he said, had been too prevalent in the sixteenth century thus far. He argued that as the ancients in their day had advanced natural science, so modern men were not so weak-minded that they could make no further new discoveries. He felt that at present there was a keener spirit of investigation in the air. In the text he recommended metallic and alchemical medicines, the bezoar stone, occult medicaments, the bone from the heart of a stag, the stone from the head of an asp, and the chick of a stork, not yet able to fly but already feathered, burned alive to ashes in an earthen pot, taken with wine, as most efficacious for the pest. Another ingredient in one of his compounds was one hundred and eighty scorpions captured at the rising of Sirius. A remedy of pure quintessences prepared from one hundred and fifty simples in such artful proportions that it seemed sent from the sky, he refused to divulge further at present.

[98] *J. Jessenii . . . Zoroaster. Nova brevis veraque de universo philosophia,* Witebergae, 1593, 8vo. Copy: BM 527.b.6.(2.).

[99] *De vera curandae pestis ratione,* Frankfurt, 1568. BM 1167.c.30.(1.).

He discussed for some eight pages, however, the question whether there was curative power in words.[100] But of this more presently.

Nearly twenty years later Pistorius began the publication of his library of writers on the Cabala but does not seem to have carried it farther than the first volume.[101] He says he began to study the doctrine of the Cabala when little more than a boy and collected many books on it in Hebrew and Latin. Of these he now printed Reuchlin's *De verbo mirifico* and *De arte cabalistica,* Riccio's *De coelesti agricultura,* Archangelus de Burgo Novo, Leo Hebraeus *De amore,* rabbi Joseph's *Gate of Light,* and one or two other treatises.

Fourteen years later Pistorius was attacked by Jacob Heilbronner in a work entitled *Daemonomania Pistoriana* and dedicated to Frederick, duke of Wurtemberg and Tech, and count of Montbéliard (1593-1608). This title rather suggests a book on witchcraft or a collection of exorcisms, but the sub-title reads, "A Magical and Cabalistic Method of Curing Disease by Johann Pistorius of Nidde, once doctor of medicine, now of papist theology, drawn from Jewish and Gentile ditches and then offered to Christians to drink. With a Prophylactic Antidote by Jacob Heilbronner, doctor of theology."[102] In short, it is not even primarily an attack upon the cabalistic library of Pistorius but upon his pest tract. The animus of the attack, however, seems to be found in large measure in the fact that Pistorius had changed his religion and had written against Luther. Heilbronner says that from a physician Pistorius became a politician, from a politician a theologian, from a Lutheran a Calvinist, from a Calvinist a papist. Pistorius turned Calvinist in 1575, and became a Catholic after 1586.

[100] *Ibid.,* fols. 64v-69v.

[101] Joh. Pistorius, *Artis cabalisticae hoc est reconditae theologiae et philosophiae scriptorum Tomus I,* Basel, 1587.

[102] *Daemonomania Pistoriana. Magica et cabalistica morborum curandorum ratio a Ioanne Pistorio Niddano medicinae quondam nunc theologiae Papisticae doctore ex lacunis Iudaicis ac Gentilitiis hausta post Christianis propinata. Cum antidoto prophylactico Iacobi Heilbronneri doctoris theologi.* Excusa Lavingae typis Palatinis Anno MDCI.

Heilbronner has found this magical book which Pistorius wrote while practicing medicine, in which he asserts that there is power in words and names to cure disease, and talks of a ladder of angels, three horizons, and the Cabala of the rabbis. Heilbronner declares that all pious men believe that good and holy angels of God lend no aid to magical and theurgical incantations, characters, words, names and letters, even the *Tetragrammaton.* The inference is that Pistorius has for many years been an associate of demons. The following statements ascribed to Pistorius by Heilbronner are in fact all contained in the section of his pest tract above mentioned. To the three chief parts of medical cure—diet, drugs and surgery—he would add a fourth, the power of certain words. He speaks of fifty gates of intelligences and of marvelous power which emanates thence in words. "Nature first exercised magic in the voice. Therefore magic resides especially in words." The Cabala is the tree of rarity and most solemn discipline. Consequently Pistorius is convinced that there are great operative forces in certain words, and that this discipline of names is worthy of priests, philosophers and kings. Such was the effect of mixing too much Cabala with medicine.

We have not quite done with Pistorius, however. In 1607 he published a work on the microcosm,[103] in which he contended that the human head alone is the microcosm and not the vile human body as a whole, which furthermore is not spherical like the head and the universe. Moreover, it is in the head and intellect that man surpasses other animals. Pistorius then proceeded to a detailed comparison of the parts of the brain and head with those of the universe. Had someone suggested to Pistorius the objection that the human head is not exactly spherical, he might have retorted that the celestial orbs are not perfect spheres either.

[103] *Microcosmus . . . seu Liber de proportione utriusque Mundi in quo quid homo et quid unusquisque sit aut debeat demonstratur,* (Paris, 1607). An edition of Lyons, 1612 has the somewhat different title, *Microcosmus seu liber cephale anatomicus de proportione utriusque mundi: in cuius calce reviviscit Pelops (seu, libellus de nobilitate et excellentia cerebri).* A third edition was added to Plutarch, *De fluviorum . . .*, Tolosae, 1618.

In the preface to a work printed at Paris in 1611[104] which has already been noticed in our chapter on the Lore of Gems, P. Constantius Albinius traced the history of science and magic from Adam, Noah and the Magi of Persia. He represented the Greeks, influenced by the devil who tries to obfuscate the light of nature as worst he may, as the first corruptors of all arts who substituted superstition for religion, necromancy for magic, and idolatry for astronomy. Thereby they brought the name of magic into bad odor for a long while, but today many praise Trithemius and Agrippa for their knowledge of it. Albinius defines magic as an art by which one comes to know elements and compounds, their properties and abstruse operations, while the Cabala shows the way to God and is as full of divine mysteries as magic is of natural secrets. It predicts the future and knows the bonds between things celestial and terrestrial. Natural magic, however, is presently represented as tracing its origin from the divine ternary and Trinity. We are told that three with the magical four produces the perfect seven. Subsequently in the text Albinius dilates further on the power of numbers and the computation of the numerical value of names and of astrological times.[105]

Number mysticism and the like were not confined in the sixteenth century to special works on such topics or to writers on occult and cabalistic philosophy. They were also found disseminated in works of natural and political science from Rheticus's reference to the number six in his *Narratio prima* on the Copernican theory to Kepler's attempt to relate the five regular solids to the orbits of the planets in his *Mysterium cosmographicum*. Modern historians have represented this as an aberration on Kepler's part, but it was taken very seriously by his contemporaries. So able an astronomer as Maestlin praised it as based not on mere observation or logic or conjecture but confirmed "by genuine and most germane reasons which cannot be contradicted drawn from both the nature of things and ge-

[104] *Magia astrologica . . . P. Constantii Albinii Villanovensis . . .*, Paris, 1611. Copy used: BM 718.b.15. (2.).

[105] *Ibid.*, fols. 32, 34.

ometry." Maestlin doubted not that all astronomy would be reformed in consequence.[106]

Jean Bodin in his *Republic* discoursed on the influence of number and music upon the destiny of states, stressed the importance of squares, cubes and multiples of seven and nine in determining periods in the life either of individuals or of nations, but held that there were only four perfect numbers between 1 and 10,000, namely, 6, 28, 496 and 8128. However, he believed that 729, the cube of 9, often brought changes in states. According to the Roman Fasti, "which cannot lie"—a choice bit of historical criticism—729 years elapsed between the founding of Rome and the battle of Actium, and 729 years had also intervened between Charlemagne's conquest of the Lombards and Louis XII's defeat of Sforza and the Venetians. The perfect number, 496, also marked political periods such as that from Augustus to Augustulus and from the latter to Charlemagne.[107]

[106] Maestlin's preface of 1596 to his re-edition of the *Narratio prima*, in Kepler, *Prodromus dissertationum cosmographicarum*, 1621, p. 90.

[107] *Les six livres de la republique de I. Bodin Angeuin*, 1576, pp. 442-49 (IV, 2).

CHAPTER XLV

DIVINATION

Nemo hactenus divinationes has revocavit ad artem sicut olim astromantia chiromantia physiognomia geomantia nomantia et aliae revocatae fuerunt.

—George of Ragusa

Although astrological predictions continued rife in the early years of the sixteenth century, while the works of Cocles and Indagine attested the vogue of chiromancy, other forms of divination seem not to have received much attention in print. Only as the century wore on, did such publications become frequent. Interest especially among the learned seems to have been aroused largely by and based mainly upon allusions to divination in classical literature. Thus Melchior Guilandinus, a Prussian who became prefect of the botanical garden at Padua, touching upon the sibylline books, remarked that, since most learned men had had faith in the sibyls, it seemed worth inquiring whence this power of vaticination came to men, whether by nature or by art. If by art, by what aids and means it was acquired. If by nature, whether from within or without us. If from within, why we do not all have such foresight. If from without, whether from celestial or infernal parts. Guilandinus did not regard terrestrial exhalations as a sufficient explanation of pagan oracles and concluded that they were the work of demons.[1] Be that as it may, works on other methods of predicting the future than by the stars or the lines in the hand were now apt to be the result of classical scholarship and historical interest rather than of a superstitious demand for practical purposes. The latter, however, continued to manifest itself in certain types of divination such as geomancy.

[1] Melchior Guilandinus, *In C. Plinii maioris capita aliquot . . . commentarius . . .*, Lausanne, 1576, pp. 144-47.

Opposition to divination, on the other hand, appeared early in the century in the *De rerum praenotione* of Giovanni Francesco Pico della Mirandola, a work which was written at least in part in 1502, eight years after his uncle's death,[2] and published with Francesco's letters and other works at Strasburg in 1506-1507.[3] Its nine books cover more than three hundred folio pages and are an erudite but labored and confused medley from past literature on the subject, scholastic and Arabic as well as classical and patristic. Francesco as a writer was well compared by Campanella a century later to a cuttle-fish which conceals itself with its inky fluid.[4]

Prophecy and revelation are distinguished by Francesco from natural foreknowledge or divination. They are to be had neither from the stars, as Roger Bacon and Artephius erroneously contended, nor by nature and study, as various writers in Arabic have held. Most arts of divination are superstitious and involve pacts with demons. Geomancy, augury and auspices, omens, signs, lots and superstitious dreams are singled out for particular attack, as is the magic of Proclus, Alkindi, Roger Bacon, certain Hebrews, the Brahmans and gymnosophists, and Apollonius of Tyana. In the fifth book Francesco attempts to answer the counter-arguments of Bellantius and others to his uncle's attack on astrology. Throughout the entire work his attitude is not unlike that of Jean Gerson towards science and superstition in the previous century. Indeed, he often cites Gerson approvingly.

On the other hand, his particular *bête noire,* even more so than Roger Bacon, is Peter of Abano, instances of whose favoring attitude to astrology and incantations in the *Conciliator* are cited here and there as errors.[5] We have already indicated the debt

[2] As Giovanni Francesco remarks in his fifth book against divining astrology.

[3] Since the pages are unnumbered in this early edition, and it is less accessible than that of Basel, 1572-1573, my subsequent citations will be to the latter.

[4] Campanella, *De Gentilismo non retinendo,* 1636, p. 24: "Franciscus Picus quoniam est plenus subtili verbositate et taediosa, in necessariis deficiens et in subtilibus abundans, difficultates varias instar piscis sepiae fugiens atramentoque obnubilans."

[5] *Opera,* Basel, 1572-1573, II, 447 (De rerum praenotione, III, 4): "iustus et integer liber ex eius erroribus se-

to Francesco of Symphorien Champier's discussion of Peter of Abano's errors. Francesco further supplies a bit of information concerning the relations of Peter of Abano with the inquisition, stating that he had seen in the records of the inquisition that Peter, when accused of denying the existence of demons, cleared himself of this charge by bringing forward two of his students to testify that during his stay in Constantinople he had consulted a woman who practiced necromancy.[6]

Francesco shows a fairly wide acquaintance with the literature of magic, occult science and arts of divination. He objects that a certain Arab had extended the scope of the word necromancy to include astronomical magic, and that Picatrix had further stretched it to cover the divination of all hidden things whose causes and mode of production are unknown.[7] He cites Algazel on fascination[8] and is familiar with the work of Almadal or Almadel on the *Firmness of Six Sciences*.[9] Of these, however, Francesco lists only five: chiromancy, pyromancy, geomancy, hydromancy and aeromancy. Presumably he uses the last name to embrace both the auruspicia and augury of Almadal's work. Against divination and astrology he cites Henry of Hesse in his commentaries on the Book of Genesis and Innocent V on the *Sentences*.[10]

Although Francesco rejected astrology and other arts of divination and was inclined to class almost all magic as diabolical rather than natural, he still believed in the occult virtues of inferior things like the peony and magnet[11] as well as in divine prophecy and revelation. He alluded credulously to a recent celebrated miracle in Germany, where crosses, lances, nails, crowns of thorns, and other insignia of Christ's passion fell from the sky in raindrops which left figures of these shapes, mostly in red but some in black, upon men's bodies and clothing as a divine warn-

orsum colligi posset." See also pp. 482, 493-94, 518-22, 552, 585, 597-98, 660, 662 (De rerum praenotione, IV, 7, 9; V, 4, 7, 11; VI, 2; VII, 7).

[6] *Ibid.*, pp. 493-94 (IV, 9).

[7] *Ibid.*, p. 482 (IV, 7).

[8] *Ibid.*, pp. 418-19 (II, 4).

[9] *Ibid.*, pp. 485, 597-98, 607 (IV, 7; VI, 2-3).

[10] *Ibid.*, p. 556 (V, 7).

[11] *Ibid.*, p. 527 (V, 5).

ing against their abuse of supercelestial grace.[12] Francesco also recounted the apparition in an aerial body of a woman who had been dead for months. She answered many questions and spoke at different times to about a thousand persons, for which Francesco had the word not only of the prefect of Augsburg but of the emperor himself.[13] It thus becomes apparent that Francesco did not oppose divination from any want of credulousness, but on religious grounds as the work of demons. His *De rerum praenotione* represents no rational or scientific advance.

Geomancy was a type of divination with a medieval and recent rather than classical background. There had been printed at Vicenza about 1485 in Italian and reissued in French translation a decade later a work on lot-casting and geomancy by Lorenzo Spirito.[14] It was reprinted several times during the sixteenth century,[15] and was later translated into Dutch and English. The interest in geomancy of Cocles, Agrippa and Scepper has already been noticed, and we have heard Gian Luigi de' Rossi assert that he had learned geomancy from Luca Gaurico.[16] But the latter seems to have published nothing on geomancy. A long bibliography of writings on the occult arts and sciences which is contained in a manuscript at the British Museum[17] states that in his *Opera* published at Lyons in 1556 Joachim Forlius treated of geomancy, physiognomy, the interpretation of dreams, and other kinds of divination. The author meant is Joachim Fortius Ringelberg of Antwerp, whose *Opera* first appeared at Lyons in 1531. They discuss very briefly the subjects mentioned and also horoscopes, astrology and chiromancy. A geomancy ascribed to Geber was printed in Italian at Venice in 1550.[18]

In 1527 there was printed at Venice, with a Proemio addressed

[12] *Ibid.*, pp. 703-4 (IX, 5).

[13] *Ibid.*, p. 641 (VII, 4).

[14] Reichling, III, 118; Panzer, IV, 126; Hain 14957-14959; Art ancien, Bulletin XI (1924), Item 3253. Haym, *Biblioteca italiana,* 1803, IV, 99, lists a folio ed. Brescia, 1484.

[15] Brunet, V, 495, lists editions of 1528 and 1583; Haym, of Bologna, 1508, and Perugia, 1532; at BM, Rome, 1535, Paris, 1559, Lyons, 1560 and 1583. Also Venice, 1537.

[16] Pèrcopo, XVII, ii, 12.

[17] Sloane 696.

[18] *De la geomantia dell' eccell. filosofo Gioanni Geber . . .*, Vinegia, 1550, 8vo. Copies: BN V.21838 and V.29315.

to Clement VII and a privilege for ten years by the same pope, the *Triumph of Fortune* of Sigismondo Fanti of Ferrara.[19] This elaborate volume is sumptuously illustrated with astrological figures and pictures of famous men and women: popes, emperors, generals, giants, writers, artists, musicians and scientists. Although the pretense is made that the method is that of natural science and astrology, it is really chance divination after the manner of Amalricus the king and the *Experimentarius* in the twelfth century. Depending on the hour of the day or the throw of the dice, one obtains a number of reference to answer any one of seventy-two questions as to the future. One is referred first to a Fortuna, of which there are twelve named after the winds and points of the compass, then to a Casa, named after twelve Italian families, then to a wheel, then to a sphere, and finally to a sibyl or an astrologer, each with twenty-two astrological figures and answers. In the pictures of famous men such scholastic celebrities as Aquinas and Albertus Magnus are omitted. But this may be inadvertent, since even Ptolemy seems to have been left out, while Albumasar and Mandeville appear, Campanus is represented thrice, and Leonardo of Pisa and Fanti himself

[19] *Triompho di Fortuna di Sigismondo Fanti Ferrarese* (on title page). On the verso is the papal privilege to his "dilectus filius, Sigismundus Fantus," that of the Rogati, and a poem of Sempronius Amaranthius commending the work of Fanti to the pope. At fol. AA ii recto, "Proemio del Triompho di Fortuna di Sigismondo Fante Ferrarese al sommo pontifice Clemente papa septimo nel quale tratta delli accidenti del mondo et de molte discipline con varie questioni casi et conclusioni pieno de gravissime sententie et maturi documenti si per scienza naturale come per astrologia opera a ciascuno utilissima et sollazzosa." At fol. BB recto, "Tavola del Triompho di Fortuna de Sigismondo Fante Ferrarese el quale tratta delli accidenti del mondo si per scienza naturale come per astrologia da Mercurio Vannullo Romano fedelmente esposto." Vannullo's name had already appeared at fol. (AA v) recto, "Notando primo de Mercurio Vannullo Romano de la presente opera espositore," and at fol. (A vi) verso, "Tavola delli errori de la presente opera de Mercurio Vannullo," etc. At fol. (BB x) verso, col. 2, "Qui finisse la expositione degli Prohemii et Tavola de l'autore da Mercurio Vannullo Romano exposta." The various tables then occupy 3 unnumbered and 128 numbered leaves. Then on a last unnumbered page the colophon, "Impresso in la inclita citta di Vinegia per Agostin da Portese nel anno del virgineo parto MDXXVII nel mese di Genaro ad instatia di Iacomo Giunta Mercatante Florentino con il privilegio di Clemente Papa VII et del senato Veneto a requisitione di l'autore," etc. In folio. Copy used: BM 719.m.2.

twice each. Medicine and geometry seem better represented than either astronomy or astrology.[20] The title page is adorned by a figure of a pope seated with figures representing virtue and pleasure on a sphere of the world supported on the shoulders of Atlas, while its axis is turned by an angel and a demon. Below are buildings with a huge sun-dial or clock on a tower and two human figures holding respectively an astrolabe and a die bigger than a man's head. I do not know whether this Sigismondo Fanti was of the same family as an Antonius de Fantis who edited the astrological *Isagoge* of Alcabitius and the same author on conjunctions, with the commentary of John of Saxony, in 1521.[21]

As skill in geomancy was imputed by Rossi to Gaurico, so the latter states that Jacobus de Panico of Padua (1490-1548) was learned in geomancy. But Luca does not specify any work by him on the art. He says that his family came from Bologna, and that he was good-looking, of refined manners, and always wore white garments. But he was nearly blind in both eyes.[22]

In the *Index* of prohibited books for 1559 are listed works on *Nomantia* and *Geomantia* by Gaudentius Tervisinus,[23] or Gaudentius of Treviso. His *Nomantia* at least is preserved in manuscript in Italian. It uses numerical values for the letters in proper names to determine such questions as which of two combatants will win.[24]

As the works of Spirito and Fanti, at least, were in Italian, so in the second half of the century such books of divination were

[20] The same page cuts of pictures are repeated with different names, that of a mounted general being used for Pompey, Hannibal, Belisarius etc., while the same figure of a geometer serves for Pythagoras, Campanus of Novara, and Leonardo of Pisa.

I made lists of all the personages named in the hope that they might reflect the interests of the time, intellectual and otherwise, but I doubt whether any definite conclusions can be safely drawn from them.

[21] Alchabitius, *Praeclarum opus ad scrutanda stellarum magisteria isagogicum restitutum ab Antonio de Fantis qui notabilem eiusdem autoris libellum de planetarum coniunctionibus nusquam antea impressum addidit, cum Joannis de Saxonia commentario,* Venice, M. Sessa et P. de Ravanis, 1521, 4to.

[22] Gaurico (1552), fol. 120v.

[23] F. Reusch, *Indices librorum prohibitorum des 16ten Jahrhunderts,* 1886, p. 187.

[24] FL Plut. 89 sup., cod. 41, fols. 92-105, Opera dela anticha et honorata scientia di Nomandia . . . per Gaudentio Trivisano astrologo, geomante, chiromante et fisinomo, opening, "Non è dubio che per instinto naturale . . ."

apt to be in the vernacular languages rather than in Latin, which suggests that they were falling under the stigma of being popular superstition. In 1552 again appeared at Venice the Italian translation of the geomancy ascribed to Geber,[25] and in the same year and place was printed *l'Oracolo* of Girolamo Parabosco.[26] This *Oracle* answered questions by chance selection of a letter and number, and by reference via a table of constellations and degrees to a day of the month, where the answer was given in three lines of verse. Christophe de Cattan or Cattano published a geomancy in French at Paris in 1558. It was reprinted in 1567, 1572 and 1577, and at London in English translation in 1591. The bibliography in the Sloane manuscript lists another geomancy in French by Bandaroy, published at Paris in 1574.

The very next year G. de la Tayssonnière, "gentilhomme Dombois," printed his geomancy in French at Lyons. He claimed in the title to have purged the art of obscurities, to have separated it from astrology, and to have reduced it to its pure simplicity and true ancient purity.[27] In the dedication to her majesty, the queen of Navarre, the author numbers among the great inventions of antiquity the numerous arts of divination, which he says compare favorably with our evil modern inventions of gunpowder and artillery. Indeed, he is not certain that the invention of printing may not have brought more evil than good. "Madame, as for poor geomancy, so ancient, gentle and delectable (and useful too, since by it one can pleasantly relieve oneself of vicious idleness)," once it predicted to our author that that day he would meet a princess. The forecast was happily fulfilled when another princess playfully threw Madame's chapeau high in the air and it fell at our author's feet, enabling him to restore

[25] *De la geomantia dell' eccel. filosofo G. Geber parte prima. Con una brevissima chiromantica phisionomia. Novamente dal nobil huomo M. G. Piceno tradotti e pur hora dati in luce.* Vinegia, 1552, octavo: copy used, BM 719. c.7.

[26] Girolamo Parabosco, *l'Oracolo,* Venice, 1552: copy used, BM 718.e.8. (1.).

[27] G. de la Tayssonnière, *La geomance, par laquelle on peut prevoir deviner et predire de toutes choses doubteuses et incertaines. Science repurgee des superfluitez qui l'offusquoyent separee de l'astrologie et reduicte à sa pure simplicité et vraye purité ancienne pour les gens d'esprit par tables briefves et familieres.* Lyon, Benoist Rigaud, 1575, 4to.

it to the queen. His method of divination is the usual one by the casting of points and reference to sixteen geomantic figures. Tayssonnière's dedication reinforces the impression given by the publication of geomancies in the vernaculars rather than in Latin, namely, that if the art was gaining more widespread popularity among laymen, it also had lost what standing it once possessed among the learned. There are other geomancies found in manuscripts whose authors I have failed to identify but whose names sound as if they might be of this period. One by Burnettus de Viella is apparently in Latin.[28] Another by Villanova de Papiniano is in Italian.[29] A third anonymous work covers 112 leaves in a sixteenth century manuscript but is almost certainly of earlier composition, since it contains revolutions for the years 1474 and 1475 cast by geomantic methods.[30] A geomancy in French by a Nicolas Monnel in another manuscript which the catalogue dates as of the sixteenth century[31] appears to be by Nicolas Monvel de Blaringhem (Nord),[32] author of "Le livre des passions astrologiques," a work of astrological medicine found in a manuscript of the fifteenth century.[33]

Another treatise on *Nomandia,* printed at Venice in 1549 in Italian by Annibale Raimondo Veronese, has exactly the same title as that ascribed in manuscript to Gaudentius of Treviso.[34] It sets forth the same method of divination by names, the letters of which are given numerical values. The planets and signs of the zodiac are again assigned numbers and related to letters of the alphabet. On the title page the author is again described as an astrologer, geomancer, chiromancer and physiognomist. But a

[28] FR L.II.XXV (Lami, p. 373).

[29] Vatic. Reg. Suev. 1319.

[30] BMsl 1437, ff. 1-112.

[31] BMsl 3810, paper quarto, ff. 1-79, opening, "Pource que plusieurs personnes et la plus grant partys du monde desirent scavoir leurs adventures. . . ." I have not examined the MS itself.

[32] E. Wickerheimer, *Dict. biog. des médecins,* 1936, p. 574.

[33] BN fr 2074, ff. 1r-88v. So far as I could decipher the writing, the author appeared to describe himself on fol. 1r as "Je Nicolas Monvel natif demorans ay[?] la paroisse de Blazinghem ou diocese de Thezolbane."

[34] *Opera dell' antica et honorata scientia de Nomandia specchio d'infiniti beni e mali che sotto il cerchio della luna possono alli viventi intervenire . . . ; aggiuntovi la fisionomia.* Venetia per Iovita Rapirio, 1549. Unfortunately I did not note the opening words.

tract on physiognomy is added to this edition. The papal *Index* of 1559 adds to Annibale's *Nomandia* an "Item de geomantia et de chiromantia."[35] The work was reprinted at Venice in 1550 and 1551, and so seems to have achieved immediate currency.[36] An "Instruction pour la Nomence ou Nomancie" occurs in a manuscript which seems to be of the sixteenth century.[37]

Luca Gaurico gave the date of Raimondo's birth, or perhaps conception, since the figure of the horoscope is marked as "Per conceptum examinata," as November 19, 1505. A patrician of Verona, as a boy he could run and jump like a deer. Engaging in military activities, he suffered many wounds and imprisonments which Gaurico specifies in detail. He had been more than once charged with homicide and put to torture.[38] Yet Raimondo predicted of himself that he would probably live to be eighty and die a natural death.

This Annibale Raimondo was active in astrology as well as Nomandia. He composed annual astrological predictions in Italian of which the first noted by Hellmann was for 1553 and the last for 1565.[39] The British Museum, however, contains a prediction by him for the year 1550 addressed to the Doge and Grand Council of Venice and printed that year at Mantua.[40] He further wrote on comets, notably that of 1577,[41] and on the new star of 1572. He held that it was not a new star but the eleventh in the constellation of Cassiopeia, thereby exciting the wrath of Tycho Brahe[42] and Thaddeus Hagecius.[43] That nevertheless he was sincerely interested in natural science and astronomy as

[35] Reusch (1886), p. 178.

[36] I have used the edition of 1550.

[37] BMsl 2879, ff. 118-29.

[38] Gaurico (1552), fol. 117r.

[39] Hellmann (1924), p. 34.

[40] Annibale Raimondo, *Al Sereniss. Principe et allo Illustrissimo Maggior Consiglio di Venetia. Pronostico de A. R. Veronese sopra la dispositione de l'anno 1550,* Mantova, 1550, quarto.

[41] Annibale Raimondo, *Discours sur la noble Comette apparue à Venise au mois de Novembre 1577, la plus notable, gracieuse et benevole que l'on ait veu de nostre temps . . . Fait en Italien par M. Hannibal Raimondo de Veronne et depuis traduit en langue Françoise,* Lyon, Jean Patresson, 1578, 8vo.

[42] Tycho Brahe, *Opera omnia,* Frankfurt, 1648, I, 428.

[43] *Thaddaei Hagecii ab Hayck . . . Responsio ad virulentum et maledicum Hannibalis Raymundi scriptum quo iterum confirmare nititur stellam quae anno 72 et 73 supra sesquimillesimum fulsit non novam sed veterem fuisse,* Pragae, ex officina G. Nigrini, 1576, 4to.

well as in astrology and divination is shown by treatises by him dealing with the tides, the movement of trepidation of the eighth sphere, and a supplementary declaration to the rule of Giovanni Bianchini for finding the altitude of the poles or latitude.[44]

In 1550 Jacques Gohorry published at Paris under his pseudonym of Leo Suavius a work on somewhat the same order as Raimondo's *Nomandia,* which may have suggested its composition. It explained the ancient meaning of letters, numbers and divine names "from the sibyl," but also was concerned with shorthand and mystic writing after the fashion of the *Steganographia* of Trithemius.[45] It perhaps should be classed with cabalistic and mystic writings rather than divination.

We now turn from geomancy and cognate methods to divination of the future by interpretation of dreams. Whereas there had been several incunabula of the *Dream-Book of Daniel,* the only analogous publication in Latin from the first half of the sixteenth century seems to be an edition of Venice, 1516, in which it is combined with *Dreams of Solomon.*[46] Two years later the Aldine press at Venice issued the much fuller Greek text in five books of the *Oneirocritica* of Artemidorus, together with the work of Synesius of Cyrene on dreams. While the *Dream-Book of Daniel* appears not to have been published in Latin again after this, its place among learned readers presumably being taken by the *Oneirocritica,* it continued to make an appeal in vernacular translations. One in French had appeared about 1510,[47] an English version was issued around 1542,[48] and an

[44] Annibale Raimondo, *Trattato utilissimo et particolarissimo del Flusso e Riflusso del Mare . . . Aggiuntavi una piena dichiaratione alla regola gia data dal astrologo . . . G. Bianchini per trovar col mezzo dell' hore l'altezza de' Poli et appresso un discorso fatta sopra il moto della trepidatione dell' ottava sfera,* etc., Venetia, 1589, 4to.

The last-named tract had already appeared in 1580: A. Raimondo, *Discorso sopra'l moto della trepidatione dell' ottava sfera indirizzato a tutti quelli che hanno desiderio di viver lungamente,* [Verona?], 1580, 4to, 8 fols. This fuller form of the title shows that the tract was also astrological.

[45] Leo Suavius, *De usu et mysteriis notarum liber in quo vetusta literarum et numerorum ac divinorum ex sibylla nominum ratio explicatur,* Paris, 1550. BM 1043.b.24.

[46] *Somnia Salomonis David regis filii una cum Danielis prophete somniorum interpretatione: novissime ex amussim recognita omnibusque mendis expurgata,* Venetiis, 1516.

[47] *Les songes Daniel prophete, trans-*

Italian translation was published in mid-century.[49] A Latin translation of Artemidorus by Janus Cornarius came out at Basel in 1539. In the same year Scaliger edited with a commentary the *De insomniis* attributed to Hippocrates which had already been translated into Latin for Sixtus IV by Andrea Brenta in the previous century. The widespread currency of the work of Artemidorus was attested by two further editions of the Latin translation of Cornarius at Basel in 1544 and at Lyons in 1546, by the first appearance of Fontaine's partial translation in 1546, and by two printings of the Italian version of Pietro Lauro at Venice in 1542. These were followed by other editions of it there in 1547 and 1558. To give some idea of the great vogue which this work had throughout early modern times without stopping to enumerate too many particular editions, we may simply note that the twentieth edition of it in English translation was reached in 1722 and the twenty-fourth in 1740. Meanwhile the *Dream-Book of Daniel* for a time found readers even in Latin, as is shown by its appearance in manuscripts of the sixteenth and seventeenth centuries.[50]

The interpretation of dreams was discussed at considerable length by Ferdinand Ponzetti, first president of the apostolic camera, in his *Third Part of Natural Philosophy,* dedicated to cardinal Giulio de' Medici, brother of Leo X, and printed at Rome on October 10, 1515.[51] Ponzetti's treatise on poisons is considered in another chapter. He notes that some thought that dreams came from the Intelligences; others, from species derived from some influence; others from idols cast off from ob-

latez de latin en francoys. (Extracted from the "Interpretationes seu somnia.") Paris, 1510(?): copy used, BM c.36.a.8.

[48] *Dreams of Daniel,* Robert Wyer, London, circa 1542, 8vo: Dibdin.

[49] *Insonio de Daniel. Questo sie el modo de veder la significatione de Daniel propheta secondo li di de la luna.* Venetia, 1550(?), 4to: copy used, BM 1073.i.43.

[50] Sompnia Danielis: BM Sloane 3542, 16th century, fol. 43, imperfect. Sompniale Danielis: BM Sloane 2561, 16th-17th century, fol. 53.

[51] *Tertia pars naturalis phylosophie Ferdinandi Ponzetti Camere Apostolice Presidentis Primatis.* Impressum Romae apud Iacobum Mazochium Romanae Achademiae Bibliopo. Anno MDXV Die x mensis Octobris Triumphante divo Leone X Pontifice maximo Anno eius tertio. cxxxiii fols.

jects; while astrologers referred them to the sky.[52] He recognizes that the interpretation of dreams is a complicated and difficult matter, since the senses even while awake are deceived by hallucinations and much more so in sleep. Moreover, images are not formed in the same way by different persons; external influences such as climate and the aspects of the stars vary; and the words by which ideas are expressed are not the same among different peoples. The interpretation of dreams cannot approach in certainty such sciences as grammar and medicine, and even in these mistakes are made. Nevertheless Ponzetti felt that what had been observed and found true over long stretches of time could not be ignored. He gives five pages of things seen in dreams and their significance.[53]

Ponzetti touched on such cognate matters as the power of an emerald to liquefy the eyes of serpents,[54] fascination, and cure of minor diseases by the exercise of strong imagination and emission of vapors, and other arts or modes of divination. Characters and unguents are deceptive, not producing the effects attributed to them except by aid of evil spirits. But for Ponzetti the question whether nigromancy has all its efficacy from demons, as many believe, is difficult to solve, since the subject is "unknown to us," and there has been no reliable book on it since the time of Zoroaster and Democritus. Ponzetti inclines to interpret figuratively the reported transformations of men into beasts.[55] But he believes, like Pomponazzi, that certain persons, whose organs and spirits are better composed and proportioned and clearer than those of a normal healthy being, can rise above man's usual physical powers, acquire some similitude to the celestial bodies or union with God and other separate substances, and predict the future by instinct or goodness of nature or by power bestowed on them by the stars at the time of their generation. Such natural divination, however, is not to be confused with divine prophecy.[56]

A much less favorable attitude towards divination from dreams

[52] *Ibid.*, III, iv, 1; fol. cxi verso.
[53] *Ibid.*, fols. 124v-26v.
[54] *Ibid.*, fol. 117r.
[55] *Ibid.*, III, iv, 4; fol. 115r-v.
[56] *Ibid.*, III, v, 1; fol. 116r-v.

was displayed a half century later in the compendium of natural philosophy by Sebastian Fox Morcillo of Seville. He accepted prophetic dreams sent by God but completely rejected "that divination which is made by some instinct of nature or power of the rational soul when free from cares."[57]

Christopher Hegendorff, whose eight-page *Praise of Sleep,* printed at Leipzig in 1519, consisted chiefly of gleanings from the classics, in 1536 published a Latin translation of Aristotle's treatises on longevity and brevity of life and on divination through sleep or dreams. Jean Thibault, who flourished about 1530, had written *La phisionomie des songes,* but the work was published without indication of the date or the place of printing. The *Scholia* of Michael of Ephesus to certain works of Aristotle were translated by Conrad Gesner and published at Basel in 1541.[58] In a preface to that on divination by dreams, Gesner, addressing his old schoolfellow, Melchior Wirzius, who was now professor of mathematics at Zurich, said that he had no doubt that many would be offended by that title, because observance of dreams seemed to be prohibited in the Old Testament. But Gesner protested that as here set forth it was not superstitious.[59]

In 1549 at Lyons, together with the Latin translations by Julius Caesar Scaliger and Guinther of Andernach of the *De insomniis* of Hippocrates and Galen respectively, and of that by Ficino of Synesius on dreams, there was printed a treatise on dreams by Oger Ferrier or Augerius Ferrerius,[60] a physician and native of Toulouse who lived from 1513 to 1588. According to Sudhoff he was for a time physician to Catherine de' Medici.[61] De Thou does not mention this but says that Ferrier followed

[57] Foxius Morzillus, *De naturae philosophia seu de Platonis et Aristotelis consensione libri V*, 1560, V, 16; fol. 208v. Copy used: BM 524.e.26.

[58] *Michaelis Ephesii Scholia in Aristotelis libros aliquot nempe De iuventute senectute vita et morte, De longitudine et brevitate vitae, De divinatione per somnum. E Graeco nunc primum conversa Conrado Gesnero Tigurino medico interprete,* Basel, 1541.

[59] *Ibid.*, p. 77.

[60] Augerius Ferrerius, *Liber de somniis. Hippocratis de insomniis liber (J. C. Scaligero interprete). Galeni liber de insomniis (G. Andernaco interpete). Synesii liber de somniis (translatus a M. Ficino).* Lugduni, 1549, 16mo.

[61] *Abhandlungen z. Gesch. d. Medizin*, 1902, p. 52.

Jean Bertrand, cardinal-elect, to Rome; that he was a physician famous for his proficiency in astrology and other arts less known to the vulgar; that he was highly esteemed by Scaliger but had a sharp literary controversy with Cardan.[62] He had already published at Lyons in 1541 a treatise on critical days according to Pythagorean doctrine and astronomical observation, of which there was a second edition at Leyden in 1549, and which was to appear again in 1602.[63] A book on nativities in French by him was printed at Lyons in 1550.[64] Erastus states that he attributed power to words and characters, if employed by a learned and intelligent man, and if the patient did not resist them.[65]

Bodin tells a tale of Ferrier's renting a house in Toulouse in 1558 very cheap because it was said to be haunted. A young Portuguese student at Toulouse resorted to captromancy and had a young girl gaze into her finger nails. She said that she saw a woman richly clad holding a torch near a pillar. The Portuguese then advised Ferrier to dig for treasure near a pillar in the cellar of the house. But when he did so, a whirlwind put out the light, burst forth from the cellar, and brought down the eaves on the adjoining house, breaking a pitcher of water which a woman was carrying. After that the house was no longer haunted, and the Portuguese explained that the spirit had gone off with the treasure, and that Oger was lucky that it had not injured him. Oger himself told Bodin of the incident only two days after it happened on December 15, 1558, when the weather was as clear as during the halcyon days.[66]

[62] Thuanus, *Historia,* lib. 89.

[63] *De diebus decretoriis secundum Pythagoricam doctrinam et astronomicam observationem,* Lyons, 1541. Sudhoff, *op. cit.,* mentions the first two editions but was unable to consult any copy of the work. There is a copy of the 1549 edition at the British Museum: shelf-mark, 545.a.2.

[64] Oger Ferrier, *Des jugemens astronomiques sur les nativitez,* Lyon, 1550, 220 small pages in coarse italic type.

I have seen a later edition of Lyons, J. de Tournes, 1582, 16mo, 181 pp., of which there are three copies at the Bibliothèque Nationale, Paris. It is in three books and employs Arabic terms freely.

[65] Thomas Erastus, *Disputationum de medicina nova P. Paracelsi pars prima,* 1572, p. 179.

[66] Jean Bodin, *Démonomanie,* 1580, III, 3, fol. 135r. I assume that Bodin mentions this subsequent serenity of the air to show that the violent wind of two days before had been supernatural.

In his preface to the work on dreams Oger Ferrier expresses gratification that some of the occult philosophy and science of the ancients has survived, and his text is full of classical examples. But he has a poor opinion of the dream-books ascribed to Solomon and Daniel and of a work on the interpretation of dreams according to the Persians, Indians and Egyptians which is probably that of William of Aragon.[67] Ferrier classifies dreams as of either divine, natural or diabolical origin. Natural dreams of patients are useful for their physicians to know. Diabolical dreams have natural significance in part but in part are treacherous. Divining dreams do not occur often, and one should pay heed only to those dreams which remain impressed upon the mind after one wakes. It might seem difficult to attend to those which did not. Ferrier believes, however, that there is a correct and by no means superstitious art of interpreting dreams, partly from a divine force affecting our minds, partly from a certain convenience and conjunction of nature, and based and built up further upon constant daily observation. In interpretation he would take astrological considerations into account. In closing he states that learned friends have advised him to omit, as not proper for vulgar ears, certain doctrines which he had taken from the Platonists, Chaldeans and Indians. He has consequently expunged these passages and committed them "to burning flames."

In 1550 there was printed at Mainz a little volume by Ioannes Benedictus, a royal doctor and canon of Breslau and Cracow. entitled, *Of Visions and Revelations Natural and Divine.*[68] It was addressed to a Polish count,[69] and deals more particularly with dreams, divinations and sleep-walking. The five causes of the

[67] T II, 300-301.

[68] *De visionibus et revelationibus naturalibus et divinis libellus elegans ac compendiosius nunc primum ęditus per clariss. et doctiss. D. Ioannem Benedictum, regium doctorem, canonicum Vratislaviensem et Cracoviensem, MDL.* Moguntiae apud S. Victorem excudebat Franciscus Behem typographus, Anno MDL. Copy used: BN D.13792 (6.), ColR.

[69] *Ibid.*, fol. a iii recto, "Illustri et magnifico heroi Ioanni comiti a Tarnow castellano Cracoviens. etc. Ioannes Benedictus regius doctor salutem." The author alludes to a recent fire at Breslau in 1541.

last are given as memory, sense of touch, obedience to the appetitive faculty, movement of the limbs, and reason. The others are accounted for primarily by the strength of imaginative virtue which can act by its intrinsic nature without the external senses just as the earth can produce plants by putrefaction without seed. Concerning the imaginative virtue Benedictus cites both Avicenna, *Sextus naturalium,* and Abdala the Arab. He purposely remains silent as to a celestial cause because it is universal and remote, and because God shuts up the stars as with a seal. Remedies have often been learned from dreams and warnings received, of which many historical and other examples are given. But many persons cultivate forbidden arts of the Chaldeans and vanities of magic which Christians should shun. Demons may influence visions and revelations, there is also the possibility of hallucination, and sometimes identical effects can be produced naturally and miraculously. As a Roman Catholic, Benedictus indulges in some recrimination at the expense of Protestantism. But he holds that the pagan sibyls attained the spirit of prophecy by their adherence to virginity. In closing he cites "the concourse of all cabalists" as well as Augustine for the opinion that an angelic power is set over every visible thing in this world.

In 1575 there was printed at Padua a paper on dreams and divination from dreams which Alessandro Carreri, a priest and jurisconsult of that city, had read before the Academy of Animosi.[70] Its publication was approved by the local inquisitor. We have considered in another chapter Carreri's disputation whether metals can be produced artificially. Carreri used the *De somno et vigilia* of Aristotle and contended that the heart and not the brain was the seat of the sentient soul, imaginative virtue, and of dreams. Dreams were produced either by the spirits which serve the senses and retain some images as they return to the heart during sleep, or by memory being aroused. Carreri believed that the intellect also operated in sleep, and that dreams had a purpose and end. Though many were "empty, negligible and

[70] A. Carreri, *De somniis deque divinatione per somnia,* Patavii, 1575: copy used, BM 719.g.37.

utterly to be despised," others were signs, bodily or mental, or even causes, or foreshadowed the event of human action. But the Platonic doctrine that dreams are divinatory because connected with the ideas in the divine mind was not consonant with the thought of Aristotle. Avicenna's theory of dreams is not acceptable to Carreri, because he supposes a hierarchy of creating Intelligences, whereas God alone can create; because Avicenna has mortal forms produced by the giver of forms, whereas like is not produced by like; because Avicenna says that by intelligence is produced the soul of the sky endowed with sentient and imaginative virtue; and because Avicenna incorrectly represents the *intellectus agens* as distinct from our rational soul. Carreri also rejects the doctrine of certain Arabs that Intelligences which they call forms of the world not only assist the heavens and impart some perfection to them but pour out a virtue like light through the universe and reveal the future to the rational soul in dreams and prophecy. Others ascribe dreams to the emanation of idols or similitudes from objects. But Aristotle in *De sensu et sensibili* denies the reality of such emanations, and, even if we admit them, it is not clear how the incorporeal can be revealed by such corporeal idols or how colors would be emitted at nightime.

That God can send dreams directly is denied by some on such grounds as that God knows only Himself and not particular things, or that separate intelligences cannot present particular objects to the imagination. The theologians, however, insist that God can send dreams directly, and Aristotle grants that God contains all things in virtue as in cause. Nor would the philosopher deny that intelligence through the light and motion of the sky so disposes mortal bodies as to move melancholy and the other humors in a way which excites some divining dreams. Carreri concludes with the theologians that God can act either through media or directly on anything, and with Aristotle that God excites dreams by alterations depending on the heavens, received in the air, and impressed on the humors and spirits of the body. Then through hidden channels by which the mind is united to the body the bodily spirits offer images to the imaginative faculty. It is hard to see, except that it is ascribed to Aristotle and mentions God, how this explanation is any different from the doctrine of the astronomers, earlier mentioned by Carreri, who ascribe dreams to the influence of the stars through the air upon our bodies and minds. Yet he had objected to it that in that case all men should have the same dream simultaneously. Without recognizing that this objection would seem equally applicable to his own theory, Carreri passes on to explain away the interdiction in the Book of Genesis as levelled only at curious and superstitious observance of dreams. He further hazards the suggestion, subject to correction by the Roman Catholic church, that observance of the song and flight of birds is not absolutely forbidden Christians but only the superstitious variety called augury or auspices. Carreri died only in 1625 or 1626, when he was almost an octogenarian.[71] How his youthful attitude of 1575 may have been affected or altered by the bull of Sixtus V against astrology and divination I do not know.

Thomas Hill or Hyll, who translated Cocles on chiromancy into English about 1550, published a work on the interpretation of dreams in English at London in 1567 and again in 1576.[72] His interest in divination of the future is further shown by an annual astrological prediction for 1572[73] and a work on the effects and significations of certain comets.[74]

In 1577 the Arabic work on interpretation of dreams of Achmet or Ahmed ibn Sirin was printed at Frankfurt under the misleading designation, *Apomosatis Apotelesmata sive de significatis . . . somniorum*. It was again published with the work of Artemidorus at Paris in 1603 by Rigaltius.[75]

[71] Tomasini (1630), pp. 366-67.

[72] *The most pleasaunte Arte of the interpretacion of Dreames . . .*, London, 1576, 8vo: copy used, BM 719.e.32.(1.). The earlier printing was by Wm. Copland at Lothbury.

[73] Hellmann (1924), p. 32, citing Eustace F. Bosanquet, *English Printed Almanacks and Prognostications*, London, 1917, LXXV.

[74] *A Contemplation of Mysteries: contayning the rare effects and significations of Certayne Comets . . . Gathered and Englished by T. Hyll*, London, (1590?): cited in the article on Hill in DNB by Gordon Goodwin.

[75] On the earlier history of the work and the modern bibliography of it see T II, 291 *et seq.*; GS I, 558-59.

Another work on dreams of an Aristotelian cast was addressed in 1591 to the duke of Urbino by Celso Mancini of Ravenna, a professor of moral philosophy at Ferrara and canon at the Lateran.[76] It certainly shows little effect of the bull of Sixtus V, as to the possible influence of which on Carreri we speculated above. In the preface Mancini warns the reader not to take offense when he hears him asserting that dreams are not sent by God. The Bible of course states that they are, but in the present disputation Mancini intends not to mix the sacred with the profane. Nor if he gives the Aristotelian reasons for denying the existence of demons, should the reader hold him any more responsible than if he explained how Luther arrived at his damnable heresy. In short, if he wears the Peripatetic wolfskin for the moment, let the reader remember that beneath it he is at heart a Christian lamb. Much like Carreri, Mancini agrees with Aristotle that dreams are caused by images brought from memory especially by the blood returning to the heart where the imaginative virtue resides. He thinks of such images as sprinkled through the spirits in the blood as stars are scattered through the eighth sphere. Anent the Aristotelian attribution of divination to melancholy, Mancini adds that this may be either from some occult property, or because that humor acts as a bridle or mainspring of our rational soul and spurs it on, or because, as Ficino had suggested, the most subtle, lucid and agile spirits are generated from that humor. Asking the cause of true dreams, Mancini reviews the opinions of Democritus, Synesius, Porphyry, Iamblichus, Aristotle, Averroes, Avicenna, Albertus Magnus and Jean de Jandun before setting forth his own defense of Aristotle.

The chief work on the subject of augury during the sixteenth century was by Agostino Nifo, who wrote a treatise *De auguriis* in the field of divination just as he touched on well-nigh every other mooted topic of his time. He did not do so, however, until relatively late in his career. According to Graesse the first edition of Nifo's *De auguriis* was printed at Bologna by the heirs of Hieronymus de Benedictis in 1531. The edition which I have

[76] C. Mancini, *De somniis*, 1591: copy used, BM c.76.b.1.

used and which is more commonly cited is that of Basel, 1534, in which the work of Nifo is bound with that of Horapollo on hieroglyphics.[77] In this edition, however, the text is dated at its close, "January 2, 1524." This cannot be a misprint for 1534, if there really was an earlier printing of 1531. The work is addressed to count Guido Rangoni who lived until 1537, so that his dates do not help to determine that of the composition of the work as between 1524 and 1534. This treatise by Nifo was published in a French translation by Antoine du Moulin at Paris in 1547, together with a French translation by Charles Fontaine of the first three books of the *Oneirocritica* of Artemidorus. The Latin text was reprinted at Marburg in 1614 with Nifo's work on critical days and the *Urania divinatrix* of Goclenius.

Nifo states that Aristotle and many others put faith in auguries, and that he composes two books on the subject lest their example lead others astray. In the first book he will narrate all the vanities they handed down. In the second he will disprove the reasons they gave for trusting auguries and will show in what auguries one may put faith and how far augury may go. The first book includes such topics as augurific sneezes, jumpings and tremors, and the opinions of Pliny, Plutarch and the astronomers as to auguries, with tables of the moon in the twelve signs of the zodiac.

The Peripatetics contend that auguries are neither cause nor effect of future events. Yet Aristotle in *De somno et vigilia* holds that a dream is *per accidens* a cause of the future, and this line of reasoning might equally well be applied to auguries. Some persons say that augury is not a cause *per se* but shares the causal effect of the constellation under which it is performed. But Nifo calls them insane and points out that any superstitious art of divination like pyromancy or geomancy might be justified by a like argument. He then repeats approvingly the position of Aquinas in *De sortibus* that, if even the stars cannot cause con-

[77] Aug. Niphus Suessanus, *De auguriis libri II. . . . Ori Apollinis Niliaci de hieroglyphicis notis libri II . . .*, Basel, Joh. Hervagius, 1534: copy used BM 718.f.20.

tingent events, much less can the acts of animals and other bases of augury do so. Nifo also rehearses the arguments of Pliny and Favorinus against augury. In another passage he takes too seriously Pliny's statement that auguries are valid as they are received by us, that is, are valid for those who accept them. Nifo argues against it that our imaginative power has no virtue over birds or beasts, whereas Pliny probably had reference to the effect of credulity in augury upon the conduct of the believer himself.

Like dreams, auguries may be classed as divine, natural and fortuitous. Natural ones are akin to the symptoms which the physician notes in his patient. Or if a meteorologist on seeing three suns predicted rain, he would not exceed natural reason. But most sneezes, tremors, flight and singing of birds Nifo dismisses as fortuitous, and hence divination therefrom is nugatory and superstitious. He then concludes that the true cause of superstitious auguries is the demon. He denies that a good demon moves auguries by intervention of the moon, as recent writers (*iuniores*) think. But it is true that evil demons concur with the observance of certain stars, especially the moon, in order to lead men into error.

This is perhaps the best place to mention Nifo's work on weather signs, printed at Venice in 1540.[78] No doubt, however, he would have classified it as natural science rather than divination and have associated it with his books of meteorology, which it often cites, rather than with his work on augury. In any case it is chiefly a compilation from classical authorities such as Pliny, Theophrastus, the commentary of Theon on Aratus, Vergil, Alexander of Aphrodisias, and the anonymous interpreter of Ptolemy of whom Nifo had made so much in his astrological treatise on the calamities of our times. Nifo also, however, cites

[78] *Magni Augustini Niphi Medici philosophi Suessani de verissimis temporum signis commentariolus ad illustrissimam Mariam Aragoniam Vasti Marchionissam,* Venetiis apud Hieronymum Scotum, 1540, 143 pp. in italics. Copies used: BN R.12808, where it is bound with the Bologna, 1520 edition of Nifo's work on the predictions of a flood from the conjunctions of 1524, and BM 538.a.31.

the venerable Bede, Averroes and Albertus Magnus. There are also statements and chapters without any citations. In the chapter on signs of rain from diseases of animals comes a personal touch, Nifo stating that he is wont to joke with his students and say that his rectum is an astronomer because its actions indicate the coming of rain, while "we have observed in our much beloved dog, Falcon, in fair weather rumblings of the belly paining him so that he would not eat. When rain came and the pain ceased, he would be ravenously hungry."[79] The arrangement of Nifo's work is topical: first chapters on signs of fair weather, then of rain, and so on. In the last chapter on the revolution of scarcity and fertility and their duration,[80] he states that it is the common opinion of men "in our locality" that they cannot last more than thirty years, and that the astronomical explanation is that Saturn causes fertility or paucity of crops and that its revolution in its orbit is completed in thirty years. He then proceeds, without making any attempt to reconcile the ensuing inconsistency, that Scripture tells of seven successive years of scarcity, "which we too have observed more than once in our locality," but that according to astronomers it cannot last more than three years, because Jupiter every three years alters the force of the angle in the figure of sixteen sides (which he had elsewhere stressed as Ptolemaic)[81] which it describes with Saturn.

In 1616 Paul Minerva, a Dominican, master of sacred theology, and commentator on Aristotle, published an elaborate work on weather prediction, dedicated to cardinal Galemini.[82] He cited a great number of authorities from the Greeks, Indians and Arabs down, including such less common authors as Vettius Valens, Teucer of Babylon and Conrad Wimpina,[83] and utilizing the scholia of Noviomagus on the *De natura rerum* of Bede.[84] He succeeded in finding the tract of Nifo on weather

[79] *Ibid.*, pp. 82-83.

[80] *Ibid.*, pp. 135-36.

[81] In his *De figuris stellarum Helionoricis,* Naples, 1526, folio: copy used, BN Rés. R.112 (2).

[82] Paulus Minerva Barensis, *De praesagiendis temporum mutationibus iuxta triplicem viam coelestem metheorologicam et terrestrem libri tres,* Neapoli, 1616, folio. Copy used: BM 719.m.9.

[83] I, 8 and 12; II, 32 (p. 263). For Wimpina see T IV, 268-73.

[84] II, 5 (p. 210).

signs only after a vain search of twelve years and while his own book was in the press.[85] He accepted the influence of the stars and astrological weather prediction and noted the rains and floods which followed the conjunction of Saturn and Jupiter in Pisces in 1583 while he was going from Milan to Bologna as a student in September, 1587.[86] Each star, he affirmed, had its particular influence fixed by divine decree at creation.[87] He here repeated the effects of comets according to those who classed them as meteors but he proposed to write a special tract upon comets demonstrating that they were celestial.[88] Minerva distinguished between superstitious and natural divination from thunder. He accepted as by Bede tracts on the signification of thunder. He also listed various supposed safeguards against lightning, such as wearing a gem, although for some of them he seemed not to wish to assume responsibility.[89] He believed in weather prediction from natural dreams, and that boys because of their tender age were sensitive to aerial impressions and weather change.[90] He says that prediction from the weather on January 25 of the year has prevailed since antiquity. If that day is clear, there will follow abundance. If it is windy, wars are denoted. The reason for this, he admits, is occult and hidden from us.[91]

Belief in portents and prodigies had found frequent support in both ancient historians and medieval chroniclers, and continued to do so in sixteenth century historians. Jacob Mennel in 1503 dedicated to the emperor Maxmilian a treatise on signs, prodigies and portents, old and new, especially during the years 1500-1503.[92] In an astrological judgment by Gaspar Torrella, printed in 1507, portents and prodigies are defined, while omens are recounted from Roman and medieval history.[93] The next year, 1508, saw the publication of the text of the ancient Latin writer, Julius Obsequens, on prodigies.[94] Polydore Vergil, while in Eng-

[85] Preface to the reader.

[86] I, 9 (p. 19).

[87] II, 8 (p. 214).

[88] II, 10 (pp. 218-19).

[89] II, 12-13, pp. 223-29.

[90] III, 21, pp. 331-32.

[91] II, 29, p. 258.

[92] Vienna 4417*, 24 ff.

[93] *Epistola de portentis presagiis prodigiisque admirabilibus, de solis et lune defectibus deque cometis.*

[94] It was printed with the Aldine edition of Pliny's letters at pp. 495-525.

land in 1526, wrote a dialogue on prodigies which was perhaps not printed until 1531.[95] The work of Camerarius on portents, published in 1532, has already been mentioned in our chapter on The Circle of Melanchthon. Conrad Lycosthenes' (c.1518-1561) chronicle of prodigies and portents was printed at Basel in 1557.[96] Two years later its author's name appeared on Paul IV's *Index* of prohibited books but without reference to any particular work by him. "Licosthenes" was much cited in the posthumous edition in 1642 by Bartholomaeus Ambrosinus of Aldrovandi's work on monsters, although he was censured as having written many idle things. A work similar to that of Lycosthenes which appeared at Wittenberg some thirty years later was the *Catalogue of Prodigies and Marvelous Things of Recent Occurrence* by B. Dubenus.[97] An enumeration of prodigies during the years 1531-1585 is found in manuscript.[98]

Michael Stanhufius in his work on meteors was inclined to regard as prodigies such apparitions in the air as that recently seen in Switzerland of two lions fighting, one of which tore off the other's head, or one of a dragon fighting with a snake, which was seen by himself in September, 1551, and which lasted for two hours. Many such were observed before and after the captivity of Johann Frederick, elector of Saxony. Some argue that the clouds are invested with such forms by the imaginations of the beholders, but Stanhufius rejects this explanation and holds that these phantasms appear contrary to the natural order as signs of divine wrath at human sin. He would so interpret a cloudburst of 1551 in Franconia which destroyed the walls of towns and splendid buildings and many vineyards, or the damage done on the Baltic and in Saxony by a great wind of the same year.[99]

[95] There is a copy of the Basel, 1531 edition of *De prodigiis* in the British Museum: 697.b.18.(4.).

[96] Conrad Lycosthenes, *Prodigiorum ac ostentorum chronicon quae praeter naturae ordinem . . . ab exordio mundi . . . ad haec . . . tempora acciderunt*, Basel, 1557, folio, pp. 20, 670. In MS Strasburg 65 (Latin 63) the work is continued from 1557 to 1638.

[97] B. Dubenus, *Catalogus prodigiorum rerumque aliquot mirabilium quae paulo ante acciderunt*, Witebergae, 1591, duodecimo.

[98] Vienna 2945, 16c, 243 ff.

[99] Michael Stanhufius, *De meteoris,*

A Catalogue of Prodigies and Portents Divinely Manifested in Heaven and Earth in Punishment of Crimes and Signification of Great Changes in the World was published by Marcus Frytschius in 1563 together with his treatise on meteorology, dedicated to the emperor Ferdinand from Breslau and printed at Nürnberg.[100] Frytschius says that he first presented the work to Ferdinand at Augsburg. He added the brief tract of Albohazen Hali on the significance of comets in the twelve signs of the zodiac.[101] The prodigies begin with Noah's flood and come down to 1562, including earthquakes, comets, swarms of locusts, eclipses, pests, falls of buildings, two-headed calves, and planetary conjunctions. In the revised edition of 1583 of *De meteoris* by Johannes Hagius, whose preface is dated September 8, 1581, the catalogue of portents was omitted.[102]

That historians of the sixteenth century continued to deal in prodigies may be illustrated from the pages of de Thou. He details such events as a rain of grain in Carinthia near Klagenfurt and Villach in March, 1548, or the birth in Meissen in the same year of a child with a divided forehead and cranium, and without lips, right ear, hands or feet, or the hatching of a chick at Paris with four wings and four feet. For 1560 he lists such signs in the sky as fires, a great number of horsemen, a comet, "most sure announcer of death to the king," and a church struck by lightning, not to mention an earthquake. In 1572 a flying dragon was seen in the air. Or we are told how Condé had a fatal

---

Wittenberg, 1562: fols. P 3 r-v, P 5 r-v, Q 5 verso.

[100] *Meteorum hoc est impressionum aerearum et mirabilium naturae operum loci fere omnes methodo dialectica conscripti et singulari quadam cura diligentiaque in eum ordinem digesti ac distributi a M. Marco Frytschio Laubano Hexapolensi Lusatiae superioris alumno. Item Catalogus prodigiorum atque ostentorum tam coelo quam in terra in poenam scelerum ac magnarum in mundo vicissitudinum significationem iam inde ab initio divinitus exhibitorum ab eodem conscriptus. Omnia ab authore recognita et locupletata.* Noribergae anno 1563, in officina Ioannis Montani et Ulrici Neuberi, 8vo. Copy used: BM 538.a.4.

[101] It has a separate title page, although there are but two pages of text.

[102] *De meteoris sive impressionibus aereis . . . nunc . . . pluribus in locis auctiores et emendatiores opera Iohannis Hagii,* Witebergae, excudebat Iohannes Lufft, 1583, 8vo. Copy used: BM 538.a.7.

dream and met an old hag before the battle in which he was captured.[103]

With the literature of portents and prodigies may be associated the seven books of marvels published at Cologne in 1532 by Frederick Nausea, a theologian of Wurtemberg, doctor of laws, and preacher in a church at Mainz, who in 1541 became bishop of Vienna.[104] He raises the question whether anyone can foreknow the future from marvels of rare occurrence and answers it in the affirmative. He doubts, however, whether marvels which are entirely natural, like the magnet attracting iron or the salamander living in fire, can be signs of the future, since they always act in the same way and therefore cannot be special signs of unusual events. He then turns to marvels seen in the sky and on earth in the year 1531. These included three suns which are a sign of prolonged rain, the image of the upper half of a man holding in his hand a bloody sword which was probably a sign of sanguinary strife, a fiery citadel, an army with the implements of war, a prodigious birth in Germany, a girl of seven or eight years at Rome from whose breasts spouted limpid water, bloody crosses in the sky, a shower of black bread in Apulia, and a comet. After giving historical examples to show what has followed when such phenomena appeared before, Nausea comes to the conclusion that the end of the world is near, although he refuses to try to set a definite date for it. In his last book he goes back to an earthquake in 1528 and what it portended. Earlier he had discussed the differences in meaning between the Latin words for prodigy, portent, monster, omen, presage and *ostentum*, in a tiresome style which made one feel that he was well named Nausea. He omitted from consideration auguries and auspices as too superstitious and passed over dreams as signs of the future in the present work because he had already composed a separate treatise on them which he might sometime publish. Later, when he was bishop of Vienna, Nausea addressed to the archduke

[103] *Iac. Aug. Thuani Historiarum* lib. 5, 27, 56, 34. There are many other such passages.

[104] F. Nausea, *Libri mirabilium septem*, Cologne, Petr. Quentell, 1532, 4to. Copy used: BM 444.d.22.(1.). Gesner (1545), fol. 261v, lists other works by Nausea but not this.

Ferdinand a treatise preserved in manuscript, entitled "A Booklet of Secrets," and considered the problem of the origin of the calamities of the time and how they could and should be removed.[105]

Eight books of Sibylline oracles in Greek verse were first printed at Basel in 1545 by Oporinus, with excerpts of Lactantius from them, annotations of Xystus Betuleius Augustanus, and a Latin translation of the predictions as to Christ of various sibyls: the Persian, Delphic, Cimmerian, Samian, Cumean, Hellespontine, Phrygian, European, Tiburtine, Agrippan and Erythraean. Gesner, writing in the same year, noted that some of the verses were corrupt and that others did not scan.[106] Ten years later a complete translation of the *Oracles* was issued by Sébastien Châteillon, professor of Greek at Basel.[107] Among his numerous works on classical antiquities Onufrio Panvinio of Verona (1529-1568) included a discussion of the sibyls and sibylline verses, published at Venice the year before his death.[108] Annotations on the *Oracles* by Joannes Opsopoeus (1555-1596) were first printed in 1589 and subsequently in 1599, 1607 and 1689, sometimes with Châteillon's translation.

The theme of fate is closely related to that of divination, so that we may record the publication in 1508 of a *Question Concerning Fate* by Petrus Feltrus or Pietro d'Afeltro (da Feltre). He was a physician, philosopher, Aristotelian commentator, and professor of Naples. The work was dedicated to cardinal Oliviero Caraffa, to whom Nifo in 1504 had dedicated his astrological *De nostrarum calamitatum causis*.[109] Pomponazzi's treatise on fate and free will has been mentioned in our chapter upon him. In 1563 at Venice appeared the nine books on fate of Julius

[105] Vienna 9616, 16th century, 43 fols. It opens and closes as follows: "Inter tam multas quam varias . . . / . . . Deus deorum in Sion. Amen."

[106] Gesner (1545), fol. 597v.

[107] *Sibyllinorum oraculorum libri VIII interprete Sebastiano Castalione*, Basileae, 1555.

[108] *De sybillis et carminibus sybillinis*, Venetiis, 1567: according to the list of his writings given by Domenico Antonio Gandolfo, *Dissertatio historica de ducentis celeberrimis Augustinianis scriptoribus*, Rome, 1704.

[109] N. Cortese, "L'età spagnuola," in *Storia della Università di Napoli*, 1924, p. 325, citing Toppi, Nicodemo and Tafuri. I have not seen a copy of Pietro's work.

Serenius, a philosopher of Brescia, whose work was called erudite by Gabriel Naudé in the next century.[110] There was a treatise against fate in thirteen chapters by Quenay of Evreux in 1575,[111] while Baccio Baldini treated of the subject in a work published in Italian at Florence in 1578.[112] Other writers on fate listed by Naudé in 1647 were Sepulveda, Lactantius Domeninus, Ulpian of Verona, Jacobus Carpentarius, Omphalius and Riolan.[113]

Nicolaus Leonicus Thomaeus or Niccolò Leonico Tomeo, professor at Padua where he died in 1531 at the age of seventy-four, in dialogues published at Venice in 1524 had among other topics touched upon divination. I have been unable to find sixteen books on the art of divining ascribed by Gesner to Ludovicus Ponticus Virunius or Virmius of Treviso.[114] The two chief general works on that subject during the sixteenth century were by the Protestant scholars of Wittenberg, Peucer and Camerarius. *Mantice* was the first word in the title of a work published at Lyons in 1588 by Pontus de Thyard, Tyard or Thiard, but, as the full title suggests,[115] the work was devoted exclusively to astrology and not to other arts of divination, and we have considered it in a chapter on astrology.

The work of Caspar Peucer (1525-1602) on various kinds of divination was first printed at Wittenberg in 1553,[116] again in 1560, 1576 and 1580 at the same place, then at Frankfurt in 1593,[117] forty years after its first appearance but still within the

[110] Io. Hallevord, *Bibliotheca curiosa*, Regiomonti et Francofurti, 1676, p. 223.

[111] *Quenaei Ebroicensis De fati expugnatione libellus*, Paris, 1575. Ad clarissimum officialem Rothomagensem Christophorum Eude, Mecoenatem suum. At the close ecclesiastical approvals of the work by two doctors of theology, David Berot and Ioannes Paradis, are respectively dated Dec. 12 and 16, 1574. Copy used BN Rés. R.885.

[112] *Discorso dell' essenzia del fato e delle forze sue sopra le cose del monde e particolarmente sopra l'operazioni degl' huomini.*

[113] *Gabrielis Naudaei . . . Πεντὰς questionum iatro-philologicarum*, Geneva, 1647, p. 160.

[114] Gesner (1545), fol. 568v.

[115] Pontus de Tyard, *Mantice ou discours de la verité de divination par astrologie*, Lyon, 1558.

[116] Caspar Peucer, *Commentarius de praecipuis divinationum generibus, in quo a prophetiis divina autoritate traditis et physicis praedictionibus separantur diabolicae fraudes et superstitiosae observationes* . . . Wittebergae, Johannes Crato, 1553, 335 fols., 8vo.

[117] Caspar Peucer, *Commentarius de praecipuis divinationum generibus, in quo a prophetiis authoritate divina*

lifetime of its author who composed a long preface dated in 1591 for this new edition. Meanwhile the book had been published in a French translation in 1584.[118] There was at least one more Latin edition, at Hanover in 1607 after Peucer's death. Thus it seems to have been the most influential of his numerous writings which were concerned with the varied fields of medicine, astronomy, mathematics, natural history, and psychology.[119] Alsted made considerable use of it in his encyclopedia in the following century.

Peucer, a doctor of medicine and philosophy, had studied at Wittenberg under Melanchthon, whose daughter he married. In 1545 he became professor of philosophy, in 1554 of mathematics, in 1560 of medicine at the university of Wittenberg, and most of his writings were printed there. John Garcaeus, writing at Wittenberg in 1556, spoke of Peucer as a "most celebrated professor of mathematics in this academy and my most dear preceptor."[120] In matters of religious belief Peucer followed Melanchthon rather than the strict Lutherans and became a violent opponent of consubstantiation as well as of transub-

---

traditis et a physicis coniecturis discernuntur artes et imposturae diabolicae atque observationes natae ex superstitione et cum hac coniunctae: et monstrantur fontes ac cause physicarum praedictionum: diabolicae vero ac superstitiosae confutatae damnantur ea serie quam tabella praefixa ostendit, Francofurti, apud Andreae Wecheli heredes, Claudium Marnium et Ioan. Aubrium, 1593, 738 pp. and Index. I have used a copy of this edition in which a few pages (275-86), containing the end of the section on theomancy and the opening of that on magic, were missing.

[118] *Les Devins, ou commentaire des principales sortes de devinations. Nouvellement tournée en François par S(imon) G(oulart) S(enlisien.),* pp. 653. H. Cornix, Anvers, 1584.

[119] The chief titles are: *Volucrum et piscium appellationes collectę a P. Ebero et C. Peucero,* 1549. *De dimensione terrae et geometrice numerandis locorum particularium intervallis,* Witebergae, 1587. *De essentia, natura, et ortu animi hominis,* 1590; other eds., 1594, 1597. *Elementa doctrinae de circulis coelestibus et primo motu,* 1551. *Logistice astronomica hexacontadωn et scrupulorum sexagesimorum quam algorythmum minutiarum physicalium vocant, regulis explicata,* 1556. The following medical treatises were published posthumously: *Practica seu methodus curandi morbos internos,* ed. P. Uffenbach, Francofurti, 1614. *Tractatus de febribus, ab autore ipso primum publice praelectus, nunc vere in lucem emissus,* Francofurti. 1614.

[120] In the Epilogue to his *Tractatus brevis . . . de erigendis figuris coeli* etc., printed at Wittenberg, 1573. This work has been discussed in a previous chapter. See above, pp. 102-103.

stantiation in the eucharist.[121] He is regarded as a leader of crypto-Calvinism in electoral Saxony. He was imprisoned for twelve years by the elector from 1574 to 1586, a matter to which he refers feelingly in his long preface of 1591. After his release he became physician to the duke of Anhalt.[122]

Peucer's discussion of divination is colored by his classical scholarship and his Protestantism. He often indulges in snatches of Greek, although he usually gives immediately afterwards a Latin translation of the Greek words. These classical passages include the quotation of numerous ancient oracles. His Protestantism is shown in religious digressions and a hostile attitude to Roman Catholicism. In the latter part of the first section of his work, at least in the edition of 1593, he seems for a time to forget about the subject of divination and embarks upon a long consideration of the different degrees of divine presence. These are: first, in all creatures which are in the universe generally; second, in the blessed angels and in mankind; third, in the Church and those who are saved; fourth, in the Son.[123] Elsewhere he discusses the sacraments and Holy Spirit in opposition to the church of Rome, and declares that Mohammedanism and popery are two kingdoms contrary to Christ and works of the devil.[124]

The general arrangement of Peucer's text is as follows. After discussing divination in general, he turns to oracles and theomancy, then to magic—which he thus incorrectly implies is a

[121] His position in this regard may be briefly illustrated by quoting a passage from the preface of 1591 to his work on divination in which he affirms that Melanchthon consistently opposed "both magics of the pontiffs: the one of the conversion of holy bread by the consecration of the shaven priest, differing in no wise from magic, into the substance of the body of Christ, though all Scripture together with the nature of things and the character of miracles as extraordinary works of God are utterly opposed to this; the other of the connection and copulation with the bread by the same magic logic of the body included and involved in it."

[122] On Peucer's religious position and career see: Friedrich Coch, *De vita D. Caspari Peuceri*, 1856; E. L. T. Henke, *Kaspar Peucer und Nikolaus Kriel,* Marburg, 1865; Calinisch, *Kampf und Untergang des Melanchthonismus in Kursachsen,* Leipzig, 1866.

[123] *Commentarius de praecipuis divinationum generibus,* 1593, p. 131 et seq.

[124] *Ibid.*, p. 198.

variety of divination, whereas the opposite is true—then to divination from entrails, to augury and aruspicina, to lot-casting under which he puts geomancy and divining from names and numbers, and to dreams and their interpretation. Next he considers medical prognostications, meteorology and weather prediction, physiognomy and chiromancy, astrology, and last prodigies and portents. There does not seem to be much logic to this arrangement and it includes subjects which otherwise we do not consider in this chapter. But we shall have to present Peucer's work as we find it.

Peucer criticizes the Aristotelian doctrine of the eternity of the world and accepts the account of creation in the Book of Genesis.[125] He asserts that God may act directly on nature by miracles and special providences, not merely through secondary causes and the forces of nature. But he more than once insists that God is not the cause of sin and that the human will is free. Miracles, moreover, have their limits. Nothing is ever absolutely annihilated in them, nor can two things occupy the same space simultaneously. When the water was changed to wine at Cana, it was not both water and wine at the same time.[126] In these strictures Peucer's objective seems to be denial of the miracle of the mass and of the doctrine of consubstantiation, affirming that Christ cannot at the same time be body and not body.

Natural divination Peucer in general regards as licit. He recognizes, however, that the Bible sometimes seems to forbid it, while in other passages it appears to encourage divination from natural causes.[127] The explanation of this apparent contradiction is that natural divination is permissible, if it is not admixed with superstition, if due order is observed, and if divine power is duly kept in mind. While permissible, natural divination may fail because matter is in a state of flux and instability, the mixtures of the primary qualities keep changing and forms alter, so that the outcome varies.[128] Even the influences of the stars may fail to produce their usual effects because of the intractability of

[125] *Ibid.*, pp. 557-64.
[126] *Ibid.*, p. 138.
[127] *Ibid.*, p. 117.
[128] *Ibid.*, pp. 71-72.

matter. Furthermore, in natural divination the person essaying to predict must not only observe the rules of the art but should be born with a natural talent for it.[129]

The discussion of illicit or diabolical divination leads to much the usual estimate of the nature and power of the demons who lure men into the practice of such arts. Peucer believes that the demons act with divine permission and that they cannot create any species. But they have marvelous art and are able to simulate creative activity by means of apparitions and phantasms. They have power especially in the air where they congregate the clouds to produce marvelous phenomena, and they know the science of astrology down to the last detail.[130] Moreover, while they cannot create species, Peucer has no doubt that they can abuse creatures.[131] As a Protestant, Peucer attributes the frequent success of invocation of the saints and the working of cures and other marvels by relics to the fraud of demons, whose purpose in this is to keep men from calling directly upon God.[132] But Peucer does not believe that even an angel, much less a demon, can cover an immense distance in a moment and be in heaven and earth practically simultaneously. Witches have simply been deluded in their imaginations by demons, when they assert that they have travelled hundreds of miles in a moment. Peucer, however, experiences some difficulty in explaining away the flight of the prophet Habakkuk.[133] He is more credulous in describing the case of a girl who was supposed to be possessed by demons, and states that he himself saw the demon running to and fro under the skin in a form which looked like a mouse.[134]

There is little that is novel in Peucer's discussion of oracles.

[129] *Ibid.*, pp. 76-78.

[130] *Ibid.*, pp. 41-44.

[131] *Ibid.*, p. 147.

[132] *Ibid.*, p. 47.

[133] *Ibid.*, p. 148. The flight of Habakkuk is recounted in the thirteenth and fourteenth chapters of the Book of Daniel which were omitted in the King James version. This passage and that in which the devil takes Jesus up on a pinnacle of the temple were the chief scriptural reliance of those who argued for the flight of witches in the medieval and early modern periods. A good deal may be found on this point in Hansen (1900), but unfortunately there is no index. The weight of learned opinion was against the flight of witches or their transport through the air by demons, but during the delusion (1400-1700) many rabid witch-hounds asserted its reality.

[134] *Ibid.*, p. 258.

In the main he rehearses the familiar classical accounts of them. He holds, however, that the oldest oracles, such as those of Jupiter Ammon in Egypt and of Dodona, were perversions affected by the devil from the domestic school which Noah established after the flood for his children and grandchildren who set up similar schools when they scattered over the face of the earth. These schools were then gradually perverted into the seats of oracles which owed their efficacy to demons.[135] In another passage Peucer states that the ancient Chaldeans converted religion into philosophy, that the Egyptians converted religion into superstition, that the Greeks converted it into disputations and allegories, while the Romans turned it into monarchy and papacy.[136] He further asserts that as the pagan oracles ceased to function at the coming of Christ, so when Luther purged the church, many deceits and illusions of the demons were done away.[137]

This last point had already been made by Johannes Rivius of Attendorn (1500-1553) in his work on specters and apparitions or old superstition in 1541.[138] He further asserted that the dreams and silly fables of the monks were now a thing of the past, that bells were no longer consecrated, adjured, baptized and anointed as they once were, that no one today suspended verses of the Gospels from his neck or wore wax consecrated by the pope. Rivius admitted, however, that a few vestiges of superstition remained even among Protestants, some of whom still sought hidden treasure by crystal-gazing or employed incantations and arts of divination. Witches also had not disappeared even with the Reformation, and Rivius urged that they be put to death. This Rivius, after teaching boys for twenty-five years at Cologne, Zwickau, Anneberg and Meissen, and editing notes on Terence, turned to theology and canon law but died in his fifty-third year of a local pest after losing his son, nephew and wife by it. George Fabricius of Chemnitz who succeeded him in

[135] *Ibid.*, pp. 224-25.
[136] *Ibid.*, pp. 264-65.
[137] *Ibid.*, pp. 250-51.
[138] Ioh. Rivius. *De conscientia libri iiii. Eiusdem de spectris et apparitionibus umbrarum seu de veteri superstitione,* Lipsiae, 1541, 8vo: copy used, BM 847.b.1.(1.).

his school also wrote his life. His educational treatise, *De institutione puerorum,* was printed at Lyons in 1550 and perhaps earlier. In 1537 he printed a work at Wittenberg on the familiar genius or guardian angel of each person, which is primarily religious and of no importance for our investigation.[139] De Thou placed his death in 1553. Peucer may have owed more than he acknowledges to Rivius.

As we have already implied, Peucer makes no clear distinction between divination and magic. Under the magic arts he takes up necromancy at some length, adducing many historical examples, then more briefly runs over lecanomancy, gastromancy, the inspection of lucid surfaces by pure boys, catoptromancy, crystallomancy, dactyliomancy, onychomancy, hydromancy, and aeromancy, all of which might properly be classed as varieties of divination. But then he devotes a distinct book to the subject of incantations, after which he digresses to discuss pharmacy, poisoning and sorcery, but also various other 'mancies or divining arts.

Peucer declares himself in opposition to the Cabala, yet he was much impressed by the significance of numbers. In his introductory section he notes that great changes of empires are apt to occur every five hundred or every seven hundred years.[140] In a later passage he calls attention to the fact that in the year 1449, after an abnormal inundation of the river Pegnitz, war broke out between the margrave of Brandenburg and the city of Nürnberg. Exactly fifty years after the expiration of this war, there was another flood of the Pegnitz and another war with the margrave. Finally, fifty years after that came a third inundation and a third war.[141]

Towards astrology Peucer was even more favorable than towards natural divination. It was for him the part of physical science which investigated the celestial causes of the alterations of inferior bodies. It might of course be abused by charlatans

[139] It is printed with the 1614 edition of the *Opera* of Rivius at pp. 709-30.

[140] *Comm. de praecip. divinationum generibus,* 1593, pp. 30-34.

[141] *Ibid.,* p. 709.

and superstitious persons. But Peucer demonstrated to his own satisfaction by the stock arguments from the manifest effects of the sun and moon and from the tides that the influences of the stars are efficacious, and that prediction of the future can be made from them. He held that critical days were governed by the moon, that fixed stars as well as planets gave significations for the future, that a conjunction of Saturn and Mars was almost invariably unlucky, that the relation of the planets to the eighth sphere was important, and that the customs and morals of different peoples corresponded to the stars to which they were subject. Peucer answered the arguments against astrology of such church fathers as Basil and Chrysostom. He held that observation of the stars was necessary for the successful practice of medicine. He asserted that he did not accept all the Chaldean art, but he treated of genethlialogy and referred the reader further to Ptolemy's *Quadripartitum,* Firmicus, Pontano and Cardan.[142] Things which are not in the sight of all and are not understood by everyone when they are investigated and which do not produce the same effects every year are nevertheless due to the virtue of the stars, with whose motions and influxes they are in remarkable and almost divine agreement.[143] Dreams from which the future may be predicted are influenced by the stars, whereas ordinary dreams are caused by the humors or temperament, although both are formed by the brain in the same way.[144] Peucer's faith in astrology stopped short of astrological images. He reasoned that there was no force from the stars in objects fabricated by human art because in such no new combination of qualities is instituted and no new form is given to matter.[145]

Peucer put much trust in occult virtues and marvelous sympathies.[146] Such sympathies and antipathies between things in nature come from their forms and qualities, whether first, secondary, or occult. The force of the occult qualities is greatest, since they are closest akin to the forms themselves. But since we do not know the forms, we have little hope of discovering the nature

[142] *Ibid.,* pp. 645-93, for Peucer's attitude to astrology.

[143] *Ibid.,* p. 59.

[144] *Ibid.,* p. 453.

[145] *Ibid.,* p. 333.

[146] *Ibid.,* pp. 572, 615, etc.

of the occult qualities which flow from and depend upon them. Peucer accepted such remedies as the peony and the emerald for epilepsy, dung of a white dog for quinsy, the lungs of a fox for asthma, and wearing a belt made of a wolf's intestines for colic,[147] all of which we have already heard from Fernel. He believed in the divining rod.[148] He also accepted spontaneous generation, although he denied that any very new species could be so produced, since things generated from putridity have their limits divinely set.[149]

Creatures generated from putrefaction have, however, an especially close connection with the influence of the heavens, and so furnish a very favorable basis for prediction. For example, if under certain conditions worms are generated, this is a sign of abundant crops. But if flies are produced, wars are portended, while spiders indicate pestilence. The explanation is that the worms are due to a hot and wet sky which fertilizes the soil, while the flies are caused by a dry sky which inflames human bodies and stirs up turbid, acrid and bellicose humors. The generation of spiders, which are venomous creatures, indicates an excess of poisonous putridity and consequently a condition favorable to the outbreak of plague.[150] Peucer further suggests that the pest follows periods of time such as have been mentioned above.

After all this it is something of a surprise to find Peucer hostile to alchemy. He asserts that the transmutation of metals is not possible by any human art, since the transmutation of species is reserved to God alone. Alchemists are apt to be dupes of the devil who blinds their eyes or deludes them into thinking that they have succeeded and have actually produced gold from quicksilver, copper, or some other metal.[151]

After having described with some fulness the work of Peucer, there is the less reason for dwelling on the briefer treatise of like title by Joachim Camerarius (1500-1574) which was printed only in 1576 after his death.[152] As the second half of its title

[147] *Ibid.*, pp. 542, 549.
[148] *Ibid.*, p. 640.
[149] *Ibid.*, p. 539.
[150] *Ibid.*, p. 58.
[151] *Ibid.*, p. 147.
[152] Joachim Camerarius, *Commen-*

shows, it was largely concerned with the Greek and Latin words used for the various types of divination. Based almost wholly on the classics, it discusses oracles, astrology, dreams, physiognomy and chiromancy, symbolica, divination from the flight of birds and from sacrifices, magic incantations, lots, luck, the wheel of fortune, and necromancy. In a digression on climacteric years we are reminded of the fact that Luther and Melanchthon both died at the age of sixty-three. Camerarius not only believed in witches' sabbats but tells on supposedly reliable authority a story of a man leaving his head as surety with a fish-wife while he went home to get money to pay for the fish. In the same year 1576 appeared another posthumous publication by Camerarius, the work of Plutarch on demons with notes. Taken together with his astrological publications and his book of 1532 on portents, these works illustrate the credulity and interest in the occult of a distinguished classical scholar who further possessed a wide acquaintance with almost all fields of learning that were then developed. In fact, Camerarius wrote rather too many books, some one hundred and fifty.

Various kinds of divination were distinguished by George Pictorius in his discussion of ceremonial magic of 1563.[153] All of them were censured by him as diabolical. Necromancy Pictorius subdivided into necyomantia which actually raises the corpse and scyomantia which merely evokes the shade. Anthropomancy is divination by the entrails of boy victims. Lecanomancy, gastromancy and captromancy seem much alike. In the first, water in a basin is exorcized to raise a demon. In the second a boy gazes into a basin of water, a practice usually designated as captromancy, but Pictorius reserves that term for such gazing when a mirror is placed beneath the water. Onimancy is when the boy gazes into his fingernail or palm which has been oiled. Of the forms of divination by the four elements Pictorius distinguishes four varieties of hydromancy and two of geomancy, of which art he pronounces Almadal the Arab the first author.

---

tarius de generibus divinationum ac Graecis Latinisque earum vocabulis, Lipsiae, J. Steinmann, 1576, 154 pp.

[153] *De speciebus magiae ceremonialis quam goetiam vocant*, in his *Pantopolion*, Basel, 1563.

Capnomancy is divination by smoke, caeromancy by dripping wax from Turkey, ichthiomancy with fish, onomancy by names —a Pythagorean table is given. Thephramancy is by ashes, botanomancy by the leaves of sage, sycomancy by fig-leaves, axiomancy by driving an axe into wood or casting it into water, libanomancy by casting incense into the fire. To chiromancy also pertains metoposcopy. Pictorius himself over thirty years ago had three times tried coscinomancy or divination by a sieve but then had abandoned the practice lest demons seduce him. The art of the haruspex, auspices, omens and dreams complete the list except for those who impose upon the populace by superstitions and signs. For these arts Cardan is often cited, Petrus Crinitus on capnomancy, and Giovanni Francesco della Mirandola on geomancy by casting of points and on axiomancy.

The treatise of Camerarius was not the only posthumous publication on the subject of divination. In the following paragraphs we consider two other such works. That of Hieronymus Zanchius of Bergamo (1515-1590) was printed by his heirs only in 1610.[154] He had left Bergamo for Strasburg a little after Peter Martyr whom he succeeded at Strasburg in 1554, when Peter was called to England. Subsequently Zanchius taught at Basel, Nîmes and Heidelberg, where he died.[155] The work on divination reproduces his class-room lectures and is a cut-and-dried performance. He still accepted the Aristotelian doctrine of comets and thought that one could predict to a certain extent from them. But he regarded most divination as diabolical. He also, however, made much use of the arguments against divination in Cicero's *De divinatione*. He discussed omens, specters, lots, physiognomy, divination from dreams and by madness or fury. He distinguished the usual three types of divination: natural, divine and diabolical. He admitted no natural divination from specters but a certain amount from natural dreams. He believed in the significance of the life-line of the hand in chiromancy and in the

[154] Hieron. Zanchius, *De divinatione (ab haeredibus editus). Accessit tract. T. Erasti de astrologia divinatrice.* 2 pt., Hanoviae, 1610, 8vo. The work of Zanchius runs to p. 183.

[155] For these facts I follow Thuanus. *Hist.*, annum 1590.

influence of the stars, but saved free will and attacked nativities. In the case of divination through fury, he admitted only divine inspiration and diabolical possession, denying such human power or that melancholy enables one to foretell the future.

Jean Jacques Boissard, born at Besançon in 1528, died at Metz on October 30, 1602. He appears to have been primarily an antiquarian and poet. His treatise on divination and magic seems to have been printed only in 1615.[156] It is of little importance and in the main a stale farrago of bits from various past authors such as Trithemius, naming and defining different occult arts, telling stories about them, and dealing with such particular themes as lycanthropy, Simon Magus, incubi and succubi. Much Greek verse and Latin translation thereof is included. The chief original feature is an account of the oracle-gods and seers of antiquity with a full length picture of each person heading the discussion of him. Among those so considered are Jupiter of Dodona, Ammon, Themis, the Pythian Apollo, Trophonius, Serapis, the Palisci, Branchus (Branchidae), Mercurius Trismegistus, Proteus, Nicostrata, Telemus, Iapyx, Tiresias, Idmon, Tages, Amphiarus, Thyodamas, Mopsus, Helenus, and the sibyls. The work seems purely literary and antiquarian with no relation to science.

Thaddaeus Hagecius (Tadeáš Hájek z. Hájku) played a considerable part in the controversies stirred up by the new star of 1572 and was well spoken of by Tycho Brahe as an astronomer. He served the imperial family as physician. He was also interested in divination by astrology and in signatures in plants and gems. Fairly early in life the idea occurred to him that, if prediction was possible by chiromancy from the lines in the hand, one's character and destiny might equally well be read in the lines of the forehead, especially if one joined genethlialogy with this art of metoposcopy. Hagecius believed that metoposcopy had

[156] This is the edition which I have used. Émile Auguste Bégin, *Histoire des sciences, des lettres, des arts et de la civilisation dans le pays Messin*, Metz, 1829, who at pp. 404-406 lists eight works by Boissard, calls the *De divinatione et magicis praestigiis* a posthumous publication but dates it at Metz, 1602.

been cultivated by the ancients but was now almost extinct. He began to make and record observations of the foreheads of various persons. As a result he dedicated on December 23, 1560, from Prag to the emperor Ferdinand a brief and partial but, as he believed, new and original treatment of the subject.[157] He says that the emperor often conversed with him about the hidden things of nature and especially concerning astronomy.[158]

Hagecius waited some time for Cardan to publish the treatise on metoposcopy which he had announced, but Cardan would not even show him the manuscript of it, when Hagecius visited him at Milan. Hagecius therefore printed his own work in the hope, he says, that it might move Cardan to publish his and so further develop interest in the art. But no such work by Cardan appeared during the remaining fifteen years of his life nor in those immediately following his death. Meanwhile there was a demand for a new edition of the treatise by Hagecius which had been out of print for many years. He had not pursued the subject farther, partly because occupied with his medical studies and his duties as physician to the emperor Maximilian II and then involved in controversy with Graminaeus and Lindanus as to the star of 1572, partly because with advancing years his curiosity as to methods of divination had waned—not so much, he adds, because of uncertainty of the arts of divination as because some curious men carried them too far and claimed too much for them. "Of this sort of lying diviners and seers this age of ours has many." Finally, however, he yielded to the demand for another edition, which he dedicated to the archdukes Ernest, Matthias and Maximilian, from Vienna on October 1, 1583; and which was printed at Frankfurt in 1584. The treatise consists of two parts: first, aphorisms such as that an oblong

[157] I have had access to the second edition of 1584: *Thaddaei Hagecii ab Hagek doctoris medici Aphorismorum Metoposcopicorum libellus unus.* Editio secunda. Francofurti apud haeredes Andreae Wecheli, MDLXXXIIII, 79 small pages. Copy used: BM 1141.b.11. (2.).

The dedication to Ferdinand is here reprinted at pp. 3-15. That of October 1, 1583, to the three archdukes follows at pp. 16-18, while an Epistola ad lectorem fills pp. 19-28.

[158] *Ibid.*, p. 16.

forehead with an oblong face and thin chin indicate cruelty and tyranny; second, a series of pictures of faces showing various lines in the forehead and each accompanied by a legend such as "Fall from a height," or "Peril in water," indicating the fate or character of the type in question.

The interest in this form of physiognomy manifested by the reprinting of the treatise by Hagecius was shown further by a series of publications in the first part of the next century. In 1603 and again in 1608 and 1618 appeared the work of Rudolphus Goclenius (Göckel) on *Uranoscopia chiroscopia et metoposcopia,* not to mention his *Physiognomica et Chiromantica Specialia* of 1621, 1661 and 1692. In 1615 at Strasburg Samuel Fuchs published his *Metoposcopia et op[h]thalmoscopia.* It is the sole work by him found in the British Museum, where there are two copies of it, while the Bibliothèque Nationale of Paris has only one other treatise by him, on the euphony of Latin oration. In 1616 at Wittenberg Christian Moldenarius printed *Exercitationes physiognomicae* in four books, described as collected from various Greek and Latin authors, and devoted respectively to physiognomy, chiromancy, metoposcopy and interpretation of dreams. It is the only work by him in both the British Museum and Bibliothèque Nationale. From Germany the interest spread to Italy, where in 1626 at Milan, if not before, appeared *De naevis* of Ludovicus Septalius (Lodovico Settala), reprinted at Pavia in 1628. The second impression of Cyrus Spontonus (Ciro Spontone), *La metoposcopia overa commensuratione delle linee delle fronte,* was edited by Gioanni Battista Spontone at Venice in 1629, with other reprintings in 1637 and 1642. Finally in 1658 was issued at Paris by Claudius Martinus Laurenderius in thirteen books with eight hundred figures of human faces what at least purported to be the work on metoposcopia of Cardan, which Hagecius had sought in vain to inspect and whose publication he had awaited a century before.

Johann Rothmann, a physician and philosopher of Anhalt who is mentioned several times in the correspondence of Tycho Brahe, published at Erfurt in 1595 a work on chiromancy and its agreement with astrology.[159] In the dedication of his treatise to a quartet of most illustrious men Rothmann expresses his belief in the doctrine of signatures in plants and in the influence of the stars. He has tried to set forth the canons of chiromancy in a brief systematic form, to contribute some observations of his own, and to substantiate the asserted harmony of chiromancy and astrology by a number of living examples. He knows of no one who has done this last before. Among such individual genitures are three brothers of Wittenberg and a person born at Breslau on August 17, 1567. He further holds that the influence of the planets can be judged from the condition of certain parts of the hand which are assigned to each. He asserts that Scripture in the Book of Job is favorable to chiromancy. If there is divergence between the signs of the hand and the horoscope, it is due to some impediment to the influence of the stars, inherited from the parents.[160] Rothmann digresses concerning the world soul and spirit of the universe, which he locates in the incorruptible heaven and makes of a fiery substance.[161] Back in the dedication he had stated, probably with regret, that the name of magic is now in disrepute.

The continued cultivation of chiromancy and physiognomy into the seventeenth century despite the papal bulls of 1586 and 1631 against divination has already been touched on in a chapter dealing with the bulls, but may be here illustrated further by two works having a closer connection with other arts of divination.

In 1619 Jean Belot, whose *Flowers of Christian and Moral Philosophy* of 1603 have been noticed in a previous chapter, published in French at Paris a book on chiromancy and physiognomy with an astrological discourse on the recent comet of 1618.[162] The discussion of chiromancy includes its relations to

[159] Johann Rothmann, *Chiromantiae theorica practica concordantia genethliaca vetustis novitate addita,* Erphordiae, 1595, quarto minori, 55 fols. Copy used: BM 1141.c.7. An English translation appeared in London, 1652.

[160] *Ibid.,* fols. 54v-55r.

[161] *Ibid.,* fol. 44r: "Commentatiunculae de anima mundi et spiritu universi."

[162] Jean Belot, *Instruction familière et tres facile pour apprendre les sciences de chiromance et phisiognomie . . .*

other occult arts and brings in more superstitious matter than might be expected, including not a little on other forms of divination. The opening chapter deals with the planets; the second, with the signs of the zodiac, their qualities, sympathies, antipathies, and harmonies with chiromancy and other divining sciences. For magic twelve spirits or angels of the signs are noted. We are also told that in the Jewish Cabala twelve anagrams of the *Tetragrammaton* are engraved on as many stones of different colors, and that the future is judged according to their changing order. The fourth chapter treats of sacred letters found in the lines of the hand, their association with the heavenly bodies, and divination from them. The fifth chapter returns to the planets and signs, while the seventh explains how to learn the day of birth, the temperament and heredity from the hand. The third, sixth and eighth chapters are more strictly chiromantical. The ninth, however, expounds how to tell the dreams of princes by geomancy as well as chiromancy, while the tenth instructs how to find one's genius or governing angel by engraving astrological figures on metal plates, as directed by Paracelsus in *Archidoxes magiques*. This method, of which Belot hopes to treat more fully elsewhere, he regards as wholly natural and involving neither pacts with demons, nor other illicit practices, nor anything against the honor of God and the Christian religion. Eleven chapters then deal with the technique of chiromancy or astrological chiromancy, such as connecting twenty-eight possible incisions of the quadrangle of the hand with the mansions of the moon.

In the twenty-second chapter, however, on divination from the nails Belot again digresses to discuss several kinds of divination. In onimancy one invokes the angel Uriel and oils the nail of the right hand of a young virgin girl. Coscinomancy, for which Pictorius is cited, detects a thief by poising objects on the thumbs or fingernails of two persons and then repeating the names of suspects until the objects tumble off at mention of the

---

plus un Discours astrologique, Paris, 1619. Copies: BN R.28141 et V.21880. I have read the work, however, in the Lyons, 1654 edition of Belot's works: BM 8632.bb.3.

guilty. Belot also marvels at the discovery of lost articles and secrets which he saw Sieur Colmet make in the fauxbourg S. Germain des prez. In alectromancy grains of corn are placed on the letters of the alphabet while the moon or sun is in Aries. An entirely white cock is then selected, its nails are cut, and it is ticketed with a cabalistic prayer and 72 verses from the Psalms. Belot notes that 72 such verses were chosen by the ancient Hebrews and cabalists and are faithfully recorded by Reuchlin in *De verbo mirifico* and *De arte cabalistica*. Belot further speaks of the triliteral names of 72 angels. Returning to alectromancy, we note that an answer to the question put is spelled out by writing down the letters in the order in which the cock eats the grains of corn. Clidomancy employs a suspended key and scroll. Dactilomancy is operated by rings put on the fingernails. Yet in the same chapter Belot voices a somewhat sceptical attitude as to statements of the Bible, representing Vadianus in his commentaries on the Pentateuch as saying that the water of probation of the ancient Hebrews really possessed no such virtue but was merely a device to impress the simple.

Of the two closing chapters on chiromancy the twenty-fourth represents the hands as a compendium of three worlds, with some secrets of astrology and astronomy, elementary, celestial and intellectual. The twenty-fifth assures us that chiromancy comprehends all sciences of divination and magic, and that from the hand of the dead one can discover all that one could by necromancy.

The second part on physiognomy presents a similar mixture. It opens by citing Hippocrates as favoring astrological medicine and in the second chapter repeats from Pasquier's *Researches concerning France* stories of an astrologer's successful predictions. Presently some quatrains are quoted from Belot's *Centuries* about the horoscope of a young German prince. Instructions are given how to learn anyone's physiognomy by geomancy, then metoposcopy receives attention and oneirocratie or the physiognomy of dreams. Writers of recent centuries on that theme are condemned, and what Artemidorus, Cardan and

"Niphius" (Nifo?) have said concerning it is called mere lies. But Belot soon lists seventy-two divining dreams which he associates not only with the twelve astrological houses but with the names of God and with the aforesaid seventy-two cabalistic verses from the Psalms.

Such was the persistence of trifling as well as more serious methods of divination into the seventeenth century. And such was the curious mental outlook of Belot, who mingles a few bits of scepticism as to religion and the Bible with a great mass of occult science and superstition as to which his attitude often appears to be one of extreme credulity.

Maurice Froger, a physician of Montpellier, on August 13, 1622, completed a work on physiognomy with sections on chiromancy, metoposcopy or the physiognomy of the forehead, and the interpretation of dreams.[163] It is preceded in one manuscript by a briefer elementary treatise on astrology by him.[164] Some years later Dominicus de Rubeis, a citizen of Venice, dedicated tables of physiognomy to cardinal Richelieu.[165]

[163] BN 7484, paper: p. 1, de physionomia. Most of the first chapter, to page 27 is written at the end of BN Rés.p.R.215, but the name of Froger does not appear in the catalogue of printed books of the Bibliothèque Nationale. Our MS continues: p. 95, de chiromantia naturali sive chiroposcopia, opening, "Ordo naturae . . ."; p. 125, de metoposcopia, opening, "Metoposcopia de lineis frontis effectus . . ."; p. 141, de oneirocritica, opening, "Oneirocritica est in somniis. . . ." At p. 192 the text closes, ". . . de omnibus partibus phisiognomiae dicta sufficiant ad dei gloriam et studiosorum gratiam. Per me, Mauricius Froger, huius tractatus de Phisionomia finis impositus die 13e Augusti anno domini millesimo secentessimo vingesimo secundo a domino Mauritio Frogero doctore medico Montispelerii."

In another MS at Paris, Ste. Geneviève 2234, early 17th century, fols. 102-173, the author's name is given as Robert Froger: "Tractatus physiognomiae chiroscopiae metoposcopiae et quirocriticae (*sic*). Hunc tractatum dictavit vir doctissimus Robertus Frogerius medicus Monspeliensis Parisiis anno 1622." Incipit, "Hic tractatus quatuor complectitur partes. . . ."

[164] In BN 7484 it occupies 41 fols. followed by blank leaves to fol. 47 after which a new pagination starts for the treatise on physiognomy.

[165] *Dominici de Rubeis civis Veneti Tabulae Physiognomicae*, Venice, 1639, 144 pp. Copy used: BN Rés.p.R.214. With it is bound the earlier work of Corvo and Molinius, mentioned in our fourth chapter, and a work of Scipio Claramontius of Cesena, addressed to Gabriel Naudé, *De atra bile quoad mores attinet*, Paris, 1641. Besides these printed treatises, the volume concludes with two physiognomies in manuscript, one a portion of the work of Froger mentioned above.

The tradition of Pomponazzi, Nifo and Cardan may be traced farther into the seventeenth century, and even the influence of Vanini, although he had been burned at the stake for atheism in 1619, in a work printed at Frankfurt in 1632 on divination by dreams and prophecy by Hieronymus Franzosius.[166] In the preface to the reader he says that he does not write for tyros or those who are disturbed by philosophical heresy but for those who cherish true wisdom. What he says will perturb only monks and friars and those who ignorantly utter fallacies. He speaks of Cesare Cremonini as his teacher and quotes Vanini for a page on the subject of demons, concluding that they cannot produce the species of anything and impress these on a corporeal subject. Before this Franzosius has quoted a passage of three pages on prophets from Cardan's work on the immortality of the soul.[167] Cardan had said that no prophet is trained or erudite, that they ought to be free from all mental disturbance, and proceed from knowledge of universals, not of particular things. Hence it is usually only after the event that the particular verification of prophecy becomes clear. Prophets are not found near the poles, where bodies are dense, but flourish in a land like Palestine, which is temperate and with favoring skies. Prophets are neither timid nor wrathful, moderate eaters, and abstain from sexual intercourse. They are as far removed from men as men are from beasts and may be regarded as a mean between separate mind and man. Franzosius explains that by "separate mind" Cardan meant either one of the intelligences or some sidereal virtue. Some say that he meant the Averroistic unity of the intellect, but Franzosius defers discussion of this point to his commentary on *De anima*. Meanwhile he has further quoted Cardan to the effect that persons about to die sense it first. "For then the intellect already has begun to separate from the body and from the rest of the soul, and hence soul and body are aware of this separation not as some object but as the eye feels darkness and blindness."

[166] Hieronymus Fronzosius, *De divinatione per somnum et de prophetia*, Francofurti, 1632, 4to. Copy used. BM 719.g.45.

[167] The passage has been noticed in our chapter on Cardan.

Franzosius also quotes Agostino Nifo not a little. First as to the influence of the stars on the rise of prophets. Albumasar ascribed it to a conjunction of Saturn and Jupiter; Ptolemy and Almansor attributed it to other conjunctions, while Avicenna agreed with Albumasar. The prophet as the image of the Intelligence of the sphere of Jupiter knows the future in particular and proves and confirms his power by miracles. To this contention Franzosius objects that the Intelligence merely moves the sphere of Jupiter and does not know inferiors any more than demons do. He says that Nifo also opposed this contention but by a different argument. He again cites Nifo as strenuously opposing the attempt of Arnald of Villanova to base the art of interpreting dreams on three things: contrary and dissimilar appearances, direct metaphor, conjecturing times through the proportion of the metaphor. Aristotle based interpretation solely on similitude, and so Nifo rejected Arnald's first and third methods.

While Franzosius quotes Nifo, Cardan and even Vanini with apparent approval, he attacks the arguments of Julius Caesar Scaliger in the latter's commentary on the Hippocratic *Liber de insomniis*.

Franzosius holds that divination from dreams is sometimes true, often false. He denies the view of Albertus Magnus that dreams are produced by the influence of the sky. But he thinks that objects entering the soul often contain in themselves some indication of the order of things to come, and that the soul, led by a certain connection of things and events, may divine the future. In such divination atrabiliar persons are the most proficient.

Prophecy, like dreams, is entirely a matter of the imagination and not of the intellect. As in dreams, so in prophecy the imagination of melancholy persons hastens on from one thing to another and so may hit upon future possibilities but also may stray along false leads. Although Franzosius had denied that dreams were produced by the influence of the sky, he attributes the rise of prophets and new religious sects to the stars. Moreover, at certain times sudden cures occur and raising of the dead, just as at other times diseases arise which make men appear as if dead. If we accept such occult powers in certain individuals as Tacitus asserted of Vespasian, or the unburnable finger of Pyrrhus, or the two boys in Germany before whom doors mysteriously opened, according to Albertus Magnus, why may certain men not possess innate powers of expelling diseases, walking through fire, and working other miracles? In feats of this sort the force of fixed imagination is of much moment. Men of profound phantasy so alter the blood that they effect changes in near-by objects, as old-wives fascinate children. Prophets also require faith in those whom they heal, and in this one thing is founded the force of incantations, if they have any. In this discussion of prophecy it is easy to trace the influence of Pomponazzi and Cardan.

Although Franzosius's title mentions only prophecy and divination by dreams, he also discusses demons, as we have seen. He not only quotes Vanini concerning demons but asserts himself that they cannot perceive or understand sensible things, that no action of an abstract substance is to be referred to imagination and that demons cannot possess human bodies.

To such bold asseverations Franzosius occasionally and rather incidentally adds a Christian qualification and exception. Before asserting that demons cannot possess human bodies, he is careful to explain that his remarks have no reference "to those true demons mentioned in holy writ," who enter bodies, excel in divination, and work marvels, preserving after their fall the intelligence with which they were divinely endowed at creation. Of prophets, too, he treats only those mentioned by ancient writers, ever venerating the inexpungable truth of the holy Roman church, "which to the confusion of our blindness rambles gloriously over any reasons whatsoever." Peripatetically speaking, those prophets are not admitted who foresee certainly future contingents or who establish their claims by miracles. "I have added, 'Peripatetically,' " says Franzosius, "in order that I might make no mention of holy prophets." In the eleventh chapter on changes of religions, after affirming that all sublunar things change—morals, customs, rites, states, languages, and even religions—he adds that God sent His Son who by great miracles laid the foundations of the holy church to endure until the great day of final conflagration. "To this end were divinely sent the prophets Abraham, Moses, Isaiah, Ezekiel and others mentioned in the Scriptures, whom I have never touched upon when I was disputing as to prophecy, always attending to those things which, being produced by the industry of nature, are knowable by their causes." Whether these exceptions were sincere or ironical, at least Franzosius survived to publish at Verona in 1645 an Apology for Aristotle against Galen as to semen.

CHAPTER XLVI

THE LITERATURE OF WITCHCRAFT AND MAGIC AFTER WIER

. . . mere baggages . . . mere cousenage . . .
—REGINALD SCOT

The work with which we open this chapter, that of Johann Wier, physician to the duke of Cleves, on the magic illusions of demons,[1] not only comes first chronologically but is further distinguished by its attitude of opposition to the witchcraft delusion. Wier did not question the existence of demons: rather he attributed the witchcraft delusion to their activity. He contended that the so-called lamiae or witches were persons whose minds had been deranged and imaginations corrupted by demons, but that they were not responsible for their actions and confessions any more than the insane, and that they were guilty neither of heresy nor entering voluntarily into pacts with the devil. Their illusions were also partially owing to the credulity and weakness of the feminine sex, and women should be punished less than men. Wier distinguished sharply between these lamiae and criminal poisoners or infamous magicians. The latter wilfully consulted magic books and employed superstitious procedure, and in Wier's opinion were more blameworthy than the lamiae who did neither but merely suffered from delusions. Yet the lamiae were put to death while the magicians found praise and frequent employment.

Wier held further that the supposed sexual intercourse of demons with women was purely imaginary, that lycanthropy was a disease, that demons were not attracted by herbs or other

[1] *De praestigiis daemonum et incantationibus ac veneficiis libri V recogniti et valde aucti authore Ioanne Wiero Graviano illustrissimi ducis Cliviae Iuliae etc. medico . . .*, Basileae per Ioannem Oporinum, 1564, is the edition I have used (Col 156.4 W6361), but it purports to be an enlarged edition, the first having been in 1563.

earthly matter, and that the tests employed in distinguishing witches were most fallacious. He also found abuses to criticize in the ecclesiastical procedure used in remedying sorcery and in magic cure of diseases. He opposed the employment of incantations and strange words, which he held did not possess celestial virtue or concur with the images of the sky—thereby suggesting that he was not so sceptical as to astrological influence. He admitted that some medical writers had been too given to use of characters and superstitious names, mentioning as examples Alexander of Tralles, Bernard Gordon and recently Oger Ferrier. He was opposed to such occult arts as those of Almadel and Artephius, the *ars Bulaphiae*, the notory art, the Pauline art, and the art of revelations.

But Wier praised natural magic as contrasted with the diabolical variety and with goetia or theurgy. Natural magic was most profound speculation into abstruse natural things, true knowledge and a holier philosophy. And he believed not only that the lamiae sometimes were subject to illusions from unguents with which they had anointed themselves or natural soporific drugs which they had taken, but that eating the brain of a bear might make one imagine himself to be a bear. He cited such past authorities as the Conciliator and Pomponazzi.

On the other hand, Wier had exposed cases of supposed prolonged fasting, such as that of the child Barbara, aged ten, who was said to have gone for thirteen months without food, drink or elimination.[2]

While Wier opposed the witchcraft delusion and urged milder treatment of the so-called witches, he not only retained faith in the existence and activity of demons and in occult marvels of nature, but he also decked his work out with much the same anecdotes and tales of magic as were to be found in other books on witchcraft and with discussion of stock questions and topics like Pharaoh's magicians, the witch of Endor, necromancy and other occult arts. It was perhaps these features which won many readers for his book and insured a number of subsequent editions.

[2] *De commentitiis ieiuniis,* with his *De lamiis,* 1582, pp. 109-38.

He also restated his views more succinctly in a treatise of 108 pages and 24 chapters, *De lamiis,* published in 1582.[3] Despite the fact that Wier continued the appeal of witch-books to prurient ears, his book made a serious impression as well. "Slowly," says Burr, "here and there, the burning words of Weyer stirred up a disciple, more or less ardent: Ewich and Neuwaldt and Witekind and Loos and Godelmann and Anten in Germany, Reginald Scot and Gifford and Harsnet and Cotta in England. But," Burr adds, "they stirred up adversaries tenfold more numerous and influential."[4]

Into such writings we shall dip a little farther, since the specimens given by Hansen came only to 1540. They form a sorry enough epilogue to our work but also a necessary one, with more cruel reality back of them than the academic discussions of divination in our preceding chapter. Our survey is only illustrative and in no sense exhaustive,[5] while it is to be remembered that some writers on the subject from the second half of the century, like Pictorius, Cesalpino and Erastus, have already been treated in other chapters. On the other hand, since some of the writers now to be considered attributed to pacts with demons not only witchcraft, sorcery and evil magic, but nearly all occult arts and sciences, these too will come in for occasional mention. Works on witchcraft and books on diabolical magic are difficult to separate and distinguish, while there is much disagreement between our writers as to the boundaries and ramifications of these subjects. We shall also note discussions by Peripatetics and medical men unfavorable either to witchcraft itself or to the conceptions of demons and nature on which the belief in it was based.

Such a discussion was dedicated in 1567 to the duke of Urbino. This publication was in the nature of a belated reply to

[3] Copy used: BM 719.i.3.(2.).

[4] Geroge L. Burr, "The Literature of Witchcraft," *Papers of the American Historical Association,* IV, 3 (1890), 58-59, where the titles of the works referred to are given.

[5] For further detail and bibliography consult George Lyman Kittredge, *Witchcraft in Old and New England,* Harvard University Press, 1929. On the other hand, many of the authors whom I shall discuss are not mentioned by Kittredge.

questions which Matthaeus Gentilis Sanctogenesiensis had addressed to Ianus Matthaeus Durastantes on January 21, 1560.[6] To the first of these questions which concerned a medical dogma of Fernel and Gentilis's teacher Argenterius as to a triple variety of disease, Durastantes had already replied on March 20, 1560, that he was unable to answer it, since he did not have the works of Fernel and Argenterius in which they had expressed the view in question. The remaining three questions, to which he now in 1567 published his replies, were as follows: 2) are demons sometimes the cause of disease? 3) what treatment should be given to a patient who part of the time was full of bad juice (*malo succo*) and part of the time was very weak? 4) whether the recent fashion of burning rhubarb for dysentery and other complaints was in accordance with Galenic procedure? I mention these other questions, although we are here primarily interested only in that concerned with demons, in order to show how the problem of their existence and activity could obtrude itself into medical and natural discussions. Similarly Jacopo Aconzio of Trent, after writing in 1558 on scientific method,[7] in 1565 published eight books on the stratagems of Satan.[8]

Gentilis recognized that Hippocrates never referred the cause of disease to gods or demons, but Fernel asserted that his own eyes had convinced him that demons were sometimes the cause of disease, and Gentilis suspected it in a recent case. Durastantes opens his reply with the statement that he is about to write "many novel and marvelous things concerning their (i.e. demons') essence, qualities and effects, but this promise he scarcely fulfills. He further asks readers not to blame him if there is anything in his volume against the Catholic faith, for which he would willingly die a martyr. He is merely stating the views of Aristotle, Hippocrates, Galen and Averroes. Christian and Pla-

[6] Janus Matthaeus Durastantes, *Problemata de daemonibus, an sint et an morborum sint causae,* Venice, 1567. Copy used: BM 1169.c.2. I have also seen cited an edition of Venice, 1587 with the title *Problemata, an sint daemones, et de eorum viribus.*

[7] *De methodo, hoc est de recta investigandarum tradendarumque scientiarum ratione;* also at Genoa, 1582. Copy used: BM527.b.28.(2.).

[8] Jacobus Acontius, *Stratagematum Satanae libri octo,* Basel, 1565. Copy used: BM 847.h.6.

tonic theologians accept the existence of demons, but Aristotelian metaphysics has no place for them, whether actually or potentially, whether as bodies, incorporeal substances, or as accidents. Except for reason and appetite, Durastantes has never read nor found any demons, good or bad, in the works of Peripatetic moral philosophers or indeed of moral philosophers generally. A certain Arrivabenus who was interested in chemistry and the fallacies of alchemy, after he had vainly expended most of his patrimony in prolonged experiments, resorted to a book of magic but was frightened by the demons who appeared and burned the volume, as he told Durastantes in 1541. But the Peripatetics would explain that he suffered from melancholy and delusions. And dogmatic medicine, being subordinated to philosophy, will not admit demons as a cause of disease.

Turning to a discussion of proper causes of disease, Durastantes holds that, since health is a condition of symmetry, disease is disorder. He censures both Leonicenus and Fuchs, the former for "certain new dreams and figments," the latter for saying that between cause and effect, and between the antecedent cause of disease and disease itself there was no mean.

A few more passages illustrate the attitude of Durastantes to nature and to occult science. He denies that the salamander can remain unburned in fire. Its frigidity may enable it to endure the flames for a time, but it will be burned in the end. "For fire (*ignis*), as its etymology proclaims, generates nothing, that is, consumes everything." Setting etymology against folklore does not seem a very convincing argument in a matter of natural science. Durastantes rejects the doctrine of Theophrastus that plants have a sensitive soul. He denies that demons, granting that they exist, would be subject to gems set in rings. It is noteworthy that both the question of Gentilis and the reply of Durastantes hold aloof from the question of witchcraft.

The work of Franciscus Cataneus Diacetius the Younger on the superstitions of the magic art which was published at Florence in 1567 in Italian[9] covers only thirty-six leaves and seems

[9] *Discorso del reverendo M. Francesco de Cattani da Diacceto . . . sopra la superstizzione dell'arte magica,* Firenze, 1567.

to contribute nothing new on the subject. The author was a canon of Florence and apostolic protonotary who later became bishop of Fiesole (1570-1595); his dedication of April 14, 1567, is addressed to the cardinal Michele Bonello; at the close of the work are ecclesiastical and inquisitorial imprimaturs.

In 1568 was printed at Basel the book of Richard Argentinus on the illusions and incantations of demons and necromancers.[10] The dedication to Reginald Wolsius of Strasburg is dated five years earlier from Exeter on January 31, 1563. Whether the Argentinus of Richard's name indicates that he was also of Strasburg seems doubtful. He appears to have received the degrees of master of arts and bachelor of medicine from Oxford and in 1541 that of doctor of medicine from Cambridge. He took orders during the reign of Mary Tudor and had a living at Ipswich. His other writings include translations of Zwingli and Luther in 1548, when he was a Protestant, and a plea for restoring the study of Arabic at Oxford and Cambridge.[11]

Argentinus lists and describes various occult and diabolical arts in about the usual manner and recounts a number of stock stories. A show of Hebraic scholarship is made by giving the Hebrew words for ventriloquism, observance of days, of points, figures and numbers, demonic operative magic, too extreme astrology or augury, necromancy and the Greek iunx. Among the chapter topics are: crystal gazing, pacts with demons, Beelzebub, Ur of the Chaldees in which Abraham was deceived, the sibyl in the sixth book of the Aeneid, superstition, specters, omens and anathema, and divine permission and tolerance of such doings. The author is concerned with "magical and diabolical predictions" (and other occult arts) "which have no physical cause." His most novel, not to say original, argument seems to be this. As some evangelicals thought that Aristotle should be entirely renovated, not because his philosophy was inherently bad but because it had so occupied all theology that the

[10] Ricardus (or, Richardus) Argentinus, *De praestigiis et incantationibus daemonum et necromanticorum liber singularis numquam ante hac aeditus,* Basel, 1568. Copy used: BM 719.a.1.(1.).

[11] DNB, article, "Argentine, alias Sexten, Richard."

Bible had been silenced and neglected, so all divination without a physical foundation should be done away, not because all conjecture as to the future is evil but in order to save true and sacred astrology. Natural astrology is thus defended rather than attacked by Richard, but he calls Chaldean astrology "the mother of all superstition."

The foregoing allusion to Aristotle suggests the thought that it is rather odd that he should be held to have denied the existence of demons or their influence on nature on the one hand, yet be charged on the other hand with excessive influence upon scholastic theology.

The stories of Argentinus are not entirely of the doings of demons. He also tells of a man born naturally from the earth. He cites Cardan frequently, also Caspar Peucer, and accepts as Agrippa's the fourth book of the *Occult Philosophy*. He compares the *Steganographia* of Trithemius to the superstitious volumes of Numa Pompilius. From Pico della Mirandola he draws "the history of unheard-of lust," which was to appear again in the seventeenth century treatise of Thomas Bartholinus (1616-1680),[12] of the man who required chastisement as an incitement to cohabitation. Argentinus also cites Pomponazzi, Coelius Rhodiginus, and the *Malleus maleficarum*.

In medical theses, *De incubo*, perhaps of 1570, over which Simon Grynaeus presided, the view was maintained that an incubus was not a demi-god or demon or an external pressure such as that of a witch lying upon one or anything of that sort, as was popularly believed, but a symptom of an internal organic or functional complaint.[13] This had been the opinion of leading physicians and medical writers like Gentile da Foligno and Antonio Guaineri in preceding centuries, but its reaffirmation in the

[12] *Epistola de usu flagrorum in re medica et venerea lumborumque et renum officio*, Frankfurt, 1670, 8vo. The tercentenary of Bartholinus's birth was celebrated in *Janus* 31 (1916), 271-378, by various contributors.

[13] *De incubo theses . . . ad quas praeside Simone Grynaeo D. respondebit M. Sebastianus Caesar Themarensis in auditorio medico die 26 Martii Hora 7 Matutina.* No year is given, the work being a broadside folded into a smaller volume. It is dated "1570(?)" in the catalogue of the British Museum: copy used BM 7306.f.6.(5.).

midst of the witchcraft delusion and persecution is worth noting. Wier had already taken this position,[14] except that he had allowed also for incubus in the sense of an illusion of the devil.

The work of the Calvinist, Lambert Daneau (1530-1595), on sorcerers was widely read, running through a dozen editions in Latin, French, German and English before the end of the century,[15] though it first appeared in French and Latin only in 1574.[16] Of Daneau's life and *Christian Physics* we have treated in another chapter. Daneau can remember the time, he says, when the Parlement of Paris would dismiss a charge of sorcery as an idle laughing matter. But recently it has been considering an almost infinite number of such cases and pronouncing judgments daily upon men from various provinces, including even nobles and the learned. By its decree there had been executed an Honoratus who was the head of a college of three hundred blind men.[17] Daneau grants, however, that there are still many sceptics as to witchcraft, that the question is today much disputed, and that some persons change their opinion as to it twice a day.[18] For the rest his treatise proceeds largely along traditional lines. His belief in insensible spots on the bodies of witches was to be rejected by Binsfeld.

Francesco Verini the Younger, a Florentine professor of philosophy at the university of Pisa, addressed a work on demons to Petrus Jacobus Borbonius, archbishop of Pisa. Since he held that office only from 1574 to his death in 1575, the work must have been addressed to him and presumably composed at that time. It appears not to have been printed but is preserved in a Riccardian manuscript at Florence.[19]

[14] *De praestigiis daemonum,* 1564, II, 33, p. 238, "De incubi daemoniaci illusione et incubo morbo naturali."

[15] These editions are listed by P. de Félice, *Lambert Daneau . . . , Sa vie, ses ouvrages, ses lettres inédites,* 1881, pp. 158-60. N. Paulus's chapter on "Die Hexenschrift des Calvinisten Lambert Daneau," pp. 172-82 of his *Hexenwahn und Hexenprozess,* 1910, consists chiefly of excerpts from the German translation.

[16] I have used the Latin edition of Frankfurt, 1581: *L. Danaei De veneficis quos vulgo sortiarios vocant dialogus,* BM 719.b.12. Also that of Cologne, 1575: *De veneficis quos olim sortilegos nunc autem vulgo sortiarios vocant dialogus,* BN R.32908.

[17] Edition of 1581, pp. 184-87.

[18] *Ibid.,* pp. 186-89.

[19] FR 1223 D. VI, 16th century, fols. 1r-53v: Liber Francisci Verinii secundi Florentini et philosophi ordinarii de

Tycho Brahe tells us that the theological arguments against astrology which he refuted in his oration of 1574 at Copenhagen had been put forward there by Nicolaus Hemmingius in the classroom and in his commentaries on the Pauline epistles, and were taken for the most part from the work of Calvin against astrologers. After delivering his oration, Tycho was invited to dinner by the legate with other professors including Hemming or Hemmingsen. In conversation Tycho held that astrology was not contrary to evangelical doctrine, if it was pursued soberly, without superstition, and within due limits. Hemming then went so far as to accept this position with the two further stipulations that complete freedom of action be left to God and free will to man. Tycho assured him that no astrologer even among the pagans, unless he was a complete atheist and Epicurean, ever denied the first proposition and that he personally would gladly concede the other.[20] It may be that this conversation had some influence upon the book which Hemming published the next year, 1575, against magic arts, since he did not include astrology in its condemnation, although such forms of divination as augury and auspices were forbidden. Hemming held that magic was of diabolic, not human, invention, and that man alone could accomplish nothing in it. It was not permissible to resort to it even to free the bewitched, nor should they appeal to a witch for aid. After discussing such usual topics as why God permits magic, the different kinds of magic, and how demons know the future, Hemming in conclusion treated of three matters: how the individual should guard himself against magic, how a minister of the Gospel, and how a judge should deal with offenders. In short, Hemming's book seems much the usual sort of theological treatise on witchcraft.[21] Hemming lived from 1511 or 1513 to

---

demonibus ad d. Petrum Iacobum Borbonium ex marchionibus Montis S. Mariae . . . archiepiscopum Pisanum Corsice et Sardinie primatem. After the dedication, which occupies fols. 2r-4r, the text proper opens and closes; "Qui demonum notitiam expetunt . . . / . . . quod utinam mihi aliisque foeliciter contingat."

[20] *Opera*, ed. Dreyer, I (1913), 170-173.

[21] Nicolaus Hemmingius (Niels Hemmingsen), *Admonitio de superstitionibus magicis evitandis*, Copenhagen, Joh. Stockelman and Andreas Gutterwitz, 1575, small 8vo. The work was

1600, was successively professor of Greek, of dialectic and Hebrew, and of theology at Copenhagen, and wrote many works on theological subjects. In 1579 he was dismissed from the university of Copenhagen because he seemed too favorable to Calvinism. He became a canon at Roeschilde. [22] A letter of June 27, 1598, by him to Tycho Brahe is preserved.[23]

In 1578 was published at Paris in French *A Declamation against the Execrable Error of Wizards, Sorcerers, Enchanters . . . and Similar Observers of Superstitions,* by Pierre Nodé, a Franciscan friar.[24] Contending that such persons had dangerously increased in numbers throughout the realm, he called for their punishment and expulsion. He regarded sorcery as worse than all other heresy and as the beast of the Book of Revelation, while medical empirics, *urinaires,* physiognomists, prognosticators and writers of almanacs were little better. He further discussed why the devil did less harm to persons of rank with his sorcerers than to the common people. With his oration he printed the articles of 1398 of the faculty of theology of Paris and the preface of Gerson thereto. In the course of the declamation he had cited Ulric Molitor and other Latin writers.

The following year a similar work was printed at Paris, also in French, by Pierre Massé, an advocat of Le Mans, *On The Imposture and Deceit of Devils, Diviners, Enchanters, Sorcerers,* and so forth.[25] Massé began with divination, then took up magic,

listed by Albertus Bartholinus, *De scriptis Danorum, liber posthumus,* published in Johann Mollerus, *Bibliotheca septentrionis,* 1699. as follows: "Admonitio de magicis artibus. Item 33 propositiones adversus magiam. Item propositiones de vaticiniis, Hafniae, 1575."

[22] Dreyer in the notes to *Tychonis Brahe Opera omnia,* I (1913), 313, and Albertus Bartholinus, *De scriptis Danorum liber posthumus anno MDCLXVI acutior editus a Thoma Bartholino, nunc denuo recensitus . . . a Johanne Mollero,* Hamburg, 1699, pp. 105-6, 340, to whom I am indebted for these facts of Hemming's life, disagree as to the date of his birth which Bartholinus gave as 1511, Dreyer as 1513.

[23] Tycho Brahe, *Opera,* ed. Dreyer, VIII (1925), 77.

[24] Pierre Nodé, *Declamation contre l'erreur execrable des maleficiers, sorciers, enchanteurs . . . et semblables observateurs des superstitions,* Paris, 1578. Copy used: BM 719.b.10.(1.).

[25] Pierre Massé, *De l'imposture et tromperie des diables devins enchanteurs sorciers noueurs d'esguillettes Cheuilleurs Necromanciens Chiromanciens et autres qui par telle invocation*

and after that amulets. Asking whether astrology, divination from dreams, lot-casting and chiromancy were good or bad, he argued that such arts were false and useless.

At Rostock in 1580 there was published by Francis Joel or Ioel, professor of medicine at Greisswald, a work on preternatural diseases and magic, with an appendix concerning the sabbats of witches on a certain mountain.[26] His medical experience and training did not lead him to any scepticism as to witchcraft. Rather he accused Paracelsus of being a magician and made all varieties of magic diabolical. Godelmann, to whom Joel's son Timothy communicated the volume, later complained, while copying the attack on Paracelsus, that Joel had made no distinction between magicians and witches but had condemned all to be burned.

Adam a Lebenwald in eight tracts printed at Salzburg in the same year 1580 on cabala, judicial astrology, the four elements, alchemy, spirits of mines, weapon ointment, transfer of disease, and magic, seems to have been interested only in tracing the participation of the devil in these matters. Unlike Joel, however, he defended Paracelsus from the charge of magic.[27]

In few persons did credulity as to the powers and attributes of witches take so extreme a form as in Jean Bodin (1530-1596). Yet he has a great name in the history of political thought, of historiography, and even of religious toleration. He should perhaps be as infamous for his *Démonomanie* as he is famous for his *Republic, Method in History,* and *Heptaplomeres,* in which representatives of seven different viewpoints with reference to religion amicably discuss their varying opinions. The last, however, remained unpublished until the nineteenth century.

Diabolique ars Magiques et Superstitions abusent le peuple, Paris, 1579, 250 pp. Copy used: BM 719.b.10.(2.).

[26] *Francisci Joelis de morbis hyperphysicis et rebus magicis . . . cum appendice de ludis lamiarum in Monte Bructerorum quem Blocksberg vocant,* Rostock, 1580. I have not seen the work, but E. D. Hauber, *Bibliotheca sive Acta et Scripta Magica,* etc., 1738, I, 683-89, summarizes it. Godelmann reports the title somewhat differently, *Collectanea disputationis suae de morbis hyperphysicis et rebus magicis.*

[27] Adam a Lebenwald is treated of by Hauber, *op. cit.*, I, 349-66, and his defense of Paracelsus is reproduced there at pp. 382-98.

The *Démonomanie* appeared in 1580[28] and may be described as a formless screed and dribbling mess. The chapter headings do not well cover what is included under them: the work is full of digressions and meanderings. But in the course of it Bodin asserts that witches are transported through the air, that demons assume human form, and that men are transformed into animals. He believes in lycanthropy or werwolves and in the marks of sorcerers. In their professed cures they employ unnatural remedies and poisons like the brain of a cat or head of a raven. Really the only maladies which they can cure are those which they have inflicted, and in this case they must pass the ailment on to someone else. When a dealer in wood of Orléans agreed to such a transfer of his mortal disease to his infant son, the nurse overheard the agreement and escaped with the child. The devil then killed the sorcerer instead, and the corpse turned black. At Nantes, when the judge ordered a woman to touch the neighbor whom she was accused of bewitching—which Bodin assures us is the usual procedure in Germany and even in the imperial Chamber—she refused and when forced to do so, cried out, "I am dead." The victim instantly recovered while the witch dropped dead. A scholar of the Parlement of Bordeaux, when a friend was sick unto death of quartan fever, suggested that he transfer it to one of his enemies. The sick man said that he had none. The scholar then suggested that he transfer it to his servant but the patient would not agree. Finally the sorcerer said, "Give it to me"; the sick man agreed and recovered, while the wizard died.[29] Surely an altruistic and self-sacrificing sorcerer, though Bodin does not say so! His book is full of such tales, its very preface opening with the recent trial of Jeanne Harwillier on April 30, 1578. She had been given as a child by her mother to the devil who visited her invisibly and lay with her without her husband's noticing it. It was found that she had been whipped

[28] *De la Demonomanie des sorciers, A Monseigneur M Christofle de Thou Chevalier Seigneur de Coeli premier President en la Cour de Parlement et Conseiller du Roy en son privé Consil, par I. Bodin Angevin,* A Paris, Chez Iacques du Puys Libraire Iuré à la Samaritaine, MDLXXX. Avec Privilege du Roy. Copy used: BM 8631.1.4.

[29] *Ibid.,* III, 2; fols. 128r-130r, for these tales of transfer of disease.

for this thirty years before and her mother burned alive by decree of Parlement confirming the sentence of the judge of Senlis. Now the daughter suffered the same fate, which Bodin twice[30] explicitly states is the general custom of Christendom and the very ancient practice in all Europe, although Boquet tells us that in Burgundy witches were commonly strangled before being burned.

Bodin said in the dedication of the *Démonomanie* dated December 20, 1579, that he did not expect that anyone would attack his work, unless it were some sorcerer who defended his profession. As the work was about to go to the press, the printer called the attention of Bodin to Wier's *De lamiis* which had recently appeared, and publication was delayed until Bodin could compose a refutation of it which, aside from personal abuse, does little but repeat what he has previously said. The *Canon episcopi,* to which Wier had appealed, Bodin rejected as not passed by a general council and as opposed "by all theologians."[31]

Bodin distinguished from witchcraft "natural means of knowing secret things." Astrology was licit, if not carried to forbidden extremes, as was metoposcopy. But Bodin would not rank chiromancy with physiognomy. He criticizes Pico della Mirandola's praise of natural magic, and opposes the use of figures, characters and barbarous words. He further denies that sorceries can be worked by the virtues alone of herbs, animals, stones or stars.[32]

Giovanni Lorenzo d'Anania, a native of Calabria, whose *Cosmography* has been noticed in a previous chapter, wrote a work on the nature of demons which was printed separately more than once[33] and was also included in the *Malleus maleficarum.*[34] Its dedication is dated from Naples on March 1, 1581. Anania be-

[30] In his preface where the pages are unnumbered and later at fol. 206v. At fol. 192r he tells of a witch who was sentenced to be strangled first, but the executioner couldn't strangle her.

[31] *Ibid.,* fol. 249r.

[32] *Ibid.,* I, 5; fols. 28r-41r.

[33] The first edition seems to be: Giov. Lor. Anania, *De natura daemonum libri iiii,* Venetiis, 1581, 8vo, 211 small pp. in italics. Copy used: BM 719.a.1.(2.). BM 719.d.28.(2.) is an edition of Venice, 1589. Yet other editions are mentioned.

[34] In the edition of 1669, for instance.

lieved in the existence of both aerial and subterranean demons. He held that demons only pretend to shun certain constellations and regarded both astrological and necromantic images as operative only by demon aid. He thought that demons could inflict diseases which differed from those that arise naturally from the humors. Diseases from demons come on more suddenly and are rarely curable by medicines. He believed that demons are terrified by the relics of the saints, but that they are cast out now less frequently than formerly. He appears to hold the devil responsible for peoples not employing their own vernaculars in religious services, which suggests Protestant leanings on his part, although Caraffa is said to have been his patron. He further discusses how brutes know remedies with which to cure themselves but does not seem to attribute this to the influence of demons. Whether he possessed any medical competence or training I have not discovered. He left in manuscript a treatise on fortune and another against the Hebrews.[35]

The work of Leonardus Vairus on witchcraft or diabolical magic appears to have been composed in Latin and was published in French translation at Paris in 1583.[36] The earliest Latin edition I have seen was that of Venice, 1589.[37] Vairus became bishop of Pozzuoli from 1587 until his death in 1603.[38] The Latin title of Vairus's work, *De fascino,* denotes witchcraft rather than fascination. He defines *fascinum* as "a pernicious quality induced by art of demons because of tacit or express pact of men with the same demons." He denies fascination by power of imagination, by strength or morbidity of vision, by touch and contact, or by words, characters and observation of the stars. Nor are there any born fascinators. In his last chapter Vairus treats

[35] Mazzuchelli, *Scrittori d'Italia,* Brescia, 1753-1763.

[36] *Trois livres des charmes sorcelages ou enchantemens . . . faicts en Latin par L. Vair . . . et mis en François par J. Baudon,* Paris, N. Chesneau, 1583, 8vo, 553 pp.

[37] Leonardus Vairus, *De fascino libri tres . . . in quibus omnes fascini species . . . describuntur . . . necnon contra praestigias imposturas allusionesque daemonum cautiones et amuleta praescribuntur,* Venetiis apud Aldum, 1589. Copy used: BM 719.c.36.

[38] See Eubel, Zedler, Jöcher, Iacobilli, *Bibliotheca Umbriae,* 1658, Ughelli, *Italia sacra,* 1717-1722, and Toppi, p. 187. Toppi lists five other works by Vairo but not *De fascino.*

of safeguards and amulets against the impostures and illusions of demons, a topic to be developed more fully in the work of Codronchi in the next decade, which much resembles the treatise of Vairus in other respects.[39]

The opposition of Wier to the persecution of witches was continued and carried farther by Reginald Scot in *The Discoverie of Witchcraft,* published at London in 1584. Already in the dedicatory preface he attacked the "witchmongers," as he called them, and asked, if the devil really worked the sorcery, "why should the witch die for it?" Other leading arguments were that the so-called witches were "mere baggages" and poor old women who could harm no one, and that to ascribe to witches powers which were fit for God alone was to belittle the miracles of Christ by crediting the like to witches. Scot made less of demon activity and delusion than Wier. In a supplementary *Discourse upon Divels and Spirits* in thirty-four chapters he stated that he himself regards them as purely spiritual, that we are not thoroughly informed concerning them, and have to satisfy ourselves with what the Bible says concerning them. Scot continued, however, to fill his pages with questionable stories and at one point suggests that readers who are loath to hear or read "filthie and bawdie matters (which of necessitie are heare to be inserted)" should skip the next eight chapters. At their close he says, "Now, being wearied with the rehearsall of so manie lecheries most horrible, and verie filthie and fabulous actions and passions of witches, together with the spirit Incubus, I will end with a true storie taken out of Iason Pratensis."[40]

Scot contended that neither the devil nor Samuel was raised by the witch of Endor but that it "was a mere cousenage."[41] He held that miracles, prophecies and oracles have ceased. He opposed the interpretation of dreams, augury, cabala, and judicial astrology except weather prediction and perhaps some other natural astrology. He puts the argument for amulets and ligatures

[39] If I give a fuller account of Codronchi's contents, it is because I happened to read and take notes on his book first.

[40] *The Discoverie of Witchcraft,* London, 1584, III, 20 and IV, 9.

[41] *Ibid.,* VII, 10; p. 142.

in the mouth of "Argerius Ferrarius" (Oger Ferrier?) who "citeth a great number of experiments" out of classical authors.[42] Scot includes many charms and a long discussion of natural magic and legerdemain, with an exposé of such a trick as seeming to behead a boy. Another book deals with the deceits of alchemy; in another he compares popish exorcists with other conjurors. He believed, however, that "there is fascination and witchcraft by malicious and angrie eies."[43] In fine, while attacking the witchmongers, he still attempts to satisfy, not to say, panders to, the interest in occult arts and magic, which, although disapproving, he illustrates at length.

In the previous chapter on Divination we had occasion to mention the work on specters and apparitions by John Rivius, first printed in 1541. About thirty years later Ludwig Lavater, then a preacher and later head of the Zwinglian church at Zurich, published a work on the same subject, first in German and then in Latin.[44] French and English translations followed almost immediately in 1571 and 1572, and there were later Latin editions, showing the popularity of the subject. Except that his treatment was longer, and that he added to specters strange sounds and other presages of deaths, slaughters and changes of empires, Lavater's position was essentially the same as that of Rivius. Both were Protestants and denied that souls or ghosts of the dead could appear. Yet both maintained that such apparitions were seen, but were not the souls of the dead but the work of demons. Lavater says in his preface, however, that there are many persons who have never seen or heard such specters and noises themselves and who think that what others tell of them are mere nonsense and old wives' tales. He recognizes that in many cases such apparitions are imaginary and that the books of the monks are full of fables. But the Bible, church fathers,

[42] *Ibid.*, XII, 12; p. 239.

[43] *Ibid.*, XVI, 10; p. 487.

[44] I have used the Latin text: *De spectris lemuribus et magnis atque insolitis fragoribus variisque praesagitionibus quae plerunque obitum hominum magnes clades mutationesque imperiorum praecedunt liber unus, Ludovico Lavatero Tigurino autore.* Apud Ioannem Crispinum (Geneva, 1571). Copy used: BN Rés.R.2503. The preface to Ioannes Steigerus, consul of Bern, of this Latin version is dated at Zurich, January, 1570.

other qualified writers and daily experience attest that specters do appear. Lavater is said to have aided Gesner in his study of birds and published a catalogue of comets down to that of 1556.[45]

The problem of the appearance or materialization of spiritual beings was further reviewed in 1586 by Pierre Le Loyer (1550-1634).[46] His work in four books fills two volumes. Le Loyer was a Roman Catholic and a lawyer at Angers who passed as one of the most learned Frenchmen of his time and was something of a poet. He had studied the humanities at Paris and law at the university of Toulouse. He had been in attendance at the Parlement of Paris[47] as well as the courts of Angers. In his work on specters he displays a wide range of reading, including such medieval authors as the pseudo Raymond Lull, John of Rupescissa and Johann Nider or such sixteenth century writers as Pomponazzi, Cardan, Levinus Lemnius and Sprenger's *Malleus maleficarum*. His work which first appeared at Angers in French was reprinted at Paris in 1605 and in English translation at London the same year.

After noticing the arguments "of the Sadducees, Epicureans and Peripatetics" against the appearing of angels and demons, and the contentions of those who deny that such spirits can assume bodies, Le Loyer admits that many natural things are mistaken by our sight or hearing for specters or prodigies. Artificial objects, too, may deceive the senses, especially when they are deranged and in an abnormal state. A disordered imagination is another source of false impressions. But against naturalist philosophers, Averroes and Pomponazzi, and some medical men, Le Loyer contends that the devil sometimes intermingles with

[45] *Cometarum omnium fere catalogus qui ab Augusto quo imperante Christus natus est usque ad hunc 1556 annum apparuerunt ex variis historicis collectus, Tiguri per A. et J. Gesnerum fratres (s.d.).* Copy used: BN V.21082.

[46] Pierre le Loyer, Conseiller au siege presidial d'Angers, *iiii livres des spectres ou apparitions et visions d'esprits anges et demons se monstrans sensiblement aux hommes,* A la Royne Mere du Roy, Angers, 1586, 2 vols. Copy used: BM 719.f.6.

[47] *Ibid.*, I, 131, 294-310, where the speeches on both sides of a case of sorcery before the Parlement are reported.

such "corrupted senses and phantasy." He further insists that good and bad specters appear visibly to men, and that the pagans recognized the existence of angels and demons. Such apparitions are also recounted in both the Old and the New Testament. Demons have appeared to men both in corpses and in aerial bodies. Other indications of their presence are the strange voices which are sometimes heard, other marvelous sounds and visible signs, dreams, revelations, and ecstatic states.

With the second volume and third book we approach the question of the apparition of souls of the dead. After discussing the essence and origin of the soul and the opinions of the Gentiles as to its separation from the body, Le Loyer devotes two chapters to legal opinion on the question, then turns to the views of Jewish rabbis and cabalists and of Moslems. The arguments adduced by "Lavatier[48] and other dogmatists" to prove that souls do not appear after the decease of their bodies are refuted. So is the contention of "the Pomponazzists and astrological libertins" that the apparitions come from the constellations and are mirages formed in the clouds, as in the case of the supposedly miraculous apparition of St. Coelestinus. The Church maintains the apparition of souls after the death of their bodies, and holy doctors and councils have so held.

The fourth book opens with the problem of the professed raising of Samuel by the witch of Endor. Some persons are deceived by the devil with false visions or deceive other men by feigning visions. John of Rupescissa is represented by Le Loyer as one who had false revelations. False visions of the pagans and oracles given by demons are also discussed. In ancient theurgy devils were evoked who pretended to be gods or angels, and in necromancy they present themselves in the guise of the dead. Le Loyer then considers how one can distinguish demons from good angels and souls of the dead. Finally, means of expelling demons are taken up. Some herbs are believed to have this power. Le Loyer also tells how the ancient pagans routed

[48] Presumably the reference is to Ludwig Lavater.

demons or performed rites of expiation after having seen some horrible vision.

From some passages in the work we may infer that Le Loyer was a foe of Paracelsus and of alchemical medicine. He says that he saw a medical empiric at Paris who boasted in full Parlement that he could tell the qualities and temperament of any herb at first sight, even including herbs from America whose virtues were as yet scarcely known to medicine. "But this Paracelsite was refuted and prohibited with his Paracelsus, and his ignorance was sufficiently disclosed by those appointed to examine him."[49] Le Loyer also rejects "Raimond Lulle . . . with his fifth essence to which he ascribes such power that it can purge dark and bilious humors from the body and chase away devils."[50] It is probable that Le Loyer here has in mind the work of John of Rupescissa on the fifth essence which had been printed in a Lullified version under Raymond's name, but in any case the animus against alchemical medicine is clear.

There were later works on apparitions and specters by the Jesuit, Petrus Thyraeus,[51] whose writings I have not seen, and by Scherertzius in 1621, of which a word may be said here.

Scherertzius, in his treatise on specters of 1621,[52] believes in the apparition of angels and demons partly because Luther did so, partly as a result of his own experiences, of which he has kept a record. He does not, however, limit the various tales of apparitions with which he regales us to his own experience. He makes some generalizations withal, as that the devil is always present in the appearance of specters, that the souls of the dead cannot appear to us, and that specters have become of rarer occurrence since the Reformation, the same point as had been made by Rivius in his work on specters eighty years before and by James I more recently. Meteorologists explain cer-

[49] *iiii livres des spectres* . . . , I, 131.

[50] *Ibid.*, II, 309.

[51] His works in Latin on varied apparitions and on demoniacs appeared at Cologne in 1594 and that on infested places in 1598. Further editions of all three soon followed. Zedler, under the heading "Disputationes variae" notes a *De apparitionibus spirituum* printed at Mainz, 1582.

[52] Sigismundus Scherertzius, *Libellus consolatorius de spectris, hoc est apparitionibus et illusionibus daemonum*, Wittebergae, 1621. BM 719.b.21.

tain phenomena in the sky as natural and caused by vapors, but Scherertzius is more interested in seeing or detecting the devil everywhere. The second part of his treatise contains consolations against the attacks of specters. The third part is devoted to pious admonitions such as not to fabricate or feign an apparition and to have nothing to do with necromancers or nigromancers. He charges Trithemius in his *Steganographia* and Jacobus de Clusa[53] with having written necromantic books which deserve to be burned rather than read.[54]

Martin Biermann, in seventy-four theses on magic actions which were published first in 1590 at Helmstadt[55] and later at Wittenberg in 1613,[56] opposed some of the extreme contentions of Bodin in his *Démonomanie* but still allowed a considerable magical activity to demons. He does not concern himself with natural magic, saying that today a magician is described as one who makes a pact with the devil to obtain the devil's aid. Thus he identifies magicians and witches. He denies cohabitation of demons with magicians and holds that the latter experience many things only in dreams and even when awake are deceived by varied phantasms so that they seem to themselves to behold and to effect things which have no reality. He further denies that demons can assume true bodies apparent to the sense, "because in eternal beings nothing new happens, nor can that transformation be made without alteration, from which separate forms are entirely immune." The transformation of Lot's wife into a pillar of salt and Nebuchadnezzar's eating grass he classes as divine miracles contrary to the laws of nature and entirely distinct from magic illusions. Biermann would also wholly separate voluntary human action from natural phenomena. He rejects the weapon ointment of Paracelsus and speaks slightingly of ligatures and the placing of herbs under one's pillow as love-

[53] Concerning him see T IV, 285-91.

[54] *De spectris,* III, 10, ". . . Trithemius abbas Spanheimensis peculiarem librum de Steganographia edidit et Jacobus de Clusa tractatum de ratione agendi cum spiritibus scripsit qui libri igni potius fuerant tradendi quam edendi et legendi."

[55] Martinus Biermannus, *De magicis actionibus exetasis succincta: sententiae Johannis Bodini . . . opposita,* Helmstadii, 1590. Copy used: BM 8630.e.31.

[56] BM 526.g.4.

charms. Biermann wrote a treatise on the internal principles of the generation of natural things which I have not seen.[57]

The work or works of Johann Georg Godelmann, a doctor of both laws, *On Magicians, Sorcerers and Witches*[58] appeared in print at Frankfurt in 1591. The dedication of the first part on magic to Christian III of Denmark is dated from Rostock, April 4, 1590, but the author says he wrote it five years ago. This is not true of the second section on witches, however, for although it is without a dedication, it contains an allusion to the author's having spent the year 1587 in Livonia. The third part on judicial procedure in witch cases is dedicated to Udalric, duke of Mecklenburg, i.e. Ulrich who actually was only Administrator von Schwerin.

Godelmann attempts to take middle ground between what he regards as the extreme positions of Bodin and Wier. He reproves Scribonius for attempting to revive the cold water test for witches which was rejected by the law faculties in German universities. He also pooh-poohs the idea that witches have distinguishing physical marks. In the matter of witch trials he utters many wise cautions, such as that in no other kind of crime is a judge so apt to wander from the path of justice, that no one should be imprisoned or subjected to torture on the testimony of sorcerers and witches, that confessions of witchcraft made under fear of prison or torture prove nothing, that many witches eagerly seek death, that death-bed depositions are often false, and that the actions of witches resemble those of sleepers. Noting that persons consulting magicians and sorcerers are never punished, and that many books of magic are printed, sold and read with impunity, Godelmann pleads for gentler and more circumspect treatment of witches. Like Wier, he regards them as deceived in dreams by Satan, with whom they have no express pact, nor do they sin with their eyes open, as magicians and sorcerers do. Lycanthropy, too, he terms a species of melancholy

[57] *De principiis generationis rerum naturalium internis*, Helmstadii, 1589.

[58] *De magis veneficis et lamiis recte cognoscendis et puniendis libri tres*, Francofurti . . . Nicolai Bassaei . . . 1591. The three books are separately paginated.

or delusion of the demons. Although he admits that the devil may sometimes transport human beings through the air, he denies that witches fly on broomsticks to sabbats, that they have sexual intercourse with demons, or that they can raise storms.

But Godelmann credulously repeats tales of feats of magic in the same way as other writers. Such stories are told of Albertus Magnus, Trithemius and Faust, who is represented as living at Wittenberg in Luther's time. Albertus filled the imperial palace at Cologne with flowers, foliage and songbirds in winter. Trithemius raised a specter of Mary of Burgundy, the wife of Maximilian, that was true to life even to a wart on her neck. Faust carried his comrades through the air, turned a peasant's pigs into bundles of straw in mid-stream, devoured another rustic's horses and cart, and allowed his foot to be pulled off. From Camerarius is repeated the story of the citizen of Nürnberg who owned a crystal which always foretold the future. Godelmann himself had been assured by a leading citizen of Rostock who had lived in Norway that the Lapps by means of their incantations could learn of any event within twenty-four hours after its occurrence.

Godelmann furthermore holds that natural magic is licit, disagreeing with Erastus who had pronounced all magic illicit. Godelmann feels, however, that Paracelsus went too far in advising magic cures of disease, and that his books are full of superstitious rather than natural amulets. He discusses Paracelsus in a chapter on sleight-of-hand or illusory curers of hyperphysical diseases,[59] which imitates the title of the work of Joel on hyperphysical diseases which we have already considered and admits being indebted to it. Godelmann himself had seen a magician cure the sick by employing diabolical names, and he regards the use of weapon-ointment as diabolical. He denies that magic images and characters derive their force from the stars, and rejects the authority of Avicenna and Pomponazzi as well as of Paracelsus. Augurs and chiromancers he believes should not be called magicians.

[59] *Ibid.*, I, 8, De curatoribus morborum hyperphysicorum praestigiosis.

Godelmann reveals his Protestantism in holding that the exorcists of the Roman church are to be classed with enchanters and magicians. Exorcism existed in the primitive church as a peculiar gift but then ceased, so that Ulpian defined *exorcisare* as "to be an impostor." Godelmann further classes the Jewish Cabala, whether old or new, as a species of incantation. His attitude to Jews is indeed very hostile. He wonders that there are Christian princes and republics "who put up with and defend this blasphemous and magical people" and he commends the noble refusal of Christopher, duke of Wurtemberg, to admit them in return for financial aid, and the kings of Denmark and Sweden and "electors, princes and cities of Saxony" for excluding them.

Godelmann was widely read in the literature of his subject and cites many past authors. If his work is a mixture of sanity and credulity, of religious prejudice and a feeling for law and nature, it was perhaps the more effective on that account than a more strictly rational and scientific work would have been then in doing something to check the excesses of the witchcraft delusion.

Peter Binsfeld came from Luxemburg, studied at Rome and became a doctor of theology, then was a canon at Trier and grand vicar, suffragan or Weihbischof to the archbishop. He is said to have died of the plague on November 24, 1598, but "about 1606" is also given as the time of his death.[60] "From his pen in 1589," says George L. Burr, "came that learned defense of the credibility of the witch-confessions which for a century played the part of a code to the witch-persecutors of Germany, Protestant as well as Catholic."[61] It was reprinted at Trier in 1591 in a revised and enlarged version together with Binsfeld's commentary on the Title of the Code, *De maleficis et mathematicis*. I have used an edition of Trier, 1596, in which Binsfeld says that since "our earlier treatises" are out of print, he issues

[60] See Hoefer and Michaud. Valerius Andreas, *Bibliotheca Belgica*, 1643, p. 724.

[61] Geo. L. Burr, "The Fate of Dietrich Flade," *Papers of the American Historical Association*, V (1891), 199.

"this third edition, fuller than the others."[62] The commentary on *De maleficis et mathematicis* is also described in this 1596 edition as newly revised and augmented in many places. Binsfeld further added in this third edition papal bulls and *Extravagantes* against the occult arts from the *Extravagans* of John XXII to the bull of Sixtus V against astrologers. German translations of his work on the confessions of witches had appeared in 1590 and 1591, and there were posthumous Latin editions of it in 1605, 1611 and 1623.

Binsfeld is conscious of an insistent opposition to the witchcraft persecution. Many are asking when there will be an end to the burning of witches, but he has no sympathy with this attitude.[63] Many regard the confessions of witches as too marvelous and impossible, as mere dreams and phantasies.[64] Franciscus Ponzinibius held that by Christ's passion and death the devil was bound in hell and cannot vex mankind until the advent of antichrist. But Bartholomew Spina showed that this view savored of heresy.[65] On the other hand, some of the notions of the witch-hounds are too superstitious for Binsfeld. He regards the floating in water as a test of witches, recently advocated by Scribonius, as a mortal sin and a work of superstition introduced by the devil.[66] He likewise rejects the opinion of Grillando and Bodin that witches cannot shed tears, Bodin's idea that the child of a witch is almost certain to become a witch, and the belief of Daneau and Bodin in bodily marks or insensible spots by which witches may be detected.[67]

For the rest, Binsfeld's book displays the usual features and tenets of tracts on witchcraft. He holds that the enormous and ever increasing depravity of the age has provoked God to let demons and witches do their worst against mankind. To the old

[62] Petrus Binsfeldius, *De confessionibus maleficiarum et sagarum*, Aug. Trevirorum, 1596. Copy used: Bern Theol. XII, 41.

[63] *Ibid.*, dedication.

[64] *Ibid.*, p. 1.

[65] *Ibid.*, p. 11.

[66] *Ibid.*, pp. 355-60. Another to reject this test was the colleague of Dodoens at Leyden, Ioannes Heurnius (1543-1601) in a Response to the president and councillors of the supreme court of Holland. Valerius Andreas, *Bibl. Belgica*, 1643, p. 517.

[67] *Ibid.*, pp. 750-53.

stories he adds many recent anecdotes, of which some are dated as late as 1595 and so are peculiar to this third edition. As each man has a guardian angel, so to each is assigned a tempting evil spirit. Witches cannot work miracles, imprint a natural form, or transform themselves or others into animals. But they can with demon aid make imperfect animals such as are generated from putrefaction, they can have sexual intercourse as incubi or succubi with demons, they can impede the force of generation between husband and wife or other persons, inflict diseases and even kill men and animals, and also cure many diseases which are beyond the resources of medical science—the demon being a most skilled physician—but not all. They can produce storms and cause sterility, injure the crops, transport bodies from place to place. However, they are not always borne bodily to their assemblies but sometimes are the prey of illusions.

So much for the first chief question of Binsfeld's book, whether the deeds to which witches confess really happen? His second principal query is whether their testimony implicating others may be accepted. Against this might seem to militate a constitution of Charles V that no one shall be arrested or tortured on denunciation of enchanters and diviners. But Binsfeld interprets this merely as a prohibition of having recourse to magic and divination to discover hidden criminals and holds that it does not apply to witches' implicating their associates, which is testimony as to past fact and involves no divination or occultism. Binsfeld does not agree with Bodin that a judge may deceive the accused with false promises of immunity, he would give the sacrament to the penitent, and he informs us that it is the general custom not to burn witches alive but to strangle them first.[68] He also recognizes that torture is a dangerous and not very dependable instrument of criminal procedure, and that persons under torture have confessed to the murder of men who were afterwards found alive.[69]

Especially in the commentary on the *Titulus, De maleficis et mathematicis,* does Binsfeld branch out into a discussion of other

[68] *Ibid.,* p. 375.

[69] *Ibid.,* pp. 679-98.

occult arts than sorcery and witchcraft, although already in *De confessionibus* he has denied the possibility of souls of the dead returning to this world and participating in magic, has discussed nocturnal apparitions, and has held that exorcisms are not always effective against demons.

The disgorging or emission of objects of incredible size, shape or hardness and sharpness from the human body in certain cases and whether it was due to witchcraft and demons had already perplexed previous writers. Grillando stated that if they were preserved for a few days they would liquefy and lose their apparent forms especially if they had been vomited or voided at stool. Others held that hard objects were introduced into the flesh by demon motive power so swiftly that this was invisible and unnoticed. To Paracelsus is attributed the explanation that the pores were distended so that there was no abrasion of the skin, but this theory is rejected and the Paracelsan method of cure in such cases is omitted as "ridiculous and full of superstition."[70] Cosmas Philiarchus of Pistoia, a canon and theologian of Florence, held that such objects might be either illusions of the devil or real, in the former case the air being condensed and colored to imitate solid objects, in the latter the objects having been introduced piecemeal and invisibly.[71]

As to the extent of the occult virtue possessed by natural objects Binsfeld's attitude seems somewhat wavering and inconsistent. He denies that demons can be expelled from the body of a possessed person by the force of melody or of any herb or stone, although he admits that these may indirectly mitigate the vexation which the demon causes the person possessed. He holds that no natural explanation can be given for the bleeding of the corpse of the victim at the approach of the murderer. It must be considered a divine miracle "in horror and detestation of so great a crime." Yet he believes that witches and demons are impeded by the sound of bells from injuring crops and vines by thunder storms. At first, it is true, he ascribes such marvelous

[70] *Ibid.*, p. 578 *et seq.*

[71] *Ibid.*, p. 581, citing "lib. de officio sacerdotis in 2. part. lib. 3 cap. 8 in primo praecepto Decalogi."

effects of bells to the fact that they have been blessed and have received the Holy Spirit. He denies, however, that church bells are baptized, as Calvin and Brentius have calumniously charged. But soon he states that the motion of pulsation rarefies the air and disperses and dissolves dense matter, so that the weather is moderated in the vicinity.[72] This natural explanation might seem to suffice without the preceding supernatural ascription.

An opposite view had been maintained by Gaspar Hombergius who, passing over the baptism of bells, had held that the ringing of them during storms was idolatrous and portentous.[73]

If Binsfeld ascribes far greater powers over man and nature to witches and demons than to unaided human and natural forces, he is more equable in the case of foreknowledge of the future, where, perhaps without realizing it, he grants to astrologers almost the same powers as to demons.[74] God alone can know future events in themselves. Those coming events which have a cause determined necessarily and infallibly, demons can know by natural knowledge and astrologers can predict without sinning against any law. Effects which often follow from the stars and heavenly movements but not infallibly, astrologers may predict conjecturally but not infallibly, and demons are subject to the same limitation. Demons cannot know naturally contingent and undetermined future events or human thoughts that are dependent on our own free will. But they often predict truly by guess work concerning human actions or foretell acts of the will and intellect indirectly and by conjectural knowledge. Similarly an astrologer cannot predict with any certainty concerning fortuitous events and human acts dependent on free will. But, as Bartholomaeus Medina points out, astrologers sometimes predict by four other methods than by observing the constellations. One is by lots or luck, another by their own prudence, a third

[72] For the passages cited in this paragraph, *Ibid.*, pp. 129-30, 131, 136, 380-83.

[73] Gaspar Hombergius, *De superstitiosis campanorum pulsibus ad eliciendas preces quibus placentur fulmina excogitatis responsio*, Francofurti ad Moenum, 1577, 8vo. Copy used: BM 719.e.5.

[74] Binsfeld does not compare them or discuss them together. His treatment of demon foreknowledge occurs in the edition of 1596 at pp. 427-33, that of astrology at p. 450 *et seq.*

through the stupidity of those who consult them, the fourth by pacts with demons. But the last method would seem of little advantage to them, since their own scope of foreknowledge is practically as broad as that of the demons. The latter, however, know about secrets, thefts, lost articles and hidden treasures which escape human cognizance and which Binsfeld declares it is damnable and contrary to Scripture, the canons and laws to investigate astrologically. But these are, it should be noted, really past and present rather than future matters. In foreknowledge and prediction strictly interpreted, astrology remains equipped with all the avenues and possibilities that are open to the demons.

Regardless of the new stars of 1572 and subsequent years, Binsfeld still explains comets as terrestrial exhalations in the upper air caused by the sun's rays. He says nothing of any influence of other planets on them. They may rise either from natural causes or by miraculous disposition of God. In the former case they may signify drought and consequent famine, or by infecting the air they may cause pestilence, or war by inflaming human spirits. By heating the air they are likely to induce disease especially in kings who live delicately and who may die of the disease, or in case of war suffer a violent death. Hence the death of kings is apt to follow the appearance of a comet—a rather tenuous line of reasoning. When comets appear by divine miracle, they always signify imminent calamity or death of kings and princes. He illustrates this by recalling those which marked respectively the death of St. Thomas Aquinas, of the duke of Milan in 1400, and many ills early in the pontificate of Eugenius IV.[75] If to the modern reader these examples are as unconvincing as Binsfeld's previous reasoning, conversely they attest the hold that belief in comets had upon him and his age, if it could be maintained by such feeble props and supports.

Of physiognomy, if kept within proper limits, Binsfeld did

[75] Of these three comets the last two were recorded by Antonino, archbishop of Florence. Binsfeld discusses comets at pp. 459-66.

not disapprove. He noted that Grillandus *de sortilegiis* and Troilus Malvetius *de sortibus* had approved of chiromancy as natural science. He himself held that signs in the body show the individual's inclination but do not impose necessity. The physiognomist should not try to judge concerning divine gifts or external matters like honor, wealth, good or bad fortune, and violent death. He should observe the face especially. After these qualifications Binsfeld added some details as to the physiognomy of the members of the human body.[76]

Although according to divine, canon and civil law consultation of diviners was a most serious sin, Binsfeld notes that it went on in his time with the knowledge and tolerance of magistrates, and that no one thought of inflicting any penalty either on those consulting diviners or on the diviners and lot-casters themselves. In this he agrees with Wier and Godelmann that other forms of magic and occult arts than witchcraft were much practiced and seldom punished. Whereas the Code prescribed burning for an aruspex who entered another's house and deportation to an island for the householder receiving him, even the legists admitted that such penalties were obsolete and substituted other milder ones. As for augury, Binsfeld granted that it was sometimes lawful to predict the future from the song, flight or other disposition of birds, if such future events came within the scope of the natural instinct of the birds as influenced by the stars or as moved by the angels. Citing Aquinas, Antoninus, Turrecremata, Coelius Rhodiginus and Benedictus Pererius on divination from dreams, Binsfeld maintained the usual Aristotelian position that we ought neither entirely to despise nor entirely to be concerned as to dreams. If the cause of the dream was within the body, one might foresee the corresponding result, and it was quite proper to predict from dreams having extrinsic causes such as the heavenly bodies or the surrounding air, in so far as the influence of these extended. But it was wrong to predict from such dreams contingent future events or acts involving free will. It was proper to predict the

[76] *Ibid.*, pp. 468-74.

future from divine revelation in dreams but not from demonic revelation.[77]

Binsfeld would punish the use of charms for injurious or lustful purposes, but not for medicinal or agricultural ends. He notes that it is the general opinion of civil lawyers that magical incantations employed for beneficial purposes may not be punished, but that such are not held licit in the forum of conscience and divine and canon laws.[78]

Alchemy is discussed by Binsfeld for some twenty pages.[79] Its close relation to the occult arts and sciences in his mind is indicated by the fact that his treatment of it follows those of astrology and physiognomy and immediately precedes that of other arts of divination. His attitude towards it is nevertheless not wholly unfavorable. Having raised the question whether the art of alchemy works any true effects so far as transmutation is concerned and whether it may be licitly practiced without incurring suspicion of magic, he cites authorities on either side and decides that it is still unsettled whether gold can be made alchemically. "Morally speaking," however, gold-making seems well nigh impossible and beyond human reach. But the art of alchemy can produce other true and useful effects, and is not illicit from its nature and object. But if it seeks to make true gold or silver or precious gems, it is useless and dangerous to the state, and perilous to the body and soul of the alchemist. In many instances, too, alchemists are guilty of invoking demons, and the art is often combined with magic. Among Binsfeld's citations in the course of this discussion are the decretal "Spondent" of John XXII, various legal writers, two writers on heresy—Bernardus de Lutzenburgo and Gabriel Prateolus—Eymeric, Cajetan, Janus Lacinius, Cardan, Gregorius Valentianus, Thomas Bartholomaeus Chassanaeus, Antonius Mirandulanus, and Michael de Palario.

Witchcraft was again discussed in 1595, when Baptista Codronchi printed at Venice his *De morbis veneficis ac veneficiis*

[77] *Ibid.*, pp. 500-516.

[78] *Ibid.*, pp. 525-26, 542, 566-71.

[79] *Ibid.*, pp. 475-97.

libri quatuor.[80] The rest of the long title is worth translating: "in which not only by sure reasons are bewitchments shown to exist, but their species, causes, signs and effects are disclosed by a new method; finally, concerning their cure and preservation is treated exactly, and true, new and tested remedies are set forth." The work is useful for both physicians and exorcists. The talk of a new method and new remedies appears to be mere humbug intended to attract new readers to a time-worn but still vital theme. For Codronchi, *veneficia* are the same as *maleficia,* not poisons but bewitchments, and he ascribes them all to demons in the usual way. His work much resembles *De fascino* of Leonardus Vairus, published in the previous decade, except that Codronchi is fuller on the theme of natural remedies against witchcraft.

In a preface to the senate of Imola, where he had formerly been engaged in public administration and medical practice, presumably as municipal physician or health officer, he states that considerations of personal health had forced him to retire from that office and devote the rest of his life to writing. Even before his retirement he had written on certain baths which lay within their jurisdiction. Next he printed two books on a safe and Christian method of healing, a title slightly suggestive of present Christian science. He had not yet finished this work, when not only at Imola but in many other towns of Italy numerous persons were found to be affected by various bewitchments. Among these sufferers was one of his own daughters, so that he worked at and read extensively on the subject and now publishes his findings. The change from public office and medical practice to a literary career seems to have agreed with Codronchi, if he was still living when in 1620 at Bologna and

[80] Baptista Codronchius philosophus et medicus Imolensis, *De morbis veneficis ac veneficiis libri quatuor in quibus non solum certis rationibus veneficia dari demonstratur sed eorum species caussae signa et effectus nova methodo aperiuntur, postremo de eorum curatione ac preservatione exacte tractatur veraque nova et experta remedia proponuntur,* Venice, 1595. Copy used: BM 1191.f.1.(2.).

The dedication is dated, "Ex aedibus meis octavo idus Ianuarii anno a Chrysto nato MDXCV."

1623 at Cologne was printed his treatise on climacteric years, the way to avoid their perils, and methods of prolonging life.

Codronchi proves the existence of witchcraft from the Bible, decrees of church councils, canon law, the church fathers, and the philosophers, Plato and Aristotle. Like Cesalpino, he holds that the Peripatetics knew of demons and their sorceries, while unlike Cesalpino he admits that they could not demonstrate their existence from philosophical principles. According to Codronchi, physicians also admit their existence, historical records are full of their doings, and their reality is attested alike by the poets, common report and the judgment of inquisitors. The diseases and injuries which witches inflict are not caused by imagination, vision or rays from the eye, touch, occult natural properties, celestial influences or intelligences, or by melancholy, but by the art of demons. Instruments, characters and images have no force in themselves. Their efficacy must be produced by demons. Witches can make married couples impotent and bring on sterility, remove the genitals by magic, produce abortion, dry up the milk, and retain the urine. By the aid of demons they can transform themselves or others into the semblance of brutes and other shapes. Some by mental excess know all that goes on at the sabbat, although themselves absent, while others are borne there in the body. By *veneficium* the demons can possess human bodies. Turning to the problem of incubus and succubus, Codronchi affirms that the incubus of the theologians differs greatly from that of medical men, which is the first sane remark he has made for some time.

Coming to the cure of the bewitched, Codronchi makes some sensible criticisms of the remedies which are employed by exorcists without the knowledge of physicians and which often injure the sick. Exorcists sometimes require that the patient be entirely immersed in a bath of lye, ashes of olives, and river water in which have been boiled rue, sage, hypericon, artemisia, vervain, palma Christi, and aristolochia rotunda. Codronchi would advise omitting this treatment, since many conditions of which he is suspicious must be observed in the use of the bath.

He also cautions against an ointment which exorcists put on the eyes, forehead, ears and breast.

It is a vexed question how things of nature can act on demons, who are not physical agents. But the story of Tobias and the heart of a fish burnt on coals seems to justify, in Codronchi's opinion, the employment of natural objects against demons. The schoolman, Richard of Middleton, had suggested that such objects cannot entirely cure ailments inflicted by demons but afford some alleviation by their action, not on the demon, but on the person afflicted. Others had suggested that the demon is insulted or offended by the disagreeable character of the things employed and so retires, possibly because they are signs of hell fire to him. But for Codronchi the best explanation is that God especially endows these natural objects with power against demons, and this the more so, if they are piously offered and duly blessed and exorcized. Among the natural remedies he considers are emetics, baths, suffumigations, liniments and oils.

The notion that men can be transformed into animals such as werwolves, to which Bodin had given support in his *Démonomanie,* was denied by Claude Prieur in a treatise of 1596 addressed to the pastor and magistrates of Wavre. He held that lycanthropy was an illusion of the devil or of magic.[81] J. de Nynauld was likewise to oppose it in a work published in 1615.[82] It had further been rejected in 1597 in the work to which we shall next turn by king James I, who did not even attempt to explain "war-woolfes" or "men-woolfes" as illusions of demons but attributed to "a naturall super-abundance of Melancholy" and to a vitiated imagination the belief of some men that they were wolves or other animals.[83]

[81] Claude Prieur, *Dialogue de la lycanthropie ou transformation d'hommes en loups vulgairement dit loups-garous et si telle se peut faire,* Louvain, 1596, 8vo. Copy used: BM 719.e.6.(1.).

[82] J. de Nynauld, *De la lycanthropie,* Paris, 1615. At p. 82, "Refutation des opinions et arguments que Bodin allegue au 6 chapitre de sa Demonomanie pour maintenir la realité de la lycanthropie des sorciers."

[83] *Daemonologie, in forme of a Dialogue, Diuided into three Bookes,* Edinburgh, Printed by Robert Waldegraue, Printer to the Kings Majestie. An. 1597. Cum Privilegio Regis, III, 1, pp. 61-62.

I have used the reprint edition of London, 1924, edited by G. B. Harrison.

This sceptical attitude and natural explanation by James is the more remarkable, because as a rule in the *Daemonologie* he accepts the extreme contentions and more superstitious beliefs of writers on witchcraft. He holds that witches cannot shed tears, "thretten and torture them as ye please."[84] He believes that the devil gives them his mark upon some secret place of their body, "which remains soare unhealed" until their next meeting with the devil, after which it becomes insensible.[85] James also believes that witches may be detected by their floating in water.[86] In this connection he accepts the bleeding of a corpse in the presence of the murderer but, like Binsfeld, attempts no natural explanation of it, "God having appoynted that secret super-naturall signe, for tryall of that secrete unnaturall crime." Witches, aided by the devil, can make men or women love or hate one another, transfer disease from one person to another, take life by roasting wax images of the individuals in question, raise storms and tempests, drive men crazy, haunt houses and make men possessed by demons.[87] The devil can transport witches through the air, but not very far or they lose their breath. This transportation can be effected invisibly by the devil so thickening and obscuring the air surrounding the witch "by contracting it strait together, that the beames of any other mans eyes cannot pearce thorow the same to see them." Apparently James believed in vision by extramission of rays from the eye, an antiquated theory. He does not believe that witches can be transformed into small animals and birds, pass through closed doors or small apertures, or leave their bodies and return to them.[88] He believes that "faire banquets and daintie dishes" are actually carried "in short space fra the farthest part of the worlde," but that armies of horse and foot, castles and forts, that appear by magic are only "impressions in the air."[89] The devil is far more cunning than man in the knowledge of all the occult properties of nature, has great agility and power over

[84] *Ibid.*, p. 81, III, 6.
[85] *Ibid.*, pp. 33, 36; II, 2-3.
[86] *Ibid.*, p. 80, III, 6.
[87] *Ibid.*, II, 5, pp. 45-47.
[88] *Ibid.*, II, 4, pp. 38-41.
[89] *Ibid.*, I, 6, p. 22.

the air and some knowledge of the future but cannot read men's minds.[90]

James advocates the death penalty for all magicians and witches, and their customers, patrons and abettors. Since the penalty is so severe, he agrees that "Iudges ought to beware to condemne any but such as they are sure are guiltie, neither should the clattering reporte of a carling serve in so weightie a case." But as in a treason trial, ordinary safeguards as to evidence must give way, and the testimony of children and guilty persons be admitted. "For who but Witches can be . . . witnesses of the doings of Witches."[91] James would even accept their accusations against persons whom they think they saw at imaginary sabbats which they really did not attend but were only illusions presented to their imaginations by the devil. His reason is that God would not permit the devil to represent anyone but witches in such illusory gatherings, "so iealous is God I say of the fame of them that are innocent."[92]

There is one thing to be said for James's treatise or dialogue. Except for an occasional lightness of tone, appropriate enough to the dialogue form but incongruous with the grimness of the subject, it is a serious piece of reasoned argument without any of the indecent and incredible stories that fill so many of the books on witchcraft. Also Philomathes occasionally strikes some sparks of scepticism, although Epistemon hastens to put them out. Even he makes a dangerous admission when he says that simple jugglers "will make an hundred things seeme both to our eies and eares otherwaies then they are."[93] The first book deals with magic or necromancy, the second with sorcery or witchcraft, the third with spirits and the punishment of witches. Although James now and then sneers at the superstitious ways of the papists, he adopts almost precisely the attitude of the recent bull of Sixtus V towards astrology, holding that only a moderate amount of astrological medicine and weather predic-

[90] *Ibid.*, II, 5, p. 44; I, 1, p. 4; I, 6, pp. 21-22.

[91] *Ibid.*, III, 6, pp. 77-79.

[92] *Ibid.*, III, 6, pp. 79-80. James also relies on the three tests of insensible marks, inability to weep, and floating in water as means of distinguishing the guilty from the innocent.

[93] *Ibid.*, I, 6, p. 23.

tion is licit, and that the rest of astrology leads on to the black and unlawful science of magic.[94]

James maintains that since the coming of Christ and planting of the church "all miracles, visions, prophecies and appearances of angels or good spirites are ceased."[95] Before the Protestant Reformation more ghosts and spirits were seen than since it, but witchcraft and other unlawful arts have increased since the Reformation.[96] He recognizes that many of the learned would not agree with his condemnation of astrology, and that there are many who deny the existence of any spirits whatsoever.[97]

Professor Kittredge has shown that James's bark was much worse than his bite, that there were only about two executions a year in England during his reign there, that he personally exposed impostors who had pretended to be bewitched, and demonstrated that upon one occasion innocent persons had been executed.[98] We, too, may pursue the subject a little further into the period of the reign of James I and early seventeenth century.

The book on magic of Strozzi Cicogna is not much different from the many others on that theme which appeared during the period of the witchcraft delusion, and so is of more importance as attesting the popularity of the subject than for any new ideas or method of treatment and presentation. First printed at Venice in 1605 in Italian with the title *Palace of the Enchantments and of Great Marvels of Spirits and of All Nature,*[99] it appeared the next year in Latin at Cologne under the caption *Theater of Every Kind of Magic or Rather of Universal Nature in which by a disputation founded on the first principles of things the universal nature of spirits and incantations is explained.*[100] Cicogna was a noble of Vicenza, a theologian, phi-

[94] *Ibid.*, I, 3-4, pp. 10, 13.

[95] *Ibid.*, III, 2, p. 66.

[96] *Ibid.*, II, 7, p. 54.

[97] *Ibid.*, I, 4, p. 14; II, 7, p. 55.

[98] George Lyman Kittredge, *Witchcraft in Old and New England,* 1929, Chapter XVII, King James the First, pp. 276-328.

[99] *Palagio de gl'incanti & delle gran maraviglie de gli spiriti & di tutta la natura, divisi in libri xlv & in iii prospettive, Spirituale, celeste & elementare,* Venetiis, 1605, 4to.

[100] *Magiae omnifariae vel potius universae naturae theatrum in quo a primis rerum principiis accessita disputatione universa spirituum et incantationum natura etc. explicatur,* Coloniae, 1606, 8vo.

losopher and doctor of laws, and nuncio of his city to the republic of Venice. His attitude throughout is orthodox. He believes in creation and argues against the eternity of the world, plurality of worlds and the *magnus annus*. His closing chapter is on the uncertainty of human science and the truth of holy Scripture. He believes in the existence of demons whom he divides into fiery, aerial, watery and terrestrial, and the last into genii, lares, specters, wood sprites, satyrs, fauns, familiar spirits, and subterranean spirits who shun the light. He denies the existence of white magic, and holds the usual views as to the powers of demons maintained by believers in witchcraft. He represents the Council of Rome under pope Zacharias as condemning Aldebert or Adalbert and Clement for heresy for invoking demons. Most of the eight names invoked by Aldebert in his prayer were of demons, not angels, since we know the names of only three angels—Michael, Gabriel and Raphael—and of these only one, Michael, was included among Aldebert's eight names. Cicogna discusses the Cabala somewhat and attributes to the rabbis and cabalists, the doctrine that angels rule the signs of the zodiac and four elements, and that nine choirs of angels correspond to the celestial spheres: namely, the seraphim to the *primum mobile,* cherubim to the eighth sphere of the fixed stars, Thrones to Saturn, Dominions to Jupiter, Virtues to Mars, Powers to the sun, Principalities to Venus, archangels to the sphere of Mercury, and angels to that of the moon. Like other books of the same type, Cicogna's delights in incredible stories, some of which we recognize as old acquaintances. He gives cases of marvelous rejuvenation from the pages of Cardan, of Torquemada, and of Petrus Maffeius.

A lurid light is shed upon the witchcraft delusion by the *Discourse on Sorcerers,* with an account of six actual cases, by Henri Boquet, a lawyer of the county of Burgundy, which ran through three editions in the first decade of the seventeenth century.[101] We are told, however, that the author's family sub-

[101] *Discours des sorciers avec six advis en faict de sorcelerie et une instruction pour un juge en semblable matière.* I have used the third edition

sequently suppressed all the copies that they could lay hands on.[102] The work seems distinctly inferior to that of Binsfeld which it cites frequently along with Delrio and various other authors. It illuminates practice more than theory, giving the text of an edict of February 19, 1604, by the duke and duchess, decreeing death for attendance at witches' sabbats in the county of Burgundy and praising the local Parlement as "the sole and true flail of sorcerers" and as keeping the fires of execution burning continually "in infinite number," whereas some parlements are so blind that they cannot see "these vermin." Whereas, however, Binsfeld had intimated that unrepentant witches were burned alive, Boquet notes that even they were strangled first in his country unless guilty of some enormity such as being taken as a werwolf. He further states that it was not the custom in Burgundy to verify by torture the testimony inculpating other persons as present at the sabbat, and blandly remarks that in sorcery not so exact proofs are required as in the case of other crimes. Like James I, he accepts as proofs that a person is a witch the inability to weep and the presence of marks on the neck and right shoulder, although both Delrio and Binsfeld had rejected these indications. Witnesses for the accused count for little with Boquet. Thus one woman was condemned to death although she produced twenty-nine witnesses to her good character and orthodoxy, including two confessors, while two doctors of medicine and two surgeons had visited her immediately after she was imprisoned and found no marks on her body. But Boquet explains that the devil sometimes effaces the marks. Only as to the confiscation of the property of persons condemned as witches does Boquet show any signs of relenting, remarking that if their children are left without goods, they are the more likely to be won over by the devil, and that therefore as a matter

of Lyons, 1610, 73 caps., 550 and 93 pp. From the permit to print which is dated 1607 I judge that the first edition appeared then. The second was at Lyons, 1608. There are copies of the second and third editions in the British Museum. I used a copy in the Stadtbibliothek of Bern. An English translation by E. Allen Ashwin was edited by Montague Summers in 1929 under the title, *An Examen of Witches*.

[102] Michaud, IV, 545.

of expediency it may be better to leave them some means of honest subsistence. One example may be given of Boquet's beliefs. He says that it is well known that chaplets are formidable to demons, since they bear the cross and are used in works of piety and devotion.

Jacques Fontaine of St. Maximin (Var) in Provence will serve to illustrate one phase or extreme of medical opinion towards magic and science during the last quarter of the sixteenth and the first quarter of the seventeenth century. He had studied philosophy at the university of Paris and had taught it at the royal court. He then passed on to the study of medicine, received the doctorate at the newly founded university of Aix in his native Provence, and practiced medicine there. He received the title of royal councillor and doctor ordinary after the death of Henry IV in 1610. Becoming engaged in a bitter controversy and war of pamphlets on mineral waters with persons whom he regarded as charlatans but who enjoyed popular favor, he retired for a time to Avignon where in 1601 and 1603 he published works on theriac and other subjects of orthodox Galenic medicine. He had earlier published a work on chicken pox at Aix in 1596 and one on medical prognostication at Tournon in 1597. He was presently recalled to Aix as first professor of medicine at the university and installed in 1606, and continued to publish works on medical subjects. His lectures are said to have been attended by large audiences.[103] A collected edition of his medical works appeared during his lifetime in 1613. He wrote against the Paracelsists and, as we have seen in a previous chapter, against astrology.

In the interim between the publication of the two aforesaid works against Paracelsanism and astrological medicine, Fontaine had shown himself a credulous believer in the existence of signs elsewhere than in the sky by two books issued in the same year 1611. One was a commentary in Latin upon the *Physiog-*

[103] For the facts in the foregoing paragraph see J. Félix E. Chavernac, *Deux médecins* [Jacques Fontaine et Antoine Mérindol] *et un spagyrique* [Nicolas Coningo "le chevalier de Catelmont,"] *à Aix, en l'an 1600,* Aix, M. Illy, 1875, octavo, 96 pp.

nomy of Aristotle addressed to queen Margaret, the divorced wife of Henry IV.[104] The other work, in French, addressed to the queen regent, Marie de' Medici, concerned the marks of sorcerers or the spots insensible to pain and the touch supposed to exist on the bodies of witches and to be stigmata of Satan.[105] In connection with an actual trial of a reputed sorcerer, Louis Gaufridy, before the local Parlement of Aix, the court had requested Fontaine's opinion on the subject as a learned physician and professor of medicine. His reply was no credit to either profession. The opponent of alchemy, Paracelsanism and astrology now reveals himself as a supporter of demonology in one of its most debased details. He puts full credence in the marks which even such rabid writers on witchcraft as Daneau, Bodin and Delrio had slighted, as Fontaine complains. He holds that they are confirmed by daily reports of doctors of medicine, and that in the present case a splinter was inserted three fingers deep in some thirty different places chiefly on the abdomen without the accused feeling it. In the previous case of a Magdeleine de la Palud, who was possessed by a great number of demons, similar spots were found at her first examination, but after she repented and was exorcized, these spots became soft and emitted blood. This Fontaine attributed to the withdrawal of the devil from her body and not to a divine miracle. His physical explanation of the marks is that those parts of the body are deprived of their radical humor and natural heat. Some sorcerers say that Satan marks them with a hot iron and an unguent, others by a touch of his finger. Fontaine prefers the former explanation. He affirms that the evil spirit so marks all sorcerers and never without their consent. He further asserts that the devil makes some persons who are not possessed act as if they were and then yield to medical treatment, so that men may think that the actions of

[104] Iacobus Fontanus, *Phisiognomia Aristotelis ordine compositorio edita ad facilitatem doctrinae commentariis illustrata brevissimis . . . ad serenissimam reginam Margaretam*, Paris, 1611.

[105] Jacques Fontaine, *Des marques des Sorciers et de la réelle possession que le Diable prend sur les corps des hommes. Sur le subject du procès de l'abominable . . . sorcier L. Gaufridy*, Lyon, 1611. I have used the reprint of 1865 (BM 8630.cc.3).

those who are truly possessed proceed from humors and maladies afflicting their bodies and not from the devil. Likewise the devil makes some dream of sabbats, so that men like Wier may incorrectly conclude that all sabbats are mere dreams. Or demons impersonate persons who are really present at sabbats, so that they may seem to be at home asleep in their beds. Fontaine further rejects the explanation of Levinus Lemnius that the gift of tongues is due to excessive melancholy and is lost when the person is medically purged of melancholy. Fontaine denies that the soul can spontaneously evolve a new language, failing to take into account at all subconscious memory and the fact that such persons usually speak only a few words or phrases.

Such was the unscientific attitude and subservience to superstition of the royal physician and first professor of medicine at Aix. A century after Cattaneo and Pomponazzi he holds views as to demons and astrological influence almost diametrically opposed to theirs. Even more discouraging than to find writers at the beginning of the sixteenth century denying the existence of demons but accepting the influence of the stars and occult virtues, is it to find an opponent of astrological medicine at the beginning of the seventeenth century accepting the most superstitious details of the witchcraft delusion. Probably it was after 1611 that he looked at the moons of Jupiter through the telescope, but there is no reason to believe that doing so altered his views as to the activities of demons and marks of sorcerers. But this new telescopic way of looking at things came to him only late in life, when his ideas were set. Had he had the advantage of it earlier, perhaps he would have spent more of his time in looking at new-found things in the heavens, and less in searching with pins and needles for insensible spots on the bodies of those accused of witchcraft. In this new opportunity lay hope for the future.

Fontaine's interests and his combination of attitudes towards alchemy, astrology, occult virtue and witchcraft are very similar to those of Thomas Erastus a generation earlier. But the only connection in which Fontaine cites Erastus, so far as I have noted, is concerning purgatives and there he disagrees with him.[106]

In connection with the belief in witchcraft and the activity of demons something should be said of the literature of exorcisms, which in printed form becomes especially noticeable in the last quarter of the sixteenth and first part of the seventeenth century.[107] Hieronymus Mengus or Girolamo Menghi published several works of this sort. In 1573 he had edited exorcisms of Sylvester Prierias, inquisitor early in the century.[108] His *Flagellum daemonum* appeared at Bologna in 1577-1578, again in 1581 and at Frankfurt in 1582. In 1586 it was reissued at Bologna with his *Fustis daemonum,* which appeared separately or with the *Flagellum* in several subsequent editions. A *Compendium artis exorcistae* was printed at Bologna in Latin and at Macerata in Italian in 1580. It was reprinted in 1582 and 1590 in Italian at Bologna, in 1595 at Venice, and in Latin at Venice in 1601. Finally we find it prohibited in the *Index* of March 4, 1709. Yet another work for the exorcist by Menghi, entitled *Fuga daemonum* had appeared at Venice in 1596. The British Museum also has an *Eversio daemonum e corporibus oppressis* by Menghi printed at Bologna in 1588.

The character of such works may be illustrated by one dedicated to Sixtus V, author of the bull against judicial astrology and divination of January 5, 1586. This was the *Practica of Exorcists* of Valerio Polidoro of Padua, a conventual Franciscan and doctor of arts and sacred theology, and professes at least to be published with the license of his superiors.[109] Among things to be learned from the exorcized spirit are: his name, in order that

[106] *Opera,* 1613, p. 609, "Pharmacia medica generalis in qua medicamentorum omnis generis facultates explicantur et maxime purgatrices contra sententiam peritissimi Erasti." At p. 648 *et seq.,* "De medicamentis purgantibus in genere," he often cites Erastus.

[107] Laevinus Crucius of Flanders who lived and published other works in the first half of the sixteenth century composed an *Eruditorium exorcistae* which remained unprinted: V. Andreas, *Bibl. Belg.,* 1643, p. 607.

[108] *Aureus tractatus exorcismique pulcherrimi . . . Sylvestri Prieriatis . . . liber recognitus auctus atque a mendis innumeris repurgatus* (opera R. P. F. Hieronymi Mengi), Bononiae, 1573. BN E.4642.

[109] *F. Valerii Polidori Patavini ord. min. conventualium artium et sacrae theologiae doctoris Practica exorcistarum . . . ad daemones et maleficia de Christi fidelibus ejiciendum,* Patavii,

it may be written down and put above an image of the demon on paper to be burned; the names of his associates and satellites and their number; the cause of his entering the body of the possessed in order that a contrary remedy may be applied, or, if it be by witchcraft, that the appropriate exorcisms may be read; what order or chorus of angels or what saint he fears, in order to invoke the same for aid; what holy words he especially abhors in order that these may be repeated; what other demon is his bitterest foe and rival, to the end that he may be cited against him; by what exorcist he should be expelled and at what day and hour it is best to work for his expulsion. The exorcist is warned, however, to beware of curious digressions and not to repose too much trust in the demon's replies, in fact to shut him off if he volunteers too much information and seems fraudulent. Instructions are also given how to tell whether a person is actually possessed by a demon and not afflicted by some unusual bodily disease.

Another such work was the *Antidotarium against Demons* by Alessio Porri, a theologian, Carmelite of the Observance, consultant of the Holy Office and public exorcist in the city of Venice, where his book appeared in 1601 with the approval of the Council of Ten and an ecclesiastical censor.[110] Porri quotes cases from the Bible and lives of the saints a great deal but also relies upon his own experience as an exorcist. When he has asked demons how they entered the body of the possessed, they have almost invariably replied that it was in food or drink. It is therefore recommended that Roman catholics make the sign of the cross over their mouths before eating or drinking, although no doubt demons can enter by other ways. The degree of difficulty which the exorcist has in controlling the demon gives some gauge of how high or low an order of spirits it is. The part of the body which they especially occupy is that about the heart, since their object is either to agitate the body with violent motions or to impede its natural operations. Apparently Porro still agreed with

Apud Paulum Meietum MDLXXXVII. Cum superiorum licentia. Copy used: BM 8630.ccc.8.

[110] Alessio Porri, *Antidotario contro li Demonii . . . Nel quale si tratta come entrano ne' corpi humani*, etc., Venetia, 1601. Copy used: BM 719.f.10.

Aristotle rather than Galen that the heart and not the brain was the center of the nervous and motor system. But demons may occupy other parts of the body, and therefore approved exorcisms order them not to hide themselves in the four humors, flesh, bones, nerves, and other parts of the body. Demons torment the body in five chief ways: by fascination of the mind and senses, infirmity of corporal forces, corruption of the organs, contraction or distraction of the limbs, and violent movement in the entire body. Porri lists fourteen sins which are likely to lead to demoniac possession, but would not deprive the possessed of the privilege of communion. He tells a story of Luther failing to exorcize a demon in 1545 in the sacristy of the parish church at Wittenberg and of the demon blocking the doors of the sacristy so that they would not open inward or outward and so keeping Luther a prisoner until they were forced open. Porri speaks of demons being constrained by magic art and gives various instances to show that they haunt houses and certain places.

A *Thesaurus Exorcismorum,* published at Cologne in 1608 covers in all 1272 pages, including two works by Polidoro, the *Flagellum* and *Fustis* of Menghi, and two more works of other authors, Zacharias Visconti, an exorcist of Milan, and Petrus Antonius Stampeus, a priest of Cleves. The volume is full of prayers, exorcisms and blessings of water and other substances, and the use of oil, myrrh, vervain and the like in fumigations.

Alexander Albertinus, a Franciscan of the Observance, whose family came from Rocha Tallada, in 1620 addressed to the bishop of Verona from Mantua a *Hammer of the Demons or Four Most Experimented Exorcisms Collected from the Gospels.* The text consists of short paragraphs of Scripture alternating with prayers or conjurations. For example, "Then came Jesus with his disciples to the garden called Gethsemane. And do you with your associates go to the bottomless pit by the journeys of Christ to the garden of Gethsemane and by His labor." Besides the Verona edition of 1620,[111] the work was reprinted at Milan

[111] Alexander Albertinus, *Malleus daemonum sive quatuor experimentatissimi exorcismi ex evangelis collecti* . . . , Verona, 1620. Copy used: BM 719.d.15.

I append a few other examples of

in 1624, and again in 1628. An Italian version, partly in Latin and partly identical with the foregoing, was addressed to the same bishop in 1621. Sbaralea says that it, like the aforementioned work of Menghi, was condemned by the *Index expurgatorius* on March 4, 1709.

If such ecclesiastical censure seems quite belated, it is to be remembered that medical men continued to believe in demons and witchcraft into the seventeenth century. Jacopo Caranta, doctor of medicine and philosophy, had a good deal to say on both these subjects in 1624 in a discussion of the question whether a man born without testicles or with only one could have sexual intercourse and generate,[112] suggested by an actual case of a man married for nine years whom Caranta and a surgeon examined. Caranta cites both Delrio and Codronchi frequently, and agrees that virility may be removed by incantations and sorcery, although impotency may also be induced by an evil constellation, such as Saturn and Mars in the fifth house at the time of birth. Even if such impotency is the work of demons, Caranta follows Pomponazzi and Mizauld in advising that the body be purged first. Obsessed persons are often afflicted in both mind and body, of which the Church can cure the former, medicine the latter. Caranta has scruples against superstitious ceremonial and devices, even questioning whether the use of a ring in marriage is not superstitious. Towards the close he remarks that natural remedies should be employed without words and incantations, stated numbers and figures, or set day and hour, and that superstitious remedies should not be resorted to even to remove witchcraft.

---

the literature of exorcisms in the first part of the seventeenth century:

E. Pauls, "Der Exorcismus an Herzog Johann Wilhelm von Jülich 1604 und 1605," *Annalen des historischen Vereins für den Niederrhein,* 63 (1896), 27-53.

Christoph. Johann. Dalbya, *De exorcismo. Item de gynaeco baptismo,* Herborn, 1612. The author was a Calvinist.

Maximilianus ab Eynatten, scholasticus and canon of the cathedral of Antwerp who died in 1631, *Manuale exorcismorum,* Antwerpiae, 1619, and again in 1649.

Hilarius Nicuesa, a monk of Chieti, *Exorcismarium magnum,* Venetiis, 1639.

[112] Jacobus Caranta, *De nato cum uno testiculo* . . . , 1624. Copy used: BM 784.l.3.(3.).

CHAPTER XLVII

THE SCEPTIC AND THE ATHEIST: FRANCESCO SANCHEZ AND LUCILIO VANINI

Tu igitur quisquis es eiusdem mecum conditionis temperamentique quique de rerum naturis saepissime tecum dubitasti, dubita modo mecum: ingenia nostra naturamque simul exerceamus.

—FRANCESCO SANCHEZ

From the credulity evidenced as to witchcraft, demons and supernatural marvels we now turn to two representatives, the one of scepticism, the other of atheism, in the last quarter of the sixteenth and the early years of the seventeenth century. It was at Toulouse that Francesco Sanchez in 1576 at the age of twenty-four wrote the preface to his *Quod nihil scitur,* and it was at Toulouse on February 9, 1619, that Lucilio Vanini at the age of about thirty-four "went blithely to die in the arms of Philosophy," denying with his last words the existence either of God or the devil.[1] Let us examine the attitude of these two men towards natural science and the occult arts and sciences.

Francesco Sanchez[2] was from Portugal, where he was born at Braga in 1552, and in a sense may be regarded as an example of that country's intellectual activity in the sixteenth century following the voyages of trade and discovery. It is intimated in Bayle's *Dictionary* on the dubious authority of *Patiniana* that he was of Jewish descent. At any rate his father was a physician,

[1] See the account of his death in *Mercure françois,* 63 (1619), 63-65. According to it, he was arrested in November and executed early in February. Gramond or Gramundus, president of the Parlement of Toulouse, recounted the process of Vanini in his *History of Gaul,* and connected it with the recent comet of 1618, according to Voetius, *Exercitatio de prognosticis cometarum,* 1655, p. 75. Copy used: BM 532.e.16.(3.).

[2] On Sanchez there is the work of L. Gerkrath, *Franz Sanchez. Ein Beitrag z. Gesch. d. philos. Bewegungen im Anfange d. neueren Zeit,* 1860. So far as the facts of Sanchez's life are concerned, Gerkrath's account is based mostly on the Vita by Delassus in the 1636 posthumous edition of Sanchez's works.

and he was to follow in his footsteps as a professor of medicine. While he was born in Portugal, most of his intellectual activity and career centered in southern France. He was educated at Bordeaux, with which were associated other sixteenth century writers who were tinged with scepticism, namely, Charron and Montaigne. Its Collège de Guyenne had rather close relations with Portugal, numbering Portuguese scholars on its faculty and having some of its teachers called away to Portugal to found schools there. Having finished his studies at Bordeaux and taken the M.D. degree at Montpellier in 1574, Sanchez went to Italy for a while and may possibly have been influenced, directly or indirectly, by the teaching of Telesio. He returned to southern France in 1576 to become professor of medicine at Montpellier at the age of only twenty-four. The Wars of Religion soon drove him from this post to Toulouse, where he practiced medicine, was head of a hospital, for a time professor of philosophy, and then royal professor of medicine.

It was also in 1576, as we have said, that he composed the preface to his most original and noteworthy work, *Of the Right Noble and First Universal Science, That Nothing is Known,* although the book was not printed until 1581.[3] In the meantime in 1578 he had published a poem on the comet of 1577 in which he disagreed with the contention of the astrologer Giuntini that comets are always portents of evil.[4] On the basis of this poem and a treatise on divination which seems to have first been printed in the posthumous edition of Sanchez's *Opera,* Gerkrath devoted a chapter to "The Struggle of Sanchez against Superstition,"[5] while he remained silent as to his hero's belief in natural marvels and occult virtues, of which we shall presently have more to say.

The *Quod nihil scitur* of Sanchez is written in short sentences,

[3] I have not seen the first edition of Lyons, Apud Ant. Gryphium, 1581, but have used that of 1618: Franciscus Sanchez, *De multum nobili et prima universali scientia quod nihil scitur.* Copy used: BM 528.b.3.(2.).

[4] J. Baudrier, *Bibliographie lyonnaise, recherches sur les imprimeurs, libraires, relieurs et fondeurs de lettres de Lyon au XVIe siècle,* VIII, 374.

[5] Gerkrath, *op. cit.,* pp. 104-23, "Dritter Abschnitt, Der Streit des Sanchez gegen den Aberglauben."

some of them a single word, with much rapid fire of question and answer, perhaps indicative of the nervous haste and impatience of youth. There is little discernible plan and order, much digression, reversion to a previous thought, and repetition. The text does not lead up cumulatively and progressively to a climax and conclusion. But these last are characteristics of sixteenth century learned works in general rather than of our author in particular. He seems to have a dual purpose in writing the work. His first aim is to question the validity or certainty of all knowledge, after the fashion of Socrates' claim to wisdom in knowing that he did not know, or the scepticism of Sextus Empiricus, or the more recent book of Agrippa on the *Incertitude and Vanity of the Sciences*. Sanchez's second aim, less pessimistic and more constructive, is to attack certain methods and aspects of the learning of the time and to urge more emphasis upon the study of nature and of things themselves.

The preface to the reader opens with the statement that while men want to know, few do. Sanchez then describes his own experience. From his earliest days—a favorite form of expression with young authors like Porta and Sanchez—he has been addicted to minute contemplation of nature, in which remark we may detect a sign of the growing interest in nature for its own sake. As a student he for years gulped down anything that was offered him, but then was taken with indigestion and began to throw it all up. He sought everywhere for help but could find no one to tell him sincerely and downrightly what to think of things. He then, much like Descartes in the next century, turned back upon himself, called everything into question, as if nothing had ever been said by anyone, and began to examine things themselves, which is the true method of science, and to resolve them to their ultimate principles. "I despair. Nevertheless I persist." If Sanchez anticipates the Cartesian stage of universal doubt, his insistence on things rather than words and some of his phrases are reminiscent of Galen,[6] from whose works he may have im-

[6] Compare Sanchez's statements in this preface with the quotations from Galen prefixed to the chapter on him in T I, 118-19.

bibed them as a medical student consciously or unconsciously. "You then," he continues, "whoever you are, of like mind and temperament with me, who have doubted ofttimes within you concerning the natures of things, doubt now together with me. Let us ply our talents and nature simultaneously." But since Sanchez seeks after truth, let no one expect from him the meretricious attractions of style of the humanist or the servile reverence for authority of the schoolman. "I follow nature only with reason's aid."

As the reader may have by this time guessed, the thesis that nothing is known is something of a tour de force, developed to give room for the play of the author's talents. He may assert that God alone has perfect knowledge, that our knowledge is limited by sense, that the senses are deceptive, and that the mind adds further errors of its own. We do not know God, we do not know whether the stars are of the same material as the sky, we really know nothing of the forces of sympathy and antipathy between things. Many things in the depths of ocean or bowels of the earth are unknown to us. We do not live long enough to become properly acquainted with phenomena which are of perpetual duration, while transient things are ever changing and so escape exact knowledge. Species are nothing: science is concerned only with individuals. Indeed, Sanchez goes so far as to affirm that science can be of only one thing, and that, on the other hand, to know any one thing perfectly we must know all things. Even the Cartesian "Cogito, ergo sum" might not satisfy him, for he feels that his own cogitation concerning cognition will not agree with that of another person. He has no faith in the Platonic doctrine that the soul knew all things before it was merged in the flesh, then forgot them, but may gradually recall them as it is purged of sensuality. Experience is difficult and fallacious, and, even if perfect, shows us only the external event and not the inner natures of things. One's personal experience is very limited, and "Of what profit is it to me that another has tested this or that, unless I myself experience it?" Moreover, books are innumerable. If one lived a million years, one could not read them all. Human opinion is constantly altering with the succession of centuries. Each philosopher thinks that he has found the truth but has really only hit upon one of a thousand different opinions. Now that so many new parts of the globe have been visited, we are the more keenly aware of the dissimilitude of species in different parts of the world, the varied types of humanity, of customs, and of human thought and convictions.

But Sanchez does not really mean that we know nothing. His scepticism is not so sweeping but that there are a number of things which he thinks he knows or at least assumes the truth of, and he sometimes goes to the length of dogmatic generalization. He may ask, what do we know of sympathy and antipathy, but he has no doubt that there are such relationships in nature or that they are of prime importance. If it is permissible for us to turn for a moment from *Quod nihil scitur* to the work in which he attacks belief in divination, we there find him affirming that "all nature consists of contraries and is preserved by contraries," that "there is nothing in the universe which does not have its contrary, and that there would be no universe unless there were all contraries."[7] In *Quod nihil scitur* he is confident that all things in the world are closely related and interdependent. He denies that science is knowing a thing through its causes, but he does not question the Aristotelian conceptions of final, formal, material and efficient causes. He does not hesitate to call the sun the most perfect of all bodies and like to God in its action. He declares that no existing thing acts for nothing or intends nothing, that heat is the most perfect of all qualities, that autumn and winter are perpetual death and that he himself lives only in spring and summer, that the human mind is the most perfect of all God's creatures, that nothing is so important in teaching as method. He makes some thirty different assertions as to the action of heat.

Sanchez's scepticism does not even extend to certain beliefs to which it might have been very profitably applied, such as spontaneous generation from corruption, the notion that nature ab-

[7] *De divinatione: Opera* (1636), p. 73.

hors a vacuum, the attribution of marvelous power to the torpedo and the remora. He does prefix a qualifying, "if they say truly," to the statement that "from the ashes of its burnt parent arises a worm from which another phoenix is produced," and to the account of barnacle geese. But the statement that the bear licks its cubs into shape escapes without such qualification. When Sanchez says that to ascribe this or that to an occult property is to confess one's ignorance of the cause, this does not mean that he doubts the reputed phenomenon. Rather he is credulous as to the existence of marvelous anomalies in nature.

If then Sanchez's scepticism and agnosticism are far from thorough-going, let us turn to his second aim and see what methods and aspects of contemporary learning he attacks. Reliance on words and verbal erudition is one object of his criticism. He does not have the faith of Ramus in definitions and deductions therefrom. He complains that everyone builds up his baseless labyrinth of words. He objects that language is unscientific and of popular origin. The names of things have no fitness or real significance. They were not bestowed in accordance with the natures of things. Furthermore, they soon become corrupt with the passage of time. "Therefore there is no virtue in words of explaining the natures of things."

Sanchez is equally mistrustful of mere logic and syllogisms, to the attack on which he returns several times. He questions Aristotle's dictum that "science is had by demonstration." Other sciences are founded in real things: logic consists only of subtle figments. Dialecticians reach many conclusions but have no real knowledge. The most certain knowledge of all is that by sense perception: the most uncertain of all is that by discourse. Sanchez further criticizes the terminology and classifications employed in logic. Thus before Francis Bacon our young Portuguese scholar writing from Toulouse rejects the subtleties and figments of dialectic and insists on the study of things themselves. He also, like many writers both before and after him, warns against putting excessive trust in Aristotle who, though "among the most acute examiners of nature," was a man like us and sometimes made mistakes.

Although Sanchez stated that from his earliest days he had been addicted to minute contemplation of the world of nature, he does not in the present work elaborate any method of scientific research or systematic experimentation by which a better knowledge of things may be attained. In point of fact, his own scientific qualifications at the time of writing *Quod nihil scitur* were probably scarcely adequate for such a task. For instance, he represents as inexplicable the bringing within the range of vision a coin which had previously been invisible at the bottom of a glass by filling the glass with water. But surely it was explicable in terms of the laws of refraction and principles of optics already enunciated for centuries by Alhazen and Witelo. Sanchez does, however, at least by implication, emphasize the need for greater specialization in scientific investigation. "To me," he writes, "even the least thing in the universe is enough and more for the contemplation of an entire lifetime, nor should I hope to know it finally even then. How therefore can one man know so many things?"

Sanchez proposed to take up the investigation of nature and scientific method in one or two further works, but of these no trace has come down to us. Probably they were never written. It was easier to criticize than to construct.

Indeed, Sanchez seems to have published little else during his lifetime. His medical lectures, a brief commentary on the *Physiognomy* attributed to Aristotle, an unoriginal treatise on the prolongation and brevity of life, and another assailing Cardan's theory of demons and divination, were published after his death by his son. In these works he shows flashes of his former scepticism and attacks certain superstitions, but he fails to evolve any new scientific method. "For what is our knowledge but rash confidence conjoined with every sort of ignorance? Or who would venture to say that he understands anyone of those things that are contained in the vast scope of nature in so great variety, inconstancy, contrariety and obscurity?"[8] He accepts demons on Christian faith but otherwise rejects them. He criticizes various

[8] *De divinatione per somnum ad Aristotelem: Opera* (1636), p. 43.

explanations offered of divination. In a tract on phlebotomy he abandons astrological observation in bleeding as superstitious. But to abandon blood-letting would be, he feels, to upset all medicine. He questions the genuineness of some of the works in the Hippocratic collection. He opposes the multiplication of compound medicines. He would reduce the number of medicaments, but adds six pills of his own invention. He does not often prescribe the parts of animals but sometimes recommends taking the liver of a bull or a pig.

In the Exordium to his medical lectures for 1612 Sanchez describes his method as the rejection of all the logical questions which are wont to be piled up in the schools for the training of youth rather than the profit of the profession, and the discarding of any medicament which seems dubious. Otherwise he proposes to set forth the remedies and modes of cure of ancient or recent physicians. In another undated Exordium he mentions as a most difficult and laborious but also most useful part of his task the exposition of the opinions of many authors concerning the essence, causes, signs and cure of each disease, and the exercise of discriminating judgment between their views when they disagree. Thus his method in teaching medicine is still largely one of compilation from authorities rather than the study of things themselves. He follows Galen especially and also wrote commentaries on several of Galen's works. In his *Pharmacopeia* he follows Mesue chiefly. Such is the rather tame ending in the harness of medical tradition of the spirited and sceptical colt of *Quod nihil scitur*. Is that work to be regarded as primarily a youthful ebullition, a momentary reaction and expression of discouragement before the vastness of the field of learning and the perplexity of science's task? Or did Sanchez fail to develop his position further and more positively because of lack of encouragement from his contemporaries? There were students and salary for a continuation of the exposition of medicine largely along traditional lines, whereas *Quod nihil scitur* may not have attracted sufficient readers and applause to stimulate its author to a further elaboration of scientific method. Or perhaps he simply did not have it in him. In either case, the charger of 1576 seems to have thereafter dropped back into the ranks.

If Vanini had been made a professor of medicine instead of being burned at the stake, perhaps he would have grown orthodox with advancing years. Perhaps his tongue was torn out too soon. But the charges of Sanchez and Vanini were to be repeated and improved upon by others, until eventually, instead of their dropping dead or falling back into the ranks, a considerable section of the line moved forward and occupied the position at which they had aimed.

In 1615 Vanini published his *Amphitheater of Eternal Providence* professing to set divine magic, Christian physics and Catholic astrology over against the ancient philosophers, atheists, Epicureans, Peripatetics, and Stoics.[9] Having escaped censure with this somewhat daring composition, he tried the next year to skate on even thinner ice with his *Dialogues or Four Books Concerning the Admirable Arcana of Nature, Queen and Goddess of Mortals*,[10] and had to flee from Paris in consequence. These two works, however, contained little or nothing new, although Vanini asserts that his philosophy is superior to the scholasticism of the Sorbonne and to common opinions. They were even in many respects somewhat behind the times. Vanini seems to have been either quite unacquainted with or uninterested in the scientific activity of the last half century. He makes no reference to

[9] *Amphitheatrum aeternae Providentiae divino-magicum christiano-physicum necnon astrologo-catholicum adversus veteres philosophos Atheos Epicureos Peripatheticos, et Stoicos,* Lugduni, 1615, 8vo. Copy used: BM 224.e.34.

[10] The title page reads: *Iulii Caesaris Vanini Neapolitani theologi philosophi & Iuris utriusque Doctoris De Admirandis Naturae Reginae Deaeque Mortalium Arcanis libri quatuor,* Lutetiae Apud Adrianum Perier via Iacobaea MDCXVI. Cum privilegio regis. Copies used: Col B85V31 P5, BM 976.b.1. But the division of the sixty dialogues (actually there are 59, there being no Dialogus XXXV) into four books is the work of the printer: see the note "Typographus Lectori." The "Approbatio" of two ecclesiastical censors refers to the work as "Dialogos Iulii Caesaris Vanini," and in the dedication Vanini speaks of "his meis philosophicis colloquiis." The running head at the top of the right hand pages is "Dialogi" throughout: it also appears on the back of the binding. The interlocutors are Alexander and Julius Caesar, as Vanini now styled himself. I shall henceforth cite the work as *Dialogi.*

the recent discoveries of Galileo or Gilbert's book on the magnet or the previous work of Tycho Brahe. He does not allude to the new star of 1572 or others since. It is against Cardan, not some later astronomer, that he defends the Aristotelian theory of comets. Indeed, he is more apt to cite sixteenth century astrologers, like Mizaldus and Iunctinus, than astronomers. He scarcely mentions either Vesalius in the field of anatomy or Paracelsus in that of chemistry and allied subjects. With unimportant exceptions such as the very recent work of the Jesuit Alexander de Angelis against astrology,[11] he hardly cites authors later than Fernel and Fracastoro, Pomponazzi and Cardan. It is from the last two that he derived most of his ideas and material. He praises them both to the skies. Cardan was a man "never sufficiently lauded . . . to whom the most noble republic of astrologers owes much . . . so great in letters and of virtue so outstanding that he lacked little of perfect condition in all sciences."[12] Pomponazzi was "a most acute philosopher, into whose body Pythagoras would have said that the soul of Averroes had migrated," and his work concerning the causes of the natural effects of things is called admirable.[13] Or elsewhere he is termed "the chief of the philosophers of our age" and "the divine teacher in his golden work on incantations,"[14] or "my master."[15] But this master had written a century ago, although his work on the causes of natural effects or on incantations from which Vanini chiefly draws, was not printed until 1556. It is true that Vanini also professes to condemn some of their views. He criticizes Cardan for attributing the Sibylline prophecies to astrology. He notes his ascribing the origin of religions to the stars, but then exclaims: "O most impudent mouth! O execrable tongue! O most foul utterances! O detestable words!" Or he utters similar ejaculations of horror after quoting for four solid pages Cardan's "most absurd fables." Or he alludes to "this diabolical bulwark of Pomponazzi and

[11] Alexander de Angelis, *In astrologos coniectores libri quinque*. Rome, B. Zannetti, 1615; also Lyons, 1615.

[12] I here combine passages at pp. 265, 41, and 21 respectively of the *Amphitheatrum,* 1615 edition.

[13] *Ibid.*, p. 36.

[14] *Dialogi* (1616), pp. 373-74.

[15] *Ibid.*, p. 379.

Cardan," or states that he has absolutely and brilliantly disputed against Pomponazzi in his *Apology for the Mosaic and Christian Law* against physicists, astronomers and politicians.[16] But even more than in the case of Machiavelli, "easily the chief of atheists," whom he mentions only to censure, and of the arguments advanced by anonymous atheists whom he professes to have actually met and which he pretends to refute, is it evident that his sympathies are really with Pomponazzi and Cardan, and that a main feature of these two works of his is to circulate their astrology and other occult science and their "natural" or magical explanation and substitute for miracles and demons. Trithemius and Cornelius Agrippa are other authors congenial to Vanini, although he once condemns them, too.

In any truly scientific discussion Vanini is apt to choose the worse part and to defend an erroneous against the correct view. And this again is in large measure because he is behind the times and still adheres to some outworn doctrine found in or ascribed to Aristotle. In the *Dialogi* he denies that fish breathe, although his disciple and interlocutor, Alexander, has all the better of the argument, noting their gills, the fact that water contains air, and that the fish die if the water is shut off from the air. Vanini asserts, however, that this happens because the water then corrupts and not because the supply of air is exhausted. He affirms that one species of plant can be turned into another by the influence of the stars, the nature of the soil, and the quality of the ambient sky. He holds that birds are generated from driftwood. While Alexander is sceptical as to this, they both agree that mice are generated from putrefaction. Bees, however, Vanini says, are generated from sexual intercourse. But he still believed that bears grew fat through sleep. Some writers in speaking of opposition to new discoveries and scientific progress in early modern times have confused conservative adherence to Aristotle with conservative opposition on religious or theological grounds. The atheist Vanini shows us that the two might be quite distinct and found in opposing camps, and suggests that much opposition

[16] *Amphitheatrum* (1615), pp. 57, 38.

which has carelessly been called theological was really only scientific conservatism as against more progressive scientific views.

There are limits to Vanini's acceptance of natural marvels. He denies many of the great powers attributed to gems by Albertus Magnus and agrees with Scaliger that there is more virtue in one flea than in all precious stones. Words have no force except that of affecting the hearing. Vanini doubts if imagination moves men to other than sexual acts, he somewhat questions the belief that the foetus is affected by the imagination of the mother during pregnancy, and he denies—perhaps with his tongue in his cheek—that the stigmata of St. Francis were produced by imagination. He does, however, include vehement imagination during sexual intercourse as one of six causes of the generation of monsters or monstrous births. The other five are inordinate lust, parents who are too much alike, a defect or excess of semen, malformity of the feminine receptacle, and, most potent, the influence of the stars. The witches' sabbats are delusions which Vanini, like Cardan, ascribes to the unguents with which they anoint themselves. As for divination from dreams, Vanini was himself born under the moon, and therefore "from the rules of the astronomers" his dreams should come true. But he can remember few that have proven to be so.

Such scepticism in turn has its limitations. Vanini tells of a German who engaged in private devotions during Holy Week rather than attend public services from fear of catching an excess of vapors of melancholy from the suspirations of the sad worshippers assembled. "And why should you marvel thereat? Has it not been proved by experience that a person goes mad who lies under a tree which a mad dog has gnawed?"[17]

Belief in the all-encompassing and all-penetrating influence of the stars was a chief article in the creed of Vanini as of Pomponazzi. Since Aristotle held that God ruled the spheres by the aid and ministry of intelligences, Vanini enters upon a discussion of them, especially since the scholastics have treated of them

[17] *Dialogi*, p. 448.

so ineptly that it almost makes him sick. However, whether because of continued hostility of the theological faculty at Paris to astrology or because of the bull of Sixtus V of 1586 against astrologers, Vanini finds it advisable occasionally to condemn the art. When in the *Amphitheatrum*[18] an atheist held that the cure in Apulia of a man blind from birth by an image of the Virgin was due to the stars and further accounted for the fact that, on rising with sight restored, the Apulian found himself lame, as a pretense so that he might continue begging, Vanini retorted that he had observed his physiognomy and that he was not fraudulent "by the rules of the astronomers" (i.e. astrologers). But, adds Vanini, "Away with the fables and madness of the astronomers which I declare I utterly detest and execrate and have adduced them only to uncover their weakness." In the *Dialogi*[19] Vanini states that human morals are sometimes modified by the varying positions of the stars. The will cannot operate without consulting the intellect, and there is nothing in the intellect which was not previously in the senses. Moreover, the senses are subject to the celestial bodies. "Hence I infer that if our animal spirits are made from our aliment, then on our food also depends probity or corruption of morals." But presently he warns that the foregoing remarks are not to be taken seriously.

The atheism of Vanini was based on occult science and astrology rather than the progress of modern science which he ignored and apparently had little interest in. Sanchez made more of an effort to relate his agnosticism and scepticism to a minute investigation of nature. But he did not get far with it, and beliefs which he continued to cherish seem to us as erroneous and objectionable as others which he questioned. These two cases lend support to the point which we have made more than once: that there was no regular correlation or variation in inverse ratio between theology and science, scepticism and the occult, or science and superstition. In one man's mind they made one combination: in another, another. The hope for improvement, for a

[18] *Amphitheatrum*, pp. 73-77.

[19] *Dialogi*, pp. 345-49.

further advance from magic towards science, lay not in bulls against divination or arguments against astrology, in persecution of witches or tracts against the witchcraft delusion, in pillorying the principles of Paracelsus or even in adopting the Copernican theory, in scepticism or in atheism. The hope lay in an increased positive attention to scientific problems, finding satisfaction in their solution, and thus negatively allowing the mind less time to occupy itself with, and more opportunity to forget, erroneous notions and methods. The serpent does not shed its old skin until the new has grown.

CHAPTER XLVIII

SUMMARY AND BY-PRODUCTS

How index-learning turns no student pale
Yet holds the eel of science by the tail.

POPE

The intellectual drama of the interrelations between magic and science which we have been watching has in the present volumes assumed somewhat confusing proportions and multiplicity of detail. The *dramatis personae* in this last act of the sixteenth century have exceeded three thousand in number, of whom about twelve hundred were writers and men of learning of the period under consideration, not including a chorus of more than three hundred printers mentioned by name, and considerably over three hundred patrons, patients, princes, prelates and other lay figures and passive participants in the play of ideas. While the stage has been cluttered up with all these personages—many of whom have appeared but once, while others have made repeated entrances and exits—the number of ideas themselves may be roughly inferred from the fact that our index includes some seventeen hundred topics and names of things in addition to its more than three thousand names of persons. The latter may be further distinguished as comprising over thirty Jewish and Biblical authors, over a hundred Greek and Byzantine, nearly forty Latin classical writers, nearly sixty Arabic authors, a dozen church fathers, about twenty-five early medieval Latin writers and as many more of the twelfth century, about seventy each for the thirteenth and the fourteenth centuries, and approximately 130 from the fifteenth. We have looked back upon our period through the eyes of some 140 writers of the later seventeenth and eighteenth centuries, 150 of the nineteenth century, and 190 of the twentieth.

If we institute a comparison between the present and previous volumes, we find that the number of classical authors, whether genuine or spurious, is naturally greatest in the first volume which starts from the classical period. But it is surprising that the fourth volume on the fifteenth century does not exceed the third on the fourteenth century in this respect, and that the second volume on the twelfth and thirteenth centuries should not merely exceed either of the following but contain more names of classical authors than both of them together, excluding duplications. The present volumes name about 130 classical authors as against some 230 in the first volume, about 108 in the second, and 58 and 59 in the third and fourth. Thus the reading and citation of classical authors in science and occult science seems not to have increased until after the fifteenth century, while the not great superiority of the present two volumes to the second is well nigh discounted by their greater length and opportunity for such mentions. On the other hand, the frequency with which a few much cited and commented ancient authorities like Aristotle, Pliny, Ptolemy, Galen and Dioscorides are mentioned is greatly increased in the present volumes, where we have so many more persons citing them. Here again it is to be remembered that Aristotle and Ptolemy were mentioned more times in every subsequent volume than in the first, and that in this respect the second volume on the twelfth and thirteenth centuries took the lead, citing Ptolemy twice as many times as the first volume and Aristotle almost four times as often. Indeed its 172 references to Aristotle compare favorably with the 300 odd of the present volumes. The number of references to Hippocrates, Pliny, Dioscorides and Galen, however, declined steadily after the first volume until the present volumes, except for the controversy as to Pliny at the end of the fifteenth century and an improvement for Dioscorides with the fourth volume. The number of references to Plato and to Euclid increased in the second volume over the first but then fell off again with the third and fourth volumes.

Although recognizing that any particular mention of a name may be partly or even largely a matter of accident, it may be somewhat illuminating to list the following names which, in addition to those just mentioned, occurred in each of the first four volumes and in one or both of the present volumes: Apollonius of Perga, Apollonius of Tyana, Cicero, Democritus, Dorotheus the astrologer, Epicurus, Julius Firmicus Maternus, Ovid, Seneca, Theophrastus and Vergil. Several others are missing only from the third volume on the fourteenth century: Aesculapius, Alexander of Aphrodisias, Philostratus, Plotinus, Porphyry, while Euripides is mentioned neither in the third nor the present volumes. Apuleius, Posidonius, Vitruvius and Zoroaster are names missing only from the fourth volume on the fifteenth century. Empedocles is missing from the fourth and present volumes. Livy and Socrates are absent only from the first volume; Anaxagoras, only from the present volumes; while Archelaus appears only in the second, third and fourth volumes. Many more are found only in the first two and the present volumes.

The number of Arabic and Jewish writers was about fifty in our first volume, more than doubled in the second on the twelfth and thirteenth centuries when they were translated into Latin, fell off to about 49 in the third volume and to only some 28 in the fourth. The number increases in the present volumes to nearly ninety despite the outcry in the early sixteenth century against Arabic medicine and astrology. Testing frequency of mention in a few representative cases, we find Albumasar, the great Arabic astrological authority, cited fourteen times in the first volume, twenty-four in the second, twenty-three in the third, twelve in the fourth, and over thirty times in the present volumes. Alkindi has ten mentions in the index of our first volume, six in the second, ten in the third, and six in the fourth. In the present volumes also six. Avicenna, mentioned only four times in our first volume, thereafter is repeatedly cited and without much fluctuation: forty times in our second volume, thirty-seven in the fourteenth century, twenty-six in the fifteenth, and eighty-eight times in the sixteenth and early seventeenth century. Rasis does not hold his own quite as well, rising from five to twenty-nine, but then dropping to sixteen, eleven and sixteen. Geber has his greatest number of mentions in the third volume in connection with alchemy, while Averroes after about the same number of citations in the second, third and fourth volumes—eleven, seven and ten—jumps to sixty odd in the present volumes, as might be expected from their attention to the Averroists of Padua. Costa ben Luca, Johannitius and Messahala all disappeared in the fourth volume but the three names reappear in the present. That these figures have their significance may be seen by comparing them with those for a patristic writer like Augustine to whom there are 55 references in the index of our first volume, 27 in the second, only six in the third, but then 22 in the fourth, which in general cites church fathers more than the third volume does.

Our third volume on the fourteenth century had occasion to cite or mention about a score more medieval Latin writers before 1300 than our present volumes do, while it named about ten less Arabic authors. Our fourth volume cited about sixty less medieval authors before 1300 than the third volume or forty less than the present volumes, and only half as many Arabic writers as the present volumes and about a score less than the third volume. Roger Bacon was named thirty times in the volume on the fourteenth century but only fourteen times in that on the fifteenth. Albertus Magnus and Thomas Aquinas, on the other hand, were mentioned somewhat oftener in the later volume. The astrologer Bonatti had nine mentions in either volume. Vincent of Beauvais fell off from seven to three, while the brief text of Sacrobosco advanced from six to thirteen.

The scene on which our intellectual drama has been played is a matter of some interest and significance. In the period covered by the present volumes the most striking fact is the prominence assumed by Germanic lands, including Germany, Austria, the German speaking cantons of Switzerland and the Dutch provinces of the Netherlands. These now take the lead over the Italian peninsula and islands in the number of places that we have had occasion to mention, some 225 (or 236, if the Scandinavian peninsula is included) as against some 163 Italian place names.[1] This climaxes a steady rise from about eight mentions in our first volume, twenty-four in the second, 46 in the third and 89 in the fourth. Italy, which had almost equalled the Near East and North Africa on the one hand, and the Balkan peninsula and Asia Minor on the other in our first volume, had led all other cultural regions in the second, third and fourth volumes, although in the first, second and third volumes France and Flanders had been a fairly close second and well ahead of Germanic lands, which equalled them in number of mentions only in the fourth volume. Somewhat similarly the British Isles, after slightly leading the Germanic lands in our first two volumes and falling somewhat behind in the third, fell far in the rear in the fourth and relatively even more so in the present volumes. The Spanish peninsula had fewer places mentioned than the British Isles in our first three volumes but equalled them in the fourth and outstrips them in the present.

The explanation of these rough figures seems to be that our first volume, covering the first eleven centuries of the Christian era, was especially concerned with ancient and Arabic science and superstition. With the expansion of Christendom and the development of scholasticism, France and England as well as the Italian peninsula became intellectually prominent, presumably because they contained the chief universities, wealthier religious foundations or more developed urban life. With the decline of scholasticism, the foundation of universities in Germany, the invention of printing there, the spread of humanism from Italy first to Germany, and the increased economic prosperity of the German cities, came a diffusion of culture there which flowered in the Age of the Reformation, just as Italy reached its highest point relatively in our rough statistics in the fifteenth century. There is nothing new or startling in this interpretation. Our particular line of investigation simply tends

[1] These figures are of course only roughly approximate, varying slightly according to where one draws linguistic frontiers or how one reckons a man's last name as indicating his place of origin.

to substantiate the general picture which historians have drawn of the progress of civilization. It even tends to support quantitatively, if not qualitatively, the belief in an Italian Renaissance and a German Reformation. The influence of the classical revival is further attested by an increase—not great, however—in the present volumes of mention of place names in the Balkan peninsula and Asia Minor, and in North Africa and the Near East. Central and Eastern Europe, on the contrary, after a steady, if modest, advance from the first to the fourth volumes, have no more places named in the present volumes than in the fourth, although most other regions increase their quota.

The next most notable point in the present volumes, after the prominence of German place names, is the mention of localities in the New World, Far East and southern part of Africa.

The number of places mentioned seems a fair index of the diffusion of culture and distribution of scientific interest, indicating as it does where our authors came from, studied, taught, wrote, published, practiced, and died. But the fact that many places are mentioned but once, while others like the seat of the great university of Paris occur frequently, raises the question what inference we may draw from the total number of mentions or citations in our indices[2] as distinguished from the number of place names. In our first volume the majority of places in Italy are mentioned but once, while a good many of those in Greece and Asia Minor or North Africa and the Near East are cited a number of times, so that these regions seem much richer in the history of magic and science for that period than the Italian peninsula. In the second volume the area of France and Flanders slightly overtops Italy in this frequency of citation, although behind it in the number of place names, while in the third volume Italy has the lead in both respects, and in the fourth has an even greater advantage in the number of citations than in the number of names.

Here arises the difficulty that certain individuals, especially

[2] I realize that such citations are not of equal value and so furnish a basis only for very rough approximation.

before 1500, like Adelard of Bath and Vincent of Beauvais, constantly carry with them the mention of their place of origin, while others, like Albertus Magnus and Roger Bacon, do not. Some places are mentioned only in connection with a single author, like Alexander of Aphrodisias in antiquity, Gentile da Foligno in the fourteenth century, and Guinther of Andernach in the sixteenth.

After 1500 there are fewer personal names of this sort and they are not so reiterated. I have therefore usually counted each such place only once for the present volumes. On this basis there seem to be 415 place names which occur only once, 186 which occur between two and four times, 67 which are found from five to ten times, 23 between eleven and twenty times, and 37 that occur more than a score of times. Aside from countries like Egypt, England, France, Germany, Italy, Portugal, Saxony, Spain and India, these places of most frequent mention are: Antwerp, Augsburg, Basel, Bologna, Cologne, Ferrara, Florence, Frankfurt on the Main, Heidelberg, Leipzig, London, Louvain, Lyons, Milan, Naples, Nürnberg, Padua, Paris, Pavia, Pisa, Rome, Strasburg, Tübingen, Venice, Verona, Vienna, Wittenberg and Zurich. These cities may be regarded as the leading intellectual centers and were in most cases either or both seats of universities and centers of printing. Twelve were German; eleven, Italian; four, French; one, English. After them, in the second group of frequency, come Amsterdam, Brescia, Bergamo, Cracow, Erfurt, Geneva, Ingolstadt, Leyden, Mainz, Mantua, Marburg, Montpellier, Rostock, Toulouse, Turin, and Valencia.[3] Here seven are Germanic and four Italian, three are French, one Spanish, and one of Central or Eastern Europe.

Because the present volumes are longer than any single preceding volume and also because the place of printing has commonly been noted, the number of such mentions is proportionally great. However, in no previous volume did any German town have so many as ten mentions. In the first volume Alexandria

[3] With the regions of Chaldea, the Palatinate, Persia, Poland, Switzerland, Turkey and Wurtemberg.

and Rome had over twenty-five mentions; Antioch and Athens over ten each. In the second volume Paris alone had more than twenty-five, but Toledo, Bologna and Padua, as well as Alexandria and Rome, exceeded ten. Toledo dropped below ten in the third volume, as Athens had done in the second. Paris still was the only city with over twenty-five counts, but Bologna had risen from twenty to twenty-four, while Florence and Padua had twenty-three each. Others over ten were Naples, Parma, Rome, Venice, Montpellier, Avignon and Oxford. The two last, which owed their prominence respectively to the presence of the papal court at Avignon and the prominence of Oxford dons in scholasticism, mathematics and astronomy in the first half of the fourteenth century, disappear from our list in the fourth and present volumes. Parma too falls below ten mentions, while in the fourth volume Milan, Pavia and Siena are added to the cities just mentioned, while Bologna, Florence and Padua pass the twenty-five mark.

Although the Germanic area now exceeds Italy in the number of places mentioned and equals it in the number of leading intellectual centers, the titles of our chapters, which suggest Italy or individual Italians about twice as often as they do Germany and Germans, indicate that Italy still leads in men of first prominence, although this appears truer of the first than the second half of the period, when the repressive influence of Index, Inquisition and Counter Reformation begin to be felt in Italy. In this respect, too, France is again a poor third. It is perhaps fair to say that Italy still provides the more leading minds but that Germany now offers a greater number of followers and disseminators.

Paris, although no longer monopolizing so large a share of the learned world as it had from the twelfth to the fourteenth century, nor as yet such a center of courtly and mundane culture as it was to become under Louis XIV, was the chief printing place in France and still a magnet that attracted many a scholar and intellectual vagabond. There they trod the pavements of the Rue St. Jacques and the Rue de Latran or frequented the colleges of Cambrai and Reims, of Navarre and Beauvais, or even the cemetery of the Innocents. There we have found not only an Aristotelian like Achillini or a continuer of fourteenth century scholasticism such as David Douglas, but scientists who were to rank first in their fields like Vesalius in anatomy and Brasavola in pharmacy. There came the physician Champier from southern France, the mathematician Cirvelo from the Spanish peninsula, and the astrologer-theologian Pigghe from the Low Countries. There Agrippa, Servetus and Bruno, and the impostor, Paul Skalich, spent a brief portion of their troubled careers. The chiromancer Tiberto had been there and Brucaeus, the correspondent of Tycho Brahe at Rostock. Men were drawn there not only to study the subjects for which the university was famous but to fill vacuums which seemed to exist in its curriculum, as we have seen in the case of mathematics and astrology. The university and Parlement were seldom hospitable to such intruders. The theological faculty was hostile to astrology and other occult arts. The medical faculty not only opposed unlicensed practitioners but censured alchemy and Paracelsan medicine. We have seen some expelled and others flee, while Mayerne de Turquet beat a more or less dignified retreat to England. While there were still Germans at Paris, the humanistic tendency for them to complete their education in Italy becomes also increasingly true of the men in whom we have been interested.

It is a rather striking indication of the wide spread of medical practitioners, the learning and culture of members of that profession, and the continued prominence of local hearths of civilization, that we should have had occasion to mention physicians of no fewer than seventy towns and for the most part to have made such mention only once each for these places. They include not only seats of universities like Paris, Padua, Montpellier, Cracow, Toulouse, Vienna, Erfurt, Marburg, Prag, Louvain, and Valencia, or homes of printing like Venice, Basel, Nürnberg, Augsburg, Strasburg and Cologne, or populous metropolises like Antwerp, Brussels, Bruges, Liège, Lyons, Milan, Naples and Turin, but twelve other Italian cities, sixteen German towns including smaller places like Anhalt, Hensisheim and Schwäbisch Hall, eight in France including Beaune and Seurre-sur-Sâone, and others in Spain, Portugal, Belgium, Holland and Central Europe.[4] Yet such a metropolis as London or such a university center as Bologna happens to escape mention in this particular connection.

The influence of humanism upon the method of presentation has been attested by the fairly frequent employment of such literary forms as verse, the dialogue, the letter and the oration. Many of our authors were occasional poets, though few of them could equal Fracastoro. Two or three were professors of, or lecturers on, poesy. Their publications are accompanied by prefatory poems or by complimentary and introductory verse addressed to the author. Some are interlarded by quotation from the classical poets. The relation between poetry and science has been touched on three or four times. There have been verses for and against alchemy, while geomancy and oracles have been expressed in verse. But these occult subjects had all been similarly treated in verse in the preceding medieval period. We have had occasion to cite the correspondence of Tycho Brahe alone some seventeen times, while letters between other individuals—not including dedications and prefaces—have engaged our attention in over fifty instances. The dialogue form had already been used in twelfth century science by Adelard of Bath and William of Conches, while in the fourteenth and fifteenth centuries alchemical dialogues between master and disciple were fairly frequent. But against seven cases each of treatises in dialogue in our third and fourth volumes, some twenty-six will be found in the present. The oration, which scarcely received recognition in our indices until the fourth volume on the fifteenth century, when there were ten entries, now receives about twice that number.

Another channel of intellectual activity and co-operation which was later to vie in importance with the universities, namely, the learned and scientific societies or academies, has

[4] For the full list see in the Index, Physician, location.

appeared only a few times in the present volumes. Besides four references to the Old Academy of Plato, there have been only one each to the Sodalitates of the Rhine and the Danube, the Secreti of Porta, Animosi of Padua, Gelati of Bologna, Selvaggi and Umoristi of Rome. We have, however, seen the way prepared for such associations by the interchange of specimens between naturalists, the publication of medical letters like those of Manard, and the extensive scientific correspondence of men like Benedetti and Tycho Brahe.

Over three hundred printers, booksellers and publishers have been mentioned of the period under review in these volumes. Venice was the leading center for the publication of volumes in the subjects of which we have treated. Fully a sixth of all those mentioned had their presses located there. Paris came second with almost one eighth of the total number and Lyons third with slightly less than a tenth. Rome had seventeen of our printers; Frankfurt, Basel and Naples, thirteen; Strasburg, twelve; Antwerp, eleven; Nürnberg, Bologna, Cologne and London, nine each; Wittenberg, seven; Mainz, five; Vienna and Augsburg, four. Fourteen cities had two or three each of the printers named here, while forty odd printers were distributed singly between as many towns from Cracow to Lisbon and Copenhagen to Messina.

A picturesque touch has been added to the sometimes dull tone and content of our authors by the signs of the shops where their books were sold or their drugs purchased. These have comprised figures from classical mythology like Minerva and Pegasus as well as a Christian golden Missal, Saint Christopher and Samaritan. Even abstractions and virtues such as Hope and Truth have been met as shop signs but more often concrete objects like a bell or well, star or pyramid, golden circlet or shield of Basel, two basins or three crowns. Animals were especial favorites, whether legendary and fabulous like the phoenix and monoceros, dignified as the falcon and pelican, or homely and familiar like the storks, two cocks, and the fat hen opposite the Collège de Cambrai.

In the number of things and topics—as distinct from persons and places—treated, our first volume, although two hundred pages shorter than the second, exceeds it and the third and fourth, having nearly thirteen hundred items, while they each include only a little over or more or less under a thousand respectively. This is partly because it covers a much longer period of time, eleven centuries instead of one or two, and deals with a more varied background, classical, pagan, early Christian, Arabic and early medieval; partly because as the initial volume it introduces many matters, some of which do not need repetition. Whatever the reason, some three hundred things and topics are found only in the index of this first volume. If our present publication, though restricted to the sixteenth and a few years of the following century, exceeds even the first volume in the total number of things and topics, this is partly because of its much greater length and fulness of treatment, which reflect the more abundant literary remains available for study after the spread of the invention of printing. It is further partly because, as the result of the classical reaction and the close combing of classical books and sources in which writers of the sixteenth century engaged, far more of the things and topics included in our first volume are repeated than was the case in our third and fourth volumes, while many—though not all—of the new things and topics which first appeared in the second, third or fourth volume, likewise continue in our present volumes, which thus constitute a sort of catch-all for the previous history of thought. Indeed, the majority even of words which appear for the first time in the present index—some six hundred in all—designate classical and medieval matters which we had not happened to mention in previous volumes rather than new things and ideas. For example, numerous medieval names of herbs are first mentioned in the chapter on the Naturalists in the present volumes, while various machines of the past are first named in the chapter on Three Technologists. Fireplace and chimney-flue are now first mentioned but were found in castles as early as the twelfth century, while the Post-Glossators go back to the fourteenth century.

Our third volume on the fourteenth century, which embraces the smallest total of things and topics, takes the lead in the introduction of new conceptions and processes, reflecting—a little tardily perhaps—the development of scholastic and alchemical literature, although it contains the smallest number of names of plants, animals, gems and minerals. This suggests a richness and originality in the intellectual life of the fourteenth century which has hitherto hardly been sufficiently recognized.

I have tried to subdivide and classify the things and topics mentioned under the following headings: animals and their products, vegetation, minerals, the human body's parts, characteristics and processes, disease and ailments, medicine, celestial phenomena, inferior natural phenomena other than those already named, alchemical and chemical matters, art and technology, including utensils and instruments, mathematics and time (not including astronomy), linguistic and literary, other sciences and intellectual concerns, occult arts and sciences, religion, political, crime and penal, occupations, and other phases of human life. It of course has often been difficult to tell in which of these compartments to shelf a topic, so that any figures I may give should be regarded as only roughly approximate.

In the first two volumes many more animals were named than anything else. As between these two volumes, not only were some thirty more animals named in the first volume, but it mentioned seventeen ten or more times each, while only five of these were named that often in volume two. In volumes three and four on the fourteenth and fifteenth centuries occult and other intellectual matters (exclusive of medicine, mathematics and literature) vied for the lead, the occult leading slightly in volume three and other intellectual concerns in volume four. In the present volumes the occult is second in the number of items to vegetation, while other intellectual is a close third, animals a good fourth, and religion fifth. In the first volume vegetation, the occult, and religion were close together in that order, with other intellectual considerably behind them. In the second volume the occult, religion, and other intellectual were practically tied for second place, with vegetation considerably behind. In volume three animals were far back of the two leaders and likewise in volume four, where this topic was further outstripped by religion. Also in either volume only two or three animals were indexed as many as ten times or more, and in the present volumes ten.

If we take those things and topics which have been mentioned in all previous volumes and the present as a standard of comparison, we find that of over three hundred and forty such forty-five are occult, thirty-eight animal, thirty-six other intellectual, twenty-eight concerned with religion, thirty-three with the human body, twenty-six with inferior natural phenomena, twenty-one with minerals, but only ten with vegetation, which ranked so high in some volumes. A few random examples may be listed of these topics which run through the entire work: adamant, aerimancy, allegory, apoplexy, arithmetic, ashes, astrolabe, basilisk, brain, cock, corpse, cow, coral, creation, credulity, diet, dolphin, dropsy, earthquake, egg, emerald, empiricism, encyclopedia, form, fountain, furnace, glass, gold, heredity, heresy, humanism, imagination, intestines, laurel, logic, love, magnus annus, matter, melancholy, modern, name, Neoplatonism, optical, painting, papacy, plagiarism, quality, radiation, rainbow, ring, scorpion, sea, secrecy, sermon, ship, storm, theft, tree and Trinity.

Far fewer in number are the topics not found in the first volume which begin with the second and occur throughout the others. But many of them signify an intellectual development or change in civilization. The following list is practically complete: arsenic, bezoar, Black Death, camphor, castle, Cistercian, clergy, *complexio,* confession, copyist, cucumber, dialogue, Dominican, error, Franciscan, hypnotism, inquisition, intellect, Latin, marvel, narcotic, patriarch, pearl, Peripatetic, quadruped, sacrament, sal ammoniac, scholasticism, Tetragrammaton, treasure, visions, vomiting, weight and wound.

Few in number and of slight significance compared to the foregoing seem those topics which occur only in volumes two and three, in volumes three and four, or in volumes two, three and four. The same may be said of those which first occur in the fourth volume and are found again in the present publication.

A different judgment must be passed upon those subjects which, first found in the third volume on the fourteenth century, continue in those on the fifteenth and sixteenth centuries. In this category we find accident, aqua ardens, aqua permanens, aqua vitae, Aries and Cancer, antimony, apostume, calcination, Carmelite, catoptromancy, causation, ceration, cherubim, coin, counterfeiting and money, chronicle, climacteric, contagion, crops, custom, density and rarefaction, directions (astrological), disputation, epicycle, era, essence, falling body, fisherman, fixation, fortune, garden, happiness, hospital, hypothesis, individual, infinite, Intelligence, intension and remission, international, lye, metaphysics, motion, national, natural place, noble, orpiment, pact, Parlement, peace, philter, annual prediction, price, *primum mobile,* prison, privation, putrefaction, recipe, Scotism, specialization, solution, sublimation, tartar, terminus (astrological), theory and practice, Thomism, university, velocity and vegetation. Such topics, although in part derived from Aristotle and antiquity, the Arabic world, or the thirteenth century, indicate a broadening and a deepening of civilization, of science, and of thought.

In the present volumes the occurrence for the first time of about thirty names designating very minor and outré forms of divination from Biteromancy to Venamancy is artificial and of slight importance. A group of military and political terms is of somewhat more significance: general, cavalry, infantry, explosive, shrapnel, revolver and military engineering, communes, conventicle, court and courtier, demagogue, estates, execution, gallows, government, heraldry, knight, magistrate, patriotism, prince and public service. Others concern mathematics and astronomy, as conic sections, stereometry, secant, sine and tangent, or Cor leonis, ecliptic, equant, globe-maker, gnomon, nebular hypothesis, observatory, parallax and prostaphaereses. Scientific progress in other fields is suggested by acid,

Volume	I	II	III	IV	V-VI	Topics common to all vols.
Animal	173	141	74	80	151	38
Vegetable	126	78	52	64	188	10
Mineral	76	54	53	44	97	21
Human body	80	68	52	59	99	36
Disease	56	50	45	45	78	12
Medicine	51	40	34	36	53	14
Celestial	25	20	25	26	37	15
Nature	60	51	63	50	75	35
Alchemy and Chemical	15	16	46	28	51	7
Technical (Utensils and Instruments)	87	67	36	47	88	12
Mathematics and Time	35	27	30	21	32	15
Linguistic and Literary	45	35	28	42	74	16
Intellectual	94	92	108	115	169	33
Occult	122	94	119	108	174	46
Religion	119	93	67	100	139	31
Political	12	13	13	16	38	5
Crime and Penal	13	9	9	14	16	4
Occupations	18	13	10	14	34	3
Other human life	85	65	60	71	115	4
Total	1292	1026	924	980	1708	357
Found only in	294	120	146	119	615	
First occur in		275	330	205	615	
Cited ten or more times in the index	149	120	123	139	288	33

camera obscura, circulation of the blood, sulphate of potash, voyages of discovery and several anatomical terms. But there also are new astrological terms and absent treatment, prodigy, weapon ointment and Rosicrucian. Another group reflect the religious change: atheism,[5] deism, free-thinking, conscience, fundamentalism, intolerance, materialism, pantheism, Calvinist, layman and Lutheran. A few new words mark the continued development of printing: broadside, dissertation, posthumous and proofreader. Changing conditions of civilization and modes of thought are marked or forecast by such topics and things as coach and four, monad, museum, mosquito, news,

[5] Also mentioned in Vol. I, but only once.

romanticism, spinning-jenny, telephone and tourbillon. But they are not numerous.

Of thirty-three topics which occur at least ten times in all six volumes under review, eight deal with the occult: alchemy, astrology, divination, image, incantation, magic, necromancy and occult virtue; only one with a science, astronomy. Four more, however, may be classed as intellectual: authority, experience, experiment and manuscript. Three or four deal with religion and the supernatural: God, theology, demon and spirit. Five are cosmic and celestial: universe or world, sun, moon, planet and zodiac. Three or four concern inferior nature in general: element, fire, generation and weather. Four deal with the three kingdoms, animal, vegetable and mineral: namely, animal, snake or serpent, herb and gold. Three are human: blood, dream and soul. If we add nineteen more topics which occur with almost equally regular frequency in all volumes, we raise the occult to eleven by adding secrecy, sorcery and witchcraft; the intellectual to seven by music and observation; religion to eight by creation, miracle, prayer and prophecy; cosmic and celestial to six by the addition of day; inferior nature to six by earth and matter; animals to four by dog and dragon; minerals to three by gem and magnet; human to five by sex and woman. Such is a very rough but objective enumeration and recapitulation of the subjects which have most persistently attracted our attention in this series of volumes.

In the accompanying table a considerable allowance should be made for possible error. The different volumes have not in every respect been indexed on quite the same basis, so that points indexed in one may sometimes have been omitted or overlooked in another, or noted under another caption. Some rectification of this, however, has been made in composing the table. Another person, or even I at another time, might make a different count or classify items under different headings. The figures for the present volumes are even more liable to error than those for the preceding volumes, since they have necessarily been based upon a tentative index and not the final printed form. But while not pretending to numerical or statistical accuracy, the table may suffice to give a rough idea of the number of topics treated and their distribution between various fields of interest in the several volumes.

In closing a point occurs to me which perhaps has as yet not been sufficiently emphasized. While faith in natural magic and astrology, in sympathy and antipathy, and the like, may seem as great and widespread during the period which we have just reviewed as in any preceding age, use of superstitious ceremonial and magical rite, of incantation, word and number, has fallen off markedly. Occult virtues and relationships in nature are still believed in, but magical procedure is largely abandoned. Thus the way is open for mathematical and scientific method.

APPENDICES

APPENDIX 4

GENITURES OF MEN OF LEARNING

from Garcaeus, *Astrologiae methodus* . . . , Basel, 1576, with a few additions from Sixtus ab Hemminga, *Astrologia ratione et experientia refutata*, Antwerp, 1583

In the first column is given the page of Garcaeus or Hemminga where the geniture occurs, in the second column the person's name, and in the remaining columns the year, day and hour of his birth.

62[1]	Petrarch	1304	19 July	16.20 P.M.
126	Regiomontanus	1436	6 June	4.40 P.M.
126[2]	Erasmus Reinhold	1511	21 Oct.	13.30
131	Hermann, archbishop of Cologne	1477	13 Jan.	At second hour[3]
136	Jacob Milich	1501	20 Feb.	12.52 P.M.
137	Victorinus Strigelius	1524	26 Dec.	4.43 P.M.
137	Johannes Garcaeus	1530	13 Dec.	13.28 P.M.
138	Copernicus	1473	10 Feb.	4.38
139	Peurbach	1423	30 May	3.05 P.M.
140	Andreas Osiander	1498	19 Dec.	1.12 P.M.
140	Pico della Mirandola	1463	24 Feb.	2.42 ante occasum
141	Cornelius Agrippa	1486	14 Sept.	15.24 P.M.
142	Melanchthon	1497	16 Feb.	7.06[4]
142[5]	Vesalius	1514	30 Dec.	17.45 P.M.
143	Eobanus Hessus	1488	5 Jan.[6]	17.50 P.M.
144	Erasmus	1467	27 Oct.	16.31 P.M.
	Justus Jonas Sr.	1493	4 Jan.	17.20 P.M.
145	Ulrich von Hutten	1488	21 April	9.30 P.M.
146	Alciati	1492	8 May	1.30 post ortum[7]

[1] And again at p. 145.

[2] And again at p. 323. It is added that he died of phthisis, aged 42, on 19 Feb. 1523 (*sic.*)

[3] It is added that he died 13 Aug. 1552. Eberus gave his day of birth as January 14.

[4] In an anonymous note on the inside cover of Basel O.III.4, the hour of Melanchthon's birth is given as "7 minus 30" on Feb. 16, 1497.

[5] And again at p. 337. Sixtus ab Hemminga, p. 237, gives the date of his birth as 31 Dec. 1513.

[6] Sixtus ab Hemminga, p. 282, gives 6 Jan. as the day.

[7] But at p. 166 the hour of his birth is given as 18.23 P.M.

147	Georgius Sabinus	1508	22	April	19.00	
	Iacobus Micyllus	1503	5	April	17.30	
148	Pietro Bembo	1470	28	May	1.03	P.M.[8]
	Albrecht Dürer	1471	20	May	22.30	P.M.
149	Hermolaus Barbarus	1453	21	May	5.10	ab occasu
150	Joachim Camerarius	1500	11	April	22.15	
	Caspar Crucigerus Jr.	1526	19	March	5.45	P.M.
151	Matthias Flacius (Illyricus)	1519	3	March	21.00	P.M.
152	Paulus Crellius	1531	3	Feb.	14.30	
	Ioh. Willenbrochius Dantiscanus	1531	5	June	22.40	P.M.
153	Georgius Valcurio physicus	1514	15	Feb.	15.26	P.M.
	Christianus Egenolphus	1502	22	July	15	P.M.
154	Franciscus Burchardus, chancellor of Weimar	1505	9	July	18.20	
	Joachim Minsingerus, chancellor of Brunswick	1514	12	Aug.	20.30	
155	Hieronymus Wolf	1516	13	Aug.	6.30	
	Johann Virdung von Hassfurt	1463	14	March	30.32	(*sic*)
156	Wolfgang Lazius[9]	1514	30	Oct.	15.24	
	Johann Sueidewein, jurisconsult	1519	20	Dec.	12.30	noctis[10]
157	Hadrian Albinus, Dr. and chancellor of margrave Johann	1513	20	Oct.	15.05	
	Cornelius Scepper[11]	1501	18	Dec.	5.26	
158	Matthias Stoius[12]	1526				
	Iacobus Homelius	1528	31	July	15	
159	Johann Sturm à Schleiden	1507	7	Oct.	2.00	P.M.
	Galeatius Capella historicus Mediolanensis (died 1537)	1487	7	March	17	
161	Simon Pistorius, chancellor of duke George of Saxony	1489	28	Oct.	4.46	
165[13]	Ioh. Iacobi medices principis	1498	13	Feb.	3.22	A.M.
166[14]	Paulus Praetorius	1521	23	Jan.	14.00	P.M.
168	George of Trebizond	1396	4	April	12.20	
169	Cyprian Leowitz	1524	8	July	21.52	P.M.
	Conrad Glaser[15]	1490	30	March	1.30	

[8] But at p. 341 the date is given as 20 May, 0.20 P.M.

[9] "Medicus et historicus imperatoris Ferdinandi."

[10] A marginal note adds that he began the study of law in 1538, was betrothed on July 29, 1539, and married October 28 of the same year, and died of apoplexy about midnight December 3, 1568.

[11] "Aulicus Belgicus in omni genere disciplinarum insignis."

[12] "Medicus et insignis astronomus."

[13] Repeated at p. 356.

[14] Repeated at p. 267.

[15] He is described as an arithmetician who went insane.

170	Erasmus Ebnerus, consiliarius Brunswicensis	1511	21 Dec.	4.52	
	Alexander Pistorius	1524	3 May	4.30	
170bis	Eusebius Moenius	1527	19 Jan.	3.55	
	Georgius Moenius	1533	24 Sept.	4.48	P.M.
171	Geo. Fabricius Chemnicensis	1516	22 April	17.30	
	Caspar Brusch	1518	19 Aug.	17.45	P.M.
172	Caspar Othmar, musician	1515	12 March	2.30	P.M.
	Franciscus de Canona, musician	1497	18 Aug.	0.02	
173	Caspar Brusch Jr., organist	1508	23 Sept.	15	
	Paul Hoffhamer, organist	1459	25 Jan.	15	
174	Johann Buchner, organist[16]	1483	27 Oct.	10.50	
	Laurentius Stauber, organist	1486	8 April	14	
175	Johann Reiffenstein	1522	20 -?-	20.30	
	Johann Fischer, sculptor	1492	4 Dec.		
184	Martin Luther	1483	10 Nov.	11.00	P.M. Islebiae
	Caspar Crucigerus	1504	1 Jan.	13.00	P.M. Lipsiae
185	Paulus Eberus	1511	7 Nov.	13.00	P.M.
	Geo. Major, theologian	1502	25 April	1.30	P.M. Nürnberg
186	Iohannes Brentius	1499	24 June	4.10	P.M. Halae Suevorum
	Iacobus Rungius	1527	25 July	18.10	P.M.
187	Iohannes Forsterus	1496	10 July	12.00	P.M.
	Iohannes Bugenhagius	1485	24 June		
192[17]	Hieronymus Savonarola	1452	21 Sept.	5.44	P.M.
193	Albert Hardenberg, theologian	1507	14 March	0.00	
194	Georg Suartzerd, father of Melanchthon	1458	26 Nov.	19	
197	Johann Agricola	1492	20 April	5.00	P.M. Islebiae
231	Rupert à Mosheim	1493	22 Sept.	4.20	
253	Valerius Cordus	1515	18 Feb.	4.04	P.M.
272	Hermann Finck, musician	1527	21 March	5.17	P.M.[18]
301	Wilibald Pirckamerus (i.e. Pirckheimer)	1470	4 Dec.	13.31	
	Hector Scollius	1536	14 Nov.	16.15	"Dunckelspul"[19]
321	Ioh. Hanusius Bohemus	1516	11 May	22.05	P.M.[20]
334	Geo. Sigismund Seldius Augustanus	1516	20 Jan.	13.?	P.M.

[16] This and the two preceding genitures are repeated at pp. 252-54.

[17] And again at p. 378.

[18] It is stated that he died a sudden death, "miserrime."

[19] A master of arts and student of medicine, he was for three years unable to retain food and died at Brandenburg on 21 Jan. 1565 at 14.30 P.M.

[20] As a result of excessive study he fell into a frenzy.

	Franciscus Zazius	1532	21	March	1.00 ab ortu
336	Caspar Peucer	1525	5	Jan.	12.00 P.M.
	Vitus Ortel Winsemius	1501	1	Aug.	0.30 P.M.
337	Georgius Curio	1498	10	June	0.30
338	Johann Dryander	1500	27	June	20.09 P.M.
	Johann Kentmann	1518	21	April	1.37 P.M.
339	Ambrosius Scala, physician	1495	30	March	18.41
	Andreas Aurifaber	1513	29	Nov.	2.40
340	Johann Carion	1499	22	March	1.46
	Erasmus Flock	1514	1	Jan.	8.20 or 8.30
341	Joachim Rheticus	1514	15	Feb.	13.30
344	Hieronymus Rudolphus, arithmetician	1496	2	April	8
359	Conrad Celtes	1459	1	Feb.	3 mane
362	Justus Jonas Jr.	1525	2	Dec.	16.00 P.M.[21]
387	Politian	1454	14	July	1.28 P.M.
389	Caspar Busch Sr., "magnus nigromanticus"	1467	30	Sept.	3.30
	Trithemius, "nigromanticus"	1462	1	Feb.	11.30
401	Ioh. Gelenius, mathematician	1535	25	Dec.	17.57 P.M.
	Thomas Holtzhoder, mathematician	1532	14	Dec.	16.15

The remaining items are from Sixtus ab Hemminga.

236	Viglius Zuichemus Frisius	1507	18	Oct.
	Gemma Frisius	1508	8	Dec.
	Nicolaus Biesius, royal physician	1516	27	March
	Ioannes Stadius	1527	19	April
	Ioannes Iseltius, medicus	1524	31	March
279	Carolus Crusius	1526	18	Feb.
280	Valentin Nabod	1523	13	Feb.
	Chilianus Goltsteyn	1499	25	March
	Justus Mengus, theologian	1499	13	Dec.
	Ioannes Ramus, jurist and royal professor	1527	10	Nov.
281	Cornelius Gemma	1535	28	Feb.
282	Ioannes Velsius Frisius	1532	19	July

[21] He was decapitated at Copenhagen in 1567.

APPENDIX 5

ZIMARA AND THE TRINUM MAGICUM OF LONGINUS CAESAR OR CAESAR LONGINUS

Marcantonio Zimara was born in 1470 of poor parents at Galatina and studied at Padua. He was teaching philosophy there in 1507 but was probably forced to leave in 1509 by the war of the League of Cambrai. In 1514 he was in his native city, and in 1522 went to Naples to defend it against the overlordship of Ferdinando Castriotto. In 1523 he lectured publicly on theology at Naples in S. Lorenzo Maggiore, then taught at Padua from 1525 to 1528. Tiraboschi states that the date and place of his death are unknown,[1] but 1532 has sometimes been suggested as the year of his death.

Zimara composed Aristotelian commentaries, and in 1539 *Theorems or Propositions* were published under his name, presumably posthumously.[2] However, the title page indicates that the work had been printed previously and that additions had been made in this edition by the author himself. This work included such propositions as follow. The motion of the sky is made up of two movers, of whom one is of finite motion and is the soul existing in it, and the other is of infinite motion and is power which is not in matter. The whole is nothing else than its parts joined together. Science which is subordinate to speculation is speculative. Intelligence and its orb constitute an entity more truly than a compound of form and matter does. The first intellect knows itself alone. Intellect knows all things. The mean is nobler than the extreme. The influence of the heavens does not prevent the existence of matter but does prevent its taking on form. If there were no abstract substances, physics would become first philosophy.[3] The

[1] Tiraboschi, *Storia della letteratura italiana,* Milan, 1824, VII, ii, 847, correcting statements of Facciolati and of his own earlier editions. I follow him for the foregoing facts.

[2] *Theoremata Marci Antonii Zimarae Sancti Petrinatis . . . seu memorabilium propositionum limitationes. Cum additionibus ab ipso authore post primam impressionem factis quas sub hoc signo * noviter reperies,* Venetiis, apud Octav. Scotum, 1539. It will be noted that Zimara is here spoken of as "Sancti Petrinatis," not of Galatina. Copy used: BM 527.m.11.

[3] For the propositions thus far listed see fols. 43, 53, 56, 60, 67, 73, 82 and 83.

proposition common through the schools that nothing acts beyond its species is false if taken too literally. For the ingredients in a compound may act together in a way which they could not achieve separately.[4] Thus Zimara seems to envisage chemical change and union.

There were published in 1537, 1556[5] and again in 1564[6] comments by Zimara on statements of Aristotle and Averroes.

So far there has been no suggestion of magic in the works published under the name of Zimara, but in 1609 at Frankfurt Longinus Caesar edited a volume entitled *Trinum magicum*[7] in which he included Conclusions by Zimara which are described as "physical, metaphysical, elemental, celestial, infernal, moral and doctrinal." In the text, however, they are called "Problems of Aristotle," while towards its close they are more correctly described as "problems concerning the parts of the human body from various statements of Aristotle and other philosophers and medical manuscripts." They begin with the question why man alone among the animals has his face turned towards the heavens. Other queries ensue as to the head, eyes, nose, mouth, teeth, tongue, palate, neck, hands, stomach, blood, urine, sexual intercourse, and whether a hermaphrodite should be baptized as male or female. But there is nothing infernal or magical about these questions, nor about the problems of Alexander of Aphrodisias which follow them. Only in the three treatises ascribed to Albertus Magnus[8] which ter-

[4] *Ibid.*, fol. 92, "Nihil agit ultra suam speciem. Vagatur per scholas ista propositio sed est falsa si absolute intelligatur, miscibilia enim in mixto agunt ad actum mixti qui est praeter actum miscibilium." Zimara's text ends at fol. 94r.

[5] *Tabula dilucidationum in dictis Aristotelis et Averrois*, Venetiis, 1556, in fol.: BM 29.f.8. For the 1537 edition see Gesner (1545), 494r.

[6] *Tabulae et dilucidationes in dicta Aristotelis et Averrois recognita et expurgata*, Venice, 1564, 2 vols. in fol.: BM 519.k.18.(2.). But I quote the title (of which the wording seems questionable) from the article on Zimara in Michaud, based on Tafuri, *Scrittori Napolitani*, III, 118.

[7] Longinus Caesar, *Trinum magicum sive secretorum naturalium coelestium infernalium opus continens: I Marci Antonii Zimarae Conclusiones Physicas Metaphysicas Elementales Coelestes Infernales Morales ac Doctrinales; II Alexandri Aphrodisei (A. Politiano interprete) questiones et solutiones physico-mathematicas; III Alberti Magni tractatus tres de virtutibus herbarum lapidum et animalium. Accessere eiusdem Alberti* . . . , Francofurti, 1609. Copy used: BM 1141.a.7.

In the text the *Secreta* or *Experimenta Alberti* or *Liber aggregationis* on virtues of herbs, stones and animals is preceded by the *De secretis mulierum* ascribed to Albertus Magnus and is followed by the *De mirabilibus mundi* also attributed to him.

[8] As to their spuriousness or authenticity see T II, chapter 63.

minate the volume is there any justification for the title *Trinum magicum*.

The title, however, seems to have proved an attractive one, for in 1614 it was employed for another volume by the same editor, known now as Caesar Longinus rather than Longinus Caesar.[9] But the three constituents of the volume are now almost wholly different from what they had been before, a fact which cataloguers have sometimes ignored. There is nothing by Zimara in the *Trinum magicum* of 1614. Its first member is rather an anonymous treatise in more than twenty chapters on natural, artificial and superstitious magic, followed by an appendix[10] on marvelous operations effected by natural magic—a collection of secrets, tricks and recipes—and then by Albertus Magnus on the virtues of herbs, stones and animals.[11] This last seems the only connecting link with the *Trinum magicum* of 1609. The second constituent of the *Trinum magicum* of 1614 is a Theater of Nature concerning the magnetic cure of wounds, magical and astrological seals and images, and conclusions physical, elemental, celestial and infernal.[12] The third part consists of the Oracles of Zoroaster in verse and the mysteries of the mystic philosophy of the Hebrews, Chaldeans, Egyptians, Arabs, Persians, Greeks, Orphics, Pythagoreans and Latins in prose.[13]

The first of these component treatises bears no resemblance to the problems of Zimara in the other volume, nor can it be called favorable to magic, since astrological images are said to have no efficacy, and imagination is thought to affect another body, if at all, only *per accidens*. Words and incantations cannot cure diseases, magicians have no control of the heavens, the transformation of men into beasts is denied. About as far as the author will go is to admit that amulets and ligatures may cure by sympathy and antipathy, and that the future may be divined by pacts with demons. He holds that witches are carried through the air to their sabbats only in fancy, and lists such Protestants as Luther, Melanchthon and Camerarius among those

[9] C. Longinus, *Trinum magicum . . . editum a . . . continens 1) De magia naturali artificiosa et superstitiosa disquisitiones axiomaticas; 2) Theatrum naturae praeter curam magneticam et veterum sophorum sigilla et imagines magicas etiam conclusiones physicas elementales coelestes et infernales exhibens; 3) Oracula Zoroastris et Mysteria mysticae philosophiae Hebraeorum Chaldaeorum Aegyptiorum Arabum Persarum Graecorum Orphicorum Pythagoricorum et Latinorum. Accessere nonnulla secreta secretorum et mirabilia mundi.* Francofurti, 1614. Copy used: BM 1035.a.5.(3.). Duodecimo, 615 pp.

[10] At p. 128.

[11] At p. 241.

[12] At pp. 346-493.

[13] At p. 494 and p. 549 respectively.

who agree with his view—also Alciati, Molitor, and Vairus (*De fascinatione*, II, 3). The opposing opinion that they are moved locally by the demons he attributes chiefly to Roman Catholics.[14]

As a specimen of the natural marvels and tricks contained in the appendix which follows this first treatise may be given the apparent raising of an egg in the air by emptying the shell, filling it with May dew and exposing it to the heat of the sun at noon.[15]

The author of the Theater of Nature is denoted by the initials, "R.G.M.D.," of which the two last probably indicate that he is a doctor of medicine. After retailing many instances of occult virtue and of sympathy and antipathy, and listing seals and images for sixty more pages, he finally comes to the doctrine of weapon ointment.

A *Trinum magicum*, published at Frankfurt in 1616,[16] was presumably simply a reprint of that just described. But in 1625 there appeared under the name of Zimara on *Antrum magico-medicum*[17] which differed a good deal in its contents from the *Trinum magicum* either of 1609 or of 1614. Its first part, arranged alphabetically by diseases, gave modes of curing various ills of the human body. Its second part dealt with magic signatures, considered first in top to toe order, then alphabetically by diseases. The third part took up medicaments which help by likeness. The fourth part on seals and images repeated that section from the *Trinum magicum* of 1614. Parts 5 and 6 consisted of medicaments from minerals and vegetables; parts 7 and 8, of experiments. A second volume appeared the following year and was chiefly made up of a mixture of cures and recipes with the Chaldean Mysteries printed at the end of the volume.[18]

[14] *Ibid.*, Cap. 15, "Huic opinioni ut plurimum Romanae fidei asseclae adhaerent.

[15] *Ibid.*, pp. 190-91, "et si difficilis aliquando fuerit ascensus baculi vel tabulae adminiculo dum ascendere incipiat facilius elevabitur."

[16] It was also in duodecimo: BM 719.a.8. The old printed catalogue of the British Museum lists under the name of Zimara a *Tractatus magicus* as found in this edition and that of 1614, but we have seen in the 1614 edition that this is not the case.

[17] M. A. Zimara, *Antrum magico-medicum in quo arcanorum magico-physicorum sigillorum signaturarum et imaginum magicarum secundum Dei nomina et constellationes astrorum cum signatura planetarum constitutarum ut et curationum magneticarum et characteristicarum ad omnes corporis humani affectus curandos . . .* , Francofurti, 1625, 8vo. Copy used: BM 1034.e.13-14.

[18] *Antri magico-medici pars secunda in qua arcana naturae sympathiae et antipathiae . . .* , Francofurti, 1626, 8vo, 749 pp. Of these pp. 221-362 are Liber 2, *De affectuum humanorum curatione Hermetica et Galenica.*

APPENDIX 6

PRINTERS OF THE SIXTEENTH AND EARLY SEVENTEENTH CENTURIES MENTIONED IN THESE VOLUMES

Accoltus, Vincentius, Rome
Adriaen Van Berghen, Antwerp
Alantsee, Lucas, Vienna
Albinus, Ioannes, Mainz,
Aldus (Manutius), Venice
Andreae, Lazarus, Cracow
Angelino, Pietro, publisher, London
Anshelmus, Thomas, Hagenau
Antonius, Ioannes, Venice
Antonius, Marcus, Bologna
Antonius a Mariis, Coimbra
Apiarius, Matth., Berne
Arrivabeni, Andrea, publisher, Venice
Arrivabenis, Georgius de, Venice
Aubrius, Joannes, Frankfurt
Avantius, Ludovicus, Venice

Baldinus, Victor, Ferrara
Balsarin, Guillaume, Lyons
Barilatto, Giovanni, Venice
Barricat, E., Lyons
Bassaeus, Nicolaus, Frankfurt
Bawman, Georg, Erfurt
Becker, M. Frankfurt
Behem, Franciscus, Mainz
Bellono, Antonio, Genoa
Benalius, Bernardinus, Venice
Benedictis, Benedictus de, Bologna
Benedictis, Hieronymus de, Bologna, and his heirs
Benedictis, Ioannes Antonius de, Bologna
Bericchia, Iacomo, Rome
Bernardinus de Garaldis, Pavia

Bernia, Antonius, publisher (1642), Bologna
Bertellus, Petrus, Padua
Berthelin, Andrea, Paris
Berton, Barthelemy, La Rochelle
Besicken, Iohannes, Rome
Bevilaqua, Nicolaus, Turin
Binderiana officina, Hamburg
Bindonus, Franciscus, Venice
Birckmann, Arnold, Cologne
Birckmann, Joannes, Cologne
Bladus, Antonius, Rome
Bogardus, Iacobus, Paris
Bonardus, Vincentius, of Parma, Bologna
Bondevillaus, Guido, Toulouse (University)
Bonfadino, Bartolomeo, publisher, Rome
Bonhomme, Mathias, Vienne
Bontius, Gregorius, bookseller, Antwerp
Borculoius, Hermannus, Utrecht
Bordogna, Sigismund, Venice
Borgarucci, B., Venice
Bourges, G., Tours
Brocarius, Arnaldus Guil., Alcalà
Brubacchius, Petrus, Hagenau
Bry, Th. de, Frankfurt

Cacchius, Josephus, Aquila, Naples
Cammerlander, Jakob, Strasburg
Camotio, Gioan Fran., Venice
Cancer, Matthias, Naples
Carlinus, Io. Iacobus, Naples
Catherina de Silvestro, Naples
Cavellat, Guillaume, Paris
Cervicornus, Eucharius, Cologne and Marburg
Chesneau, N., Paris
Ciottus, Ioannes Baptista, Venice
Clottus, Io. Bapt., of Siena, Bergamo
Cocus, Simon, Antwerp
Colinaeus, Simon, Paris
Copland, Wm., Lothbury

Cornix, H., Antwerp
Corneus, Conradus, Wolfenbüttel
Cratandrus, Andreas, Basel
Crato, Johannes, Wittenberg
Crespin, J., Lyons
Crispinus, Ioannes, Geneva

David, Matth., Paris
Day, John, London
Diani Nel Pelegrino, Tito, Rome
Dives, Nicolaus, Paris
Donnis, Sebastianus a, Verona
Dorico, Luigi, of Brescia, Rome
Dorico, Valerio, of Brescia, Rome
Du Bois, Simon, Paris
Du Val, Dionysius, Paris

Egenolphus, Christianus, Frankfurt
Eguia, Michael de, Alcalà
Emmel, Samuel, Strasburg
Episcopius, Nicolaus, Basel
Estienne, see Stephanus

Falckenburg, Henr., Cologne
Feyerabendt, Iohannes, Frankfurt
Figulus, Benedictus, Strasburg
Foucher, J., Paris
Franceschi, Venice
Franceschini, Camillo, Venice
Franciscis, Franciscus de, of Siena, Venice
Frellonius, Lyons
Frizis, Antonius de, Naples
Froben, Johannes, Basel
Frobenius, H., Basel
Froschauer, Christopher, Zurich
Furmannus, Valentinus, Nürnberg

Gabiano, fratres de, Lyons
Garaldis, See Bernardinus de
Gaudoul, Pierre, Paris

Gauoti, V., Milan
Gazeau, Guil., Lyons
Gesner, Andrea, Zurich
Gesner, A. et J. fratres, Zurich
Gillius, David, bookseller, Paris
Giolito, Gabriele, of Ferrara, Venice
Giunti, Florence
Giuntus, Iacobus, Lyons
Gothinus, Aegidius, Paris
Gourmontius, Hieronymus, Paris
Graminaeus, Theodore, Cologne
Grangier, Pierre-I., Dijon
Grapheus, Jo., Antwerp
Grassi, Bartolomeo, Rome
Grieninger, Johann, Strasburg
Grimm, Sigismund, Augsburg
Gromon, Paris
Gromorsus, Petrus, Paris
Grothenius, Conradus, Lemgo
Grüninger, Strasburg
Gruppenbach, Georg, Tübingen
Gryphius, Ant., Lyons
Guarischo, Marco, Venice
Gueralda, Bernardinus, Ancona; and see Bernardinus
Gueullartius, Ioannes, Paris
Guillard, Guillaume, Paris
Gunter, Wolphgang, Leipzig
Gutterwitz, Andreas, Copenhagen
Gymnicus, Ioannes, Cologne

Haller, Johannes, Cracow
Hamann, Johann, Venice
Harnisch, Matthaeus, Neustadt
Haselberg, Jo., Nürnberg
Hector, Benedictus, Bologna
Helianus, Victor, Rome
Henricus, Nicolaus, Ursel
Henricus Petri, Basel
Hervagius, Johannes, Basel

Herzog, Johann, Venice
Hillenius, Michael, Antwerp
Honoratus, Bartholomaeus, Lyons
Horst, Petrus, Cologne
How, W., London
Huguetan, I. A., Lyons (1649)
Hupfuff, Strasburg
Huyon, Guillaume, Lyons

Iesus, la libraria dal (Nicolo and Domenico, brothers), Venice
Iobin, Bernhardus, Strasburg
Iordan, Petrus, Mainz
Isingrinius, Michael, Basel

Jacobus, Cyriacus, Frankfurt
Jesu, see Iesus
Jove, M., Lyons
Junta, house of, Venice
Junta, Lucas Antonius, Venice
Junta, Philippus, Venice
Juste, François, Lyons

Kerver, Iacobus, Paris
Kingston, John, London
Knorrn, Nicolaus, Nürnberg
Koebel, Jacob, Oppenheim

Lapicida, F., Venice
Le Preux, Franciscus, Lausanne
Le Prince, Pierre, Lyons
Locatellus, Bonetus, of Bologna, Venice
Loë, Ioannes, Antwerp
Lucius, J., Rostock
Lufft, Johannes, Wittenberg

Madrigal, Petrus de, Madrid
Manger, Michael, Augsburg
Manilius, Gislenus, Ghent
Marchetti, P. M., Brescia
Margarit, G., Barcelona
Marnet, Hier. de, Paris

Marnius, Claudius, Frankfurt
Marsh or Marshe, Thomas, London
Martinus, Iodocus, Strasburg
Masius, Gilbert, Louvain
Mazochius, Jacobus, Rome and Mirandola
Meietus, Antonius, of Padua, Venice
Meietus, Paulus, of Padua, Venice and Padua
Meiettus, Robertus, Venice
Melgar, Alfonso de, Burgos
Michel, Claude, Tournon
Montanus, Ioannes, Nürnberg
Morellus, Federicus, Paris
Morhard, Ulrich, Tübingen
Morin, Jehan, Paris
Myliander, Stephanus, Rostock
Mylius, J., Würzburg

Navò, Curtius Troianus, Venice
Neuber, Ulric, Nürnberg
Nicolaus, Gerardus, Antwerp
Nicolinis de Sabio, Petrus et Ioannes Maria de, Venice
Nigrinus, G., Prag
Nivellius, Sebastianus, Paris
Nourry, Claude, Paris
Nutius, Antwerp

Ohr, Philippus de, Hamburg
Olmo, Venice
Oporinus, Ioannes, Basel
Ostenius, Leonardus, Basel

Paganus, Theobald, Lyons
Palthenius, M. Zacharias, Frankfurt
Parcus, J., Basel
Parvus, Ioannes, Paris
Pasinus, Mapheus, Venice
Pasquet de Sallo, Ioannes, Naples
Pasquetus, Ioan. et Dominicus, Naples
Patavinus, Jo., Venice
Patresson, Jean, Lyons

Pax, Antonius, Naples
Pederzanus, Io. Baptista, Venice
Perchacinus, Gratiosus, Padua and Venice
Perez, Franciscus, Seville
Perier, Adrian, Paris
Perier, Th., Paris
Perna, Petrus, Basel
Pesnot, Loys, Lyons
Petit-Jean, Athanase, Lyons
Petit-pas, Ioannes, bookseller, Paris
Petreius, Iohannes, Nürnberg
Peypus, Federicus, Nürnberg
Phaellus, Ioh. Bapt., Bologna
Pietrasanta, Plinio, Venice
Pinocier, G., Paris
Plantin, Christopher, Antwerp
Pontius, G., Milan
Portese, Agostin da, Venice
Portonariis, Vincentius de, publisher, Lyons
Praesenius, Cominus, Brescia
Pré, Galiot du, Paris
Princeps, Petrus, see Le Prince
Prost, J. A. & M., Lyons
Pullon da Trino, Gioanni, Lyons
Puys, Jacques du, bookseller, Paris

Quentell, Petrus, Cologne
Querengis, Petrus de, of Bergamo, Venice

Rapirio, Iovita, Venice
Ratdolt, Erhard, Venice and Augsburg
Rauard, M. A., Lyons
Ravanis, P. de, Venice
Rebartus, Thomas, Jena
Regnault, G., Lyons
Resch, Conrad, Paris
Reynaud, R., Tournon
Rhau, Georg, Wittenberg
Richis, Petrus Maria de, of Pavia, Naples
Richterus, W., Frankfurt

Rigaud, B., Lyons
Rigaud, S., Lyons
Roberto, Felippe, Tarragona
Rodericus, Ludovícus, Lisbon
Roffinello, Venturino, Venice
Rose, Germanus, Lyons
Roussin, Nevers
Rovillius, Paris
Rovillius, Gulielmus, Lyons
Roy, Maurice, Lyons
Royerius, Ioannes, Paris
Ruberia, Justinianus de, Bologna
Ruffinellis, Venturinus de, Venice

Sabio (Io. Ant.) et fratres de, Venic
Sabio, see Nicolinis de
Salvianus, Horatius, Naples
San Vito, Aniello, publisher, Naples
Sansovino, F., Venice
Schoeffer, Ivo, Mainz
Schoeffer, Johann, Mainz
Schoenstenius, Iohannes, Cologne
Schott, Johann, Strasburg
Schwertal, Ioh., Wittenberg
Scotus, Hieronymus, Venice
Scotus, Octavian, Venice, and his heirs
Secerius, Johannes, Hagenau
Selfisch, Samuel, publisher, Wittenberg
Sessa, Venice
Sessa, J. B., Venice
Sessa, Melchior, Venice
Seuberlich, Laurent, Wittenberg
Sevestre, Carolus, bookseller, Paris
Silber, Eucharius, Rome
Silber, Marcellus, Rome
Silvano, Horacio, Naples
Simon, G., Antwerp
Simoneta, Giovanni Maria, of Cremona, Faenza and Pavia
Singrenius, Johannes, Vienna

Somaschus, J. B., Venice
Soncinus, Hieronymus, Pesaro
Soubron, Thomas, Lyons
Spies, Joannes, Frankfurt
Spira, Petrus, Messina
Steinius, N., publisher, Frankfurt
Steinman, J., Leipzig
Stephanus, Henricus, Paris
Stephanus, Robertus, Paris
Stockelman, Joh., Copenhagen
Strubius, G., Wittenberg
Stuchssen, Ioannes, Nürnberg
Subtilis, Joh. Bapt., Naples
Sutton, Henry, London
Sybold, Henry, Strasburg

Tacuinus, Ioannes, Venice
Thibault, Jean, Antwerp
Tiletanus, Ioannes Lodoicus, Paris
Tinghi, Philip, Lyons
Tornieri, Iacomo, Rome
Torrentinus, Laurentius, Florence
Tosius, Bartholomaeus, Rome
Tournes, Jean de, Lyons
Tozzi, Pietropaolo, Vicenza
Trechsel, Lyons
Trot, Bartholomew, bookseller, Lyons

Ulmus, Marcus Antonius, Venice
Ulricherus, Geo., Strasburg

Valgrisius, Vincent, Venice
Vascosanus, Michael, Paris
Ventura, Cominus, Bergamo
Vergilius, Ioannes, of Urbino, publisher
Vianis, Bernardinus de, Venice
Victor, Hieronymus, Vienna
Vignon, Eustathius, Venice
Villiers, Gilbert de, Lyons

Violati, Venice
Viotto, Seth, Parma
Vitali, Bernardinus de, Venice
Vitali, Matthias de, Venice
Vuyrsung (Wirsung), Marcus, Augsburg

Wachter, Georg, publisher, Nürnberg
Walde-graue, Robert, Edinburgh
Weale, A., publisher, London
Wechel, Andreas, Paris
Wechel, Andreas, heirs of, Frankfurt
Wechel, Chr., Paris
Winter, Robert, Basel
Winterburg, Johann, Vienna
Withagius, Ioannes, Louvain
Wolf, Reginald, London
Wolfgang of Strasburg, Cracow
Wyer, Robert, London

Zalterius, Bologninus, Venice
Zannetti, B., Rome
Zannetti, F., Rome
Zassenus, Servatius, bookseller, Louvain
Zenarius, Damianus, Venice
Zetznerus, Lazarus, Strasburg and Basel
Ziletti, Giordano, Venice

GENERAL INDEX

GENERAL INDEX

nec solum videri aliquibus parum rem advertentibus aut sciolis ingloriosum laborem Indices parare sed etiam superfluum . . . non illaudatum nec inutilem esse laborem imo fere necessarium maioribus libris Indices apponere idque recte praestare non omnium esse sed solummodo ea in facultate peritorum et iudicio exercitatorum.—GRATAROLO

Aaron, book of, VI, 454
Abano, baths of, VI, 209, and see Peter of
Abbot, V, 309, 555, VI, 218, 300, 439, 458
Abdala the Arab, cited, VI, 481
Abdomen, pain in, VI, 431
Abel, Charles (1870), V, 313, 435
Abel, E. (1885), VI, 460
Abelard, cited, V, 220
Abenhaen, Arabic alchemist, V, 623
Aberdeen, bishop of, V, 296
Abhandlungen der preussischen Akademie, V, 160, and see Hellmann, G. (1924)
Abhandlungen zur Geschichte d. math. Wiss., V, 343, 347-8, 350, 352, 354, 357, 415
Abhandlungen zur Geschichte der Medizin, V, 494, VI, 478
Abiosus, Iohannes Baptista, V, 166, 179, 220-1, 335, 341, 541, cited, V, 199
Abraham (the patriarch), V, 403, VI, 353, 514, 520
Abraham Avenezra (or, ibn Ezra), V, 124, 207, 261, 267, 269, 278, 284, 309, 333, 521, VI, 104, 180
Abraham ben Chija, VI, 16
Abraham Judaeus, see Abraham Avenezra
Abraham e Porta Leonis, see Portaleone
Absent-mindedness, VI, 443
Absent treatment, V, 474, VI, 221, 233
Absinthium, an herb, VI, 265
Abstemius, Vinc. Fran. V, 265-6
Abuhali, alchemist, V, 623
Acacia, V, 453
Academic freedom, V, 295
Academie royale de Belgique, V, 410
Academy, alchemical, V, 621; Animosi of Padua, VI, 481; Gelati of Bologna, V, 250; Old, VI, 228, 350, 378-9, 432; scientific, VI, 269; Secreti of Porta, VI, 156; Selvaggi, V, 250; Sodalitates of Rhine and Danube, V, 407; Umoristi of Rome, V, 250
Acakia, Martin (1538), V, 430
Acanthius, an herb, VI, 272
Acciaiolus, Zenobius, VI, 101
Accidens, per, and Accident, V, 103, 151, VI, 181, 198, 232, 485, 601
Accoltus, Vinc. pr Rome, V, 484
Achaea, flood in, V, 203
Achates, a gem, V, 457, 614
Achilles, VI, 376; shield of, V, 329
Achillini, Alexander, *Anatomicae,* V, 45-47; anatomy by, V, 43-47, ignored, V, 38-39; appearance, V, 37-38; career, V, 38-39; *Chyromantiae,* V, 49, 52, 63-64; cited, VI, 48, 370; *Distinctionibus,* V, 39, 42; *Distributionibus,* V, 39; *Intelligentiis,* V, 39; occult arts, V, 42-43; *Opera,* V, 39, 42; *Orbibus,* V, 38, 42; *Physico auditu,* V, 39, 41; picture of, V, 45-46; *Proportione,* V, 39, 41; *Septisegmentatum,* V, 47-48; *Universalibus,* V, 48; unprinted works, V, 48-49; *Viridario,* V, 51
Achillini, Claudius, V, 43
Achillini, Philotheus, V, 45
Achmet on dreams, VI, 483
Achryuasmus, interlocutor, V, 647
Acid, V, 635, 650, 659
Aconite, V, 481
Aconzio, Jacopo, VI, 518
Acorn, V, 608

Acosta, Christophorus, VI, 319
Acosta, José de, V, 468, VI, 274-5
Actium, battle of, VI, 465
Actor, V, 618
Actuality, see Potentiality and
Actuarius, V, 144, 463, VI, 228
Adalbert, heretic, VI, 551
Adam (first man), V, 6, VI, 75, 464; and astrology, V, 403; and Eve, V, 399; celestial and terrestrial, VI, 444; knowledge of, angelic, VI, 391, of names of animals, VI, 352, 356, of herbs, V, 651, VI, 259; founder of first school of physics, VI, 352
Adam ab Invidia, V, 255, 274, VI, 181-2
Adam a Lebenwald (1580), VI, 525
Adam, Melchior, V, 127, 152, 246, 298, 303, 346, 367, 383, 385, 391, 404, 406, 619, VI, 38, 61, 123, 303, 395
Adamant, see Diamond
Adda river, V, 29
Adelandus Sarracenus, cited, V, 227
Adelard of Bath, Chiromancy, V, 675; *Quaestiones naturales,* V, 144, 570, VI, 402; tr Euclid, V, 279
Adelman, Bernard, V, 180
Adelphus, Joh., medical, V, 437
Adelung, *Fortsetzung,* V, 269
Adige river, V, 488
Admont, see Engelbert of
Adolescence, V, 149, 152, VI, 10
Adriaen Van Berghen, pr Antwerp, V, 206
Adrian, VI, pope, V, 253, 282, VI, 148; dedic to, V, 208, 211, 213-4, 241
Adrian Castellensis (1507), V, 142
Adriatic Sea, V, 28
Adros, alchemist, V, 623
Adros, king of Arabia, V, 623
Adulteration, of drugs, V, 451-2, 465, 469-70, 511; of gems, V, 455-6
Adultery, revealed, V, 455, 474, VI, 320
Advertising, academic, V, 205; humanistic, V, 113; publisher's, V, 335
Advogarius, see Avogaro
Aegidius of Corbeil, V, 54, 510
Aegidius eremita, V, 623
Aegidius, Hebraist, V, 130
Aegidius, master of the Hospital, V, 548
Aegidius Romanus, cited, V, 54, VI, 48, 378, 399, 411; opposed, V, 40, 42, VI, 369; praised, V, 75
Aegidius, William, VI, 298
Aegina, see Paul of
Aelian, V, 144; cited, VI, 205, 256, 277, 280, 294, 319, 358; tr, VI, 255
Aemilia or Aemilius, V, 270
Aeneas (of Vergil), V, 486
Aeneas Sylvius, VI, 289, 338
Aeromancy, VI, 468, 499; opposed, VI, 430; put on Index, VI, 147
Aesculapius, V, 300
Aetites (eagle stone), V, 455, 457, 485, VI, 277, 419
Aetius of Amida, V, 430, 449, 478
Aevolus, Caesar (1580), VI, 414
Affaydatus or Affaytatus, Fortunius (1549), V, 269-73
Africa, V, 27, 31, 581, VI, 187, 225, 346, 392
Agate, a gem, V, 478; and see Achates, Gagates
Agent, material and final, V, 506
Ages, seven, of world, VI, 442; last, V, 374, 631; of man, VI, 140, 459
Agnello, Giovanni, alchemist, V, 624
Agnus Dei, VI, 168-9, 498
Agostini, Giovanni degli (1752-1754), V, 262
Agricola, Georg, VI, 295; cited, V, 477, VI, 285, 308, 319; disputed, V, 458, 643
Agricola, Johann, VI, 597
Agriculture, V, 609, VI, 378, 419, 426; astrology in, VI, 157
Agrippa, Henry Cornelius, career and character, V, 127-9; cited, V, 261-2, 636, VI, 170-1, 197, 361, 402, 424-5, 570; criticized, VI, 245; *Epistolae,* V, 130-3, 285, 307, 541, VI, 452; *Incertitudine,* V, 65, 128-9, 133, 138, 586, VI, 562; geniture, V, 138, VI, 105, 595; interest in alchemy, V, 127, 132-3, 541, in applied science, V, 133, in medicine, V, 127-8, 286, in the occult, V, 129-36, VI, 439, professed recantation, V, 129; legends of, V, 136-7; *Occulta philosophia,* V, 127, 129-30, 133-6, 138, its spurious fourth book, V, 136, VI, 154, 360, 406, 521; plagiarized, V, 586, VI, 456; put on Index, VI, 146-7, 150
Aguilera, Juan de (1542), astrologer, V, 255, 266-7
Ahmad ibn Sirin, see Achmet

Aicha or Aichach, V, 345
Ailly, Pierre d', cited, V, 140, 166, 227, 486, 584, VI, 131, 176-7, 432; criticized, V, 120, 140, 192, 199, 223, 280, VI, 412; pr, V, 346
Air, VI, 221; cause of fever, V, 314; corruption of, V, 97, 496-7, VI, 366, 432; extent of, V, 421, VI, 71, 78, 83, 380; midpoint of, VI, 110; not expose to, VI, 240; pressure, VI, 387; pure, cannot be separated by alchemy, V, 633; regions of, V, 428, 568, VI, 50, 93, 96, 167, 342, 369, 396; transformed into water, V, 10
Aisestain, Volfardus, VI, 137-8
Aitchison Robertson, W. G. (1926), VI, 241
Aix-en-Provence, parlement of, VI, 554; pr at, VI, 553; university of, VI, 553
Aix-la-Chapelle, V, 183
Alabaster, VI, 225
Alantsee, Lucas, pr Vienna, V, 353
Alaska, VI, 436
Albadaran, V, 527
Albano, cardinal of, V, 259
Albategni, V, 427, VI, 35; cited, V, 360, 421, VI, 43; disproved, V, 407; ed., V, 360
Albert II, emperor, V, 373
Albert, archbishop of Mainz, dedic to, V, 66, 175
Albert, archduke of Austria, V, 137, VI, 235
Albert V, duke of Bavaria, V, 619
Albert of Brandenburg (15c), VI, 89
Albert of Brandenburg, duke of Prussia, dedic to, V, 417, VI, 3; letter to, V, 365; nativity of, V, 384
Albert of Perugia, V, 534
Albert du Puy, physician, V, 124
Albert of Savoy, prince of Carpi, V, 95
Albert of Saxony, V, 23, 24, 25, 41, 95, 157; copied, VI, 43, 369
Alberti, Salomo (1574), VI, 229-30
Albertinus, Alexander (1620), VI, 558-9
Albertus Magnus, V, 27, 57, VI, 112, 291; cited, or used, V, 23, 46, 48-49, 92, 157-8, 167, 335, 475, 478, 480, 506, 564, 570, 614, 633, 643, 646, VI, 132, 276, 280, 285, 300, 315, 318, 334, 361, 378, 399, 402, 420, 429, 431, 433, 446, 484, 487, 513; cited as an alchemist, V, 141, 533, 538, 541-3, 604, 624, VI, 411, denied, VI, 244; cited for astrology, V, 159, 166, 195, 209, 213, 215, 219, 221, 227, 248, 588, VI, 125, 174, 176-7, 188; criticized and disagreed with, V, 41-42, 75, 450-1, 478, 523, 564, 647, 663, VI, 244, 256, 285, 309, 367, 385, 401-2, 416; 512, 571; follower of, V, 195, 213; his scientific superiority, VI, 283-4, 295; ignored, VI, 412, 470; magic wrought by, VI, 536; praised, VI, 424; works, alchemical, V, 679, *Animalibus,* V, 41, 54, *Ars ciromancie,* V, 674, *Fato,* ascribed to, VI, 304, *Mineralibus,* V, 443, 536, VI, 299, 305-6, 312, *Natura locorum,* V, 225, 316, 390, *Negotio naturali,* see *Philosophia pauperum, Perigenesis,* V, 538, *Philosophia pauperum,* V, 148-9, *Proprietatibus elementorum,* V, 207, *Secreta,* V, 33, VI, 600-1, *Secretis mulierum,* VI, 300, 600, *Speculum astronomiae* V, 54, 131, 199, VI, 304, *Vegetabilibus et plantis,* V, 29, 463
Albertutius, see Albert of Saxony
Albinius, P. Constantius (1611), VI, 324, 464
Albinus, Hadrian, VI, 596
Albinus, Ioannes, pr Mainz, VI, 429
Albizzi, Francesco, cardinal, VI, 149
Albohali, V, 394-5, VI, 105
Albohazen Haly, V, 317, 419, VI, 490
Albrecht, see Albert
Albubater, cited, V, 269, VI, 180; ed., V, 364, VI, 448
Albucasis, cited, V, 458, 504
Albugazel, alchemist, V, 624
Albumasar, VI, 470; cited, V, 54, 120, 163, 180, 194, 207, 227, 269, 277, 309, 326, 588, 623, VI, 89, 93, 176-7, 180, 399, 512; criticized, V, 117, 184-6, 198, 223, 277, 511, VI, 197, 200, 412; defended, V, 209; edition of, proposed, V, 395; pr, V, 346
Alcabitius, V, 307, 432; based on, VI, 119; cited and used, V, 120, 163, 207, 309, 317, VI, 104, 160, 163, 180; comm. VI, 119, 122; criticized, VI, 120; published, V, 292, 308, VI, 471
Alcalà, pr at, V, 210, 276, 283, 318, 475; university of, V, 210, 275-6, 318, 476

Alcasar de Sal, V, 292
Alce, a beast, V, 484
Alchemical, Alchemist and Alchemy, V, 532-49, 601-4, 638, VI, 218, 292, 454; Agrippa and, V, 127, 132-3, 541; allusion to, V, 439; antiquity denied or affirmed, V, 643, VI, 246; apparatus, V, 540, 590, 621, and see Furnace, Instrument; astrology in, V, 634, VI, 416; Binsfeld on, VI, 544; Brahe and, VI, 68; criticism of, V, 33, 58-59, 125-6, 262, 287, 315-6, 362, 458, 545, 571, 598, 642-3, VI, 107, 193, 244, 246, 252-3, 335, 411, 501; dabbled in, VI, 219, 519, by monks, VI, 440; deceits of, VI, 245, 434, 530; defended, V, 619, VI, 242; defined, VI, 242; demons and, V, 643, VI, 519, 525; difficulties of, V, 648, VI, 144; explained, VI, 279, in mystic terms, VI, 438, 442; favored, V, 141, 397; founders of, V, 126; law and, V, 535, 622; magic and, VI, 416, 544; medicine and, V, 620, VI, 252, and see Iatrochemistry, Paracelsus; not on Index, VI, 147; poverty of, V, 32, 141, 548-9, 643, VI, 245, 411; predicted, V, 219; pr, V, 4, 535-7, 601-3, 621-5; prohibited, V, 537, 539, 549, 604; remedy, V, 479, 632, 634, 640, VI, 224, 461, 533; spurious books of, VI, 244; stories of success of, V, 416, 540, 548-9, 648, VI, 247, 318; synonyms, V, 603; transmutation denied, V, 598, 659, VI, 244, 250, possible, VI, 435; universities and, VI, 251; vocabulary, VI, 278; and see Experiment and the names of individual alchemists
Alchimia, Das ist alle Farben . . . , V, 543
Alciati, Andreas, cited, VI, 602; nativity of, VI, 105, 595
Alcochoden, VI, 200
Alcocodea, V, 269
Alcofribas, V, 313-4, 435
Alcohol, V, 650, VI, 243; and see Wine, spirit of
Aldana, Cosimo (1578), VI, 222
Aldebert, heretic, see Adalbert
Alderotti, Taddeo, V, 42, 600
Aldine press, V, 555, VI, 475, 488, 528
Aldrovandi, Ulysse, V, 575, VI, 257-8; as a scientist, VI, 269-70; correspondence, VI, 266; inquisition and, VI, 153; later estimates of, VI, 296-7; method of treatment, VI, 276-8; pupil of, VI, 235; works, V, 7, *Animalibus insectis,* V, 249, VI, 268, 281-2, 284, 290, *Avibus,* VI, 258, 269, 277, 281, 292-3, *Dendrologiae,* VI, 289, 294, *Exanguibus,* VI, 268, 284-5, 291, *Monstrorum historia,* V, 247-8, VI, 276, 281, 292, 294, 452-3, 489, *Musaeum metallicum,* V, 247, 249-50, 547, VI, 216-7, 282-3, 295, 308, 310, 321-2, *Piscibus,* VI, 257, 281-2, *Quadrupedorum,* VI, 285, 293-4, *Serpentum et draconum,* VI, 280, 283-4, 290
Aldus (Manutius), pr Venice, V, 343, 555
Aleander, Jerome, cardinal, V, 70, 282-3, 447, 454, VI, 101
Aleardus de Indemontibus or Pedemontibus, of Verona, V, 538, VI, 209
Alectromancy, VI, 509
Alegnos, Germain, astrologer, V, 283
Alembert, Jean le Rond d', V, 555
Alembic, V, 621
Aleotti, Giov. Batt., tr, V, 364
Alessandri, Alessandro (1522), V, 142-3, 636, VI, 436
Alessio of Piedmont, *Secreti,* V, 147, VI, 215-6, 418, cited, VI, 429, 431
Alexander the Great, V, 485, VI, 363, 420
Alexander VI, pope, V, 51, 60-61, 62, 142, 171, 472; death predicted, V, 124
Alexander of Aphrodisias, V, 48, 75, 325, 410, VI, 600; cited, V, 83, 109, 514, VI, 48, 366, 486
Alexander of Hales, VI, 125
Alexander, an interlocutor, VI, 568, 570
Alexander of Tralles, VI, 516
Alexandria and Alexandrian, VI, 374, 410; see Theon of, Hero of
Alexandrinus, VI, 231; and see Olympiodorus
Alexipharmaca, VI, 338
Alfarabi, V, 114, 586
Alfonsine Tables, V, 282, 300, 333, 411, VI, 82, 112; annotated, V, 327; compared with Prutenic, VI, 5, 13, 15, 19, 24, 30, 42, 52-54, 120, 139; criticized, V, 200-1, 284, VI, 18, 23, 29, 47, 65, 118; defended, VI, 35-36, 51; difficulty of, V, 6; followed, V, 131,

172, VI, 11, 21, 37, 64, 118, 430; pr, V, 192, 291, 334, 346, 421
Alfonso X, the Wise, VI, 21; cited, V, 166, VI, 11, 49, 62, 131; misrepresented, V, 333, VI, 192; praised, V, 200, VI, 77
Alfonso I, duke of Ferrara, see Este
Alfraganus, V, 360, VI, 43, 180
Alfridaria, denied, VI, 138
Algazel, VI, 405, 468
Algorithmus demonstratus, V, 359
Alhazen, V, 366, VI, 566; cited, V, 140, 421, VI, 78
Alicorno, a beast, V, 484
Alidosi, G. N. P. (1623), V, 43-44, 49, 51-52, 234, 244
Alive, eaten, VI, 420-1; heart torn from, V, 527, 560; eye from, V, 560
Alkali, VI, 243
Alkindi, V, 24; cited, V, 54, 227, VI, 180, 429; criticized, VI, 467
Allectory, a gem, VI, 316
Allegory and Allegorical interpretation, V, 133, 150, VI, 313, 447, 498
Allen, D. C. (1938), VI, 318
Allgemeine Deutsche Biographie, V, 175, 323
Allut, P. (1859), V, 112-3, 544
Allwoerden, Henricus ab (1727), V, 288
Almadal or Almadel, V, 673, VI, 361, 430, 468, 502, 516
Almagest, see Ptolemy
Almagià, Roberto (1921), VI, 27
Almanach, V, 309, 313, 318, 345-6, VI, 111, 170, 361; of Cracow, V, 173; Fině's, V, 290-2; peasants', V, 291; use of, V, 223, 290-3; vulgar condemned, V, 329, VI, 524; and see Ephemerides
Almansor, cited, V, 269, VI, 512
Almazatus, alchemist, V, 623
Almeon, mathematician, 1139 A.D., VI, 130
Almond, V, 611
Almoner, ducal, VI, 130; royal, V, 311
Alms, V, 117
Almuten, V, 361
Aloe, V, 449, 467, 650, 662
Alofresant of Rhodes, astrologer, V, 314
Aloisius, Petrus, natural son of Paul III, see Farnese, Pierluigi
Alost (Flanders), VI, 38
Alpetragi, cited, VI, 62, 399
Alphabet and Alphabetical, letters, use of, V, 538, virtue of, VI, 444, 457; order, VI, 270-1, 299, 332, 602; revolution, VI, 456
Alphidius, cited, V, 538, 623
Alpinus, Prosper (1553-1617), VI, 319
Alps, V, 26, 27, 613, 627, VI, 254; beyond or north of, V, 111, 279, 600-1
Alsace, V, 331, VI, 74, 399
Alsted, J. H. (1630), V, 143, 418-9, 429, 651, VI, 433-6, 494
Altavilla, Benedictus (1581), VI, 139
Altdorf, pr at, V, 339; professor at, VI, 59, 73, 331
Alteration, physical, modes of, V, 101
Alterius, Julius, V, 267
Alterius, Marius (1548), V, 267-9
Althaea or Althaia, an herb, VI, 223, 262
Altimarus, Joh., physician, VI, 213-5
Alto Saxo, patrician ab, VI, 126
Altomari, Donatus Antonius ab, VI, 212, 228
Alum, VI, 307, 310, 334; four kinds, V, 457; in mineral waters, VI, 209; papal monopoly of, V, 457
Alumen catinae or catinum, V, 457-8
Alumen plumae, V, 457-8
Alumen rochae, V, 457
Alumen sciolae, V, 457
Alumen scissile, V, 458
Alumen zucharinum, V, 457-8
Alva, duke of, VI, 394
Alvarez, Antonio (1585), VI, 129
Amadis de Gaule, V, 636
Amalricus rex, VI, 470
Amanuensis, V, 129, VI, 257; and see Copyist
Amaranthius, Sempronius, poet, VI, 470
Amatus Lusitanus, cited, V, 647, VI, 258
Ambassador, V, 324, 607, 613
Amber, V, 327, 470, 651, VI, 302
Amberg, V, 440
Ambix (1938), V, 532
Ambrose, St., V, 142, 295, VI, 429
Ambrosinus, Bartholomaeus, V, 247, 249, VI, 216, 280, 290, 294, 489
Amenduni, G. (1890), V, 274
Amerbach, Boniface, legist, V, 431
Amerbach, Vitus (1549), V, 394, 405
America, V, 581, 614, VI, 323; represented as a distinct continent, V, 200; North, VI, 436; South, VI, 345; and see Voyages of Discovery

American Historical Association, see *Papers of*
Americus Polonus, astrologer, V, 179
Amethyst, VI, 419
Amico, Giov. Batt. (1536), V, 489
Amiens, V, 556, VI, 440
Ammon, oracle of, V, 458; and see Jupiter Ammon
Ammonius, comm. Porphyry, V, 167
Amorfortius, Steph. Laur., physician, dedic to, V, 602
Amphiarus, VI, 504
Amphitheater, VI, 316
Amsterdam, pr at (1650 and later), V, 333, 444, 656, VI, 7, 61, 87, 222, 253, 286, 380, 393; professor at, VI, 7
Amulet, V, 176, 455-6, 485, 628, VI, 211, 221, 233, 292-3, 309, 315, 335, 338, 420, 525, 529, 544; astrological, V, 249, 650, VI, 175, 303; disbelieved, V, 478; for travelers, V, 610-11; gold not an, V, 646; natural or superstitious, VI, 536, 601
Anabaptist, VI, 148
Anacardus, an herb, V, 467
Anael, spirit of Venus, V, 569, VI, 441
Anania, Giov. Lorenzo d' (1576), VI, 42; (1581), VI, 527-8; cited, V, 486
Anastomosis, VI, 329-32
Anathema, VI, 520
Anatomia vivorum, V, 46
Anatomy, V, 498-531; discoveries claimed, V, 43-47, 508, 515, 517-8, 525, 530-1, VI, 229-30; of brutes, V, 517; progress in, V, 498, 557, 630, VI, 296, 340, 353, 371; recent criticized, V, 515-6; taught, V, 45, 500, 524, VI, 213, 361; touched on, V, 88, 160, 387; and see Achillini, Andreas de Laguna, Carpi, Colombo, Dryander, Falloppia, Fernel, Galen, Leonardo da Vinci, Massa, Mundinus, Paracelsus, Vesalius, Zerbi
Anaxion, patient of Hippocrates, VI, 215
Anchusa, VI, 280
Ancients, devotion to, and defence of, V, 516, 565; decried, VI, 461; outdistanced, V, 545, 662-3; things known to, lost, V, 454; things unknown to, or unnoticed by, V, 453-4, 460, 540, VI, 27, 280; and see Classical and Classics
Ancona, V, 269; Jews of, VI, 151; pr at, V, 218, VI, 285
Ancusaeum, an herb, VI, 333
Andalusia, V, 468
Andernach, see Guinther of
Andrea, M. D., tr, V, 644
Andreades, Iambonus, astrologer, VI, 135-6
Andreae, Lazarus, pr Cracow, V, 347
Andreas (ancient author cited by Vesalius), V, 523
Andreas de Laguna, anatomist, V, 514, VI, 258
Andreas, pupil of Champier, V, 116
Andreas, Valerius (1643), V, 147-8, 282, 303, 329-30, 648, VI, 38, 45, 72, 101, 268, 311, 394-5, 537-8, 556
Androgyn, see Hermaphrodite
Androicus episcopus, alchemist, V, 623
Andromachus, ancient physician, V, 470
Angel, V, 88, 399; aid, V, 118, in acquiring magic, VI, 132; and demon turn axis of world, VI, 471; ceased to appear, VI, 550; divine revelation by, V, 397; existence, denied, VI, 550, proved experimentally, VI, 455; experiments with and invocation of, VI, 392, 454; external form of sky, VI, 435; faculties, VI, 351; fall, V, 87, VI, 350, 362; guardian, affirmed or denied, V, 105, VI, 157, 481, 499, 508; hierarchies, V, 584, VI, 324, 336, 340, 350, 451, 557; names, VI, 509, 551; relation to stars, signs and elements, VI, 551; reside in virtuous men, VI, 362
Angelino, Pietro, publisher, V, 624
Angelis, Alexander de, VI, 202-4; cited, VI, 172, 569
Angelus, Andr. (1597), V, 375
Angelus, Jacobus, tr, V, 336, 342, VI, 131
Angelus, Johannes, see Engel, Johann
Angers, VI, 531; pr at, VI, 531; studied at, VI, 341; written at, VI, 453
Angina, V, 559, VI, 233
Anglican, V, 653
Anguilera, see Aguilera
Anguillara, Luigi (1561), VI, 258, 333
Anhalt, VI, 506; duke of, VI, 495
Anian, kingdom of, VI, 436
Animal, anatomy, V, 517; classification,

V, 570, VI, 349, under planets, VI, 434; cries of, V, 570; cruelty to, V, 454; divination by, V, 29, 142; domestic, damage to, V, 172, 232, magic to protect, VI, 404; gathered or dispelled, VI, 434; habitat of, V, 570; hieroglyphs of, VI, 447; hybrid, VI, 419; marvelous ways, VI, 310; minute, V, 157; names, VI, 273; occult virtues of, V, 551, VI, 277; parts of, as medicine etc., V, 432, 454, 462, 475, 560, 646, VI, 216, 225, 257, 277, 293, 358, 567; questions about, V, 146; remedies learned from, V, 476, 480, 651, VI, 423, used by, V, 29, VI, 277, 315, 349, 423, 528; sacred, VI, 353; semi-human qualities, V, 20, 98, 141-2, 513, VI, 277, 281, 290; signs from, V, 104, VI, 292-3, 367, 397, 487; soul, V, 517; speak to men, V, 104; study of, V, 29, VI, 353; works on, VI, 166, 255, 257-8; and see Generation

Animism, V, 424, VI, 386; of Paracelsus, V, 628

Animodar, V, 361, VI, 115

Anjou, V, 483, VI, 130

Annalen des historischen Vereins f. den Niederrhein, VI, 559

Annales de géographie, V, 285

Annales du cercle archéologique d'Ath, V, 580

Annales Guébhard-Séverine, VI, 318

Annales internationales d'histoire, VI, 55

Annali della R. Scuola Superiore di Pisa, V, 533, VI, 438

Annals of Medical History, V, 493, VI, 141, 143

Anne of Brittany, V, 159

Anneberg, taught at, VI, 498

Annunciation, V, 257; church of the, V, 512

Anomalies, in Copernican system, V, 424, 427, VI, 5

Anonymous, V, 201, 521, VI, 601

Anselm of Genoa, V, 513

Anselm, bishop of Marsi, VI, 456

Anselmi, Giorgio, V, 118

Anshelmus, Thomas, pr Hagenau, VI, 444

Ant, and moon, V, 464; kept off trees, VI, 282

Anten, disciple of Wier, VI, 517

Anthonius, son of Gondisalvus of Toledo, V, 159

Anthropology, germ of, V, 512

Anthropomancy, VI, 502

Antichrist, VI, 456, 538; predicted, V, 124, 179, 202, 221, 311

Antidotarium Nicolai, V, 460, 464, 503

Antidote, V, 462, 476, 483, VI, 423; and see Mithridatic, Theriac

Antimony, V, 249, 478-9, 620, 628, 638-9, 651, 661, VI, 250, 252; confused with lead, VI, 313; dangerous, V, 664

Antiochus Tibertus, chiromancer, V, 49, 54-55, 65, 521, 531, 673, 675

Antipathy, see Sympathy and

Antipodes, V, 209; action of magnetic needle, V, 271; denied or affirmed, V, 389, VI, 27, 436; influence of stars there, VI, 240

Antiquarian and Antiquities, V, 141-2, VI, 270, 279, 492, 504

Antiscia, astrological, affirmed and rejected, VI, 138, 144

Antonino of Florence, cited, VI, 125, 542-3

Antonio of Cartagena (1530), V, 318-9, 475-6; cited, V, 486-7, VI, 172

Antonio, Nicolás (1672), VI, 96, 166-7

Antonius of Forlimpopoli, V, 59

Antonius, Ioannes, pr Venice, V, 391

Antonius, Manilius, chamberlain, VI, 136

Antonius, Marcus, of Carpi, pr Bologna, V, 245-6

Antonius a Mariis, pr Coimbra, VI, 35

Antonius de Magistris Galathei, see Petrus Antonius

Antonius de Monte Ulmi, V, 258, 362-3

Antwerp, V, 127-8, 148, 189, 320, 430, VI, 45, 74, 268, 285, 291, 559; born at, V, 303, VI, 235; route from, V, 585; pr at, V, 129, 206-7, 210, 226, 286, 328-9, 444, 462, 466, 469-70, 477, VI, 9, 13, 19, 31-32, 47, 102, 127, 135, 193, 208, 221, 273, 275, 310, 393-5, 397, 406, 409, 418, 449, 469, 494, 559

Anzinas, see Encinas

Aomar, cited, V, 267, VI, 180

Ape, anatomy of, V, 517-8

Apennines, V, 21

Aphrodisias, see Alexander of

Apianus, Petrus, V, 246, 349, 352-3, 364, 372, 410, 421, 623, VI, 21, 131, 382

Apianus, Philippus, V, 246
Apiarius, Matth., pr Berne, VI, 448
Apium, an herb, VI, 265
Apocalypsis spiritus secreti, V, 624
Apollo, V, 431; Pythian, VI, 504
Apollonian magic, VI, 457
Apollonius of Perga, V, 364
Apollonius of Tyana, VI, 304; dead raised by, V, 272-3; magic of, VI, 457, 467
Apoplexy, V, 46, 87, 250, 455, 459, 488, 651, VI, 311, 596
Apostema, V, 367
Apostles, V, 399; and see names of individuals
Apostolic age, VI, 117
Apostolic Canons, V, 390
Apothecary, see Pharmacy
Appetite, V, 151, VI, 221
Apple, sniffed at, VI, 281; to prevent decay of, V, 145-6; wormy, V, 145
Apuleius, as alchemist, V, 624; cited, V, 82, 119, VI, 404; *Golden Ass,* VI, 337; *Herbarium,* V, 437, 610, 614, VI, 280
Apulia, V, 24, 239, VI, 444, 491, 572
Aqua ardens, VI, 166
Aqua fortis, VI, 224
Aqua permanens, VI, 244
Aqua vitae, V, 542, 639, VI, 393
Aquapendente, Hier. Fabr. ab, V, 44, 498
Aqueduct, V, 361, 591
Aquila, V, 104, 106, 644
Aquileia, V, 269
Aquinas, Thomas, authority of, V, 97; cited, V, 92, 96, 219, 270, 475, 507, VI, 48, 229, 361, 378, 399, 411, 413, 433, 446, 543, as an alchemist, V, 541, 623, VI, 244, denied, VI, 244, 411, against astrology, VI, 170, for astrology, V, 159, 166, 209, 213, 215, 221, 246, 248, 277, 661, VI, 125, 139, 172-4, 176, for astrological images, V, 561; comm. V, 504; death of, VI, 542; followed, V, 75, VI, 398, 418; ignored, V, 175, VI, 412, 470; levitation of, VI, 451; opposed, V, 40, 42, 523, 554, VI, 369; works, *Contra Gentiles,* V, 134, VI, 173, *Esse et essentia,* VI, 431, *Fato,* V, 134, 561, VI, 174, 304, *Occultis operibus,* V, 106, *Sententiis,* V, 200, *Sortibus,* VI, 485
Aquino, V, 258
Aquitaine, V, 546
Arab, V, 135, 470; conquest, VI, 187; philosophy, VI, 601
Arabia, VI, 286; king of, V, 623
Arabian Gulf, VI, 345
Arabic, V, 75, 468; alchemy, V, 604, 623; astrology, V, 120, 175, 206, 221, 233, 260-1, 266, 269, 278, 361, 395, VI, 89, 113, 133, 180, 199, 458, opposed, V, 180, 184-5, 191, 227, 250, VI, 23, 42, 99, 118-9, 141, 165, 172-3, 194, 379, publication of, ceases, VI, 99; astronomy, VI, 11, 97; authors, cited, V, 54, 91, 206-7, 247, 374, 421, 455, 473, 485, 513, 608, 623, 647, VI, 48, 161, 180, 215, 309, 315, 335, 364, 399, 467, 487, misdated, V, 115, 387, not cited, VI, 318, opposed, V, 3, 532, VI, 468, printed, V, 4; barbarism, V, 298, 347; dispute with Greeks, VI, 365-6; language ignored, V, 356; magic, false, VI, 302; medicine, collated, V, 529, defended, V, 436-7, 446, 467, 516, VI, 251, opposed, V, 114, 122-3, 317, 430, 454, 523, VI, 211, 213, 315; pharmacy, criticized, V, 448, 466; simple, name of, V, 447, VI, 332, new from, V, 449, 453-4, 459-60; studied and taught, VI, 61, 520; tr from, V, 450, VI, 449; word used, VI, 479
Arabist, VI, 227; criticized, V, 465
Aragon, V, 14, 92, 284, VI, 42, 240; and see Ferdinand of
Aranicus, see Jacob Aranicus
Aratus, VI, 486
Arbatel, VI, 457
Arcana, V, 639, 645, 650, 659, VI, 216
Arcandam, V, 291; put on Index, VI, 148
Archaeology, V, 143
Archangelo de Burgo Nuovo, VI, 430, 462
Archbishop, V, 66, 129, 175, 226, 288, 376, 390, 399, 509, 582-3, 623, 666, VI, 123, 166, 170, 235, 316, 335, 522, 527, 542
Archdeacon, VI, 218
Archduke, V, 137, 631, VI, 225, 230, 491, 505; and see Austria
Archeion, V, 344
Archimedes, and Copernicus, V, 429, VI, 21; crane of, V, 594; editio princeps,

V, 369, 421
Architecture, VI, 430
Archiv d. Math. und Physik, V, 410, 426
Archiv f. die Geschichte d. Naturwiss., V, 464
Archiv f. Geschichte d. Medizin, V, 536
Archiv f. Gesch. d. Philosophie, V, 94
Archiv f. hessisch. Geschichte, V, 319
Archiv f. Kulturgeschichte, V, 130
Archiv f. österreichische Geschichte, V, 221
Archivalische Zeitschrift, V, 549, VI, 245
Archives des Missions, VI, 89
Archivio di storia della scienza, V, 466, VI, 27
Archivio storico lombardo, V, 161
Archivio storico per le province Napoletane, V, 258
Arcolani, Giovanni, V, 46, VI, 402
Arctic and Antarctic, VI, 10, 436
Ardoino, see Sante Ardoino
Areod, Pierre, physician, V, 125
Aretaeus, VI, 110
Aretino, Paolo, V, 230; and see Pietro Aretino
Arezzo, see Pietro Aretino, Ristoro d'Arezzo
Arfoncinus, Thomas, jurist, V, 535
Argellati, Filippo (1745), V, 161, 547, VI, 311, 368
Argenterius, Bartholomaeus (?), VI, 226
Argenterius, Ioannes (1556), VI, 212, 226-8, 518
Argentinus, Richard (1568), V, 134, VI, 520
Argonautic expedition, VI, 246, 456
Argüello, S. (1935), V, 32
Argyropulos, tr, V, 74
Ariano, V, 81
Aries, the sign, V, 177, VI, 344
Ariolus, V, 297
Ariosto, VI, 278
Aristarchus of Samos, VI, 11, 21, 32, 35, 47-48, 50, 56, 155
Aristocracy, V, 224
Aristodemus, V, 478
Aristolochia or Aristologia, an herb, VI, 261, 546
Aristotle, attitude towards, VI, 363-89, of Alexander Achillini, V, 41-42, Amerbach, V, 394, Basso, VI, 386-8, Benedetti, VI, 372, Cardan, V, 564-5, 569-70, Cesalpino, VI, 325-6, 334, Chassin, VI, 382-5, Cureus, VI, 364-6, Gassendi, VI, 389, Gilbert, VI, 380, Landi, VI, 363-4, Maffei, V, 141, Paris, VI, 337, Patrizi, VI, 373, 376-7, Piccolomini, VI, 379, Pomponazzi, V, 104, Ramus, VI, 363, Sanchez, VI, 565, Suiseth, V, 95-96, Telesio, VI, 370-1, Vimercati, VI, 368, Zabarella, VI, 369; cited, V, 167, 215, 272, 473, 647, 661, VI, 228, 280, 288, 300, 312, 326, 329-30, 350, 396, 399, 402, 546, not, VI, 319; criticized, V, 205, 254, 407, 439, 530, 582, 585, 643, VI, 137, 340, 344, 354, 363, 423, 432-3, 461, 496, 565; defended, V, 643, VI, 95, 238, 446, 484, 514; followed, V, 142, 151, 153, 157, 494-5, 514, 521, 551-2, 557, 643, VI, 32, 49, 186, 226-8, 271, 377, 406, 418, 429, 484, 570, slavishly, VI, 460; opposed, V, 204, 421, 551, 555, 642, VI, 65, 205, 227, 370-4, for exercise, VI, 63; resembled, V, 36; return to, urged, V, 281; tr of, V, 502; venerated, VI, 382
Aristotle, opinions, alchemy, V, 545, 547, 643; astrology, V, 42, 120, 290, VI, 139, 199; astronomy, V, 489, VI, 47-48, 376, 413, and see Heavens, Milky Way; Bible, Christianity and theology, V, 91, 545, VI, 343, 520-1; causes, four, of, VI, 415, 564; comets, theory of, see Comet; demons, V, 82, 88, 100-1, 104, 109, 118, 568, VI, 131-2, 336, 386, 484, 518-9; divination, VI, 482, 484-5, 512, 543; earth and water, V, 24; First Cause, V, 104; form and matter, VI, 368; Galen, disagreement with, V, 46-47, 503, 508, 515, VI, 365, 514; geological change, V, 25; heavy and light, VI, 83, 198, 369, and see Natural Place; logic, V, 336, VI, 363; metals, V, 545, VI, 317; motion, moved and mover, VI, 365, 369, arguments against earth's moving, VI, 16, and see Intelligences, moving; occult virtue, VI, 199; physics, V, 9, VI, 320; Pliny, V, 388; relation to previous thinkers, VI, 373, 386, 460; silence of, VI, 281, 283; soul and immortality, V, 94, 96-99, 105, 660, VI, 125, 198, 343, 386
Aristotle, works of, lost, V, 545, dubious, VI, 197, epitomized, V, 151, 153, VI,

32, old translation bad, V, 502, *Anima,* V, 153, VI, 433, *Cyromantia,* V, 673-4, *Coelo et mundo,* V, 153, 614, *Coloribus,* V, 555, *Epistola ad Alexandrum,* V, 48, *Generatione et corruptione,* V, 153, *History of animals,* V, 105, 511, 551, VI, 164, 225, 256-7, 277, 360, 365, *Longitudine et brevitate,* VI, 478, *Mechanica,* V, 343, VI, 142, *Metaphysics,* V, 49, VI, 378, *Meteorology,* V, 26, 31, 48, 97, 153, 248, 644, VI, 80, 366, *Mineralibus,* V, 624, *Parva naturalia,* V, 73, 325, *Physico auditu,* V, 153, 586, VI, 354, 372, 410, *Physiognomia,* V, 53, 57, 63-64, 67, *Problems,* V, 103, VI, 227, *Rhetoric,* V, 49, *Secreta secretorum,* V, 48, 246, 284, VI, 420, *Sensu et sensato,* V, 555, VI, 482, *Signis,* V, 48, 284, *Somno et vigilia,* VI, 478, 481, 485, *Theologia,* VI, 449-50

Aristotle, commentators on, Greek, V, 75, 95, 144, VI, 378, 478, medieval, V, 25, 14th century, V, 156, 16th century, V, 163, VI, 8, 202, 326, 334, 341, 356, 364, 369-70, 377, 382, 387, 487, 492, 599-600, *Anima,* V, 72, 74, 90, 100, 273, 402, VI, 368, 511, *Animalibus,* V, 254, *Coelo et mundo,* V, 73-74, 96, 158, *Elenchi,* V, 75, *Genealogy of the gods,* V, 88, *Generatione et corruptione,* V, 81, 545, 547, logic, V, 48-49, *Metaphysics,* V, 72, *Meteorology,* V, 100, 156, 183, VI, 300, 368, *Mundo,* V, 379, *Parva naturalia,* V, 73, 100, 325, *Physics,* V, 41, 48-49, 72, 75, 100, 158, 199-200, 273, 345, VI, 341, 368, *Physiognomy,* V, 54, 73, VI, 553-4, 566, *Poetics,* V, 75, *Prior Analytics,* V, 75, *Problems,* V, 62, 379, 551.

Arithmetic, V, 168, 564, VI, 77, 94, 442, 596, 598; and medicine, V, 431, VI, 142; problems, VI, 372; speculative and practical, VI, 429; taught, V, 246, 402, by playing cards; V, 278; works on, V, 152, 174, 255, 392, VI, 82, 119, 124, 137, 143, 166, 344, 494

Ark, see Noah

Arlensis, see Scudalupis

Arles, V, 71, VI, 169

Arlunus, Bernardinus, V, 161

Arlunus, Hieronymus, astrologer, V, 160-2

Arlunus, Jacobus, V, 161

Arlunus, Joannes Petreius, V, 161

Arlunus, Joannes Petrus, V, 542

Armagnac, VI, 247

Armenia, V, 458, VI, 460

Armentières, V, 329

Armeus, cited, V, 188

Arms, clashing, against demons, VI, 405

Army, see War

Arnald of Villanova, cited, V, 323, 463, VI, 280, 300, 311, not, VI, 318; cited as an alchemist, V, 141, 541-3, 547, 619, 624-5, 637, 679-80, VI, 242, 244; compiled from, V, 621; criticized, V, 120, 124, VI, 218; defended, VI, 246; life of, V, 114-5, 125-6; on dreams, VI, 512; on medicine, V, 323; on wines, V, 432; works pr, V, 443, 532-3, 602-3

Arno, river, V, 28

Aroma, see Odor, Spice

Aron, an herb, VI, 273-4

Arquato, Antonio, V, 179, VI, 75

Arras, VI, 326, 395

Arrigonius, Horatius, dedic to, V, 274, VI, 181-2

Arrivabeni, Andrea, publisher, Venice, V, 558

Arrivabenis, Georgius de, pr Venice, VI, 298

Arrivabenus, alchemist, VI, 519

Arrow withdrawn from wound apparently by magic, V, 101-3

Ars Bulaphiae, VI, 516

Ars chemica (1566), V, 622

Arsenic, V, 458, 465, 480; called eagle, VI, 279

Arsoncinus, see Arfoncinus

Art, pagan revival of, V, 37; effect on occult virtue, V, 662

Art ancien, l', V, 178, 181, 188, 197, 206, 208, 210, 225, 228, 283, 314, VI, 433, 469

Arteaga, E. E. (1917), VI, 165-6

Artefius, see Artephius

Artemidorus, *Oneirocritica,* VI, 177, 293, 475-6, 483, 485, criticized, VI, 509-10

Artemisia, an herb, V, 610, VI, 261-2, 546

Artephius, V, 574, 637, VI, 467, 516
Artery, V, 562, VI, 329-32, 381
Arthritis, VI, 223
Artillery, V, 34, 544; Cardan on, V, 567; invention of, justified, V, 585; master of, V, 171, 472; trajectory of, VI, 137
Artis auriferae, see *Auriferae artis*
Artisan, cure by, V, 465; knowledge of, V, 596-7; training of, V, 338
Artist, criticized, V, 587; interest of, V, 25; materials of, V, 34; nativities of, VI, 100; pictures of, VI, 297; training of, V, 17
Arts, fine, once more exact than physics and chemistry, V, 13
Arts, liberal, V, 114, 139, 141, 165, 206, VI, 40, 217, 382, 531; and astrology, V, 379; bachelor of, V, 397, 402, 488; doctor, master and professor of, V, 201, 288, 345, 402, VI, 124, 165, 520, 597, for doctor of arts and medicine see Medicine; essential for the physician, V, 431; present state deplored, V, 394; revived, VI, 441; should include elementary spherics, VI, 35
Arts, illicit, VI, 156
Arts, useful, V, 543, 589, VI, 419; and astrology, V, 165; and see Mechanic, Technology
Artù, Claudio, V, 258
Aruspex, Aruspicium and Aruspicina, VI, 176, 496, 503; condemned, V, 297, VI, 193, 430, 543
Arzachel, V, 300, 359, 421
Ascalon, see Eutocius of
Ascanio, cardinal, addressed to, V, 167
Ascendent, V, 66, 308, 319, 345, 367, VI, 104, 115
Aschbach, J. (1865-88), V, 407
Asclepius, V, 113, 116
Asclepiades, V, 642
Ascoli, see Cecco d'
Ash tree, VI, 262; antipathy to serpents, VI, 186, 289, 416
Ashes, as remedies, VI, 546; divination by, VI, 503; reduction to, VI, 243, 461
Ashmole, Elias, VI, 392-3
Ashwin, E. Allen (1929), VI, 552
Asia, VI, 392; visited, V, 581, VI, 154; southern, VI, 187
Asia Minor, V, 27
Asola, see A. Bladus of
Asp, V, 474, 480; stone from head of, VI, 461
Aspalathus, V, 453, VI, 272
Asphalt, V, 449
Ass, lotion of, V, 614; turned into, or made to resemble, VI, 337; use in medicine, of bones, V, 432, marrow, VI, 216
Assisi, see St. Francis of
Assyria and Assyrian, V, 135, VI, 352-3, 379
Asthma, V, 559, VI, 230, 501
Astorgius of Faenza, V, 50
Astrolabe, VI, 471; used, V, 259, 309, VI, 342, to detect thieves, V, 384; works on, V, 330, 343, 365, 371, 434, VI, 13
Astrolabium planum, V, 61, 345; and see Engel, Johann
Astrologer, called impostor, VI, 162; cited rather than astronomer, VI, 569; consulted, VI, 201; court and royal, V, 24, 168, 381, 401, 406, VI, 202; disagreement among, V, 140, 190, 210-2, 233, VI, 108, 113-4, 170, 177, 184, 204, 212, and see Controversy; death, predicted or not, see Death; demons aid, V, 92-93, VI, 200, 204, 542; errors of, V, 120, 191, VI, 394; expelled, VI, 149, 204; German, V, 655; good, defense of, VI, 131; inference from parodies of and satires on, V, 312; Jewish, VI, 301; municipal, V, 177, VI, 133; praised, V, 93, VI, 569; prediction true, V, 80, 226, VI, 101, 509, incorrect, VI, 70, 212, 349; some at fault, V, 198, 227, 279, 294, 298, 321-2, 433, 572, VI, 112, 144, 180; some more scientific than their opponents, VI, 185, 187; stories of, V, 294, 313, 402, VI, 114, 121-3, 130, 509; works against, refuted, VI, 431
Astrological medicine, VI, 219, 596; at Antwerp, V, 127, 189; attacked, V, 116, 119, 121, 329, VI, 189, 196-7, 200, 232, 412; believed in, defended or urged, V, 172-4, 176, 250, 322, 329, 384, 386, 400, 572, VI, 76, 126, 136, 140-1, 144, 159, 198, 390, 408, 479, 500; of Cardan, V, 572, Chriso-

gonus, V, 314-5, Croll, V, 649, Essler, V, 172-3, Fries, V, 433-5, Geuss, VI, 126, Grammateus, V, 174, Indagine, V, 176, Lemnius, VI, 393-4, Magini, V, 250, VI, 164-5, Monantheuil, VI, 142, Schröter, V, 224, 328, Schylander, VI, 127, Siderocrates, VI, 123, Tannstetter, V, 316-7; permitted, VI, 157, 549-50; "scientific," V, 315; works of, V, 73, 79-80, 160-3, 224, 250, 296, 300-3, 308, 323-6, 328, 356, 433, 443, VI, 106, 127-9, 158, 298, 448, 473

Astrology, antiquity, VI, 353, approved, V, 521, 547, VI, 527; attitude towards, of, Adam ab Invidia, VI, 181, Agrippa, V, 128, 131-2, Alsted, VI, 435, Angelis, VI, 202-4, Benedetti, VI, 137-9, Binsfeld, VI, 541-2, Bodin, VI, 118, 527, Brunfels, V, 318, Casmann, VI, 197-8, Champier, V, 119-21, 124-5, Cocles, V, 58, Daneau, VI, 349, Dariot, VI, 105-6, Dasypodius, VI, 88-90, Dee, VI, 18, Dorn, V, 633-4, Dryander, V, 521, Engel, V, 345-6, Erastus, V, 652-6, Feild, VI, 18, Fernel, V, 557-8, Finck, VI, 140, Fontaine, VI, 188-90, Fracastoro, V, 489, 491, Freige, VI, 186-7, Frischlin, VI, 191-2, Fulke, VI, 180, Garcaeus, VI, 102-4, Gaurico, V, 165-9, Gemma, C., VI, 30-31, Gemma, F., V, 319, George of Ragusa, VI, 198-201, Giannini, VI, 205-6, Giuntini, VI, 43, 129-33, Harvey, John, V, 374, Hebenstreit, VI, 106, Hemminga, VI, 193-6, Indagine, V, 175-6, Index, VI, 147, Inquisition, VI, 149, James I, VI, 549-50, Leonardo da Vinci, V, 28, Leowitz, VI, 111-2, 115-8, Maestlin, VI, 81, Maffei, VI, 399, *Margarita philosophica,* V, 140, 164, Maurolycus, VI, 179-80, Mercator, VI, 179, Mercurio, VI, 198, Meurer, VI, 50, Milich, V, 386-7, 389, Nabod, VI, 119-23, Nifo, V, 79-80, Nunes, V, 293, Offusius, VI, 108-11, Paduanius, VI, 124, Palissy, V, 599, Peletier, VI, 33, Pererius, VI, 412-3, Peucer, VI, 499-500, Philalthaeus, VI, 180, Philologus, V, 204-6, Piccolomini, VI, 180, Porta, VI, 162-3, Praetorius, VI, 60, Ranzovius, VI, 135-7, Robyns, V, 320-1, Rocha, V, 92-93, Ronsard, VI, 106, Russilianus, V, 78, Santbech, VI, 30, Satler, VI, 143-4, Scevolini, VI, 124-6, Scribonius, VI, 354-5, Sordi, VI, 94, Squarcialupus, VI, 184, Stabius, V, 347, Stadius, VI, 15, 29, Taisnier, V, 587-8, Turrel, V, 307-12, Tyard, VI, 107-8, Vallesius, VI, 359, Vanini, VI, 569-72, Vesalius, V, 527, Vespucci, V, 164-5, Winckler, VI, 134-5, Wolf, VI, 112-5, Zabarella, VI, 369-70; Catholic, VI, 568; Chaldean, VI, 113, 174, 427, condemned, VI, 172, 521; criticized, V, 293, 400, 652-6, VI, 240, 412, 445, from within, V, 172, VI, 23, and see Church fathers, Pico, Savonarola; decline, V, 298, VI, 87, 114; defended, V, 175, 212, 235, 238-9, 243, 264, 298-9, 311-2, 322-3, 386, 393-4, 396, 398-400, 402-3, 572, VI, 33, 104, 124-6, 134, 172, 222; defined, V, 165; diabolical, VI, 525, and see Demon; difficulty of, VI, 144; divisions of, VI, 113-4, 430; experimental, VI, 99-101, 193, and see Experience, Experiment; extreme, attacked, V, 296, 553, VI, 170-1, 520; false and useless, VI, 525; fatal to kings, VI, 202, 204; history, V, 165, 403, VI, 353; illicit, V, 198-9, 312, VI, 359, 550; introduction to, V, 251, 582-3; inventors of, V, 165, 218; licit, V, 198-9, 312, 384, 403; magic and, V, 92, 655, 660, VI, 144, 190, 550; natural, V, 175-6, 399, 655, VI, 61, 99, 115, 140, 156, 160-1, 171-3, 186, 521, 529; no mere youthful folly, V, 240, 558; now almost perfect, V, 315; oration praising, V, 164-6, 204, 218, 265-6; other occult arts and, V, 61, 65-66, 67-68, 296-7, 587, VI, 16, 176, 496; popular, VI, 99-100; practiced, by Servetus, V, 289-90, Stadius, V, 303, Turrel, V, 312; reform of, V, 281, 416; religion and, V, 131, 165, 403, VI, 114, 192-3, 198, 412, 523, and see Religion, Theology; rules and technique of, criticized, V, 227, 262, 298, VI, 88, 138, 180, 199-200, 412, upheld, VI, 158-60; scepticism as to, V, 38; science and, VI, 176; superstitious, VI, 415; true and false, V, 283, VI, 143-4, 529; uncertain, VI, 114,

179; universities and, V, 204-5, 341, 385-6, and see Bologna, Paris, Salamanca; works of, V, 262-3, 320, 407, VI, 454, 510; and see Arabic, Comet, Eclipse, Election, Image, Interrogation, Nativities, Prediction, Ptolemaic, Stars, influence of
Astronomy, V, 21-22, 142, VI, 190-1, 326, 430, 504-5; Antwerp, at, VI, 74; attacked, VI, 374-7; delighted in, V, 293; dignity of, V, 9; discovery in, claimed, V, 205; history, VI, 62, 353; how studied, V, 154-5; neglected, VI, 40; Nürnberg, at, V, 350; prerequisite, V, 58, 152, 431; progress in, VI, 20-21, hoped for, V, 411-2, 416, VI, 77, 82, predicted, VI, 173, 465; relation to astrology, V, 175, 250-1, 377, VI, 85, 138, replaces it, VI, 71, 77, 180, 186; renaissance or restoration of, V, 3, VI, 37; support for, VI, 17; taught, V, 204-5, 222, 314, 371, VI, 28, 126, 289; terminology, V, 161, 208; varieties, V, 627; Vienna, at, V, 349; works, V, 152, 319-20, 347, 521, VI, 143, 344, 377, 494; and see Comet, Copernican, Eclipse, Instrument, Observation, Peurbach, Planet, Regiomontanus, Sphere, Star, Table
Astrucius (1748), VI, 331
Asula, see Asola
Athanasia, an herb, VI, 261-2, 264
Atheism and Atheist, V, 35, 37, VI, 302, 511, 523, 568-72
Athenaeus, VI, 280
Athens, V, 295, 579, VI, 363
Atlas, VI, 3, 471
Atmosphere, see Air, height of
Atomism, V, 552, VI, 388, 391
Atrabile, see Melancholy
Atractylis, an herb, VI, 272
Attendorn, VI, 498
Atti d. Reale Accademia, Napoli, V, 51
Atti del R. Istituto Veneto, V, 494
Atti e Memorie della R. Deputazione di Storia Patria per le Provincie di Romagna, V, 231
Atti e Memorie della Società Istriana, VI, 373, 375
Attraction, V, 551; and see Sympathy
Aubel, Thomas, tr, VI, 211
Aubert, Jacques, VI, 247
Aubrius, Joannes, pr Frankfurt, VI, 494
Aucha, an herb, VI, 261-2
Aucheta, an herb, VI, 261-2
Auditorium, public, VI, 41
Augenius, Horatius, VI, 211-2
Augsburg, V, 160, 204, 217, 342, 383, 484, 640, 658, VI, 142, 457, 490; annals of, V, 391; born at, VI, 121, 492; library at, VI, 112; magistrates of, VI, 143, 469; meridian of, VI, 111; patrician of, V, 524, VI, 105; pr at, V, 34, 187, 226, 346-7, 440, 536, 596, 642, VI, 111, 134, 143, 230, 232, 301, 446
Augurellus, Joh. Aurelius, V, 534-5, 604
Augury, V, 58, 573, VI, 278, 361, 468, 496, 520; forbidden, V, 399, VI, 180, 292, 483, 523; history of, VI, 353; justified, V, 104-5, 511, VI, 536; natural distinguished, VI, 543; Nifo on, VI, 484-6; opposed, VI, 222; Paracelsus on, V, 627, 660; put on Index, VI, 147; superstitious, VI, 135, 430, 467, 491
Augustine, St. of Hippo, cited, V, 92, 140, 295, VI, 172, 232, 280, 399, 404-5, 481; criticized, V, 576; followed, V, 153; used, V, 142, VI, 204
Augustinian Order, V, 148, 302, 544, VI, 371
Augustinus, disciple of Cocles, V, 53
Augustulus, Romulus, VI, 465
Augustus, as title, V, 183, 188
Augustus Caesar, VI, 75, 465
Augustus, duke of Saxony, dedic to, V, 619, VI, 11
Augustus, elector of Saxony, VI, 105
Auratus, see Dorat
Auray, V, 391
Auria, Joseph, V, 364
Auricalchum, a mineral, V, 481
Auricula leporis, an herb, VI, 261
Auriculus leporis, VI, 264
Aurifaber, Andreas, tr, V, 327, 482, VI, 598
Auriferae artis . . ., V, 625
Aurigea duplex, an herb, VI, 261-2, 264
Auripigmentum, V, 458
Auruspicia, VI, 468; and see Aruspicia
Ausonius, V, 477, VI, 255
Auspices, VI, 278, 503; illicit, VI, 180, 292, 483, 523; put on Index, VI, 147;

superstitious, VI, 430, 467, 491
Austrasia, Chronicles of, V, 115
Austria, V, 331, 348, 644, VI, 16, 157; archduke of, V, 631, VI, 192, 230
Authorities, anatomical, V, 500-1, 514; attacked, V, 626; cited, V, 89, 310, VI, 197, 237, indiscriminately, VI, 276, 279-81, wide range of, VI, 361; classical, V, 564-5, VI, 361; compilation from, V, 53, 56, 174, 206, 368, 480, 551, VI, 88, 217, 232-3, 276, 303, 398-9, 404, 431, 486, 504, 506, 567; disagreement of, V, 46; errors in, see Error; experience and, V, 367, 460; Gentile impugned by sacred, V, 631; listed, VI, 130, 318, and see Bibliography; medical, V, 140; medieval, VI, 271, 276, 399, respect for, V, 247, 305; modern, VI, 399, and see Modern; not given, V, 19-21, 56; not slavishly followed, V, 295
Autolycus, VI, 27, 88
Automata, V, 360, VI, 434
Autun, V, 307
Auvergne, V, 598; and see Peter of, William of
Avalanche, V, 592
Avantius, Ludov., pr Venice, V, 549, VI, 208
Avempace, cited, VI, 399
Aventinus, V, 331
Averchinus, Benedictus, V, 10
Averroes, V, 25, 387, VI, 569; alchemy, V, 141, 604, 643, VI, 411; astrology, V, 646, VI, 188; cited, V, 41-42, 46, 102, 167, 215, 236, 270, 317, 460, 480, 502, 554, 647, 662, VI, 48, 229, 350, 364, 369, 399, 484, 487; comm. V, 48-49, 80, 144, VI, 370, 600; criticized, V, 75, 123, 144, 204-5, 284, 317, 452, 467; demons, V, 82, 88, VI, 405, 518, 531; Galen, and, V, 500; heavens, VI, 19, 62; misstatements concerning, V, 115, 121, VI, 405; works, *Beatitudine animae,* V, 48, *Colliget,* V, 503, 647, *Destructio destructionis,* V, 72, *Mixtione,* V, 80, *Substantia orbis,* V, 49, 72, 80
Averroism and Averroist, V, 37, 42, 71-72, 91, 94, 163, VI, 366; and see Intellect, unity of
Avicebron, cited, VI, 48
Avicenna, V, 115, 468; alchemy, V, 538, 547, 604, 623, 625, 680, VI, 244, 411; biography, V, 387; cited, V, 46-47, 54, 167, 449, 453, 456, 473, 480, 504, 512-3, 516, 518, 541, 554, 646, 662, VI, 48, 210, 217, 252, 280, 289, 299, 309, 350, 364, 399, 403, 420, 512; comm. V, 485, 507, VI, 211; criticized, V, 314, 430, 439, 465, 467, 515, 640, VI, 213, 231, 235, 313, 401-2, 536; defended, V, 435-6, 452; dreams, theory of, rejected, VI, 482, 484; Galen, and, V, 500, 523; power of soul or of imagination, V, 90-91, 100-1, 235, 561, 639, VI, 236, 336, 358-9, 416, 481; stars, generative power of, V, 157, 247, VI, 291; works, *Animal.,* V, 503, *Canon,* V, 438, 502-4, *Congelatione,* V, 26, 41, 48, 537, *Sextus naturalium,* V, 91, VI, 236, 481, spurious, V, 604
Avignon, V, 156, 269, VI, 553; Agrippa at, V, 127; pr at, VI, 553; university of, V, 391, VI, 219
Avogaro, Augustino, astrologer, V, 169, 220
Avogaro, Caesar, V, 169
Avogaro, Pietro Buono, astrologer, V, 169, 239
Axiomancy, VI, 503
Azalus, Pompilius, V, 4, 588
Azophi, astrologer, 1062 A.D., VI, 130
Azores, VI, 275
Azoth, VI, 243-4
Azov, sea of, V, 23, 27
Azzolino, Decio, cardinal, V, 484

Babel, tower of, VI, 408
Babylonian sibyl, VI, 75
Bacchus, V, 144
Bacci, Andrea, V, 484-5, VI, 315-6; cited V, 646, VI, 258, 319; quoted, V, 472
Baccolidianius, Gerardus, see Bucoldianus
Bachot, Gaspard, VI, 221-2
Backnang, VI, 76, 78, 80
Bacon, Francis, emphasis on spirits in human body, VI, 226, 371; probable debt to others, V, 627-8, VI, 421-2, 565
Bacon, Roger, V, 14, 19, 22, 24, 33, 291,

VI, 26; as alchemist, V, 541, 604, 637, 693, VI, 250; cited, V, 227, VI, 431; criticized, VI, 244-5, 467; defended, VI, 246; *Epistola de secretis operibus,* V, 291; on perspective, V, 140; Paracelsus and, V, 637; *Speculum alchemiae,* V, 537
Bactria, VI, 460
Baden, margrave of, V, 631, VI, 123
Baduarius, Sebastian, V, 75, 78
Baduel, Claude, VI, 340
Bagnoli, V, 220, 335, 541
Baifius, I. Ant., tr, VI, 460
Bairo, Pietro (1561), VI, 217-8
Balani, shellfish, VI, 289
Baldini, Baccio, physician, VI, 128-9, 493
Baldinus, Joh. Jac., V, 10
Baldinus, Victor, pr Ferrara, V, 44, VI, 375
Baldness, V, 146, VI, 402
Balduinis, Balduinus de, dedic to, V, 446
Baldus, John, physician, V, 507
Baldwin of Ninove, *Chronicon,* V, 509
Balneum Mariae, V, 590
Balsac, François de, dedic to, V, 589
Balsam, V, 590, 639, 659, VI, 217
Balsamella or Balsamillo, an herb, VI, 265
Balsarin, Guillermus, pr Lyons, V, 116
Baltic, fish in, VI, 255; wind in, VI, 489
Baluzius, Stephanus, V, 312
Bamberg, V, 171, 362, VI, 45; pest at, V, 354; pr at, V, 355
Bandaroy, geomancer, VI, 472
Baptism, of Agnus Dei, VI, 168, Aristotle, V, 42, bell, V, 135, VI, 498, 541, Christ, V, 257, hermaphrodite, VI, 600, monstrous birth, V, 509-10, unborn child, V, 509; why water used in, V, 213
Baptistery, VI, 404
Barba, Pompeo della, put on Index, VI, 148
Barbara, a child impostor, VI, 516
Barbarism, V, 557-8, VI, 456; medieval, V, 3, VI, 83; fifteenth century, V, 464; sixteenth century, V, 49, 436; and see Arabic
Barbaro, Ermolao, V, 164, 443, 538; cited, V, 122, 457, 637, VI, 246, 279, 282, 285, 333, 402; nativity, VI, 105, 596
Barbarossa, Frederick, emperor, VI, 117
Barber, ignorant, V, 51, 111, 222, 522; and practice of medicine, V, 459, 465, VI, 220; shop, V, 380
Barberini manuscripts, VI, 149
Barbi, Andrea de, bishop of Lübeck, VI, 136
Barcelona, pr at, VI, 96, 166; Tables of, V, 344
Bardinet, L. (1880), VI, 220
Bari, VI, 63
Barilatto, Giovanni, pr Venice, VI, 218
Barnacle geese, see Goose
Barocius, Petrus, bishop of Padua, V, 78
Barotius, Petrus, V, 122
Barozzi, Francesco, VI, 199; and Inquisition, VI, 154-5; *Cosmographia,* VI, 25, 47, 155
Barozzi, Jacopo, VI, 154
Barricat, E. pr Lyons, V, 607
Barros, João de, V, 470
Bartholinus, Albertus (1666), VI, 124, 524
Bartholinus, Thomas (1670), VI, 521
Bartholomaeus Anglicus, see Bartholomew of England
Bartholomaeus de Ripa Romea, cited, VI, 300
Bartholomaeus de Spina, V, 71
Bartholomew of England, V, 148, VI, 280, 300, 318, 361
Bartholomew of Messina, translator, V, 48, 284
Bartholomew of Parma, V, 54, 131
Bartholomew of Pisa, V, 106
Bartholomew of Usingen, V, 148
Bartholoti, J. J. (1498), V, 115
Bartolini, Gioanni, astrologer 17c, VI, 171
Bartolist, V, 503
Bartolommeo della Rocca, see Cocles
Basel, V, 66, 269, 484, 600, VI, 341; astrologers of, V, 177; patients at, V, 438; pr at, V, 99, 100, 121, 134, 136, 139, 152-3, 165, 169, 172-3, 185, 229, 246, 252, 265, 314, 331, 341, 343, 357, 364, 369-70, 373, 391-2, 398, 400, 402, 409, 412, 418, 434, 444, 446, 448, 454, 456, 472, 514, 518, 529, 535, 542,

545, 547, 597, 602-3, 605-10, 619, 622, 624-5, 627-8, 636, 640, 644, 654, 656, 664, 666, VI, 11, 16, 29-30, 35, 37, 45, 61, 104, 114, 143, 183, 186, 216, 255-6, 268, 275, 351, 372-3, 400, 403, 439, 444, 447-8, 455, 457, 462, 467, 476, 478, 485, 489, 492, 502, 515, 518, 520; university of, dean of, V, 609, Paracelsus at, V, 438-9, 665, professor of, V, 331, 431, 652, VI, 140, 143, 267, 492, 503, studied at, V, 652, VI, 16, 247; written at, VI, 161, 352

Basil, St., V, 295, 399, 480, VI, 346, 429, 500

Basilica, an herb, V, 482

Basilisk, V, 299, 639, VI, 186, 349, 366; dead seen, V, 480, VI, 310; deaf, V, 474; existence doubted, V, 477; killing by its glance denied, V, 474, 477, VI, 286, 358; not hatched from cock's egg, VI, 283

Bassaeus, Nicolaus, pr Frankfurt, VI, 224, 535

Bassanus Politus, see Politus

Basso, Sébastien (1621), VI, 386-8

Bate, Henri, V, 195, VI, 130

Bath, V, 62; against demon, VI, 546-7; disease from, VI, 208; dry, VI, 207; golden, V, 646; keeper, V, 618; lye and herbs, VI, 546; mineral, V, 125, 435, 440, 514, 605, VI, 208-9, 553; mixed bathing, V, 270; only on medical advice, VI, 208; Rapard on, VI, 207-8; works on, V, 54, 211, 254, 484, 537, VI, 545

Bath, bishop of, V, 142; and see Adelard of

Batoreus de Somlio, Steph. dedic to, V, 155

Battistella, Antonio (1895), VI, 150, 153; (1905), VI, 148-50

Battus, Levinus, Paracelsist, VI, 126

Bauchinet, Guillaume, physician, VI, 248

Baudon, J., tr, VI, 528

Baudrier, J. (1895-), VI, 160, 561

Baudry de Saunier, L. (1936), V, 596

Bauhin, Gaspar, VI, 258

Bauhin, Jean, V, 466, VI, 258

Baumgarten-Crusius (1845), VI, 49, 255, 267

Baumgartner, Philip, disputant, VI, 414

Bavaria, V, 331, 345, 549, VI, 227; duke of, V, 402, 548, 619, 631, VI, 45, 235, 245

Bawman, Georg, pr Erfurt, V, 418

Bayle, Pierre, V, 78, 231, 312, VI, 389, 560

Bayonne, VI, 181

Bayro, see Bairo

Bear, eating brain of, VI, 516; grows fat during sleep, VI, 570; licks its cubs into shape, VI, 565

Beaugency, VI, 346

Beaune, VI, 105

Beauvais, V, 556; count of, V, 300; and see Vincent of

Beaver, V, 454; castrates self, V, 19, disbelieved, V, 448

Becanus, Ioannes Goropius, naturalist, VI, 291

Becker, M., pr Frankfurt, VI, 286

Bed, feather-, VI, 221; spend March and September in, VI, 221-2

Bede, V, 600; cited, V, 420, VI, 391, 487; on divination from thunder, VI, 488

Bee, V, 570, VI, 290; generation of, VI, 281-3, 570; wild, VI, 268

Beelzebub, VI, 520

Beer, V, 611

Beetle, as remedy, V, 646; specimen, VI, 268

Beggar and Begging, VI, 572

Bégin, E. A. (1829), VI, 504

Beheim, Lorenz, V, 171, 350, 472, VI, 444

Behem, Franciscus, pr Mainz, VI, 480

Behemoth, V, 135

Beiträge zur Geschichte der Meteorologie, V, 178

Beiträge zur Inkunabelkunde, VI, 447

Belaus, Baptista, cardinal, V, 272

Beldomandi, see Prosdocimo de'

Belgian and Belgium, V, 282, 550, VI, 201, 409, 596

Belief, see Idea

Belisarius, VI, 471

Bell, baptism of, V, 135, VI, 498, denied, VI, 541; falling of, V, 92; repels demons and storms, V, 107, 231-2, VI, 540-1

Bellantius, Lucius, V, 159, 199; cited,

V, 165-6, 212, 263, 393, VI, 112, 180, 189; opposed, V, 227, VI, 190, 193, 201-2, 467
Bellay, Jean du, cardinal, preface to, VI, 340
Bellis, an herb, VI, 262
Bellono, Antonio, pr Genoa, V, 259
Belluno, V, 44, VI, 447
Bellutus, Bonaventura (1688), VI, 430-1
Belmisserus, Paul, VI, 257
Belon, Pierre, naturalist, V, 453, 470, 597, VI, 154, 254, 257-8, 273, 286, 295; charged with plagiarism, VI, 257; cited, VI, 267
Belot, Jean, VI, 360-2, 507-10
Belt, of wolf-gut, V, 559, VI, 501
Bembo, Pietro, nativity of, VI, 105, 596
Benalius, Bernardinus, pr Venice, V, 56
Benancio, Lisset, see Colin, Seb.
Benatius, Jacobus, astrologer, V, 236-7, 244
Benatius, Lactantius, astrologer, V, 237, 244
Bencius, Ugo, see Hugh of Siena
Benckendorff, Martin, professor, VI, 105
Benedetti, Alessandro, V, 454, 501, 612, VI, 353
Benedetti, Giov. Batt., V, 580, VI, 50-51, 137-9, 372-3, 382; correspondence of, VI, 137-9, 372
Benediction, V, 474
Benedictis, Benedictus de, pr Bologna, V, 229
Benedictis, Hieronymus de, pr Bologna, V, 45, 95, 214, 499, 513; heirs of, VI, 484
Benedictis, Ioannes Antonius de, pr Bologna, V, 50
Benedictus, Ioannes (1550), VI, 480-1
Beneszewicz (1934), V, 390-1
Beneventanus, see Marcus
Benevento, see Marcus Beneventanus
Benivieni, Antonio, copied, VI, 401
Benjamin, Francis S., Jr., V, 407
Bentivogli, fall of, V, 39
Bentivoglio, Alessandro, V, 50, 241
Bentivoglio, Annibale, V, 241
Bentivoglio, Ermete, V, 51
Bentivoglio, Giovanni, V, 51, 235-8
Beraldus, Nicholaus, cited, VI, 402
Berarodino, instrument-maker, VI, 28
Berdoe, Edward, (1893), V, 497
Berengario da Carpi, see Carpi
Berga, Antonius, V, 24
Bergamo, V, 66, 99, 600, 613, VI, 172, 458, 503; baths near, V, 605; died at, V, 601; pr at, V, 261, 264, 457, VI, 458-9; printers from, V, 72, 75, and see Locatellus
Berghen, see Adriaen Van
Bergis, Robertus de, dedic to, VI, 28
Bergkrankheiten, V, 442
Bericchia, Iacomo, pr Rome, VI, 139
Berlin, VI, 78
Bernaldo, St., Order of, V, 201
Bernard of Como, inquisitor, V, 70
Bernard of Luxemburg, VI, 544
Bernard, majordomo, V, 130
Bernard of Modena, V, 257
Bernard of Treves, V, 601, 622-3
Bernardinus de Garaldis, see Garaldis
Bernardus de Gravia, alchemist, V, 623, 637
Berne, V, 317, VI, 448, 530; excavation at, in 1460, V, 157; pr at, V, 537, 548
Bernhardt, Wilhelm, (1865), V, 391, 393, 401
Bernia, Antonius (1642), publisher, V, 247
Béroald, François, ed, V, 594
Beroaldus, Philip, cited, VI, 402
Berot, David, theologian, VI, 493
Bertacchi, Domenico (1584), VI, 228-9
Bertellus, Petrus, pr Padua, V, 44
Berthelin, Andrea, pr Paris, VI, 451
Berthelot, P. E. M., V, 537
Bertipaglia, see Leonard of
Berton, Barthelemy, pr La Rochelle, V, 596
Bertrand, Jean, cardinal elect, VI, 479
Bertrand, Léon (1922), V, 330
Besançon, VI, 504
Besicken, Iohannes, pr Rome, V, 179
Besongne, Jean B. pr Rouen (1698), V, 65
Bessarion, cardinal, V, 336, 352, VI, 432
Besson, Jacques, V, 588-96; *Absoluta ratione,* V, 589-90; *L'art et science,* V, 588, 590-3, VI, 38; *Cosmolabe,* V, 593-4; *Théâtre des instruments,* V, 594-6
Bestiary, VI, 257, 346

Bethem, cited, V, 267
Bethen, VI, 130
Bethlehem, star of, a special divine creation, V, 120, VI, 177, 198, 349; not comparable with new star of 1572, VI, 69; and see Magi, three
Betonica or Betony, an herb, V, 483, 610, VI, 262
Betoun, David, primate of Scotland, preface to, V, 294
Betti, Claudio, professor, V, 336
Bettinelli, Saverio (1774), V, 256, VI, 48
Betuleius, Xystus, VI, 492
Betzendörfer, W. (1919), V, 94
Beughem, Cornelius van (1688), VI, 380
Bevilacqua, Bonifacio, cardinal, VI, 386
Bevilaqua, Nicolaus, pr Turin, VI, 137
Bezaar, see Bezoar
Bèze, Theodore de, V, 307, VI, 267
Bezoar stone, V, 249, 316, 457, 474, 476, 571, VI, 235, 241, 269, 275, 310-2, 315, 323, 335, 420, 461
Bianchini, Giovanni, cited, V, 131, 166, 565, VI, 11, 21, 120, 131; supplemented, VI, 82, 475
Bias, ancient philosopher, V, 307
Bible, V, 103; as authority, V, 87, 97, 118, 192, 403, VI, 25-26, 76, 85, 192, 253, 341, 364, 367, 411, 442, 454, 458, 478, 484, 487, 529-30, 542, 546, 551, 557, not always to be taken literally, V, 105, VI, 82, 85, 356; comm and interpretation of, V, 147, 279, 397, 544-5, VI, 76, 174-5, 268, 356, 377, 445, 468, against alchemy, VI, 246, for and against astrology, V, 198, 655, VI, 174, 349, 359, against motion of earth, VI, 11-12, 22, 34, 41, 43, 45, 54, 63, 81, 352; manuscript of, V, 393; nature in, VI, 306, 356, 394, 432; neglect of, V, 281, VI, 520-1; only Jewish book permitted, VI, 151; prediction from, VI, 134; problems of, VI, 451; science and, VI, 347; study of, V, 295; text of, VI, 445; tr, V, 279; use in charms and exorcisms, V, 477; Genesis, V, 192, VI, 239, 246, 357, 359, 452, 468, 483, 496; Deuteronomy, V, 397; Judges, VI, 359; Job, VI, 357, 360, 507; Ecclesiastes, VI, 357; Psalms, V, 442, VI, 148, 359, 454, 509-10; Isaiah, VI, 349; Ezekiel, VI, 349, 451; Daniel, VI, 76, 497; Apocrypha, VI, 356; Tobias, V, 462, VI, 357; Gospels, V, 391, VI, 498, 558; Gospel of John, V, 526, 544; Pauline Epistles, V, 544, VI, 523; Apocalypse, VI, 75, 306, 524
Bibliography, V, 318, VI, 12, 458; of alchemy, V, 547-8, 623-5, 679-95; botany, VI, 268; Brusch, V, 373; cabala, VI, 454; geography, VI, 42; Meurer, VI, 49; occult, V, 134, VI, 469; physiognomy, VI, 167
Biblioteca de autores españoles, VI, 222
Bibliotheca Mathematica, V, 359, 370, VI, 459
Bibliothèque Mazarine, V, 182
Bicardus, Ariel (1549 etc.), VI, 10
Bichardus, Horatius, V, 50, 64
Bielman, Josef, (1937), V, 130
Biermann, Martin, (1590), VI, 534
Biesius, Nicolaus, (1556), VI, 19, 394-8, 598
Bigazinus, Hieronymus, astrologer, V, 214, 220
Bigot, Guillaume (1549), VI, 339-41
Bilfinger, G. (1892), VI, 152
Billing, Henry, VI, 268
Binder, F. (1878), V, 352
Binderiana officina, pr Hamburg, VI, 141
Bindonus, Franciscus, pr Venice, V, 514
Binetus, Petrus, a patient, V, 302
Binsfeld, Peter (1589), VI, 522, 537-44, 552
Binz, Gustav, V, 401
Biog. nat. de Belgique, V, 152, 582
Biography, V, 113-5, 390
Biondo, Michelangiolo, V, 261-3
Birckmann, Arnold, pr Cologne, V, 583; heirs of, V, 622, 624, VI, 14, 28, 119
Birckmann, Joannes, pr Cologne, V, 622, 624
Bird, affinity to waters above firmament, VI, 347; creation of, VI, 347; dung of, V, 470; eyelids of, V, 29; names of, VI, 256, 271; sign of pest, V, 608, of future, VI, 293; song imitated, V, 102; tartar in flesh of, V, 649; works on, VI, 256-7, 310, 531

Biringucci, Vannuccio, V, 7, 543-4
Birkenmajer, A. (1921), V, 86; (1933), V, 406, 408
Birkenmajer, L. A. (1926), V, 265
Biron, Signor di, nativity, VI, 161
Birth, illegitimate, VI, 236; in seventh month, V, 326, in ninth, VI, 403; miscarriage, VI, 404; moment of, VI, 126, to determine, VI, 104, uncertain, VI, 114, 204; monstrous, see Monster; nine at one, VI, 221; of great men, V, 104
Biscuit, V, 611
Bishop, V, 78, 79, 81, 142, 166, 217-8, 226, 228, 238, 241, 256-8, 264, 296, 309, 311, 321, 342, 410-1, 413, 437, 446, 472, 505, 586, 623, VI, 28, 72, 100, 102, 104, 106, 123, 136, 151, 158, 162, 169-70, 183, 235, 257, 303, 360-1, 395, 401, 440, 442, 491, 520, 528, 558-9
Bishop, William, alchemist, V, 548
Bismalva, an herb, VI, 262, 264
Bissy, seigneur de, VI, 106
Bistorta, an herb, VI, 265
Bitaudus, Iohannes, VI, 388
Biteromancy, V, 561
Bitumen, V, 466, VI, 334; from springs in sea, V, 470; in prescriptions, V, 455; iudaicum, V, 455
Björnbo, A. A. (1907), V, 343, 347-8, 350, 352, 354, 357, 415
Black Death, see Pest, of 1348
Black Sea, V, 27
Bladder, V, 508, VI, 223
Bladus, Antonius, of Asola, pr Rome, V, 258, 445, VI, 370
Blaeu, Guilielmus (1668), VI, 7-8
Blaeu, Ioannes, pr Amsterdam (1668), VI, 7
Blanc, Richard le, V, 597
Blancus, Vincentius, knight of Venice, VI, 200
Blangy-sur-Ternoise, V, 449
Blaringhem (Nord), VI, 473
Blasius of Parma, V, 23, 54, 586
Blasius, G. (1665), VI, 286
Blavven or Blawin, Andreas de, physician, VI, 224
Blazin, Jean (1574), VI, 222-3
Bleeding, see Corpse, Phlebotomy
Blemidas, Greek alchemist, V, 623-4
Blereius, Philippus Iollianus (1539), V, 291
Blind, almost, VI, 471; born, VI, 572; case of father of Tobias, VI, 358; college of 300, VI, 522; lead blind, V, 509, 513; snow-blindness, V, 612
Blocksberg, VI, 525
Blois, Estates of, VI, 106
Blonde, V, 34
Blondet, André, an official, dedic to, V, 292
Blood, V, 29, 503, 523, VI, 331; altered by imagination, V, 103, VI, 513; as carrier of images for dreams, VI, 484; as instrument of ideas, V, 101-2; medical use of human, V, 462, 602, 639, 660, VI, 240, 243, 292, condemned, V, 663, VI, 243; movement of, V, 116, 495; rain of, VI, 284; sensitive after death, VI, 241; spring of, V, 399; staunched by a gem, VI, 314, 321; sweating, VI, 355; and see Circulation of, Goat, Phlebotomy
Boar, wild, VI, 277
Boat, see Ship
Boccaccio, *Genealogia deorum,* V, 512
Boccaferrea, Ludovicus, cited, V, 643
Bock, see Tragus
Bocxsteghe (Antwerp), V, 208
Bodenstein, Adam a, V, 619, 636, VI, 267
Boderius, see Bodier
Bodier, Thomas (1555), V, 301-3
Bodin, Jean, VI, 156; cited, VI, 112, 234, 361, 554; Copernican theory, VI, 42-43; criticism of Leowitz, VI, 118; *Démonomanie,* V, 137, VI, 43, 240, 479, 525-7, 534-5, 538-9; *Heptaplomeres,* VI, 525; *Methodus,* VI, 118, 525, quoted, VI, 99; *République,* V, 418, VI, 42-43, 118, 465, 525; *Universae naturae theatrum,* VI, 43
Boethius, tr, estimate of, V, 74
Bogardus, Iacobus, pr Paris, V, 296
Bohemia and Bohemian, VI, 111, 597; king of, V, 606; queen of, VI, 225; travel in, V, 650, VI, 254, 322
Boissard, Jean Jacques (1528-1602), VI, 504
Bojano, V, 79

Bokel, Johann, on philters, V, 485-6; on pest, VI, 210-1
Bokelnheim, V, 399
Boll, Franz (1908), V, 358
Bollettino della Società di Verona, V, 488
Bologna, V, 50, 105, 107, 130, 269, VI, 457, 471; admitted to citizenship at, VI, 152; astrology at, V, 124, 204-5, 213-4, 228, 234-51, VI, 150; discovery of a biped dragon near, VI, 289; disputation at, V, 59, VI, 455; dissection at, V, 509, 525; doctors of, criticized, V, 509; February, 1524 in, V, 231; geomancy at, V, 252-3; government of, V, 236, 238, 240-1, VI, 152-3, and see Bentivoglio; inquisition in, VI, 149-50; instauration of, V, 244; nativities of leading men of, V, 251; of, V, 38, 168, 230, 259, 273, 499, VI, 153, 402, 450; pharmacists of, V, 451; pr at, V, 42, 43, 45-46, 48, 50, 95, 96, 142, 179, 187, 211, 213-4, 229, 240-1, 245-7, 249, 260, 334, 336, 364, 499, 513, 521, 528, 547, 562, VI, 211, 268, 277, 281-6, 290, 293-5, 452, 469, 484, 486, 545, 556, not, VI, 165; prediction concerning, V, 235, 243-4, 247; siege of, V, 39; slur on inhabitants of, V, 505; tumults in, V, 39; university of, V, 37, 99, 213, 640, call from, refused, V, 74, studied at, V, 403, 426, 446, 652, VI, 38, 488, taught at, V, 38-39, 61, 90, 94-95, 234, 237-40, 244-5, 247, 250, 261, 325, 499, 501, 505, VI, 48, 56-57, 152-3, 257-8, 280, 285, 289-90, 431; weather at, in 1524, V, 193, 231-2; written at, VI, 221, near, V, 167
Bolognetus, Pompeius, professor of medicine, VI, 290
Bolton, H. C. (1901), V, 545
Bolum armenum, a drug, V, 451
Bolzeta, Francesco, VI, 368
Bombast von Hohenheim, see Paracelsus
Bonafides, Franciscus, V, 493
Bonafides, Nicolaus, dedic to, V, 228
Bonardus, Vincentius, of Parma, pr Bologna, V, 245-6
Bonatti, Guido, V, 63; cited, V, 163, 166, 227, 265, 267, 309, VI, 11, 120, 131, 163, 180, 458; condemned, V, 278, VI, 107; praised, V, 587; pr, V, 346
Bonaventura, VI, 369; cited, against astrology, V, 120, for it, VI, 304, concerning conception, V, 504
Boncompagni, Baldassare (1851), V, 165; library of, V, 234, 238
Boncompagni's Bullettino, V, 355-6, 359-60, VI, 180
Bondevillaus, Guido, pr Toulouse, VI, 340
Bone, Achillini on, in ear, V, 43-45; in foot, V, 327; broken, healed by gem, VI, 321; incorruptible, V, 526-7; nourished by marrow, V, 48-49; number in head, V, 508; unguent from, V, 432; venerated, V, 435-6; virtue in V, 106; and see Os, Relics, Sinciput, Stag
Bonello, Michele, cardinal, VI, 520
Bonfadino, Bartolomeo, publisher, Rome, VI, 139
Bongo, see Bungus
Bonhomme, Mathias, pr Vienne, VI, 257, 268
Bonincontri, Lorenzo, V, 166, 257, 361-2, 392, VI, 298
Bonn, VI, 335; Agrippa at, V, 129, 137; Longolius buried at, VI, 256
Bontius, Gregorius, bookseller, Antwerp, V, 320
Bontius, Jacobus, physician, VI, 319
Bontius, William, brother of Jacobus, VI, 319
Bonucci, cardinal, V, 99
Bonus of Ferrara, VI, 285
Bonus, Petrus, alchemist, V, 546
Boodt, Anselm de (1609), V, 327, VI, 318-23
Book, allegory of, V, 150; binder, V, 354; condemned, V, 275, 290; forbidden, V, 106, VI, 153, 169; innumerable, VI, 563-4; permit to read, VI, 151; shelf, fall of, V, 226, VI, 130; shop, VI, 125; spurious, V, 262; and see Burning of, Censorship, Jewish, Library, Magic
Book knowledge deprecated, V, 52-53
Boquet, Henri, V, 136, 559-60, VI, 527, 551-3
Borax, does not purify antimony, V,

479; not found in toad's head, V, 451
Borbonius, Petrus Jacobus, archbishop, addressed to, VI, 552
Borculoius, Hermannus, pr Utrecht, VI, 102
Bordeaux, Parlement of, VI, 526; pr at, VI, 220, 449; studied at, VI, 561
Bordogna, Sigismund, pr Venice, VI, 215
Borgarucci, B. pr Venice, VI, 218
Borgia, Cesare, V, 472, VI, 301; character, V, 59, 61, 187; crimes, V, 163; dedic to, VI, 299; horoscope, V, 171; prediction for, V, 179
Borgia, Roderico, cardinal, see Alexander VI
Borsetti, Ferrante (1735), V, 168
Bosanquet, Eustace F. (1917), VI, 483
Bosch, Arnold, letter to, VI, 440
Bosea, P. P. librarian (1673), V, 49
Bosmans, H. (1907), V, 152
Boswell, William (1651), VI, 380
Botanomancy, VI, 503
Botany, VI, 227; Christian, VI, 259; controversy, VI, 224; descriptive, VI, 263, 333; excursions, V, 8, 445, 460, 463, VI, 254, 268; history of, V, 609; low rank in university curriculum, VI, 266, 334; medieval background, VI, 261-5; method, V, 390, 463, 651, VI, 259-60, 266-7; of Leonardo da Vinci, V, 28-29; works on, VI, 167, 258, 270; and see Garden, botanical, Herb
Bouchel, Laurent (1615), VI, 170-1
Bouelles, Charles de, V, 535, 637, VI, 438-43; his absent-mindedness, VI, 443
Bouillon, duke of, VI, 28
Bourbon, duke of, V, 128, 131
Bourbonnais, V, 299
Bourges, G. pr Tours, V, 464
Bourgoing, historian, VI, 361
Bousuit, see Nicolaus de
Bovillus, see Bouelles
Boy, apparently beheaded, VI, 530; beaten, V, 297; diseases of, V, 486; divination by, VI, 240; guarded by amulet, V, 455; pure, used in divining, VI, 499; sacrificed, VI, 502; scientific curiosity of, V, 448; two, before whom doors opened, VI, 132, 513; weather prediction by, VI, 488; with worms, V, 451, VI, 313
Brabant, V, 189, 303, 648
Bracesco, Giovanni, V, 545-6, 601
Bracket, telescoping, V, 595
Bradwardine, Thomas, V, 41, 275, 557
Braga, born at, VI, 560; see Council of
Bragadino, Marco, alchemist, V, 549, VI, 245
Brahe, Tycho, VI, 11, 60, 81, 95, 185, 376; accused of plagiarism, V, 350; anteceded, VI, 20; attitude towards Aristotle, VI, 84, astrology, V, 324, 345-6, 382, VI, 69-71, 143, astronomy, V, 426, VI, 64; background, V, 408, 421; cited, VI, 381; correspondence, V, 250-1, 304, 324, 376, 388-9, 397-8, 642, VI, 38, 53-55, 74, 84-85, 114, 124, 183, 357-8, 506, 524; estimate of Agrippa, V, 138, Campanus, V, 407, Copernicus, V, 406, 427, VI, 51-54, Dasypodius, VI, 90, Erastus, V, 656, Fracastoro, V, 490, Hagecius, VI, 504, Hemming, VI, 523, Leowitz, V, 111-12, Offusius, VI, 24, 111, Pena, VI, 72, Regiomontanus, V, 376, Reinhold, VI, 4, Squarcialupus, VI, 185, Stadius, V, 304, Vallesius, VI, 358, Vögelin, V, 322; ignored, VI, 75; influence, V, 575, VI, 569; observations of, V, 11, 366, VI, 53-54, 64, 68, 70; Paracelsan, V, 629; praised, VI, 190; star of 1572, V, 388, VI, 53, 67-69, 73-74, 474; system of, VI, 54-55, 62
Brahman, VI, 353, 467
Braillier, Pierre, apothecary, V, 465-6, 470
Brain, V, 45; Carpi on, V, 508; cavities of, V, 87, 512, 523; center of nervous system, V, 508, and see Heart; devoid of sense, V, 660; disease of, V, 444, VI, 196; encircled by fire, VI, 362; excrement of, VI, 355; forms dreams, VI, 500; imagination in, V, 478; in microcosm, V, 521, VI, 463; mover, not moved, V, 522; pia mater called soul, VI, 362; scorpion and worm in, V, 482
Bran, V, 474
Brancaleone, Giov. Fran., physician, V, 254
Branchiis, Joh. Richard or Rigaud de, V, 533-4
Branchus, oracle of, VI, 504

Brandenburg, VI, 457, 597; elector of, V, 202; margrave of, V, 380, 382, dedic to, V, 412, VI, 3; war with, VI, 499; and see Albert of

Brasavola, Antonio Musa, VI, 255; career, V, 446; cited, V, 647, VI, 258, 333; criticized, V, 467-9, VI, 313; early works, V, 446; *Examen*, V, 123, 445-61; family, V, 445; index to Galen, V, 609; influence, V, 460-1, 464, 467, VI, 256, 299; other works, V, 461; quoted, V, 307, 445

Brauchius, Balthasar, physician, V, 657

Braunmühl, A. v. (1900), VI, 140

Brazil, V, 614; wood, V, 469

Bread, V, 145, 474; mouldy, V, 608

Breathing, see Respiration

Breisgau, V, 297; see Freiburg-im-

Breit, E. (1912), V, 94, VI, 335

Brennonius, curé, alchemist, V, 132

Brenta, Andrea, tr, VI, 476

Brentius, cited, VI, 541

Brentius, Iohannes, VI, 597

Brescia, V, 269, 446, 454, 545, 613, VI, 128, 230, 257, 405, 493; pest at, VI, 214; pr at, V, 625, VI, 231-2, 469

Breslau, V, 404, VI, 90, 461, 480, 490, 507; see Michael of

Bresse, Maurice, professor, V, 303

Brest, V, 598

Bretschneider, C. G., V, 400

Breventano, Stefano (1571), V, 157

Briançon, V, 285

Briau, André, physician, V, 124

Bridge, V, 133

Brie, V, 434

Brindisi, V, 269

Brissac, maréchal de, VI, 33

Britain, V, 280, 610, VI, 338

Brittany, see Anne of

Broadside, V, 222, 339, 359, VI, 287, 344, 521

Brocarius, Arnaldus Guillelmus, pr Alcalà, V, 277

Brochier, Jean, astrologer, V, 271

Brosserius, Simon (1536), V, 152-3

Bronze, VI, 235

Brubacchius, Petrus, pr Hagenau, V, 387

Brucaeus, Henricus, V, 376, VI, 38-39, 53-54, 84-85

Brucker, Jakob (1742-44), V, 134, VI, 388, 451-2

Bruges, V, 328; born at, VI, 318; grammar school at, VI, 38

Brunet, J. C. (1860-80), V, 125, 287, VI, 433, 469

Brunfels, Otto, V, 316-8; *Herbarum vivae icones*, V, 322, VI, 261, 265, 273-4, 280; letter to, V, 66; put on Index, VI, 147

Bruno, Giordano, V, 495, VI, 386, 423-8, 459-60; artificial memory, V, 606, VI, 426; Copernican theory, V, 51, 62, 155; magic, ten kinds of, V, 573; quoted, V, 617

Brunschwig, Hieronymus, V, 432, 460, 532

Brunswick, V, 399, VI, 191, 596; duke of, V, 298, 393, VI, 116

Brusch, Gaspar, V, 373-5, VI, 597; put on Index, VI, 147

Brusch, Gaspar, Jr., VI, 597

Bruscus, an herb, VI, 262, 264

Brusoni, Livio Francesco, astrologer, V, 214

Brussels, V, 329, 524, VI, 140, 235; pr at, VI, 418

Bry, Th. de, pr Frankfurt, VI, 286

Brydges, Sir Egerton, V, 313

Bucephalus, V, 98

Buchner, Johann, VI, 597

Buckets, chain of, V, 595

Buckingham, V, 320

Bucoldianus, Gerard, V, 273, VI, 431-2

Budé, Guillaume, defended, VI, 340; distributes charms indiscriminately, V, 176; letter to, VI, 442

Buffon, G. L. L. de, naturalist, VI, 254, 296

Bugenhagius, Iohannes, VI, 597

Buglossa, an herb, VI, 333

Building, V, 141, 219; constellations at, VI, 100; fall of, VI, 489-90; laying corner stone, V, 259, 277, 324; restored, V, 205

Bulaeus, see Du Boulay

Bull, VI, 447; antipathy with fig, VI, 416; liver, as remedy, VI, 567

Bull, papal, V, 438, VI, 538; and see name of pope issuing

Bullarium romanum, VI, 148, 156, 171

Bulletin of Institute of History of Medicine, VI, 258

Bullettino di Bibliografia e di Storia delle

Scienze . . ., see *Boncompagni's Bullettino*
Bullón y Fernandez (1929), V, 288
Bungus, Petrus, VI, 458-9
Buoninsegni, Tommaso, VI, 187
Buphthalmos, an herb, VI, 262
Burchardus, Franciscus, VI, 596
Burckhardt, A. (1917), V, 438, 601, 609, VI, 143
Burger, Konrad (1907), V, 339
Burgher, V, 112; well educated, V, 177; and see names of towns
Burgo nuovo, see Archangelus de
Burgos, pr at, V, 92, 174, 208
Burgundian and Burgundy, V, 533, VI, 89, 527; county of, VI, 551; duchy of, V, 307; duke of, V, 168, 314; parlement of, VI, 552; prediction for, V, 310; travel in, V, 613
Burial, as magic ceremonial, VI, 243, 282
Buridan, Jean, V, 23, 156-8
Burnettus de Viella, geomancy, VI, 473
Burning of books, V, 94, 438-9; advised, V, 291, VI, 420, 534; by the author, V, 529, VI, 480; of superstitious, decreed, VI, 150
Burning glass, see Lens, Perspective
Burr, Geo. L. (1890-91), VI, 517, 537
Bursa pastoris, an herb, VI, 262
Busch, Caspar, Sr. VI, 598
Buschbell, G. (1910), VI, 149
Business, V, 140, 245, 363, VI, 168; partnership, V, 172
Busson, Henri (1922), V, 287
Buteo, John (1559), V, 293, 305, VI, 33; cited, VI, 347
Butter, V, 145
Butterflies, VI, 290; swarms of, V, 249

Cabala, V, 13, 124, 213, 218-9, 233, 316, 324-5, 636, 639, 650, 660-1, VI, 25, 361, 378, 444-6, 452-4, 457, 459, 462-4, 481, 508-9; Agrippa and, V, 130, 132, 134-5; alchemy and, V, 539, 604, 645; cited, VI, 532, 551; diabolical, VI, 525; medicine and, VI, 219, 240, 461, 463; opposed, V, 262, VI, 388, 411, 430, 499, 529, 537
Caballus, Franciscus (1499), VI, 257, 310, 348
Cacabo, V, 585
Cacchius, Josephus, pr Aquila, Naples, V, 644, VI, 370
Cadmia, a mineral, VI, 307, 312
Caelatura, V, 17
Caelius, Ludovicus, humanist, V, 503
Caeresarius, see Ceresara
Caeromancy, VI, 503
Caesar, as title, V, 182-3, 188
Caesar, Julius, V, 568-9, VI, 76; condemned, V, 578
Caesar, Julius, interlocutor, VI, 568
Caesar, Longinus, see Longinus
Caesar, Sebastianus, VI, 521
Caesius, Ferd. Calorius (1860), V, 164
Caesius, Georgius (1579), VI, 91
Cahors, VI, 442
Caius, John, VI, 267
Cajetan de Thienis, arguments rejected, V, 95; cited, V, 504, VI, 48, 125, 174, 176, 300, 412, 544
Cajetan, Thomas de Vio, cardinal, V, 75
Cajori, Florian (1929), VI, 50
Calabria, V, 78, 582, VI, 129, 449, 527
Calamities, V, 71-72, 80, 124, 163-4, 184-6, 222, VI, 492
Calamum aromaticum, V, 468
Calcagnini, Celio, V, 370, 409, VI, 63
Calcination, V, 479, 533-4, 635, 645
Calculator, V, 41; and see Suiseth
Calculus Pisanus, V, 326
Calcutta, V, 453
Calderia, John, *Concordances,* V, 263
Calendar, astrological, VI, 133; of Etzlaub, V, 348; Gregorian, V, 427, VI, 5-6, 65, 129, 191; Julian, VI, 6; movable feasts, V, 284; of Regiomontanus, V, 340-2; reform, V, 251, 265, 281, 349, 408, VI, 36-37, 45; Roman and Gallic, V, 186; works on, V, 257, 308-9, 407, VI, 124, 143
Calends, divination from, superstitious, VI, 144
Calepinus, dictionary of, V, 502
Calf, fell from clouds, V, 157, VI, 285; generated in air, VI, 342; given mercury, VI, 313; two-headed, VI, 400
Cali, Arabic name for an herb, V, 457
Calicut, VI, 314
Calid Babylonius, alchemist, V, 623
California, VI, 276

Calinisch (1866), VI, 495
Calippus, classical astronomer, VI, 97
Calvi, Gerolamo (1909), V, 28
Calvi, Giovanni (1777), VI, 331
Calvin, Jean, V, 37, 128, VI, 541; against astrology, V, 324, VI, 131, 523
Calvinism and Calvinist, V, 600, 649, 652-3, VI, 105, 148, 462, 522, 524, 559; crypto-, VI, 495; science and, VI, 346
Camaldulensian, VI, 377
Cambrai, bishop of, V, 584; League of, V, 95, VI, 599; Peace of, V, 286
Cambridge, University, VI, 238, 520
Camel, V, 399
Camera obscura, V, 32
Camerarius, Joachim, V, 337; and astrology, V, 384; called to Nürnberg, V, 338; cited, VI, 49, 536, 601; criticized, VI, 184; ed. Theon, V, 364; letters, V, 381; nativity by, V, 384, of, VI, 105, 596; pupil of, V, 397; put on Index, VI, 147; tr, V, 358, 400; at Tübingen, V, 383, VI, 341; works, *Comm. de generibus divinationum,* VI, 493, 501-2, *Norica sive de ostentis,* V, 383, VI, 489
Camerarius, Joachim, Junior, naturalist, VI, 258, 268
Camerino, V, 50, 269
Camillo, Giulio, cited, VI, 431
Camillus, Hannibal, verses by, V, 46
Cammerlander, Jakob, pr Strasburg, V, 323, 543
Camomilla, V, 448, VI, 262
Camotio, Gioan Fran., pr Venice, V, 157
Campana, an herb, VI, 263
Campanatius, Vincentius, astrologer, V, 259
Campanazzo, Antonio, astrologer, V, 167-8
Campanella, Tommaso, forerun, V, 495, VI, 386; influenced, VI, 370; on astrology and bulls against it, VI, 173-7; on death of Nabod, VI, 121-2; on Giovanni Francesco Pico della Mirandola, VI, 467; works, *An bullae SS. Pontificum,* VI, 175; *Apologia,* VI, 175; *Astrologicorum libri,* VI, 121-2, 173-6; *Atheismus triumphatus,* VI, 175, 177; *Lettere,* VI, 173, 175; *Syntagma de libris propriis,* VI, 175
Campanus of Novara, V, 25; called Arabic, VI, 43; transalpine, V, 166; cited, V, 41, 257, 557, VI, 180; depicted, VI, 470-1; disregarded, V, 407-8; errors of, V, 292-3; imitated, V, 564; method of dividing zodiac into houses, V, 336, 359-60, VI, 103-4, 120; misdated, V, 407-8, VI, 130; praised, V, 587; works, V, 407, 574, *Theory of the Planets,* V, 4, 406-8, 425, 490, tr Euclid, V, 407, comm. V, 343, 407
Campeggio, Lorenzo, cardinal, V, 130, 132, 321, 446, VI, 452
Campeggio, Tommaso, bishop, V, 321
Camphor, V, 449, 465, 468, 621, VI, 209
Campi, Francesco, physician, VI, 212
Campifulgosus, see Fregoso, Batt.
Campis, Nicolaus de, a patient, V, 302
Cana, miracle at, VI, 496
Canada, VI, 436
Canal, at Panama and Suez, envisioned, VI, 345
Canamusali, cited, V, 506
Canappaeus, J. V, 501
Canary islands, V, 469
Cancer, sign of zodiac, V, 60
Cancer, Matthias, pr Naples, V, 273, VI, 418
Candelabra, VI, 454
Candle, VI, 148; marvelous, VI, 434
Canella, V, 468
Canibas, VI, 436
Cannani, Giov. Batt., anatomist, V, 531
Cannavale, Ercole (1895), V, 72-74
Cannibal, VI, 408
Cano, Juan Sebastian del, VI, 256-7
Canon, V, 66, 160, 171, 207, 320, 407, 426, VI, 106, 371, 480, 484, 520, 524, 537, 540, 559; and see Avicenna, *Canon,* Law, canon
Canon episcopi, VI, 527
Canonicus, see John
Cantabria, V, 585
Canter, G. ed. Stobaeus, VI, 449
Cantharides, VI, 284
Cantimpré, see Thomas of
Canusula, an herb, VI, 262
Capasso, C. (1923-24), V, 255
Cape of Good Hope, V, 212, 553, VI, 346
Capece, see Capicius
Capella, see Martianus Capella
Capella, Galeatius, VI, 596

Capellani, father and son, astrologers, VI, 142
Capellanus, Ioannes, V, 125
Capicius, Scipio, V, 254
Capnio, see Reuchlin
Capnomancy, VI, 430, 503
Capo d'Istria, VI, 162
Capon, for the sick, cooked with gold coins, V, 459
Capparoni, P. (1925), V, 39, 45-46, 505
Capponi, Antonio, murderer of Cocles, V, 51
Capponi, Giorgio (1610), V, 250
Capponi, Giovanni Battista (1645-76), V, 48, 250, 273
Capracola, V, 261
Capreoli or Caprioli, Giovanni, cited, VI, 48
Caprilius, Caesar, V, 540
Captromancy, VI, 430, 479, 502
Capua, V, 269; cardinal of, V, 411
Capuano, Francesco, da Manfredonia, V, 166
Capuchin, VI, 268
Caput galli, an herb, VI, 262
Carab, alchemist, V, 623
Carafa, see Caraffa
Caraffa, Diomede, V, 81
Caraffa, Giovanni Pietro, cardinal, see Paul IV
Caraffa, Giuseppe (1751), V, 74, 582-3
Caraffa, Oliviero, cardinal, dedic to, V, 72, VI, 492
Caranta, Jacopo (1624), VI, 559
Carbachius, Nicolaus, a teacher, V, 323
Card, playing, VI, 200, 278
Cardamomo or Cardamomum, an herb, V, 467, VI, 272
Cardan, Facius, V, 365, VI, 105
Cardan, Girolamo, V, 563-79; astrology of, V, 382, 564, 571-3, 579, VI, 195, 201, 253; attitude towards past and present writers, V, 51, 256, 564-5; cited, V, 261-2, 328, 403, 410, 477, 563, 614, 641, 647, VI, 21, 29, 93, 102, 112, 120-1, 131, 148, 167, 176-7, 180, 193, 197, 234, 267, 293, 311, 319, 361, 366, 382, 411, 431, 500, 503, 521, 531, 544, 551; controversy, VI, 479, with Scaliger, VI, 283-4; copied from, V, 441-2, 621; credulity, V, 568, VI, 279, 285; criticized, V, 382, 636-7, VI, 193, 202, 283-4, 293, 384, 509-10, 566, 569; ed. V, 602; estimates of, V, 579; extracts from, V, 475; family of, V, 568, 574, 577; Index and, VI, 148; influence, VI, 511, on Bruno, V, 573, VI, 424, 426; on Palissy, V, 597; on Vanini, VI, 569-71; Inquisition and, VI, 152-3; metoposcopy of, VI, 505-6; nativities by, VI, 101, 148; on Agrippa, V, 138; praised, V, 612, VI, 569; quoted, V, 3, 563, VI, 511; style of, V, 563; subjects covered by, V, 563-4; superstition of, V, 579, VI, 292; testament, VI, 153; works, *Aethere,* V, 602, *Almanach,* VI, 102, *Animorum immortalitate,* V, 575, VI, 511, *Ars magna,* V, 421, *Comm. Quadripartitum,* V, 571, VI, 90, 102, 122, *Exemplis centum geniturarum,* V, 51, 162, 565, VI, 101, *Encomium Neronis,* V, 578, *Fulgure,* V, 576, *Libris propriis,* V, 573, *Opus novum,* V, 565, *Propria vita,* V, 563, 566, 575, 579, VI, 152-3, *Rerum varietate,* V, 563-79, VI, 152-3, 419, *Subtilitate,* V, 563, 565, 567, 569, 571, 597, VI, 71, 110, 419
Cardinal, V, 70, 99, 130, 132, 142, 171, 205, 245, 261, 268, 410-1, 486, 488, 552, 582, 584, VI, 48, 149, 349, 452; college of, VI, 150, 153, 438; conclave, in, V, 252; Congregation of, VI, 150-1; costume of, V, 259; dedic to, V, 72, 74, 75, 155, 167, 197, 208, 215, 226, 238, 240-1, 246, 255, 258, 272, 300, 304, 321, 446, 472, 484, 499, 540, 644, VI, 63, 159, 202, 208, 227, 273, 315, 340, 344, 386, 476, 487, 492, 510, 520; genitures of, V, 255, 259, 274, VI, 100, 105, 195; letter to, VI, 173; patrons, V, 336, 352, 362, VI, 227, 479; prediction for individual, V, 30, 255-6, VI, 101, 171; youthful, V, 274
Carduus benedictus, VI, 272
Carduus, Sextus, cited, V, 610
Carello, Gio. Bat., tr, V, 369
Carinthia, VI, 490; Estates of, V, 440
Carion, John, *Chronicle,* V, 382; cited VI, 361; death and epitaph, V, 382-3; geniture, VI, 598; *Prognosticatio,* V, 202, 381-3, VI, 253; relations with Luther and Melanchthon, V, 381-3; *Weissagung,* V, 204

Carl, Ph. (1864), V, 410
Carlinus, Io. Iacobus, pr Naples, VI, 273
Carlo, Giovanni, astrologer, V, 168
Carlstadt, A. Bodenstein de, V, 128; and see Karlstadt
Carmagnola, pr at, VI, 160
Carmelite, V, 67, VI, 127, 130, 557
Carmona, see Juan de
Carnelian, VI, 314
Carniola, VI, 191
Carpenter, V, 165
Carpentras, VI, 298
Carpi, V, 59, 95
Carpi, Berengario da, V, 499-513, 561-2; anatomical discovery, V, 44, 508; attitude towards occult arts, V, 510-1; citations, V, 502-6; copied, V, 516; criticized, V, 515; Falloppia's estimate of, V, 498, 529; not mentioned by Vesalius, V, 523; textual criticism by, V, 501-2; works, *Comm. Mundinus,* V, 499-513, 528, *Fractura calve,* V, 513-4, 528, *Isogogae breves,* V, 528
Carreri, Alessandro, against alchemy, V, 642-4; on dreams, VI, 481-4
Cartagena, see Antonio of
Carthage, V, 579, VI, 435
Carthusian, VI, 361, 459
Cartier, Alfred (1889), V, 287
Cartulaire de l'Université de Montpellier, VI, 223
Casaubon, Meric (1659), VI, 392
Case system, in astrological medicine, V, 302; in physiognomy, V, 57, 59-60; and see *Consilia*
Casimir, son of king of Poland, VI, 89
Casmann, Otto (1599), VI, 197-8
Caspian Sea, V, 23, 27
Cassaneo, Bartolomeo, see Chasseneux
Cassanus, Ferdinand, medical, VI, 213
Cassel, VI, 161
Casserio, Giulio, V, 43-44
Cassia, V, 468
Cassian, cited, VI, 412
Cassiano, V, 218
Cassiel, spirit of Saturn, V, 569
Cassinis, Samuel de, V, 70
Cassiopeia, VI, 97, 474
Cassius, Angelus, death of, truly foretold, V, 313
Castalio, see Châteillon
Castañega, see Martin de
Castaneolus, Dominicus Maria, astrologer, V, 236, 253
Castellamare, bishop of, dedic to, V, 218
Castellani, Pietro Nicollò de, tr, VI, 449
Castellanus, Honoratus, VI; 340
Castellanus, Petrus, see Duchastel, Pierre
Castellione, cardinal à, V, 300
Castelnuovo (Piedmont), VI, 227
Castle, V, 202; in air, VI, 548
Castor and Pollux, VI, 400
Castor oil, V, 614, VI, 219
Castres, VI, 346
Castriotto, Ferdinando, VI, 599
Castro, duke of, V, 267
Castro, Rodericus de, cardinal, VI, 197
Cat, abhorrence of, V, 662; brain of, VI, 526; chopped up, V, 432; liver of a black, V, 118
Catalan and Catalonia, V, 115, 174, 430, 625
Catalogue of Books Printed in the Fifteenth Century Now in the British Museum, V, 56, 341, 536
Catalogus codicum astrologorum Graecorum, V, 358
Cataract, operation for, V, 436; cured by swallow-wort, VI, 260
Catarrh, V, 280, VI, 367
Cathay, V, 287, 323
Catherina de Silvestro, pr Naples, V, 220
Catholic Encyclopedia, VI, 168
Catholic Reformation, see Reformation
Cato, Angelo, V, 450
Catoplepa, an animal, VI, 241
Catoptric, VI, 392, 430
Catoptromancy, VI, 499; forbidden, VI, 157
Cat's eye, a gem, VI, 314
Cattan, Christophe de, geomancer, VI, 472
Cattaneo, Andrea, V, 90-92
Cattani, Francesco de, VI, 458, 519-20
Cattle, VI, 277; to protect from smallpox, VI, 294-5; to protect trees from, VI, 282
Caudebec, V, 302
Cauliculus agrestis, VI, 262, 264
Causation and Cause, V, 151, 571, VI, 350, 384, 410, 414-5, 419, 564; ap-

parent and true, VI, 321; astrological denied, V, 164, other than, V, 393; final, VI, 384; First, VI, 343; how to determine, VI, 415; infinite, VI, 396; inevitable series of, VI, 397; natural, VI, 414; and see Demon, Marvel, Star

Cautery, V, 660

Cavalry, V, 164

Cavanete, see Tanevete

Cavellat, Guillaume, pr Paris, V, 379, VI, 10, 286

Ceccarelli, Alfonso, astrologer, VI, 156

Cecco d'Ascoli, accused of putting Christ under the stars, VI, 176-7; defended from charge of magic, V, 102, VI, 132; quoted, V, 219

Cecil, William, preface to, V, 377, VI, 73

Celestin, Claude, see Coelestinus

Celestines, Order of, V, 199

Cellanus, see Sarzosus

Celonitides, a gem, V, 614

Celsus, Cornelius, V, 439, 514; corrected, VI, 402; quoted, V, 477

Celtes, Conrad, V, 333, 346, 407, VI, 598

Cementation, V, 645, VI, 242

Cemetery, see Graveyard

Cenanus, John, anatomist, VI, 214

Ceneda (Treviso), V, 261

Censorship of the press, V, 11; deletion by, VI, 303-4, 418; ecclesiastical approval, V, 247, VI, 166, 334, 493, 520, 556-7; edition destroyed, V, 290; effect of, V, 129, 136, 287, VI, 471; expurgated edition, VI, 418; inspection required, VI, 170; passed by, VI, 9, 163, 175, 409; printing forbidden, V, 440; reply to, VI, 304; theological hinted, V, 526; theses suppressed, VI, 388; and see Index, Inquisition, Venice, Council of Ten

Census of Medieval and Renaissance Manuscripts, V, 385

Centaur, VI, 408

Centaurea maior, media, minor, VI, 262

Centaurium maius, V, 447

Centiloquium, see Cirvelo, Hermes, Ptolemy

Centralblatt für Bibliothekswesen, see *Zentralblatt*

Centumgumma, an herb, VI, 263

Century, fourteenth, VI, 131, 279; thirteenth, VI, 130, called barbarous, VI, 83

Ceradini, G. (1876), VI, 325, 328

Ceration, alchemical, V, 534

Cerauneus, a gem, V, 614

Cerdonis, Matheus, fl 1484, V, 56

Ceremony, cabalistic, VI, 446, 454; magic, V, 84, 136, 560, VI, 282-3, 404, 425; relic of paganism, V, 135; superstitious, V, 477, VI, 237, 240, 320, 546, 559, its decline, VI, 591; vain, V, 262

Ceresara, Paride, astrologer, V, 63, 256, VI, 15, 107

Ceretti, Felice (1901), V, 173

Cermisone, Antonio, V, 54, VI, 164

Cerreto, Io. Bapt. a, astrologer, VI, 126-7

Cervicornus, Eucharius, pr Cologne and Marburg, V, 520, VI, 255

Cervinus, Marcellus, cardinal, dedic to, V, 552; nativity of, VI, 105

Cesalpino, Andrea, VI, 266, 546; and circulation of the blood, VI, 328-31; cited, VI, 284, 319; works, *Appendix,* VI, 327, *Ars medica,* VI, 326, 328, other medical, VI, 326, 330-1, *Daemonum investigatio,* VI, 325, 335-8, *Metallicis,* VI, 284, 334-5, *Plantis,* VI, 258, 328-9, 331-3, *Quaestionum Peripateticarum,* VI, 325-32

Cesena, V, 50, 54-55, VI, 510

Ceylon, V, 469, VI, 314

Chael, Israelite, cited, VI, 301; and see Zael

Chair, of Fracastoro, V, 488

Chalcanthum, V, 450, 458

Chalcidius, *Comm. Timaeus,* V, 87

Chalcitis, V, 450, VI, 310

Chaldea and Chaldean, V, 135, 403, 539, VI, 113, 172, 174, 382, 427, 460, 480, 498; Cicero against, V, 165; forbidden arts of, VI, 481, 521; *Oracles,* cited, VI, 374, pr, VI, 460, 601-2

Chalk, VI, 209

Challonius, Renatus, prince of Orange, horoscope of, VI, 15

Chalons-sur-Saône, VI, 106

Chambery, V, 131

Chameleon, VI, 277

Champeaux, Ernest (1918), V, 307, 311

Champier, Symphorien, V, 208, 387, 430,

436, 468; against alchemy, astrology, magic, V, 115-22, 124-6, 541; *Annotamenta,* V, 119-21, 551; *Apologetica epistola,* V, 114; biographies by, V, 113-5; career, V, 111-2; *Castigationes,* V, 114, 122-3, 447, 449, 451, 454, 460-1; cited, V, 465, 470, VI, 306; defended, V, 289; *Dyalogus,* V, 116-8; geography by, V, 122; history by, V, 115; medical V, 114, 122-3; plagiarism of V, 112, 118, 122; *Pronosticon,* V, 124-5, 241; quoted, V, 69; works, significance of, V, 113-4
Chance, denied, V, 164, 396; discussed, V, 363, VI, 204, 410
Chancellor, VI, 596; of France, V, 291; imperial, VI, 235; university, V, 112, 207, 552, VI, 220
Chaplet, VI, 533
Character, VI, 439; astrological, V, 639, VI, 378, 457, denied, VI, 236, 536; cabalistic, VI, 444; deceptive, VI, 477; denied operative virtue, V, 100, 103, 645, VI, 133, 398, 405, 408, 416, 527-8, 546; diabolical, V, 476, VI, 425; divine, of nature, VI, 406; Greek, and Hebrew, V, 538, VI, 302, 457; magic, V, 134, VI, 302, 421, 460; medical, VI, 479, 516; monstrous, VI, 108; mnemonic, V, 606; Paracelsan, V, 635, VI, 243; superstitious, VI, 233, 320
Charcedon, a gem, VI, 305-6
Charlemagne, V, 224, VI, 75-76, 117, 435, 465
Charles I of Spain, see Charles V, emperor
Charles IV, emperor, V, 547
Charles V, emperor, V, 267-8, 314, VI, 76; addressed to, V, 204, 206, 373, 421; Agrippa and, V, 128-9, 133, 137; buys astronomical instrument, VI, 41; comet and, V, 410; constitution of, VI, 539; dedic to, V, 182-3, 187-8, 194, 203, 588; Farnese family and, V, 267; Francis I and, V, 243; horoscope of, V, 246, 588; prediction to, VI, 136; Taisnier and, V, 582
Charles VIII of France, V, 636
Charles IX of France, VI, 106, 109
Charles, archduke of Austria, dedic to, VI, 192
Charles the Bold, VI, 89
Charles, cardinal of Lorraine, V, 304
Charles II, duke of Savoy, VI, 217
Charles, margrave of Baden, V, 631
Charles, a young future emperor, V, 373
Charm, see Amulet
Charpentier, Jacques (1558), V, 556, VI, 450
Charron, Pierre, VI, 561
Chart, V, 11, 142, 538, VI, 406-7, 442
Chartres, V, 123
Chasm, meteorological phenomenon, VI, 80
Chassanaeus, Thomas Bartholomaeus, see Chasseneux, Barthélemy de
Chasseneux, Barthélemy de (1526), VI, 432, 544
Chasseneuz, jurist, V, 307
Chassin, Godefroy (1614), VI, 382-6
Chastity, to preserve, VI, 416, 429; test, VI, 429
Châteillon, Sébastien (1555), VI, 492
Chauliac, See Guy de
Chavernac, J. F. E. (1875), VI, 553
Cheese, distaste for, V, 662
Chelidonia, herb, V, 132, 448, VI, 260; stone in swallows' gizzards, VI, 310
Chemical and Chemistry, V, 17, 458, 462, 588-90, 632, VI, 309, 323; astrology observed in, VI, 201; called evil, V, 564; change, approach to concept of, V, 40, 635, VI, 243, 600, not admitted, V, 643, 647, 659; laboratory, VI, 251; Libavius on, VI, 242-3; part of alchemy, VI, 242, of natural magic, VI, 430, of pharmacy, VI, 250, 252, of physics, VI, 426, 433; remedies, VI, 248; resemble magicians, VI, 238, 243; trained or experienced, V, 634, 657; works, V, 417, VI, 242-3, 438
Chemnitz, VI, 49, 498
Chenevière, A. (1886), V, 287
Cherso, island, VI, 373
Cherubim, VI, 451, 454
Chesneau, N. pr Paris, VI, 528
Chestnut tree, V, 21
Chevalier, Ulysse (1905), V, 505
Chevigny, J. de (1570), V, 271
Chick and Chicken, V, 454; divination by plucking, V, 58; kept alive by an incantation, V, 574; monstrous, VI, 490
Chicken-pox, VI, 553

Chicory, VI, 404
Chieti, VI, 559; and see Theatinus
Child, anatomy of, V, 520; born in eighth month, dies, V, 28, 495, 510, VI, 206, 402-3; complexio of, VI, 165; crying of, VI, 230; easily fascinated, V, 475-6; head compressed, V, 512; injured by kissing rather than by evil eye, V, 477; legitimacy tested, V, 474; mortality, V, 445, 599; murdered, V, 527; signs of sex of, V, 47, and number of, VI, 428; nourishment of, VI, 221; sickens, if cradle is moved often while empty, VI, 404; and see Education, Foetus, Generation
Chimney flue, V, 595
Chin, oblong, V, 510-1
China, VI, 323
Chirico, abbot and alchemist, VI, 218
Chiromancy, V, 50-68, 132-3, 160, 575, 635, VI, 468, 496; Achillini on, V, 42-43; anatomy and, V, 511, 521, 527; astrological, V, 313, VI, 163-4, 360, 431, 506-9; Carpi on, V, 511; condemned, V, 297, 321-2, VI, 162, 177, 193, 199-200, 430-1, 525; defended, V, 586, VI, 170; election of Leo X forecast by, V, 252; experiments in, V, 582; evil, V, 564; forbidden, VI, 169; interest in, V, 49; justified, V, 105, VI, 176; medicine and, V, 651; natural, VI, 360, 536, 543; of Piccioli, V, 261-2, Taisnier, V, 587; physiognomy and, V, 62, VI, 510, 527; put on Index, VI, 147, 150-1; taught, V, 582; works on, V, 673-8, VI, 360, 506
Chiusi, bishop of, V, 228
Choler, V, 503
Cholera, V, 496
Chora, alchemist, V, 623
Chorographia, VI, 430
Chrisogonus Iadertinus, Federicus, V, 314-6; cited, V, 647, VI, 159; and see Polydorus, Chrysogonus
Christ, V, 78, 85, 108, VI, 75, 451, 456; circumcision, V, 257; conception, V, 504; crucifixion, V, 257, 506-7, 526, VI, 468, 538, seen in sky, V, 399, time of, V, 256-7; herbs and, VI, 259; miracles of, V, 107, 273, VI, 342, 427; prediction as to, VI, 492; second coming of, VI, 117; springs and, VI, 342; stars and, V, 192, 199, 295, 588, VI, 108, 117, 176-7, 180, 201; sweating blood by, IV, 355; tempting of, VI, 497; theses concerning, VI, 455
Christchurch (Oxford), V, 320
Christian II, king of Denmark, VI, 136
Christian III, king of Denmark, VI, 136; dedic to, VI, 535
Christian IV, king of Denmark, VI, 52, 70, 105
Christian, elector and duke of Saxony, dedic to, V, 405, VI, 192
Christian and Christianity, V, 117, 120, 142, 206, VI, 72; attacked, V, 270, 287; change in, about 1800, predicted, V, 572; decline at hand, V, 108; faith professed, V, 84, 89, 91, 99, 100, 109, 311, 567, VI, 94, 292, 301, 306, 350, 484, 513-4, 518; instructed by Jews in diabolical arts, VI, 149; method of healing, VI, 545; orient won for, V, 272; revelation, V, 558; scepticism as to, V, 38; sign of triumph, VI, 184-5
Christmann, Jakob (d. 1613), VI, 61
Christmann, Jakob (d. 1630), V, 350
Christmas eve, VI, 240
Christopher, duke of Wurtemberg, VI, 76, 537
Christopher de Honestis, V, 42, 460
Christopher of Paris, V, 682; cited, V, 541, 604, VI, 250
Chronicle and Chronicler, see Historian and History
Chronology, V, 395; of Alfonsine Tables and the Book of Genesis, V, 192; dating the deluge, V, 190; erroneous, VI, 88-89, 353; of life of Christ and crucifixion, V, 257; studied, VI, 61; works on, V, 152, VI, 37, 442; and see Dating
Chrysanthemum, V, 448
Chrysippos, V, 523
Chrysogonus Polydorus, see Polydorus
Chrysolite, a gem, VI, 315
Chrysostom, St. V, 295, VI, 500
Chrysostom, a Dominican, *Solutiones*, V, 96, 98
Chrysostom, father, V, 130
Church, attitude towards anatomy, V, 514, 520, witchcraft, V, 105; educated for, VI, 76; fathers, V, 87, 567, VI, 293, cited, V, 120, VI, 361, 399, 445,

467, 530, 546, against Antipodes, VI, 436, against astrology, V, 140, 198, VI, 197, 199, 204, 347, 412, 500, compiled from, V, 142, esteemed, V, 295, prediction from, VI, 134; prediction as to, V, 202, 280-1, VI, 75; primitive, VI, 537; reform predicted, V, 272, 280; return to (Roman Catholic), V, 394; submission to, V, 81, 221, VI, 165, 168, 391, 409, 483, 513; and see Council
Church, Frederic C. (1932), V, 600, 613
Chyle, VI, 340
Chytraeus, David, V, 298, 397-8
Cicada, and the cuckoo, VI, 281
Cicer imperatoris, an herb, VI, 263
Cicero, V, 307, 421, VI, 353; against astrology, VI, 199, Chaldeans, V, 165; as a poet, V, 296; cited, VI, 32; *Divinatione,* VI, 503; quoted, V, 650; *Topics,* VI, 148
Cicogna, Strozzi (1605), VI, 550-1
Cilicia, V, 21, 229
Cimmerian Bosphorus, VI, 289
Cinaedus, V, 62
Cinaprium, V, 452
Cinnabar, V, 451-2 469, VI, 186, 310, 313
Cinnamon, V, 453, 463, 468-9, 663, VI, 186
Cinoglossa, an herb, VI, 263-4
Cinquarbres, Jean de, VI, 141
Ciottus, Ioan. Bapt. of Siena, pr Venice, VI, 410
Cipher, V, 22, 34, 567, 606, VI, 419
Circle, magic, V, 83
Circulation, of the blood, V, 30-31, VI, 328-32; of elements, V, 632-3; of humors, V, 122; of the spirits, VI, 330
Cirvelo, Pedro, V, 178, 210-1, 275-8; cited, V, 486, VI, 170; and Pigghe, compared, V, 281
Cistercian, V, 295, 535
Cisthon and Cisson, V, 452
Citation, see Authorities, Classics, and the names of authors
City, V, 579; astrology and, V, 191, 269, VI, 100, 114, 116, 204
Civilization, decline of, predicted, V, 566
Civitate nella Capitanata, bishop of, VI, 100
Clangor buccinae, V, 547, 624
Claramontius, Scipio (1641), VI, 510
Classical, allusions, V, 444; antiquities, .VI, 492; astrology, V, 358, VI, 133; citation, V, 4, 484-5, VI, 412, 420, 466; erudition, V, 153, 206, 300, VI, 112, 466, 480, 495, 502; names, V, 447, 523, VI, 271-4, 280, 303; philology, V, 383, 653; place names, V, 615; quotation, VI, 184; reaction, V, 3-4, 388, 408, 421, 430, 447-8, 459, 463, 489, 514, 529, VI, 83, 200, science secondary in, VI, 270, why unfavorable to alchemy? V, 620; teaching, V, 547, VI, 418
Claudia, queen of France, V, 124
Claudinus, Julius Caesar, VI, 431
Claues, Stephanus de (1624), VI, 388
Clauser, Christopher, owner of MSS, V, 362, 441
Clausum brunelli, V, 308
Claveus, see Duclo
Clavis sapientiae, V, 533
Clavius, Jesuit astronomer, VI, 45-46, 74, 97
Clay, blue, V, 28
Clemens, *De secretis naturae,* V, 623
Clement VI, V, 54, 229
Clement VII, addressed, V, 214, 217, 227, 229, 241, 243, 253, 294, 442, VI, 450, 470; astrology and, V, 214, 217, 227, 229, 241, 243; Copernican theory, V, 325, 410; disliked by Gaurico, V, 256; in the favor or service of, V, 260, 282, 325; nativity of, V, 230
Clement VIII, VI, 151, 374; bull of, VI, 374; dedic to, VI, 334
Clement, a heretic, VI, 551
Clementinus, Clementius, astrologer and physician, V, 169, 253
Cleomedes, V, 154, VI, 82
Clermont (near Beauvais), V, 477
Cleves, duke of, VI, 515; priest of, VI, 588
Clichtowe, Josse, VI, 443-4
Clidomancy, VI, 509
Clifton, C. E. (1842), V, 488
Climacteric, see Year, climacteric
Climate, V, 347; effect of, V, 34, 577, 593; of England, V, 578; temperate, V, 575; tropical and torrid, V, 195
Clime, VI, 21, 345, 436
Clinical method, V, 302
Clirosastre, see Sponnela
Clock, V, 614, VI, 471; astronomical,

V, 323, 584, VI, 88; common, at Rome, V, 271; manufacture of, V, 132, 338, 365; water, V, 146, 594, VI, 403; and see Watch
Clothing, VI, 221, 471; and see Costume
Clottus, Io. Bapt., of Siena, pr Bergamo, V, 261
Cloud, height over-estimated, VI, 22, 50, 366; forms assumed by, VI, 489; regions free from, V, 195
Cloven heel, V, 60
Clusa, see Jacobus de
Clusius, Carolus, tr, V, 466, 468, 470, VI, 258, 275, 314
Clyster, V, 114, 663
Coach and four, V, 202
Coblenz, VI, 255
Cobra, V, 476
Coburg, VI, 36; physician of, V, 654; rector of gymnasium of, VI, 238
Coch, Friedrich (1856), VI, 495
Cochran, John (1829), V, 247
Cock, employed in divination, VI, 509; frightens a lion, VI, 281; inferior to eagle, VI, 277; seems to know the stars, VI, 281; sometimes lays an egg, VI, 283; and see Lion
Coclearia, an herb, VI, 262-3
Cocles, Bartholomaeus, V, 43, 49, 580, 587, VI, 100, 163-4, 189; *Anastasis,* V, 42, 50-65, 671-2, 676; career, V, 50-51; death, V, 51-52, 234; geomancy of, V, 57; predictions of, 51-52; put on Index, VI, 146
Cocus, Simon, pr Antwerp, V, 208
Codronchi, B. *De morbis veneficis* (1595), V, 483, VI, 529, 544-7; cited, VI, 559
Coelestinus, St. V, 104, 106-7, VI, 532
Coelestinus, Claudius, V, 291, VI, 188, 278-9
Coeruleus, a gem, VI, 299
Coimbra, commentators of, VI, 205, 382, 387; pr at, VI, 35; university of, V, 284, 292, VI, 382, 387
Coin, gold, cooked with a capon, V, 459
Colaptic, V, 17
Colchester, VI, 63
Colemondus, Allanus, a patient, V, 302
Colic, V, 280, 559, 660, 662, VI, 208, 221, 233, 292, 423, 501
Colin, Sébastien, V, 464-5
Colinaeus, Simon, pr Paris, V, 153, 201, 264, 284, 291, 557
Collar, magic, V, 137
Colle Gonzoli, V, 28
Collection, see Museum
College of, All Souls, Oxford, V, 320; Beauvais, Paris, V, 298-300; blind men, VI, 522; Cambrai, Paris, V, 296, 464, VI, 10, 324, 344; Coquereti, V, 155; endowed at Padua, for Ravennese, V, 205; Guyenne, Bordeaux, VI, 561; Jesuit, at Rome, VI, 202; maître Gervase, Paris, V, 285; Montaigu, Paris, V, 285; Navarre, Paris, V, 156, 285, VI, 459; poets, Vienna, V, 347; Reims, Paris, V, 148-9, VI, 343-4; trilingual, Louvain, VI, 31; truth, VI, 126; and see Electoral, Physician
Collemesius, *Gallia orientalis,* VI, 106
Colliculus, an herb, VI, 264
Collimitius, see Tannstetter
Collier, K. B. (1934), VI, 362
Collyria, V, 461
Colmar, V, 430, 440, VI, 216
Colmet, Sieur, VI, 509
Cologne, V, 127, 269, 437; abbot of, VI, 218; archbishop of, V, 129, 390, 582, 666, VI, 123, 235; astronomical observations at, VI, 29; government of, VI, 119, 255; imperial palace, VI, 536; naturalists, VI, 255; pest at, VI, 211; pr at, V, 110, 142, 153, 155, 226, 232, 254, 256, 282, 303, 321, 355, 390, 548, 583, 601, 610, 621-2, 624-5, 648, VI, 14, 28, 45, 119, 137, 188-9, 211, 246, 253, 255-6, 259, 268, 271, 302, 369, 377, 393, 400, 410, 413, 445, 448-9, 456, 491, 522, 533, 546, 550, 558; studied at, V, 365; taught at, VI, 119, 122, 498; theologians of, VI, 364; university of, V, 129, VI, 119; visited, V, 407, 642
Colombo, Ealdo, anatomist, V, 45, 254, VI, 329; criticizes Vesalius, V, 530
Colonna, Antonio, V, 184
Colonna, Antonio, cardinal, VI, 273
Colonna, Fabio, VI, 258, 260, 273, 289
Colonna, Prospero, V, 73
Color, V, 54, 273, 555, VI, 175, 242, 354; altered, V, 147; angels and, VI, 324; books of, V, 34, VI, 216, 313; definition, VI, 365; diabolical, V, 60;

fallacies of, VI, 434; in combustion, VI, 342; of comet, VI, 90, element, VI, 343, gem, VI, 303, 322, herb, VI, 259, mineral, V, 593, planet, VI, 138, star, VI, 159, water, VI, 209-10; particular required, V, 559, VI, 216, 501, 509; relation to eye, V, 152; seven chief, V, 555; significance, VI, 367-8
Columbus, Christopher, V, 275, VI, 275, 346, 436
Columna, Fabius, see Colonna, Fabio
Combach, Ludwig (1649), VI, 161
Comedy, satiric, V, 229
Comet, VI, 41, 155; Aristotelian theory of, a misfit, VI, 86-87, abandoned, V, 570, VI, 67-68, 71, 74, 81-82, 84, 183, accepted, V, 141, 294, 389, 656, VI, 84, 88-89, 91, 93, 95-96, 143, 367, 379, 399, 503, 542, 569, compromised, V, 376, 553, VI, 79, 252-3, 381, 408; astrology and, VI, 86-88, 184; celestial, VI, 78-81, 190, 252, 355, 488, monsters, V, 248; effects, V, 163, 239, 320-1, 329, 401, VI, 78, 428, 488, appear later, V, 321, good, V, 321, VI, 474, 561, ill, V, 141, VI, 89, 167, 354, 367, 399, 542, denied, VI, 561, kings, death of, V, 156, 248, VI, 86, 89, 367, 542, denied, V, 294, 657, VI, 92, 185, questioned, VI, 92, 184, weather only, V, 657, VI, 92; Erastus on, V, 656-7; investigation of, value questioned, VI, 85; miraculous, VI, 542; movement of, V, 389, VI, 94, 96, 381; in regular orbit, VI, 75, 77, 79-80; observations of, V, 320, 366, VI, 54, 184; planets' influence on, V, 321, 389, VI, 87, 89, 95, 542; predicted, V, 230, VI, 79, 90, 94, 117; prediction from, V, 639, VI, 80, 87-88, opposed, V, 185, VI, 253; Regiomontanus on, V, 356-7, 365-6, 370; return of, not predicted, VI, 93-94; reviewed, V, 248, 299, 342, VI, 89-90, 117, 367, 399, 531, of 1470, VI, 89, of 1472, V, 362, 600, VI, 77, of 1477, VI, 89, of 1500, V, 351, of 1517, VI, 381, of 1531, V, 243, 293-4, 320, 322, 357, 382, VI, 90, 92, of 1532, V, 320, 322, VI, 90, 92, 381, of 1533, V, 410, 421, VI, 90, of 1547, V, 269, of 1554, VI, 92, of 1556, V, 330, 342, 397, VI, 75, 111, 183-4, 531, of 1558, VI, 92, 183-4, of 1572, see Star, new, of 1577, V, 398, VI, 46, 70, 73-80, 84, 90-93, 128, 134, 143, 183, 409, 474, 561, of 1578, VI, 57, 123, of 1580, VI, 74, 80-81, 143, of 1585, VI, 71, 74, 95, of 1596, VI, 143, of 1604, VI, 87, 252-3, of 1618, VI, 61, 166, 236, 360-1, 507, 560; signs, as, VI, 92, 190, 490; sun and, VI, 381; terrestrial exhalations, see Aristotelian theory of; where generated? in sphere of fire, V, 553, intermediate sphere, VI, 408, special orb, V, 490, VI, 79-80; works on, V, 299, 370-1, VI, 133, 483; zodiac, significance in, VI, 490
Comitibus, Lotharius de, dedic to, V, 261
Comitibus, Niccolò de, cited, VI, 300
Communes, revolt of, in Spain, V, 208
Como, see Bernard of
Compass, mariners', V, 614; points of, VI, 454; and see Magnetic
Compendium, attitude towards, V, 35, 148-9, 388; prevalence of, V, 5-6, 152-4, VI, 32
Compilation, abandoned, VI, 137; professed, V, 174; and see Authorities
Complexio, V, 59-60, 117, 323, 473, 551, VI, 164, 221; dream from, VI, 417; fine distinctions as to, V, 506-7; human like that of gold, V, 639; latitude of, V, 475; signs of, VI, 428; work on, VI, 393
Compluti, see Alcalà
Compostela, V, 585
Compound, chemical, VI, 242; medicine, V, 461, 483-4, 489, 608, VI, 230, condemned, V, 35, 598, VI, 567, approved V, 420; method of preparing and mixing, VI, 419, 461
Computus, see Calendar
Conception, VI, 221; aid to, V, 444; conditions of, V, 504; effect of imagination during, V, 107; sign of, V, 147; stars at, V, 371, VI, 203; time of, V, 242, VI, 204
Conches, see William of
Conchites, V, 597
Conciliator, see Peter of Abano
Concoction, V, 289, VI, 355
Condé, prince of, VI, 490-1
Condensation and rarefaction, V, 495

Confederate, in magic, V, 103
Confession, V, 117; Barozzi's, V, 154; death without, VI, 164; to priest, V, 86; under torture, V, 103; and see Witch
Conflagration, final, V, 223, 418, VI, 26, 29, 367-8, 514, conjunction favorable to, V, 195, not under stars, V, 124, 195, predicted for 1654, VI, 76, universal unlikely, V, 158
Congress, International, history of medicine, V, 330, 505, VI, 241, 247, 300, 341, history of science, VI, 55, 168
Conic sections, V, 353
Coningo, Nicolas, VI, 553
Conimbricenses, see Coimbra
Conjunction, of planets, death from, V, 60; disease from, V, 195, 227, 489, 497, VI, 211, 408; effect, long continued, V, 203, 218, 225, 248, not immediately felt, V, 180, 193, 203, 207, 217, 230, on kingdoms and sects, VI, 354, on nativity, V, 163, 277, on prophets, VI, 512, on the weather, VI, 199; Melanchthon's fear of, V, 400-1; past reviewed, V, 223, VI, 490, before the flood, V, 120, 189-90, 193, 198, 227, before birth of Christ, VI, 117, in 630 A.D., VI, 187, in 670, V, 223, 226, in 1345, V, 195, VI, 187, in 1365, V, 229, 278, in 1405, V, 278, in 1425, V, 278, in 1444, V, 124, in 1464, V, 124, VI, 187, in 1483, V, 434, in 1484, V, 58, 63, 195, 204, 206-7, 227, 235, 489, 497, VI, 187, 500, in 1496, V, 195, in 1502, V, 162, in 1503-1504, V, 179-80, 223, 235, 238-40, in 1507, V, 238, in 1509, V, 238, in 1513, V, 227, in 1522, V, 242, in 1524, V, 158, 178-233, 239, 294, 386, 396, 400, VI, 144, 187, 197, in 1544, V, 182, 212, 260, 311, 392, 396, in 1554, V, 400, in 1563, V, 415, VI, 95, in 1564, V, 248, VI, 117, in 1583, V, 374, VI, 95, 117, 253, 488, in 1584, V, 325, in 1603, VI, 173, events of 1789 from, V, 202, 311; six great, VI, 75; six types, V, 265; theory of, V, 164, 168, 214, VI, 139, 253, 471, 500, and see Ptolemy, accepted V, 318, 417, VI, 114, 118, 174, in part, V, 277, VI, 121, 138, attacked, V, 120, 180, 185, 191, 227, developed, V, 216; works on, VI, 116-17; and see Triplicitas
Conjuration, V, 472
Conrad a Liechthenau, cited, VI, 458
Conscience, VI, 204; physical effect of guilty, VI, 241
Consecration, of rings, V, 176; and see Angus Dei, Bell
Consilia, medieval medical, V, 59, 442, 536, 600, VI, 100; 16th century, V, 327, 391, 617, 645, VI, 128-9, 230
Consilium coniugii, V, 622
Constance, V, 392
Constantine, emperor, V, 539, VI, 76, 117
Constantinople, VI, 468; fall of, V, 373, VI, 202, misdated, VI, 89; specimens from, VI, 268; and see Yesid
Constantinus Africanus, V, 494; cited, V, 54
Constantinus, Robertus (1555), V, 289, 318, 409, 548, VI, 12, 454
Constantinus, Sebastian, V, 215-7
Constantius, see Costanzo
Constipation, V, 612
Consubstantiation denied, VI, 494, 496
Consumption, V, 280, VI, 223; cured, V, 540
Contact, no action without, V, 100, 495, VI, 388
Contagion, relation to poison, V, 496, to putrefaction, V, 496, to sympathy and antipathy, V, 493-7; and see Disease
Contarini, Gasparo, cardinal, V, 559; *Elementis,* V, 254, 552-5, VI, 350; cited, VI, 349; plagiarized, V, 555-6
Contarini, Giov. Gabriele, VI, 349
Contarini, G. P., VI, 142
Contarini, Jacopo, dedic to, VI, 458
Contarini, Marco Ant., podestà of Padua, V, 524
Contarini, Niccolò, *De perfectione rerum,* VI, 349-51
Continuum, division of, V, 23
Contraries, V, 495, 527, VI, 231, 251, 311, 414, 564
Controversy, V, 9, VI, 238, 354, 406; alchemical, V, 640-2, 648, 665-6, VI, 245, 247-52; astrological, V, 180, 189-90, 197-201, 204, 206-8, 215-7, 221-9, 328-30, VI, 113; astronomical, VI, 7,

and see Star, new; botanical, VI, 224; comet of 1533, V, 410; grammatical, VI, 190; immortality, V, 96-98, 493; logical, VI, 238; medical, V, 260-7, 326, 464-6, 493, VI, 212-5, 479, 553; recent as to discovery of circulation of the blood, VI, 328-30; tone of, V, 653; Wier and Skalich, VI, 456
Convent of saints John and Paul, V, 517
Conventius, Stephanus, VI, 450
Cook, V, 618
Cookbook for invalids, V, 443
Cooperation, intellectual, VI, 267-9
Cop, Bernard, preface to, VI, 352
Copé, E. tr., V, 607
Copenhagen, VI, 598; museum, VI, 269, 311; pr at, VI, 523; university, V, 388, VI, 69, 124, 523
Copernican theory, V, 32; "absurdity" of, VI, 39, 43, 46, 52, 57, 275; astrology and, V, 367, 411, 414-9, VI, 8, 29-31; attitude towards of, Aristotelians, VI, 47-48, Barozzi, VI, 47, 155, Belot, VI, 361-2, Benedetti, VI, 50-51, Besson, VI, 38, Blaeu, VI, 8, Bodin, VI, 42-43, Biesius, VI, 19, Brahe, Tycho, and his correspondents, V, 429, VI, 51-55, Brucaeus, VI, 38, Bruno, VI, 51, 427, Cardan, V, 570, Chassin, VI, 384, Christmann, VI, 61, Clavius, VI, 45-46, Constantinus, VI, 12, Crusius, VI, 36-37, Dee, VI, 18, 26, Digges, VI, 39-40, Dodoens, VI, 9-10, 47, Feild, VI, 18, Femelius, VI, 6, Forster, VI, 42, Freige, VI, 45, Galileo, VI, 62-63, 428, Garcaeus, VI, 19, Gemma, Cornelius, V, 31, Gemma Frisius, VI, 13-14, Gesner, VI, 8-9, Gilbert, VI, 61-62, Giuntini, VI, 44-45, Hortensius, VI, 7, Inquisition, VI, 63, Leonicerus, VI, 45, Leoninus, VI, 45, Maestlin, VI, 4-5, 46-47, 78, Magini, V, 251, VI, 56-59, Maurolycus, VI, 27, Mesmes, VI, 21, Minerva, VI, 63-64, Nabod, VI, 40, Nunes, VI, 35-36, Origanus, VI, 61, Patrizi, VI, 376, Peletier, VI, 33-34, Pena, VI, 19-20, Peucer, VI, 11-12, Praetorius, VI, 59-60, Recorde, VI, 16, Rothmann, VI, 84, Schreckenfuchs, VI, 3, 16-17, 37-38, Stadius, VI, 14-15, 28-29, Stanhufius, VI, 32, Theodoricus, VI, 34-35, Tyard, VI, 25; church and, V, 410, VI, 63, 145, 428; circles, number required, V, 406; figure or model of, VI, 38, 44, 55, 60; hypothesis, regarded as, V, 413, 591, VI, 11, 14, 17-18, 21, 39, 46, 56; ignored, VI, 10, 27, 29-31, 36, 87, 92, 201, 326, 348, 355, 399; more interest in Prutenic Tables, VI, 4-5, 64-65; New Star of 1572 more startling, VI, 68; not presented in elementary textbooks, VI, 7-8; preparation for publication of, V, 408-12, 489; reception of, stages in, V, 413, VI, 64-66, contrasted with Paracelsan revival, V, 629-30; religious opposition to, overestimated, VI, 7; supported by comet of 1577, VI, 78; Wittenberg and, V, 384-5
Copernicus, and astrology, V, 419-20, VI, 29; authors used by, V, 341, 360, 421-2; background, V, 408; cited, V, 418-9, 429, VI, 10, 21, 29, 34, 41, 71, 82, 103, 396, 430; comet, on, V, 410; *Commentariolus,* V, 406, 408-9; compared with contemporaries, V, 422, 550, 629; criticized, VI, 35; encouraged to publish, V, 367, 410-13; geniture, VI, 595; medicine of, V, 419-20, 629; observations by, V, 412, 425-7, VI, 3-4, 133, used without acknowledgment, VI, 17; other occupations, V, 426; praised, V, 411-2, 415, VI, 6, 11, 17-19, 30, 45-46, 57-58, 376, 424; Ptolemy and, V, 422-5, VI, 35; relative distance and magnitude of sun, moon and earth, VI, 10-11, 24, 34, 53; reputation during lifetime, V, 408-9; *Revolutionibus,* V, 254, 406, 408-9, 413-4, 420-9, 528, 629, VI, 3, 9, 28, 36, 52; teacher of, V, 180, 234; triangles, on, V, 414, VI, 35; Werner and, V, 353, 406, VI, 36
Copho, *Anatomia porci,* V, 460, 520
Copingen, W. A. (1895-1902), V, 116
Copland, Wm. pr Lothbury, VI, 483
Copp, Ioannes, Dr., astrologer, V, 217
Coppé, Estienne, tr, V, 607
Copper, VI, 209; fusion of, VI, 217
Coppin, Nicolas, of Mons, V, 207
Copyist, faults of, V, 100, 602-3
Coquille, Guy, historian, VI, 202

Cor leonis, a star, V, 289
Coracinus, a fish, VI, 282
Coral, VI, 307; amulet, V, 455, 462; fishers, V, 591; generation of, V, 108; purifies water, V, 611; remedy, V, 457, 651; suffumigations, in, VI, 405; theriac, in, V, 453
Corbeil, see Aegidius of,
Corbett, James (1939), V, 543
Corbett, Walter, nativity of, VI, 30
Cordial, see Heart
Cordova, of, VI, 391; pr at, VI, 96, 166
Cordova, see Hernandez de
Cordus, Euricius, V, 454, VI, 254, 280
Cordus, Valerius (1515-1544), V, 452, 470, VI, 254-6, 258, 261, 265, 272, 280, 597
Coriander water, V, 454
Corinaldo, V, 200
Cornarius, Ianus, tr, VI, 213, 476; cited, V, 470
Cornelius, Fantinus, VI, 105
Cornix, H. pr Antwerp, VI, 494
Cornucopiae, VI, 300
Corneus, Conradus, pr Wolfenbüttel, VI, 210
Cornuty, George, VI, 252
Coronel, Ludovicus, V, 158
Coronobachius, Wendalinus, medical, V, 437
Corpse, animated by demon, V, 136, VI, 532; bleeds at approach of murderer, VI, 239-42, 354, 408, 540, 548; contagion ceases in, V, 497; form of, V, 40; hair grows on, V, 511; hand of, divination from, VI, 509; heavier than living body, VI, 403; medicinal use of, see Mumia, condemned, V, 455; species from, VI, 403; why so cold, V, 146; and see Post mortem
Corpus reformatorum, V, 375, 379, 381-2, 384, 386-7, 390-1, 393, 396, 399-401
Correctio fatuorum, V, 547
Correctorium, V, 537
Correggio, V, 46
Corruption, see Generation and, Putrefaction
Corsica, V, 446
Corte, Bartolomeo (1718), VI, 129, 368
Cortés, Gerónimo, on comets, VI, 95-96; *Lunario,* VI, 96, 166-7; *Phisonomia,* VI, 96, 166-7, 428-9; other works, VI, 166
Cortese, Isabella, VI, 218
Cortese, N. (1924), V, 74, 254, 274, VI, 492
Cortesius, Paul, V, 8
Cortusus, Iacobus Ant., botanist (1591), VI, 258
Corvinus, see Matthias
Corvus, Andreas, chiromancer, V, 55-56, 64-65, 587, VI, 163, 177, 510; put on Index, VI, 147
Coscinomancy, VI, 503, 508
Cosenza, VI, 370
Cosmetic, V, 543, VI, 218, 248, 419
Cosmography, V, 9, 152, 319, 347, 431, 521, VI, 47, 155, 430
Costá, à, see Acosta
Costa ben Luca, V, 560, 562
Costaeus, see Costeo
Costanzo of Bologna, astrologer, V, 246-7
Costeo, Giovanni, botanist (1578), VI, 258
Costil, Pierre (1935), VI, 183
Costume, V, 141; cabalistic, VI, 454
Costus subamarus, VI, 267
Cotta, John (1612), VI, 222, 517
Cottula foetida, VI, 262, 264
Cough, V, 280, VI, 367; dry, VI, 212
Council, Church, V, 87, VI, 532, 541, of Braga, VI, 125, Lateran in 1512, V, 94, 408, VI, 36, Maulbronn, V, 652, Rome, VI, 551, Trent, V, 488; VI, 48, 148, 159, 172, 176, 178, 183, 292-3; of Ten, see Venice
Count palatine, V, 74
Counterfeiter, V, 539, 664
Covarrubias, VI, 355
Court and Courtier, V, 128, 132
Coutances, bishop of, V, 309
Cow, Alpine, V, 627; changes color, V, 463; dissected, V, 519; scorpion and, V, 481
Cowherd, VI, 294
Coxe, H. O., V, 170
Crab, stone from, VI, 323; suspended, VI, 282
Crabbe, Johannes, VI, 253
Cracow, almanach of, V, 173; books sent to, V, 339; composed at, V, 320; eclipse at, V, 425; in, V, 415-6, 619,

VI, 59, 393; of, V, 6, VI, 267, 480; pr at, V, 173-4, 218, 347, 354, 625; taught at, VI, 449; university of, V, 173, 180
Cradle, VI, 404
Craig, H. (1916), V, 673-6
Crane, bird, V, 104; machine, V, 595
Crasso, Lorenzo, VI, 163
Cratander, And., pr Basel, V, 331
Crato, Johann, imperial physician, V, 327, 620, 658, VI, 136, 269
Crato, Johannes, pr Wittenberg, VI, 11, 34, 493
Crawfurd, R. (1917), V, 176
Creation, affirmed, VI, 26, 352, 450, 551; Aristotle and, V, 42; biblical account of, accepted, VI, 346, 356-7, 382, 496; daily, VI, 259; date of, V, 192; divine, VI, 482; of birds and fish, VI, 347, disease, V, 659, elements, V, 591, metals, VI, 347, mountains, V, 592; position of planets at, V, 309; questioned, V, 120; special, see Star, of Bethlehem, of 1572
Credulity, V, 82-83, 89, 103, 535, 568, VI, 247, 285-6, 401, 502; limits to, V, 474, 476; of lay princes and magistrates, V, 7-8, modern scientists, V, 22, Pico, Francesco, VI, 469; and see Faith, Scepticism, Truth
Crellius, Paulus, VI, 596
Crema, V, 269
Cremona, V, 269, 529; virgin birth at, V, 270
Cremonini, cardinal, V, 488
Cremonini, Cesare, Aristotelian, VI, 202; disciple of, VI, 511
Crespin, J. pr Lyons, V, 122
Crete, VI, 154
Crime, charge of, V, 505; homicide, V, 61; prevalence of, V, 164, VI, 441; revealed by astrology, V, 384; and see Corpse, bleeding, Theft
Criminal, VI, 121-3; boldness of, V, 613; Cardan on, V, 578; corpse dissected, V, 520; executed, examined, VI, 164; esteemed saint, V, 102; freed, V, 142; made to restore stolen goods, VI, 440; physiognomy of, V, 59; treatment of, V, 578
Crinitus, Petrus, cited, VI, 503
Crisis, see Day, critical, Disease
Crispinus, Ioannes, pr Geneva, VI, 530
Criteria of truth, see Truth
Critias, Andreas, dedic to, V, 218
Critical attitude, VI, 137
Croce, Maddelena della, VI, 391
Crocodile, V, 474; and wren, VI, 416
Croesus, V, 389
Croll, Oswald, Paracelsan, V, 649-51, VI, 212, 294
Cronaca Seccadenari, V, 51
Crops, ceremonies to save, V, 231; cycles of, VI, 487; failure of, V, 230, VI, 119; prediction as to, V, 172, 192, 211, 225, 235, 392, VI, 119, 501; suffer from witches, VI, 539
Cross, form of, VI, 404; signs of, V, 102, 108, VI, 241, 302, 434, 553, 557
Croton, VI, 213
Crow, V, 55, VI, 277; in alchemy, V, 538; sign of evil, V, 104
Crown of thorns, VI, 438
Crucifix stone, VI, 321
Crucigerus, Caspar, Sr. VI, 597
Crucigerus, Caspar, Jr., VI, 596
Crucius, Laevinus, VI, 556
Cruelty to animals, V, 454-5, VI, 420-1
Cruserus (Peter Creutzer?), VI, 381
Crusius, Martin, V, 380, VI, 190
Crusius, Carolus, VI, 598
Crusius, Paul (1567), VI, 36-37
Crystal gazing, V, 399, VI, 498-9, 520, 536
Crystals, VI, 243
Cucchius, Ioannes Aug., surgeon, VI, 290
Cuckoo, see Cicada
Cucumber, forced growth of, VI, 431
Cues, see Nicholas of Cusa
Culm, bishop of, V, 411
Cumae, V, 269
Cummin, an herb, V, 444
Cuneus, Gabriel (1563), VI, 213-4
Cunningham, astrologer, VI, 180
Cure, marvelous, V, 99-103, VI, 512
Cureus, Adam, V, 404
Cureus, Joachim (1532-1573), V, 381, 403-4, 559, VI, 229, 364-6
Curieus, or, Curieux, Le, interlocutor, VI, 25-26, 107
Curieux, Le, interlocutor, See Curieus
Curio, Geo. VI, 598
Curio Hofemianus, Jacobus, V, 298

Curtius, Matth., V, 325-6, 410; cited, VI, 317; comm. Mundinus, V, 501; opposed, V, 260
Curtius Symphorianus, Benedictus, V, 445
Curtze, Maximilian (1874), V, 410-1, 425-6; (1878), V, 409
Custom, force of, VI, 204
Customs duties, V, 74
Cutica, Hieronymus, astrologer, V, 162
Cuttle fish, VI, 467
Cyaneus, a stone, VI, 299
Cycle, astrological, V, 427; of fertility and scarcity, VI, 487
Cyclometer, V, 594
Cyclops, VI, 408
Cynocephalus, V, 513, VI, 278
Cyprus, VI, 337; Jew of, VI, 449; trip to, VI, 373; terebinth from, V, 461
Cyrene, see Synesius of
Cyrus, V, 389
Czerny, Albin (1888), V, 221

Dactilomancy or Dactyliomancy, VI, 499, 509
Dalbya, Chr. Joh. (1612), VI, 559
Dalechamps, V, 466; ed Pliny, VI, 258
Dallari, Umberto (1888-1924), V, 39, 61, 90, 95, 237, 246, 250, 261, 325, 505, VI, 48, 152, 257
Dalmatia, V, 314, VI, 373; died in, V, 505
Dalmatius, astronomer, VI, 344
Damascus, VI, 449; see John of
Dançay, Charles de, V, 324
Dandolo, Matteo, addressed, V, 552
Dane, V, 642, VI, 136; and see Denmark
Daneau, Lambert, career, VI, 346; cited, VI, 538, 554; *Physice Christiana,* VI, 346-9; *Veneficis,* VI, 522
Daniel the prophet, V, 403, VI, 76; Dream Book of, VI, 475-6, 480
Dantiscus, John, see John
Danube, V, 24, 407; low, V, 223
Danzig, V, 327, 641, VI, 596; pr at, V, 391, 412; town council of, V, 481; and see John Dantiscus
Dardanus, alchemist, V, 624
Dariot, Claude, astrologer and physician, VI, 105-6
Dark, afraid of, VI, 403; ages, V, 336; sensation in, V, 146
Darmstaedter, Ernst (1925), V, 536-7; (1931), V, 625; (1933), V, 625
Daroca, V, 275
Dastin, John, cited, V, 623
Dasypodius, Conrad, cited, VI, 184, and criticized, VI, 194; on comets, VI, 88-90; ed., V, 364
Dating, problem of, V, 182-8, 308-11, 613, 641, VI, 115, 387; misdating, VI, 102, 104, 111, 127-8, 130, 134, 136, 152, 162, 224, 244, 303
Daucus asininus, an herb, VI, 263-4
Dauphin of France, V, 318
Dauphiné, V, 589
David, VI, 353; plays before Saul, VI, 234
David, Matth. pr Paris, V, 556
Davis and Orioli, V, 85
Davolos, Alfonsus, dedic to, V, 258
Davy, Jacques, bishop of Evreux, VI, 361
Day, critical, V, 78, 122, 174, 250, 260-3, 284, 301-2, 314-5, 318-9, 475, 557, VI, 76, 106, 128, 144, 165, 198, 378, controversy as to, V, 260-1, due to sun and moon, V, 572, explained astrologically, V, 317, 325, VI, 127, 159, 479, 500, Fracastoro on V, 491-2, not due to moon, V, 318, 491-2, VI, 188, 200, 205, 388; Egyptian, VI, 124, 144, 174-5; equation of, VI, 15, 103; fatal for blood-letting, V, 420; feast, V, 95, VI, 151, 208, movable, V, 284; length of, explained, V, 388, reckoned, V, 339; lucky and unlucky, V, 420, 537, 614, VI, 174, 221; observance of, VI, 520, censured, V, 283; Friday and Sunday in the life of Christ, V, 257; Sabbath, VI, 88, 404; Saints', VI, 88-89; Tuesday, VI, 404; January 25, VI, 488
Day, John, pr London, VI, 72
De balneis omnia quae extant, V, 254, 438, 514, 537, 605, VI, 208
De cometis dissertationes novae (1580), VI, 183
De congelatis, V, 48
Deacon, V, 354, VI, 76
Dead Sea, fables concerning, V, 448

Dean, ecclesiastical, V, 586; medical, V, 112, 288-90, 328, 609, VI, 229, 252, 284; philosophical, VI, 229, of via antiqua, V, 406
Death, VI, 369; apparent, VI, 513; early, VI, 195; house of, V, 216; natural, VI, 385; predicted of others, V, 55, 212, 236, 256, 313, VI, 15, 127, 136, own, V, 51-52, 234, 250, VI, 136, incorrectly, VI, 114, 138, kind of, VI, 195, of Pico, VI, 107, 170, of the pope, V, 268; sensed, VI, 511; signified, V, 172, VI, 530; suicide, V, 253, VI, 123; violent, V, 51-52, 587, VI, 100, 164, 194, 385, 543; warning of distant, V, 574-5
Debt and Debtor, V, 297
Decan (astrological), V, 122, VI, 124, rejected, VI, 138
Declamation, see Oration
Decretal, against alchemy, see John XXII; cited, V, 384; lecturer on, V, 261; and see Law, Canon
Dee, John, V, 422, VI, 36; cited, VI, 381, 459; letter of, VI, 17-18, 392; *Monas hieroglyphica,* VI, 457; *Parallaticae,* VI, 72; praised, VI, 42; *Propaedeumata,* VI, 26, 392
Deer, V, 517, VI, 277; burnt horn of, V, 454; dissected, V, 454; eats snakes, VI, 315; stone from tears of, VI, 310, 315; tears of, VI, 311
Deformity, V, 61
Degeneracy, see Heredity
Degree, academic, V, 288, 325, 431, VI, 267, 322, cheap, V, 112; decline of doctoral, VI, 112; honorary and misnamed, V, 111-2; of medicines and simples, V, 440
Deism, V, 37
Delambre, J. B. J. (1819), V, 319-20, VI, 28
Delandine, A. F. (1812), V, 112
Delassus (1636), VI, 560
Delaunay, Paul, VI, 247, 254, 257, 341
Delfino, Federigo, V, 327, VI, 28; cited, VI, 382
Delhi, V, 466
Delirium, V, 626
Delius, Matthaeus, VI, 136
Delmineo, see Camillo
Delphic oracle, VI, 107
Delphinus, see Delfino
Delrio, Martin, V, 136, 487, VI, 148, 163, 552, 554, 559
Deluge, see Flood
Demagogue, V, 224
Demetrius, alchemist, V, 624
Democritus, cited as alchemist, V, 624, on dreams, VI, 484, on necromancy, VI, 477, on secrets of nature and poisons, VI, 388; not an alchemist, VI, 250
Demon, VI, 400; accused of dealings with, V, 102, VI, 156; aerial, V, 639, VI, 352, 428, 528, 532; Agrippa on, V, 135-6, his dog considered one, V, 137; alchemy and, VI, 244, 247, 250, 544; as mean between, V, 88; astrology and, V, 92-93, VI, 200, 497, 541-2; augury and, VI, 486; bodies assumed by, V, 88, 136, 666, VI, 337, 417, 526, 532, denied, V, 33, VI, 513, 531, 534; bodies of, V, 88, 486, 568, VI, 405; bonds of, VI, 425; Cardan on, V, 567-9, 579; cause future events, V, 210; classes, kinds, orders and types of, V, 84, 88, 118, VI, 336, 405, 425, 440, 551; coerced or not, V, 84, 140-1, VI, 519, 558; cure revealed by, V, 463; communicating with, V, 569, VI, 425; disagreement of Peripatetics and theologians as to, V, 42, 100-101; disease and, V, 627, VI, 425, 518-9, 528; divination and, V, 84, VI, 149, 156, 190, 360, 532; effects attributed to, futile and petty, V, 109, 568; existence, accepted on faith, V, 10, 568, VI, 131, 566, proved experimentally, V, 100, VI, 455, questioned or denied, V, 78, 270, 567-8, VI, 468, 484, 519, 550, 570; familiar, see personal; expelling, VI, 532-3, 540, and see Exorcism; games of chance and, VI, 200; gem and, VI, 305, 321-2, 324; herb mistaken for, V, 458; illusions of, V, 143, VI, 515, 531-2, 547; incubus and succubus, see Incubus; intelligence of, V, 568; invoked, V, 458, 564, 569, VI, 108, 132, 148, 154, 551; knowledge, V, 118, VI, 386, none of particular objects, V, 101, VI, 513, or of men's minds, VI, 549, of future, V, 84, 568, VI, 523, 541, 549, denied, VI,

391; location of, V, 568-9, VI, 391, 428, 534, 538, in Elbe, V, 401, and see aerial, underground; magic and, V, 83-84, 399, VI, 397-8, 411, 416, 525, 558; medicine and, V, 101, VI, 553, 559; miracle and, V, 100; moon and, VI, 486; names of, VI, 556-7; natural explanation of, VI, 336; nature and, V, 69, 92, 104, 117-8, 486, 628, 639, VI, 104, 132, 235, 391, 426, 515-6; Nifo on, V, 82-86; nutriment, V, 89, VI, 385; oracles and, V, 104, VI, 466; pact with, V, 69, 119-20, 140-1, 487, 574, VI, 200, 405, 408, 467, 508, 515, 517, 520, 526, 528, 534, 542, 601, personal, V, 568, 574, VI, 539, 551; persons sensible to, V, 568; purely spiritual, VI, 529; possessed by, see Demoniac; powers of, V, 70, 92, 101, 117-8, VI, 337, 497, 511, in air, VI, 548, introducing foreign substances into human body, VI, 540, moving bodies, V, 101, 568, VI, 417, 536, sexual intercourse, V, 666-7, VI, 362, 405, 515, 526, 534, 536; quoted, V, 219; remedies, from, V, 660, VI, 219, 234; against, V, 462, VI, 405, 547; revelation and, VI, 481; routed by occult virtues, VI, 354; safeguards against, VI, 169, 529, 553; sense of touch in, V, 88; senses deceived rather than affected by, V, 568; souls of dead and, VI, 530; specters attributed to, VI, 530, 533; speech of, V, 84; stories of, V, 136; stratagems of, VI, 518; suggestion, V, 215; underground, VI, 295, 528, 551; weather and, V, 92, VI, 391; Witelo on, V, 86-89; works on, V, 82-89, VI, 287, 445

Demoniac, V, 89, 118, VI, 336, 546, 554-5; lunar, V, 242; melancholy, V, 444; reputed, V, 97, VI, 497; signs of, VI, 337, 532; and see Exorcism

Denbighe, baron of, VI, 41

Denguetus, Petrus, a patient, V, 302

Denmark, V, 324, 630; king of, V, 371, 401, VI, 136, 535, 537; royal family of, VI, 70; and see Dane

Descartes, anticipated, VI, 362, 382-4, 562-3

Design, V, 23; argument from, V, 592

Despars, Jacques, see Jacobus de Partibus

Des Périers, Bonaventure, V, 286-7; quoted, V, 275

Despot, see Machiavelli, *Prince:* Bentivoglio, Malatesta, etc.

Desvernay, Felix (1904), V, 161

Deusing (Ant.), V, 10

Deutsch, Joseph (1910), V, 348

Deventer, taught at, VI, 255

Devil, see Demon

Dew, V, 29; and see May dew

Deweert, Jules (1912), V, 580

Diacceto, see Cattani, Francesco de

Diacetius, see Cattani, Francesco de

Diagnosis, not the sum total of medicine, VI, 251

Diagram, alchemical, V, 538; astronomical, VI, 40, 44, 182, 406; geometrical, VI, 442; of the hand, V, 56, 67, 587; and see Figura coeli

Dialectic, attacked, V, 128, 280, VI, 128, 565; defended, VI, 446; Lullian, VI, 361; of Erastus, V, 653; of Melanchthon, V, 390; of Patrizi, VI, 374; taught, see Logic

Dialogue, V, 139, 206, 254, 445, 461, 538, 545-6, 645, 653, 666, VI, 25, 107, 112, 181, 219, 244, 256, 313, 347, 377, 390, 400, 489, 493, 549, 568

Diamond, rapid generation of, VI, 314; virtues, VI, 314-5, denied, VI, 305, 314, proved false, VI, 282, 420; and see Goat, Magnet

Diani nel Pelegrino, Tito, bookseller, Rome, VI, 139

Diarrhoea, V, 612; caused by excess of salt, V, 626

Diary, VI, 219

Dibdin, T. F., VI, 476

Dictation, V, 441

Dictionary, V, 502

Dictionary of National Biography, VI, 483, 520

Dido, V, 486

Diego de Tores, *Pronostico,* V, 201

Dienheim, Johann Wolfgang, Paracelsist (1610), V, 651

Dieppe, VI, 108-9

Diet, V, 651, 659, VI, 222-3, 463

Dieterici, F. (1882-1883), VI, 449

Dietrich of Bern, V, 229

Digby (Kenelm), V, 10
Digestion, V, 554, VI, 221, 403
Digges, Leonard, VI, 39-40
Digges, Thomas (1573), V, 377, VI, 39, 72-73; cited, VI, 381
Dijon, V, 307-11, VI, 341; pr at, V, 309
Dinkelsbühl, VI, 597
Dino (del Garbo?), V, 502
Dino Junior, V, 503
Diocletian, VI, 117
Diogenes Laertius, VI, 460
Dionysidorus, V, 353
Dionysius, compiled from, V, 551
Dionysius of Alexandria, cited, VI, 300
Dionysius the Areopagite, V, 109
Dionysius the Carthusian, cited, VI, 361
Dioscorides, as an authority, VI, 260, cited, V, 46, 451-2, 460, 473, 663, VI, 223, 259, 292, 300, 303, 305, 308-9, 311, 319, 334, 353; comm. V, 462, VI, 224, 227, 254, 261, 286, 312; disagreement with Theophrastus, Pliny and Galen, V, 463; ed, V, 443, VI, 267; extracts from, V, 475; names of herbs in, V, 447-9, VI, 271-3; omissions etc., V, 467-8, VI, 260, 274; tr, V, 463
Dipsas snake, V, 477, 551
Direction (astrological), V, 58, 171-2, 266, 319-20, 351, VI, 36, 115, 120-2, 131, 138, 140, 160; rejected, VI, 144; and see Regiomontanus, Tables of
Discovery, natural, aimed at, VI, 156; reputed scientific, V, 22; and see Voyages of
Disease, V, 102, 367, 444, VI, 221, 226, 230, 513, 602; acute, VI, 251; astral, V, 659, VI, 190; cause of, V, 651, 659, VI, 212, 519; conjunctions and, see Conjunction; contagious, V, 483, 493, 496-7, VI, 229, 232, seminaries of, V, 496, 659; demon and, see Demon; forecast, V, 225, 235, 280, 392, 399; four kinds, V, 627, 649, 651, 659; from bathing, VI, 208; from fear, VI, 241; internal, V, 482; invisible, V, 627; lethal, V, 163; local remedy for, VI, 423; magic cure of, VI, 516, 536; magic transfer of, VI, 243, 525-6, 548; minor, cured by imagination and exhalation, VI, 477; new, VI, 408; none incurable, V, 638; occult, V, 559; of animals, VI, 487; of boys, V, 486; Paracelsus on, V, 626-7, 638; physical predisposition for, V, 63; predicted, VI, 243, not predicted, VI, 394; preternatural, VI, 525, 536; produced by sorcery, V, 483; splenetic, V, 506; triple variety of, VI, 518; witch and, see Witch
Disputation, V, 38, 59, 95, 274, 381, 403, 531, VI, 63, 214, 227, 423, 498; and see Theses
Dissection, V, 44, 47, 146, 288, 501, VI, 214, 281, 296, 326; by Brasavola, V, 451, 454, Carpi, V, 507-8, Massa, V, 516-7, Vesalius, V, 519, 523, 525, 530; in the schools, V, 500; medieval, V, 498; obtaining cadavers for, V, 520, 525-6; of animal, V, 454, 519, 523, VI, 269; of executed criminal, V, 454, 520; public, V, 509, 520; "professors of," V, 524
Dissertation, doctoral, VI, 229
Distillation, V, 416, 432, 532, 542, 544, 621, 643, 657, VI, 209, 217, 242-3, 250-1, 292, 378; of head, VI, 223; of metal simply by fire and evaporation, V, 635
Dithmarus, see Ursus
Dittany, V, 102
Diver's suit, V, 34
Diversus, Petrus Salius, see Salius
Dives, Nicolaus, pr Paris, V, 552
Divination and Diviner, V, 307, VI, 166, 454; abandoned except astrology, VI, 107; abused by some, VI, 505; animal, from, V, 29, VI, 501, and see Augury; born, VI, 497; Cardan on, V, 574-6; demon and, V, 574, 660, VI, 360, 497, 502-3; defended, VI, 134-5; disease and, V, 87; forbidden, VI, 156-7; fury, by, VI, 503-4; gem, by, VI, 320, 416; herb, by, VI, 275; idol, of, V, 90; imagination, by, VI, 328; law and, VI, 543; letter, numerical value of, by, see Number; magic and, VI, 427, 460, 495-6, 499, 504, 524; medicine and, V, 419-20; natural, V, 627, VI, 360, 477, 496-7, 503, rejected, VI, 478; opposed, V, 140, 283, VI, 407, 564; personal power of, V, 574, VI, 108, 497, denied, VI, 359; political,

VI, 434-5; practised, V, 55; salt, from, V, 240; sleep, in, VI, 360; superstitious, V, 297; tables, by, see Geomancy; universal, VI, 162; urine, from, V, 381; varieties of, V, 136, 627, 655, VI, 359, 397, 434-5, 496, 499, 502-3, forbidden kinds, VI, 135, 467, 521; works of, VI, 337, 361, 493-504
Divining rod, believed in, VI, 501; not mentioned, V, 593
Dobenek, Job de, bishop, VI, 303
Dodecathemoria, denied, VI, 138
Dodo, Vicenzo, V, 70
Dodoens, Rembert, VI, 268, 393, 538; *Cosmographica,* VI, 9-10, 47; *Stirpium historia,* VI, 258, 261-5, 272-3, 293-4
Dodona, VI, 498, 504
Dog, V, 106; Agrippa's, V, 137; barking prevented, V, 611, VI, 421; behavior, V, 144; blood of, VI, 241; carrying stones, V, 577; character, VI, 277; charm against, V, 611; color, changed, VI, 421; dung, V, 559, 663, VI, 233, 501; eats grass, VI, 367, not wild goose, VI, 285; hunting, V, 493; mad, V, 475, VI, 571, signs of, V, 481, 484, and see Hydrophobia; medical experimentation with, V, 480, VI, 335; neighbor's, V, 454; Nifo's, VI, 487; oil of red-haired, VI, 216; philter and, V, 486; seen in urine or water, V, 485; sign of rain from, VI, 367, 487; water distilled from, V, 543; worm under tongue of, V, 482; word used as term of reproach, V, 175, 311
Dogma, see Theology
Dolce, Lodovico (1565), VI, 313; (1575), V, 607; cited, VI, 319
Dôle, university of, V, 127
Dolphin, VI, 186; likes to be called Simon, V, 577; love for man, VI, 416
Dombes, VI, 472
Domenico Maria Castaneolo, see Castaneolus
Domenico Maria Novara, V, 62, 160, 234-6, 352, 408, 426, 672, VI, 11, 136
Domeninus, Lactantius, VI, 493
Dominican, V, 71, 96, 98, 129, 131, 148, 215, 349, 358, 674, VI, 63, 166, 187, 487; apostasy from, VI, 427; of the Observance, V, 197; opposed to astrology, V, 434
Dominions, VI, 451, 551
Don, river, V, 27
Donato, Leonardo, dedic to, VI, 349
Donatus, grammarian, V, 521
Donazzolo, P. (1912), VI, 373-6
Dondi, Giovanni de', V, 166, VI, 209
Donis, see Nicolaus Donis
Donnis, Sebastianus a, pr Verona, VI, 214
Donzellini, Geronimo, VI, 214
Doppelmayr, J. G, (1730), V, 297, 338, 342-3, 353, 357, 359, 361, 364-5, 393-4, 414, VI, 142
Doppler, Erasmus, nativity of, V, 351
Dorat, Jean, V, 270-1
Dorez, Léon (1932), V, 255
Dorico, Luigi, of Brescia, pr Rome, V, 258
Dorico, Valerio, of Brescia, pr Rome, V, 258
Dorn, Gerard, Paracelsan, V, 619, 630-6; *Admonitio,* V, 665; *Chymisticum artificium,* V, 631-2, 634-5; *Clavis,* V, 617, 631-5, 639; *Compendium,* V, 635; *Congeries,* V, 441; *Lapis metaphysicus,* V, 631-2, 635; quoted, V, 617; Suavius and, V, 638-40; tr, V, 417, 627-8, 630
Dorn, John, instrument maker, V, 349
Dorotheus, astrologer, cited, VI, 163, 180
Dorstenius, Theodericus, *Botanicon,* V, 464
Dorveaux, Paul, V, 464-6
Dost, David, see Origanus
Douai, taught at, VI, 194
Douglas, A. H. (1910), V, 93
Douglas, David, *De naturae mirabilibus,* V, 155-8
Dove, sign of good, V, 104; wooden, V, 360
Dovrez, Valerand, apothecary, V, 466
Dowry, V, 270
Dragon, biped, VI, 289; celestial, head of, VI, 15, and tail of, V, 138, 216, VI, 200; flying, VI, 286; mechanical, VI, 421; seen in air, VI, 490; viviparous, VI, 348-9
Dragon's blood, V, 451-2, 469
Drake, Sir Francis, VI, 436
Drayton, Michael, poet, VI, 318

Dream, V, 143, VI, 287; affected by diet, VI, 420; astrology and, V, 259, VI, 116, 132, 480; attentive to, V, 401; bad, prevented, VI, 314; Cardan on, V, 575; cast in form of, V, 226, 245; cause, VI, 412, 423, 476-7, 485; divination from, V, 500, 574-5, VI, 177, 503, 509-10, 512, 543, doubted, VI, 571, false and useless, VI, 525, superstitious, VI, 467; fatal, VI, 490-1; forecasting, V, 85-86; from ideas in divine mind, VI, 482; interpretation of, V, 50, 57-58, 64, VI, 135, 293, 353, 417, 422, 469, 475-84, 496, 506, 510, 512, by chiromancy and geomancy, VI, 508, opposed, V, 140, VI, 412, 478, 529; marvelous, VI, 408; medicine and, VI, 411; natural distinguished from divine and diabolical, V, 283, 401-2, VI, 411-2, 480; not from idols of objects, VI, 476, 482; Pererius on, VI, 411-2; sick, V, 263; theses on, VI, 455; truer towards morning, VI, 403; weather prediction from, VI, 488; witch's, examined, V, 117; works on, V, 286, VI, 361, 491

Dredger, V, 594

Drepana or Drepanum, V, 512, 585

Dresden, VI, 229, 269

Dreyer, J. L. E., V, 251, 376, 388-9, 398, 406-8, 642, 656, VI, 4, 11, 38, 52-53, 55, 69, 72-74, 81, 84, 90, 111-2, 143, 183, 358, 523-4, questioned, V, 423, VI, 111; (1890), VI, 140; (1906), V, 406, 423-5

Dropsy, V, 368, 626-7, 659

Drosera, an herb, VI, 265

Drowning, VI, 195

Drug, VI, 417, 420, 463; and see Adulteration, Narcotic, Pharmacy

Druid, VI, 353

Drum, VI, 241

Drusianus, Carolus, astrologer, V, 179

Dryander, Johannes, V, 520-2, 525, VI, 254, 598; *Anatomia,* V, 392, 520

Dubenus, B. (1591), VI, 489

Dubia, V, 173, 480-1

du Bois, Pierre, VI, 344

du Bois, Simon, pr Paris, V, 284

Du Boulay, C. E. (1665-73), V, 286, VI, 368

Dubravius, Joannes, VI, 255

Duchastel, Pierre, V, 311-2

Duchesne, Joseph, Paracelsan, VI, 247-51; cited, VI, 319

Duchess, V, 218, VI, 552

Duck, V, 662; twenty kinds of, VI, 267

Duclo, Gaston, V, 666

Ductus choledochus, V, 44

Dudith, Andreas, V, 656, VI, 59, 183, 185-6

Duhamel, Pasquier (1545), V, 291

Duhem, Pierre, V, 12, 16, 18, 20-21, 25-27, 30, 95, 156-8, 408, 442, 565, 597, VI, 43, 52, 284, 369, 449

Duke, V, 111, 115, 168-9, 209, 226, 246, 267, 294, 298, 304, 314, 326, 357, 365, 384, 393, 399, 402, 405, 417, 483, 548, 619, 631, 645, VI, 3, 11, 27-28, 37, 45-46, 76, 80, 82, 101-3, 116, 126, 128, 138, 140, 192, 195-6, 217, 231, 235, 245, 316, 373, 394, 462, 484, 494-5, 515, 517, 535, 537, 542, 552, 559

Dulciatus, Antonius, hermit, V, 257

Dulcis, Ludovicus, see Dolce

Dumbeleius, alchemist, V, 623

Dung, as remedy, V, 462; and see Dog

Duns Scotus, see Scotus

Du Plessis d'Argentré (1755), V, 345

Dupuis, Guillaume, medical, V, 449-50

Durand, Dana B., V, 343-4

Durand, William, cited, VI, 125, 205, 385

Durandus, monachus, alchemist, V, 623

Durant, Jean, physician, VI, 340

Durante, Castore, botanist (1585), VI, 258

Durastantes, Janus Matth. (1567), VI, 518-9

Dürer, Albrecht, V, 343-4, VI, 596

Duret, Loys, VI, 141

Dutch, VI, 7; descent, V, 430; tr, VI, 469

Du Val, official, V, 292

Du Val, Dionysius, pr Paris, V, 483

Dynachrysus, interlocutor, V, 647

Dysentery, V, 455, VI, 223, 518

Eagle, V, 25, VI, 269-70, 277-8, 416

Eames, W. (1886), V, 139

Ear, big, VI, 276; bones in, V, 44-46; burns, VI, 221; moving the, V, 102, 525; study of, VI, 422

Earth, caverns in, VI, 362, and see Water, subterranean; center of gravity and magnitude, V, 24, 156, 428; compared to an animal, V, 29-30; Gilbert on, VI, 317; habitable, V, 40, 167, 389, VI, 345, 392; internal heat, VI, 183, 388, 396; length of shadow, VI, 21; magnetic, VI, 381; motion, V, 156, 380, 383, 409, 419, 423, 428, VI, 13-14, 24-25, 60-61, 73, 326-7, 376, opposed, V, 358; political influence of orbit of, V, 414-5, 419, VI, 75; qualities of, V, 40, 271, 569; surface, V, 9, 121, 389, 552, 588, VI, 343; unmoved, V, 29-30, 385, VI, 9, 11-12, 16, 21, 27, 31-32, 39, 41-42, 44, 63, 155, 375; water and, relative amounts, V, 9, 24, 427-8, 552, 569, 591, 614, VI, 60, 380; water and air mere effluvia of, VI, 380; and see Sea, Sphere

Earthquake, V, 155, 231, 241, VI, 367, 490; at Passion, V, 125; of 1528, VI, 491; of 1561, VI, 398; predicted, V, 124, 219, 230, 232; prediction from, VI, 460; sign of pest, V, 497

Earthworm, V, 451, 608, VI, 240

East and West, relative, VI, 318

East, Near, V, 223

Easter, V, 86, 281; as New Year's day, V, 186; correction of date of, V, 225

Ebenhaen, see Abenhaen

Eberus, Paul, theologian, VI, 105, 595, 597

Ebner, Erasmus, geniture of, VI, 597; preface to, V, 400

Ebner, Hieronymus, horoscope of, V, 352

Ebony, VI, 272

Eccardus, J. G. (1723), VI, 439

Eccentric, see Epicycle and

Echeneis, V, 101, 495, 570, 646, VI, 131, 186, 205, 291, 565

Echium, an herb, VI, 280

Eck, Johann, V, 282, VI, 446

Eclipse, description, V, 392; duration, V, 190; four in 1544, VI, 392; generate comets, V, 321; influence, V, 163, 177, 180, 190-1, 225, 299, 329, 374, 392, 400, 417, VI, 96, 121, 211, denied, VI, 192, evil, VI, 22, exaggerated, VI, 174, explained, V, 272, fortunate, V, 280; listed, VI, 117, 490; lunar, V, 145, 235, VI, 343, calculation of, VI, 5, of 669, V, 223, denied, V, 226, of 1457, V, 366, of 1500, V, 425, of 1509, V, 425, of 1511, V, 240, 425, VI, 17, of 1522, V, 425, VI, 17, of 1523, V, 191, 194, 210-2, 214, 220, 224, 396, 425, VI, 17, of 1548, V, 268, of 1573, VI, 53, of Mars, 1538, V, 289; miraculous, at crucifixion, V, 109, 125, 256-7, VI, 198, called local, VI, 22; not sign, VI, 192; observation of, V, 366; Paracelsan explanation, rejected, V, 658; predicted, VI, 111, 117; predicted from, V, 219, VI, 126, 143; prodigy, VI, 490; shape of earth inferred from lunar, VI, 343; solar, V, 239, listed, VI, 117, of 1485, V, 204, of 1518, V, 186, 190, 222, 280-1, of 1519, V, 190, of 1524, V, 216, of 1540, V, 322, 392, 400, of 1547, V, 271, of 1563, VI, 117, of 1574, VI, 42, of 1598, VI, 53; unspecified, of 1534, V, 255, of 1574-1614, VI, 76; works on, V, 257, VI, 21, 111, 133

Ecliptic, obliquity of, V, 172, 234-5, 282, 352; and see Zodiac

Economics, V, 578, VI, 28, 187

Ecphantus, VI, 63

Ecstasy, VI, 355, 532

Ecttyposis, V, 17

Edinburgh, pr at, VI, 547

Edinburgh Medical Journal, VI, 330

Editions, compared, V, 141, 528, VI, 15, 173, 373, 419, 456, 463, 490, 505, 515, 537-8, 550, 559, 646; enumerated, V, 17, 39, 45-46, 63-64, 66, 121, 143, 148-9, 152, 181, 187, 197, 210, 217, 254, 265, 273, 283, 308-9, 313, 320, 330, 341-2, 357, 360, 372, 375, 385-7, 398, 418, 433, 437, 450, 461, 466, 483, 489, 513, 528, 536-7, 540-1, 543-4, 552, 558, 589, 605-6, 623, 625, 630, 636, 648-9, 656, VI, 4, 10, 15, 31, 35, 38, 40, 42, 45, 96, 116, 118, 127-8, 137, 159, 162, 166, 211, 216-8, 222, 230-1, 235, 266, 272, 286-7, 301-2, 306, 318, 325-6, 346, 359, 361, 364, 366, 369-70, 377, 393-4, 398, 410, 418, 433, 438, 441, 447-51, 458-9, 469, 472, 474, 476, 479, 483-5, 492-4, 506, 518, 522, 527, 533-4, 538, 551-2, 556, 558-9, 561, 600-2; pirated, V, 228, 594, VI, 31; suppressed, VI, 551-2

Education, V, 529, VI, 190-1, 211, 414;

and astrology, V, 386; desire to ease, V, 5-6, 149, 152, 154-5, 331, VI, 21, to save time, V, 35, 148, 152, 154-5; effect on temperament, VI, 204, 394; for the church, VI, 76; method in, VI, 564; object of, VI, 414; of Erastus, V, 652; traditional, VI, 7-8, 31-32; trend towards modern, V, 6; works on, V, 152, VI, 499; would-be innovators, V, 175; see Punishment, corporal, Student, Textbook
Edward IV, king of England, VI, 89
Edward VI, king of England, advice to, V, 578; horoscope of, V, 572, VI, 193; preface to, V, 322-3
Eel, generation of, VI, 283; live, excreted, VI, 409; poisonous, V, 481; snake and, VI, 416
Egenolphus, baron of Rapolstein, V, 610
Egenolphus, Christianus, pr Frankfurt, V, 330, 398, 464, VI, 213, 272; geniture of, VI, 596; heirs of, VI, 308
Egg, bewitched by eating, VI, 337; not eat, for three years, VI, 404; raised in air, VI, 602; shells to be broken, VI, 404; squeezed into a bottle, V, 429; that rots not, V, 572; white of, V, 458
Eggolsheim, V, 365
Egidius, see Aegidius
Egmondanus, see George, count of Egmond
Egmund, astrologer, VI, 130
Eguia, Michael de, pr Alcalà, V, 318
Egypt and Egyptian, VI, 286, 323, 348, 480; ancient, V, 135, 437, VI, 291, 349, 353, 374, 447, 458, 461, 498, 601; astrology, V, 329, 403, VI, 23, 113, 174, 379; astronomy, V, 416, 426; once covered by the sea, VI, 291; see Day, Year
Ehrenbach, pr at, V, 355
Eisenach, V, 375
Eisenmenger, see Siderocrates
Eisleben, V, 396, VI, 597
Elbe, river, V, 401
Election, astrological, V, 140, 208, 241-2, 245, 292, 354, 361-2, VI, 116, 124, 430; approved, VI, 114, 144, 174-5; condemned, in part, V, 276-7, VI, 187, in whole, V, 655, VI, 107, 172, 200, 204, 359; defended, V, 199, 362-3; for cutting wood, V, 165, founding a university, V, 338, 379, 393, laying a corner stone, V, 259, erecting papal statue, VI, 150, studying, VI, 167; of medicaments, V, 163, times for taking, V, 161, VI, 158, 165; practiced, VI, 199; tracts on, V, 265, 296, VI, 169
Election, imperial, of 1519, V, 183, 188, 319
Elector, see Brandenburg, Mainz, Palatine, etc.
Electoral college instituted, V, 435
Electricity, VI, 317
Electrum, VI, 243
Electuary, V, 461, 463, VI, 218, 314
Element, V, 557, VI, 189, 457; alteration of, V, 141, to cease, VI, 379; celestial suggested, VI, 357-8; colors of, VI, 343; compound and, V, 40, 141, 290, 554, 558, VI, 198, 354, 396, 419; consent and dissent of, V, 495; Contarini on, V, 552-5, VI, 350; demons in, V, 628; Dorn on, V, 633; four traditional, V, 29, 40, 550, VI, 83, 335, 525, reduced to three, V, 569, VI, 83, 355, rejected, VI, 96, 380; generation of, V, 538, 591; new, of Bruno, VI, 425, Paracelsus, V, 626, Patrizi, VI, 375; origin of, V, 591; poisonous, V, 473; proportion of, VI, 364; qualities and, VI, 366; rational and irrational in, V, 639; rotation of, V, 632-3; ruled by angels, VI, 551; separation of, V, 132, 541; transmutation of, V, 40, VI, 129; two original, V, 538, 633; works on, V, 40, 48-49, VI, 202
Elephant, VI, 447; dragon and, VI, 310, 313, and see Dragon's blood; ear of, VI, 269; mouse and, VI, 416; pig and, V, 662
Elephantiasis, V, 659
Elias, prophecy of, VI, 29
Eligerus, Ioh. (15c), V, 348
Eliot, naturalist, VI, 259
Elisaeus, V, 105
Elisianus, Elisius or Elysius, Andrea, V, 213
Elisianus, Elisius or Elysius, Joannes, V, 211-3
Elisabeth, queen of France, VI, 109

Elisha the prophet, VI, 356
Elixir, VI, 224
Elizabeth, queen of England, VI, 196; dedic to, V, 477, VI, 141, 160; fond of quacks, VI, 219
Ellenbog, Nicolaus, V, 180
Ellerton, William, VI, 287
Elluchasem, tables of, V, 501
Elm tree, VI, 416
Elmer, Edward, VI, 268
Eloquence, belittled, V, 631; cultivated, V, 335, VI, 201, 320; disclaimed, V, 552; humanistic, V, 430; not found in men of great understanding, VI, 413; of Champier, V, 111; opposed, V, 626; over emphasized, V, 436; and see Oration, Style
Eltz, see Georgius de
Elysian Fields, V, 213
Elzevir, Ludwig, pr Amsterdam, VI, 380
Emanation, VI, 476-7, 482; and see Exhalation, Species
Embalming, V, 509
Embryology, VI, 371
Emerald, V, 456-7, VI, 186; breaks during sexual intercourse, VI, 315; cures poison, VI, 315; liquefies eyes of snakes, VI, 477; loses color in the presence of poison, V, 481; medicinal properties, V, 456, VI, 311, 501; not good for putrid fevers, VI, 315; Peruvian, VI, 319; powdered, V, 474, 478; virtues, V, 614; Tablet, see Hermes, *Tabula smaragdina*
Emetic, VI, 547
Emmel, Samuel, pr Strasburg, V, 622
Emotion, V, 101; among primitive peoples, V, 577; explained, V, 495
Emperor, Holy Roman, V, 128-9, 133, 373, VI, 291, 469, see Charles V, Ferdinand, etc.; Roman, V, 141, 468, 470, VI, 76, 117
Empetron, an herb, V, 460
Empire, see Political
Empiric and Empiricism, V, 589, VI, 371; attacked, VI, 164; defended, V, 128; Jewish, V, 513; medical, V, 286, 316, 432-3, 437-8, 513, 551-2, 621, 630, VI, 217, 219-20, 249-50, 420, 533, attacked, V, 380-1, 431-2, VI, 524; of a herbalist, VI, 274; punished, V, 286
Encelius, Christopher, V, 397, VI, 308-10
Enchanter, see Incantation, Magic
Encinas, Ferdinand, answered, V, 208-10
Encyclopedia and Encyclopedic, V, 139, 563, 597, VI, 400, 455; first children's, VI, 352; interest, VI, 270; medieval characteristics retained, VI, 271, 276-7
Encyclopedia Britannica, VI, 23
Encyclopédie, l' V, 471, VI, 436
Endinoydea, V, 505
Endor, see Witch of
Enemy, triumph over, predicted, V, 230, 236
Eneström, G. (1896), V, 359, 370
Engel, Johann, V, 344-7
Engelbert of Admont, V, 373
Engineering, military, V, 34, 133, 584, 598, VI, 33, 154
England and English, V, 149, 333, 416, 437, 485, 497, 537, 553, 604, VI, 42, 155, 253, 288, 328, 517; as a haven, VI, 248; called to, VI, 503; executions of witches in, VI, 145-6, 338, 550; king of, V, 247, 322-3, 572, 578, VI, 89, 193, 240; Latin books in, V, 12; names of simples, VI, 271; naturalists, VI, 258-9, 267; queen of, V, 477, VI, 248, and see Elizabeth; tr, V, 65, 66, 286, 313, 528, 603, 606, 608, 618, 641, 649, VI, 106, 215, 222, 266, 302, 393, 405, 410, 469, 472, 475-6, 507, 522, 530-1; visited, VI, 488-9; written in, V, 674, VI, 13-16, 483
Enlightenment, period of, V, 14
Ennery, V, 434
Enoch, V, 373, VI, 75; as an alias, VI, 438
Enriquez de Cabrera, Ferdinand, grand admiral, dedic to, V, 208
Ens, VI, 371, 396; non, V, 658
Ensisheim, V, 610, VI, 399
Entzelt, see Encelius
Enula, an herb, VI, 263; and see Helenium
Environment, influence of, VI, 204
Eobanus Hessus, V, 330, 338, 355, VI, 595
Ephemerides, V, 6, 251, 264, 346, 349, 357, 361, 415, 565, VI, 15, 17-18, 22-

24, 51, 60-61, 108, 111, 118, 140; German and Italian compared, V, 654, VI, 158; use defended, VI, 139; and see Maestlin, Regiomontanus, Stadius, Stoeffler
Ephemerus, an animal, VI, 288-9
Ephestion, see Hephaestion
Ephesus, see Michael of
Ephistus, alchemist, cited, V, 623
Epicurus and Epicurean, V, 25, 380, VI, 391, 523, 531, 568
Epicycle and Eccentric, V, 388-9, 414, 418-9, 422-5, 429, 557, 569-70, VI, 20, 25, 38-39, 46, 58, 62, 97, 326, 375, 396; an eccentric of the eccentric, VI, 46; hypothetical, V, 82, VI, 19; imaginary, VI, 25; of a comet, VI, 79; rejected, V, 489, 491
Epilepsy and Epileptic, VI, 195, 212, 356; amulet for, V, 455, 470, 647, 662, VI, 169, 338; Paracelsus and, V, 619, 627, not incurable, V, 638; remedy for, V, 476, 659-60, VI, 225, 501; treatise on, VI, 169; why subject to visions, V, 87
Epiphanius, VI, 315, 319
Episcopius, Nicolaus, pr Basel, V, 605, 609
Epistemon, an interlocutor, VI, 549
Epistritides, a gem, V, 614
Epitaph, V, 333, VI, 401
Epitome, V, 391, 468; see Regiomontanus
Equant, omitted, V, 423; retained, VI, 57
Equinox, and solstice, V, 281-2, 284; anticipation of, V, 407; diversity of, VI, 17; Nunes prefers Alfonsine Tables on to Regiomontanus, VI, 35-36; precession of, VI, 45, 57, Copernicus on, V, 427, VI, 17, 29, 65; vernal, V, 264, 282, VI, 19, 118, 120
Eranthemum, V, 448
Erasistratus, V, 530
Erasmus, Didimus, V, 37; on astrology, V, 176-7, VI, 113, 194; on Bouelles, VI, 442; geniture, VI, 105, 595; on medicine, V, 578; Paracelsus, V, 438; sanitation, V, 497; superstition, V, 176
Erastianism, V, 652
Erastus, Thomas, V, 652-67, VI, 183, 479; cited, V, 482, VI, 183, 382, 431, 555-6; compared with Jacques Fontaine, VI, 555; criticized, V, 656; epitaph, V, 652; life, V, 652; on Paracelsus, V, 619-20, 657-60; opponents of, VI, 114; works, *Astrologia divinatrice,* V, 654-5, *Cometarum,* V, 656-7, 664, *Confutatio,* V, 654, *Defensio,* V, 653-5, 662, *Disputatio de auro potabili,* V, 664-5, *Disputatio de lamiis,* V, 664, 666-7, *Disputationum,* V, 619-20, 642, 655, 657-61, *Examen de simplicibus,* V, 468, 470, 663, *Occultis pharmacorum potestatibus,* V, 661-4
Ercole I of Ferrara, see Este
Erfurt, VI, 106, 122, 457; born at, V, 173; composed at, V, 217; pr at, V, 149, 375, 418, VI, 106, 506-7; university of, V, 149, 338, 354-5, VI, 5-6
Erhard à Marka, cardinal, V, 226
Erler, G. (1895), V, 407
Ermland (Warmien), bishop of, V, 410, 413
Ernalsteen, J.A.U., V, 303
Ernest, archbishop, dedic to, V, 666, VI, 235, 505
Ernest, archduke, dedic to, VI, 505
Erolo, cardinal, VI, 48
Error, V, 436, 449; accused of, V, 464-5, 505, 515-6, 557, VI, 272; corrected, V, 143, 461; of ancients, VI, 226; of Aristotle, V, 205, 585, VI, 364, 423, 432-3; of authorities, VI, 280, 400-2; of Galen, V, 525, 530; of La Faye, VI, 423; of Peter of Abano, V, 119-22, 551; of Pliny, V, 502, VI, 254, 280, 402; of Skalich, VI, 456; of Sacrobosco, VI, 155; of senses and intellect, VI, 563; persistence of, V, 181, 485; popular, VI, 198, 220-2; purged from, V, 546; relation to science and magic, V, 12-13, VI, 328; works on, V, 501, 515-6, 551, VI, 226
Erudition, see Classical
Erythraeus, Janus Nicius, (1642), VI, 377
Eschenden, see John of
Esdras, V, 130
Essence, fifth, V, 541-2, 561, 590, 602, 632, 638, 640, 651, 659, VI, 242, 249-52, 397, 435, 461, 533; is sky com-

posed of? VI, 384, 435; knowledge by, V, 118
Essenes, VI, 456
Essler, Johann, V, 172-3, 437; and Pigghe, V, 200-1, 282
Estates, see Blois, Carinthia
Este, Alfonso I d', duke of Ferrara, V, 169, 445-6
Este, Alfonso II d', duke of Ferrara, VI, 228
Este, Borso d', duke of Ferrara, V, 342
Este, Constance, VI, 135
Este, Ercole I d', duke of Ferrara, V, 168, 513
Este, Ercole II d', duke of Ferrara, V, 168, 247, 445
Este, Ippolito d', cardinal, V, 258
Este, Lodovico d', cardinal, V, 540
Este, Obizzo, marquis, VI, 135
Estotilandia, VI, 436
Estramadura, VI, 196
Esula, an herb, VI, 263
Ether, V, 602
Ethics, V, 607, 652; and see Philosophy, moral
Ethiopian, V, 444; Sea, V, 585
Etterlin, Petermann, V, 177
Etymology, VI, 278, 345; versus folklore, VI, 519
Etzlaub, Erhard, map and instrument maker, V, 348
Euandrophilaetes, VI, 214
Eubel, *Hierarchia catholica,* VI, 162, 528; corrected, V, 274
Eucharist, V, 652, VI, 395, 495; and see Sacrament
Euclid, V, 305, 574, VI, 88, 137; cited, V, 41, 557, as an alchemist, V, 624; comm. VI, 372, 377; criticized, V, 416, 642; *Elements,* V, 155, 279, 340, 343, 360-1, 407, VI, 88, 119, 154; errors of translators of, V, 293; *Optica et catoptrica,* V, 293, 304
Eude, Christophorus, dedic to, VI, 493
Eudemus, cited, V, 109, 523
Euerarthus, Martin (1583), VI, 13
Eudoxus, cited, V, 419, VI, 43, 97
Eugenics, VI, 414, 423
Eugenius IV, VI, 542
Eunuch, VI, 402
Euonymus Philiatrus, V, 543, 548, 621
Eupatoria, an herb, VI, 263
Europe, V, 336, 391, VI, 75, 119, 187, 289, 392, 408; central, V, 27, VI, 319, and northern, VI, 273, and southeastern, VI, 185; pest in, VI, 210; to rule all, VI, 118; transmitted to, VI, 274; traversed, V, 581, VI, 154
Euscathius, see Marianus Euscathius
Eusebius, a Jesuit, VI, 276
Eustachio, Bartolomeo, anatomist, V, 498
Eustratius, cited, VI, 48
Eutocius of Ascalon, V, 369
Evans, A. H. (1903), VI, 271, 279; criticized, VI, 287-8
Evaporation, V, 31, 157, 496; no rain without preceding, V, 592; and see Exhalation
Evax, cited, VI, 300, not cited, VI, 318
Evidence, see Truth, criteria of
Evil, problem of, V, 107, VI, 347
Evoli, see Aevolus
Evolution, theory of, V, 598
Evreux, bishop of, VI, 360-1; and see Quenay of
Ewich, disciple of Wier, VI, 517
Exaltation (astrological), V, 216
Example, force of, VI, 204
Excavation of a ship in 1460, V, 157
Excommunication, of Bruno, VI, 423; Calvinistic, V, 652; of worms and locusts, V, 135
Excrement, medicinal, V, 621, VI, 233; of venomous animals odorless, V, 481
Execution, attended, V, 505; predicted, V, 587; why crowded? V, 146
Exercise, V, 146, VI, 394
Exeter, dedic from, V, 134, VI, 520
Exhalation, attracted by comet, VI, 355; caused by stars, V, 92, 552; from bones of dead, virtue of, V, 106; from human bodies, V, 102-3, 106-7, VI, 241, 322, 477, 571; from poisonous animals, V, 474, 477; marvelous, V, 155; metals formed from, V, 125; oracles and, VI, 466
Exorcism and Exorcist, V, 117-8, VI, 545; books of, VI, 556-9; criticism of, V, 283, VI, 454, 530, 537, 540, 546-7, forbidden, VI, 434; of an herb, VI, 404; of water, VI, 502; public, in Venice, VI, 557
Experience, anatomical, V, 499, 507, 517;

appeal to, V, 19-21, 104, 460, 478-9, 662, VI, 316; astrology and, V, 216, 235, 258, 312, VI, 122, 138, 185, 193; chemical, V, 634; clinical, see Consilia; confirms the Bible, VI, 342, reasoning, V, 249; fallacious and limited, VI, 563; future inferred from, VI, 417; long, V, 412, 499; manual, V, 650, VI, 434; medical, V, 123; "mistress of all things," V, 460; natural science and, V, 634, VI, 268, 419; occult virtues and, V, 551, VI, 358; of Copernicus, V, 412, Corvus, V, 56, an exorcist, VI, 557, herbalists, VI, 273-4, iatrochemists, V, 650, of specters, VI, 533; of the weather, V, 156; own, V, 258, 473, 482, 506-9, 571, 597, 612, VI, 283, 533, 557; personal, V, 59; prediction and, V, 374; that of others, VI, 233; third column of science, VI, 434; and see Empiricism, Experiment

Experiment, V, 10, 33, VI, 316-7, 602; agricultural, V, 609; alchemical, V, 127, 265, 548, 637, VI, 244, 248, 419, 519; anatomical, V, 508; astrological, V, 303, VI, 99-101, 427; authority and, VI, 530; botanical, VI, 274; chiromantic, V, 67, 582; collection of, V, 147, VI, 421, 429; conjuring, VI, 154, 392; exorcism and, VI, 558; hunting, VI, 421; isolated, V, 634; magical, V, 120, VI, 133, 398; mechanical, VI, 421; medical, V, 462, 621, VI, 216, 260, 321, 421; method, V, 303, 305, 441, 494, 650, VI, 78, 374; necromancy and, V, 635; numerical, VI, 442; occult arts and, V, 634; of ghosts, V, 97; perspective, VI, 419; physical, V, 581, VI, 248; pneumatic, VI, 421; proving existence of angels and demons, VI, 455; static, VI, 421; testing this and that, V, 448, 451-2, 460, 478, 646, 662, VI, 193, 241, 282, 335, 420; trick and, V, 147, 567, VI, 419

Experimentarius, VI, 470

Experimentum, see Experiment

Expiation, rites of, VI, 533

Explosive, V, 34

Extravagantes, see Decretal

Eye and Eyesight, V, 32, 116, 140, 144, VI, 402, 511; clouded, V, 459; disorder of, V, 506, VI, 222; double pupil, V, 473; evil, see Fascination; emerald and, V, 474; eyewash, V, 430, 436; glasses or goggles, V, 519, 612; muscles, V, 531; nerve, V, 305; of frog, V, 560, wolf, V, 610; protected, VI, 294; restored, VI, 358; sore, V, 496; structure, V, 301, 436; suffusion, VI, 229; vision by extramission, V, 305, 475, VI, 387, 548, denied, V, 31, VI, 425; visual species, VI, 340; weak human, V, 31

Eymeric, Nicolaus, V, 648, VI, 246, 544

Eynatten, Maximilian ab (1619), VI, 559

Ezechias, V, 647

Ezekiel the prophet, VI, 514

Ezra the prophet, VI, 435

Faber, Jacobus, see Lefèvre d'Etaples

Faber, Wenceslaus, astrologer, V, 160

Fable, V, 29, 469

Fabre, Claude, physician, V, 328

Fabricius, Paul, imperial astrologer, VI, 184

Fabricius, George, *Epistolae,* V, 143, VI, 49, 255, 267, 366; geniture, VI, 597; *Metallicis,* V, 420; *Vita,* VI, 302, 498-9

Fabricius, Wilhelm, surgeon, VI, 321

Fabroni, Angelo (1791-95), V, 74, 90, 274, 325

Facciolati, Jacopo (1757), V, 71, VI, 599

Facies (astrological), V, 309, VI, 144; rejected, VI, 138

Facts, need of new, not felt, V, 11

Faenza, V, 50, VI, 209, 211, 449; despot of, V, 235; pr at, V, 214, 227-8

Fair, V, 329, VI, 212

Falckenburg, Henr., pr Cologne, V, 648

Faith, cured by, V, 106; and works, V, 289; justification, V, 309; lack of, VI, 440; required, VI, 513

Fall, from height, V, 367; from horse, VI, 322; of man, see Sin

Falloppia, Gabriele, VI, 260, 292; called an Aristotelian, VI, 364; cited, V, 647, VI, 319; controversy with Rondelet, VI, 212; criticized, VI, 317; dissections of, VI, 214; estimates of Carpi

and Vesalius, V, 529-30, of Carpi and Ingrassia, V, 44-45; letters, VI, 266; *Medicatis aquis,* VI, 208-9; *Metallis,* V, 548-9, VI, 311-3; *Observationes anatomicae,* V, 45, 529-31, VI, 209; praised, V, 336, 531; quoted, V, 498; *Secreti,* VI, 208, 218; *Ulceribus,* VI, 208
Famiensis, Odoardus, astrologer, V, 179
Famine, VI, 89
Family, V, 601, VI, 160, 470; cares, V, 262, VI, 80, 440; tree, V, 445
Fanianus, J. C. (1560), V, 622; (1576), V, 535, 541, 622
Fano, V, 50, 269; scheme for a university at, V, 265-6
Fanti, Sigismondo, *Triompho di Fortuna,* V, 253-4, 409, VI, 470-1
Fantis, Antonius de, ed., VI, 471
Fantuzzi, Giovanni (1781-94), V, 51
Farmer, advice to, V, 211; prediction and, V, 121; and see Agriculture, Peasant, Rustic
Farnese, Alessandro, cardinal, VI, 255
Farnese, Alessandro, son of Octavio, V, 267-8
Farnese, Carolo, son of Octavio, V, 267
Farnese, Orazio, duke of Castro, V, 267-8
Farnese, Pierluigi, death predicted, V, 256, VI, 195
Farnese, Rainutio, duke of Parma and Piacenza, VI, 231
Fasciculus medicinae, V, 323
Fascination, V, 90, VI, 237, 357, 477; accepted, V, 101, 455, 475-6, 562, VI, 233, 301, 315, 419-20, 513, 530; affects heart, V, 116; counteracted, VI, 277, 338, 434; doubted, V, 477, 486-7; no physical basis, VI, 358, 528, 546
Fascinum, VI, 528
Fasti, VI, 465
Fasting, V, 478, VI, 378, 402; exposure of pretended, VI, 516; feats of, V, 273, VI, 431-2; long, VI, 220
Fat, cold? V, 506-7; human, V, 454, 518; of bear in weapon ointment, VI, 240; of snake or viper, V, 451
Fate, V, 573, VI, 182, 350, 453, 492-3; and see Necessity
Faun, VI, 408, 551
Faust, magic of, VI, 536
Favaro, Antonio (1879), V, 359
Favaro, G. A. (1928), V, 529
Faventinus, Leonellus, see Leonello of Faenza
Favorinus, cited, VI, 197, 206, 232, 486
Fear, see Disease, Flood, Popular
Feast, see Day
Feild, John (1557), VI, 17-18
Feinis, Francisca de, VI, 109
Feldhaus, F. M., V, 34, 596
Feldkirch, V, 384, 391
Félice, P. de (1881), VI, 346, 522
Felicity, V, 297, 314
Feltre, VI, 492; bishop of, V, 321
Feltrus, Petrus, VI, 492
Femelius, Christopher (1599), VI, 5-6
Ferdinand I, emperor (also earlier archduke of Austria and king of the Romans), V, 222; dedic to, V, 210, 221, 347, 370-1, VI, 341, 345, 455, 490-1, 505; nativity of, V, 246, VI, 105, 196; physician of, V, 602, VI, 136, 596; prediction concerning, V, 167
Ferdinand of Aragon, king of Spain, V, 124, VI, 136
Ferdinand of Aragon, duke of Calabria, V, 209
Ferdinand, archduke of Austria (1576), V, 631, VI, 230
Ferdinand, count in Ortenburg, etc., V, 603
Ferdinand III, grandduke of Tuscany, preface to, V, 247
Ferdinand, king of Sicily, V, 270
Ferguson, John, (1906), V, 535, 541-3, 545, 624, 648, VI, 217, 251-2; (1930), VI, 215-6
Ferinarius, Ioannes, V, 404, VI, 366; quoted, V, 378
Fermo, V, 218; pr at, VI, 211
Fern, VI, 295
Fernando of Cordova, VI, 455
Fernel, Jean, V, 556-60; astrology of, V, 557-8; called superstitious, V, 477, VI, 202; cited, V, 416, 484, 486, 559-60, 630, 641, VI, 49, 234, 365, 407, 518, 569; compared with Fracastoro, V, 494; criticized, VI, 228, 245, 365; defended, VI, 215; quoted, V, 550; repeated, VI, 501; works, *Abditis causis,* V, 548, 558-60, VI, 202, 430, *Cosmotheoria,* V, 284, 557, VI, 409,

medical, V, 7, 556, VI, 212, *Monalosphaerium,* V, 284, 557, *Physiologia,* V, 550, 556, 558, *Proportionibus,* V, 284, 557
Ferrara, V, 233, 370, 460, 531, 540, VI, 63, 402, 470; apothecaries of, V, 445, 461; astrology at, V, 168-9, 253, 274; cardinal of, V, 258; duke of, see Este; old, V, 269; pr at, V, 44, 540, VI, 373, 375, 449; taught at, V, 94-95, 167, 169, 446, 581, 586, VI, 48, 205, 373, 484; university of, V, 115, 164-5, 169, 426, 640; visited, V, 445; and see Domenico Maria of
Ferrari da Grado, Giamatteo, V, 535-6; cited, V, 503, VI, 402
Ferrariis, see George de
Ferrarius de Fenaco, Damianus, V, 207
Ferrarius de Gradibus, see Ferrari da Grado
Ferrault, Jean, VI, 432
Ferrerio, Giovanni, on comet of 1531, V, 293-5; cited, VI, 131
Ferrier, Oger, VI, 478-80; cited, V, 481, VI, 516, 530
Ferrus, Alphonsus, surgeon to Paul III, V, 254
Festgabe an H. Grauert (1910), V, 349
Festschrift f. Max Neuburger, V, 345
Festschrift Hermann Baas (1908), V, 381
Fettich, Theobald, herbalist, VI, 274
Feuerwerksbuch, V, 34, 596
Feyerabendt, Iohannes, pr Frankfurt, VI, 134
Fever, V, 313, 454, VI, 136, 208, 212, 223, 367; acute disease not without, disputed, VI, 251; caused by excess of sulphur, V, 626; controversy as to, VI, 212, 215; cured, by fright, V, 146, gem, VI, 321, single draught, V, 416; died of, V, 38; drink advised in, V, 465; dry, V, 496; ephemeral, V, 612; intermittent, VI, 213, 223; long, V, 239; melancholy, V, 258; pestilential, V, 264, 457, 514, VI, 211, 223, 409; putrid, V, 456, VI, 315; quartan, V, 146, 280, 416, 479, 646, VI, 419, 526; signs of, V, 315, 475; tertian, V, 560; tides compared to, VI, 388; typhoid, VI, 248; works on, V, 314-5, 326, VI, 494
Ficalho, Conde de, V, 466
Ficino, Marsilio, cited, V, 637, VI, 48, 197, 212, 303, 375, 399, 403, 484; criticized, VI, 220, 232, 245, 378; imitated, V, 114; lectured on, V, 127; not followed, V, 119; pr, VI, 158; tr, VI, 447, 478
Fienus, Thomas, (1608), V, 106, VI, 235-7
Fiesole, bishop of, VI, 520
Fig, VI, 416; leaf, VI, 503
Figard, L. (1903), V, 556-8
Figgis, J. N., V, 652
Figulus, Benedictus, pr Strasburg, V, 641
Figulus, Carolus, botanist, V, 390, VI, 255-6, 259-60
Figulus, Nigidius, see Nigidius
Figura coeli, V, 131, 171, 197, 299, 315, 367, VI, 18-19, 100, 102-3, 158-9, 406, 494; at creation, V, 309
Figure of sixteen angles or sides, V, 185-6, 302, 315, 434, VI, 159, 487
Filelfo, geniture of, VI, 30
Filiarchi, see Philiarchus
Filipendula, an herb, VI, 263
Fillon, B. (1888), V, 596
Finck, Hermann, VI, 597
Finck, Thomas, (1591), VI, 140
Finé, François, V, 285
Finé, Oronce, V, 284-6, 290-3; addressed, V, 298; *Aequatorium,* V, 285; alchemy, V, 543; astrology, V, 285, 290-2; career, V, 285; cited, VI, 21, 131; criticized, V, 292-3, VI, 137; dedic to, V, 301-2; publications, V, 139, 284-6, 290-2
Finger, frozen, V, 146; unburnable, VI, 513; and see Nail
Fioravanti, Lionardo (1561), VI, 217
Fiorentino, F. (1868), V, 94; (1879), VI, 338; (1884), VI, 459; (1911), VI, 266, 338
Fire, action of, VI, 381, against demons, VI, 405; colors of, VI, 342; combustion explained, V, 554, 569, VI, 355; nourished by humidity, V, 593; divination from, see Pyromancy; engine, V, 595; house on, V, 446; in the air, V, 497; not an element, V, 428, 569, 604, VI, 49, 83, 355, 380; of St. John, V, 439; only element suited to man, VI, 362; recipe for infernal, VI,

428; sky made of, VI, 48; sphere of, see Sphere; to strike, VI, 309; walking through, VI, 513; wettest of all bodies, VI, 389; would it burn tow, if motion of sky ceased? VI, 188; writings lost in a, V, 331
Fireplace, V, 488, VI, 404
Fireworks, V, 544, VI, 434
Firmicus Maternus, Julius, VI, 20-21; cited, V, 120, 165, VI, 102, 104, 112, 163, 180, 500; compiled from, V, 317; criticized, V, 242, 278; ed., V, 318, 322, 343, 345, 448; interpolation in, VI, 246
Firminus de Bellavalle, V, 291
Firpo, Luigi, (1939), VI, 173
Firstborn and Firstfruits, why superior? V, 146
Fischart (1574), V, 417
Fischer, Hermann, (1929), VI, 264-5
Fischer, Johann, VI, 597
Fischer, Joseph, (1932), V, 342
Fish, VI, 355; breathe air, V, 570, denied, VI, 570; comet and, VI, 367; creation of, VI, 347; dead on shore, V, 497; divination by, VI, 503; fossil, V, 597; found alive in rock, VI, 285; gall of, VI, 358; heart of, VI, 547; live on silver, V, 22, 29; liver of, V, 470; man would be, VI, 343; marine, VI, 349; not to be eaten in 1524, V, 211; rain of, VI, 366; stone in head of, VI, 315; tartar in, V, 649; works on, VI, 255-7, 271, 310
Fisherman, V, 663
Fistula, V, 621, VI, 423
Fixation, alchemical, V, 534
Flacius Illyricus, Matthias, VI, 105, 596
Flade, Dietrich, VI, 537
Flamel, Nicolas, cited, V, 637
Flanders, V, 582, VI, 38, 207, 556
Flatulence, VI, 367
Flavor, see Taste
Flayderus, Fridericus Hermannus, ed., VI, 191
Flea, VI, 429, 571
Flemish, written in, V, 286, 330
Flessa, Ioh. Adam (1744), V, 382
Flisco, Laurentius de, V, 509
Flisco, Nicolaus de, cardinal, V, 215
Flock, Erasmus (1514-1568), V, 341-2, 397, VI, 194, 598
Flood, astrology and, V, 120, 124, 195, 202, 227-8, 311, 588, VI, 194; conjunction and, V, 158, 196-9, 206-12, 217; drought and, V, 195, 209; eclipse and, V, 224; fossil shells and, V, 27-28, 597, VI, 291; Noah's, V, 213, VI, 76, 490, date of, V, 190-5, disbelieved, V, 195-7, miraculous, V, 36, 220, VI, 345, natural, V, 592; partial and particular, V, 158, 194, 196, 199, 202-3, 211-2, 215-7, 219, 221, 229, denied, V, 217-8, 223; past listed, V, 218-9; second deluge, feared, V, 178, 180-2, 188-9, 193-4, 213-4, 222, 230, rejected, on biblical grounds, V, 195, 217, 223, on natural grounds, V, 156, 195, 216, 220, ridiculed, V, 215, 219; universal, V, 78, 181-2, 247
Flora, see Joachim of
Florence, V, 80, 184, 187, 253, 257, 326-7, 336, 501, 518, 582, VI, 27, 101, 128, 131, 158, 187, 470, 520, 522, 540, 542; born at, V, 164, 507, VI, 129; patrician of, VI, 226; pr at, V, 17, 182, 184, 187-8, 197, 273, VI, 148, 221-2, 225-7, 326, 447, 493, 519; prediction concerning, V, 214, 235; taught at, V, 325, 581
Florida, VI, 346, 436
Florimontius, Galeatius, V, 184
Florus, alchemist, V, 623
Flöter, Balthasar, Paracelsan, V, 619
Florens, M. J. P. (1857), VI, 328
Flower, in alchemy, VI, 243, botany, VI, 333, pharmacy, V, 448
Flussas, see Foix de Candalle
Fly, house, VI, 282, 290, 429; generated by a dry sky, VI, 501; portend war, VI, 501
Foetus, baptism of, V, 509; effect of imagination of mother on, V, 107, 147, 363, VI, 203, 236, 407, 571, of father, VI, 237; freak, VI, 269; period of, V, 172, 272, 345, VI, 104; superfoetatum, V, 510; temperament of, VI, 190; work on, V, 503; and see Birth, Child, Stars, influence on
Foix de Candalle, François, VI, 449
Foligno, see Gentile da
Folklore, see Superstition, popular
Fonseca, Gabriel, V, 10
Fontaine, Charles, tr, VI, 476, 485

Fontaine, Jacques, VI, 253, 553-7; against astrology, VI, 188-90; *Astrologia medica,* VI, 189-90; comm. Aristotle, *Physiognomy,* VI, 553-4; *Des marques de sorciers,* V, 70, VI, 554-5; *Diebus criticis,* VI, 188; *Discours,* VI, 188; *Magiae Paracelsicae detectio,* V, 644-5; *Pharmacia,* VI, 189; *Une dispute des elements,* V, 644
Fontana, Giovanni da, V, 4, 34, 580, 588, 595, 597
Fontenay, V, 464
Food and drink, VI, 221, 271, 277, 394, 403, 597; concentrated, V, 611; effect on morals, VI, 572, temperament, VI, 204; laid up, V, 401; selection of, V, 662; various specified, VI, 207-8; see Nutrition
Fool, V, 59, VI, 32
Foot, ailing, V, 327; care of, V, 612; club, V, 241; sole of, as sign, VI, 164; why go to sleep, V, 145
Forberger, Geo., Paracelsan, V, 619
Forchheim, V, 365
Forest dweller, VI, 287, 338; and see Wood sprite
Forgery, V, 472
Forlì, V, 60, 166, 479; and see James of
Form, VI, 419; action by, VI, 424; alteration of, in chemistry, V, 635, no new, in art, VI, 500; devil and, V, 70; giver of, V, 236, VI, 291, 482; human, lost by witch, VI, 352; implanted by God, V, 661; intension and remission of, V, 48-49, 95-96, 170; material, V, 98; matter and, VI, 350, 362, 368, 414, 441, 599; new from stars, see Star; occult virtue and, VI, 500; of celestial bodies, V, 104; of element and compound, V, 554; of metals unknown, V, 316; origin and plurality of, VI, 198; specific, see occult virtue; spiritual, V, 496; substantial, V, 40, 559, 661-2, VI, 366
Forman, Simon, VI, 219
Fornix, V, 45
Forschungen zur Geschichte Bayerns, see Reicke, E.
Forster, Richard (1575), V, 422, VI, 41-42
Forsterus, Iohannes, VI, 597
Forte, Angelo di, V, 263-4
Fortianello, V, 92
Fortification, see Engineering, military
Fortius, Joachim, see Ringelberg
Fortschritte der Medizin, V, 119
Fortunate Islands, VI, 346
Fortune, V, 19, VI, 350, 399, 410, 470, 528; denied, V, 164; place of (astrological), V, 308, VI, 20, and see Pars fortunae; wheel of, VI, 470, 502
Foschi, Placido, physician, VI, 127
Fossel, Viktor (1908), V, 381
Fossil, VI, 308; Aldrovandi on, VI, 291; amber a, V, 470; Cardan and Palissy on, V, 597-8; Falloppia on, VI, 312-3; Leonardo da Vinci on, V, 22, 27-28, VI, 292, 313
Fossombrone, bishop of, V, 217; pr at, V, 217
Foucher, J. pr Paris, V, 544
Fountain, in Sicily, V, 21; of blood, V, 399; origin of, V, 23, VI, 396; virtues of, VI, 377, 419, 428; why cold in summer? VI, 391
Fournier, André Le, see Furnerius
Fowler, VI, 267
Fox, VI, 277; lung of, V, 454, 559, VI, 501; oil of, VI, 219
Fox Morcillo, Sebastian, VI, 478; cited, VI, 49
Francanzano, Antonio, V, 39, 94
Fracastoro, Hieronymus, career, V, 488; cited, V, 641, VI, 232, 267, 407, 430, 569; homocentric theory of, V, 489-90, 570, VI, 62, 376; letter to, V, 456; on contagion, V, 493, 496-7, critical days, V, 261, 491-2, lenses, V, 490-1, sympathy and antipathy, V, 493-6, vis plastica of stars, VI, 292; refuted, V, 261, 263; *Syphilis,* V, 488-9; minor works, V, 493
Fragoso, Juan (1572), V, 469-70, VI, 314-5
France, V, 115, 123, 280, 298, 326, 445, 454, 466, VI, 145, 220, 269, 287, 304, 409, 419; astrology in, VI, 170-1; book from, V, 200; circulation in, V, 143; epidemic in, VI, 212; export to, VI, 209; flight to, VI, 175; foreigners in, V, 476, VI, 22; herbs of, VI, 225; king of, V, 35, 102, 113, 168, 230, 247, 589, VI, 133, 142, 240, 361, 432;

left, VI, 248; mathematics in, V, 297; Mediterranean coast of, V, 455; most perfect man in, V, 296; press in, VI, 170; queen of, V, 128, 159, 589, VI, 109, 178, 368; return to, V, 546, VI, 341; southern, VI, 561; travel in, V, 55, 650, VI, 255, 373; universal monarchy for, VI, 344; war with, V, 72; and see French
Franceschi, pr Venice, V, 100
Franceschini, Camillo, pr Venice, VI, 218
Francesco Capuano, see Capuano
Francesco da Ferrara, cited, VI, 125
Francesco de Melzi, V, 16
Franche Comté, VI, 311
Franchi, de, family, V, 10
Francis I, V, 137, 184, 233, 243, 260, 399, 476, VI, 142, 368; addressed to, V, 168; almoner to, V, 311; cabala, interest in, VI, 453; captivity of, V, 396, VI, 116, predicted, VI, 15; defeat at Pavia, predicted, V, 310; liberality to learning, V, 295, VI, 257, 341; preface to, V, 285
Francis, duke of Anjou, V, 483, VI, 130
Francis of Assisi, St., VI, 362; stigmata of, VI, 571
Francis of Florence, inquisitor, V, 121
Francis of Piedmont, V, 46
Franciscan, V, 70, 116, 127, 147-9, 252, 331, VI, 66, 430, 444, 450, 524, 556, 558; astrology and, VI, 15, 194; education by, V, 148-9; occult books and, VI, 150-1
Franciscis, Franciscus de, of Siena, pr Venice, VI, 213
Franciscus Maria Ferrariensis, VI, 136
Franciscus de Canona, VI, 597
Franck, alias for Silber, which see
Franconia, V, 331, 362, VI, 238, 409, 489
Frankfurt am Main, V, 442, VI, 191; book fair, VI, 212; dean of, V, 586; pr at, V, 44, 65, 375, 380, 387, 398, 405, 416, 441, 464, 474, 483, 547, 556, 619, 622, 636, 648-9, 665, VI, 126, 134, 173, 190-1, 197, 211-2, 224, 239, 242, 255, 267-8, 272, 286, 306, 308, 316, 331, 393-4, 426, 457, 460-1, 474, 483, 493-4, 505, 511, 521-2, 535, 541, 556, 600-2
Frankfurt an der Oder, pr at, V, 289, VI, 61, 377; studied at, VI, 341; taught at, V, 381, VI, 60, 105, 377
Franz, Günther (1933), V, 181
Franzosius, Hieronymus (1632), VI 511-4
Fratelli dal Jesu, see Jesu
Frati, Lodovico, V, 170
Frauenburg, V, 629, VI, 53
Fraxinus, see Ash tree
Freak, see Monster
Frederick I, king of Denmark, VI, 136
Frederick III, emperor, V, 373; geniture, V, 399; knowledge of herbs and gardens, VI, 353
Frederick III, elector Palatine, V, 652
Frederick, count Palatine, dedic to, V, 631
Frederick, duke of Wurtemberg and Tech, VI, 462
Free-thinking, V, 11-12, 37, 526, VI, 532
Fregoso, Battista, *Dictis factisque,* V, 157, VI, 401
Freher, M., *Scriptores,* V, 44
Freiburg-im-Breisgau, of, V, 173, 385; pr at, V, 139, VI, 302; taught at, VI, 16, 37, 191, 399
Freige, Ioan. Thom. VI, 37; *Paedagogus,* VI, 352; *Quaestiones physicae,* VI, 27, 45, 186-7, 351
Freistadt, V, 403
Frellonius, pr Lyons, VI, 220
French, V, 466, VI, 304; ambassador, V, 324; cavalry, V, 164; court, V, 303; in Milan, V, 162; invasion, of Italy, V, 60, of Navarre, V, 174, 208; league, VI, 22; names of plants, V, 463; naturalist, V, 550, VI, 258; place names, V, 614; readers, V, 189; taught, V, 582; tr, V, 65-67, 189, 271, 291, 310, 466, 541-2, 589, 597, 606, 618, 636, VI, 105-6, 118, 215, 266, 318, 393, 438, 447, 451, 469, 474-5, 494, 530; tr from, V, 477, VI, 215; written in, V, 122, 206, 284, 286, 297, 299, 330, 433, 477, 543, 590, 594, 596, 623, 642, 644, VI, 20, 24, 38, 107, 128, 160, 169, 220, 311, 360-1, 453, 459, 472-3, 478-9, 485, 507, 522, 524, 528, 531
Freyenstain, V, 603
Friar, V, 78, 201; attacked or sneered

at, V, 36, 63, VI, 175, 511; and see Dominican, Franciscan, etc.
Fribourg (Switzerland), V, 127, 132, 541; taught at, V, 542
Fridaria, V, 269
Friedenwald, Harry (1937), VI, 258
Friedlein, Gottfried (1865), VI, 89
Friedrich, Johann (1864), V, 177, 255, 433
Friend and Friendship, V, 239, 260, 336, 363
Fries, Laurent, V, 331; career, V, 430-1; cited, V, 460; compared with Champier, V, 430-1; controversy with Gengenbach, V, 229, 435; estimate of, V, 437-8; parodied by Rabelais, V, 313, 435; quoted, V, 430; relations with Agrippa and Paracelsus, V, 431, Luther, V, 433, Murner, V, 434-5; works, *Defensio,* V, 436-7, *Dialogus,* V, 434, ed. Ptolemy, *Geography,* V, 173, 437, *Ein kurtze Schirmred,* V, 433, *Epitome,* V, 434, *Prognostication,* V, 229, *Spiegel der Artznei,* V, 431-3, 435-6, *Synonyma,* V, 435
Frischlin, Nicodemus, V, 380, 405, VI, 190-2, 197
Frisia, V, 430, VI, 436
Friuli, Inquisition in, VI, 149-50
Frizis, Antonius de, of Corinaldo, pr Naples, V, 200
Froben, Johannes, pr Basel, V, 409, 438, 535, VI, 255, 267
Frobenius, H. pr Basel, V, 609
Frog, eye of live, as remedy, V, 560; found alive in marble, VI, 285; generated in air, V, 599; not eaten in antiquity, V, 481; red, as sign of pest, V, 574; suspended, as remedy, V, 646; thought to fall with rain, V, 599, 658, VI, 283, 349, 366
Froger, Maurice, VI, 510
Froger, Robert, VI, 510
Froschauer, Christopher, pr Zurich, VI, 291
Frostbite, V, 612
Fruit, preserving, V, 555, VI, 419
Frytschius, Marcus, (1563), VI, 490
Fuchs, Johann, medical, V, 437
Fuchs, Leonhard, V, 6, 443, 449, 455, VI, 280, 353; attacked by Massa, V, 515-6, Servetus, V, 289; cited, V, 465, 470, VI, 256; controversy with Ryff, VI, 212-3, with Scheck, VI, 212; criticized, VI, 225; *Errata,* V, 501; *Historia stirpium,* VI, 261, 265; put on Index, VI, 147
Fuchs, Remaclus, see Fusch
Fuchs, Samuel, (1615), VI, 506
Fuentes, Alonso de, *Somma,* VI, 390-2
Fugger, brothers, dedic to, V, 399; family, V, 619, VI, 112
Fugger, Georg, V, 416
Fugger, Jacob, preface to, V, 581, 583
Fugger, Jacob the Elder, VI, 116
Fugger, Johann Jacob, VI, 227
Fugger, Philip Edward, VI, 121
Fugger, Ulrich, dedic to, V, 391
Fugitives, pursuit of, V, 363; and see Religious, exile
Fulda, abbot of, VI, 300
Fulgosius, see Fregoso
Fulke, Wm., *Antiprognosticon,* VI, 180
Fulwod, W. tr, V, 607
Fumanello, Antonio, physician, V, 493
Fumes, danger from, V, 459, 462
Fumi, Luigi, VI, 149
Fumigation, V, 639, VI, 558; and see Suffumigation
Fundamentalism, V, 192
Funeral and burial, V, 520; monument, VI, 401
Fünfkirchen, bishop of, VI, 183
Fungi, V, 480
Furies in sleep, V, 628
Furmannus, Valentinus, pr Nürnberg, VI, 91
Furnace, V, 540, 590, 635, VI, 95; death from descent into, VI, 366
Furnerius, Andreas, V, 543, 621
Furnius, Dionysius, copyist, V, 666
Fusch, Remaclus, V, 464, 544

G. C., VI, 106
G. Parisiensis, alchemist, V, 623
Gabelchover, Wolfgang, tr, VI, 316
Gabiano, fratres de, publishers, Lyons, VI, 74
Gabotto, F. (1892), V, 258
Gabriel, angel, V, 102, VI, 551; spirit of moon, V, 569, VI, 441
Gadaldinus, Aug. tr, V, 530

Gaddi, cardinal, VI, 227
Gaetanus, Camillus, patriarch, VI, 410; and see Cajetan
Gaffarel, Jacques, VI, 302
Gagates, a gem, V, 457
Gaignaeus, Ioannes, ed., V, 552
Gaillard, Gabriel H. (1819), V, 636, VI, 368
Gaiono, Bart., physician, V, 493
Galactites, a gem, VI, 320
Galantinum, a disease, VI, 212
Galatina, VI, 599
Galatinus, Petrus, *De arcanis,* V, 130, VI, 444-5
Galemini, Agostino, cardinal, dedic to, VI, 63, 487
Galen, V, 125, 295, 387, 470, 502, VI, 353; against Aristotle, V, 46-47, 503, VI, 327, 340, 514; anatomy, V, 500-1, 505-6, 508, 514, 516, 518-9, 525, 530, VI, 213, 353; astrology, V, 290, VI, 210; attitude towards, of Cardan, V, 564, of Vesalius, V, 523, 525, 530; cinnamon extinct since, V, 468, 663; cited, V, 172, 195, 450, 456, 473, 506, 512, 523, 561, 661-2, VI, 210, 223, 232, 234, 272, 313, 317, 319, 334, 338, 358, 399, 402; comm. V, 550, VI, 356, 400, 567; compiled from, V, 42, 551, VI, 217, 406; critical days, on, V, 314, 325, 491, comm., VI, 128; criticized, V, 271, 289, 314, 439, 465, 467, 508, 519, 527, 564, 630, 640, VI, 212-3, 215, 226-8, 336, 461, from experience, V, 662-3; defended, V, 79, 261, VI, 238, 365; disputed, V, 491; edited, VI, 230; errors of, V, 525, 530; fascination, V, 476; followed, V, 430, 467, 521, 552, 557, VI, 226-7, 271, 562-3, 567, against experience, V, 501; lectured on, V, 436; life of, V, 387; medicines of, superior, VI, 225; not read, VI, 260; omissions of, V, 449, 453-4, 640; praised, V, 492, 499, 564; procedure of, VI, 518; soul, on the, V, 559; text, V, 501-2, revised, V, 524-5; tr, V, 61, 430, 437; venerated, VI, 382; works, burned by Paracelsus? V, 438, by Vesalius, V, 529, dubious, VI, 215, indices to, V, 609, lost, V, 523, titles, *Administrandis sectionibus,* V, 525, *Comm. Aphorisms,* V, 446-7, *Decubitu infirmorum,* V, 328, VI, 158, *Insomniis,* VI, 478, *Iuvamentis membrorum,* V, 502, *Medicinalis,* V, 541, *Methodo medendi,* V, 430, VI, 230, *Praesagiis ex pulsibus,* V, 564, *Remediis parabilibus,* V, 614, *Secreta,* V, 448, *Techni,* V, 504, *Utilitate partium,* V, 502, VI, 402
Galenism and Galenist, VI, 215, 602; self-styled, V, 525; traditional, V, 492, 557
Galenus, Joannes, see Pediasimus
Galeotto Marzio da Narni, V, 503, VI, 402
Galeum Rhodeum, a fish, VI, 257
Galileo, V, 585; and biology, VI, 334; and Campanella, VI, 173; and Copernican theory, V, 249-50, VI, 7, 62-63, 428; and Tyard, VI, 26; ignored, VI, 64, 87, 201, 569; praised, VI, 97, 190
Gall bladder, V, 503
Galland, Pierre, V, 312
Gallianus, Conrad, astrologer, V, 202; cited, 227
Galliera, a castle of Julius II, IV, 150
Gallizioli, G. B. (1788), V, 600
Gallois, L. (1890), V, 200, 285-6, 292, 331; (1935), V, 285
Gallows, robbing the, V, 526
Gallucci, Giov, Paolo, astrological medicine, VI, 158; *Speculum,* V, 155, VI, 60, 159-60; *Theatrum,* V, 8-9, 151, VI, 60, 158-9
Gambalunga family, VI, 127
Game, Gaming and Gambling, V, 246, 363, VI, 200, 470-1
Ganay, Germain de, VI, 438-42
Gandelot, Abbé (1772), VI, 106
Gandolfo, D. A. (1704), V, 545, VI, 492
Ganivet, Jean, V, 159, 443
Ganymede, VI, 278
Ganzenmüller, W. (1935), V, 532
Garaldis, Bernardinus de, pr Pavia, V, 64; and see Gueralda
Garbo, Dino del, V, 502-3, 513; disciple of, V, 502
Garbo, Tommaso del, V, 503-4, 510
Garcaeus, Joh. V, 384, VI, 19, 102-5, 111, 595

Garcia da Orta, see Orta
Garcia, Pedro, refuted, VI, 431
Garden, VI, 259, 296, 353; botanical, at Bologna, V, 247, Padua, V, 446, 531, VI, 258, 466, Pisa, VI, 332; private, VI, 154, 268
Gardo, Lago di, V, 488
Gargantua, *Deux publications* (1925), V, 313, 435
Gargionius, Fabritius, VI, 152
Garlic, supposed effect on magnet denied, VI, 282, 317, 420
Garnet, V, 457
Garnier, Joseph (1918), V, 307, 309, 311
Garrison, F. H., V, 496
Garsias, alchemist, V, 548
Garzo, Marcellus, V, 242
Gascon and Gascony, V, 299
Gassar, Achilles Pirminius, astrological predictions, V, 392; censure of Paracelsan propositions, V, 640-1; cited, VI, 267; *Consilia,* V, 391; historical writings, V, 391; relation to Melanchthon and Wittenberg, V, 390-1
Gassendi, Pierre, V, 234-5, VI, 389
Gastmansdorf, V, 362
Gastromancy, VI, 499, 502
Gattinaria, Marcus, VI, 402
Gaudentius of Treviso, VI, 471, 473; put on Index, VI, 147, 471
Gaudoul, Pierre, pr Paris, V, 308
Gaufridy, Louis, reputed sorcerer, VI, 554
Gaul, V, 113, 115, 200, 512; Cisalpine, VI, 227; from Gal, VI, 345; and see France
Gauoti, V. publisher, Milan, V, 543
Gaurico, Luca, V, 51, 213, 255-9, 312, 488, 586, VI, 105, 157; admirers of, V, 379, 383-4; cited, VI, 21, 121, 131, 180, 193; criticizes Regiomontanus, V, 360; descriptions of contemporaries, V, 38, 94, 241, VI, 471, 474; disciple of, V, 246, 267; ed., V, 192, 306, 365; lecture on astrology, V, 239; Paris and, V, 279; prediction by, V, 160, 229-30, 257, 392, at fault, V, 382, VI, 101; put on Index, VI, 147; quoted, V, 37; relations with popes, V, 230; tr, V, 167; works, *Directiones,* V, 375, *Eclipsi solis miraculosa,* V, 256-7, 301, *Nativitatibus,* V, 258-9, 363, *Opera nuova,* V, 259, *Oratio,* V, 165-7, 334, *Praedictiones,* V, 257-8, *Pronostico,* VI, 101, *Questio,* V, 167, *Super diebus decretoriis,* V, 263, *Tractatus astrologicus,* V, 38, 51, 94, 252, VI, 100-1, 471, 474
Gaurico, Pomponio, V, 17
Gaza, Theodore, V, 342, 570, VI, 279
Gazeau or Gazeius, G. pr Lyons, V, 398, VI, 24
Gazius, Antonius, physician, V, 170-1
Gazius, Simon, V, 167
Gazulus, V, 336, 359-60, VI, 103, 180; Ragusinus, VI, 131
Geauschelius, Jacobus, VI, 459
Geber, alchemist, V, 126, 536-7, 626, 648, 684-5, VI, 218; cited, V, 141, 538, 604, 623-5, 637, VI, 224, 252; comm. V, 545; debt of Paracelsus to, V, 658; geomancy by, VI, 469, 472; of Spain, V, 565; pr, V, 536-7, 545-6, 548, 602
Gechauff, see Venatorius
Geiger, L. (1871), VI, 444
Gelenius, Ioh., VI, 598
Gelyra, V, 674
Gem, composition, VI, 312; dissolved, V, 541; engraved, see Image; in breastplate of high priest, VI, 315; liquor of, V, 621; magic power of, V, 475, 610, 614, 646, VI, 305-6, 309, 324, 335, denied or doubted, V, 455, VI, 305, 316, 320, 416; occult virtue of, V, 456, 551, 570-1, 579, VI, 299, 302-3, 316, 320-2, 419, 428, 435-6, 488, denied, V, 663, VI, 571; passed through alimentary canal, V, 456-7; pulverized, V, 273, 456, 478; scepticism of dealers in, VI, 285; seven and planets, VI, 315; virtue lost with age, VI, 300; works on, by Bacci, VI, 315-6, Boodt, VI, 318-23, Cesalpino, VI, 334-5, Fragoso, VI, 314-5, Gabelchover, VI, 316, Garcia da Orta, VI, 313-4, Gesner, VI, 304-5, 307-8, Lang, VI, 316, Lunardi, VI, 298-301, Rueus, VI, 303-6, Stella, VI, 302-3
Gemma, Cornelius, VI, 598; *Arte cyclognomica,* VI, 100, 406; cited, V, 248-9, 482, VI, 79-80, 184, 382; *Ephemerides,* VI, 30; finishes his fa-

ther's work, VI, 13, 102; inferior to his father, VI, 30; inspired by star of 1572, VI, 68; *Naturae divinis characterismis,* VI, 406-9; praised, VI, 42, 75; tale of lucky forecast, VI, 99-100
Gemma Frisius, V, 372, 526, VI, 406; and comet, V, 410; and Copernican theory, V, 319, VI, 13-14; cited, VI, 18; combined science and astrology, V, 319; criticized, VI, 184; horoscope of, VI, 102, 196, 598; on monstrous races, VI, 275; observations of, VI, 14-15; works, *Astrolabio catholico,* VI, 13, 102; *Ephemerides,* V, 249; Letter to Stadius, VI, 13-14; *Principiis astronomiae,* V, 357
Gemusaeus, Hieronymus, V, 609
Genealogy, V, 112-3
Genebrard, Gilbert, VI, 141
General, VI, 471
Generation and corruption, V, 40, 151, 554, VI, 369, 433, 535; animal, VI, 95; applying seminal virtue, VI, 391; from earth, VI, 521; from stars, V, 157, 247, VI, 188, 198; human, V, 503-4, VI, 221, aid to, V, 444, VI, 459, artificial, VI, 431; of metals and minerals, V, 593, 643; spontaneous, V, 27-28, 141, 236, 574, 599, 655, VI, 188, 199, 283-4, 286, from ideas, V, 236, from putrefaction, V, 43, 570, VI, 281, 283, 290, 327, 357, 379, 421, 481, 501, 539, 564, 570, from saliva, VI, 283, human, V, 90, 270, in air, VI, 342, in fire, denied, VI, 95, of animals, V, 157, 236, of fossils, VI, 291, 312, of insects, VI, 283, 290, 570, of plants, VI, 333, 481, of scorpion in the brain, V, 482, of stones in air, V, 659, within stones, VI, 284-5; and see Eugenics, Goose, barnacle, Monster
Genethliaci and Genethlialogy, see Nativities
Geneva, Agrippa at, V, 127; council of, VI, 247; flight to, VI, 247, 423; pr at, VI, 326, 346, 386, 493, 530; studied at, VI, 247, 346; taught at, VI, 346
Gengenbach, Pamphilus, V, 229, 314, 434-5
Genista, an herb, VI, 263
Geniture, see Nativity
Genius, V, 573, VI, 354, 551; familiar, VI, 449, 508; identified with geniture, V, 105
Genoa, V, 113, 269, 455, 513, VI, 364; head compression at, V, 512; merchants of, VI, 337; placenta of, V, 611; pr at, V, 259, VI, 518
Gentile, VI, 532
Gentile da Foligno, VI, 521; cited, V, 475, 485, 502-4, 513, VI, 229; criticized, V, 437, VI, 365
Gentilis, Matthaeus, VI, 518-9
Genua, Marcus Antonius, V, 524
Genuissa, an herb, VI, 263-4; and see Genista
Geography, V, 141, 285-6, 331, VI, 430, 436; at Nürnberg, V, 348, 350, 352, 354-5, 357-8; brief treatment of, VI, 31; instruments, V, 354; lectures on, V, 288; new world separated from Asia, V, 200; recent discovery, V, 630, not reflected, V, 122; taught, V, 288; works on, V, 372, VI, 40, 42, 361; and see Cosmography
Geology, V, 19, 25-28, 156, VI, 342, 396
Geomancy, V, 50, 54, 57, 68, 135, 466, VI, 468-73, 503, 509; Agrippa and, V, 131; alchemy and, V, 634; astrology confused with, VI, 16; election of Leo X predicted by, V, 252; illicit, V, 660, VI, 169, 180; inquisitor to leave cases of, to ordinary, VI, 150; learned from Gaurico, V, 168; natural, V, 105, VI, 176; opposed, VI, 193, 199; put on the Index, VI, 146-7, 150-1; relation to lot-casting, VI, 496; stimulates mind, V, 575; superstitious, VI, 430, 467, 485; varieties of VI, 502,
Geometry, V, 282, 284, 386, 512, 564, 589, 642, VI, 77, 81, 253, 443, 471; appealed to, V, 428, VI, 374; certainty of, VI, 464-5; Copernican, VI, 3, 10; demonstrations by Regiomontanus, V, 360; held in contempt, V, 155; medicine and, V, 431, VI, 142; new, VI, 373; speculative and operative, VI, 429; works of, VI, 88-89, 140, 142, 373
George, count of Egmond, bishop of Utrecht, VI, 102
George de Ferrariis, V, 450

George, duke of Saxony, VI, 596
George of Paris, cited, V, 220
George of Ragusa, VI, 198-202; quoted, VI, 179, 466
George of Trebizond, V, 570, VI, 279; cited, V, 166, 227, 403, VI, 170; geniture, VI, 105, 596; tr, V, 336, 343
George of Venice, see Giorgio
Georgius de Eltz, V, 167
Gerard of Cremona, V, 252; attacked by Regiomontanus, V, 336-7; cited, V, 437; criticized, V, 468, 502; *Geomancy,* V, 54, 131; *Theory of the Planets,* V, 85
Gerardus, Aegidius, VI, 311
Gerbus, see Zerbus
Gerhardus, Joannes, botanist, (1597), VI, 258
Gerkrath, L. (1860), V, 579, VI, 560-1
Germ, see Disease, Seminaries of
German, authors, V, 143; choristers at Toledo, V, 582; contribution to useful arts, V, 34-35; girl, case of, V, 273; grateful to France, VI, 22; infantry, V, 164; inquisitors, VI, 338; inventions, V, 335; language, VI, 142, lectured in, V, 438; low, V, 618; mile, V, 614, VI, 50; names, VI, 256, 308, 319, VI, 85; naturalists, V, 550, VI, 258; nation, at Paris, V, 285; praised, V, 334-5, 589, prince, V, 598, VI, 509; self consciousness, V, 335, 416; readers, V, 189; saying, VI, 221; spoken in Spoleto, V, 578; tale of a, VI, 571; taught Latin temporarily, VI, 440; tr, V, 64-66, 210, 218, 391, 398, 432, 541, 655, VI, 117-8, 142, 218, 393, 457, 522, 538; troops in Calabria, V, 582; works in, V, 12, 202-3, 206, 217, 229, 286, 291, 314, 322, 327, 330-3, 342, 345, 347, 356-7, 361-2, 365, 373, 382, 396, 417-8, 421, 430-43, 521, 532, 536, 543, 610, 618, 620, 642, VI, 56, 60, 70, 106, 111, 126, 134, 143, 184, 262, 400, 530
Germany, V, 280, 288, 321, 350, 378, 466, 601, 612, VI, 80, 132, 145, 459, 506, 513, 516, 526; alchemy in, V, 604, VI, 242; astrology in, V, 210-1, 654, VI, 157-8; astronomy and mathematics in, V, 297-8, 366, 567, VI, 31; floods not predicted for, V, 229; herbs from, VI, 268; inns of, V, 613; Lower, VI, 75, 310; map of, V, 331, 348; mineralogy of, VI, 319; mines of, V, 457, VI, 308-9; miracle in, VI, 468; pest in, V, 354, VI, 185; return to, V, 171, 652, 654; South, cities of, V, 344; travel in, V, 650, VI, 255, 439; Turk to rule, V, 375; war of 1546 in, VI, 409; witchcraft in, VI, 337-8, 535; wretched state of, in 1549, V, 299
Germisone, see Cermisone
Gernardus, *Algorithmus demonstratus,* V, 359
Gerona, see Moses of Gerunda
Gerson, Jean, V, 242, VI, 304, 524; cited, V, 277, VI, 467; others compared with, V, 116, 652, VI, 467
Gesamtkatalog der Wiegendrucke, V, 39, 55, 116, 179, 345-6, 535, 675, 677
Gesner, Andrea, pr Zurich, V, 589, 621
Gesner, A. et J. fratres, prs Zurich, VI, 531
Gesner, Conrad, V, 6, 8, VI, 273, 531; *Bibliotheca* (1545), V, 8, 49, 55, 71-75, 81, 129, 142, 144, 149, 152-4, 160, 254, 260, 324, 330, 346, 348, 362, 386-7, 407, 430, 435, 438-41, 443, 445, 448, 460, 464, 500-1, 514, 528-9, 541-2, 618, VI, 8-9, 255-7, 267, 270, 341, 443, 445, 447, 491-3, 600; *Bibliotheca* (1583), V, 318, 417; *Bitumine,* V, 466; botanizing excursions, VI, 254; cited without title, V, 641, VI, 177, 256, 294, 319, 349; compiler, VI, 270; correspondence of, VI, 224, 255, 267, 288; ed., V, 470, 609, VI, 449; extracts from, V, 475; friend of, V, 391; *Historia animalium,* VI, 257-8, 259, 267, 270, 280, 286, 353; *Historia insectorum,* VI, 254; *Historia plantarum,* VI, 268; influenced by, VI, 349; inquiry by, V, 605; not cited, VI, 259, 335; *Omni rerum fossilium genere,* VI, 269, 271, 303-4, 307-8; other works, VI, 265-6, 291; pupils, VI, 393; pseudonym of, V, 543, 621; question by, V, 605; specimens sent to, VI, 269; tr, VI, 478
Gesture, VI, 427, 446
Gethsemane, VI, 558
Geuder, Christofer, dedic to, V, 361
Geuder, Johann, dedic to, V, 361

Geuderus, horoscope of, V, 352
Geuss, Wolf., astrologer and physician, VI, 126
Ghent, VI, 125, 378, 394; born at, VI, 126; pr at, V, 410, VI, 393; school at, VI, 38
Ghilini, Camillo, tr, V, 157
Ghini, Luca, naturalist, VI, 258, 260, 333
Ghirardacci, Cherubino, V, 51, 234
Ghost, V, 97, 143, 628, VI, 469, 532; denied, VI, 530, 533, 540; and see Specter
Giannini, Tommaso, (1618), V, 424, VI, 48, 97-98, 205-6, 386
Gianotti, Tommaso, see Philologus
Giant, V, 512, 639, VI, 408, 470; and see Patagonia
Gibraltar, see Straits of
Giffoni, bishop of, V, 256, 586; feudal lord of, 257
Gifford, William, VI, 517
Gifftiger, (1567), V, 474
Gift, must be reecived as a, VI, 322
Giglio, see Lilio
Gilbert, William, V, 547; astronomy of, VI, 61-62; authors criticized by, V, 270; cited, VI, 63-64; *Magnete,* V, 580, VI, 63-64, 316-8; not cited, VI, 308, 319, 569; *Philosophia nova,* V, 656, VI, 61-63, 379-82; quoted, V, 333
Gilbertus Cardinalis, V, 623
Gilgil, alchemist, V, 604
Gilles, see Aegidius
Gilles, Pierre, see Gillius
Gilliszoon, Willem, see Aegidius, William
Gillius, David, bookseller, Paris, VI, 324
Gillius, Petrus, naturalist, VI, 255-7
Gimma (1723), V, 63
Giolito, Gabriel, of Ferrara, pr Venice, V, 233
Giorgio, Francesco, V, 130, 247, VI, 450-3
Giovanni da Fontana, see Fontana
Giovio, Paolo, V, 51, 137, VI, 255-6
Giraldus Cambrensis, VI, 288
Girard de Vienne, V, 310
Girl, see Woman
Gita or Gith, an herb, VI, 263-4
Giulio Fl., VI, 125
Giunta, Iacomo, VI, 470; and see Junta
Giunti, pr Florence, VI, 221
Giuntus, Iacobus, pr Lyons, V, 158
Giuntini, Francesco, V, 67, VI, 129-33; cited, VI, 202, 569; *Comm. Sphere,* V, 288, 418, VI, 24, 27, 43-44, 130, 275-6; disagreed with, VI, 201, 561; *Speculum astrologiae,* V, 199, 326-7, VI, 44, 115, 130-3; used, VI, 430
Giustiniano, Paolo, abbot, V, 555
Glacier, V, 31
Glareanus, V, 331
Glaser, Conrad, VI, 596
Glass, broken, V, 613; burning-, see Lens; making, V, 141, 604; painter, V, 596; purified, V, 457; window, V, 116; worker, V, 596
Glaucon, Galen to, V, 430
Globe, V, 372, 583; divining, VI, 243; maker of, V, 354; works on, VI, 103
Glogau, V, 404; and see John of
Glossators, VI, 276
Gmunden, see John of
Gnome, V, 628, 639
Gnomics and Gnomon, V, 397, VI, 373, 430
Goa, pr at, V, 466
Goat, V, 58, 462; bezoar from, VI, 235; blood of, V, 559, breaks the stone, V, 663, VI, 241, 314, effect on magnet denied, VI, 282, 314, 420, softens diamond, V, 158, VI, 186, 285, 309, 314; he, V, 476, gives milk, VI, 225; liver of, VI, 225; milk, V, 621, child weaned on, VI, 204
Göckel, see Goclenius
Goclenius, Rodolphus (1618), V, 326, VI, 136-7, 368, 485, 506
God, V, 150, VI, 349, 414; acts through the stars, V, 105, 194, VI, 199, 481, directly, V, 403, VI, 187, 347, 407, 496; aid invoked, V, 508, VI, 33; ascent to, VI, 426, 450-1; chosen by, V, 439; Copernicus on, V, 424; cursing, VI, 200; disease from, V, 627; dreams and, VI, 482, 484; fear of, V, 215; First Mover, VI, 198, 369; freedom of action, VI, 523; future, alone knows, VI, 156, reveals only effects, not causes, V, 298, shows signs, VI, 135; grace of, VI, 77; image of, in sky, V, 399; in the east, VI, 138;

limbs of, VI, 451; magic and, VI, 239; majesty of, VI, 367; man and, V, 390, 398, VI, 451; marvelous works of, VI, 290-1; medicine and, V, 626; names of, see Name and Tetragrammaton; nature and, VI, 81; order and, VI, 164; perfect knowledge of, VI, 563; presence, degrees of, VI, 495, in all, VI, 239; sons of, V, 108; sun as symbol of, VI, 188; super omnia, VI, 166; supreme cause, VI, 384-5; unity and, VI, 442; warning from, VI, 78, 468-9; witches and, VI, 549; wrath of, VI, 92, 211, 489, 538; and see Prayer, Providence, Trinity

Godelmann, Johann Georg, VI, 517, 525, 535-7

Goebelius, *De succino,* V, 466, 470

Goeppingen, V, 412

Goetia, VI, 415, 516; called false, VI, 193, 460; varieties of, VI, 400

Gogava, tr, V, 364

Gohorry, Jacques, V, 636, 640; and see Suavius

Gold, V, 540, VI, 434; acquisition predicted, V, 236; affected by lead, V, 315, quicksilver, VI, 404; bath of, V, 646; called eagle, VI, 278; chain of, worn against leprosy, V, 420; defined, V, 626; divine, V, 645; fire and, V, 146; flour of, V, 457; fowl and, V, 645, VI, 388; growth of, V, 33; impervious to heat, V, 645; leaf, see Herb; made of mercury and sulphur, V, 459, 634; marvelous, VI, 315; medicinal, V, 459, 599, 639, 645-7, 651, VI, 250, 316; mine, V, 33; name, see called; not an amulet, V, 646; not reducible to a salt, V, 638; potable, V, 540-2, 598, 628, 634, 645-7, 665, VI, 218, 224, 250, 252; praised, V, 547, VI, 435; protects from sorcery, V, 646; purified by antimony, V, 249; quenched in wine, V, 647; refiner of, V, 540; vulgar, chemical and divine, V, 645

Goldberg, V, 153

Golden Fleece, V, 643

Goldfinch, V, 29, VI, 285

Goldsmith, VI, 245

Goltsteyn, Chilianus, VI, 598

Gomez-Miedes, Bernardino, VI, 281-2

Gómez Pereira, (1558), VI, 215

Gondersleven, V, 348

Gondisalvus of Toledo, V, 159

Gonon, Benedictus, (1626), V, 535

Gonzaga, Federico or Federigo, marchese, dedic to, V, 63, 230

Gonzaga, Francesco, dedic to, V, 250

Gonzaga, Gianfrancesco, marchese, dedic to, V, 55-56

Goodwin, Gordon, VI, 483

Goose, barnacle, V, 570, VI, 279, 288-9, 401, 421, 436, 565, 570; eaten cooked alive, VI, 420-1; long-lived, VI, 285; modest and cautious, VI, 277; stuffed with cat, V, 432; tongue of, V, 444; tough, VI, 285

Gordon, Bernard, V, 437, VI, 516

Görlitz, pr at, V, 369, 387, and dedic to senate of, VI, 90

Gotha, VI, 457

Gothinus, Aegidius, pr Paris, V, 464

Goths, filthy inflow of, V, 522

Göttingen Abhandlungen, V, 344

Goulart, Simon, tr, VI, 494

Goulin, Jean, V, 558

Goulin, Nicolas, VI, 141

Gourmontius Hieronymous, pr Paris, VI, 344

Gout, V, 619, VI, 106, 212; caused by too little sulphur, V, 626; one of four types of disease, V, 627, 659; remedy for, VI, 243, 422

Government, V, 142

Govi, G. (1885), V, 365

Gozadinis, Laurentius de, V, 61

Grabmann, Martin, V, 14

Grado, Matth. de, see Ferrari da Grado

Graesse, J. G. T. (1859-69), V, 65, 79, 182, 486, 541, VI, 215, 433, 458-9, 484

Graevius, *Thesaurus,* V, 545

Graminaeus, Theodore, pr Cologne, VI, 72, 456, 505

Grammar and Grammarian, V, 57, 112, 142, 255, 285, 431, VI, 28, 190, 455, 477; school, VI, 38, 190-1; science subordinated to, VI, 270

Grammateus, Henricus, V, 173-4

Gramond or Gramundus, *History of Gaul,* VI, 560

Gran, archbishop of, dedic to, V, 376, VI, 316

Granada, pr at, VI, 159
Granger, Thimothy, VI, 287
Grangier, Pierre-I. pr Dijon, V, 308-9
Grapheus, Jo. pr Antwerp, V, 320, 462
Grassi, Bartolomeo, pr Rome, VI, 315
Gratarolo, Guglielmo, V, 545, 600-16, 621; alchemical publications (not listed below), V, 602; *Chrysorrhoas*, V, 603-4; *Consilium*, V, 608; criticized, VI, 285; family, V, 601; index to Galen, V, 609; ed., V, 99-100, 107, 542; *Literatorum . . . valetudine*, V, 601, 605, 608; *Memoria reparanda*, V, 606-7; *Pestis descriptio*, V, 607-8; *Physiognomy*, V, 66; *Praefationes*, V, 609; quoted, V, 600; *Regimine iter agentium*, V, 605, 609-16, VI, 400; *Theses*, V, 609-10; *Verae alchemiae*, V, 545-8, 601-3, VI, 224; *Vini natura*, V, 608
Gratian, alchemist, V, 624
Gratian, *Decretum*, cited, V, 120, VI, 175
Gratiola, an herb, VI, 265
Grato, Giov. Carlo, astrologer, V, 246
Graux, Charles, (1889), VI, 89
Grave and Graveyard, air near, corrupt, V, 97, VI, 403; ceremonial at, VI, 404; of the Innocents, Paris, V, 525; phantasms seen at, V, 97
Gravity, center of, V, 24, 156, 586; force of, V, 271, 365; same for other planets as for earth, V, 429, VI, 381
Gray, Dr. Robert, VI, 267
Greece, V, 612
Greek, alchemy, V, 532, 548, 623-4; ancient, V, 104, 577, VI, 94, 211, 330, 353, 498; astrology, VI, 174; authors, enthusiasm for, V, 3, 336, 430, 467, 550, 620, preferred to Arabic, V, 3, 114, 501; characters, V, 538; cited, V, 455, 513, 608, VI, 487; commentators, V, 185, VI, 365-6; corrupted arts and religion, VI, 464; debt to Egypt, Arabs and India, V, 437; language, V, 349, 356, 379, 596, VI, 91, 256, 275, 296, 362; magic, VI, 154, 293; manuscripts, V, 185, 393, VI, 154; medicines not for Frenchmen, V, 466; modern, V, 463, 501-2, 585; names, of arts of divination, VI, 502, of birds, VI, 256, 271, of simples, VI, 254, 332; New Testament, V, 393; not omniscient V, 449; philosophy, VI, 601; Pliny preferred to, V, 388; pretense of, V, 349; quoted, VI, 120-1, 134, 278, 495, 504; scholarship, V, 176, VI, 275, 279; taught, V, 152, 338, 582, VI, 30, 194, 255, 492, 524; text, V, 369, 421, VI, 447, 449, 460, 475, 492; things unknown to, V, 453, 467; words interspersed, V, 402-3, misspelled, VI, 275, 408; and see Translation, from
Greekling, modern, V, 436
Greene, E. L. (1909), VI, 261-2, 265, 290, 295
Gregoire, Père, see Marchand, Henri
Gregoire, Pierre, VI, 431
Gregorius, Martin, tr, V, 430
Gregory the Great, V, 87, 142; cited, VI, 157
Gregory XIII, VI, 148; addressed to, V, 251, VI, 45; deceived by an alchemist, VI, 245; nativity of, VI, 156; and see Calendar, Tables
Gregory XIV, dedic to, VI, 373-4
Gregory, brother, VI, 268
Gregory of Rimini, V, 95
Gregory the theologian, V, 390
Greisswald, professor at, VI, 103, 525
Grenoble, V, 125, 303; death of Agrippa at, V, 129, 137; university of, V, 449
Grévin, Jaques, *Deux livres*, V, 477-8; *Discours*, V, 478-9
Grieninger, Johann, pr Strasburg, V, 356; probably same as Grüninger
Grillando, Paolo, V, 71; cited, VI, 538, 540, 543
Grimani, cardinal, V, 72, 205, VI, 227
Grimm, Sigismund, physician, pr Augsburg VI, 446
Griphus, Thomas, astrologer, V, 255
Grisons, V, 605
Grisostomo, Giovanni, a prior, VI, 153
Griteus, Andrea, doge of Venice, V, 314
Grohmann, J. C. A. (1801-2), V, 393
Gromon, pr Paris, V, 308
Gromorsus, Petrus, pr Paris, V, 544
Gronau, (1794), V, 202
Gronetus, Guilelmus, a patient, V, 302
Grosseteste, Robert, cited, V, 166, 399
Grosseto, bishop of, V, 472
Grothenius, Conradus, pr Lemgo, VI, 352
Grüninger, pr Strasburg, V, 433; and see Grieninger

Grünpeck, Joseph, V, 206; put on the Index, VI, 146-7
Gruppenbach, Georg, pr Tübingen, VI, 5, 76
Gryllus, Laurentius, medical, VI, 227
Grynaeus, Simon, V, 343, 364, 656, VI, 91-92, 521; dedic to, V, 379-80
Gryphius, Ant., pr Lyons, VI, 561
Gryphius, Thomas, see Griphus
Gryuel, François, copyist, VI, 453
Guadalajara, V, 486
Guaiaco or Guaiacum wood, V, 440, 446, 454, 460
Guaineri, Antonio, V, 437, VI, 210, 319, 521
Guardian angel, see Angel
Guareschi, Icilio, (1904), V, 544
Guarico, see Gaurico
Guarino, *Supplementum,* (1740), V, 168
Guarischo, Marco, pr Venice, VI, 398
Guazzo, Marco, (1540), V, 233
Gueralda, Bernardinus, pr Ancona, V, 218; and see Garaldis
Guerra, Vincentius, censor, VI, 334
Guerrini, Olindo, (1879), VI, 373
Gueullartius, Ioannes, pr Paris, VI, 343-4
Gugler, Nicolaus, V, 368; father and son, V, 370-1
Guibert, Nicolas, V, 648; *Alchymia . . . expugnata,* VI, 244-5, 451-2; *Apologia,* VI, 245-6; *Interitu alchemiae,* VI, 245-7, criticized, VI, 246
Guido da Bagni, V, 55
Guido, John, Villariensis, V, 296-7, VI, 131
Guilandinus, Melchoir, botanist, V, 336, 531, VI, 224, 258, 279, 466; works by, VI, 260
Guillard, Guillaume, pr Paris, V, 622-3
Guimarães, Rodolphe, (1915), V, 421, VI, 35
Guinther of Andernach, (1571), VI, 219, 368, 478
Guise, duke of, V, 111
Guise, Charles, cardinal of Lorraine, V, 304, VI, 71; preface to, VI, 344
Guise, Charles, duke of, V, 294
Guise, Mary of, V, 294
Gulielmus, Joannes, dedic to, V, 355
Gum, V, 589-90; Arabic, V, 449
Gundelfinger, Ursula, horoscope of, V, 352
Gunpowder, see Invention
Gunter, Wolphgang, pr Leipzig, V, 354, 415
Gunther, R. T. (1921-39), V, 320
Günther, Siegmund, (1878), V, 349, 353; (1896), V, 370; (1900), VI, 55
Gutterwitz, Andreas, pr Copenhagen, VI, 523
Guy de Chauliac, V, 501, 504, 506, 513
Guyton, Louis Marie, (1874), V, 307-11
Gymnasium, see School
Gymnicus, Ioannes, pr Cologne, V, 153, VI, 256, 410
Gymnosophist, VI, 353, 456, 467
Gypsum, V, 457, VI, 310

Habakkuk, the prophet, VI, 497
Habebacar (Rasis), V, 623
Habitat, VI, 271
Habitus, VI, 244
Haeser, Heinrich, (1853), V, 44
Hafner, Peter, surgeon, dedic to, VI, 254, 290-1
Hagecius, Simon, V, 416
Hagecius, Thaddeus, VI, 474; *Aphorismorum,* **VI,** 72, 504-6, cited, **VI,** 79, 381; in error, **VI,** 79; letters to, **V,** 415-6, **VI,** 84; praised **VI,** 75
Hagen, von, see Indagine
Hagenau, pr at, V, 386-7, 501, VI, 439, 444
Haghen, Theodoric ab (1552), VI, 101-2
Hagius, Iohannes, ed, V, 360, VI, 490
Hague, The, pr at, V, 483, 630, VI, 178
Hahne, Hans (1929), V, 379
Hail, formed from hot vapors, VI, 387; marvelous images on, VI, 366-7; and see Weather
Hain, *Repertorium,* V, 55, 56, 139, 179, 339-41, 343, 385, 521, 536, VI, 298, 447, 469
Hainault, V, 580
Hainzelius, Jo. Henr., V, 607
Hair, dyed, VI, 429; grows on corpse, V, 511; makes metal ductible, VI, 224; relation to the teeth, V, 146; removed, V, 543; when to cut, VI, 167, 429; why turns white from fright? V, 146; witchcraft and, VI, 404
Halcyon birds and days, V, 614, VI, 310, 429, 479
Hales, see Alexander of

Hali, see Haly
Hallam, Henry, quoted, VI, 363, 452
Halle, VI, 238
Haller, A. v., V, 170, VI, 331
Haller, Johannes, pr Cracow, V, 173
Hallevoordius, Joannes, (1676), V, 262, VI, 395, 493
Hallevvin, Franciscus de, bishop of Amiens, VI, 440
Halley, Edmund, VI, 94
Halliwell, J. O. (1841), V, 320; (1849), VI, 219
Hallucination, V, 87, VI, 477, 481, 530-1; of disordered brain, V, 478; produced by herbs and drugs, VI, 420
Halm, Erich, (1923), V, 128
Halo, V, 399
Halosanthos, V, 470
Haly, cited, V, 46, 502, 510, VI, 163, as alchemist, V, 623; compiled from, V, 317; condemned, VI, 107; followed Galen, V, 500; *Geomantia,* V, 54, 131; on astrology, V, 207, VI, 139
Haly Abenragel or ibn Ragel, V, 104, 266-7, 269, 361, 434, VI, 113, 180; discarded, V, 278
Haly Heben Rodan or ibn Ridwan, V, 198, VI, 180; comm. Ptolemy, *Quadripartitum,* V, 216, VI, 107, 121
Hamann, Johann, pr Venice, V, 179, 341, 346
Hamburg, VI, 39; pest at, VI, 210; pr at, V, 485, VI, 140-1, 301, 460; received religious refugees, VI, 211
Hamech or Hameth, alchemist, V, 624
Hamelius, see Duhamel
Hamilton, Robert (1876), VI, 257, 272
Hamman, see Hamann
Hammer, mechanical, V, 594
Hand, dexterity, V, 103; lines of, VI, 459, 503; "mountains" of, V, 527, 531, VI, 164, 459; neglect of, V, 522; proportion of, V, 587; and see Chiromancy
Hannibal, VI, 471
Hanover, pr at, V, 654, VI, 318, 494, 503
Hansen, Joseph, V, 69-71, 89, VI, 517; (1900), VI, 497; (1901), V, 70, 116, 283
Hanusius, Ioh., VI, 597
Happiness, problem of, V, 204
Hapsburg, Ludwig Wolfgang ab, preface to, V, 603
Hardenberg, Albert, VI, 597
Harder, Hieronymus, botanist, VI, 266
Harderwijk, pr at, VI, 211
Hare, VI, 277; fat of, VI, 421; young, cure for stone, V, 432
Hargreaves, V, 35
Hariolus, see Ariolus
Harnisch, Matthaeus, pr Neustadt, VI, 41
Harris, D. Fraser, (1911), VI, 330
Harrison, G. B. (1924), VI, 547
Harsnet, Samuel, VI, 517
Hartfelder, Karl, (1889), V, 193, 401
Hartmann, B. (1889), V, 407
Hartmann, Georg, V, 337, 353, 357, 364-5, 414, VI, 60
Hartmann, J. (1919), V, 344
Hartwig, O. (1857), V, 567
Haruspex, see Aruspex
Harvet, Israel, medical, VI, 248, 251
Harvey, John, physician, V, 374
Harvey, William, VI, 328, 330-2
Harwillier, Jeanne, burned as witch, VI, 526-7
Haschard or Haschaert, Peter, physician, V, 329-30
Haselberg, Jo., pr Nürnberg, VI, 441
Hasselt, V, 147
Hassfurt, see Virdung, Johann von
Hat, effect on head, V, 512; green, V, 252
Hate, see Love and
Hauber, E. D. (1738), VI, 525
Haunted house, see House
Haym, N. F. (1803), VI, 469
Head, afflictions of, V, 651; alone is the microcosm, VI, 463; anatomy of, V, 520; left as surety, VI, 502; most divine member, V, 511; small pointed, V, 59-60; why created round, VI, 391; why inclined in thought, VI, 402; see Skull
Headache, V, 482, 612, VI, 208, 212
Health, contagious? V, 103; preservation of, V, 170, VI, 399
Hearsay, V, 474; accepted, VI, 278; condemned, V, 564, 576
Heart, V, 362; affected by fascination, V, 116; brain or, center of sensory and motor activity, and seat of sen-

tient soul? V, 31, 508, VI, 327-8, 364-5, 379, 481, 557-8; Cesalpino on, VI, 331-2; cordial for, V, 457, VI, 314; corresponds to first moving Intelligence, V, 510; dropped every fourth beat, V, 564; eaten, to predict, V, 560; fat around, V, 506-7; fatty, V, 509; in demoniac, VI, 557; in microcosm, V, 510, 521, VI, 443; noblest part of, V, 511; of swallow, V, 560; of vulture, V, 610; parts and movement of, V, 387; source of spirits, VI, 330; source of veins as well as arteries, VI, 327; torn out, V, 527; ventricles of, V, 46, 517; very hot, V, 145; very large, V, 517; water in, V, 526; work on, V, 44; worn over, V, 480, VI, 211, 294, 420

Heat, V, 538, 571-2; action of, V, 125, VI, 564; alchemical, V, 640; and cold, VI, 370, 372-3, 381; cause of sleep and waking, VI, 226; celestial, VI, 369, 403, same as elemental, VI, 381; direct from sky, V, 558; in emotion, V, 495; innate, V, 497, 557-8, VI, 365; latent, VI, 385; most perfect quality, VI, 564; motion and, V, 207, VI, 370, 385; natural, V, 146, 641, VI, 554, in summer of 1557, VI, 312; of sun extinguishes fire, V, 463; raises water underground, VI, 284; and see Weather

Heavens, V, 150-1, VI, 350; animate or no? VI, 198, 203, 369, 379, 446, 482; chart of, VI, 344; crystalline, VI, 428; empyrean, VI, 354, 399, 428; eternal and incorruptible, V, 78, VI, 49, 73, 84, 95, 97-98, 228, 348, 358, 413, questioned or denied, VI, 67, 84, 137; form of, VI, 370, and matter of, VI, 384, 435; rational, VI, 443; simple body, VI, 205, 369; substance of, VI, 198, fire, VI, 84, 371-2, water, VI, 354; two parts distinguished, VI, 327; will come to rest, VI, 379; and see Sphere, Star

Hebenstreit, Johann, VI, 106

Hebraeus quidam, V, 395

Hebrew, V, 395; against, VI, 528; alphabet, V, 130; ancient, VI, 509; books, VI, 151, 462; characters, V, 538-9, VI, 457; magic, VI, 467; names of herbs, VI, 259-60; oldest language, VI, 362; philosophers cited, VI, 378, 453, 601; physics, VI, 433; taught, V, 16, at Basel, V, 331, Copenhagen, VI, 524, Heidelberg, VI, 61, Paris, V, 295; words used, V, 523, VI, 520; written in, VI, 353

Hector, Benedictus, pr Bologna, V, 48, 528

Hegendorff, Christopher, VI, 478

Heidelberg, V, 269, VI, 457; comet seen at, VI, 92; disputations at, V, 503; pr at, V, 470, 642, VI, 41, 80; university of, V, 402-3, studied at, V, 298, 397, VI, 248, taught at, V, 652, 661, VI, 61, 80, 503; written at, V, 139, 203, 654, 659, 666

Heilbronn, V, 328, 334

Heilbronner, Jacob (1601), VI, 462-3

Heinfogel, Conrad, V, 337, 339, 344

Heingarter, Conrad, V, 362

Helenium, an herb, VI, 263

Helenus, son of Priam, V, 57, VI, 504

Heliamandus or Helinandus, cited, VI, 300

Helianus, Victor, pr Rome, VI, 45

Helias, Jacques, VI, 141

Helias, Thesbaeus, V, 373

Heliodorus ad Theodosium, V, 624

Heliotrope, gem, VI, 309, checks haemorrhage, V, 646; herb, turns towards sun, VI, 416

Hell, V, 106, 272; doubted on natural grounds, V, 84; location of, V, 156, VI, 25, 60

Hellebore, cures, insanity, V, 481; white, VI, 335

Heller, August (1882), V, 391

Heller, Joachim, V, 337, 365, 394-6

Hellmann, C. Doris, (1934), VI, 74

Hellmann, G., *Neudrucke,* V, 160, 201, 231, 353, 365; (1914), V, 178; (1917), V, 345; (1924), V, 160-2, 167-70, 173-4, 181, 184, 187-8, 193, 197, 202-4, 206, 209-11, 214, 217-8, 228-9, 234, 237, 244-6, 255, 283, 286, 291, 299, 313, 318, 322, 326-7, 330-1, 353, 361, 382, 391-2, 396, 400, 433, 443, 466, 605, 654, VI, 56, 60, 84, 106, 108-9, 111, 123, 133-4, 143, 147, 157-8, 474, 483, omissions by, V, 167, 326, 440, VI, 124

Helmstadt, pr at, VI, 534-5; university of, V, 393

Helsinger, Adam, teacher, V, 323

Hemmingsen, Nicolaus, VI, 523-4
Hemminga, Docon ab, VI, 196
Hemminga, Sixtus ab, VI, 112, 193-6, 595, 598, cited, VI, 197, 202
Hen, and gold, V, 645, VI, 388
Henisch, Georg, (1549-1618), VI, 142-3
Henke, E. L. T. (1865), VI, 495
Henneberg, count of, V, 652
Henricus Euforbiensis, V, 213
Henricpetri, Sebastianus, pr Basel, VI, 186
Henricus, Nicolaus, pr Ursel, VI, 286
Henricus Petri, pr Basel, V, 99, 372, 603, 608, 644, VI, 16, 29, 37, 104
Henry IV, emperor, VI, 117
Henry II, king of France, V, 284; dedic to, VI, 368; failure to predict violent death of, VI, 101; geniture of, VI, 131; preface to, V, 558
Henry III, king of France, V, 483, VI, 106, 138, 142
Henry IV, king of France, V, 486, VI, 117, 130, 247, 553-4; addressed, VI, 142; horoscope of, VI, 161
Henry VII, king of England, tale of astrologer and, V, 294
Henry VIII, king of England, discusses comets, V, 320; geniture of, VI, 196
Henry, prince, son of James I, VI, 248
Henry, duke of Brunswick, VI, 116
Henry, Infante of Portugal, brother of John III, V, 293
Henry of Ghent, cited, VI, 125
Henry of Hesse, V, 567; cited, V, 220, VI, 431, 468
Henry of Malines, see Bate, Henri
Henry of Mondeville, V, 513
Henry of Saxony, V, 166, VI, 300
Hensisheim, see Ensisheim
Hephaestion of Thebes, V, 120, 358
Herald and Heraldry, V, 35, 112, VI, 277
Herb, V, 141, 464, 590, VI, 230, 385, 394; astrological, V, 619, VI, 422; biblical, VI, 306; boiled and buried, VI, 243; catalogue of, VI, 184, 255; change of species, VI, 570; classification, VI, 259-60, 266-7, 280, 332-3, under planets, VI, 434; collection of, V, 446, 513, 610, 660, VI, 221, 295, 404; color, VI, 422; created before the stars, VI, 259, 347; decoction and distillation of, V, 541; diuretic, VI, 314; divining, VI, 275; dried, VI, 268; exoteric, V, 643; fertilization of, VI, 348; four faculties of, VI, 293; Galen's, no longer procurable, VI, 225; growth of, VI, 351; hieroglyph of, VI, 447; ingredient in medicine, VI, 216; juice of, in fumigation, V, 273; known at first sight, VI, 533; leaf of gold, V, 143, VI, 436; magic, VI, 295, 404, 416; mountain, V, 445, VI, 259, 428; name of, V, 462, 464, VI, 254, 259, 264-5, 273-4; not in Dioscorides, V, 454, 460, 462, VI, 260; of Saintonge, V, 599; parts of, V, 463, 476, 662, VI, 422-3; sensitive, VI, 436; soul of, VI, 519; too many used in medicine, V, 634; turn towards sun, V, 495; under one's pillow, VI, 534; virtues, excessive, VI, 260-1, expel demon, V, 462, VI, 532, occult, V, 551, 661, VI, 260, 293, 428, raise dead, V, 103; works on, VI, 255
Herbal, VI, 254, 266; medieval, VI, 271
Herbalist, V, 445, 447, 461, 611, VI, 219, 263-4, 273-4
Herborn, pr at, V, 419, VI, 433, 559; professor at, VI, 433
Hercules, V, 531
Heredity, VI, 190, 364, 507-8; and acquired characteristics, V, 577; and degeneracy, V, 577; and environment, VI, 398
Hereford, bishop of, V, 142
Heresy, V, 61, 77, VI, 107, 148, 153, 244, 538, 544; abounds, VI, 441; extirpation of, given precedence over magic arts, VI, 150, urged, V, 243, VI, 148; Nifo accused of, V, 77-78; occult arts as, VI, 145, 176; of Bruno, VI, 427; of invoking demon, VI, 551; philosophical, VI, 511; sorcery worse than other, VI, 524
Hermaphrodite, V, 270, VI, 276, 408, 600
Hermann, archbishop of Cologne, VI, 595
Hermann, Fritz, (1934), V, 319
Hermann, Johann, physician, V, 390, 620
Hermannus on rains, cited, V, 227
Hermes, V, 57, VI, 353, 461; Arabic, V, 126; as alchemist, V, 141, 532, 622, cited, V, 83, 624-5, 685, decried, V, 604, not an alchemist, VI, 250; astrologer, V, 210, VI, 114, 180, 448;

astronomer, VI, 458; book of magic to Aristotle, VI, 147; cited, V, 538, VI, 300; Trismegistus, V, 113, 116, 119, 126, 424, VI, 141, 407, 409, 458-61, 504, existence denied, VI, 461; Trutina of, VI, 104, 115; works, *Asclepius,* VI, 438, 447, 449, 460; *Centiloquium,* V, 267, VI, 197, 448; *Chiromancy,* V, 586; *Decubitu infirmorum,* V, 103; *Iatromathematica,* V, 103, VI, 158; *Pimander,* V, 127, VI, 22, 438, 447, 460; *Secret,* V, 538; *Seven Tractates,* V, 622; *Speculis et luce,* V, 173; *Tabula smaragdina,* V, 533, 537, 622, VI, 244, 438, 448
Hermetic, V, 127, VI, 190, 602; magic, VI, 457; Scott's attempted distinction, VI, 448; seal, V, 650
Hermit, V, 257, 302
Hernandez de Cordova, Gonsalvo, V, 72, 80
Hero of Alexandria, VI, 89, 154; *Pneumatics,* V, 364, VI, 421
Herodotus, cited, V, 469
Herophilus, V, 523, 530
Herr or Herus, Michael, V, 317
Herrick, Francis H. (1934), VI, 270
Hervagius, Johannes, pr Basel, VI, 485
Herwort, Wolphgang, patrician of Augsburg, V, 524
Herzog, Johann, pr Venice, V, 179
Hesiod, cited, V, 83; translated, VI, 142
Hesiodic magic, VI, 457
Hesperides, garden of, VI, 246
Hesse, landgrave of, V, 609, VI, 56, 136; and see Henry of, Philip of, William, landgrave of
Hessus, Eobanus, see Eobanus
Hessus, Ioannes, botanist, VI, 255
Heurnius, Ioannes, VI, 538
Heusinger, C. F. (1853), V, 381, 404, VI, 38, 366
Hevesy, A. de (1923), V, 407
Hidden things, investigated, V, 219; revealed, V, 83; and see Occult, Secret, Treasure
Hierarchy, V, 112
Hieroglyph, VI, 278, 447, 457, 461
Hieromnine, interlocutor, VI, 25
Hildegard, St. V, 124,
Hilden, VI, 321
Hill or Hyll, Thomas, V, 65, VI, 483; cited, VI, 180
Hillenius, Michael, pr Antwerp, V, 444
Hiller, J. E. (1935), VI, 318
Hilten, Johann, V, 375
Hindu, see India
Hipler, Franz (1876), 417; (1882), V, 409
Hipparchus, V, 415, VI, 21, 71, 97; cited by Pliny, VI, 67
Hippocrates, V, 125, 213, 295, VI, 353; *Aphorisms,* V, 289, comm. V, 446-7, 550, VI, 214; as a teacher, V, 416; authenticity of writings, VI, 567; astrological medicine of, V, 263, VI, 41, 172, 509; cited, V, 172, 195, 473, 503, 512, 514, 523, 561, VI, 232, 402; comm. V, 503, VI, 211, 356, 400; compiled from, V, 323, VI, 217, 406; criticized, V, 314, 435, 437, VI, 228, as in error, V, 465, 530, VI, 402, as out-of-date, VI, 252, 461; defended, V, 261, VI, 215, 238; demons, for, VI, 336, against, VI, 518; dreams of sick, on, V, 263; Epitome from, V, 262; *Insomniis,* tr, VI, 476, 478, comm. VI, 476, 512; lectured on, V, 436; *Morbis,* comm. VI, 211; never referred occult virtues to the stars, VI, 232; not read, VI, 260; on power of soul over matter, V, 561; text emended, V, 502
Hippopotamus, V, 651
Hircina, herb, V, 316
Hirsau, see William of
Hirsch, August, *Biographisches Lexikon,* V, 144, 324, 641, VI, 217
Hispaniola, VI, 346
Histoire littéraire de la France, V, 139
Historian, see History
Historiographer, V, 28; cited, V, 181; imperial, V, 128, 339, 347, VI, 88; of Zwickau, VI, 302
Historian, Historical and History, V, 143, 286, 401, 410, 547, VI, 247, 275, 352, 361, 396, 442, 466, 525, 560; advertising mistaken for, V, 335; annual predictions as a source for, V, 244; astrological interpretation of, V, 108, 121, 311, VI, 76, 117, 129, 441, verification of, V, 565-6; attention to prodigies, VI, 488, 490; biography, V, 390; Bodin and, VI, 525; Champier and, V, 113, 115; cited or appealed to, VI, 411, 458-9, 546; collection, V, 55; criticism, VI, 465; ecclesiastical, V, 112; examples, V, 206, VI, 78, 481,

499; local, of Augsburg, V, 391, Ferrara, V, 168, Lyons, V, 112, Milan, V, 161-2, VI, 596, Nola, V, 144, Nürnberg, V, 337-8; Maestlin's perverted, VI, 83; military, V, 208; new school of, V, 578; of astrology, V, 165, 403, VI, 353; of astronomy, VI, 62, of ideas, V, 414, 629-30, VI, 423; of learning, V, 404, of modern science, V, 377, 414, 550, VI, 94, 287-8; "of obsolete paradoxes," VI, 452-3; of "physics," VI, 352-3; of science, misapprehended, V, 377, VI, 93-94, 464; persistence of errors, V, 181; professor of, V, 397, VI, 238; relation to philosophy, V, 108-9; science larded with, V, 388; sixteenth century, V, 286; sorcery of demon attested by, VI, 546; study of, V, 35; "true Hebraic," V, 192; unimpressed by conjunction of 1524, V, 233; universal, V, 391; works of, V, 636

Historisches Jahrbuch, VI, 149, 183,

Historisches Taschenbuch, V, 193, 401,

History, see Historian, etc.

Hochstraten, Jakob von, inquisitor, V, 71, VI, 445

Hoefer, J. C. F. *Nouvelle biographie générale,* V, 580, 583, VI, 102, 537

Hofemianus, Iac. Curio, V, 17, 403

Hoff, Hans von, horoscope of, V, 352

Hoffemianus, Iac, Curio, see Hofemianus

Hoffhamer, Paul, VI, 597

Hog, see Pig

Hoghelande (1604), V, 416, 548-9, 621, 647-8, VI, 246, 318

Hohenheim, V, 439

Holcot, cited as alchemist, V, 623

Holland, V, 182, 189; countess of, VI, 401; supreme court of, VI, 538

Hollerius, Jacobus, cited, V, 482

Hollyng, Edmund (1599), V, 485

Holmyard, E. J. (1927), V, 48

Holstein, VI, 136, 377

Holtzhoder, Thomas, VI, 598

Holy Congregation, see Inquisition

Holy Land, see Palestine

Holy Roman Empire, chancellor, VI, 235; doomed, VI, 435; vice-chancellor, V, 240; and see Emperor, Elector

Holy water, see Water

Holy week, VI, 571

Hombergius, Gaspar, VI, 541

Homelius, Iacobus, VI, 596

Homelius, Iohannes, V, 397, VI, 41

Homer, *Iliad,* V, 390; nods, V, 120

Homeric magic, VI, 457

Homocentric, see Sphere

Honduras, VI, 436

Honestis, see Christopher de

Honey, made from dew, V, 570; prevents putrefaction, VI, 283; used in medicine, VI, 235

Honoratus, head of college of blind, VI, 522

Honoratus, Bartholomaeus, pr Lyons, V, 256

Honoratus de Robertis, see Robertis

Hoopoe, V, 19-20, VI, 310

Horapollo, VI, 278, 447, 485

Hornanus, Adrian Iunius, horoscope of, VI, 196

Hornet, VI, 290

Horns, why some animals have? V, 570; and see Unicorn

Horoscope, see Nativity

Horospicium, VI, 430

Horse, V, 462, VI, 447; care of, V, 612; fall from, VI, 322; hoof used in fusing copper, VI, 217; injured by, V, 246; language of, V, 570; pack-, V, 613

Horsemen, seen in sky, VI, 490

Horst, Petrus, pr Cologne, V, 610

Hortensius, M. tr (1668), VI, 7-8

Hortulanus, alchemist, V, 537, 622, 690; cited, V, 623, VI, 278, 300; not cited, VI, 318

Hospital, at Grenoble, V, 137; head of a, VI, 561; master of the, V, 548; of S. Maria Nuova, V, 90; of St. Peter and St. Paul, V, 517

Host, venerated, VI, 337

Hôtel-Dieu, VI, 251

Hour, VI, 152, 322; invented, VI, 353; observance of, condemned, V, 661; unequal, VI, 159

House, astrological, V, 201, 216, 225, 258, 292, 319, 323, 345; accepted, VI, 138, 144, division of zodiac into, V, 330, 333, 336, 348, 359-60, 395, 557, VI, 33, 99, 102-4, 108, 124, 131, 140, 158, 160, dreams and, VI, 510, prediction and, V, 258, rejected, VI, 204, sixth, V, 308; "devil's," V, 256; haunted, V, 143, 574, VI, 479, 548;

of Dürer, V, 344; of Fracastoro, V, 488; of Nabod at Padua, V, 122; on fire, V, 446
Houssay, Fr. (1937), VI, 286
Houzeau et Lancaster (1882-89), V, 173, 245-6, 308, 313, 371, VI, 10, 12, 31, 38, 45, 155
How, W. pr London, V, 608
Huarte Navarro, Juan de Dios, VI, 413-4
Huck, see Bishop, William
Hugh of Lucca, V, 513
Hugh of Siena, V, 42, 437, 448, 502, 504-5, 513
Hugo Eterianus, cited, VI, 459
Huguald, Uldrich, philosopher, VI, 267
Huguenot, V, 464
Huguetan, I. A. pr Lyons, VI, 433
Huldaric, prince of Denmark, VI, 70
Humanism and Humanist, VI, 459; astrology and, V, 176-7; belittled, V, 57, 631; capacity for self advertising, V, 113; commonplace by, V, 66; criticized, V, 336, 504; failure at Nürnberg, V, 338; insipid compliments, V, 307; letter-writing, VI, 268; narrow, V, 356; stress on style, V, 3, 5, 8-9, 133-4, VI, 134
Humanisme et Renaissance, V, 344
Humanities, see Arts, liberal, Classics
Humidum radicale, V, 590
Hummel, see Homelius
Humor, V, 374, 503, 527, 557, VI, 355, 381; affected by imagination, V, 117, by guilty conscience, VI, 241; alimentary, aqueous and radical, VI, 365; cause of critical days, V, 392; cause of disease, V, 492, VI, 214-5, not, V, 374; causes of dreams, VI, 482; contagion and, V, 497; denied, VI, 638, 664; four, V, 122, VI, 167; putrid, VI, 213; radical, VI, 554; relation to stars, V, 122, 174, 323, 475, VI, 199; work on, V, 328; and see Melancholy
Hun, count of, VI, 455
Hundt, Magnus (1501), V, 160
Hungary, king of, VI, 196, 315, 457; and see Matthias Corvinus; pest in, VI, 185; travel in, V, 650,
Hunger, animals motivated by, V, 551, 555; bodies emaciated by, V, 517; half died of, V, 548; in 1527, V, 517; warding off, V, 611
Hunter, cited, V, 582
Hunting, V, 73, 363, 493, VI, 277, 421
Huntington Library Bulletin, VI, 40
Hunting Library Photostats, VI, 287
Hunyadi, Matthias, see Matthias Corvinus
Hupfuff, pr Strasburg, V, 432
Huseneck, Rudolf von, V, 177
Huser, Johannes (1589), V, 617, VI, 224
Huss, John, VI, 117
Hutten, Ulrich von, VI, 595
Huyon, Guillaume, pr Lyons, V, 308
Hven, VI, 56
Hyacinth, a gem, V, 456, 573-4
Hybrid, VI, 419
Hydra, called fabulous, V, 474
Hydraulics, VI, 457
Hydrography, VI, 430
Hydromancy, V, 58, VI, 468, 499; alchemy and, V, 634; astrology and, V, 16, VI, 176; evil, VI, 430; false, VI, 193; forbidden, VI, 146-7, 169; four kinds of, VI, 502; superstitious, V, 297
Hydrophobia, VI, 571; advanced cases strangled, V, 484; late appearance of, V, 484-5; periodic accessions of, V, 482; remedies for, V, 477; when mortal? V, 483; works on, V, 479-80, 481-3
Hyena, VI, 416
Hyerosky, Wm. dedic to, V, 539
Hyginus, V, 343
Hyle, V, 48-49; and see Matter
Hyleg, V, 361, 375, VI, 200
Hyll, T. see Hill
Hymn, V, 173
Hypericon, VI, 546; perforata, V, 462
Hypnotism, VI, 403
Hypothesis, attitude toward, V, 13, 411, 413, 416, 422, 427, 576, 591, VI, 27-28, 46, 56, 66; precedes discovery, V, 30, 494
Hysteria, V, 442

Iacobi, Ioh. VI, 596
Iacobilli, L. (1658), VI, 528
Iamblichus, VI, 404, 409, 484
Iapyx, VI, 504
Iatrochemistry, VI, 242, 250
Ibn Sina, see Avicenna
Ice, breaking the, V, 303; formation of, V, 30
Iceland, VI, 438

Ichthiomancy, VI, 503
Idea, VI, 407, 414; association of, V, 12-13; come slowly, V, 167; history of, V, 494; implant occult virtue, V, 135; in divine mind, V, 101, 561, VI, 362, 446, 482; misplaced and contradictory, VI, 86-87; new, V, 245, 414, VI, 54, 276, from the Arabs, VI, 251; not to be torn from their context, VI, 94, 179; permutation and combination of, V, 420, VI, 54, 75-76, 81, 84-87, 91-93, 198, 225, 292, 502, 518, 521, 537, 555, 570, 572; persistence, see Tradition; power, generative, V, 236, operative, V, 101; practical consequence of, VI, 242; received only through the senses, VI, 360; words and, VI, 477
Idmon, VI, 504
Idolatry, VI, 132
Iesus, la libraria dal (Nicolo and Domenico, brothers), Venice, V, 55, 64
Image, aerial, V, 97, 107; astrological, approved, 106, 117, 135, 166, 249, 345, 533, 572-3, 650, VI, 114, 174, 299, 303-4, 424, 359, 419, 426, 508, 602, disapproved, V, 119-20, 140, 165, 278, 327, 645, 656, VI, 187, 309, 318-9, 378, 397-8, 405, 411, 416, 500, 528, 601; brought by blood to heart, VI, 484; Bruno on, V, 606; cabalistic, VI, 508; Cardan on, V, 572-3; incur charge of atheism, VI, 302; magic, V, 83, 166, 573, 636, VI, 147, 299, 301, 536, 601-2, omitted, VI, 304, 426; necromantic, V, 140, VI, 528; no force in, VI, 546; of lion in gold, V, 242, VI, 113, 303-4; of Virgin, VI, 362, 572; used in exorcism, VI, 557; wax, VI, 548, and see Agnus Dei
Imagination, VI, 446; affected by demon, V, 486, by external bodies without movement of the senses, VI, 328, 337, 481, by potions and unguents, V, 478, by species, VI, 391; cannot act on another body, V, 117, 645, VI, 601; cure by, VI, 477; deceived, V, 87, VI, 279, 515, 531-2; disease, VI, 546; historical, V, 115; in preaching, governing and medical practice, VI, 413, in prophecy, VI, 513; power of, V, 83, 91, 100-2, 106, 116-7, 235, 574, VI, 132, 235-7, 241, 336, 416, 513, doubted, V, 660, VI, 528, 571; vitiated, VI, 547; and see Foetus
Immorality, V, 52
Immortality, see Soul
Immunity from snake bite, V, 102
Imola, V, 50, 90; preface to senate of, VI, 545
Impotency, see Marriage
Imprimatur, see Censorship
Imprisonment, see Prison
Imser, Philip, astronomer, V, 371-3
Incaffi, hill of, V, 488
Incantation, V, 83, 90, 135, 560, 562, VI, 499, 502; condemned, V, 32, 399, 564, VI, 197, 467, 601; cure attributed to, V, 101-3, 120, 474, VI, 403; depend on faith, VI, 513; employed, VI, 218, 440, 498, 536, by Paracelsus, V, 628; induce impotency, VI, 559; law and, VI, 544; opposed, V, 574, VI, 516; put on Index, VI, 147; trivial, V, 574; while plucking herbs, V, 660, VI, 295, 404
Incarnation, VI, 427
Incense, divination by, VI, 503; effect on brain, V, 478; inextinguishable, VI, 243
Incubator, VI, 411
Incubus and succubus, V, 88, 118, 270, VI, 357, 504, 529, 539, 546; medical meaning, V, 118, VI, 521-2, 546
Incunabula, lack of alchemical, V, 532, 536; and see *Gesamtkatalog*, Hain, Klebs, etc.
Indagine, Johannes ab, V, 49, 319; cited, V, 586, VI, 164; friend of Brunfels, V, 318; *Introductiones*, V, 65-66, 174-6, 580, 606-7; put on Index, V, 175, VI, 147; *Rationes*, V, 319
Index, V, 445; importance of, V, 609; often faulty, VI, 262
Index expurgatorius, and other lists of forbidden books, V, 136, VI, 12, 145, 172, 452; cited, VI, 157, 178; of Milan, of 1554, VI, 146; of 1709, VI, 556, 559; Paul IV's, of 1559, V, 175, 434, 587, VI, 125-6, 147-8, 157-8, 374, 471, 474, 489; Spanish, of 1559, VI, 147-8, 167; Venetian, of 1554, V, 220, 606, VI, 146
India and Indian, V, 64, 539, 567, VI, 240, 314, 353, 480, 487; astrology of, V, 165, 395, VI, 23, 174; better known,

V, 467-8; Greek debt to, V, 437; marvels of, V, 48; medicine of, V, 468, 470; simples of, V, 466-9, 476, VI, 294, 323, 333; stones from, VI, 275; wild man of, VI, 269
Indigestion, VI, 206
Individual and Individuation, VI, 198, 369; and see Ens
Infamy, V, 59
Infant, see Child
Infantry, V, 164
Infection, at a distance, V, 496; in fascination, V, 475; and see Disease, contagious
Infelicity, VI, 144
Inferno, V, 135; and see Hell
Infinite, conception of, V, 151
Inflammation, V, 559
Influenza, VI, 212
Infundibulum, V, 45
Ingegneri, Angelo, VI, 162
Ingegneri, Giovanni, VI, 162
Ingelfingen, V, 397
Ingolstadt, V, 485, VI, 446; astrology at, V, 347; pr at, V, 460, VI, 268, 410, 414; professor at, V, 246, 394, 406, VI, 227; studied at, V, 346, VI, 16; university of, V, 345, VI, 414
Ingrassia, Giovanni Filippo ab, anatomist, V, 44-45
Inheritance, administration of, V, 219; predicted, V, 587
Ink, printing and writing, V, 450, VI, 308
Inn, experience in, V, 613
Innocent V, VI, 468
Innocent X, V, 10
Innsbruck, VI, 136
Inquisition and Inquisitor, V, 70-71, 83, 115, 127, 613, 653, VI, 63, 145, 556-7; Aldrovandi and, VI, 153; approved by, VI, 459, 481, 520; archives of, VI, 149; astrology and, V, 121, 290, VI, 126, 149, 157-8; Barozzi and, VI, 154-5; Bruno and, V, 606, VI, 427; Cardan and, VI, 152-3; Cologne, of, V, 129; exorcism and, VI, 556-7; forbidden books and, VI, 150-1, 169, 445; history of Roman, obscure, VI, 149; Jews and, VI, 151-2; license of, with, V, 250, 645, VI, 35, 160-2; magician and, V, 103, VI, 148, 150; Peter of Abano and, VI, 468; Porta and, VI, 155-6, 421; Spanish, VI, 166, 196; witch and, VI, 145-6, 338, 546
Insanity, VI, 596-7; cured by hellebore, V, 481; induced by magnet, VI, 314, philter, V, 486, witchcraft, VI, 548
Inscription, at Padua, V, 623; study of ancient, V, 115
Insect, born in furnace, VI, 95; intelligence, VI, 290; investigated, VI, 385; recipe against, VI, 429; swarm of, V, 497; and see Aldrovandi, Ant, Bee, etc.
Instant, VI, 385
Instinct, see Nature
Instrument, V, 588; alchemical, V, 590, 635; astronomical, V, 190, 285, 339, 347, 358, 365, 369, 371-2, 521, 583-4, VI, 41, 82, 124, lack of, VI, 79, large, VI, 17, limitations of, V, 423; cabalistic, VI, 454; geographical, V, 338; maker, V, 338, 348-9, VI, 28, 59; musical, V, 584, VI, 440; Regiomontanus's, V, 339; scientific, V, 12-13, 15; works on, V, 365, 369, 371, 582, 589, 593-6, VI, 82
Intellect, active, V, 90-91, VI, 369, 482; angelic, divine and human, VI, 443; divinity of, VI, 135; human, V, 151, 273, VI, 350, 369, 564; in sleep, VI, 481; list of leading, V, 564-5; separate, V, 561; unity of, V, 42, 71, 82, VI, 511, condemned in 1512, V, 94; works on, V, 48
Intelligence, animal, VI, 290; Aristotelian moving, V, 78, 87, 102, 104-5, 109, 170, 205, 552-3, VI, 342, 369-70, 414, 426, 511, 546, 571-2, 599, dream from, VI, 476, existence questioned, VI, 187, rejected, VI, 384; fifty gates of, VI, 444, 463; first, V, 510; hierarchy of creating, VI, 482; identified with forms of celestial bodies, V, 104, VI, 370, of world, VI, 482; of Mars, V, 219; planets and, V, 102, 121, 205; separate, V, 86, 575; soul of man united to, V, 87, 90-91, 116, 134, VI, 236, 353; tenth, of moon, V, 90-91, 116
Intension and remission, see Form
Interrogation, astrological, V, 199, 572, VI, 114, 430, condemned, V, 140, 276, 384, VI, 78, 200, 359
Intestines, V, 44

Intolerance, V, 653
Intoxication, cure for, VI, 419; monthly recommended, VI, 403; to excess, V, 612
Invention and Inventor, listed, V, 584-5, VI, 217; medicinal, V, 264; of astrology, V, 165, 218, cabala, VI, 454, divination, VI, 472, gunpowder, V, 335, 585, VI, 299, deplored, V, 458, VI, 472, hours, VI, 353, magic, V, 175, microscope, V, 490-1, printing, V, 5-6, 179, 335, 337, 435, 565, VI, 472, revolver, V, 34, telescope, V, 490-1, wine biscuit, V, 611; practical, V, 20; three modern, V, 558, 566-7
Invidia, see Adam ab
Invisible, demon, V, 101, 639; man, V, 83, VI, 309, 320; writing, V, 146-7, VI, 429
Ioannitius, V, 538, 623
Iobin, Bernhardus, pr Strasburg, VI, 75
Ionghe, Johannes de, physician, VI, 311
Ionsius, see Jonsius
Iordan, Petrus, pr Mainz, V, 330
Ipswich, VI, 520
Ireland and Irish, VI, 279, 288
Irenaeus, Christopher, VI, 286
Iron, VI, 305; earth in, VI, 317; in alchemy, V, 546, medicinal waters, VI, 209; medicinal virtue of, VI, 317; mountain of, V, 496; refused by ostrich, V, 647, digested by, VI, 210; spot removed from, VI, 217; and see Magnet
Isaac Israeli, V, 453, 503
Isaac the monk, V, 623-4, VI, 88
Isaachi, G. B. (1579), V, 596
Isabella, island of, VI, 346
Isaiah, the prophet, VI, 514
Iseltius, Ioannes, VI, 598
Isidore of Seville, cited, VI, 186, 280-1, 291, 300, 361; criticized, VI, 281; not cited, VI, 318
Isingrinius, Michael, pr Basel, V, 456
Isis, V, 4, 203, 319, 344, 471, VI, 50, 74, 261, 436
Island, floating, V, 155, denied, V, 591; number of, V, 614
Isocrates to Demonicus, V, 113
Israel, ten tribes of, VI, 75
Istria, V, 466
Italian, V, 167, 204, 269, 333, 482, 577-8, 615, 658, VI, 183, 328; derived from Latin, VI, 362; families, VI, 470; naturalist, V, 550, VI, 258; of Lyons, VI, 130; outclassed in warfare, V, 164; place names, V, 614; tr into, V, 64, 67, 197, 210, 263, 364, 369, 466, 555-6, VI, 148, 163, 221, 266, 302, 390, 393, 447, 472, 476, 556, 559; version, V, 229, 235, 238-40, 258, VI, 44; works in, V, 57, 64, 167, 169, 179, 228-9, 237, 245-6, 255, 259, 274, 544-5, 555-6, 624, 636, VI, 27, 62, 155, 160-1, 167, 210-1, 222, 260, 313, 315, 377, 398, 428, 469-74, 493, 519, 550
Italy, V, 78, 143, 205, 213, 336, 339, 341, 436, 466, 495, 509, 546, 548, 581, VI, 259, 279, 506; anatomy in, V, 498; astrology in, V, 164, 210-1, 279, 298, 326, 379, 654, VI, 157-8; eclipse in, V, 163; emperor in, V, 582; epidemic in, VI, 212; exile from, V, 99, 600-1, 605, VI, 423; fountain from, V, 21; foreigners in, V, 127, 350, 397, 403-4, 408, 426, 582, 652, VI, 255, 267, 394, 561; French invasion of, V, 60, 111, 187, 233, VI, 187; herb from, VI, 268; Index and Inquisition in, VI, 145; learning in, V, 261, VI, 364; left, V, 171, 529; Paracelsans in, VI, 217; personified, V, 245; pest in, VI, 89; popular errors in, VI, 198, 222; publication in, V, 328, VI, 160-1, 170, 445; return to, V, 55; spring in, V, 245; study in, VI, 235; transit from, V, 625; travel in, V, 365, 612, VI, 255; Turk to rule, V, 375; use of restricted area, V, 231, VI, 227; war in, VI, 185; witchcraft in, VI, 338, 545
Iunctinus, see Giuntini
Iuntae, see Junta
Iunx, VI, 293, 520
Iuvenis, see Ionghe
Ivrea, VI, 169

Jabir ibn Haiyan, V, 537
Jacob, the patriarch, V, 203, VI, 356
Jacob Aranicus the Jew, V, 548
Jacob the Jew, physician, V, 513
Jacobus, Cyriacus, pr Frankfurt, V, 547-8, 618-9
Jacobus de Clusa, condemned, VI, 534
Jacobus de Panico, geomancer, VI, 471
Jacobus de Partibus, cited, V, 317, 460, 503, 513; compiled from, V, 460;

criticized, V, 437; disciples of, V, 506
Jacoli (1877), V, 235
Jahrbuch der Kunstsammlungen, V, 343
Jahrbuch für Philosophie und Paedagogie, VI, 89
James I, king of England, VI, 248, 533; *Daemonologie,* VI, 547-50; exposure of impostors by, VI, 550
James V, king of Scotland, V, 294
James of Cremona, tr, V, 369
James of Forlì, V, 42, 46, 95, 170, 437, 448, 504
James of Toledo, V, 602
Januarius, Jacobus (1506), V, 535
Janus, V, 381, 625, VI, 521
Jason, V, 486
Jasper, VI, 186, 309; as an amulet, VI, 309, 322, 335; cure by, V, 321; green, V, 456
Jean de Cinquarbres, VI, 141
Jean de Jandun, V, 71, 75, VI, 369, 484
Jean de Murs, V, 190, 229, 300, VI, 28
Jena, V, 328; pr at, VI, 36, 393; taught at, VI, 30, 238-9
Jergis, astrologer, VI, 180
Jerome, St. V, 142, VI, 446
Jerusalem, destruction of, V, 311; priest of, VI, 301
Jessenius or Jessensky, J., VI, 461
Jesu, see Iesus
Jesuit, V, 110, 653, VI, 45, 148, 274, 276, 294, 362, 383, 387, 409, 414, 455, 533, 569; and prohibited books, VI, 151; schools, VI, 382, 410
Jesus, see Christ
Jew and Jewish, astrology, VI, 173, 301; books, VI, 151-2, 444; cited, V, 264, 284, 421; conversion predicted, V, 271; converted, VI, 444-5; demon, invoked by, VI, 148-9; empiric, V, 513; extraction, V, 264, VI, 560; expelled, from Spain, V, 124, from Denmark, Sweden, Saxony and Wurtemberg, VI, 537; physician, V, 381, 513, 645, VI, 259; put in mouth of, VI, 453; rabbi, VI, 361, 532, 551; tr, VI, 449; and see Hebrew, Judaism
Jeweler, V, 456
Joachim I of Brandenburg, V, 381-2
Joachim of Flora, cited, VI, 75
Joachimsthal, V, 397, VI, 59
Jobst, Wolgang (1556), V, 254, 260, 284, 289, 362, 391
Jöcher, C. G. (1750-1751), V, 152, 168, 173, 325, 550, VI, 109, 187, 210, 227, 459, 528; corrected, VI, 128, 134
Jociscus, Andrea, V, 607
Joel, Francis, VI, 525, 536
Joel, Timothy, VI, 525
Johann Frederick, elector of Saxony, captivity, VI, 489; dedic to, V, 357; geniture, VI, 105, 116, 196; image seen in sky, V, 399
Johann Frederick, duke of Stettin and Pomerania, VI, 102
Johann Wilhelm, duke of Jülich, VI, 559
Johann Wilhelm, duke of Saxony, preface to, VI, 37
Johannet, René (1932), VI, 393
Johannisberg, VI, 61
John XXII, V, 62; *Extravagans,* 'Spondent . . .,' V, 535, 539, 604, VI, 538
John III, king of Portugal, V, 293
John III, king of Sweden, VI, 311
John Albert, archbishop of Magdeburg, V, 398-9
John the Baptist, St. VI, 236; and see St. John's Eve
John of Bruges, V, 182, 311
John, duke of Burgundy, V, 168
John Canonicus, VI, 378
John of Damascus, V, 541, 624, VI, 446
John Dantiscus (of Danzig), V, 410
John, prince of Denmark, horoscope of, VI, 52, 70
John of Eschenden, cited, V, 163; not cited, V, 277
John de Fundis, V, 26
John of Ghent, VI, 378
John of Glogau, V, 6, 160, 170, 179-80, 333
John of Gmunden, V, 223, 332, VI, 11
John Grammaticus, V, 248
John de Gravia, alchemist, V, 638
John of Kepfersperg, astronomer, V, 349
John of Ketham, see *Fasciculus medicinae*
John of Legnano, VI, 136
John de Lineriis, V, 131, VI, 130
John of Lübeck, V, 179
John de Mandeville, VI, 275, 280-1
John of Padua, alchemist, VI, 161

John the philosopher, chiromancer, V, 678
John of Phortzn, astronomer, V, 349
John of Pontigny, medical, V, 437
John Pratensis, see Pratensis
John of Rupescissa, V, 126, 478; cited, V, 541-2, 604, 613, 623-5, 638, VI, 244, 250, 531; *Consideratione quintae essentiae,* V, 536, 542, 601-2, 631-2, VI, 251, 533; false revelations of, VI, 532; *Liber lucis,* V, 603
John of St. Amand, V, 460
John of Saxony, cited, VI, 107, 180; comm. Alcabitius, V, 227, 308, VI, 471; forgotten, V, 332; omitted as barbarous, VI, 119; put on the Index, VI, 148
John of Seville, cited, V, 207, 362; *Epitome,* V, 395; tr, V, 308, 673
John de Suchten, see Suchten
John of Vienna, alchemist, V, 624
Johnson, Francis R. (1934), VI, 40; (1937), V, 423, VI, 5, 16, 18
Johnson, Sir George (1882-84), VI, 330
Joke, practical, V, 613
Jonas, Justus, theologian, horoscope of, VI, 105, 595
Jonas, Justus, Jr., VI, 598
Jonsius, Joannes (1659), VI, 377, 389
Jordan, river, V, 15, VI, 356
Jordanus Nemorarius, cited, V, 41, 557; ed., V, 278, 343; errors of, VI, 137; works sought, V, 376
Joseph, interpretation of dreams by, VI, 417
Joseph, rabbi, VI, 462
Josephus, historian, VI, 353
Joshua, commands the sun to stand still, VI, 22, 69
Joubert, Laurent (1521-1583), VI, 220-1
Journal of the History of Ideas, V, 413, 424
Journal of Theological Studies, V, 652
Journalistic trend, V, 5
Journey, prediction as to, V, 236, 277
Jove, Michel, pr Lyons, V, 271, 465
Jovius, see Giovio
Juan de Carmona, physician, VI, 128, 196-7
Juan, Don, of Austria, VI, 195
Juba, cited, VI, 300
Judaism, V, 120
Judge, as patient, V, 302; in witch trial, V, 177
Judgment, last, V, 223
Jugé, Clément, abbé (1907), VI, 33
Juhasz, C. (1937), VI, 183
Julian, chiromancer, V, 57
Jülich, duke of, VI, 559
Julius II, V, 51, 505, VI, 148; dedic to, V, 141; election of favorable times, VI, 150; prediction addressed to, V, 167, VI, 136; preface addressed to, V, 8
Julius III, V, 284; longevity erroneously predicted for, V, 206
Junctinus, see Giuntini
Junior, Antonius, M.D., V, 323
Junta, pr Venice, V, 254, 514, 605, VI, 208
Junta, Lucas Antonius, pr Venice, V, 192
Junta, Philippus, pr Venice, V, 182; heirs of, prs Florence, V, 183
Jupiter, Ammon, VI, 498, 504; and Ganymede, VI, 278; the planet, casts a shadow, VI, 24, house of, V, 216; influence of, V, 119, 138, 151, 189, 196, 310, 489, VI, 487, intelligence of, VI, 512, moons of, VI, 190, 555
Jurisconsult, Jurisprudence and Jurist, V, 112, 142, 256, 261, 274, 307, 370-1, 540, VI, 182, 241, 481, 526, 596, 598; family of, V, 601; occult arts and, V, 261; praise of, V, 336; restored, V, 295; and see Law
Juste, François, pr Lyons, V, 313
Justice, eternal, VI, 456
Justin, Epitome of Trogus Pompeius, V, 35
Justin Martyr, VI, 344
Justingen, see Stoeffler
Justinian, Code of, VI, 537-9, 543
Justinianus Augustinianus, VI, 445
Justus, Guolph., see Jobst, Wolfgang

Kampen, see Pigghe, Albert, of
Karlspach, V, 603
Karlstadt, pest at, V, 354
Keats, quoted, VI, 67
Kelley, Edward, VI, 392
Kentmann, Johann, naturalist, VI, 269, 307, 319, 598
Kenwix, Margaret, herbalist and quack, VI, 219

Kepfersperg, see John of
Kepler, Johann, V, 366, 411, 413, VI, 110; cited, VI, 172; friend of, V, 251; *Mysterium,* V, 200, 391, VI, 464-5; *Prodromus,* V, 412, 429, VI, 5, 52; *Rudolphine Tables,* VI, 4; *Somnium,* V, 7
Kerver, Iacobus, pr Paris, V, 300
Ketham, Johann von, see *Fasciculus medicinae*
Keussen, H. (1919), V, 407
Key and Keys, shaken against demons, VI, 405; used in divining, VI, 509
Khorasan, V, 476
Kid, V, 621
Kidney, anatomy of, V, 47, 517; experiment with, V, 508; trouble, VI, 223
Kiesewetter, C. (1893), VI, 393
King, V, 646; astrology and, VI, 202; catalogue of, V, 391; charlatans favored by, V, 279; conduct of, V, 187; edict desired, V, 280; favor with, VI, 320; health of, VI, 223; patron, VI, 353; and see Comet, France, Francis I, Political, Scrofula (for royal touch)
King, C. W. (1865), VI, 300
Kingston, John, pr London, V, 624, VI, 41
Kink, R. (1854), V, 328
Kiranides and Kiranus, cited, V, 610, 614, VI, 300, and criticized, VI, 281; not cited, VI, 318
Kissing, V, 477, 484
Kittredge, Geo. L. (1929), VI, 517, 550
Klagenfurt, VI, 490
Klauser, Christopher, V, 180
Klebs, Arnold C. (1938), V, 39, 139, 343, 346, 447-8
Klüpfel, E. (1827), V, 407
Knight, Knighted and Knighthood, V, 111, 129, 174, 256, 404
Knivet, Edmund, knight, VI, 268
Knorrn, Nicolaus, pr Nürnberg, VI, 134
Knot, cure by, VI, 233
Knowledge, fields of, VI, 429; limited by sense, VI, 563; of the particular, VI, 198
Knusdorp, VI, 69, 84
Kobolt, A. M. (1795), V, 345-6, 394, 485
Koebel, Jacob, author, V, 330-1
Koebel, Jacob, pr, V, 330-1
Königsberg, pr at, V, 481
Korbach, school of, VI, 354
Krabbe, Otto Carsten (1854), V, 397, VI, 126
Krabbel, Gerta (1915), VI, 455
Krafftbrot, V, 611
Krauss, see Crusius
Krems, V, 346
Kreutzburg, VI, 455
Kriel, Nikolaus, VI, 495
Kristeller, P. O. (1938), V, 533, VI, 438
Krumbacher, Karl (1897), VI, 88
Kuepfner, Johann (1542), V, 460
Künstbüchlin, V, 543
Kyeser, Konrad, V, 34, 596
Kyngstonus, see Kingston

Labezzaro, V, 547
Labor, saving—and wasting—, V, 595
Lac lunare, see Galactites
Lacedaemonian, see Sparta
Lacinius, Janus, V, 546; cited, V, 623, VI, 411, 544
Lactantius, VI, 492
Lacuna, Andrea, see Andreas de Laguna
Ladislaus Oracomensis, V, 220
Laet, Jaspar, astrologer, V, 189-91
La Faye, professor, VI, 423
Laguna, see Andreas de
La Mantia, Vito, VI, 149
Lamb, V, 561, VI, 416
Lami, Giovanni (1756), V, 325
Lamia, VI, 515-7
Lamp, inextinguishable, VI, 247, 279; magic, VI, 419, 421
Lanceola, see Plantago
Lancillotti, Giovanni Francesco (1765), V, 533
L'Ancre, Pierre de (1607), VI, 287
Land and Water, see Earth, surface of
Landi, Ortensio, *Paradossi,* VI, 363-4
Landshut, born at, VI, 227; pr at, V, 206
Landus, Bassianus, Aristotelian, VI, 364
Lanfranc, medical, V, 513
Lang, Johann, physician, VI, 241; letter, V, 548, VI, 316
Language, V, 564; differences of, V, 146, VI, 477; learned in an hour, VI, 439-40; of animals, V, 570; oriental studied, VI, 61, known, VI, 106; origin of, popular and unscientific, VI, 565;

study of, flourishing, V, 295; taught, V, 582; vernaculars, VI, 273-4, derived from Latin, VI, 362; and see Name, Tongue, Translation
Lapicida, F., pr Venice, V, 179
Lapidarius, cited, VI, 300
Lapidary, sceptical, VI, 285
Lapis lazuli, V, 449, VI, 313
La Pologne au Cong. Int. des Sci. Hist., V, 406, 409
L'Apostre, Georges, VI, 459
Lapland and Lapps, magic of, VI, 536
Lar and Lares, VI, 551
Larch tree, resin of, V, 461
Lark, eating a crested, not good for colic, V, 662
Larkey, Sanford V. (1934), VI, 40
La Rochelle, V, 478; pr at, V, 596
Lateran, VI, 371, 484; Council of, V, 94, 225
Lateranus, V, 370; and see Ziegler
Lathe, V, 594
Latin, barbarous, V, 521, 528; decline of, V, 11-12; faulty, V, 182-3; ignorance of, V, 111-2, 229, 438, VI, 373; learned in an hour, VI, 439-40; medieval, criticized, V, 3; not read by women or the populace, V, 262; opinion, V, 554; taught, V, 31, VI, 255; and see Translation
Laton, Moses, V, 283
La Tour Landry, seigneur de, VI, 341
La Tourette, Alexandre de, V, 640
Lauban, VI, 490
Laubenburg, V, 355
Laudanum, V, 639
Lauingen, VI, 112; pr at, VI, 116, 118, 462
Launay, Loys de, V, 478; cited, VI, 361
Launoy, Jean (1662), VI, 377, 388
Laurel, as antidote, VI, 277; immune from lightning, V, 146; leaves no ash, V, 146
Laurenderius, Claudius Martinus (1658), VI, 506
Laurentanus, Leonardus, doge of Venice, V, 537
Laurentius, Andreas, cited, V, 486
Laurentius de Flisco, see Flisco
Laurentius de Gozadinis, see Gozadinis
Lauro, Pietro, tr, VI, 476
Lausanne, pr at, V, 336, VI, 279, 466
Lausitz, VI, 490; an alchemist of, V, 532
Laval, VI, 339
Lavater, Ludwig, VI, 530-1; opposed, VI, 532
Lavinius, Petrus, V, 131
Law and Lawyer, VI, 456, 524, 531, 551; alchemy and V, 535, 622; answers Bruno, VI, 423; astrology and, V, 198, 307, VI, 542; attacked, V, 63; belittled, V, 57; canon, V, 86, 403, 426, 438, VI, 145, 169, 498; civil, V, 70, 403, 426; customary, V, 307; credulous as to superstition and witchcraft, V, 143; disgust with, V, 142; doctor of, V, 129, 168, 203, 258, 351, 370, 406-7, 426, 446, 581, VI, 169, 255, 491, 535, 551; faculties of, VI, 535; influence on individual, VI, 204; losses at, V, 172; magic and, VI, 132-3; medicine and, VI, 218; mental faculties and, VI, 413; not enforced, VI, 543; occult arts and, VI, 543; opinion, VI, 532; professor of, V, 431, VI, 105, 352; student of, VI, 346, 382, 531, 596
Layman, V, 35-36; medicine for, V, 431, VI, 608; occult virtue learned from, V, 661
Lazarus, raising of, V, 103
Lazarus, St., feast of, V, 307
Lazius, W., astrologer, V, 179, VI, 596
Lazzarelli, Lodovico, V, 533, VI, 438
Lead, V, 315, 479; congelation of, V, 507; from cave man's club, V, 512; gains weight, VI, 403
League, VI, 22
Leapyear, see Year
Learning, flourishing in Italy in 1544, V, 261; prodigy of universal, V, 307; reform required, V, 631; transmission of, V, 179
Lebzelter, J. tr, VI, 211-2
Lecanomancy, VI, 430, 499, 502
Lecture, attendance large, V, 581-2, VI, 553; by Achillini, V, 38-39, Brasavola, V, 446, Falloppia, VI, 208, 311, Nifo, V, 79, Palissy, V, 598, Sanchez, VI, 567; cursory, V, 152; hour of, VI, 152; notes for, V, 47, on, V, 326, 479; opening, V, 164, VI, 41; preserved in manuscript, VI, 165; pr, VI, 503; royal and Ramian, VI, 142; student,

V, 204; twenty errors in one, VI, 423
Leduchet (1741), V, 313
Leeuwen, van, see Leoninus
Lefèvre d'Etaples, Jacques, addressed to, VI, 442; Agrippa and, V, 127-8; cited, V, 166, VI, 459; disciples of, VI, 443; interest in Lull, V, 535; mathematical activity, V, 278-9, 343; mystical activity, VI, 437-8
Le Fournier, see Furnerius
Left, arm, worn on, VI, 315; see Right and
Legate, papal, V, 238, 240-1, 245-6, 264, 540; preface to, V, 540; royal, see Ambassador
Le Gendre, G. C. (1733), VI, 296-7
Legerdemain, see Sleight-of-hand
Legerius, an Aristotelian, VI, 382
Legerus, Allanus, a patient, V, 302
Leghorn, VI, 254
Legius, Leonardus, V, 460
Legnano, see John of
Leib, Killian, prior, V, 232-3, 348
Leicester, earl of, VI, 41
Leipzig, born at, VI, 597; dissertation of, V, 579; medical faculty of, V, 380, 440; pr at, V, 160, 217, 354, 357, 396, 415, VI, 49, 141, 211-2, 448, 478, 498, 502; studied at, V, 341, 406, VI, 16; taught at, V, 160, 397, VI, 41, 49, 366; theologians of, VI, 364
Leisure, longed for, V, 163
Leland, John, V, 7
Le Loyer, Pierre (1586), VI, 531-3
Lemgo, pr at, VI, 352
Lemnius, Levinus, VI, 306, 393-4; cited, V, 647, VI, 237, 283, 382, 407, 430, 531, 555; described, VI, 394; tr, V, 636
Lemnius, Simon, VI, 459
Lemnos, VI, 225
Lens, V, 286, 490-1
Leo I, VI, 125
Leo X, V, 95, 142, 205, 510, VI, 195, 476; alchemy and, V, 253, 535, 537; astrology and, V, 236, 253, 489; dedic to, V, 164, 169, 253, VI, 445, 449; election predicted, V, 105, 252-3; Nifo and, V, 74, 78, 85-86, 98, 184, 196; Philologus and, V, 205; superstition of, V, 252
Leo Hebraeus, *De amore*, VI, 462
Leo, Johannes Franciscus, VI, 169
Leonard of Bertipaglia, cited, V, 463, 513, 597
Leonard of Pisa, depicted, VI, 470-1
Leonardo da Vinci, V, 16-36, 596; anatomy of, V, 17, 29, 35; attitude towards magic and alchemy, V, 32-33; botany of, V, 28-29; debt to past, V, 18, 23-24, 156-7; experience of, V, 19-21, 26; geology of, V, 25-28, 597, VI, 284, 292, 313; note-taking of, V, 16-18, 21, 23; other science of, V, 30-32; technology of, V, 34-35
Leonardus, Justinianus, V, 96
Leone, Ambrogio (1523), V, 143-7
Leone, Camillo, V, 144
Leonello of Faenza, physician, V, 509
Leonicenus, Nicolaus, cited, V, 122, 166, 227, 436, 452, VI, 215, 402; disagreed with, V, 452, 502; influence, V, 115, 388, 447, 451, VI, 254, 280; not cited, V, 477; praised, V, 166; tr, V, 343
Leoninus, Albertus (1578), VI, 45
Leonora, queen of France, VI, 368
Leopold of Austria, cited, V, 163, 166, 213, 227, 265, 317, VI, 89, 131, 163, 180
Leopoldina, V, 379
Leovitius, see Leowitz
Leowitz, Cyprian, astrologer, V, 375, VI, 111; *Brevis et perspicua ratio*, VI, 111, 115-6; cited, V, 374, VI, 21, 50, 67, 102, 131, 139, 202; *Coniunctionibus magnis*, VI, 118-9; criticized, VI, 42, 111-2, 118, 193, 195; geniture, VI, 596; put on the Index, VI, 147
Le Paulmier, see Paulmier
Leper and Leprosy, VI, 252; amulet for, V, 420; oil for, V, 432; Paracelsus and, V, 619, 627
Le Preux, Franciscus, pr Lausanne, VI, 279
Le Prince, Pierre, pr Lyons, V, 309
Lerquian, Iusepe, prior, VI, 166
Lery, Sieur de, geographer, VI, 361
Lessines, V, 582
Letter, V, 66, 113, 137, 179-80, 203, 205, 208, 218, 292, 297, 304, 343, 346, 352, 355, 365, 368, 409-13, 416, 431, 439-40, 479, 490, 497, 525, 529, 532, 546-8, 613, 617, 619, VI, 13, 17-18, 50-51, 112, 126-7, 154, 255, 260, 266, 279,

351, 444; medical, V, 327, 436, 514, VI, 129, 213, 224-5; of Bouelles, Ganay and Trithemius, VI, 438-42; of Enoch, VI, 438; of George of Ragusa, VI, 198-201; of inquisition, VI, 151-3; of Loyola, VI, 455; of Patrizi, VI, 375; scientific, VI, 267-9, 420, 433; warning, VI, 195; and see Alphabet, Agrippa, Brahe, Campanella, Geo. Fabricius, Gesner, Melanchthon, Mundella, Pirckheimer

Lettuce, V, 614

Leutershausen, VI, 91

Levant, VI, 257

Leviathan, V, 135

Levinus Lemnius, see Lemnius

Levitation, VI, 451

Ley, Willy (1929), V, 391, VI, 269, 291-2

Leyden, V, 462; pr at, V, 286, 367, 445, 513, 623, VI, 142, 318, 479; taught at, VI, 194, 346, 538

Leymbach, astrologer, V, 160

Libanomancy, VI, 503

Libavius, Andreas, career, VI, 238; cited, VI, 253, 319; opposed, V, 648, VI, 249, 252; quoted, VI, 238; works, *Alchymia*, VI, 242-3, *Alchymia triumphans*, VI, 249, *Declamatio de cometa*, VI, 87, 252-3, *Defensio*, VI, 245, *Natura metallorum*, VI, 243, *Neo-Paracelsica*, VI, 242, *Quaest. physicarum*, VI, 238, *Tractatus duo physici*, VI, 239-43, *Variarum controversiarum*, VI, 238

Liber de anatomia vivorum, V, 46

Liber de natura rerum, VI, 280

Liber receptarum, V, 180

Liber segretorum artistarum ac medicorum, V, 39

Libertin, see Free thinking

Liberty, V, 578-9

Librarian and Library, V, 112; burgher, V, 177; cabalistic, VI, 462; Ferrara, at, V, 168; French royal, V, 623; magic, V, 134; of Aldrovandi, VI, 153, Barozzi, VI, 154-5, Capellani, VI, 142, Champier, V, 123, Colbert, VI, 259, Crasso, VI, 163, Finé, V, 543, Fuggers, VI, 112, Gambalunga, VI, 127, Gassar, V, 391-2, George of Ragusa, VI, 202, Giorgio, VI, 452, Hellmann, V, 178, 181, 188, Longolius, VI, 255-6, Matthias Corvinus, V, 395, Mizauld, V, 300, Naudé, V, 178, Pirckheimer, V, 357, 369, S. Michael de Muriano, VI, 377, Simon de Phares, V, 291, 345; Palatine, V, 391; Turkish, VI, 353; Vatican, V, 407; and see Regiomontanus, Walther

Library, The, VI, 224

Libri, Gugl. (1838-1841), V, 21, VI, 154-5, 296; corrected, VI, 93, 137; quoted, V, 252, VI, 254

Libya, V, 473

Licetus, Fortunius, naturalist, VI, 286

Lichtenberger, Johann, astrologer, V, 203-4

Liddelius, Duncan, VI, 55

Liebler, see Erastus

Liechthenau, see Conrad a

Liège, V, 189, 206-8; bishop of, V, 226, VI, 28, 235; studied at, VI, 341

Liegnitz, pr at, V, 404

Lièvre, A. F. (1856-1860), V, 465

Life in movement, V, 25

Ligature and suspension, VI, 419, 529, 534, 601; and see Suspension

Ligature, in vein, VI, 330

Light, created before sun? VI, 357; medium between corporeal and incorporeal, VI, 375; reflection of, V, 32; transmission of, VI, 380-1, through solid bodies, V, 272; within human body, V, 116

Lightning, action of, V, 33, 146, 155; freak, VI, 366; protects from, VI, 323, 488; stone produced by, VI, 323; struck by, V, 202

Lignum aloes, V, 123, 453

Lignum guaiacum, V, 440, 446, VI, 272

Lignum sanctum, V, 254

Lignum vitae, V, 546, 603

Like and Likeness, VI, 419; attracts like, V, 271, 495, 527; basis of interpretation of dreams, VI, 422; cures like, VI, 248, 251, 388, 602; doubted, V, 664; relation to occult virtue, V, 135

Lilio or Lilius, astronomer, VI, 129

Lill, V, 603

Lille, V, 329, 466

Lilly, astrologer, V, 313

Lily of the valley, V, 651

Limburg, V, 544

Limousin, V, 111
Linacre, Thomas, sends rings as charms, V, 176; tr by, V, 343, 349
Lincoln, bishop of, V, 166
Lincolniensis (Robertus?), V, 321
Lindanus, William, bishop of Ruremond, VI, 72, 505
Lindau, V, 391
Lindenius renovatus, VI, 431
Lindhout, Henricus a, VI, 140-1
Liniment, VI, 547
Linnaeus, Carolus, VI, 334
Lion, V, 517, VI, 220, 447; fiery, seen in sky, V, 399, VI, 489; freightened by cock, VI, 281, 350, 403, 416, by cock-crow, V, 662; other traits of, VI, 277; and see Image, of
Lip, long, VI, 276
Lisbon, V, 550; pr at, V, 293, 550-1
Literati, V, 608
Lithosis, VI, 243
Lithospermum arvense, VI, 280
Litteramancy or Literomancy, V, 58, 561
Liver, VI, 362; as concentrated food, V, 611; dried, VI, 269; human, in weapon ointment, VI, 240; of black cat, V, 118; part of sky for, VI, 158; source of veins, V, 531, VI, 432, denied, VI, 327; treatment for, VI, 317
Livianus, Venetian condottiere, V, 488
Livonia, V, 376, VI, 535
Livy, V, 307
Lizard, VI, 284; oil of, V, 432
Llerena, VI, 196
Lobel, Matth., botanist, VI, 258, 261-4
Locatellus, Bonetus, of Bergamo, pr Venice, V, 39, 72, 163, 184
Loci communes, V, 141
Locust, V, 135, 497; plague of, VI, 89, 490
Lodi, VI, 258
Lodovicus, A. see Luiz, Ant.
Loë, Ioannes, pr Antwerp, VI, 9
Loenhut, V, 303
Logic, V, 431, 642, 653; attacked, VI, 565, 567; false, VI, 98; restored, V, 336; studied, V, 564; taught, V, 38, 61, 90, 204-5, 325, 338, 446, 488, VI, 61, 142, 289, 368, 524; works on, V, 111, 149, 152, 173, 209, 380, 390, 421, VI, 190
Lombard, see Peter
Lombardi, Ant. Maria, pharmacist, VI, 268
Lombardy, V, 161, VI, 465
London, V, 269, VI, 219, 248, 267, 472; pr at, V, 270, 374, 377, 466, 547, 603, 607, 624, VI, 17-18, 26, 39, 41, 72, 106, 111, 115, 118, 180, 215, 222, 258, 268, 271, 285, 287, 316, 405, 476, 483, 507, 529, 531
Longevity, altered since antiquity, V, 665, VI, 403; how attain, V, 205-6, 571, 627-8, VI, 423, 566; in far east, VI, 297; in hands of God, VI, 161; not predictable, VI, 200; of Artephius, V, 637, early man, VI, 391, patriarchs, V, 121, VI, 403, Pythagoras, V, 166, soldier, VI, 145; predicted, V, 260; stars and, V, 121; and see Youth renewed
Longinus Caesar, VI, 599-601
Longitude, V, 292, 319, 557; and latitude, VI, 10, 90
Longo, Giov. Batt., disciple of Porta, VI, 129, 164
Longolius, Gybertus, naturalist, VI, 255-6
Lonicerus, M. A. (1483), VI, 45
Loos, disciple of Wier, VI, 517
Looz, county of, VI, 28
Lord's prayer, repeated thrice, VI, 404
Lorente y Pérez, J. M. (1921), V, 275
Lorindt, V, 639
Lorraine, V, 111, 136, 294; cardinal of, V, 304, VI, 344; duke of, V, 111, 115; mines of, V, 125; stone of, VI, 306
Lot casting, VI, 417, 496; not punished, VI, 543; opposed, V, 399, VI, 135, 467; and see Geomancy, Sortilege
Lothbury, pr at, VI, 483
Lot's wife, VI, 534
Loubenbourg, see Laubenburg
Louis XI, king of France, VI, 89
Louis XII, king of France, V, 113, 187, 260, 636, VI, 465
Louis II, king of Hungary, VI, 196
Louis, brother of Witelo, V, 86
Louise of Savoy, V, 128, 131, 137
Louvain, V, 189, 208, 410, VI, 406, 409; Agrippa at, V, 136; dissensions at, V, 176-7; gallows outside, V, 526; pr at,

V, 106, 320, 329, VI, 235; quodlibet at, V, 206-7; taught at, V, 147, 303, VI, 31, 194, 235; theologians of, VI, 364; university of, V, 129, 147-8, 151, 176-7, 462, 640, VI, 341, 394, 406
Love, and hate, V, 242; and insanity, V, 486, VI, 223; charms, V, 105, VI, 534-5, and see Philter; falling in, VI, 351; heroic, V, 87; incitement to, V, 105-6; sexual, V, 571
Low Countries, see Netherlands
Lowe, astrologer, VI, 180
Loxus, physiognomist, V, 67
Loyola, Ignatius, VI, 362, 455
Lübeck, V, 108, VI, 210; bishop of, VI, 136
Lucca, V, 284, 648; pharmaceutical find near, VI, 294; pr at, VI, 212
Lucena, Ludovicus, V, 130
Luciani, Luigi (1908), VI, 328
Lucius, J. pr Rostock, VI, 38
Luckenwald, VI, 310
Ludwig, duke of Wurtemberg, V, 631, VI, 76, 80
Ludwig V, elector Palatine, V, 203
Ludwig VI, elector Palatine, VI, 91
Lufft, Johannes, pr Wittenberg, V, 398, VI, 490
Luiz, Antonio, V, 550-1
Lull, Raymond, V, 126, 130; alchemical Corpus, V, 443, 533-6, 541-2, 545-8, 602-4, 621-5, 632, 638, 648, 691-3, VI, 244, 531; cited, V, 141, VI, 218, 242, 250, 459, 533; defended, VI, 246; influence, VI, 424; life of, V, 648, VI, 244
Lullian art, V, 325, VI, 201, 361, 406, 434, 456, 459
Luminaries, see Sun and Moon
Luminarium, V, 460
Lunardi, Camillo, VI, 298-302; cited, VI, 361; compared with de Boodt, VI, 318-9; condemned, VI, 299; *Lunario*, V, 218; tr, VI, 313
Lunaria, an herb, V, 458, VI, 263, 292
Lungs, V, 507; function of, V, 511
Luther, Martin, V, 9, 37, 128, 287, 394, 438-9, VI, 117, 456, 484, 502, 536; and astrology, V, 233, 433; belief in apparition of spirits, VI, 533; failure to exorcize demon, VI, 558; geniture, VI, 597; praised by Bruno, VI, 424; prediction as to, V, 230, 382; prodigy announcing, VI, 409; purged church of many illusions of demons, VI, 598; routed Aristotelian theologians, VI, 364; teacher of, V, 149; tr, VI, 520; witches' sabbats and, VI, 601; written against, VI, 462
Lutheran, V, 378, 392, 397, 413, VI, 148, 183, 462; called a, V, 66, 289; division among, VI, 494
Luxemburg, VI, 537, 544
Lycanthropy, VI, 504, 515, 526, 535, 547
Lycosthenes, Conrad (1557), VI, 489; put on Index, VI, 147
Lycus, V, 523
Lydia, V, 229
Lye, V, 635, VI, 546
Lyncurium (lynx stone), V, 455-6, VI, 310, 335
Lynn, King's, V, 374
Lynx, sees through mountain, V, 158; and see Lyncurium
Lyons, V, 258, 454, 465-6, VI, 66, 267; Agrippa at, V, 128, 137, 307; Champier at, V, 111-2; Giuntini at, VI, 129-30; history of, V, 112, 115; medical college, V, 112; Mercurio at, VI, 438; pr at, V, 66-68, 113-4, 116, 122, 124-5, 136, 143, 149, 152, 158-9, 253, 256, 270-1, 287-8, 300, 308-10, 313, 326, 328, 342, 398, 445, 449-50, 461, 465-6, 493, 501, 532, 536, 542, 545, 547, 560, 594, 602, 607-8, 636, VI, 24, 33, 44, 74, 105, 107, 115, 120-1, 130, 160-1, 173, 189, 220-1, 255, 266, 268, 299, 318, 364, 382, 393-4, 410, 432-3, 447, 463, 469, 472, 474, 476, 478-9, 493, 499, 554, 561, 568-9; school at, VI, 382; trip to, VI, 201

MacCurdy, Edward (1938), V, 16, 33
Mace, the spice, V, 453, 467
Macer on herbs, V, 448; comm. VI, 400
Macerata, pr at, VI, 556
Machiavelli, *Discorsi*, V, 636; *Prince* of, V, 85; works printed posthumously, V, 6-7, plagiarized, V, 187
Machiavellianism, V, 37, VI, 570
Machine and Machinery, V, 34-35, 133, 193, 588-9, 593-6, VI, 373

Mâcon, V, 67
Madagascar, VI, 346
Madman, see Mania
Madrid, VI, 126; pr at, V, 469, 486-7, VI, 167, 221; Vesalius in, V, 530
Madrigal, Petrus de, pr Madrid, VI, 167
Maeotis, V, 447
Maestlin, Michael, V, 412, 429, VI, 52, 464-5; cited, V, 376, VI, 381; program of publication, VI, 82; quoted, VI, 69; works, *Alterum examen,* VI, 5, *Consideratio,* VI, 80-81, *Defensio,* V, 427, *Dimensionibus,* VI, 4-5, *Ephemerides,* VI, 5, 79, 82, *Epitome,* VI, 46-47, 82-83, *Observatio,* VI, 76-79
Maffei, Giovanni Camillo (1563-1564), VI, 398
Maffei, Hieronymo, V, 513
Maffei, Pietro, VI, 551
Maffei, Raphael, cited, V, 407, VI, 256; *Urban Commentaries,* V, 141
Maffei, Scipio (1732), V, 490
Magazine, a forerunner of the, V, 113
Magdeburg, V, 399
Magenbuch, Johann, physician, V, 657
Maggi, Lucilio, see Philalthaeus
Magi, V, 150; chief of, VI, 460; cited, V, 527; figments of, VI, 233; initiated learning, VI, 381; Persian, VI, 220, 353, 415, 464, not priests or sages, V, 660; Pharaoh's, VI, 391, 516; Pliny on, VI, 303, 305, 309; shield of, VI, 459; three, and star of Bethlehem, V, 166, 215, 323, 403, VI, 69, 176, 349, adoration of, V, 257, and number twelve, VI, 442
Magic and Magician, V, 91, 636, VI, 336, 441, 519; accused of, V, 19, 102, 327, 382, VI, 132; Arabic, false, VI, 302; artificial, VI, 601, rejected, VI, 450; ascending scale of, VI, 439; astronomical, VI, 468; at Toledo and Salamanca, V, 283; avoided, VI, 310; book, V, 136, 172, 177, 409, VI, 147, 150, 154, 427, 434, 515, 519, 535; born, V, 510; celestial, V, 533; ceremonial, VI, 400; condemned, V, 321, 660-1, VI, 467; counter, V, 628, 649-50, VI, 434; criticized, V, 116-7; dabbled in, VI, 219; defined, V, 13, VI, 434, 464; demon, existence of, proved by, V, 83; diabolical, V, 580, VI, 240, 378, 415, 417, 434, 517, 520, 523, 525, 534; divination and, VI, 495-6, 499, 524; divine, VI, 460, 568; ecclesiastical, VI, 168, 495; empiric and, V, 381; expelled by Christianity, V, 283; experience and, VI, 397-8, 434; faith requisite for, VI, 398; feats of, VI, 536; forbidden, VI, 169; founders of, V, 175; God hates, VI, 239; good, if not abused, V, 635; Greek, VI, 293; illusions of, V, 83, VI, 417, 534; Leonardo da Vinci and, V, 32-34; logic of, V, 34, 249, 574, VI, 367, 495; mathematical, VI, 378, 426; medicine and, V, 381; mode of acquisition illegal, VI, 132; natural, V, 13-14, 33, 104, 124, 132-5, 175, 213, 278, 478, 550, 561, 564, 573-4, 635, VI, 302, 353, 378, 392, 410-1, 418, 421, 424, 426, 430-2, 434, 438, 449-50, 460, 530, 536, 601, defined, VI, 415, 464, denied, V, 660, VI, 240, 527, doubted, VI, 597-8, praised, VI, 516; philosophical, VI, 435; Pliny on, V, 560-2; praised, V, 166; punishment of, VI, 535; reality of, V, 83; religion and, V, 85; revived, V, 55; sacred, VI, 407; science and, see Science; Thadeus of Parma on, V, 118; transfer, of disease, see Disease, of marks, VI, 237; vanity of, VI, 481; varieties of, V, 118, 573, 635, VI, 378, 426, 430, 457, 460, 523; white, denied, VI, 551; word, fear of, VI, 304, less objection to, V, 13, long in bad odor, VI, 464, now in bad odor, VI, 507, used freely by Porta, VI, 418; worse than witch, VI, 515
Magini, Ioannes Antonius, V, 250-1, VI, 129, 210; Brahe to, V, 304, VI, 52; cited, VI, 64, 172; works, *Astrologica ratione,* V, 250, 325, VI, 122, 164-5, comm. Galen, *Diebus criticis,* V, 250, *Ephemerides,* V, 251, VI, 56, *Legitimo astrologiae,* V, 315, VI, 128, *Novae theoricae,* V, 251, VI, 55-59, *Tabulae,* V, 251, VI, 57, 430
Magister Hospitalis, alchemist, V, 623; and see Aegidius
Magistrate, V, 143, 666, VI, 302
Magliabechi, Antonio, V, 229

Magnet, action of, V, 101, 108, 121, 243, 271, 495-6, 551, 571, VI, 235, 314, 350, as instance of occult virtue, V, 299, 661, VI, 316, 320, 397, 468, of sympathy, VI, 430, checked by diamond, V, 646, found false, VI, 282, 314, 420; draws nails from ships, V, 451, 585, denied, VI, 301; earth a great, VI, 381; iron goes to magnet, V, 146, VI, 206; magical virtue denied, V, 451, VI, 319; medicinal virtue, VI, 317; mountains of, V, 495, denied, V, 451, VI, 314, 319; other assertions concerning, disproved, VI, 282, 420; works on, V, 547, 580, 583, VI, 300, 308; and see Garlic, Goat
Magnetic, compass, V, 365, 527, 583, VI, 275; cure, VI, 601; pole, V, 271; virtue, of man, V, 650, of nature, V, 634, VI, 434
Magnetism, VI, 240
Magnus, Olaus, VI, 280
Magnus annus, VI, 121, 378, 551
Maimonides, cited, V, 480, 502, VI, 432-3
Maino de' Maineri, V, 637
Mainz, archbishop of, V, 66, 174; at, V, 443, VI, 191, 457, 491; born at, V, 323; of, V, 172, 282; preface from, V, 17, 321; pr at, V, 172, 330, 521, 675, VI, 429, 480, 533
Mairhofer, Matthias, S. J. VI, 319, 414-8
Major, Geo. VI, 597
Majoragio, Marco Antonio, V, 547
Malacca, V, 477
Malatesta, Pandolfo, V, 55
Malatesta, Ramberto, count, V, 228
Maleficia, VI, 427, 545
Malines, V, 128, 137, 195, 582, 621, VI, 15, 194; tables of, V, 195
Malleus maleficarum, V, 71, 487, VI, 169, 172, 521, 527; 531
Mallow, wild, VI, 223
Malta, V, 585
Maltraversi, Guido, count, VI, 135
Maltraversi, Niccolò, VI, 135
Malvetius, *De sortibus,* VI, 543
Malvezzi, Nerio (1884), V, 231, 237-8
Mameluke, V, 206
Man, V, 152, VI, 451; abnormal conduct, V, 572; aptitude for science, VI, 413; astral body, V, 633-4, 660; body a prison, V, 631; cave, V, 512; cure by breath of, V, 475; fall, VI, 391; foreign substances emitted by, VI, 540; ignorance, V, 189; magic power, V, 101, VI, 131-2, 416, 477; magnetic power, V, 650; of letters, V, 146; old, V, 145; parts of, V, 635, VI, 269, 600, used in magic and medicine, V, 454, 537, 663, VI, 233; peculiarities, V, 145, 577; perfect, V, 296; primitive, V, 577-8, VI, 382; relation to God and neighbor, V, 390, VI, 451; sensual, V, 97; star in, V, 628; symmetry of body, V, 587; wild, VI, 269, 287; world made for, VI, 81; young more docile, V, 146; and see Anatomy, Blood, Corpse, Generation, Monster, Pygmy, Skull, etc.
Manard, Jean, V, 460; cited, V, 122, 465, VI, 215, 317, 402; criticized, V, 449, 452, 457, 467, VI, 228; defended, VI, 215; remedy of, VI, 235
Mancini, Celso, *De somniis* (1591), VI, 484
Mandeville, D. C. (1927), V, 48
Mandosio, Prospero (1784), VI, 127
Mandragora, VI, 292, 401
Manes, V, 381
Manfred, son of Frederick II, VI, 448
Manfredis, Hieronymus de, V, 50, 54, 356, 443, 586
Manger, Michael, pr Augsburg, VI, 134, 143
Manget, J. J. (1702), V, 648
Mania and Maniac, VI, 287; bound, V, 297; caused by tree gnawed by mad dog, VI, 571; cure, V, 444; moon and, V, 242
Manilius, V, 142, 341; cited, V, 165, 296, VI, 112, 180; ed., V, 304
Manilius Antonius, see Antonius
Manilius, Gislenus, pr Ghent, V, 410
Manlius, Jacobus, *Luminarium,* VI, 225
Manna, Pietro, physician, V, 529
Mans, Le, VI, 53, 524
Mansion, see Moon and Sun
Mansor, king of Persia, V, 522
Mantua, V, 103, 251-3, 256, 450, 645, VI, 300; addressed from, VI, 558; astrologer of, VI, 195; duke of, dedic to, V, 645; marquis of, dedic to, V,

56, 63, 230; of, V, 63, 94, 98, 100; prince of, V, 250; pr at, VI, 48, 474
Manual, see Hand
Manuscript, alchemical, V, 532, 603; annotation, VI, 105; autograph, V, 273, 320, 339, 358-9, 393, VI, 136, 163, 392; circulation in, and of, V, 4, 6, 99, 156, 187, 340, 362, 365, 409-10, 441, 532, 539-40, 547-8, 574, 601-3, 617, 620, VI, 62-63, 72, 112, 182; collected, VI, 154; compared with printed text, V, 603, 622; concealed, VI, 505; copied, V, 393; de luxe, V, 268; employed in editions, V, 340-1, VI, 88; ignored, V, 647, VI, 265; lectures in, VI, 59; left in, V, 250, 370, 636, VI, 70, 127, 163, 172, 201-2, 265-6, 373, 377, 424, 453-4, 471, 473, 489, 492, 522, 528, 556; migration and transport of, V, 350; of Copernicus, V, 420, Inquisition, VI, 149, Leonardo da Vinci, V, 16-18, 34, Paracelsus, V, 617, Pomponazzi, V, 99-100; Regiomontanus, V, 339-40, 393; original, V, 310; stolen and pirated, VI, 257; vernacular, V, 432
Manutio, Aldo, pr Venice, VI, 300
Manutio, Paolo, (1557), V, 553-6
Map, accompanying Ptolemy's *Geography,* V, 437; cooperative, V, 331; new, V, 358; of Finé, V, 285; of Germany, V, 331, 348, heavens, V, 343, Nürnberg, V, 348; portable, V, 614; wooden world, V, 488
Maphaeus, see Maffei
Maranta, Bartolomeo, pharmacist, VI, 258, 260-1
Marathrum, an herb, VI, 349
Marble, VI, 209, 285, 307, 334
Marbod, cited, V, 571, VI, 300, 305, 319, 334, 361; comm. VI, 400; not cited, VI, 318; opposed, VI, 420; pr, VI, 302
Marburg, physician of, VI, 351; pr at, V, 7, 273, 326, 361, 392, 520, VI, 118, 137, 272, 368, 485; professor at, V, 520, 609, VI, 213, 352; studied at, VI, 341; university of, V, 520-2, VI, 254; visited, VI, 191
Marcellus, copied, V, 122-3, 443
Marcellus, Hieronymus, philosopher, V, 515
Marchand, Henri (1674-1750), VI, 66
Marchasite, VI, 309
Marchetti, P. M., pr Brescia, V, 625
Marcolinus Fanestris, Andreas, VI, 208, 218
Marcus Beneventanus, astrologer, V, 199-201, 282
Marcus Cherrhonesus, VI, 405
Marcus Damascenus, VI, 236
Marescallus, Nicolaus, VI, 255
Margaret of Austria, V, 644
Margaret, queen of France, dedic to, VI, 554
Margarit, G. pr Barcelona, VI, 96
Margarita, countess of Holland in 1314, VI, 401
Margarita, daughter of Charles V, 267-8
Margarita philosophica, see Reisch, Gregorius
Marguerite of France, queen of Navarre, VI, 220
Maria, alchemist, see Mary, sister of Moses
Maria Aragonia, marchese, VI, 486
Maria sopra Minerva, S., convent of, V, 197
Mariana, bishop of, V, 446
Mariana di Giacomo, see Taccola
Marianus Euscathius, V, 220
Marignano, V, 111
Marin, F. L. C. (1786), VI, 106
Marini, G. L. (1784), V, 325
Marinus, classical, V, 523
Mario, Gieronimo, astrologer, V, 274
Mariscottus, Jacobus Ant. tr, VI, 158
Markham, Sir Clements (1913), V, 466, VI, 314
Markos, alchemist, V, 623
Marliani, Giovanni, V, 96
Marlianus, Aloisius, V, 604, 623
Marnet, Hier. de, pr Paris, V, 379, VI, 286
Marnius, Claudius, pr Frankfurt, VI, 494
Marot, Clement, V, 287; cited, VI, 361
Marquard, Jo. ed., VI, 441
Marriage, V, 94, 127, 383-4, VI, 458, 494, 596; astrology and, V, 140, 230, 268, 363, VI, 178; conciliated, VI, 306; husband, examined, VI, 559; husband and wife, choice of, V, 297; made in May, VI, 221; wife, contrariness of, V, 145; witchcraft and, VI, 337, 428, 539, 546, 559

Mars, the planet, eclipsed, V, 289; influence of, V, 61, 92, 119, 196, 199, 209, evil, V, 121, 151, 399, not evil, VI, 451; movement or orbit of, V, 411, VI, 5, 114
Marseilles, VI, 66; fish of, VI, 255; pr at, VI, 61
Marsh or Marshe, Thomas, pr London, VI, 18, 72
Marshmallow, VI, 333
Marsi, people of Italy, V, 473
Marsilius d'Inghen, V, 95
Marstallerus, Gervasius, V, 297-300, 386, 394, 396, 581
Marsus, Ascanius, dedic to, V, 607
Martianus Capella, V, 421, VI, 40
Martin V, VI, 136
Martin of Arles, V, 73
Martin de Castañega, V, 71
Martin, Albert (1889), VI, 89
Martin, James, Ramist, VI, 238
Martinelli, Giovanni, V, 205, 484
Martinelli, Matteo, professor, V, 73
Martini, Joseph, *Catalogue,* V, 259
Martini, Raymond, *Pugio fidei,* VI, 445
Martinus, Iodocus, pr Strasburg, V, 469
Martyr, Peter, V, 178, VI, 214, 503
Martyrdom, V, 567; of science, so-called, VI, 413
Marvel, cause of V, 91, VI, 419; emphasis on, V, 151, 263, 291, 400; interest in, V, 143, 155, 462, 599, VI, 186, 220, 269, 366, 377, 399; natural, not signs of future, VI, 491
Mary of Burgundy, wife of Maximilian, VI, 89, 536
Mary Magdalene, VI, 225
Mary, sister of Moses, alchemist, V, 604, 623
Mary Tudor, queen of England, VI, 520
Mary, the Virgin, V, 270; an image of, see Image
Marzio, see Galeotto Marzio
Marzipan, V, 611
Masius, Gilbert, pr Louvain, V, 147
Mass, VI, 456; celebration of, VI, 148
Massa, Nicolaus, anatomist, V, 254, 514-9, 524, 621
Massacre of St. Bartholomew's day, VI, 142
Massalongo, R. (1914-15), V, 494
Massari, Francesco, naturalist, VI, 256, 258, 267
Massaria, Alessandro, VI, 368
Massé, Pierre (1579), VI, 524
Masses, see Populace
Masseur, forbidden to practise medicine, VI, 220
Masslieb, an herb, VI, 274
Materia medica, see Pharmacy
Materialism, V, 36, V, 340
Maternus, see Firmicus Maternus
Mathematician and Mathematics, V, 57, 61, 202, 215, 218, 221, 281, 320-1, 564, 585-6, 588-9, VI, 598; ancient and modern, V, 41; at Nürnberg, see Nürnberg; at Paris, V, 275, 278, 636; calculation, V, 409, 413, 425, VI, 4, 69, 77, 90, 111, 139; certainty, VI, 135; court or royal, V, 24, 304, VI, 28, 56; criticism, V, 282, 292-3, VI, 35-36, 137; in France and Germany, V, 297, 567; lack of, VI, 85; medicine and, V, 128, 221, 443, 557, VI, 211; method, V, 581, 588, 591, VI, 135, 374; natural magic and, VI, 410; nature and, V, 40-41, VI, 395; of Benedetti, VI, 373, Maestlin, VI, 77, Peletier, VI, 33; oration on, V, 204, VI, 69; renaissance of, V, 295, 332, 334, 366, 368; scope of, V, 14; studied, V, 350, 488, VI, 61, 77, 201; taught, V, 154, 179, 204, 223-4, 245, 250, 254, 269, 275, 285, 288, 292, 303, 321, 327-8, 338, 345, 354, 385-6, 394, 397, 412, 543, 581-2, VI, 5, 16, 19, 30, 34, 38, 41, 56-57, 60, 73, 80, 119, 123, 126, 142-3, 178, 289, 341, 478, 494; textbook of, V, 154; works of, V, 174, 328, 330, 353, 520, VI, 88-89, 124, 140, 143, 154
Mathematicus, V, 14, 313; in the Code, V, 384
Mathesis, V, 14, 218, 586
Matricaria, an herb, VI, 262
Matter, V, 40, VI, 198; duality of, VI, 350; eternity of, V, 42; first, V, 48-49, VI, 341, 368-9, 384; first principle of nature, V, 538; intractable, VI, 496; and see Form
Matthaeus de Gradibus, see Ferrari da Grado
Matthesius, Johann, V, 375, 396-7

Matthew of Sicily, alchemist, V, 638
Matthias, archduke, dedic to, VI, 505
Matthias Corvinus, king of Hungary, V, 179, 337, 374, 395, 406-7, VI, 90, 105, 116
Mattioli, Pierandrea, cited, V, 470, 477-8, VI, 258, 319, 333, 399; comm. Dioscorides, VI, 224, 261-3, 286; disagreed with, VI, 232-3, 260, 313; *Epistolae*, VI, 224-5, 255, 268; ranked first in botany, VI, 353; sent specimens, VI, 268
Maturantius, Franciscus, VI, 279
Maubisson, George de, dedic to, VI, 459
Maulbronn, council of, V, 652
Maurice, elector of Saxony, VI, 105, 116, 196
Mauroceno, Giov. Francesco, cardinal, V, 155, VI, 159
Maurolico, see Maurolycus
Maurolycus, Fran., mathematician, V, 304, 360, 421, 426, VI, 27, 74, 179-80, 382
Maximilian I, emperor, V, 339, 347, 349, 373, 391, 536; death of, V, 122; dedic to, VI, 109, 441, 444, 488; horoscope of, V, 399, VI, 105, 121
Maximilian II, emperor, VI, 118, 505; at court of, V, 480, VI, 394; dedic to, VI, 116, 219, 457; horoscope of, VI, 105
Maximilian, archduke, dedic to, VI, 505
Maximilian, king of Bohemia, V, 606
Maximilian, duke of Bavaria, VI, 235
May dew, VI, 602
Mayer, Michael, brother (1581), VI, 414
Mayerne, Theodore Turquet de, VI, 247-8
Maynardus, Petrus, V, 324-5
Mayronis, Franciscus de, V, 504
Mazochius, Jacobus, pr Rome, Mirandola, V, 164, 472, VI, 476
Mazuccum, a disease, VI, 212
Mazzuchelli, Gianmaria (1753-63), VI, 154-5, 528
McColley, Grant (1937), V, 319, VI, 44, 55
McMurrich, J. P. (1930), V, 29
Mead, G. R. S. (1906), VI, 448
Meals, V, 446, VI, 221-2
Measles, VI, 393
Measurement, VI, 72-73, 77; of contents, V, 174; of speed, V, 34; relation to science and magic, V, 12-13, 302, 581, VI, 109
Meat powder, V, 611
Mechanic and Mechanical arts, V, 57, 105, 252, VI, 137, 217, 372; and medicine, VI, 142
Mechlin, see Malines
Mecklenburg, duke of, VI, 126, 535
Meconium, an herb, V, 663
Medea, V, 486, VI, 349
Media, VI, 460
Medici, Alessandro de', VI, 194-5
Medici, Catherine de', V, 24, VI, 478; dedic to, V, 67, 593, VI, 130
Medici, Cosimo de', duke, V, 326, VI, 27
Medici, Francesco de', grand-duke, dedic to, VI, 325, 332
Medici, Giovanni Jacopo de', VI, 105
Medici, Giulio de', cardinal, V, 74; dedic to, V, 74, 197, 246, VI, 476
Medici, Lorenzo de', duke of Urbino, V, 246
Medici, Lorenzo the Magnificent, V, 252
Medici, Lorenzo, murderer of Alessandro, VI, 194
Medici, Marie de', queen of France, VI, 178, 554
Medici, Michele (1857), V, 39, 44
Medicine, V, 42, 113, 430-44, 588, VI, 194, 378, 456, 471, 477; amateur, V, 35; bachelor of, V, 328, VI, 520; candidate in, V, 618, VI, 127, 143; classical revived, V, 295; conclusions, V, 170; criticized, V, 35, 618; divisions of, VI, 214; doctor of, V, 61, 147, 164, 174, 179, 220, 234, 236-7, 250, 261, 273, 283, 314, 323, 328, 341, 362, 382, 385-6, 391, 403, 446, 469, 501, 609, 640, 644, 661, 666, VI, 38, 41, 69, 87, 123, 128-9, 140, 143, 169, 188, 213, 223, 229, 238, 247-8, 251, 255, 269, 298, 316, 331, 394, 399, 423, 462, 494, 520, 552-4, 559, 561; dogmatic, VI, 249-50, 519; faculty of, V, 7, 286, 288-90, 328, 483, 500, VI, 219; Hippocratic, VI, 247, and see Hippocrates; history of, V, 115, 609, VI, 207; influence on development of child, VI, 204; Italian schools of, VI,

227; licentiate in, V, 328, VI, 88, 223; magic and, V, 533, 610-11, 614, 626, 660, VI, 292, 410; medieval, V, 522-3; new, V, 438, 440, 558, 619, VI, 219, 248, called for by changed conditions, V, 665, VI, 251-2; Paracelsan, V, 438-42, 626, 638, VI, 219, 248, 252; practice of, V, 111-2, 298, 327, 341, 346, 385-6, 391, 404, 426, 466, 484, 488, 509, 563-4, 630, VI, 38, 109, 142, 228, 255, 291, 368, 394, 413, 553, 561, illicit, V, 128, 286, VI, 220; praised, V, 578; prerequisite, as a, V, 58; prerequisites for, V, 638; prognostication, V, 212, VI, 496, 553; progress, recent, VI, 353; record of cases, VI, 248, and see Consilia; reform desired, V, 416; scholastic, attacked, V, 280, 605, studied, V, 285, 346, 403, 426, 488, 652, VI, 201, 247, 597; scope of, VI, 354; sects in, VI, 248-50; taught, V, 38-39, 43, 61, 74, 90, 112, 114, 144, 205, 237, 244, 318, 385-6, 403, 430, 438, 476, 493, 501, 542, 609, 652, VI, 30, 38, 49, 54, 59, 124, 126, 141, 152-3, 210, 212, 214, 227-8, 235, 258, 287, 290, 325, 335, 340, 368, 399, 406, 461, 494, 525, 553, 561; theory of, V, 43, 325, 446, 563-4, VI, 152, 266, 289, 365, 413; traditional, VI, 567; witchcraft and, VI, 517; without a degree, V, 288-9, 356, 433, 439; works of, V, 170, 205, 542-3, VI, 38, 124, 142, 167, 217, 226-7, 230, 236, 326, 395, 553, 567; and see Compound, Physician, Simple

Medieval, see Latin, Middle Ages

Medina, duke of, VI, 128

Medina, Bartholomaeus, cited, VI, 541

Medina, Petrus, mathematician, VI, 137

Mediterranean Sea and basin, V, 26, 31, 212, VI, 273

Medium, VI, 417

Meerbeeck, P. J. van (1841), VI, 261

Meerbonen, a gem, VI, 309

Megietti, Paolo, see Meietus

Meiettus, Robertus, pr Venice, VI, 48, 159

Meietus, Antonius of Padua, pr Venice, VI, 370

Meietus, Paulus of Padua, pr Padua and Venice, V, 479, 666, VI, 370, 377, 557

Meissen, VI, 309, 490; taught at, VI, 498

Melancholy, V, 367, 444, 449, 455, 476, VI, 422; character and, VI, 510; criminal tendencies from, V, 578; delusions from, V, 87, 97, 576, 667, VI, 519, 535, 547; gem cures, VI, 305; gift of tongues from, V, 118, VI, 176, 555; in men of letters, VI, 206; length of life and, VI, 140; moves from fourth to fourth, VI, 209; power of prediction from, V, 106, 575, VI, 484, 512, denied, V, 236, VI, 504; thoughts, V, 162; vapor, VI, 571; work on, V, 530

Melanchthon, Philip, V, 378; astrology and, V, 193, 338, 361, 379-84, 393, 398-402, 405; at Tübingen, V, 379-80; Camerarius and, V, 381, 400; Carion and, V, 381-3; Chytraeus and, V, 397; cited, V, 298, 418, VI, 49, 361, 601; Copernican theory and, V, 385, VI, 43; courses given by, V, 390; Cureus and, V, 403-4; death of, VI, 502; dedic by, V, 391, 399-400; education, influence on, V, 383, 390, 402-4, and see pupils; Encelius and, V, 397, VI, 308; Gassar and, V, 390-1; Gaurico and, V, 383-4; Grynaeus and, V, 379-80; Heller and, V, 394; horoscope of, V, 401, VI, 105, 595; letters, V, 297, 375, 379, 381, 397, 399-401; Milich and, V, 387; Morshemius and, V, 402-3; Paracelsus and, V, 580-1; Peucer and, V, 384, VI, 494-5; praised, V, 404, VI, 354; prefaces of, V, 359-60, 367, 386, 392-4, 399-400; pupils of, V, 381, 384, 397, 402-4, VI, 123, stamp put on, V, 378; quoted, V, 332; Reiffenstein and, V, 386; Reinhold and, V, 385; resemblance of his circle to that of Paul III, V, 378; Schöner and, V, 393-4; Siderocrates and, VI, 123; Stifelius and, V, 392-3; Stoeffler and, V, 379; textbooks by, V, 380; tr, V, 400; Witekind and, V, 404; Wolf and, V, 383; works by, *Anima*, V, 390, 402-3, *Contra empiricos*, V, 380-1, 431, *Declamationes*, V, 368, 380-1, 386-7, 390, 393, *Eclipsium . . . descriptiones*, V, 392, *Initia doctrinae physicae*, V, 380, 385, 398, 402, VI, 20, *Orationes*, V, 379, 386, 401, *Quaestio de somniis*, V, 401

Melanelius, Matthias Theodorus, tr, V, 430
Melanthium, an herb, VI, 263
Melchiorius, Ioannes Odoricus, physician, VI, 225
Meldula, Mastrius de (1688), VI, 430-1
Melgar, Alfonso de, pr Burgos, V, 208
Melioratus, Remigius, medical, VI, 227
Meliorius, Philippus, dedic to, VI, 226
Melk, V, 366
Mellerstadt, see Polich of
Mellumcelli, fruit of a plant, VI, 261
Mellynays, VI, 453
Mèl-Monts, VI, 360
Melzi, Francesco de, V, 16
Memmingen, VI, 16
Memmius, Joh. Bapt., tr, V, 364
Mémoires de la société de Paris et de l'Ile de France, V, 483
Mémoires de la société royale de Bohéme, V, 429
Mémoires de Paquot, V, 152
Memorie e documenti per l'Università di Pavia, V, 325
Memory, artificial, VI, 361, 459; blood and, VI, 484; cause of dreams, VI, 481, 484, of sleep-walking, VI, 481; circle and, VI, 448; important for legal and medical theory, VI, 413; occult arts and, V, 220, 606, VI, 426; to sharpen, V, 434, 560, 607, VI, 429; works on, V, 605
Menabenus, Apollonius, physician, VI, 311
Mencke, *Series rerum* (1728), V, 391
Mendoza, Balthazar de, licentiate, VI, 165
Mendoza, Francesco de, cardinal, V, 582
Mendoza, Sánchez de, astrologer, VI, 166
Menelaus, *Spherica,* VI, 27
Menelbus, V, 478
Ménétrier, père, quoted, V, 111-2
Menghi, Girolamo, VI, 556, 558-9
Menghus of Faenza, VI, 209
Mengus, Justus, VI, 598
Meninges, V, 482
Mennel, Jacob (1503), VI, 488
Mercati, Michele, mineralogist, V, 7, VI, 210, 334
Mercator, Gerard, VI, 179
Mercenarius, Archangelus, V, 666, VI, 48, 370
Mercer, John, tr, VI, 447
Mercerius, Nicolaus (1586), V, 143
Merchant, V, 264, 285, 613, VI, 337
Mercure françois (1619), VI, 560
Mercurialis, Hieronymus, cited, VI, 258; *De venenis,* V, 479-81; other works, V, 479-80, 482-3; pupil of, VI, 235
Mercurio, Giovanni, VI, 438
Mercurio, Scipione, VI, 198, 222
Mercurius Trismegistus, see Hermes
Mercury, the metal, V, 458, 483, VI, 434; as a remedy, V, 651, taken internally, VI, 224, not injurious taken in small doses, VI, 313, three states and uses, V, 639, overworked, V, 459; effect on gums and saliva, V, 147; excess of, produces feeling of depression, V, 626; fixation of, V, 458; generation of, V, 125; hot or cold? V, 465; gold made from, V, 548, VI, 634; not the seed of all metals, V, 33; ointment, V, 62, 459; produced from iron, V, 546; substance of, V, 315, one of three principles, V, 626; virtues of, V, 661
Mercury, the planet, difficulty in observing, VI, 52, 70; in Copernican system, V, 424, VI, 30, 52, 70; influence of, V, 138, 177, 216, 224; oval orbit of, V, 205; position of, VI, 18; symbol of, VI, 457; theory of, VI, 20; transit of, predicted, VI, 23-24
Merenda, Antonio, (1640), VI, 177
Mérindol, Antoine, VI, 553
Merlin, birth of, V, 270
Mermaid, V, 570, VI, 279
Merode, Bernard de, VI, 196
Mersenne, Marin, VI, 452
Merula, Gaudentius, V, 249, 546-7
Merula, George, cited, VI, 402
Mesmes, Jean Iaques de, VI, 20
Mesmes, Jean Pierre de (1557), VI, 20-22
Messahala, cited, V, 120, 194, 207, 269, 348, VI, 163, 180; disagreement of Nifo with, V, 199; ed., V, 347, 395
Messiah, coming of, V, 124, VI, 445
Messias, Petrus, VI, 236
Messina, V, 594, VI, 179, 448; pr at, VI, 27
Mesue, cited, V, 502, 527, VI, 217, 252, 300, 335; comm, V, 501, VI, 400; criticized, V, 123, 439, VI, 402; defended, V, 446, 449, 452, 467; fol-

lowed, VI, 567; *Grabadin,* V, 460; life of, V, 114; not cited, VI, 318
Metal, V, 141; alive, V, 665; alteration and vitrification, VI, 243; as remedy, V, 604, VI, 230, 243, 251, 335, opposed, V, 665; composition, VI, 317; description, V, 625-6; formation, VI, 199; generation, from mercury and sulphur, V, 125, 664, VI, 310, 317, denied, V, 125, 643; germs of, VI, 317; lectures on, VI, 311; life in, V, 628; locating veins of, VI, 342; questions about, V, 144, 396, 589; relation to macrocosm, VI, 451, parts of body, V, 249, planets, V, 249, VI, 301, 317-8, rejected, VI, 317-8; smelting of, V, 396, VI, 309; spirit of, VI, 451; veins of, on mountain ridges, VI, 342; why rarer than in antiquity? V, 396-7; why unmentioned in Mosaic account of creation? VI, 347; works on, V, 396-7, 589, VI, 334
Metaphysics, V, 80, 142, VI, 368, 429; ancillary to natural magic, V, 561; taught, V, 63, 197
Meteor, V, 239, VI, 355, 490; at Vienna in 1520-1521, V, 203, 222; ferruginous rock, VI, 342; generation of, VI, 96; ignited, VI, 91; miraculous, VI, 349; purpose, VI, 367; seen by Buridan, V, 156; sign of the future, VI, 367, 489
Meteorology, V, 151, 155, 374, 642, VI, 496, 533-4; new, of Gilbert, VI, 380; works on, VI, 103, 377, 490; and see Aristotle, Weather
Meteoroscopium, an instrument, V, 372, 584, VI, 25
Metham, John, V, 673
Method, V, 11; alone new, VI, 186; and knowledge not to be sought simultaneously, V, 641; in astronomy, VI, 82-83; in botany, see Botany; in medicine, VI, 567; in teaching, VI, 564; mathematical, V, 583; need of, felt, V, 11; of Cornelius Gemma, VI, 406, 409; of investigating demons, V, 82; of sixteenth century learning, attacked, VI, 565; Ramian, criticized, VI, 238-9; too much attention to, VI, 239; and see Hypothesis, Scholasticism, Scientific
Methodic sect in medicine, VI, 249
Metoposcopy, V, 587, VI, 170, 176-7, 503-6, 509-10; called false, VI, 193; licit, VI, 527
Metz, V, 127, 131-2, 153, 313, 431, 434, VI, 219; died at, VI, 504; pr at, V, 433, 504
Meung, see Odo of
Meunier, Léon, (1893), V, 493
Meurer, Christopher, (1587), VI, 49, 366
Meurer, Wolfgang, (1513-1585), VI, 49-50, 267, 366-7
Mexico, VI, 436
Meyer, Ernst von, V, 650
Michael, archangel, VI, 551; spirit of the sun, V, 569, VI, 441
Michael of Breslau, V, 173
Michael of Ephesus, VI, 478
Michael de Petrasancta, see Petransancta
Michael Scot, V, 569; *Chiromancy,* V, 675, 678; cited, V, 166, 523; forbidden, VI, 164; *Phisionomia,* V, 54, 63-64, 167
Michael a Vislicza, astrologer, V, 173
Michaud, M. M. *Biographie universelle,* VI, 130, 537, 600
Michel, Claude, pr Tournon, VI, 169
Michelius, Josephus (1597), V, 648
Microchronicon . . . des Rektors Haftiz, V, 202
Microcosm, V, 28, 101, 135, 164, 249, 263, 300-1, 322, 409, 510, 521, 553-4, 626, 628, 639, 649-51, VI, 25, 75-76, 141, 143, 367, 381, 407, 443, 451, 457, 463
Microscope, antedated, V, 22; disappointing effect of, VI, 296
Micyllus, Iacobus, VI, 596
Middelburg, V, 648; and see Paul of
Middle ages, as dark ages, VI, 382; authors little cited, V, 473, 480, 485; conspiracy of silence against, V, 4, 421; continued interest in, V, 263, VI, 399; ignorance of, V, 18, 336, 463, VI, 261-5, 271; medicine and science of, attacked or belittled, V, 52, 494; prejudice against, V, 500, not shared by Cardan, V, 565; Regiomontanus and, V, 336-7; and see Classical reaction
Middleton, see Richard of
Midsummer night, VI, 295
Mid-wife, V, 58, 302, 381, 511, 561; for-

bidden to practise medicine, VI, 220; performs baptism, V, 510
Miedis, Bernardinus Gomesius, VI, 282
Mieli, Aldo (1914), V, 544
Migliorati, see Melioratus
Milan, V, 16, 33, 70, 96, 247, 457, 565, VI, 213, 311, 368, 488, 596; astrologer expelled from, V, 162; duke of, VI, 542; exorcist of, VI, 558; Index of, VI, 146; inn at, V, 613; Inquisition in, VI, 149; medical college of, V, 470-1; patrician of, VI, 336; pest at, V, 161-2; pr at, V, 159, 543, VI, 162, 506, 558; route from, V, 615; taught at, V, 547, VI, 213; visited, VI, 505
Mile, German and Italian, V, 615
Miletus, N., V, 125
Milianus, Baldassar, V, 75-77
Milich, Jakob, V, 360, 380, 382, 385-90, 405; cited, V, 298, VI, 49, 194; comm. Pliny, V, 386-8; ed., V, 359; geniture, V, 385, VI, 595; oration by, V, 386, VI, 147; *Propositiones medicae,* V, 387; put on Index, VI, 147
Military affairs, V, 143; and see Engineering, War
Milk, dried up, VI, 546; increased, VI, 320; soured, V, 476
Milky Way, V, 306, 553, 570, VI, 74, 364, 367, 408
Mill, V, 584; wheel, V, 594
Millefolium, V, 451
Millegrana, an herb, VI, 265
Mind, see Intellect, Soul
Mine, Miner and Mining, V, 133, 397, 540; alum, V, 457; arsenic, V, 458; copper, V, 598; diseases of, V, 442; German, VI, 308; gnomes in, V, 628; gold, V, 33; gypsum, V, 457; lighted, V, 584; output predicted, V, 392; silver, V, 125; spirits in, VI, 425, 525; wealth from, VI, 116
Mineral and Mineralogy, VI, 319, 385; classification, VI, 269, 307, 320; collection, VI, 269; and see Bath
Minerva, Paul, (1616), VI, 63-64, 487-8
Minimum, V, 40
Minium, V, 451-2
Minsingerus, Joachim, VI, 596
Mint, V, 483
Miracle, V, 567, VI, 22, 416, 439, 444; belittled by witchcraft delusion, VI, 529; Cana, of, VI, 496; ceased, VI, 529, with coming of Christ, VI, 550; Christ, of, V, 107, 109, 273, VI, 342, 427; demon, see Demon; denied, VI, 336; disregarded, V, 96; divine, VI, 408, 534, 540; explained, V, 103; flood a, V, 36; four kinds distinguished, VI, 434; limits to, VI, 496; magic, V, 573; natural, V, 99, VI, 513; questioned, VI, 570; recent, VI, 468; religion dependent on, V, 108; stars, from, see Star; supernatural, V, 236, VI, 416
Mirandola, V, 55; pr at, V, 164; see Pico della
Mirandolano, Antonio Bernardo, VI, 411, 432, 544
Mirror, VI, 419; concave, V, 554; divining, VI, 502; magic, V, 103, 132, VI, 147, 243, 421, 434, forbidden, VI, 147; magnifying, VI, 595; marvelous, VI, 154; telescopic, VI, 421
Misaldus, see Mizaldus
Miscellany, V, 113, 208
Missile, see Motion, violent
Misy, V, 450, VI, 310
Mithridatic, antidote, V, 471, 598, VI, 225, 230, 258
Mittag-Leffler (1914), VI, 459
Mittarelli, G. B. (1779), VI, 377
Mitteilungen des Coppernicus Vereins, V, 353, 409
Mitteilungen des Vereins für Geschichte der Stadt Nürnberg, V, 337
Mitteilungen zur Geschichte der Medizin, V, 385
Mizaldus or Mizauld, Ant. V, 299-301, VI, 127-8; cited, V, 327, VI, 18, 50, 311, 559, 569; criticized, VI, 184; medicinal secrets by, VI, 216, 429; poem, V, 286
Mocenigo, denouncer of Bruno, VI, 427
Mockius, Jacobus, cited, VI, 319
Modena, V, 257, 269, VI, 268, 364, 373; bishop of, VI, 158; citizen of, see Scotus, Octavian; duke of, V, 169
Modern, anatomists criticized, V, 516; cited, V, 55, 157, VI, 92; degeneracy, VI, 252, 538; follow Campanus, V, 408; follow Galen and authorities too much, V, 500; juniors, V, 185; progress

over ancients, in medicine, V, 46, VI, 461, in science, VI, 20-21, 353
Modern Language Notes, VI, 318
Modernity, misclaimed, V, 18-19, 493
Moehsen, J. C. W. (1783), VI, 245
Moenius, Eusebius, VI, 597
Moenius, Georgius, VI, 597
Moerbeke, see William of
Moffett, Thomas, naturalist, V, 7, VI, 268, 284-5, 308
Mohammed, conjunction preceding advent of, V, 120
Mohammedanism, VI, 495; union with, portended, V, 271
Moibanus, Ioannes, V, 475
Moiebanus, astrologer, VI, 136
Moldenarius, Christian (1616), VI, 506
Mole, V, 608
Moletius, Joseph, cited, VI, 57
Molfetta, bishop of, V, 472
Molinius, Antonius, V, 67-68, 542, VI, 485, 510
Molitor, Ulric, cited, VI, 524, 602
Moll, A. (1877), V, 181, 331
Moller, Johannes, (1699), VI, 124, 524
Mollerus, Thobias, astrologer, VI, 253
Molnar, Albert von, (1621), VI, 191
Moloch, V, 647
Molucca islands, V, 355, VI, 276, 345
Mömpelgard, see Montbeliard
Monad, VI, 396, 450, 457
Monantheuil, Henri de, VI, 141-2
Monardes, Nic. V, 468, VI, 235, 275, 319, 333
Monastery, V, 310, 343, 373, 440, 517, 619, VI, 178; English dissolution of, V, 7; imperial, VI, 414; of Lazarus, V, 525
Mönch, Walter, (1933), V, 118-9
Mondeville, see Henry of
Money, booklet giving value of, V, 329; Copernicus on, V, 426
Moneylender, VI, 187
Mongoose, V, 476
Monhemius, Ioannes (1542), V, 153-4
Monk, V, 658, VI, 511, 559; fables of, VI, 498, 530; given to alchemy, VI, 440; mistress of, V, 526
Monk, Francis, astrologer, VI, 194
Monnel, see Monvel
Monoceros, VI, 323-4, 410
Monoculus, V, 46
Mons, V, 207, VI, 211
Mons Sanctae Mariae, V, 218
Monsieur, see Dog, Agrippa's
Monster, V, 598, VI, 290, 297, 413, 453; faith in, increased by voyages of discovery, VI, 275; generation of, V, 247-8, VI, 571, monstrous births, V, 47, 509-10, 517, VI, 283, 287, 401-2, 408-9, 490-1, 571; mouthless, VI, 281; not caused by stars, VI, 203; moral, V, 393; races, VI, 275, 408; works on, VI, 286-7; and see Aldrovandi
Montagnana, Bartholomaeus de, VI, 209, 317, 402
Montaigne, VI, 561
Montalbanus, Ovidius, naturalist, VI, 289, 294
Montanus, Ioannes, pr Nürnberg, V, 358, 365, 367, 369, 395-6, VI, 490
Montanus, Joh. Bapt. V, 524, 641, VI, 224, 228, 231, 365
Montanus, Joh. Scultetus, Paracelsan, VI, 224
Montbéliard, VI, 331; count of, VI, 76, 462; pr at, V, 623, VI, 96, 145
Montefiore, VI, 127
Montegius, Philip, astronomer, VI, 15
Montescutolo, see Pacino da
Monteux, Jerome, see Montuus, Hier.
Montferrat, V, 28; duke of, V, 645; prince of, V, 250
Month, length of lunar, V, 122; lucky and unlucky, VI, 221
Montis, Thomas, astrologer, V, 206-7
Montluçon, V, 299
Montpellier, bishop of, VI, 257; chancellor of, VI, 220; first book pr at, V, 160; friends at, VI, 267; physician of, VI, 304, 510; studied at, V, 111, 391, 431, VI, 248, 561; taught at, V, 112, VI, 340, 561; theses at, VI, 222-3
Mont Royal, VI, 459
Montuus, Hieronymus, V, 125
Montuus, Sebastian, V, 501
Monvel, Nicolas, VI, 473
Moon, ants and, V, 464; attraction of earth on, VI, 62; auguries and, VI, 486; Copernican theory as to, V, 428-9; covered with water, V, 32; critical days and, V, 260-1; demons and, VI, 486; distance of, VI, 20; elements surrounding, V, 32; halo about, V, 399;

illumination of, V, 32, 417-8; in conjunction of 1564, V, 248; influence of, V, 122, 249, 417-8, VI, 128, 429, on birth of Moses, V, 222, in bleeding and pharmacy, V, 315, on earth's surface, VI, 343, on eggs, V, 572, on humors, VI, 192, on mania, V, 242, in purging and surgery, V, 121, in twelve signs, VI, 128, 485, on Vanini, VI, 571; intelligence of, V, 90-91; latitude of, VI, 15; magnitude of, V, 411; mansions of, V, 284, 292, 356, 557, VI, 124, 427, 508; moist, VI, 180; movement of, V, 200, 412, VI, 62; night and, VI, 182; observation of, VI, 53; prediction from, V, 195; theory of, VI, 29, 59

Moon milch, a gem, VI, 320

Moonstone, suspension of, V, 249

Mopsus, VI, 504

Moralizing, VI, 277, 447

Moravus, Augustinus, astrologer, V, 333-5

Morbach, Achates (1553), V, 618

Morbeth cardinalis, V, 54

Morbus gallicus, see Syphilis

More, Sir Thomas, and astrology, V, 176

Morellus, Federicus, pr Paris, V, 607-8, 623, VI, 216

Moreri, Louis, VI, 247

Moretus, Matthaeus, V, 450

Morhard, Ulrich, pr Tübingen, V, 225, 264, 372, VI, 3

Morhart, Huldenrichus, see Morhard, Ulrich

Morhof, D. G. (1732), VI, 190-1, 199, 377

Morienus Romanus, cited, V, 538, 604, 623-4, 633; ed., V, 622

Morin, Jean Baptiste, (1583-1656), VI, 178

Morin, Jehan, pr Paris, V, 287

Morley, Henry (1854), V, 563, VI, 152

Morone, Girolamo, VI, 162

Morshemius, Joh. Merc., V, 402-3

Mosellanus, V, 176

Moselle river, VI, 255

Moses the lawgiver, V, 15, 203, 403, VI, 75, 353, 435, 454, 514; account of creation, VI, 85, 433; cited, VI, 451; horoscope of, V, 221

Moses Arovas (Rova, Rouas), tr, VI, 449

Moses of Gerunda (Gerona), astrologer, V, 220

Mosheim, Rupert à, VI, 597

Moslem, VI, 532

Mosquito, V, 327, VI, 429

Moth, to protect from, V, 147

Mother, V, 83

Motion, V, 40-41, 151, 583, VI, 12, 350, 410; Benedetti on, VI, 372; circular, V, 423, VI, 384; direct, VI, 372; finite and infinite, VI, 599; free and necessary, VI, 385; heat and, V, 207, VI, 370; in vacuum, VI, 357; local, V, 17; of one carrying weights, V, 146; perpetual, V, 32, 580, VI, 144, 385, 434, of simple body, VI, 43, 46; velocity of falling body, V, 254, 565, 585-6, 594, VI, 365, 369, 372, 387; violent, V, 48-49, 144; and see Sphere

Motta, (1891), V, 161

Moufetus, see Moffett, Thomas

Moulin, Antoine du, see Molinius

Mountain, at poles, V, 495; formation of, V, 26-27, 156, 592-3, VI, 312, 343; gnomes in, V, 628; haunt of witches, VI, 525; height of, V, 23, 25, 26-27, 591, VI, 50, 366, 380; herb, see Herb; in the hand, V, 527, VI, 164, 459; refuge from flood, V, 193, 202, 222; shape of, V, 593; suspended, VI, 342; travel in, V, 614

Mountebank, V, 618, VI, 421; and see Quack

Mouse, VI, 416

Mouth, holding things in, against pest, V, 608, poison, VI, 315; thirst, V, 611; to help teeth, VI, 311

Mucius, Achilles, VI, 458

Mugwort, V, 483

Mule, born of a mule, V, 510

Mulelavellus, Hieronymus, V, 77

Mülhausen, V, 383

Mullein leaves, VI, 295

Müller, Adolf, (1918), V, 391, 411, 413

Muller, Samuel, VI, 184

Mumia, V, 455, 639, 659; of a red-headed man violently slain, V, 650

Münch, E. (1826), V, 352

Münchner Beiträge z. Gesch. u. Lit. d.

Naturwiss. u. Medizin, V, 501
Mundella, Aloysius, V, 446-7, 452-8, VI, 315; *Annotationes,* V, 446, 450, 454-5; *Epistolae,* V, 446, 450, 454, 456-7; Index to Galen, V, 609
Mundinus, attempt to distinguish others of same name, V, 500-1; Carpi on, V, 499-500, 505; cited, V, 54, 518; comm. V, 46; criticized, V, 501, 515; defended, V, 499, 521; followed, V, 44, 499, 516; forbidden, V, 500; humanistic criticism of, V, 500-1; ignored by Vesalius, V, 519, 525; misunderstood, V, 521-2; more independent than Arabs of Galen, V, 499-500; pr, V, 501, 521; text corrupt or restored, V, 500, 505, 521; variation from, V, 509
Munich, pr at, V, 625
Münster, VI, 457
Münster, Ladislaus, (1933), V, 39, 46
Münster, Sebastian, V, 288, 331
Müntz et Fabre, (1887), V, 407
Muntz, Johann, astrologer, V, 160
Munzius, Hieronymus, cited, VI, 382
Muraena or Murena, VI, 281, 416
Muratori, *Scriptores,* V, 234
Murner, Thomas, V, 434-5
Muscle, double, V, 517; intercostal, V, 531; membrane enveloping entire body, V, 518; moving tongue, V, 518, 531; of abdomen, V, 516, eye, V, 531, eyelid, V, 530, hand, V, 527, 531, head, V, 531, jaw, V, 530, nose, V, 508, 530, stomach, V, 505, thigh, V, 531; others, V, 518; work of Galen on dissection of, not read by Vesalius, V, 530
Muscovy, VI, 342
Museum, VI, 296; Aldrovandi's, VI, 270, 289; Guilandinus's, V, 336; Kentmann's, VI, 269; of natural history, at Bologna, V, 247, at Copenhagen, VI, 269, 311; other private collections, V, 598
Mushroom, VI, 335
Music, Musical and Musician, V, 524, 581, VI, 470; affects the body, VI, 234; demon and, VI, 234; designation, VI, 450; horoscopes of, VI, 100, 597; imperial choristers at Valladolid and Toledo, V, 582; medicine and, V, 431, VI, 142; of cardinals, V, 582; Taisnier on, V, 583-4; taught, V, 582; works on, V, 174, VI, 344, 373; and see Instrument
Musk, VI, 230
Mussel, VI, 285
Mustela, William, theologian, V, 299
Muteau, Chas. (1882), V, 311, VI, 341
Myconius, teacher at Zurich, VI, 8
Myliander, Stephanus, pr Rostock, VI, 39
Mylius, J. pr Würzburg, V, 560
Mylius, Martin (1582), V, 387
Myrrh, V, 650, VI, 416, 558
Myrtle, a sprig of, V, 610
Mystery play, V, 125
Mystic, Mystical and Mysticism, V, 631, VI, 374, 437, 443-4, 456-7, 601
Myth and Mythology, V, 642, VI, 278

Naaman, VI, 356
Nabod, Valentin, VI, 598, *Astronomicarum institutionum,* V, 155, VI, 40; comm. Ptolemy, *Quadripartitum,* VI, 115, 120-2; *Enarratio,* VI, 119-20; tragic death, VI, 121-3
Naiboda, see Nabod
Nail, finger-, divination from, V, 574, VI, 167-8, 479, 502, 508; monstrous, VI, 269; when to cut, VI, 167, 221, 429
Name and Names, of, angel and demon, VI, 439, 444, 556-7; animal, VI, 356; assumed, V, 74; barbaric, VI, 439, 444; bird, V, 3, 256, 271, VI, 494; classical, interest in, V, 3; diabolical, VI, 536; divination from, VI, 287, 473, 496; fish, VI, 494; gem, VI, 303; God, VI, 444, 454; herb, V, 3, 651, VI, 332; Jesus, VI, 405, 434; mythological, astrological and magical, VI, 460; no key to natures of things, VI, 565; Paracelsan, V, 649; philosophers' stone, V, 603; place, V, 610, 615-6; superstitious, VI, 516; taken in the, of, VI, 320; vernacular, VI, 273; virtues of, VI, 427
Nancy, V, 112, VI, 457
Nantes, witchcraft at, VI, 526
Naphtha, V, 466, VI, 416

Naples, V, 231, 455; born at, VI, 418; city of, V, 74, 93, 118, 142, 221, 254, 582, 585, VI, 214, 245, 335, 398; export to, VI, 209; fled from, VI, 427; kingdom of, V, 93, 179, 183, 335, 341, 533, 541; of, V, 17, 211, 259, 273-4, VI, 155; patrician of, V, 75-76; pr at, V, 73, 79, 182-3, 187-8, 200, 211, 220, 253, 273, 541, VI, 63, 129, 162, 260, 273, 289, 370, 418, 422, 487; taught at, VI, 226, 492, 599; university of, V, 45, 63, 73, 144, VI, 63, 214; written from, V, 229, VI, 42, 260, 527
Napurg, Georg, letter to, V, 343
Narbonne, V, 115, 269
Narcotic, V, 438
Nardi, G. M. (1938), V, 479
Narni, see Galeotto Marzio da
Nassau, VI, 433
Natalis, Hieronymus, V, 96
Natalis, Petrus, a patient, V, 302
Nationalism and Nationality, V, 12; due to stars, V, 247-8; influence on temperament, VI, 204
Nativities, V, 167, 170, 282-3, 434, 557-8, VI, 36, 199, 430, 469; approved, V, 276-7, 312, 318, 361-2, 398-9, VI, 114, 155, 169, 298, 500, 504; based on likeness, VI, 422; collections of, V, 345, VI, 99-101, 104-5, 507; determined by chiromancy, VI, 431, by physiognomy, VI, 452, from temperaments, V, 66; forbidden, VI, 157; individual horoscopes, Agrippa, V, 138, Benedetti, VI, 138, Charles V, V, 588, Clement VII, V, 230, Cocles, V, 50, Cureus, VI, 366, Cutica, V, 162, Duchastel, V, 311, Farnese, V, 267, Gemma Frisius, VI, 102, Gregory XIII, VI, 156, Gugler, V, 371, de Heu, V, 434, Leo X, V, 253, Cosimo de' Medici, V, 326, Milich, V, 385, Nabod, VI, 122-3, Paduanius, VI, 124, Peletier, VI, 33, Peurbach, VI, 17, Pirckheimers, V, 351-2, Raimondo, VI, 474, Regiomontanus, V, 565, Rovere, V, 274, Schöner, V, 367, Vitalis, V, 241, Wolf, VI, 113, Zabarella, VI, 370; method of drawing up, V, 176, VI, 103, 435; of cities, ridiculous, VI, 204, unknown, V, 191; of illustrious men, V, 170-1, VI, 30, 100-1, 104-5, 131, 193-6, 595-8; of long-lived, V, 588; of prince, V, 267-8, 274, 326, 384, VI, 15, 52, 70, 121, 126-7, 142, 160-1, 210, 509; of prophet, V, 510, VI, 173, 408; opposed, V, 140, 250, 661, VI, 32, 45, 144, 187, 197, 359, 412, 504; own, VI, 33; papal, V, 246, VI, 105, 156; prediction from, V, 251, 311, 313, VI, 116, 173; put on Index, VI, 148; rectified or verified, VI, 104, 115, 194, 204, by time of conception, V, 242; relation to conjunctions, V, 225, to eclipses, VI, 111; revolution of, V, 58, 246, 251, 260, 266-7, VI, 101, 114, 131, 133, 165, 430, 448; tested, VI, 193-6; use in history, V, 565-6, in medicine, V, 250, 315, VI, 159, 165; works on, V, 328, 363-4, 367-9, 394-5, 521, VI, 111, 131, 479
Natural place, doctrine of, V, 24, 40, 495, 594, VI, 12, 348, 365
Nature, VI, 268, 368-9; animate, see Vitalism; art and, V, 512, 571; attitude towards, V, 139-58, of da Vinci, V, 36; balks our curiosity, VI, 297, 566; bizarre, VI, 287; changed since antiquity, V, 665; continuity of, V, 495, VI, 424, 564; demoniacal, VI, 378; freak of, see Monster; interest in, V, 204-5, VI, 339, 347, 562-3, 566; ladder of, VI, 384-5, 398-9, 426; law and order in, denied, V, 628, 655; light of, V, 441; never idle, V, 592; principles of, V, 151, 394, 538, VI, 384, 395, 410; questions about, V, 143-7, VI, 400, 402-3, 428; regular or bizarre, VI, 390; sense of, V, 571; sentient, V, 495
Naudé, Gabriel, V, 231, VI, 510; (1625), V, 102, VI, 132; (1645), V, 71, 77-78, 178, 181; (1647), VI, 196, 493
Nausea, Frederick, V, 321-2, VI, 491-2
Navalius, Petrus Arnaldus, preface to, VI, 133
Navarre, V, 616; queen of, V, 287, VI, 220, 472; war in, V, 174
Navgerius, Bernardus, cardinal, dedic to, VI, 208
Navigation, V, 571, VI, 157; and see Voyage
Navò, Curtius Troianus, pr Venice, V, 94, VI, 100
Nazari, G. B. (1572), V, 625, 679-95

Neander, Michael (1583), **V**, 417 (1561), **VI**, 30
Nebuchadnezzar, VI, 356-7, 534
Nebula, VI, 110
Nebular hypothesis, VI, 348
Necessity, V, 28, VI, 453; fatal denied, V, 242, 552, 581, suggested, V, 310; and see Fate
Neckam, Alexander, VI, 391
Necromancy, V, 58, 136, 433-4, VI, 107-8, 154, 421, 426, 468, 499, 509, 516, 520, 549; accusations of, V, 635, VI, 150, 405, 408, 439; condemned, V, 32-33, 296, 321, 660, VI, 169, 180, 193, 411, 430, 464, 534; diabolical, V, 92, 166, 477, VI, 135, 532; divisions of, VI, 502; false, VI, 193, 411; put on Index, VI, 146-7, 151; should not include astronomical magic or divination, VI, 468; true and a science, VI, 132; unknown, VI, 477
Necyomantia, VI, 502
Negro, V, 34, VI, 276
Nemesius, cited, VI, 256
Neocoro, L. (1697), VI, 269, 311
Neo-Platonism, VI, 374, 426, 449; and demons, V, 82, VI, 425
Neoterici, V, 395, 464; criticized, V, 261; and see Modern
Nephritis, a stone, VI, 315
Nereid, V, 143
Nero, emperor, a moral monster, V, 393; praised, V, 578
Nerve and Nervous system, V, 46, VI, 292, 327
Netherlands, V, 189, 328-9, VI, 185, 211, 394; Grand Council of, V, 128
Nettesheim, see Agrippa of
Nettles, V, 462
Neubecker, Conrad, VI, 190
Neuber, Ulric, pr Nürnberg, V, 358, 365, 367, 369, 395-6, VI, 490
Neu-Brandenburg, VI, 104
Neuburg on the Danube, pr at, V, 369
Neuenburg (Switzerland), pr at, V, 666
Neustadt an der Hardt, pr and taught at, VI, 41
Neuwaldt, Hermann, disciple of Wier, VI, 517
Nevers, V, 666
New Batavia, VI, 319
New England, VI, 436
New Granada, VI, 436
New World, see Voyages of Discovery
News, craving for, V, 287
Newton, Sir Isaac, V, 388, VI, 381
Newton, Thomas, tr, V, 608
Nicander, followed, V, 477
Nicaragua, VI, 436
Nicephorus, V, 348
Nicetas, cited, **VI**, 48, 56, 63
Nicholas of Cusa, V, 23, 34, 344, 409; cited, V, 166, VI, 432, 459; criticized, V, 336; on divine numbers, VI, 441; praised, VI, 424; *Static Experiments*, V, 637, VI, 421
Nicholas of Florence (Niccolò Bertrucci), V, 437, 480, 502-4, 513
Nicholas of Lyra, cited, V, 507, VI, 361
Nicias, defeat of, VI, 192
Nicodemo, *Addizioni*, V, 229, VI, 492
Nicolas de Heu, nativity of, V, 434
Nicolaus aggregator, V, 503
Nicolaus de Bousuit (1528), V, 147
Nicolaus de Schadeck, V, 320
Nicolaus Donis, Germanus, V, 342
Nicolaus, Gerardus, pr Antwerp, V, 208
Nicolaus Nicoli, V, 504
Nicolaus a Nova Villa, dedic to, V, 296
Nicolinis de Sabio, Petrus et Ioan. Maria de, prs Venice, V, 558
Nicostrata, VI, 504
Nicuesa, Hilarius (1639), VI, 559
Nidde, VI, 461
Nidepontanus, see John of Pontigny or Niedbruck
Nider, Johann, cited, VI, 531
Niedbruck, see Pontigny
Nifo, Agostino, V, 49, 439, VI, 511; allusions to own writings, V, 78-81, 205; career, V, 71-74; cited, V, 198, 213, 226-7, 317, 328, VI, 131, 159, 370, 512; criticized, V, 199, 204, 208-11, 315, VI, 184, 510; dedic and preface to, V, 472; Leo X and, see Leo X; Pigghe and, see Pigghe; plagiarism by, V, 85, 187; Pomponazzi and, V, 94-95, 97-98, 196; praised, V, 197; works, *Auguriis*, VI, 447, 484-6, *Commentaries*, V, 72-75, 79-81, 183-6, 254, *Demonibus*, V, 72, 75-78, 80-85, 89, *Diebus criticis*, V, 78-79, 162-3, VI, 485, *Falsa diluvii prognosticatione*, V, 178, 182-4, 186-9, 193-7, VI, 486, cited or replied to, V, 197-9, 204, 208-9, 222-3, 227, *Figuris stellarum helionoricis*, V, 73, 183, 188-

9, VI, 487, *Immortalitate animae,* V, 97-98, *Intellectu,* V, 72, 75-78, 80, 82, 98, *Metap. quaest.,* V, 72-73, 504, *Meteor.,* VI, 486, *Nostrarum calamitatum causis,* V, 71-72, 80, 163-4, 184-6, VI, 486, 492, *Opuscula moralia et politica,* V, 178, *Primi motoris infinitate,* V, 72, *Re aulica,* V, 205, *Regnandi peritia,* V, 187, *Sensu agente,* V, 71-72, translations, V, 72-74, *Verissimis temporum signis,* V, 7, VI, 486-7

Nigidius Figulus, VI, 183

Nigrinus, G. pr Prag, VI, 474

Nigrisolus Carpensis, Galasius, V, 59

Nigromancer and Nigromancy, V, 88, 627, VI, 598; astrology and, VI, 16; opposed, V, 283, VI, 534; reputation as, V, 256; and see Necromancy

Nile, V, 19-20, 31; flows uphill, VI, 342; inundation of, V, 493; all water passes through, V, 22, 26, 30

Nîmes, university of, VI, 340, 503

Nimwegen, VI, 29

Ninove, see Baldwin of

Niphus, Augustinus, see Nifo, Agostino

Nitre, VI, 299; as a remedy, V, 651; generation of, V, 125; in mineral waters, VI, 209

Nivellius, Sebastianus, pr or bookseller, Paris, VI, 343-4

Nivernois, history of, VI, 202

Noah, VI, 75, 353, 464; ark of, VI, 347, 451; domestic school of, VI, 498; see Flood, Rainbow

Nobility and Noble, V, 112, 259, 274, 302, 465, 539, 606, 621, VI, 136, 153-4, 522, 550; as patients, V, 518, VI, 248; collect recipes and secrets, VI, 218; dedic to, V, 155, 310, VI, 128; harmed less by witches, VI, 524; of animals, VI, 277; prediction concerning, V, 230; student, V, 225

Nodé, Pierre (1578), VI, 524

Noens, Franc. Rassius, V, 556

Nola, V, 73, 144

Nola, Giov. Andrea, physician, VI, 213

Nolthius or Noltius, Andreas, VI, 78, 184

Nomancy, Nomandia or Nomantia, V, 58, VI, 430, 471, 473-4; forbidden, VI, 147, 471

Nomenclature, see Name

Nonius, Petrus, see Nunes, Pedro

Norfolk, V, 374

Norican Alps, VI, 409

Noricum, V, 373

Norway, V, 376, VI, 136, 536

Nose, muscles of, V, 508

Nosebleed, to check, V, 147, 462, 612

Nostradamus, cited, V, 636, VI, 170, 180

Notory art, condemned, V, 120, 141, 220, 283, 606, VI, 146, 430, 516

Notices et Extraits, V, 70, 283, 447, 454, VI, 101

Nourrisson, J. F. (1875), V, 85, 183, 187

Nourry, Claude, pr Paris, V, 309

Nova Francia, VI, 436

Novara, V, 269, 547; and see Campanus of, Domenico Maria

Novatian heresy, VI, 427

Novenaria, denied, VI, 138

Noviomagus, ed. Bede, VI, 487

Nozze Cristini-Zani (1901), V, 173

Numa Pompilius, VI, 521

Number, assigned to planets and signs, VI, 473; divination from, VI, 496; equivalent for letter of alphabet, V, 135, 538-9, VI, 362, 378, 464, 471, 473; mysticism, V, 243, VI, 110-11, 139, 350, 442, 444, 457-8; observance of, VI, 520; of candles or Psalm, VI, 148; perfect, VI, 76, 458; significance, VI, 202, 407, 499; varieties, VI, 378-9; virtue, V, 135, 561, VI, 198, 234, 358, 426, 464-5, denied or questioned, V, 491, 495, VI, 206, 378-9, 559; works on, VI, 441-2, 454; One, VI, 438, 442; Two, V, 135, VI, 438; Three, V, 634, VI, 169, 221, 281, 378, 404, 406, 438, 453, 464; Four, V, 297, VI, 454, 458, 464; Five, VI, 441-2, 454, 459; Six, V, 373, 414, VI, 350, 441-2, 450, 465; Seven, V, 491, VI, 139-40, 292, 356-8, 425, 450, 459, 464-5; Nine, VI, 350, 465; other particular numbers, VI, 357, 442, 450, 458, 461, 465, 509-10

Numidia, V, 229

Nun and Nunnery, V, 10, 351, VI, 335

Nunes, Pedro, VI, 102; criticism of Copernicus, VI, 35, Finè, V, 292-3, Pigghe, V, 282, Regiomontanus, VI, 35, Reinhold, VI, 36, Werner, VI, 35-36; himself criticized, VI, 137; works, *Annotationes,* V, 407, VI, 35, *Arte navigandi,* V, 282, 407, VI, 35, *Crepus-*

culis, V, 421, *Erratis Orontii,* V, 292-3
Nuñez, see Nunes
Núñez de Zamora, astrologer, VI, 166
Nuova Antologia, VI, 338
Nuovo archivio Veneto, V, 44
Nuovo giornale botanico, V, 29
Nürnberg, V, 370, 383, 414, 439, 657-8, VI, 59, 126, 255; astronomy and mathematics at, V, 337-41, 343-4, 354-5, 360, 366, 412, 426, VI, 17; attitude towards Paracelsus, V, 380, 439-40, Regiomontanus, V, 338-9; born at, V, 349, 369, VI, 597; citizen of, V, 348, 351, VI, 536; council, see senate, gymnasium at, V, 394; Heller has to leave, V, 396; map of, V, 348; patrician of, V, 359, 400, 472, 542; pest at, V, 354; pr at, V, 159, 210, 258, 328, 334, 339-41, 347, 349, 353-4, 356-65, 367-9, 392, 395-6, 413, 421, 433, 440-1, 536-7, 545, VI, 84, 91, 101, 126, 134, 302-3, 441, 448, 490; senate of, V, 360, 366, 368, 380, 440, VI, 91; studied at, V, 383; university a failure, V, 338, 393; war and flood at, VI, 499
Nurse, wet, V, 316
Nut, V, 146; tree, V, 578
Nutius, pr Antwerp, VI, 395
Nutmeg, V, 467
Nutrition, VI, 355, 369; and see Food
Nux Indica, V, 449
Nux methel, V, 449
Nux vomica, V, 449
Nymph, V, 628, 639
Nynauld, J. de (1615), VI, 547

Oak, V, 146; and see Acorn
Oakfern, V, 483
Oath, V, 52
Obelisk, moving an, V, 595
Oberschwyz, V, 440
Obicius, Hyppolitus (1605), VI, 429-31
Obsequens, Julius, VI, 488
Observation, V, 581, VI, 374, 382-3, 562; alone, V, 416, 441; ancient preferred to medieval, V, 337; anatomical, V, 47, 499-500, 506-9, 517; astrological, V, 216, VI, 99, 111, 159, 174; astrological medicine, in, V, 163, 302, VI, 210; astronomical, VI, 3, Brahe, V, 11, 366, VI, 53-54, 64, 68, 70, Copernicus, V, 412, 425-7, VI, 3-4, 16-17, 37, 45-46, 52-53, Ptolemy, V, 422, 425, VI, 3, 13, 35, Regiomontanus and Walther, V, 339, 366, 376, 426, Reinhold's lack of, VI, 4-5, of others, V, 190, 257, 264, 426, 490, VI, 13-15, 23-24, 28-29, 42, 61, 77, 79-82, 92, disagree, VI, 184; botanical, V, 123, 452, VI, 270, 295, 332-3; chiromantical, VI, 160, 507; clinical, V, 442, 517, 629; mineralogical, V, 597-8, VI, 306, 319-20; of Cardan, V, 569; of dreams, VI, 480; of foreheads, VI, 505; of Leonardo da Vinci, V, 17, 18, 26-29; zoological, VI, 268-9, 281, 283, 290,
Observatory, astronomical, V, 324, 344, VI, 17, 25, 158
Occamist, V, 149
Ockham, William, VI, 369; cited, VI, 48; criticized, VI, 365; edited, V, 199-200
Occult, interest in, V, 13-14, 126, 129-36, 442, 527, 605, VI, 155, 220, 371, 394, 399, 452, 502, 530
Occult science of past fouled by posterity and Satan, V, 262
Occult virtue, V, 473, VI, 230-5, 369, 540, 546; accepted, V, 101, 123, 299, 420, 462, 527, 550, 556, 573, 599, 626, 646, VI, 186, 199, 204-6, 209, 241, 277, 293-4, 306, 316, 336, 385, 392, 406-7, 419, 424, 434, 460, 468, 548, 601-2; Agrippa on, V, 135; belittled, V, 494; cure particular diseases, V, 457; difficulties regarding, V, 661-2, VI, 91, not all true, VI, 416, not mentioned by Aristotle, VI, 432, can it affect a particular member? V, 663-4; discussed by Erastus, V, 661-4, by Scaliger, VI, 293; doubted, VI, 91; explained, as from whole substance, VI, 231, 311, 354, as from stars, V, 135, VI, 231-2, not from stars, V, 661, VI, 189, 205, 232, dependent on form, VI, 354, neither form nor dependent on form alone, VI, 189, 231, not identical with substantial form, V, 661-2, relation to temperament, V, 662; Fernel on, V, 559, 630; known by experience alone, V, 664, VI, 354, 397; Luiz on, V, 551; of Agnus Dei, VI, 168-9; of compounds, VI, 189; of gems, VI, 299, 302-3; of heavens and stars, see Star;

of Paracelsan medicine, V, 626; of simples, V, 662; Olmo on, VI, 230-5; Peucer on, VI, 500-1; taking refuge in, V, 236, 479, 494, 630, VI, 293
Occupations, listed, V, 302; depicted, V, 345
Ocean, see Sea
Octavian, Irish theologian, VI, 288
Octavianus of Ghent, astrologer, VI, 199
Oddis, Oddus de, VI, 210
Odington, see Walter of
Odinton, V, 220
Odo of Meung, V, 448
Odor, V, 555, VI, 354; against demons, VI, 338; against snakes, V, 481; against suffocation, VI, 223; alchemical, VI, 242; nutritious? VI, 281, 365; of fish, VI, 271; of herbs, VI, 259; of minerals, VI, 593
Oenomancy, V, 587, VI, 420
Oeomancy, V, 587
Offusien, see Offusius
Offusius, Iofrancus, *Ephemerides* (1557), VI, 22-24, 108-11
Ohr, Philippus de, pr Hamburg, VI, 141
Oil, animal, VI, 219; distilled, V, 465, 635, 643, VI, 243; extracted, V, 479, from woods and gums, V, 589-90, from best steel, VI, 282; heavier than water, VI, 138; introduction in England urged, V, 578; medicinal, VI, 547, for leprosy, V, 432; of chrism, VI, 168; of philosophers, V, 502; of red-haired dog, VI, 216; of scorpions, VI, 218; of tartar, VI, 217; of violets, V, 608; properties, V, 555; sometimes quenches fire, V, 554; stains, V, 145; used in exorcism, VI, 558
Ointment, see Unguent
Olaus, Elias (1586), VI, 95
Old wife, see Woman
Olivarius, Jacobus, VI, 257
Olive, VI, 546
Olmedilla y Puig, Joaquin (1887), VI, 258
Olmo, pr Venice, VI, 258
Olmo, Giov. Francesco, VI, 230-5
Olmütz, V, 334
Olympian and Olympic, V, 627, 639, VI, 457
Olympiodorus, VI, 291
Olympiodorus, Alexandrinus, alchemist, V, 624
Olympus, Mt., height of, VI, 50
Omar Tiberinus, VI, 131
Omen, V, 104, 401, 563, VI, 135, 467, VI, 488, 503, 520; and see Prodigy
Omont, Henri (1897), V, 70, 283, 447, 454, VI, 101
Omphalius, VI, 493
Onimancy, VI, 502, 508
Onion, juice of, V, 146
Onomancy, V, 661, VI, 503; forbidden, VI, 169; put on Index, VI, 147
Onychomancy, VI, 499
Ophthalmia, V, 506
Opinion, fixed, V, 146; unstable, VI, 564
Opium, V, 438; modern, not that of Dioscorides, V, 663
Oporinus, Ioannes, pr Basel, V, 153, 373, 400, 402, 518, 607, VI, 30, 455, 492, 515
Oppenheim, V, 331; pr at, V, 203, 331, 348, 536
Oppian on fishes, comm. VI, 400
Opsopoeus, Joannes (1589), VI, 492
Optical illusion, V, 87, 146, 305-6, VI, 434
Optics, see Perspective
Opus mulierum et ludus puerorum, V, 547
Oracle, V, 104, VI, 135, 455, 466, 502, 504, 532; ceased, VI, 529; false or ambiguous, VI, 360; origin of, VI, 498; quoted, VI, 495; why ceased, V, 108, VI, 498 see Delphic
Oradinus, Vincentius, astrologer, V, 214
Orange, V, 112; prince of, VI, 15, 87
Oration and Orator, V, 164-6, 204, 265, 336, 386-7, 390, 400, 520, 547, 578, 607, VI, 69, 123, 141-2, 191, 230, 254, 394, 423-4, 523-4
Orb, see Sphere
Oreadini, see Oradinus
Oresme, Nicolas, V, 220, 291, VI, 278-9, 378
Oribasius, cited, V, 157, 523; used to correct Vesalius, V, 530
Orifiel, spirit of Saturn, VI, 441
Origanus, David (1558-1628), VI, 60-61
Originality, V, 563, VI, 326, 413; lack of, V, 396, 580, VI, 363, 398, 409
Origlia, G. G. (1753), V, 73
Orioli, see Davis and
Orlandi, P. A. (1714), V, 57, 244, 250
Orlandini, Niccolò, V, 327

Orléans, VI, 248; Ordinance of, VI, 170; pr at, V, 588, VI, 38; professor at, V, 588-9; studied at, VI, 346; witchcraft at, VI, 526
Orpheus, VI, 460; existence denied, VI, 461
Orphic philosophy, VI, 456, 601; theology, V, 119
Orpiment, VI, 310
Orsini, cardinal, V, 410
Orta, Garcia da, V, 466-9, 476, VI, 274; cited, V, 470, VI, 235, 258, 319, 333; influence, V, 469-70; quoted, VI, 298; sceptical, VI, 313-4
Ortel, Vitus, VI, 598
Ortenburg, V, 603
Ortona, pr at, VI, 444
Ortroy, Fernand van (1920), V, 410-1, VI, 13, 30
Ortulanus, see Hortulanus
Orvieto, V, 269
Os cruris, V, 512
Os sacrum, V, 509
Osiander, Andreas, V, 384, 413, 420, 422, 545, VI, 9, 595
Osiris, V, 291, 406, VI, 279
Ossifrage, a gem, VI, 321
Ostenius, Leonardus, pr Basel, V, 656
Osterbergius, Georgius, pr Königsberg, V, 481
Osthanes, alchemist, V, 624
Ostrich, V, 647, VI, 220
Othmar, Caspar, VI, 597
Otho, collaborator of Rheticus, V, 350, 354
Ottfried, tr, V, 391
Otto III, emperor, VI, 435
Otto Henry, count palatine, V, 548
Ottobeuern, V, 180
Ottoman empire, V, 179
Oursel, C. (1906), V, 308-9
Ovid, *Metamorphoses,* comm., VI, 129
Ovid, pseudo, *De vetula,* V, 219
Oviedo, Gonzalez, de, cited, VI, 275
Ox, bees generated from carcass of, VI, 281-2
Oxcart, VI, 289
Oxford, V, 674; chancellor of, VI, 41; reformers and astrology, V, 176; university, VI, 238, 520
Oxygen, V, 569
Oyster, V, 649
Pacchiotto, Felice, cited, VI, 94
Pacino, Ugolino, da Montescutolo, V, 336
Pact with demon, see Demon, Witchcraft
Paddlewheel, V, 34, 595-6
Padernus, Mt., VI, 268
Padovanius, see Paduanius
Padua, V, 83, 86, 91, 99, 103, 130, 166, 170, 269, VI, 56, 161, 300, 322, 377, 471, 556; astrology at, V, 164, 167, 205; astronomical observation at, VI, 28; bishop of, V, 78; botanical garden, V, 446, 531, VI, 466; college endowed at, V, 205; count of, VI, 135; death at, of Nabod, VI, 121-3; dissections at, V, 525-6; finds at and near, of chest, VI, 246, inscription, V, 623, lamp, VI, 279; libel on two citizens of, VI, 101; medical discussion at, VI, 229; met at, VI, 452; podestà of, V, 524; popular professor at, V, 205; pr at, V, 44, 56, 328, 356, 479, 493, 596, 642, 666, VI, 122, 202, 211, 260, 286, 369, 481, 556-7; siege of, V, 535; studied at, V, 44, 71, 94, 328, 403, 426, 446, 488, 601, 652, VI, 88, 128, 373, 382, 599; taught at, V, 39, 71-72, 75-76, 94-95, 163, 169, 204-5, 324-5, 327, 480, 488, 493, 501, 505, 524, 544, 548, 581, 666, VI, 28, 48, 155, 201, 208, 210, 212, 227, 229, 286-7, 364, 368-70, 493; university of, V, 37, 85, 164, 184, 250, 334, 360-1, 479, 531, 640, VI, 122, 154, 311-2, 423; written from, VI, 260
Paduanius, Ioannes (1563), V, 154, VI, 124, 161
Pagan and Paganism, VI, 278, 532; in sixteenth century, V, 631
Paganus, Theobald, pr Lyons, V, 328, 501
Pain, V, 273
Paint, Painter and Painting, V, 452, 587, VI, 289, 313
Palaeontology, V, 27
Palario, Michael de, VI, 544
Palatinate (Rhenish), V, 331, 401, 652, VI, 41; count of, V, 372, 441, 548, 631, VI, 45, 235; elector of, V, 99, 203, 391, 402, 600, 652, 661, VI, 91, 316; loss of, predicted, VI, 361
Palermo, chiromancy at, V, 582; pr at, V, 582; taught at, V, 581

Palestine, home of prophets, V, 575, VI, 511; Postel on, VI, 344
Palisci, VI, 504
Palissy, Bernard, V, 441, 465, 596-9
Palladius on agriculture, cited, VI, 282
Palma Christi, VI, 546
Palmarius, See Paulmier, le
Palthenius, M. Zacharias, pr Frankfurt, VI, 197, 331
Palud, Magdeleine de la, tried as witch, VI, 554
Paludanus, Carolus, physician, VI, 267
Pampeluna, battle of, V, 174
Pamphilia, V, 229, VI, 460
Pamplona, pr at, VI, 413
Panacea, herb, VI, 311; Paracelsan rejected, V, 659
Panama, VI, 345
Pandectarius, V, 447, 450, 453, 458
Pandonius, Sylvius, bishop of Bojano, V, 79
Panetius, Adrian, correspondent of Benedetti, VI, 138
Panico, see Jacobus de
Pansier, P., V, 161
Pantagruel's Prognostication, V, 313
Pantaleon, H. (1562), V, 609; (1565-66), V, 347, 407
Panteo, see Pantheus
Pantheism, VI, 375
Panther, attractive odor of, V, 555
Pantheus, Joh. Ant., V, 537, 633
Pantheus, Joh. Aug., V, 535, 537-40; *Ars transmutationis,* V, 537-9; *Lunario,* V, 540; *Voarchadumia,* V, 539-40, 604, 636
Panvinio, Onuphrio, VI, 492
Panzatis, Bartolameo de, a patient, V, 518
Panzer, G. W. (1793-1803), V, 355, VI, 469
Páo de Cobra, an herb, V, 476
Paoli, H. J. (1921), V, 466
Papacy, Papal, Papist and Pope, V, 81, 141, 646, VI, 156, 498; alchemy and, V, 535, 537, 539-40; alum monopoly, V, 457; apostolic secretary, V, 472; as international arbitrator, V, 212; attitude towards astrology, V, 175, 241, VI, 156-78; camera, VI, 476; curia, VI, 181, 255, 265, 274; decline predicted, V, 375; French, V, 113; horoscopes of, V, 259, VI, 100; nephews, V, 268; notary, VI, 181; pension, VI, 153; penitentiary, VI, 444; pictures of, VI, 471; prediction concerning, V, 236, 255-6, 259-60, 375, VI, 177, 204, 440, forbidden, V, 168, VI, 171, 177, 413; protonotary, VI, 106, 520; states of, VI, 149; superstition of, VI, 549; urged against Turk, V, 212; and see names of individual Popes: John XXII, Leo X, Paul III, Sixtus V, etc.
Papadopoli, N. C. (1726), V, 44, 325, 327, VI, 122
Papers of the American Historical Association, VI, 517, 537
Papiniano, Villanova de, geomancy, VI, 473
Paquot, see *Memoires de*
Parabosco, Girolamo, *l'Oracolo,* **VI**, 472
Paracelsan and Paracelsist, VI, 126, 190, 217, 224, 239, 247, 372, 437, 533; ignored, VI, 335; opposed, V, 392, 664-5, VI, 250, 252, 388, 553; revival, V, 417, 442, 617-51, VI, 224, 294, contrasted with reception of the Copernican theory, V, 629-30
Paracelsus, V, 438-42, 548, 596, VI, 365, 424, 569; accused of atheism, V, 664, blasphemy, V, 657-8, drunkenness, V, 657, inconsistency, V, 658, lying, VI, 245, magic, V, 635, 645, 660, 664, VI, 243, 525, 536, stupidity, VI, 240, 243, superstition and vanity, VI, 236, 540; alchemical medicine not originated by, V, 533, 541, 637, 657-8, VI, 219; alchemy and, V, 625-6; anatomy and, V, 626; animism of, V, 628; astrology of, V, 440, 626, 660, opposed, VI, 141; attacked by, Cardan, V, 565, Cureus, V, 381, Erastus, V, 657-60, 664, Melanchthon, V, 380-1; billingsgate of, V, 9, 440; biography of, V, 431, 636; boastfulness, V, 439; burning of *Canon* disputed, V, 438-9; cited, VI, 278, 282, 459; compared with Agrippa, V, 129, Bruno, VI, 424, Copernicus, V, 629, Fries, V, 431, 438; cures of, V, 416; deaths of patients, V, 665, own, VI, 252; defended, VI, 525; demon and, VI, 428; disease, theory of, V, 626-7, 638, 651; distinctions and

divisions made by, V, 627; Dorn and, V, 635; estimate of, V, 604, 619-20, 629, VI, 85; extracts from, V, 475; four pillars of, V, 626, VI, 433; Latin, unfamiliar with, V, 438; letters of, V, 439-40, 617; Libavius and, VI, 242-3; magic and, V, 660; names assumed by V, 74, 439; natural law and science beyond the ken of, V, 628; praised, V, 618-9, 630, 642, VI, 219; principles of, V, 626, 633, 637, 644, 658, 664, VI, 247-8, opposed, VI, 141, 250; reflections on a remark attributed to, V, 441; remedies of, V, 329, 639, VI, 243, 252, 540; sky called fire by, VI, 84; style of, V, 619; teaching at Basel, V, 438-9; weapon ointment of, VI, 420, 534; works, V, 617-9, 636, how far pr during life, V, 440, *Archidoxa,* V, 417, 625, 627, 631, VI, 508, *Astronomia,* V, 416, *Dat Secreet,* V, 618, *Defensiones,* V, 440, *Grosse Wundartzney,* V, 440, 618, VI, 106, *Labyrinthus,* V, 440-1, 618, 626, *Paragranum,* V, 439, *Paramirum,* V, 439-40, 627, pest tract, V, 330, *Philosophia magna,* V, 631, *Praesagiis,* V, 627, *Prognosticatio,* V, 617, VI, 456, religious and theological, V, 440, 442, *Secretis naturae mysteriis* (1570), V, 631, *Summis naturae mysteriis* (1584), V, 635, *Tincturis,* V, 439

Paradella, Pardelos or Paratella, an herb, VI, 262, 264

Paradis, Jean, theologian, VI, 493

Paradise, terrestrial, V, 453

Parallax, V, 306; measurement of, VI, 72-73; observation of, VI, 10, 79

Paralysis, VI, 212; from too much mercury, V, 626; checked, V, 470

Paratella, see Paradella

Parcus, J. pr Basel, V, 605

Paré, Ambrose, cited, VI, 280

Paris, V, 220, 270, 383, 477, 636, VI, 490; Achillini at, V, 38; Agrippa at, V, 127-8; alchemy at, V, 546, 625, censured, VI, 242, 247-50; articles of, VI, 351, 524; astronomy and astrology at, V, 275-306, VI, 572; Brasavola at, V, 446; Brucaeus at, VI, 38; Bruno at, VI, 423-4; Champier at, V, 111; Cirvelo at, V, 275-6, 278; Douglas at, V, 155; expelled or fled from, VI, 388, 568; Finé at, V, 284-6, 290-3; Germans at, V, 285; Guido, John, at, V, 296; Hôtel-Dieu, VI, 251; humanism at, V, 9; journey to, VI, 255; Lefèvre d'Etaples at, V, 278-9; Lull, interest in, at, V, 535; Marstallerus at, V, 298; mathematics at, V, 275, 278, 281, 285, 288, 292, 295, 304, 543, VI, 19, 141-2, 178; Mayerne at, VI, 248; medicine at, V, 286, 288-90, 640, VI, 141, 219, faculty of, VI, 242, 247-52; Mizauld at, V, 299; oath required at, V, 276; outsiders at, V, 297; Parlement of, V, 286-7, 290, 345, 483, VI, 250, 344, 346, 388, 522, 531, 533; Pena at, V, 304; Pighe at, V, 279-80; prévôt of, V, 286, VI, 522; pr at, V, 24, 48, 65-66, 129, 141, 143, 148-9, 153, 155, 157-8, 182, 184, 189, 201, 254, 264, 273, 279, 281, 283-5, 288-9, 291-2, 294-301, 304, 308-9, 330, 343, 348, 386, 418, 421, 430, 463-4, 479, 486, 489, 514, 535, 540, 542, 544, 552, 556-8, 594, 596, 601, 607-8, 622-3, 636, 638, 640, 654, VI, 10, 12, 20, 22-23, 43, 108-9 128, 141-2, 175, 182, 186, 199, 201, 216, 223, 230, 249, 251, 256, 286-7, 293, 295, 301-3, 324, 340, 343-4, 360-1, 393, 403, 410, 431, 437-8, 441, 447-8, 450-1, 454, 459-60, 463-4, 469, 472, 475-6, 483, 493, 506-8, 524-6, 528, 531, 547, 554, 568; professors of, see mathematics, medicine and university; Ramism at, VI, 142; renaissance at, V, 295; Servetus at, V, 288-90; Skalich at, VI, 457; sophistry at, V, 280-1; Stadius at, V, 303-4; streets of, V, 543, VI, 20, 324, 343-4, 568; studied at V, 55, 62, 111, 285, 446, VI, 38, 251, 531, 553; surgeon of V, 598; Thibault at, V, 286; university of, V, 155-7, 342, 345, 430, 479, 483, 552, 556, 567, 642, VI, 175, 341, 377, 382; Vesalius at, V, 525; Wier at, V, 137; and see College, Sorbonne

Paris of Mantua, see Ceresara, Paride

Parlement, see Bordeaux, Burgundy, Paris, Toulouse

Parma, V, 118, 246, VI, 127; duke of, VI, 138, 195, 231, 373; pr at, V, 596, VI, 93; see Blasius of

Parmenides, VI, 370
Parnassus, Mt. V, 203
Pars fortunæ, VI, 138, 158, 200
Parsley, VI, 309
Parson, astrologer, V, 160
Parthenium, an herb, VI, 262
Partnership, V, 172, 363
Parvulus philosophiae naturalis, V, 148, 160
Parvus, Ioannes, pr Paris, VI, 441
Paschal, Julius, ed., V, 594
Pasinus, Mapheus, pr Venice, V, 514
Pasquet de Sallo, V, 188
Pasquetus, Dominicus, pr Naples, V, 73
Pasquetus, Ioannes, pr Naples, V, 73
Pasquier, E. (1560), cited, VI, 509
Pasquinade, V, 204, 230
Passerat, Jean, VI, 141
Passerus, Antonius, Aristotelian, VI, 364, 366
Passi, Pietro (1614), VI, 431-2
Pastor, of a church, VI, 91, 547
Pastor, Ludwig, V, 255, VI, 149-51
Pastrengo, Guiglielmo da, V, 263
Patagonia, giants of, V, 578, VI, 276
Patavinus, Joannes, pr Venice, V, 326
Pathology, V, 556-7, 578
Patient, V, 123, 125, 528; live or die? VI, 275; named, V, 518
Patiniana, VI, 560
Patisson, M., pr for, VI, 230
Patresson, Jean, pr Lyons, VI, 474
Patriarch, of Alexandria, VI, 410; six before Enoch, V, 373; and see Jacob, Longevity of, Noah, etc.
Patriotism, teaching of, decried, V, 579
Patristic, see Church Fathers
Patrizi, Francesco, VI, 373-7, 449, 460-1; cited, VI, 382
Paul the Apostle, household of, V, 473-4; tomb of, V, 85
Paul III, V, 252, 282, 446, 581, VI, 148, 451; and astrology, V, 241, 243, 255-60, 264-9, 274, 379; Copernicus to, V, 411-3, 423, VI, 52; election predicted, VI, 15, 107; eulogized, V, 265, VI, 424; geniture, V, 246, VI, 105, 195; medical and scientific works dedic to, V, 254, 260-1, 263, 269-73, 514-5; occult science, V, 252, 261-2, 264
Paul IV, VI, 101; and see Index of
Paul V, VI, 173
Paul of Aegina, V, 263, 449
Paul de Haeredia, VI, 445
Paul of Middelburg, V, 178, 264, 408; cited, V, 165-6, 294; criticized, V, 257; *Prognosticum,* V, 217-8; said to've forecast appearance of syphilis, V, 207
Paul of Venice, cited, V, 248, 319; opposed, V, 41, 95
Pauline art, VI, 361, 430, 516
Paulmier, C. S. le (1894), V, 483
Paulmier, Julien le, V, 482-3, VI, 251
Paulmier, Pierre, archbishop of Vienne, V, 288
Paulmier, Pierre le, medical, VI, 251-2
Pauls, E. (1896), VI, 559
Paulsen, Friedrich, (1919), V, 338
Paulus, Nicolaus, (1893), V, 149; (1910), V, 70, VI, 145-6, 522
Pavanello, G. (1905), V, 534
Pavia, V, 70, 130, 157, 269, 325, 460; battle of, V, 310; pr at, V, 63, 121, VI, 178, 257, 506; printer from, V, 79, 183; university of, V, 111, 127, 132, 273, 325, 431, VI, 180, 213, 402
Pax, Antonius, pr Naples, VI, 273
Peace, advised, V, 290; predicted, V, 272, 280
Peach-tree, VI, 311
Peacock, VI, 277
Pearl, V, 571; in medicine, V, 420, 457, 651, VI, 314; perforated, V, 455; pulverized, V, 455, 457, 478; salt of, V, 650
Peasant, V, 302; cited, V, 482; find by, V, 512, VI, 289; and see Agriculture, Farmer, Rustic
Peasants' Almanach, V, 291
Peasants' Revolt of 1525, V, 396, VI, 90, 144
Peckham, John, *Perspectiva communis,* V, 167, 343, 365, 385; criticized, V, 305-6
Pediasimus, Joannes, VI, 89
Pederzanus, Io. Bapt., of Brescia, pr Venice, VI, 405
Pedomancy, V, 587
Pedro, Antonio, VI, 171
Pegnitz, river, VI, 499
Pelagius Aphricanus, alchemist, V, 624
Pelerin, Jean, VI, 141
Peletarius or Peletier, Jacques (1563),

VI, 33; criticized, V, 293; observation by, VI, 24
Pelican, V, 20, 98, VI, 284
Pellechet, M.L.C. (1897-1909), V, 536, VI, 298
Pellicier, Guillaume, VI, 257
Pellus, Silvius, mathematician, VI, 373
Pelster, Fr. (1923), VI, 304
Pena, Jean, V, 304-6, 356; cited, VI, 84; errors as tr, V, 293; *Euclidis Optica et Catoptrica,* VI, 19-20, 71; theories of, VI, 19-20, 71, 83
Penance, VI, 149, 154
Pendasio, Federico (1555), VI, 48
Penitence, V, 86; and see Penance
Pennius, Thomas, naturalist, VI, 268, 284
Pennyroyal, V, 611
Pension, V, 74
Peony, V, 614, 647, 662, VI, 338, 468, 501
Pepper, V, 467-8, 651
Peramato, Petrus de, physician, VI, 128
Peranzonus, Nicolaus, astrologer, V, 178, 218-20
Perazonus, Nicolaus, on notory art and memory, V, 606; put on Index, V, 606, VI, 146; and see Peranzonus
Perchacinus, Gratiosus, pr Padua and Venice, VI, 155, 214, 260
Pèrcopo, Erasmo, (1893-96), V, 51, 79, 165-6, 168, 192, 204, 229-30, 252, 256, 258-9, 279, 375, VI, 101, 157, 469
Perenoto, Antonio, cardinal, V, 644
Pererius, Benedictus, cited, VI, 232, 452, 543; ***Communibus . . . principiis,*** V, 110, VI, 409-10; ***Magia,*** VI, 410-3; quoted, VI, 390
Peretti, Alessandro, cardinal, VI, 315
Perez, Franciscus, pr Seville, VI, 197
Perez, M. tr, VI, 159
Perez Cascales, Franciscus, V, 486-7
Perez de Messa, Jacobus, astrologer, VI, 165
Perfectum magisterium, V, 538
Perga, see Apollonius of
Pericardia, V, 507
Perier, Adrian, pr Paris, VI, 568
Perier, Th. pr Paris, V, 24
Peripatetic and Peripateticism, V, 37 et seq., 98, 109-10, 236, 427, 531, VI, 24, 34, 131, 198-9, 227, 253, 317, 325-7, 334, 338, 350, 364, 379, 388, 450, 456, 460, 485, 513, 568; astronomy, V, 489, VI, 47-48; attitude towards astrology, V, 510, 643-4; attitude towards demons, V, 82, VI, 350, 484, 517, 519, 531, 546; attitude towards magic, VI, 336; controversy with Ramists, VI, 238-9; disagreement with Aristotle or inter se, V, 553; physics, VI, 433
Perlach, Andreas, V, 415; assistant to Tannstetter, V, 223, 349, 382, VI, 117; professor at Vienna, V, 223-4, 328, 358, 382
Perna, Petrus, pr Basel, V, 603, 619, 625, 628, 630, 640, 656, 664, 666, VI, 29, 183; heirs of, VI, 351
Perrenot, Antoine, addressed to, VI, 395
Perscrutator, V, 633; cited, V, 207, 227
Persia and Persian, V, 135, 476, VI, 323, 460, 480, 492; astrology, V, 395, VI, 23; bezoar from, VI, 335; king of, V, 522; magi of, VI, 220, 353, 415, 464, philosophy of, 601
Persian Gulf, V, 27
Perspective, V, 17, 24, 86, 140, 305-6, VI, 369, 566; appeal to, VI, 20, 71; medicine and, VI, 142; works on, V, 486, VI, 137, 372-3
Perspiration, provoked, V, 316
Perth, V, 294
Peru, VI, 275, 323
Peruchot or Purchot, Edemondo, VI, 129
Perugia, V, 214, 534; pr at, VI, 469
Pesaro, V, 50, VI, 298; pr at, VI, 299
Pesnot, Loys, pr Lyons, VI, 105
Pessimism, V, 242-3, 394, 516, 631, VI, 538
Pest, VI, 490; at Antwerp, V, 128, Bologna, V, 232, Brescia, VI, 214, Cologne, VI, 211, Germany, V, 354, VI, 185, Grenoble, V, 125, Hamburg, VI, 210, Hungary, VI, 185, Italy, VI, 89, Milan, V, 161-2, Poland, VI, 185, Rome, V, 161, Sessa, V, 72, Turkey, VI, 185, Venice, VI, 185; causes, V, 124, astrological, V, 161, 607, VI, 95, comet, V, 607, excess of sulphur, V, 626, occult, V, 559, VI, 235; cure for, V, 463, 541; death from, V, 331, 601, VI, 498, 537; infection, V, 103; measures against, V, 213, 608; mortality from, V, 608; nativities of individuals

and, V, 398; of 1348, V, 157, 195, 497, VI, 187; Olmo on, VI, 235; predicted, V, 280; presages of, V, 213, 497, 607-8; remedies, V, 480, 541, 574; safeguards against, V, 574, VI, 169, 420; signs of, V, 608, VI, 501; tracts on, V, 125, 297, 318, 330, 347, 439, 475, 483, 496, 542, 605, 607-8, VI, 128-9, 158, 210-2, 214, 218, 220, 461-3; warned against, V, 230
Peter the Apostle, longevity of, V, 206; tomb of, V, 85
Peter of Abano, V, 55, VI, 222; astrology of, V, 117, 124, 248, VI, 180, 203, 403; cited, V, 104, 166-7, 170, 206, 220, 274, 309, 478, 480, 485, 503, 506-7, 511-3, 541, VI, 131, 139, 300, 304, 311, 313, 386, 399, 405, 411, 516; *Chiromancy,* ascribed to, V, 53-54, 57, 676; *Conciliator,* V, 121, 434, 485, 503, 511, VI, 197, 304, 416; criticized, V, 41-42, 79, 478, VI, 197, 360, 411-2; defended from charge of magic, V, 61, 102, VI, 132; errors of, V, 119-22, 551, VI, 467-8; *Geomancy* ascribed to, V, 64, VI, 150; other works of, V, 61-62, 263, 485, 600, VI, 150, 154; relation to Index and Inquisition, V, 115, VI, 147, 150, 468
Peter of Auvergne, cited, V, 219, 227
Peter Lombard, VI, 405; *Sentences,* V, 8, 173, comm. V, 504, VI, 468
Peter Martyr, see Martyr
Peter, see also Petrus
Petit, Jean, see Parvus
Petit-Jean, Athanase, pr Lyons, VI, 160
Petit-pas, Ioannes, bookseller, Paris, VI, 324
Petramellarius, see Pietramellara
Petrarch, VI, 104, 595
Petrasancta, Michael de, V, 197-9, 213
Petreius, Iohannes, pr Nürnberg, V, 258, 297, 349, 357-8, 360-1, 363, 537, 545, VI, 101, 448
Petri Henricus, see Henricus Petri
Petrification, V, 108, 597-8
Petroleum, V, 455
Petronius, St. V, 107
Petrucius, Bellisarius, V, 134
Petrus Antonius de Magistris Galathei, VI, 171-2
Petrus de Archa, V, 586
Petrus de Argellata, V, 513
Petrus, Cornelius, V, 462
Petrus Hispanus, cited, V, 503; comm. Isaac, V, 503; doubted, V, 478; Logic of, V, 209
Petrus, Johannes, bishop of Viterbo, V, 410
Petrus monachus, alchemist, V, 623
Petrus Peregrinus, V, 4, VI, 300; ed, V. 391; plagiarized, V, 4, 580
Petrus a Villanova, alchemist, V, 623
Petum, an herb, V, 636
Petz, H. (1888), V, 337, 339-40, 364
Peucer, Caspar, V, 405, 408, 490, VI, 229, 358, 598; astrology of, V, 384, 400, VI, 103; astronomy of, V, 384-5, 426, VI, 11-12, 34; cited, V, 402, VI, 21, 435, 521; criticized, VI, 184; *Divinationibus,* VI, 407, 493-501; *Elementa,* VI, 11-12; Letters, V, 12, 52, 74, VI, 225; put on Index, VI, 12, 147; relation to Garcaeus, VI, 103, to Melanchthon, V, 384, VI, 494-5
Peurbach, Georg, V, 234, 330, 565; cited, V, 172, 421, VI, 10-11, 21, 62, 131; comm., VI, 16-17; criticized, V, 200; horoscope of, VI, 17, 595; observations by, V, 366; praised, V, 200, 587; as restorer of mathematics, V, 332-5, 347, 366; works, *Canones,* V, 365; *Epitome,* V, 172, 340-1; *Quadrato geometrico,* V, 365; *Tubulae,* V, 221, 225, 316, 332, 346-8; *Theoricae,* V, 173, 285, 341, 359, 372, 380, 412, 425, VI, 36, 430
Peutinger, Conrad, V, 331
Peypus, Federicus, pr Nürnberg, V, 353, 357, VI, 302
Pflaum, Jakob, astrologer, V, 181, 348
Phaellus, Ioh. Bapt., pr Bologna, V, 240
Phaemon the Greek, V, 482
Pharaoh, VI, 353; and see Magi, Pharaoh's
Phares, see Simon de
Pharmacist and Pharmacy, V, 445-71, 548-9, VI, 267-8, 499; Arabic, V, 448, 466; botany and, VI, 258; criticized, V, 114, 122, 464-5, 618, 634, 640, VI, 280; discovery by, VI, 294; instructions to, VI, 225; lectures to, VI, 248; medicine and, V, 522, VI, 220; nomenclature, V, 447-8; shop, V, 123, 380, 445, 447, 453-4, 612, VI, 262-3, 313
Pherecydes, V, 478

Philalethes, Eudoxus, VI, 214
Philalthaeus, Lucillus, pseudonym for Lucilio Maggi, cited, VI, 48, 50, 138; comm. *De caelo et mundo,* VI, 138, 180
Philiarchus, Cosmas, VI, 540
Philip I of Spain, VI, 136
Philip II of Spain, V, 304, 469, VI, 245, 356; dedic to, V, 303, VI, 14-15, 102, 395, 413, 418; marriage of, VI, 102; oldest son of, VI, 126; prediction from nativity of, VI, 136
Philip of Hesse, V, 520, 621, VI, 116, 196
Philip of Tripoli, translator, V, 48, 284
Philo Judaeus, VI, 22
Philobiblon, eine Zeitschrift für Bücherfreunde, V, 341
Philolaus, VI, 63
Philologus, Thomas, V, 204-6, VI, 428; called to Rome, V, 205, 253; cited, V, 213, 226-7, 621; criticized, V, 214; self-conceit, V, 204-5; succeeded by, V, 327; works of, V, 178, 204-6
Philomates, preface to, VI, 109
Philomathes, an interlocutor, VI, 549
Philomathesius, VI, 184
Philoponus, V, 75, 81, VI, 48, 97
Philosopher, V, 57, VI, 51, 183, 196, 335, 492-3, 506, 550-1, 564; absent-minded, VI, 443; contrasted with chemist, V, 634; disagree, VI, 450; god on earth, V, 110; persecuted, V, 105, 107; predicts as well as astrologer, V, 120-1, 210; and see Philosophy
Philosophers' stone, VI, 244, 250
Philosophia pauperum, V, 5
Philosophiae chimicae, V, 622
Philosophisches Jahrbuch, VI, 304
Philosophy, V, 61, 168, VI, 194, 443, 455-6; ancient, V, 150, VI, 217, 410, 416, 568; anti-Aristotelian, VI, 50-51; astrology and, VI, 70; bachelor of, VI, 414; Christianity and, V, 142, 165, 276, 631, VI, 339-62; divisions of, VI, 433; doctor of, VI, 87; errors of, VI, 318; flourishing, V, 295; Hebrew, VI, 432; history of, V, 128; martyr of, VI, 560; master of, V, 403; materialistic, V, 36; medicine and, V, 626, VI, 211-2; moral, V, 95, VI, 129, 395, 519, moral taught, V, 403, VI, 267, 289, 484; natural, V, 48-49, 269, 273, 316, 394, 416, 472, 547, VI, 129, 198, 339, 390, 395, 410, 432, natural taught, V, 148-9, 446, VI, 211, 354, essential to the state, VI, 395, natural misrepresented, V, 641, neglected, V, 143, VI, 32, natural and moral, V, 142; new, VI, 568; of love, V, 631; Paracelsan, V, 628, 630-1; prayer and, V, 107; preferred to botany, VI, 266; sacred, VI, 306, 339-62; secret, VI, 455; studied, V, 38, 285, 488, 652, VI, 77, 369, 553; subject of, VI, 378; taught, V, 38-39, 43, 74, 90, 94-95, 153, 524, 666, VI, 48-49, 105, 180, 201, 205, 210, 227, 286, 290, 341, 370, 373, 423, 494, 522, 553, 561, 599; universal, attempted, VI, 406; works on, V, 153; VI, 217; and see Aristotle
Philostratus, VI, 304
Philotheus, Greek comm. V, 448
Philter, V, 485-6, VI, 419
Phlebotomy, V, 323, VI, 221, 223, 567; astrological, V, 161, VI, 106, 127, 144, 197, 200, 298, 403, 567; between thumb and forefinger, V, 506; controversy as to in cases of pleurisy, V, 260, 326, VI, 215, of spleen, V, 506; works on, V, 529, VI, 212
Phlegm, V, 162
Phoenix, V, 122, 639, VI, 565; disbelieved in, V, 474, VI, 281
Phortzn, see John of
Phthisis, V, 597, VI, 595
Phyllitis, an herb, VI, 259
Physica, V, 90
Physician, V, 45, 233, 269, 370, 465, VI, 546, 598; at Council of Trent, V, 488; budding, V, 213; character, V, 121; chemist contrasted with, V, 634; college of, V, 111, 176, 644, VI, 219, 248; consulted, VI, 208; court, V, 652, 661; criticized, V, 465; dispute between, V, 493; ducal, V, 111, 168, 298, 390, 483, 620, VI, 126, 128-9, 140, 217, 228, 235, 399, 495, 515; electoral, VI, 229, 316; essentials of, V, 431-2; family of, V, 601, VI, 560; first of all, V, 166; ignorant and incompetent, V, 509; imperial, V, 328, 602, 620, VI, 128, 136, 318, 394, 431, 504-5, 596; Jewish, VI, 259; kinds of, V, 638-9; life of, V, 544; location of, Aix-en-Provence, VI, 553, Alost, VI, 38, Anhalt, VI, 506, Antwerp, V, 128, 189, 286, 430, VI,

74, 127, 268, 291, Augsburg, V, 391, 640, VI, 142, Basel, VI, 267, 284, Beaune, VI, 105, Bergamo, V, 99, 600, Blangy-sur-Ternoise, V, 449, Brescia, V, 446, VI, 230, Bruges, V, 328, Brussels, V, 329, VI, 140, Coburg, V, 654, Colmar, V, 431, VI, 216, Cologne, V, 437, Cracow, VI, 267, Cremona, V, 529, Erfurt, VI, 106, Feldkirch, V, 391, Franche-Comté, VI, 311, Fribourg, V, 127, 131, Glogau, V, 404, Guadalajara, V, 486, Hensisheim, V, 610, Imola, VI, 545, Krems, V, 346, La Rochelle, V, 478, Leyden, V, 462, Liège, V, 206, Lindau, V, 391, Lisbon, V, 550, Louvain, VI, 30, 394, Lyons, VI, 105, 267, Mantua, V, 98, 100, 645, Marburg, VI, 351, Metz, V, 313, Milan, V, 159, VI, 311, Mirandola, V, 55, Montpellier, VI, 304, 510, Naples, V, 211, VI, 214, 492, New Batavia, VI, 319, Nîmes, VI, 340, Nürnberg, V, 341, 439, 657-8, VI, 126, Orléans, VI, 248, Padua, V, 170, Paris, V, 296, 477, VI, 247, 251, Pavia, V, 460, Perugia, V, 534, Pontigny, V, 437, Prag, VI, 224, Rome, V, 254, VI, 129, Salzburg, V, 460, Schaffhausen, VI, 267, Schwäbisch Hall, V, 133-4, Serrasanquirico, V, 484, Seurre-sur-Sâone, V, 328, Seville, VI, 196, Strasburg, V, 317, 437, subalpine, VI, 213, Thiers, VI, 221, Toulouse, VI, 478, Turin, V, 125, Udine or Belluno, V, 44, Utrecht, VI, 101-2, Valencia, VI, 373, Valladolid, VI, 129, Venice, V, 488, 516, VI, 201, Verona, V, 324, 493, 538, VI, 267, Vienna, V, 440, Würzburg, V, 159, Ypres, VI, 311, Zurich, V, 362, Zwickau, VI, 302; municipal, V, 8, 127, 131, 313, 391, 443, VI, 221; papal, V, 10, 74, 260, 446, VI, 127, 315; pharmacist and, VI, 250; philosopher and, VI, 364; predicts, V, 120-1; prominent, V, 233; recent, V, 123, 447, criticized, V, 449; royal, V, 124, 128, 159, 170, 286, 288, 292, 469, 476, 483, 486, 630, 640-1, VI, 142, 221, 225, 247, 321, 355-6, 368, 478, 480, 553, 598; superstitious, VI, 240; surgeon and, VI, 217; to a cardinal, V, 205, 497, Grand Captain, V, 72, Inquisition, VI, 196, marshal of France, VI, 33, princes, V, 318, 327, 644, VI, 87, 123; unconcerned with occult, VI, 230

Physics, V, 149; Aristotelian, V, 9; astronomy and, VI, 238, 354; Christian, VI, 568; four schools of, V, 352-3, VI, 433; natural magic and, V, 561; professor of, VI, 352; sacred, VI, 434; study of nature, VI, 352; varieties of, VI, 433; and see Philosophy, natural

Physiognomy, V, 17, 50-68, 160, 635, VI, 413, 496, 506, 509, 542-3; Achillini on, V, 42-43; astrological, V, 247, VI, 176, 452, 572; called evil, V, 564, VI, 524; Carpi and, V, 510; fourth column of science, VI, 434, interest in, V, 49; opposed, VI, 199; put on Index, VI, 147, 150; superstitious, VI, 430; works on, V, 65-68, 261, 432, 605-6, VI, 160-4, 166-8, 170, 360, 469, 474, 510

Physiologus, V, 20; cited, VI, 300

Physiology, V, 269-70, 577, VI, 340, 355, 371; astrological, of Mizauld, V, 301; new, of Gilbert, VI, 380

Piacenza, V, 4, 43, 70, 364; duke of, VI, 195, 231; university of, V, 431

Pianero, Giovanni, medical, VI, 128

Picatrix, V, 122, 132; cited, V, 533, 637, VI, 468

Piccinino, Jacopo, VI, 136

Piccioli, Antonio, V, 67, 261-2

Picciolis de Carpo, Ant. Franciscus de, V, 261

Piccolomini, Alessandro, VI, 27-28, 363; cited, VI, 60, 93, 387, 435; *Trattato della grandezza dell'acque e della terra*, V, 24; turns from astrology to astronomy, VI, 180

Piccolomini, Francesco (1596), VI, 377-9

Piceninus, see Piccinino

Piceno, M. G. tr, VI, 472

Pico della Mirandola, Giovanni, attitude towards astrology, V, 107, 119-20, 191, 209, 227, influence of, V, 79, 319, 654, VI, 23, 160, 467, answered, belittled or criticized, V, 79-80, 164, 171, 199, 263, 276, 278, 296, 329-30, 340, 380, 393, 646, VI, 20-21, 119, 125, 169-70, 172, 193, 210, 359, 379, 527, cited, recommended or repeated, V, 140, 160, 198, 227, 262, 284, 294, 481, 637, 655,

VI, 131, 198, 201, 232, 375, 399, 412, 430, 433, 456, 521; attitude towards Ptolemy, VI, 317, Cabala, VI, 445, Chaldean Oracles, VI, 460, critical days, answered, V, 318, 325, natural magic, V, 124, criticized, VI, 431, Regiomontanus, V, 333-4, science, V, 5; death of, V, 164, exactly predicted, VI, 107, 170; disciple of, VI, 450; geniture, VI, 595; George of Ragusa compared with, VI, 202; *Heptaplus,* VI, 148; plagiarized, VI, 456; theses, VI, 431, 455

Pico della Mirandola, Giovanni Francesco, V, 71; *Auro,* V, 540-1; cited, V, 125, 262, VI, 503; daughter Julia, V, 540; influence on Champier, V, 121-2; letters, V, 173, VI, 467; *Rerum praenotione,* V, 121-2, 159, VI, 467-9; style characterized, VI, 467; *Veris calamitatum causis,* V, 124, 164

Picquet, Honoré, V, 112

Pictorius, Georg, VI, 302, 399-406, 502-3; cited, V, 610, VI, 508

Picture, allegorical, VI, 456; anatomical, V, 523, and see Plate; botanical, VI, 267; multiplied, VI, 296; of Achillini, V, 45-46, animals, VI, 447, astrological types, V, 345, Falloppia, V, 336, famous persons, VI, 470-1, insects, VI, 268, Kentmann's cabinet, VI, 269, Maestlin, VI, 80, metoposcopic types, VI, 506, monsters, VI, 281, 283, 286, 408, oracle-gods and seers, VI, 504, Pontus de Tyard, VI, 24, Schöner, V, 365, Stadius, VI, 28

Piedmont, V, 293, 296, VI, 131, 227; and see Alessio of, Francis of

Pierre du Bois, see Du Bois

Pierre, Jehan, de Tours, V, 285

Pietramellara, Andrea, son of Giacomo, V, 193, 231-2

Pietramellara, Giacomo, astrologer, V, 160, 193, 228-9, 231, 237-40

Pietrasanta, Plinio, pr Venice, VI, 390

Pietro Aretino, V, 204, 230, 312

Pietro da Torrigiano, see Turrisianus

Pig, V, 462, 480, VI, 536; fat of, VI, 240; liver as medicine, V, 621; marrow of VI, 216; sign of rain from, VI, 367

Pigafetta, cited, VI, 276, 331

Pigeons, street of, V, 85

Pigghe or Pighius, Albert, V, 182, 279-84; *Adversus prognosticatorum vulgus,* V, 184-94, 201, 279-81; *Aequinoctiorum,* V, 281; *Apologia,* V, 201, 281; astrology of, V, 184, 186, 189, 191-2, 280-3; compared with Cirvelo, V, 281; controversy with Marcus Beneventanus, V, 199-201, 282; criticized by, Cirvelo, V, 210-1, Nunes, V, 282; relations with Laet, V, 189-91, with Nifo, V, 85, 182-8, 279; repeated by Tannstetter, V, 222-4, by Rocha, V, 209

Pigment, V, 141; medicinal, V, 513

Pile-driver, V, 594

Pill, V, 461, 611, VI, 218, 567

Pinocier, G. pr Paris, VI, 459

Pinzio, Paolo, tr, V, 67-68

Pirckheimer, Charitas, V, 352

Pirckheimer, Wilibald, V, 337, 340; astrology of, V, 171, 350, 361; correspondence of, V, 171, 350, 355; family of, V, 351-2, 361; friend of, V, 369; library, V, 357, 369; nativity of, V, 351, VI, 597; poison and conjuration, V, 472; publishes Ptolemy's *Geography,* V, 288, 356

Pirovano, Gabriele, V, 159, VI, 201

Pisa, V, 81, VI, 338; archbishop of, VI, 335, 522; born near, VI, 236; leaning tower of, V, 585; prediction concerning, V, 235; university, VI, 335, taught at, V, 45, 67, 74, 90, 184, 274, 325-6, 501, VI, 226-7, 325, 332-4, 522; and see Leonard of

Pisano, Alfonso, astrologer, V, 255

Pisanus, V, 365

Pisces, see Conjunction of 1524

Piso, William, cited, VI, 317; criticized, V, 478

Pistoia, V, 269, VI, 540

Pistorius, Alexander, VI, 597

Pistorius, Jo. Niddanus, VI, 211, 240, 461-3

Pistorius, Simon, VI, 596

Pitatus, Petrus, V, 264-5, 375, 379, 581, VI, 124; cited, VI, 18

Pitch, VI, 282

Pius IV, and astrology, VI, 156; bull of, VI, 148

Pius V, VI, 127

Pius, Rudolph, cardinal, horoscope of, VI, 105
Pizzimenti, Domenico, teacher of Porta, VI, 245, 418
Placenta of Genoa, V, 611
Placidus, Sextus Papirius, V, 382
Placotomus, Io., letter to, V, 399
Plagiarism, charges of, V, 112, 134, 144, 154, 289, 331, 333-4, 350, 443, 464, 556, VI, 55, 257, 456; guilty of, V, 4, 85-86, 118, 122, 187, 441, 457, 555-6, VI, 43, 401, 473; not guilty, V, 21; of citations, V, 586
Plancy, Guillaume, V, 7, 558
Planerius, see Pianero
Planet, affixed to its sphere, VI, 12, 34, 95; aspects of, V, 319, 323, 557, 655, VI, 120, 138, 144, 159, 197, 200, 204; comet and, VI, 87, 89, 95; denser part of its sphere, V, 153; hand, and, V, 160, 527, VI, 164, 167; history, periods of, and, V, 121, 311, VI, 174; hours of, V, 345; human body and, V, 122, 309, VI, 167, 200; influence in general, see Stars, influence of; metals and, V, 249, VI, 301, 318; morning and evening stars, VI, 10; move with own motion, VI, 25, 71-72, 376, 380, 384, 387; moved by their spheres, VI, 34, 39, 58, by sun's rays, V, 388; names, VI, 198, after men, VI, 107, used in incantations, V, 135; nature and properties, V, 258, 292, 317, VI, 22, 124, 138, 158-60, 197, 200, 354, 427, 435, 451, 473, 508; observations of, V, 366; order of, VI, 432; quantity of, VI, 110; spirits of, V, 102, 206, 569, VI, 387, 441, and see Intelligences; sympathy of seven stones with, VI, 301; temperaments and, V, 237; theory of, V, 173, 205, 246-7, 284, 371, 490, VI, 3, 6, 14, 20, 27, 30-31, 58-59, 82, 159-60, 192, 299, 375, and see Copernican, Ptolemaic; winds and, VI, 212
Planisphere, V, 583
Plant, see Herb
Plantago lanceolata, VI, 263
Plantain, V, 483, VI, 263
Plantin, Christopher, pr Antwerp, VI, 31-32, 47, 409, 418
Plantsch, Martin, V, 70
Plaster, medicinal, V, 461, 483, 541; for the memory, V, 607
Plate, anatomical, V, 508, 519-20, 528; of machines, V, 593-5; of plants, VI, 265-6, 273
Platearius, V, 454, 460
Plato, and alchemy, V, 624, 643, and anatomy, V, 514, and Aristotle, VI, 363, 386, and demons, V, 82, 87-88, and witchcraft, V, 105; cited, V, 86, 119-20, 527, VI, 48, 110, 300, 312, 350, 374, 377-8, 458, 546; comm., VI, 377; compiled from, V, 551, VI, 228, 406; pseudo, VI, 197; read, VI, 382; refuted, V, 96; silent on astrology, VI, 199; *Timaeus,* V, 87
Platonic, Platonism and Platonist, V, 113, 236, 561, VI, 148, 373-4, 382, 391, 409, 450-1, 454, 456, 480, 482, 518, 563; and see Neo-Platonism
Plato Junior, alchemist, V, 624
Plato of Tivoli, V, 252
Platter, Felix, physician, VI, 284
Platter, Thomas, humanist, V, 153
Pleiad, VI, 106
Pleurisy, V, 260, 326, VI, 215
Pliny the Elder, V, 451; attitude towards the magi duplicated, VI, 303, 305, 309; cited, V, 103, 157, 272, 460, 470, 487, 514, 574, 610-1, 614, 647, VI, 21, 32, 67, 167, 246, 273, 275, 281, 292, 294, 300, 305, 308-10, 319, 334, 358, 388, 399, 402, 404, 485-6; comm. V, 370, 386-8, 560-2, VI, 256-7; compiled from, V, 418, VI, 271, 277, 303; criticized, V, 396, 447, 449, 452-3, 469, 523, 564, VI, 205, 416; ed., VI, 258; "errors of," V, 502, VI, 254, 280, 402; experiments of, V, 437, VI, 421; *Medicina,* V, 437; misrepresented, V, 561; praised, V, 388, VI, 185
Pliny Junior, *Practica,* V, 113
Pliny the Younger, *Letters,* VI, 488
Plitt, G. L. (1876), V, 149
Plonisco, John, astrologer, V, 218
Plotinus, V, 119; cited, VI, 48, 351, 375, 425, 442, 450; and *Theology* of Aristotle, VI, 449
Plough, mechanical, V, 595
Plumati and Sabachnikoff (1901), V, 33
Plusquam Commentator, see Turrisianus
Plutarch, V, 421, 463; cited, VI, 399,

403, 485; compiled from, V, 551, 562; ed., VI, 502
Poem, Poet and Poetry, V, 57, 124, 152, 168, 213, 229, 254, 267, 270-1, 286-7, 296, 435, 488, 493, VI, 28, 51, 105-6, 127, 191, 234, 257, 278, 313, 318, 341, 395, 400, 438, 443, 504, 531, 546, 561; against alchemy, V, 126, 536; alchemical, V, 534, VI, 124; ancient quoted, V, 477, VI, 458; college of, V, 347; effect on human body, VI, 234; fifteenth century, V, 114; geomancy in, VI, 472; Greek, VI, 492, 504; introductory and prefatory, V, 46, 76-77, 300-1, 322, 355, 365, 373, 380, 394, VI, 352, 453, 470; laureate, V, 581; mythological, V, 307; oracles in, VI, 472; quoted, V, 52, VI, 393, 509; science and, VI, 267; taught, V, 338, 345, VI, 238
Pogo, A. (1935), V, 319-20
Pogonia, a comet, VI, 134
Poison and Poisoning, V, 115, 459, 564, VI, 388, 499; action of, V, 496, VI, 223, by antipathy, VI, 430, without contact? V, 473; animal its own cure, V, 634; cause of disease, V, 60, 627; contrary for, VI, 311; cure for, VI, 315, 423, tested, VI, 335; danger of, from copper pestle, V, 457; death by, predicted, V, 587, VI, 195; distinguished from contagion, V, 496, veneficia, VI, 545-6, witchcraft, VI, 515; feared, VI, 201; maiden fed on, V, 473, 480, 485, 551, VI, 420; medicine and, V, 479, 639; preservation from, V, 608, 612; safeguards against, accepted, V, 481, 612, VI, 241, 310, doubted, V, 478, 485, VI, 232, 323; slow, V, 472-3, 480, 485, VI, 220, 223; of sorcerers and witches, V, 526; stars and, V, 473, VI, 209; tales of, V, 115; tip of tail of stag alone, V, 646; warned against, V, 230; works on, V, 472-4, 477-81, 484-5, 600, 605
Poitiers, VI, 230
Poland, Pole and Polish, V, 404, 539, 550; count of, VI, 480; king of, V, 170, 392, 396, 409, 479, 482, 640-1, VI, 89; pest in, VI, 185; princess of, VI, 42; travel to and in, V, 409, 650, VI, 59
Polemon, V, 67, VI, 164
Polich, Martin, astrologer, V, 379
Polidoro, Valerio (1587), VI, 556-8
Politian or Poliziano, Angelo, V, 164, 452, VI, 600; horoscope of, VI, 105, 598
Political, V, 426, VI, 28, 118, 344, 395, 570; change with earth's movement, V, 414-5, 419, VI, 75, with eclipses, VI, 22; fatal downfall of kingdoms, VI, 15, 354; four monarchies, VI, 41-42, 76, 116, 352, 498; imagination, VI, 413; medicine, VI, 407; periods of empires, V, 417-8, 427, VI, 174, 396, 435, 465, 499; prediction, V, 168, 180, 224, 230, 235, 290, VI, 136, 173, abstained from, V, 222, forbidden, V, 224, VI, 171; propaganda, VI, 344; relation of state to religion and science, VI, 395; signs, VI, 407, 530; thought, VI, 525
Politus, Bassanus, V, 557
Polium, an herb, VI, 262
Polydore Vergil, V, 586, VI, 488-9; put on Index, VI, 147-8
Polydorus, Chrysogonus, ed Geber, V, 545
Polygraphy, VI, 434, 442
Pomerania, duke of, VI, 102; travel in, VI, 254
Pomesania, bishop of, VI, 303
Pommard, VI, 105
Pompey, VI, 471
Pomponazzi, Ioannes Nicolaus, V, 95
Pomponazzi, Pietro, V, 78, 399, 552; cited, VI, 386, 407, 416, 516, 521, 531, 559; described, V, 94; disagreed with, V, 636, 660, VI, 236, 536; influence of, VI, 511, 513, 532; pupil of, V, 99, 488, 601; relation to Achillini, V, 39, 94-95, Affaytatus, V, 273, Cattaneo, V, 92, Giuntini, VI, 131, Gratarolo, V, 600-1, Nifo, V, 94-95, 97-98, Paracelsus, V, 645, Vanini, VI, 569-70; works, Commentaries, V, 99-100, *Commento inedito*, V, 100, *Defensorium*, V, 96, 98, *Dubitationes*, V, 100, *Fato et libero arbitrio*, V, 99-100, 110, *Immortalitate*, V, 94, 96-98, *Incantationibus*, V, 43, 98-110, 252, 600, 660, VI, 131, 408, 411, *Intensione et remissione*, V, 95-96, *Nutritione et*

augmentatione, V, 95, *Reactione,* V, 95, *Solutiones,* V, 98
Pontano, Giovanni, cited, V, 213, 227, 389, 403, 637, VI, 93, 131, 367; in favor of astrology, V, 165-6, 356, VI, 112, 197, 500; quoted, V, 52; reprinted, V, 299; tr, V, 342
Pontigny, V, 437
Pontius, alchemist, V, 623
Pontius, G. pr Milan, V, 543
Pontus, see Heracleides of
Pontus de Tyard, see Tyard
Ponzetti, Ferdinand, *De venenis,* V, 472-4; *Tertia pars naturalis,* V, 472, VI, 476-7
Ponzinibius of Piacenza, Franciscus, V, 70, VI, 538
Poor, demoralizing effect on the state, V, 243; extreme, VI, 453; provision for, advised for 1524, V, 211; weekly alms for, VI, 404
Pope, see Papacy and names of individual popes
Pope, Alexander, quoted, VI, 457
Poplar tree, VI, 416
Populace, VI, 338; faith in predictions, VI, 99-100; harmed more by witches, VI, 524; ignorant, V, 585; not to read, V, 262; prediction concerning, V, 255; strangle hydrophobiacs, V, 484; susceptible to impostors and innovators, V, 279, 330; tumults of, predicted, V, 272; and see Error, popular
Popular Astronomy, VI, 44, 55
Popular indignation, V, 393; medicine, V, 431, 437; report, VI, 288; rumor and panic, V, 182
Popularization, from printing, V, 5, 608, VI, 428; in education, V, 148, 642
Porchetus Silvaticensis, VI, 445
Porcupine, V, 477
Pores, distended, VI, 540
Porphyry, VI, 114, 448; cited, VI, 425, 484; comm., V, 167
Porri, Alessio, exorcist (1601), VI, 557-8
Porta, Giovanni Battista, alchemical experiments by, VI, 245-6; cited, VI, 258, 294, 319, 431; influence, VI, 429-30, 434; Inquisition and, VI, 150, 156; quoted, VI, 145; tests assertions about magnet, VI, 282; works, *Chirofisonomia,* VI, 163-4, *Coelestis physiognomiae,* VI, 162-3, *Humana physiognomia,* V, 68, VI, 164, *Magia naturalis,* V, 147, 590, VI, 215-6, 245-6, 401, 418-22, *Phytognomonica,* VI, 422-3, prohibited, VI, 150
Portaleone, Abraham, *De auro,* V, 645-7; *Consilia,* V, 645
Portent, see Prodigy
Porter, VI, 209
Portese, Agostin da, pr Venice, VI, 470
Portinarius, Bernard, V, 85-86, 253
Portius, see Porzio
Portonariis, Vincentius de, pr Lyons, V, 124
Portugal and Portuguese, V, 167, 453, 459, 469, 550, VI, 128, 314, 382, 479, 560; cited, VI, 297, 353; education, VI, 561; floods predicted for, V, 229; in the East, VI, 346; king of, V, 293; language, V, 466, VI, 274; mathematician, V, 282, 292, VI, 34; route to East, VI, 345; and see Voyages of Discovery
Portunariis, Jac. de M., V, 85
Porzio, Simone, V, 273-4, 478, VI, 459
Posidonius, V, 523; criticized, V, 448
Possevin, Antonius, VI, 201
Post Glossators, V, 503, VI, 276
Post mortem, V, 482, 509, 517
Postel, Guillaume, career, VI, 341; cited, V, 374, 418, VI, 361; works, *Causis,* VI, 343-4, *Compendium cosmographiae,* VI, 341, 345, *Nativitate,* VI, 341-2, *Orbis terrae concordia,* VI, 454-5, *Universitate,* VI, 343-6, others, VI, 454
Posthumous publication, V, 6-7, 45, 48, 99, 310, 327, 347, 353-4, 371, 375, 409, 470, 501, 540, 552, 593, 600, 620, VI, 39, 49, 61-62, 125, 161, 163, 189, 208, 210, 216-7, 227, 237, 252, 254, 256, 265, 270, 285, 291, 294-5, 308, 311, 326, 334, 368, 379-80, 441, 447, 452, 489, 494, 501-4, 506, 566, 599
Potentiality and actuality, VI, 384
Potion, magic, V, 478; medical, V, 513, 541
Potter and Pottery, V, 596
Poyet, Guillaume, chancellor of France, V, 291
Pozzuoli, bishop of, VI, 528
Practica, see Prediction, annual

Praesenius, Cominus, pr Brescia, VI, 231
Praestigiae and Praestigium, V, 385, VI, 193, 430, 456
Praetorius, Iohannes (1715), VI, 115
Praetorius, Johann, astrology of, VI, 60, 84; cited, V, 397, VI, 184; lectures of, VI, 59-60; on comet of 1577, VI, 73, 84
Praetorius, Michael (1619), V, 584
Praetorius, Paulus, VI, 596
Prag, VI, 225, 318; dedic from, VI, 505; pr at, VI, 56, 224, 227, 474; virgin of, VI, 321; visited, V, 415, VI, 59
Prantl, Carl, V, 407
Prasinus, a gem, VI, 232
Pratensis (Pratis), Jason (J. A.), V. 443-4, VI, 529
Pratensis, Johannes, V, 388; correspondence with Tycho Brahe, V, 588-9, 642, VI, 54, 69
Prateolus, Gabriel, cited, VI, 544
Prato, V, 67, 326
Prayer, VI, 168, 379; against threatening ills, V, 217; answered under certain constellations, V, 117; cabalistic condemned, V, 661; effect on body and mind, V, 106-7; for fair weather, by clergy, V, 231-2; frees from diabolical magic, V, 117; of Aldebert, VI, 551; of philosophers, V, 107; some forms of, condemned, V, 283; stops rain, V, 104
Pré, Galiot du, pr Paris, VI, 108
Preacher and Preaching, VI, 413, 491, 530; and see Sermon
Predestination, VI, 350, 446
Prediction, annual, V, 93, 160-1, 166-9, 174, 179, 186, 204, 206, 208, 210, 212-7, 220, 222, 224, 229-31, 234-47, 253, 255, 267, 271, 279-81, 283, 286, 309-10, 322, 326-7, 330-1, 345-7, 356, 361, 379, 382, 392, 396, 400, 418, 421, 431, 433-4, 439-40, 443, 466, VI, 56, 60, 106, 111, 123-4, 126, 133-4, 143, 147, 157-8, 160, 474, 483, advice as to, V, 572; criticized, V, 186, 189-90, VI, 119, 359; disinclination for, V, 239, 244; popular faith in, VI, 99-100; profitable, VI, 4; satirized, V, 286-7, 312-3; sensational, V, 222; and see World, end of
Prehistoric find, V, 512
Prelate, prediction concerning, V, 230, 258-9; and see Archbishop, Bishop
Prices, V, 469; brought down, VI, 319; rise predicted, V, 401
Pridianus, Paulinus, cited, VI, 74
Prierias, Sylvester, inquisitor, V, 71, VI, 556
Priest, V, 65, 86, 302, 349, 354, 365, 509, 537, 540, VI, 360, 453, 481, 558; astrology and astronomy of, V, 162, 296, 337, 351, 384, VI, 166, 281; blameless life, V, 296; breastplate of high, VI, 315; cited, VI, 337; crafty, V, 97, VI, 362; medicine and, VI, 520; of Jerusalem, VI, 301; on metals and gems, VI, 301; unskilled, V, 107
Prieur, Claude, VI, 547
Primrose, James (1638), VI, 222
Primum mobile, V, 282, 284, 421, 425, 557, VI, 112, 155, 210, 551; solid and impenetrable, VI, 26
Prince, V, 259, 271, VI, 109; alchemy, V, 141; collection, V, 598; death predicted, V, 290, VI, 15; dedic to, V, 153; dream of, VI, 508; exhortation to, V, 311; gullible, V, 279, VI, 245; Italy widowed of, V, 245; just, V, 579; predicted, V, 259; speaking to, V, 363; and see King
Princeps, Petrus, see Le Prince
Printing, see Censorship, Edition, Invention of, Posthumous
Prisciano, Pellegrino, V, 168-9, 253
Priscillianists, VI, 125, 157
Prison (including imprisonment and captivity), at discretion of Inquisition, VI, 154; death trying to escape from, VI, 191; for criminals, V, 578; for failure to testify aganist heretics, VI, 153; for printers and booksellers, VI, 170; for witchcraft, VI, 535; of Agrippa, V, 137, Bruno, VI, 423, 428, Campanella, VI, 173-4, Cardan, VI, 152, elector of Saxony, VI, 489, Francis I, V, 396, Finé, V, 285, Maximilian, V, 399, Peucer, VI, 495, Raimondo, VI, 474, others, V, 55, 286; predicted, V, 59, 219, 587.
Priulus, Franciscus, astrologer, V, 253
Privation, V, 40; explains fortune, chance and accident, V, 552; no regress from, VI, 244

Problem, V, 144, 225, 580; solution of, V, 90-91; stock, V, 23, 643; works of, V, 551, VI, 600
Proceedings of Royal Society of Medicine, VI, 216, 218
Proclus, V, 185, VI, 114; cited, V, 82, 154, 551, VI, 10, 48, 409; opposed, VI, 467; pr, V, 257, 343, 349, VI, 114, 448; tr. V, 257, 343, VI, 114, 154; works, *Magia,* VI, 407, *Paraphrasis,* V, 400, *Sphere,* V, 343, 349, VI, 16, *Sufformationes,* V, 343
Proctor, Robert (1898-1903), V, 116, 179
Prodigy, V, 374, 573, VI, 91, 135, 407-9, 488-91, 496, 531; as warning, VI, 367; at birth of great, V, 104, 108; contrary to natural order, VI, 186; disapproved, V, 660; divine, VI, 409; from stars, VI, 75, 77-79, 104; in nature, V, 3, 399, VI, 225, 291; in sky, V, 222, 399, VI, 75, 78-79; of first degree, VI, 408; rain, VI, 366
Profatius Judaeus, cited, V, 421
Professor, candidate for chair, VI, 222-3; dismissed for religious views, VI, 524; emeritus, VI, 289; extraordinary, V, 38, 71, 402, VI, 61; on feast days, V, 244; ordinary, V, 38, 43, 71, 90, 94-95, 234, 237, VI, 119, 201, 290; royal, V, 285, 291, 298, 304, 543, VI, 19, 141, 178, 219, 368, 561, 598; superstitious, VI, 240
Progress, idea of, see Modern; not steady, VI, 392; tradition and, V, 250-1
Projectile, V, 48
Projection, alchemical, V, 533, VI, 242
Proksch, J. K. (1875), V, 324
Promissor, astrological, VI, 160
Pronunciation, V, 145
Proof-reader, V, 346
Prophecy and Prophet, V, 87, 89-90, 104-5, 108, 124, 212-3, 236, 374, 627, VI, 441, 446, 451, 456; advent of, V, 510; astrology and, VI, 29; compared with other men, V, 575, VI, 511; distinguished from divination, VI, 467, divine from natural, V, 477; has ceased, VI, 529, 550; imaginative, not intellectual, VI, 512; knowledge of, VI, 511-2; magical, VI, 457-8; natural gift, VI, 511; pseudo, V, 60; recent criticized, V, 374; where born, V, 575, VI, 511; why understood only after the event? V, 575, VI, 511
Proportion, V, 41, VI, 373, 378, 599; arithmetical and geometrical, V, 594; demons and, V, 82, 88; finding means in, V, 292; of velocities, V, 41
Propugnatore, Il, VI, 373
Proscarabeus, an insect, VI, 268
Prosdocimo de' Beldomandi, V, 166, 359
Prost, Auguste (1881), V, 128, 131-2, 136, 286, 434
Prost, J. A. & M. prs Lyons, VI, 173
Prosthaphaereses, V, 350, VI, 55
Protestant and Protestantism, V, 11-12, 14, 37, 66, 99, 378, 411, 413, 431, VI, 46, 136, 147, 247, 419-20, 433, 481, 493, 495, 498, 520, 530, 537; cited, VI, 361, 601; inclination, V, 127-8, VI, 528; minister, VI, 346, 523; turned Protestant, V, 331, 600, VI, 38, 457
Proteus, VI, 504
Protonotary, apostolic, V, 256
Provence, V, 296, 304, 644, VI, 188, 553
Providence, divine, V, 164, 295, VI, 203, 343, 350-1, 396
Prowe, Leopold (1883-84), V, 200, 341, 353, 384, 391, 406-10, 413-4, 417, 419-20
Pruckner, Nicolaus, V, 322-3, 372, VI, 11
Prugner, see Pruckner
Prune, V, 611
Prussia, V, 404, 415, 531, VI, 455, 466; currency of, V, 426; duke of, see Albert; written in, VI, 302
Prutenic Tables, see Reinhold
Psalm, see Bible
Psalter, VI, 105
Psellus, on demons, V, 568, VI, 404-5
Psychology, V, 140, 269, 577, VI, 340, 494; and see Aristotle, *De anima,* Soul
Psylli, V, 473
Ptolemaic astrology, V, 194, VI, 161, 346, 512; abandoned, VI, 31, 187, 193; combined with Alcabitius, VI, 119; comet and, VI, 89-90; lack of student interest in, V, 400-1; Pico and, V, 317; preferred, V, 180, 184-6, 191, 196, 209, 216, 223, 233, 243, 269, 277,

367, VI, 99, 103-4, 108, 120-1, 172, 174, 193, 487; reverted to, V, 250; too childish, VI, 109, 184
Ptolemaic astronomy, V, 154, 423, 489-90, VI, 51, 155, 201; combined with Copernican, VI, 6, 8, 55-57, 66; Copernicus and, V, 408, 412, 422, VI, 15, 21, 38, 42, 46-47; criticized, V, 416, 569-70, VI, 14, 30-31, 39, 326, 375-6; followed, VI, 10, 16, 32, 47, 60, 63; form retained, VI, 55; its arguments against earth's rotating, VI, 16; taught through seventeenth century, V, 247, VI, 7-8
Ptolemaic geography, disproved, V, 630; see Clime
Ptolemy, V, 307, 333, 427, 591; *Almagest,* V, 295, 336, 364, 419, 423, VI, 16, 37, 41, 82, 430, comm. V, 364, difficulty, V, 186, Epitome of, see Regiomontanus; altitude of pole altered since, V, 235; *Apotelesmata,* see *Quadripartitum;* biography, V, 403; *Centiloquium,* V, 185-6, 242, 278, VI, 159, 199, 367, authenticity questioned, V, 403, VI, 107, comm. V, 302, 356, criticized, V, 315, VI, 197, tr. V, 342; cited, V, 57, 167, 191, 207, 267, 276, 317, 418, 510, 566, VI, 6, 13, 16, 21, 27, 62, 71, 94, 97, 103-4, 110, 115, 120, 163, 167, 180, 212, 399, 432, as alchemist, V, 624, on comet, V, 321, pro astrology, V, 236; conjunctions, theory of, and, V, 120, 209-10, 216, 242, VI, 174; *Cosmography,* see *Geography;* criticized, V, 284, 407, VI, 318; defended, VI, 36; discovery since, V, 221; first of astrologers, V, 269; *Geography,* V, 173, 200, 288-9, 295, 336, 339, 355, 437, 566, comm. V, 251, 372, 564, maps of, V, 122, 173, tr, V, 342, 352, 356; *Harmonics,* VI, 89; ignored, VI, 470; image, astrological, and, V, 106, 533; legendary telescope of, VI, 421; medieval astronomers preferred to, V, 172; misinterpreted, VI, 139; *Musica,* V, 364; ninth sphere and, VI, 62; *Optica,* V, 365; observations of, V, 353, 422, 426, VI, 3; *Planisphere,* V, 200; praised, V, 389, except as astrologer, VI, 180; *Quadripartitum,* V, 185, 190, 192-3, 277, 364, 419, VI, 41, 90, 112, 172, 199, 202, 448, 500, comm., V, 73, 79, 184-5, 257, 402, 571, VI, 102, 114, 120-2, 486, epitome, V, 320, last edition of, VI, 99, tr, V, 400, VI, 120; services to mankind, V, 389; *Tetrabiblos,* see *Quadripartitum;* text incorrect, V, 415; zodiac, division into houses, VI, 202-3
Public service, V, 378
Publishing to sell, V, 114
Pullon da Trino, Gioanni, pr Lyons, VI, 364
Pulse, VI, 381; and firmament, V, 651; tides compared to, VI, 388; treatises on, V, 44
Pumice stone, VI, 310, 416
Pump, V, 594
Pun, V, 245, VI, 223
Punishment, beheading, V, 55, 598; burning, VI, 428, 511, alive? VI, 526, 539, 552; capital opposed, V, 578; corporal, V, 149, 218, VI, 170, 526; death and confiscation, VI, 171, 552; exile, VI, 149; fine, VI, 170; galleys, VI, 149, 151; hanging, VI, 136; merely spiritual, for having or reading magic books, VI, 150; on the wheel, V, 641; strangling, VI, 527, 539; of witches, VI, 337, 515, 526-7, 539; see Prison
Purgative and Purging, V, 121, 289, 461, 551, VI, 127, 144, 197, 221, 223, 235, 251, 313, 556, 559; action on humors, VI, 235; day before bathing, VI, 208
Purification, alchemical, V, 533
Puritan, V, 653
Purple cloth, VI, 282
Purpura, generation of, VI, 283-4
Puschmann, Theodor, V, 44
Pustule, V, 280
Puteus, Franciscus, VI, 213-4
Putrefaction and Putridity, VI, 227, 355; controversy as to, V, 666; in alchemy, V, 133, 590; relation to contagion, V, 496; and see Generation, spontaneous, from
Puys, Jacques du, bookseller, Paris, VI, 526
Pygmy, V, 628, VI, 408; existence doubted, V, 41, 578
Pyramid, said to have six bases, VI, 138

Pyrausta, winged quadruped living in flames, V, 647, VI, 95
Pyrites, VI, 307, 309
Pyromancy, V, 55, 58, 68, 587, VI, 468; alchemy and, V, 634; astrology and, VI, 16, 176; evil, V, 660, VI, 430; false, VI, 193; forbidden, VI, 146-7, 169; superstitious, V, 297, VI, 485
Pyrotechnics, VI, 243
Pyrrhus (of Epirus), VI, 513
Pythagoras, cited, V, 82, VI, 378, 569; depicted, VI, 471; father of the cabala, VI, 444; longevity of, V, 166
Pythagorean, V, 113, 491, 552, VI, 63, 202, 358, 454, 456-7, 479, 503, 601
Pythian Apollo, VI, 504
Python or Pythoness, V, 399

Quacelbenus, William, naturalist, VI, 268
Quack, V, 7-8, 283, 618, VI, 219, 244
Quadrant, VI, 28; Reinhold's poor wooden, VI, 4
Quadrivium, defended, V, 243; praised, V, 164
Quadruped, tartar in flesh of, V, 649
Quality, VI, 311, 385; action by, VI, 424; agreement in, V, 571; contrary, VI, 414; dryness, VI, 284; element and, VI, 366; ethereal, V, 552-3; first, V, 40, 91, 125, 506-7, 554-5, VI, 109, 354-5, 369, 381; four orders of, VI, 293; genius and, VI, 413; manifest, V, 101, 456-7; reduced to two, V, 569, VI, 120, 370; regular solids and, VI, 110; secondary, VI, 354, 381; works of art and, VI, 500
Quarantine, V, 493
Quartan fever, see Fever
Queen, VI, 472-3; see England, France, etc.; mother, V, 128, 285, VI, 130, 531
Quenay of Evreux, VI, 182, 493
Quentell, Petrus, pr Cologne, V, 321, VI, 491
Quercetanus, see Duchesne
Querengis, Petrus de, of Bergamo, pr Venice, V, 75
Quesne, see Duchesne
Quetelet, A. (1864), V, 319
Quickelberg, Samuel, VI, 268
Quicksilver, see Mercury, the metal
Quinsy, VI, 501
Quintessence, see Essence, fifth
Quintilian, V, 642
Quiricus de Augustis, V, 464
Quirini, Vicenzo, dedic to, V, 79, 163
Quistellio, Fra Ambrogio, V, 544-5
Quivira, VI, 436
Quodlibeta, V, 206-7
Qur, used for Cur, V, 145

R.P., VI, 184
Rabanus, cited, VI, 300
Rabanus Maurus, VI, 300
Rabbit, VI, 277
Rabelais, V, 313, 435
Rabies, V, 484, 497, 608; and dog-star, V, 482, VI, 351
Race, black and white, V, 34
Race, Monsieur, surgeon, V, 598
Radiation, of force, VI, 241; and see Emanation, Species
Radl, Emil (1913), VI, 334, 371; quoted, VI, 325
Raemdonck, van (1869), VI, 179
Raggius of Florence, V, 253
Ragusa, V, 96, VI, 131; archdeacon of, VI, 218; merchant of, V, 264; and see George of
Raimondo, Annibale, V, 661, VI, 473-5; censured, VI, 185; put on Index, VI, 147
Rain, and evaporation, V, 31, 195, 592; of black bread, VI, 491; of grain, VI, 490; of minute animals, V, 157; of signs of the Passion, VI, 468; Paracelsus on, V, 658; and see Weather
Rainbow, VI, 32, 364, 399; at evening, V, 657, night, VI, 432-3; natural, VI, 657; of promise, V, 195, 217, 657, VI, 80, 356, 367; twenty-four in one week, VI, 267
Ram, disease of the, VI, 212
Ramelli, Agostino, (1588), V, 596
Ramism, at Paris, VI, 142; criticized by Libavius, VI, 238-9
Ramus, Ioannes, VI, 598
Ramus, Petrus, V, 565, 567; attack on Aristotle, V, 421, VI, 363; attitude towards Paracelsus, V, 642; cited, V, 338, VI, 96, 354; death of, VI, 450; foe of, V, 556; friend of, V, 5, VI, 38; logic of, opposed, VI, 190; pupil

of, VI, 141; quoted, V, 338; Rheticus and, V, 413, 416; stress on method, V, 11, VI, 565
Ramusio, Giov. Batt., V, 488, 493, 495
Rangoni, count Guido, V, 204, 227; dedic to, VI, 485
Rangoni, Tommaso Giannotti, see Philologus
Ranzovius, Henry, astrologer, V, 222, VI, 53, 140; *Catalogus,* V, 162, VI, 101, 135-6; geniture, VI, 194; used, VI, 430
Rapard, Francis, physician, V, 328-30, VI, 207-8
Raphael, angel, V, 102, VI, 357, 551; spirit of planet Mercury, V, 569, VI, 441
Rapirio, Iovita, pr Venice, VI, 473
Rapolstein, baron of, V, 610
Rasis, V, 387, VI, 230; abandoned, V, 317; alchemy, V, 693; Almansor, V, 529; cited, V, 46, 54, 317, 480, 504, 623-5, VI, 252, 431; criticized, V, 114; followed Galen, V, 500; *Liber luminum,* V, 541
Rassius, see Noens
Ratdolt, Erhard, pr Venice and Augsburg, V, 56, 342-3, 345-6, 419
Ratisbon, Diet of, V, 402
Ratzenberger, Caspar (1598), VI, 266
Rauard, M. A. pr Lyons (1649), VI, 433
Raut, Otto, M. D., astrologer, V, 160
Ravanis, P. de, pr Venice, VI, 471
Raven, head of, used in witchcraft, VI, 526
Ravenna, VI, 449, 484; college for students from, V, 205; and see Philologus, Tommaso da
Ravisius-Textor, Johannes, VI, 459
Raziel, cited, V, 637, VI, 301
Reaction, VI, 368
Reading, V, 605; wide, V, 134, VI, 531
Reales, Francisco, VI, 166
Reason, age of, V, 14; and experience, V, 92, 97, 521, 545, 565, VI, 193; and sense, warfare of, V, 105; indirect and tortuous, V, 563
Reatius, an enchanter, V, 103
Rebartus, Thomas, pr Jena, VI, 36
Rebdorf, prior of, V, 232, 348
Recanati, senate and people of, V, 218
Recantation, VI, 130
Receptarum, liber, V, 180
Rechter Gebrauch d'Alchemie, V, 543
Recipe, alchemical, V, 539; excess of, V, 650; medical, V, 441, VI, 219; old abandoned for new, V, 650; multiplied, V, 461, VI, 419, 601-2
Recueil des chroniques de Flandre, V, 510
Recorde, Robert (1556), VI, 15-16
Records of Civilization, V, 406
Red Sea, V, 212; dividing waters of, V, 222
References, cross, V, 17
Reformation, Catholic, V, 37, 653, VI, 126, 145-78, 419; in general, V, 37; of learning required, V, 631; Protestant intellectual illumination, V, 662, specters fewer since, VI, 533, but witchcraft increased, VI, 550, and see Protestant
Refraction, V, 366, 490
Regensburg, V, 407, 440, 529; and see Ratisbon
Reggio, VI, 209, 268
Regiomontanus, V, 232, 234, 330; astrology and, V, 342, 363; attitude towards past, V, 336-7; cited, V, 131, 172, 227, 265, 309, 421, VI, 11, 21, 23, 62, 103, 131, 180, 432; comm., V, 372; criticized, V, 200, 334, VI, 35, 377, 565; death of, V, 333-4; Diadochi of, V, 370, 377; doggerel on end of world ascribed to, V, 373-4; geniture of, V, 367, 565, VI, 595; influence of, V, 348-50, 376-7, see Schöner and; letter of, VI, 60; manuscripts of, V, 339, 358-9, 364, 370, 393; oration on, V, 368; observations by, V, 366, 376; praised, V, 200, 332, 587, VI, 37; publication, program of, V, 339-40, 355, 361, 395, executed by others, V, 342, 344, 352, 358, 364, 369-70; pupils of, V, 345; reformer or restorer of mathematics, V, 332-5, 347, 366; tables of, compared with Prutenic, VI, 5; tr, V, 342; used, V, 131; works, *Additiones,* V, 360-1, *Annotationes,* V, 356, *Calendar,* V, 340-2, *Chiromancy,* V, 673, 678, *Cometae magnitudine,* V, 356-7, 365, *Disputationes,* V, 336-7, 340-2, *Ephemerides,*

V, 232, 340-2, 348, *Epitome of Almagest,* V, 6, 172, 179, 335, 340-1, 565, *Fundamenta operationum,* V, 369, *Introd. in elementa Euclidis,* V, 361, *Meteoroscopium,* V, 352, 372, *Optio introd.*, V, 360-1, *Ponderibus et aqueductibus,* V, 361, *Problemata primi mobilis,* V, 225, *Problemata xxix Saphaeae,* V, 355-6, 359, *Quadratura circuli,* V, 357, *Tabula primi mobilis,* V, 369, *Tabulae directionum,* V, 340-2, 346, 358, 360, 371, 375-7, 399, 565, VI, 103, 111, 115, 119-20, *Tabulae sinuum,* V, 364, 376, *Torqueto,* V, 365, 370, *Triangulis,* V, 357, *Triangulis sphaericis,* V, 565; and see House, astrological, division of zodiac into

Regnault, G. pr Lyons, VI, 432

Regor, alchemist, cited, V, 623

Regulus, Sebastianus, VI, 290

Reichenbach, monastery of, V, 343

Reichling, D. (1905-1914), V, 342, VI, 469

Reicke, E. (1906), V, 171, 350, 407, 472, VI, 444

Reicurt, V, 603

Reid, Robert, abbot, preface to, V, 295

Reiffenstein, Johann, V, 386, VI, 597

Reims, V, 447; pr at, VI, 342; and see College of

Reinerius, Federicus, VI, 430

Reinhold, Erasmus, V, 376; astrology and, V, 417-8; cited, V, 418, VI, 18, 21; comm. Peurbach, V, 380, 412, 425, VI, 10-11; Copernican theory and, V, 412; copies Melanchthon, V, 380; criticized, VI, 36; ed., V, 380, 412; horoscope, VI, 105, 595; oration on Regiomontanus, V, 368, 393; praised, VI, 14; Prutenic tables, V, 251, 385, 411, 418, 429, VI, 3-6, 10-11, 13-15, 19, 24, 28-30, 37, 42-43, 57, 60, 82, 112, 140, 430, criticized, VI, 51, 139, not mentioned, VI, 11, 16, 23, 46; pupil of, V, 402

Reisch, Gregorius, *Margarita philosophica,* V, 139-41, 407, 523, 533, VI, 52

Relics of the saints, V, 106, 435-6, VI, 236; demon terrified by, VI, 528; operate how? V, 106, VI, 497

Religion and Religious, V, 142, 211, 259, 327, 677, VI, 82; astrology and, V, 5, 108, 287, VI, 133, 181, 569; bias, V, 653; Cardan and, V, 567; celibate, medical instruction for, V, 170; change, explained, V, 108, VI, 513-4, predicted, V, 180, 354; cleavage, V, 11-12; difficulties, V, 396; exile and refugees, V, 99, 600, VI, 183, 211, 423; founders of, V, 108, VI, 512; hypocrisy, VI, 362; lay attitude towards, V, 35; liberty, opposed, VI, 395; magic and, VI, 304; marvel and, V, 100; Order, see name of; personal, V, 162; past perversion of, VI, 498; prediction concerning, forbidden, VI, 171; questioned, V, 37; rather than rational or scientific, V, 140, 150; recluse, V, 87; renaissance of, V, 323; sect, V, 230; stimulates study of nature, VI, 290; works, V, 170

Remaclus Fuchs or Fusch, see Fusch

Remora, see Echineis

Renaissance, at Paris, V, 295; Cardan and, V, 565-6; Christian, V, 37; Christian Paracelsan urged, V, 631; fictitious, V, 53, 55, 335, 489; hypothesis of, V, 334; misconception of, explained, V, 5, 53; of anatomy, V, 524, 530, astrology, V, 265, chiromancy, V, 52-53, mathematical sciences, V, 304, 334, 366, 368, medicine, V, 494, religion, V, 323; "spirit of," V, 113

Renata, or Renée, duchess of Ferrara, V, 445

Renatus a Brechia, V, 308-9

Renaudet, A. (1916), VI, 439, 441-4

Rendiconti della Reale Accademia dei Lincei, VI, 424

Rendsburg, VI, 377

René de Breche, see Renatus

Renovatus, Rapitus, see Piccioli, Antonio

Resch, Conrad, pr Paris, V, 281

Resin, V, 461, 469

Resistance, V, 41; and see Motion

Reslyn, see Roeslin

Resolution, see Solution

Respiration, V, 511, 518, VI, 223, 228

Resurrection, V, 526; at certain times,

VI, 512; denied by Aristotle, V, 272; in pagan times, V, 103-4; naturally possible? V, 103, 272-3, VI, 385; signs of, in nature, VI, 259
Rete mirabile, V, 508, 519
Retz, Maréchal de, V, 304
Reuchlin, Johann, V, 9, VI, 444-5; *Arte cabalistica,* VI, 444-5, 462, 509; cabala and, V, 661; disciple of, VI, 450; put on Index, VI, 148; *Verbo mirifico,* V, 127, VI, 444, 462, 509
Reuponticum, V, 447
Reusch, Franz H. (1886), V, 220, 434, 619, VI, 146, 471, 474
Revelation, art of, VI, 516; attitude towards, V, 96; disregarded, V, 96; distinguished from divination, VI, 467
Reventlovius, Dethlevus, VI, 136
Reverberation, alchemical, V, 645
Revolution, of nativity, see Nativity; of year, V, 58, 219, 239, 251, 557, 572, VI, 169, 199, 430, 473, approved, V, 265, 318, VI, 114, 138, condemned, VI, 204, how reckoned, V, 189, 191, VI, 118, 120, tables of, VI, 30, tracts on, V, 265; popular, V, 222
Revolver, V, 34
Revue de Paris, VI, 393
Revue du seizième siècle, VI, 254, 257
Rex, a star, V, 289
Rey Pastor, Julio (1913, 1926), V, 275
Reymers, see Ursus, Nicolaus Raymarus
Reynaud, R. pr Tournon, VI, 97, 169
Rha, river, V, 447
Rhabarbarum, V, 447
Rhaetia, see Grisons
Rhaponticum, V, 447
Rhau, Georg, pr Wittenberg, V, 383
Rhazes, see Rasis
Rheticus, Joachim, V, 347, 426, VI, 598; *Additiones,* V, 391; astrology and, V, 384, 414-7; *Canon,* V, 354; *Chorographia,* V, 417; cited, V, 18, 21; Copernicus and, V, 408, 411-4; *Ephemeris,* V, 415; *Narratio prima,* V, 200, 391, 406, 412, 414-5, VI, 5, 8, 15, 52, 464; not cited, VI, 11, 46, 49; *Opus palatinum de triangulis,* V, 354; pupil of, V, 341; put on Index, VI, 147; *Quaestio,* V, 384, 403; quoted, V, 408; relation to, Flock, V, 341, 397, Gassar, V, 391, Gesner, VI, 8-9, Paracelsus, V, 416-7, Ramus, V, 413, 416-7, Werner, V, 350, 354
Rhetoric, V, 152, 168, 642, VI, 395, 443; Lullian, VI, 361; taught, V, 338, VI, 459
Rheumatism, remedy for, V, 432
Rhine, V, 407, 585, 625; and see Palatinate of
Rhinoceros, V, 476, VI, 186, 323
Rhodes, V, 314, 514; wood of, VI, 272
Rhodiginus, Caelius, cited, VI, 282, 521, 543
Rhubarb, action of, V, 101, 655; belittled, V, 479; burnt, for dysentery, VI, 518; Greek and Latin names of, V, 447; use of, V, 449
Ribas, Pedro de, VI, 167
Ricardus, Claudius, medical, VI, 311, 316
Riccardi, Pietro (1870-93), V, 245
Ricci, Ricchus or Ricius, Augustinus, V, 264, 284
Riccio, Paul, *De anima coeli,* VI, 446; *De caelesti agricultura,* VI, 462; put on Index, VI, 148
Riccoboni, Antonio (1598), V, 204, 325, 493, VI, 48
Richard of England, alchemical, V, 537, 604, 623
Richard of Middleton, VI, 547
Richard of St. Victor, VI, 459
Richardus, see Ricardus
Richelieu, cardinal, dedic to, VI, 510
Richis, Petrus Maria de, pr Naples, V, 79, 183
Richter, A. L. (1853), VI, 148
Richter, Johann, see Praetorius
Richter, J. P. (1883), V, 17-36
Richterus, W. pr Frankfurt, VI, 126
Riedel, Adolf (1863), V, 202
Riesenberg, VI, 303
Riezler Festscrift (1913), V, 232-3, 348
Rigaltius, ed, VI, 483
Rigaud, B. pr Lyons, VI, 472
Rigaud, S. pr Lyons, VI, 382
Right or left, V, 47, VI, 275
Rimini, V, 55, 269, VI, 127; pr at, V, 217; see Gregory of
Ring, amulet worn in, VI, 292; astrological, V, 327; astronomical, V, 521,

582-3; cramp-, V, 176; gem set in, VI, 232, 435, 519; magic, V, 106, VI, 147; sucking a gold, VI, 313; use in divination, VI, 509, in marriage, VI, 559
Ringelberg, Joachim Fortius, *Experimenta,* V, 147; geomancy, VI, 469; manuals, V, 152; put on Index, VI, 147; *Sphere,* V, 152
Riolan, Jean, VI, 247-9, 251-2; cited, V, 559, VI, 493
Riot, at Lyons, V, 112
Ripa Romea, see Bartholomaeus de
Ripley, George, alchemist, cited, V, 624, VI, 250; pr, VI, 161
Risigalum, V, 458
Ristori or Ristoro, Giuliano, V, 67, 326-7
Ristoro d'Arezzo, VI, 398
Rithmomachia, VI, 154
Rittmann, Alex. (1869) and (1870), V, 493-4, 556-7; quoted, V, 488
Rivari, Enrico (1929), VI, 153
River, V, 20; action of, V, 26, 156; origin of, from rainfall, V, 592, VI, 284, denied, V, 31, from sea, V, 30, VI, 284, 342, 362, 432, from vapor in earth, V, 23, VI, 432; water, VI, 546; see Nile and other particular rivers
Rivettus, Georgius (1592), VI, 211
Rivista di filosofia, VI, 173
Rivista di storia delle scienze, V, 39, 44, 46, 479
Rivius, Johannes (1541), VI, 302, 498-9, 530, 533
Rizza Casa, Giorgio, VI, 160-1
Robert, earl of Leicester, dedic to, VI, 41
Robert, king of Naples and Sicily, dedic to, V, 450, VI, 300
Robertis, Cassandra de, V, 445
Robertis, Hieronymus de, V, 445
Robertis, Honoratus de (1585), VI, 371
Roberto, Felippe, pr Tarragona, VI, 96, 166
Robertus, Gaudentius (1692), VI, 127
Robertus Vallensis, see Vallée, Robert
Robyns, John, V, 320-1
Rocha, Thomas, *Compilatio,* V, 161; *Digna redargutio,* V, 92, 208-9; *Diebus criticis,* V, 174; *Epistola contra necromanticos,* V, 92-93
Rocha Tallada, VI, 558
Rochas, Adolphe (1856), V, 125
Roderick of Majorca, V, 674
Rodericus, Ludovicus, pr Lisbon, V, 551
Rodianus, alchemist, cited, V, 538
Rodriguez, see Rodericus
Rodulphus, Volumius, V, 557
Roelants, Joachim, V, 529
Roeschilde, VI, 524
Roeslin, Helisaeus, VI, 55, 191; cited, V, 374, VI, 253; letter to Maestlin, VI, 79-80; *Theoria nova,* VI, 74-76, 123
Roffinello, Venturino, pr Venice, V, 326, 544
Rogeriis, Ioannes de, astrologer, V, 168
Roisi, Monsieur de, V, 598
Roissy, Seigneur de, VI, 20
Roland, medical, V, 513
Romagna, governor of, V, 228; legate of, V, 238; shepherds of, V, 21
Roman forests, V, 73
Romances, old French, V, 636
Romanellus, Jacobus, V, 59
Romanic Review, V, 85, 182
Romans, ancient, V, 104, 468-9, 579, VI, 316, 353, 435; king of the, V, 167, 183, 347, 372, VI, 457, 498, and see Emperor
Rome, V, 142, 171, 254, 446, VI, 38, 129, 202, 245, 491; ancient, VI, 204, fall of, VI, 202; astounded, V, 326; astronomical observation at, V, 216, 264, 366, 426; bezoar tested at, V, 316; burned at, VI, 427; called to, V, 184, 205, 256, 282, 325, 339, 544, VI, 153; chiromancy at, V, 582; churches of, visited, V, 85; common clock of, V, 271; council of, VI, 551; died at, V, 375, VI, 48, 325; empire of, VI, 117, and see Emperor, Roman; fish of, VI, 255; flight from, VI, 175, 427; founding of, VI, 465; golden age of, V, 334; hanged at, V, 505; Holy Office at, VI, 149; Index issued at, VI, 147; leisure at, VI, 226; marvel at, V, 510; Mercurio at, VI, 438; meridian of, V, 259; pest at, V, 161; pr at, V, 142-3, 169, 179, 197, 200, 204, 215, 246, 254-5, 257-8, 260-3, 364, 445, 472, 484, 536-7, 545, VI, 45, 62, 139, 202, 210, 257-8, 284, 315, 334, 370, 410, 447, 449, 469, 476, 569, pr allowed except in, VI, 163; Reuchlin at, VI, 444;

route to, V, 615; sack of, in 1527, V, 512-3; state archives of, VI, 149; studied at, VI, 537; university of, V, 74, 197, 254, 484, 505, 581, VI, 325, 373-4; went to, V, 16, 169, 407, VI, 153, 455, 457; wrote at, V, 168, 215, 362, 393, 644
Romenay, VI, 202
Rondelet, Guillaume, VI, 268, 271, 273, 290; accused of plagiarism, VI, 257; cited, VI, 49, 258, 289; controversy, VI, 212; criticized, V, 565, 570; estimate of, VI, 272; tests an assertion, VI, 282
Ronsard and astrology, VI, 106
Rosarium philosophorum, V, 547, 624
Rosarius minor, V, 537, 543, 638
Roscius, Minus, senator of Bologna, V, 235
Rose, as sign of pest, V, 608; odor of, expels demon, VI, 337; to turn a red, white, V, 147; water, V, 458
Rose, Germanus, pr Lyons, V, 449
Rosemary, VI, 166
Rosen, Edward (1937), V, 406; (1940), 413
Rosenberger, John, patrician of Augsburg, VI, 105, 116
Roseus, Franciscus, ed, VI, 449
Rosicrucian, VI, 126
Rosinus, alchemist, cited, V, 538, 604, 523
Rosinus, Stephanus, V, 160
Rosmini, Carlo de' (1820), V, 161
Rosselius, Hannibal (1585-90), VI, 449
Rossellius, C. (1579), V, 607
Rossi, G. G. (1893), V, 494
Rossi, Gian Luigi de, astrologer, V, 168
Rossi, Gioseppe de (1585), VI, 139-40, 210
Rossi, Girolamo, VI, 210
Rostock, citizen of, VI, 536; dedic from, VI, 535; pr at, VI, 38-39, 126, 255, 525; town council of, VI, 126; university of, V, 397, VI, 38-39, 126, 255
Roth, F. W. E. (1889), V, 330; (1902), V, 443; (1910), V, 464
Roth, R. (1877), V, 500
Rothmann, Christopher, mathematician, VI, 56, 74, 84
Rothmann, Johann, physician (1595), VI, 506-7
Rotting, professor, V, 338
Rouen, V, 301, VI, 493; admired, V, 579; pr at, V, 65
Rousselus, Gaspar, a patient, V, 302
Roussin, pr Nevers, V, 666
Rovere, Galeotto da, cardinal, V, 240
Rovere, Giulio da, cardinal, V, 274
Rovillius, Gulielmus, pr Lyons, VI, 33
Rovillius, pr Paris, V, 636
Roy, Maurice, pr Lyons, VI, 105
Royerius, Ioannes, pr Paris, VI, 23, 109
Rubeis, Dominicus de (1639), VI, 510
Rubeis, Johannes de, V, 168
Rubeis, Johannes Aloisius de, see Rossi, Gian Luigi de
Ruberia, Justinianus de, pr Bologna, V, 96, 240, 245
Rudio, Eustachio, V, 43-44
Rudolph II, emperor, V, 251, VI, 173, 318; bezoar of, VI, 323; preface to, VI, 320
Rudolphine Tables, see Kepler
Rudolphus, Hieronymus, VI, 598
Rue, V, 483, VI, 338, 546; wild, VI, 267
Rue, de la, see Rueus
Rueff, Jacob, V, 324
Ruelle, Jean, botanist, cited, V, 122, 611, VI, 256, 258, 277, 333; compared with later botanists, VI, 264; criticized, VI, 225; *Natura stirpium,* V, 463, VI, 261-4, 278; tr Dioscorides, V, 443, VI, 272
Rueus, Franciscus, VI, 303-6, 319, 322, 359, 394
Ruffinellis, Venturinus de, see Roffinello
Ruffus, Franciscus, V, 228
Rufinus, 13c botanist, VI, 261-5, 295
Rufus, medical, V, 430
Rumor, see Popular
Rump, Johannes (1897), V, 402
Rungius, Iacobus, VI, 597
Rupescissa, see John of
Rupeus, Hieronymus, V, 153
Ruremond, bishop of, VI, 72
Ruscelli, Girolamo, VI, 215, 431
Ruscum, an herb, VI, 262
Russia, VI, 268
Russilianus Sextus, Tyberius, V, 78
Rustic, V, 57, 484, 612, VI, 536; cited, VI, 119, 263; health of, VI, 223; inquired of, V, 463; thicker skull of, V, 512; and see Farmer, Peasant

Rustighello, Francesco, astrologer, V, 214, 228, 244-5
Rybwurte or Rybgrasse, VI, 263
Ryff, Peter (1552-1629), VI, 143
Ryff, Walther Hermann, V, 442-3, 536, 621; comm. Pliny, V, 560-2; ed Dioscorides, VI, 267, 272

Saalfeld, VI, 308
Sabbat, see Witch
Sabian, V, 421
Sabinus, George, VI, 105, 596
Sabio (Io. Ant.) et fratres de, prs Venice, V, 314, 391
Sabio, see Nicolinis de
Sachiel, spirit of the planet Jupiter, V, 569
Sachs von Lewenheimb, *Oceanus,* V, 10
Sacrament, V, 283, VI, 539; and see Baptism, Eucharist, Mass, Penance, etc.
Sacrobosco, cited, V, 337, VI, 49, as alchemist, V, 623; *Computus,* V, 391; ed., V, 379; errors of, VI, 155; misdated, VI, 130; praised, VI, 46, 83, 155; shines on, VI, 83; *Sphere* of, V, 85, 388, 394, 432, 521, VI, 6, 16, 20, 37-38, 155, comm. V, 402, 564, VI, 43, 45, 82, 122, ed, V, 275, 279, 332-3
Sadducees, VI, 531
Sadoleti, Jacopo, cardinal, V, 268
Sage, an herb, V, 483, VI, 333, 503, 546
Sagittaria, an herb, VI, 265
Sagon, François, V, 287
Saguntum, VI, 282
Sahl ibn Bischr, see Zael
Sailor, V, 211
Saint, VI, 446; apparition of, V, 107; or criminal? V, 102; easily deceived, VI, 279; life of, V, 414; power of, V, 104, 107, VI, 497, 557; prayer to, V, 104, VI, 497; and see Relics
St. Amand, see John of
St. Bartholomew's, massacre of, VI, 142, 247, 450
St. Cloud, see William of
St. Gall, V, 440
St. Germain des Pres, VI, 509
St. John, fire of, V, 439; herb of, V, 483; Eve, VI, 221, 404, and see Midsummer night
St. Lawrence, name for Zanzibar, VI, 346
St. Maximin (Var), VI, 188, 553
St. Nicholas, church of Zaragoza, VI, 167
St. Pancras, cardinal of, V, 472
St. Peter and St. Sebaldus, church of Nürnberg, V, 351, 365
St. Peter, church of, Rome, V, 259
St. Quentin, VI, 439
St. Victor (Mainz), VI, 480; and see Richard of
Sta. Susanna, Rome, cardinal of, VI, 171
Ste. Maria Annunciata, Paris, convent, V, 358
Sainte Marthe, Scévola de, VI, 257
Saintes, V, 299
Saintonge, herb of, V, 599
Sal alkali, V, 457
Sal ammoniacus, V, 458-9, VI, 278; armeniacus, V, 458; armoniacum, V, 458
Sal gemmae, V, 458
Sal nephthicus, V, 458
Sal nitrum, V, 458
Salamanca, astrology at, V, 278, VI, 165-6; dedic to, V, 276; magic at, V, 283; pr at, V, 283; studied at, V, 275; university of, V, 276, 278
Salamander, V, 628, VI, 269; and fire, V, 158, 474, 647, VI, 95, 323, 428, 519
Salary, from archduke of Austria, V, 222; large, V, 74, 184, 374, 586; of town physician, VI, 255; small, V, 128, 204; university, V, 338, VI, 341, 373
Salerno, V, 72-74, 183, 269
Salignac, baron of, VI, 161
Salius Diversus, Petrus (1584), VI, 211
Saliva, generation from, VI, 283; influence of planets on, V, 264; released by bad surgery, V, 509; virtue of, V, 474, 574, VI, 349, 393, 425
Salmon, VI, 267
Salò, VI, 158
Salt, V, 457-8, 597, 665, VI, 307, 310, 334, 434; action of, V, 146; divination from, VI, 240; extraction of, VI, 251; in metals, VI, 317; in mineral waters, VI, 209; of human skull, VI, 224; of

pearls, V, 650; principle or not? V, 626, 644, VI, 250
Saltpeter, V, 458, VI, 299
Salvianus, Horatius, pr Naples, VI, 260, 273, 418, 422
Salviati, cardinal, V, 410
Salzburg, V, 460, VI, 525
Salzinger, Ivo (1721), V, 535
Samael, spirit of Mars, V, 569, VI, 441; and see Sammuel
Sambucus, John (1531-84), VI, 88
Sammuel, intelligence of Mars, V, 219; and see Samael
Samos, see Aristarchus of
Samuel, cabala of, V, 130; and see Witch of Endor
San Andrea di Busco, convent of, V, 555
San Francesco, convent of, V, 252
San Gimignano, VI, 337-8
San Ginesio, VI, 518
San Miniato, VI, 210; and see Bonincontri
San Petronio, church of, Bologna, VI, 455
San Pietro in Vinculis, V, 240
San Severino, V, 533
San Vito, Aniello, publisher, Naples, VI, 42, 214
Sánchez de Viana, Pedro (1589), VI, 129
Sanchez, Francesco, career, VI, 560-1; examined, VI, 223; influence, VI, 567-8; on Cardan, V, 579; *Quod nihil scitur,* VI, 560-6; quoted, VI, 560; works, other, VI, 561, 566-7
Sandalwood, V, 453, 467
Sandarac, V, 458, 465, VI, 310
Sandaracha, see Sandarac
Sandri, G. (1938), V, 488
Sandritter, see Santritter
Sanitation, V, 497
Sannazaro, Giacomo, VI, 399
Sanseverino, Ferdinand, V, 74
Sanseverino, Maria, V, 73
Sanseverino, Robert II, V, 72
Sansovino, F. pr Venice, VI, 217
Santbech, Daniel (1561), VI, 29-30
Sante Ardoino, V, 472-3, 597, 637
Sante Ferrari, V, 53
Santritter, Johannes Lucilius, V, 334-5, 341, 346
Saphar, VI, 180
Saphaeae recentiores doctrinae, V, 355
Saphea, instrument, V, 355-6, 359
Sapphire, as remedy, V, 456, 478, 646, VI, 217; magical, VI, 305
Saracen, V, 347, 395; and see Arab
Saragossa, see Zaragoza
Sarcomoros, see Des Périers
Sardonyx, V, 457; medical properties doubted, V, 456
Sarnelli, Pompeo (1677), VI, 156, 163
Sarton, George, VI, 483
Sartorius, Andreas, VI, 105
Sarzosus Cellanus, Franciscus (1526), V, 284
Satan, see Demon
Satire, on astrological predictions, V, 204, 230, 286-7, 312-3
Satler, Wolfgang (1605), VI, 96, 143-4
Saturn, the planet, VI, 209; and comet of 1585, VI, 95; completion of revolutions of, V, 311, in 1789, V, 202; influence of, V, 60-61, 92, 119, 174, 177, 367, 495, 510, VI, 203, 402-3, on agricultural cycles, VI, 487, on contemplation, V, 119, denied, VI, 206, 402; movement of, V, 426; providential position of, V, 151
Satyr, VI, 408, 551
Saul, king of Israel, VI, 234, 435
Savage, S. (1922), VI, 224
Savius, Anth. Thomas, dedic to, VI, 105
Savona, Erastus, physician, VI, 201
Savonarola, Hieronymus, *Against Astrology,* V, 199, 653-5, VI, 172, 201, tr, V, 655, VI, 187; geniture, VI, 131, 597; physiognomy and character, V, 60
Savonarola, Michael, V, 492; cited, V, 54, VI, 233, 402; criticized, V, 437, VI, 164, 209; ed., V, 602
Savor, see Taste
Savoy, V, 613; duke of, V, 24, 304, VI, 28, 138, 217, 373
Saxifragia maior, an herb, V, 316
Saxo Grammaticus, VI, 404
Saxonia, Hercules, VI, 237
Saxony, VI, 537; came to, VI, 259; court of, V, 328; duke of, V, 342, 358, 390, 399, 405, 619, VI, 11, 37,

192, 196, 596; elector of, VI, 103-5, 116, 136, 192, 495; from, V, 589; in, V, 298, VI, 238, 254, 409, 489; princes and cities of, VI, 537; see Henry of, John of
Saya, Nonius Marcellus, V, 24, VI, 164
Sbaralea, J. H. (1806), VI, 559
Sbonsius, Abraham, V, 404
Scab, VI, 208; cure for, V, 459
Scala, Ambrosius, VI, 598
Scala, Cane della, VI, 135
Scala, Hieronymus, V, 410
Scala, Paolo de la, see Skalich
Scala philosophorum, V, 547
Scaliger, J. C., V, 304, 468, 479; cited, V, 418, 486, 559, 647, VI, 49, 185, 258, 266, 387-8, 571; comm. *De insomniis,* VI, 476, 478, 512; criticism of Cardan, VI, 283-4, Champier, V, 112-3, others, V, 418, VI, 257; criticized, VI, 382, 435, 512; *Exotericarum exercitationum,* VI, 293
Scaliger, J. J., geniture of, VI, 105
Scalzi (1876), VI, 328-9
Scallerus, Hieronymus, physician, V, 657
Scammony, belittled, V, 479; gives a dog dysentery, V, 454; purges bile, V, 12, 105, VI, 397
Scarab, VI, 278
Scardeone, B. (1560), V, 545, VI, 279
Scenographica, VI, 430
Scepper, Cornelius, V, 131, 226-7, VI, 596
Scepticism, V, 37, 38, 129, 196-7, 287, 448, 477-8, 567, VI, 561-4; as to alchemy, V, 648, lore of gems, VI, 313-4, 318, suspensions, V, 646, witchcraft, VI, 522, 549; doubtful V, 312; falls off in 17th century, VI, 286; growth of, V, 37; limited, V, 110, 512; mingled with credulity, V, 481-2, 560, 647, VI, 186, 220, 309, 323, 420, 564-5, and superstition, VI, 301, 510, 555; misapplied, VI, 324
Scevolini, Domenico (1565), VI, 124-6, 412
Schadeck, see Nicolaus de
Schaffhausen, VI, 267
Scheck, Jakob, controversy with Fuchs, VI, 212, with Ramus, VI, 354
Schedel, Hartmann, V, 333, 343
Schegkius, Jacobus (1538), V, 153
Schelhorn, J. G. (1738), V, 370
Scheligius, Albert (1583), V, 479
Schenck a Grafenberg, J. G. (1609), VI, 286
Schepper, see Scepper
Scherertzius, Sigismund (1621), VI, 533-4
Scheurl, Christopher (1506), V, 334, VI, 303
Scheveninger, see Zenocarus
Schewrlein, nativity of, V, 352
Schieble, J. (1855-59), VI, 457
Schilt, Ian, professor, V, 162
Schiopodes, see Skiapodes
Schlecht Festschrift (1917), V, 337
Schleisinger, see Schleussinger
Schleswig-Holstein, duke of, VI, 140
Schleussinger, Eberhard, V, 349, 361-3
Schmalkaldic war, V, 397
Schmidt, C. G. A. (1888), V, 173, 229, 313, 431, 433-7
Schmidt, Daniel, V, 354
Schmiedel, C. C. (1754), VI, 265
Schmitt, Joachim, VI, 105
Schneeberg, V, 396
Schnepf, Erhard, V, 397
Schoeffer, Ivo, pr Mainz, V, 521
Schoeffer, Johann, pr Mainz, V, 172
Schoenstenius, Iohannes, pr Cologne, VI, 259
Schoepflin, *Alsatia illustrata* (1751-61), VI, 88
Scholarships, V, 338
Scholasticism, and Schoolmen, attacked, V, 128, 280-1, 285, 515; aversion from, V, 80, 448, 516-7, 631, VI, 382, 568, 571-2; cited, V, 541, VI, 176, 378, 386, 399, 445, 467; continued, V, 4, 39-40, 95, 151, 194-5, 198, 480, 506-7, 590, VI, 188, 198, 292, 599; debt to, V, 23; defended, VI, 446; dispassionate, V, 9; form, VI, 236; ignored, VI, 470; method, V, 284, 642-3, VI, 24, 214, 383; read, V, 75; and see Disputation, Quodlibeta, Theology, scholastic, etc.
Scholderer, Victor (1938), VI, 447
Scholl, Jacob, V, 323-4
Schöner, Andreas, V, 337, 352, 368-9
Schöner, Johann, V, 331, 337, 354-71; astrology of, V, 338, 354, 356-7, 361, 367-9; astronomical observations by, V, 426; Beheim and, V, 171; cited, V, 375, VI, 21, 25, 102, 121, 131, 180, not,

VI, 11; estimate of, V, 368, 405; geniture of, V, 367, VI, 104; Heller and, V, 394-5; Melanchthon and, V, 393-4; *Opusculum astrologicum,* V, 361-4; picture of, V, 365; pupils of, V, 341, 369; put on Index, VI, 148; Regiomentanus and, V, 354-60, 364-8; Rheticus and, V, 412; *Tabulae resolutae,* V, 359-60, 371, 394; Werner and, V, 353, 368
Schonheintz, Jakob, V, 159, 334, 340
School, at Ghent, VI, 38, imperial court, V, 582, Korbach, VI, 354, Lessines, V, 582, Memmingen, VI, 16, Thorn, V, 153; domestic, of Noah, VI, 498; for choristers, V, 582; grammar, at Bruges, VI, 38, curriculum for, VI, 190-1; gymnasium, at Coburg, VI, 238, Nürnberg, V, 394; in Portugal, VI, 561; Jesuit, at Lyon and Tournon, VI, 382, 410; municipal of Dijon, V, 311-2; oration on, VI, 191
Schoolfellow, V, 323
Schoolmaster, life of, V, 218, 220, 309-12, VI, 112-15, 399, 498-9
Schorndorf, V, 153
Schosser, Iohannes, poet, VI, 105
Schott, Hans or Johann, pr Strasburg, V, 173, 322, VI, 273
Schottenloher, Karl (1907), V, 352, 355, 359, 362; (1910), V, 349, 359, 370; (1913), V, 232-3, 348; (1917), V, 337
Schrauf, K. (1904), V, 328
Schreckenfuchs, E. O., astronomer, V, 372, VI, 16-17, 37-38, 55; quoted, VI, 3
Schreiber, see Grammateus
Schreiber, W. L. (1924), VI, 213, 224, 272
Schreyer, Seb. Cl., V, 351
Schrotbanck, Hans, astrologer, V, 160
Schröter, Adam, V, 619
Schröter, Johann (1551), V, 224, 328
Schwäbisch Hall, V, 397, VI, 597; physician and astrologer to, VI, 133-4; pr at, V, 387; town council of, VI, 134
Schwarz, C. G. (1740), V, 339, 369
Schwerin, see Ulrich of
Schwertel, Johann, pr Wittenberg, V, 404
Schwilgué, clock-maker, VI, 88
Schwimmer, Johann (1935), VI, 266
Schylander, Cornelius, physician, VI, 127
Schyringham, Simon, copyist, V, 676
Science and Scientific, acquisition of, V, 91; aptitude, VI, 413; attitude, VI, 555; change, indicated by stars, VI, 173; classification, VI, 259-60, 266-7, 269-71; collaborator, sought in vain, VI, 109; combined with other interests, VI, 270, and see Idea; concerned with individual, VI, 563; defined, V, 12-13, VI, 369; general mental effect, VI, 54; how received, V, 91; inferiority of fifteenth century, V, 4-5; independence, V, 36; magic and, V, 85, 235, 263, 303, 494, 626, 650, VI, 81, 94, 132-3, 328, 400, 410, 414, 464; method, VI, 518, 566; modern, VI, 288; natural, and medicine, V, 431-2; pretense, V, 254; principles, V, 276; progress, VI, 573; Ramist conception of, VI, 238-9; recent, ignored, VI, 568-9; religion and, V, 442, 567; slighted, V, 3; speculative, VI, 599; studied, VI, 77; summary of sixteenth century, VI, 295-6; uncertain, VI, 551; uncritical historically, V, 22; universal knowledge, VI, 120, 133; Vanini's faulty, VI, 570
Sclanus Prochitanus, Salvus, VI, 214-5
Scollius, Hector, VI, 597
Scordion, an herb, V, 123
Scorpio, the sign, V, 325
Scorpion, generated in brain, V, 482; in a stone, VI, 284; pig and, V, 480-1; remedy for, V, 481, VI, 422; safeguard against, V, 249; used medically, VI, 216, 218-9, 246; work on, VI, 291
Scot, Michael, see Michael
Scot, Reginald (1584), V, 667, VI, 529-30; quoted, VI, 515
Scotism, V, 175, VI, 378
Scotland, V, 155, 157, 269, 295; barnacle geese in, VI, 279, 288; learned men from, V, 194, 295-6, VI, 238; sophists from, V, 280
Scott, Walter (1924), VI, 448-9, 460
Scotus, cited as alchemist, V, 623
Scotus, Duns, VI, 369, 431; and astrology, V, 175, 221, VI, 125, 205; cited, V, 504, 507, VI, 188, 289, 365, 433, 446; opposed, V, 40, 42, 43, 523; quoted, V, 298

Scotus, Hieronymus, pr Venice, V, 39, VI, 486
Scotus, Octavian, pr Venice, V, 39; heirs of, V, 72, 79, 96, 162-3, 184
Screw, applications of, V, 595
Scribanarius, Marcus, astrologer, V, 160, 230-1, 240, 244
Scribonius, Guilelmus Adolphus, VI, 351-5; opposed, VI, 535, 538; quoted, VI, 339
Scrofula, cured by royal touch, V, 102, 486, VI, 133, 425, 432, doubted, VI, 240, 432
Scudalupis, Petrus Arlensis de, VI, 301-2, 324
Sculpture, V, 13, 17, VI, 597
Scultetus, Bartholomaeus, VI, 183
Scultetus, John, VI, 224
Scurvy, VI, 38
Scyomantia, VI, 502
Scythia and Scythian, V, 147, 611
Sea, bed of, V, 591; compared to a tree, VI, 387-8, to sweat of earth, VI, 396; depth of, V, 591, VI, 380; displacement or shifting of, V, 156; foam, V, 470; higher than mountains, V, 25, VI, 342; movement east to west, V, 553; -serpent, VI, 286; -sickness, V, 146; sounding device, V, 594-5; water made potable, V, 584-5, 637, VI, 428; why salt, V, 25, 591, VI, 384, 391, 396
Seal, see Image
Season of year, V, 191, 475, VI, 95, 223, 564
Sebaldus Kirche, Nürnberg, V, 351, 365
Sebastian of Aragon, V, 14
Secant, use of, V, 426; word introduced, VI, 140
Secerius, Johannes, pr Hagenau, V, 501
Secrecy, V, 32; broken, V, 650; enjoined, V, 130, 136; maintained, VI, 69; from vulgar, V, 107, 132, 223, 300
Secret, V, 10, 33; alchemical, V, 534; book of, V, 33, 147, VI, 418-9, 429, 434, 492, 601; medicinal, VI, 215-8; natural, V, 204, 463, 510, 567, 599, VI, 166, 388, 390, 422, 428, 527; pleasure of prying into another's, V, 146; revealed, V, 650, by astrology, V, 253; Werner's V, 350; writing, see Cipher
Secretary, V, 228
Securis, John, V, 466
Secularism, V, 37
Sedacerius, alchemist, V, 623
Seed, VI, 290; classification by, VI, 333; collected on midsummer night, VI, 295; oil from, V, 590; and see Generation
Segovia, V, 514
Seldey, Lady, VI, 218
Seldius, Geo. Sigismund, VI, 597
Seldner, Henry, astronomer, V, 349
Self-interest, motive of, V, 577
Selfisch Samuel, publisher, Wittenberg, V, 376, VI, 6
Selling goods and lands, V, 222
Selva, Giovanni di, VI, 432
Semen, VI, 364, 408, 514, 571
Semita recta, V, 543, 604, 624
Senebier, Jean (1779), VI, 453
Seneca, agreed with, V, 157; cited, VI, 94, 199, as an alchemist, V, 623-4
Senguerdius, Arnold, Ph.D., VI, 87
Senior (Zadith ben Hamuel), alchemist, V, 622
Senlis, judge of, VI, 527
Senna, an herb, V, 460
Sense, active, VI, 369; common, V, 571, 573, VI, 379, 425; errors of, VI, 279, 477, 531, 563; external and internal, V, 151, VI, 406; internal, VI, 379; marvelous concord with its object, V, 495; of animals, V, 152; of hearing superior to that of sight, V, 295; of touch, VI, 481
Sentences or *Sententiae,* see Peter Lombard
Septalius, Ludovicus (1626), VI, 506
Septier, A. (1820), V, 622
Sepulveda, VI, 493
Serafino, Fra, of Mantua, V, 252
Seraphim, VI, 454, 551
Seraphinus, physician and astrologer, VI, 136
Seraphinus de Pisis, surgeon, V, 60
Serapion, cited, V, 451, 453, VI, 272, 300, 303, 308-9, 361; corrected, V, 114, 467; criticized, V, 123, 452; defended, V, 446; tr of, V, 450
Serapis, VI, 504
Serenius, Julius (1563), VI, 492-3
Serf, V, 172

Sermon, V, 433, 649, VI, 377, and see Preacher
Sermoneta, *Comm. Aphorisms,* V, 448
Serpent, see Snake
Serrano, Gabriel, astrologer (1593), VI, 165
Serrasanquirico, V, 484
Servant, domestic, V, 44
Servetus, Michael, *Apologetica disceptatio,* V, 288-90; *Apologia,* V, 289; astrology of, V, 288; at Paris, V, 288-91; cited, VI, 361; compared to Bruno, VI, 423; medicine of, V, 289; pulmonary circulation and, VI, 329; *Syruporum universa ratio,* V, 289
Servius, Petrus, V, 10
Sessa, V, 71-73, 76, 162, 184; and see Nifo
Sessa, pr Venice, **V**, 607
Sessa, J. B. pr Venice, **V**, 306, **VI**, 299
Sessa, Melchior, pr Venice, V, 306, 391, VI, 471
Seth, and astrology, V, 403
Setser, Hieronymus, VI, 105
Settala, see Septalius
Seuberlich, Laurent, pr Wittenberg, V, 376
Seurre-sur-Saône, V, 328
Seven cities, VI, 436
Seven Years War, V, 383
Severinus, Petrus, Paracelsan, V, 627, 630, 651, VI, 372
Sevestre, Carolus, bookseller, Paris, VI, 324
Seville, VI, 196, 478; archbishop of, VI, 197; pr at, V, 197, VI, 128-9, 197; and see Isidore of, John of
Sex, aberration and immorality, V, 62, 241, 270, VI, 408, 521; change of, V, 270, VI, 209, 287; intercourse, V, 170, 444, VI, 223, 559, 600, with a phantasm, V, 70; of insects, VI, 283, 290; of plants, VI, 422, denied, VI, 348; predetermined, VI, 261; and see Demon, Generation, Incubus
Sextus Empiricus, VI, 206, 562
Sextus Platonicus, see Placidus
Sforza, VI, 465
Sforza, Caterina Iaggelone, dedic to, VI, 42
Sforza, Francesco, V, 247
Sforza, Galeazzo, V, 50
Sforza, Giovanni, lord of Pesaro, VI, 298-9
Sforza, Ludovico, V, 59, VI, 465
Shakespeare's England (1917), VI, 219
Shame, sense of, V, 513, 551
Sheep, head dissected, V, 519; shuns wolf, V, 662, VI, 241; and see Lamb
Shell, see Fossil
Shell-fish, VI, 289; and see Fossil.
Shepherd, advice to, V, 211; basilisk killed by, VI, 310; give mercury, VI, 313; horn of, V, 21
Shin, ailing, V, 327
Ship, VI, 286, 421; building, V, 585, against flood, V, 193; excavated in 1460, V, 157; launching, V, 595; model, V, 584; proportions, V, 585; speed measured, V, 34
Shoe-blacking, VI, 308, 429
Shorthand, V, 638
Shrapnel, V, 34
Sibyl, V, 213, VI, 504, 520; Babylonian, VI, 75; Erythraean, V, 219, VI, 492; inspired by God, V, 627, by stars, VI, 569, by own virginity, VI, 481; listed, VI, 492
Sibylline books, VI, 246, 466; magic, VI, 457; oracles, VI, 492
Sicily, V, 21, 45, 115, 215, 450, 455, 512, 638, VI, 149
Siculus, Angelus, alchemical impostor, VI, 245
Sideritis, an herb, V, 451-2
Siderocrates, Samuel, Paracelsan, VI, 123
Siena, V, 227, 269, 326, 544, VI, 214, 333, 410; alchemy at, V, 534; university of, VI, 394; and see Hugh of
Sieve, divination by, VI, 503
Sifaras, VI, 359
Sigismund, emperor, V, 373
Sigismund I, king of Poland, V, 170
Sign, cure by, VI, 233; method for, VI, 407; of future, V, 47, belief in, attacked, VI, 467; of shops, V, 155, 157, 447, 464, 483, 514, 544, 556, 558, VI, 10, 20, 27, 30, 124, 343-4, 410; of Zodiac, see Zodiac
Signatures, doctrine of, V, 628, 635, 649, 651, VI, 164, 249, 294, 422, 434, 504, 507, 602; four species of, V, 635
Significator, astrological, V, 272, 473, VI, 113, 160

Siguenza, taught at, V, 275
Silber, Eucharius, pr Rome, V, 536-7
Silber, Marcellus, pr Rome, V, 197, 537
Siler montanus, VI, 309
Silesia, V, 153, 404, VI, 224
Silkworm, VI, 290
Silvano, Horacio, pr Naples, VI, 129
Silvaticus, J. B. (1597), **V**, 470-1; (1605), V, 264, 457
Silvaticus, Matthaeus, V, 450; cited, VI, 300, 402; not cited, VI, 318-9; and see Pandectarius
Silver, V, 396; defined, V, 626; flour of, V, 457; medicinal, VI, 316; mines, V, 125; ring of, VI, 292; sublimate, V, 458-9; thread of, V, 249
Silvius, see Sylvius
Simeon, rabbi, VI, 445
Simi, Niccolò, astrologer, V, 244-6, VI, 18
Simler, Josias (1583), V, 417
Simon, G. pr Antwerp, VI, 393
Simon, Italo (1931), V, 44
Simon Magus, V, 327, VI, 504
Simon de Phares, V, 189, 275, 291, 334, 345, 445, VI, 130, 254
Simon de Ulmo, V, 116
Simoneta, Giov. Maria, of Cremona, pr Faenza, V, 228; Pavia, VI, 257
Simonides, V, 478
Simonius, Simon, V, 482
Simple, medicinal, V, 113, 122-3, 445-71, 484, 527, 531, disadvantage of, V, 632, method of knowing, V, 449-50; new, V, 123, 453-4; professor of, V, 247, VI, 266, 280; when to collect, V, 446, VI, 134
Simplicius, cited, V, 215, 604
Sin, VI, 496; effect on nature, V, 397, VI, 347, 408; makes astrology imperfect, V, 403; of diviners, VI, 177; pardon from, VI, 169; preternatural events to punish, VI, 211; results in possession by demons, VI, 558; signs divine against, VI, 489; witchcraft a punishment for, VI, 538; worse than in time of Noah, V, 194
Sinciput, V, 553-4
Sine, V, 357, 364, 376
Singer, Charles (1917), V, 176, 493
Singer, D. W. (1917), V, 493; (1928-31), V, 535
Singrenius, Johannes, pr Vienna, V, 174, 221, 349
Singultus relieved, V, 462-3
Sinigaglia, V, 269
Siren, VI, 269
Sirigatti, Francesco, V, 253
Sirius, rising of, VI, 461
Sirleto, cardinal, VI, 139
Sisto da Siena, see Sixtus Senensis
Sitzungsberichte Bayer. Akademie, V, 390-1
Sixtus IV, VI, 136, 476
Sixtus V, V, 484, VI, 315; bull against astrology and divination, V, 245, 247, VI, 139, 145, 147, 149, 156-8, 160, 162, 196, 198, 232, 234, 370, 413-4, 483-4, 538, 549, 571, interpretations thereof, VI, 159, 163-5, 169-72, 175-8, 431; dedic to, VI, 158, 369-70, 556; preface to, V, 8
Sixtus ab Hemminga, see Hemminga
Sixtus the Pythagorean, V, 113
Sixtus Senensis, VI, 196, 461
Skalich, Paul, **VI**, 455-7
Skeleton, V, 524
Skendorf, Ernest à, VI, 201
Skiapodes, VI, 275, 408
Skull, compressed in infancy, V, 512; fracture of, V, 513; huge pre-historic, V, 512; powdered, VI, 233; salt of, VI, 224; scrapings of, VI, 240; shape of, V, 512; thickness of, V, 512
Slander, amulet against, V, 176
Slave, African, VI, 225
Sleep, V, 151, 611, VI, 221, 478, 535; caused by heat, VI, 226; disturbed by slight noise, V, 146; induced, V, 573, VI, 419, 423; presence of enemy sensed during, VI, 241; produced by heart, VI, 443; trance, V, 574; walking in, VI, 480; with mouth closed or open? VI, 393
Sleidan, Johann, historian, VI, 195, 361
Sleight of hand, V, 103, VI, 245, 247, 426, 530, 536, 549
Sloane collection, VI, 248; and see Index of MSS
Small pox, cured by stone pocked like, VI, 294-5; use of red bedclothes in, V, 116
Smetius, Henricus (1537-1614), V, 661
Smith, D. E. (1917), V, 328, VI, 141, 143; (1923), V, 353

Smith, Preserved, V, 287
Smoke, divination by, VI, 503
Snail, V, 621
Snake, VI, 277, 280, 291; antipathy to ash tree, VI, 186, 416; caught by stag, VI, 294; charmer, V, 473-4; cold or hot? V, 477; eel and, VI, 416; emerald and, VI, 477; fat of, V, 451; horn of, V, 481; immunity from, V, 102; odors hostile to, V, 481; restores its sight with an herb, VI, 349; saliva and, VI, 349; sign of pest, V, 608; stone produced by hissing of, VI, 323; tongue of, V, 478, VI, 232; why sheds skin? VI, 284; winged, V, 570; and see Dragon
Sneezing, VI, 367; epilepsy and, V, 660; sign of future, V, 511, VI, 485, denied, VI, 486
Snellius, Willebrodus (1618), V, 366-7
Snow, V, 31, 612, VI, 50; flake, when formed? VI, 387; why chills more than water? VI, 366
Social, customs and life, V, 143, 231; science, V, 175
Society, primitive or savage, V, 577-8
Socinian, VI, 183
Socrates, V, 568-9; fate of, V, 105
Sod, virtue of, V, 627-8
Soissons, V, 463
Soldati, B. (1906), V, 165
Soldier, V, 55, 123, 573, 611; longevity of, V, 145; preferred by women, V, 146
Solid, regular, relation to four qualities and to heavens, VI, 110
Solidago, an herb, VI, 274
Solinus, cited, VI, 280-1, 300, 303; credited, VI, 275; criticized, V, 448
Solmancy, V, 58
Solofra, V, 398
Solomon, V, 67; acquired wisdom by magic, V, 166; cited, VI, 300; *Clavicula,* VI, 147; *Dreams of,* VI, 475, 480; on gems and images, VI, 300-1, natures of things, VI, 353, plants, VI, 353; Pentagon of, VI, 405; philosophy of, VI, 434; temple of, V, 85
Solution, alchemical, V, 533, 645
Somaschus, J. B. pr Venice, V, 540, VI, 159, 349, 371, 450
Soncinus, Hieronymus, pr Pesaro, VI, 299
Sondheim, Moriz (1938), V, 434
Sophocles, *Elektra,* quoted, V, 424
Sorb tree, virtue of, V, 482, 497
Sorbinus, Arnoldus, VI, 286
Sorbonne, V, 129, VI, 568, 572; approbation of, VI, 175; censure by, V, 287, VI, 388
Sorcery, V, 297, VI, 295, 415, 499, 549; abounds, VI, 441; counter magic against, VI, 516; diabolical, V, 477; dissolved by God alone, V, 477, by an herb, V, 458; Porta accused of, VI, 419; safeguard against, denied, V, 646; worse than other heresy, VI, 524; and see Witchcraft
Sordi, Pietro, on comet of 1577, VI, 93-95
Sortilege, forbidden, VI, 148; name applied to divination from spirits, V, 627, prediction as to crops, V, 192; put on Index, VI, 147; superstitious, VI, 430; works on, VI, 154, 169; and see Lot-casting
Sory, VI, 310
Soubron, Thomas, pr Lyons, VI, 189
Soul, V, 86, 150-1, 493, VI, 354, 456; ascent of, VI, 406; body and, V, 631, 651, 658, VI, 427, 453; breathing and, V, 511; cabala on, V, 453; divining power of, V, 87, VI, 512; essence, VI, 532; faculties, VI, 369, 371; immortality of, V, 71, 90, 94, 96-98, 526, 558, 567, VI, 198, 239, 343, 350, and see Aristotle; magic power of, V, 103, 135-6, 571, 639; of divine fire, VI, 362; Paracelsus on, V, 651; rational, VI, 198, 228, 327, 340, 379, 396, 484; recovery of forgotten knowledge by, VI, 563; relation of human to celestial, VI, 236, to universe, VI, 443; sensitive, VI, 241, 365, 436, denied plants, VI, 519; separation from body, V, 87, 90, 272-3, 573, VI, 453-4, 511, 532; transformation, incredible, V, 108; vegetative, VI, 355, 436; virtue of, VI, 392; works on, V, 44, 48-49; world, V, 135-6, 561, 579, 640, VI, 236, 383-4, 407, 424-5, 434, 507
Sound, carrying power, V, 145; dependent on air, V, 474; effect on ear, V, 152; marvelous, VI, 530, 532; stars make no, V, 153
Source study, V, 154

Space, VI, 364, 375; and see Vacuum
Spachius, Isreal, tr, V, 469, VI, 314
Spagiric or Spagyric sect, VI, 249
Spain, V, 134, 159, 282-3, 326, 476, 565; astrology in, V, 211, 278, 319, VI, 145; danger of flood in 1524 slight in, V, 211; epidemic in, VI, 212; exported to, VI, 209; expulsion of Jews from, V, 124; farther, V, 208; herb of, VI, 225; king of, V, 183, VI, 136, 160-1, 356; Lullian art in, V, 535; papal bull in, VI, 166; sailing from to England, V, 553; war with France, V, 72; went to, VI, 245, 373, 394; witchcraft in, VI, 145-6
Spampanato, Vincenzo (1933), VI, 423, 427
Spaniard, V, 39, 167, 210, 275, 459, 514, VI, 304, 322
Spanish, Armada, VI, 253; astrologer, V, 210; Index of 1559, see Index; Inquisition, see Inquisition; Jew, VI, 445; naturalist, VI, 258; physician, VI, 128; soldier, V, 313; taught, V, 582; tr from, V, 468-9, into, V, 197, 283, VI, 159, 222; written in, V, 201, 210, VI, 274, 314, 390, 413, 428
Sparta, V, 579, VI, 435
Spatulomancy, V, 58
Spear, use in magic, VI, 404
Specialization, example of, set by magic, V, 102; partial, of Paracelsus, V, 442; urged by Cardan, V, 563, Sanchez, VI, 566; wanting in 16th century, V, 8, 426, VI, 334
Species, VI, 600; altered, VI, 570; are nothing, VI, 563; divine, VI, 407; dream from, VI, 476; from corpse, VI, 403; intelligible, V, 369; multiplication of, VI, 26; not emitted, VI, 365; not transmuted, VI, 244, 246, 250; of sediment in sick, VI, 213; origin of, VI, 347, 501; phantastic, VI, 236; radiation of, V, 496, VI, 392; reception of, V, 152; relation to occult virtue, V, 135; sound and color explained by, V, 152; spiritual, V, 496; visual, VI, 340
Specimen, scientific, VI, 267-8, 307
Specter, V, 401, VI, 520, 530-4, 551; feigned, VI, 534; fewer since Reformation, VI, 533; nocturnal, VI, 540
Speculum, V, 673, VI, 361
Sperm, V, 46-47, 503
Spermaceti, V, 470
Speroni, Sperone (1500-1588), VI, 123
Speyer, bishop of, VI, 123; near, VI, 431; visited, VI, 191
Sphere, dimensions of, V, 40-41; eight only, VI, 432; eighth, VI, 192, 354, 451, 551, configuration of, VI, 144, motion of, V, 264, 284, 311, 328, 333, 353, 409, 572, VI, 10, 17, 20-21, 26, 43, 46-47, 58, 60, 342-3, 378, 475, anomaly of, V, 415, VI, 13, 15, 41; elementary, V, 321; eleventh, V, 424, VI, 17, 49, 92, 97; homocentric, V, 422, 489-90, VI, 19, 62, 326; ninth, V, 185, 333, 424, VI, 17, 21, 34, 41, 44, 47, 49, 58, 62, 65, 97, 108, 343, 399, abandoned, V, 284, VI, 47, 83-84, 354; of comets, suggested, V, 490, VI, 79-80; of fire, V, 25, 553, VI, 110, 327, 369, denied, VI, 71-72, 83, 384, ignored, V, 428; of moon put next sun, VI, 44; perfect figure, VI, 34; planetary, denied, VI, 71-72, 326; single, of earth and water, V, 24, 427-8, VI, 10, 12, 27, 34, 41, 50, 60, 83, 343; solidity, VI, 357, denied, VI, 191, 384; tenth, V, 333, VI, 17, 58, 62, denied, VI, 354; works on, V, 152, 165, 167, 354, VI, 124, 447; and see Primum mobile, Sacrobosco, Zodiac
Spherics, VI, 27
Spices, V, 469, 544; trade in, V, 167, 468
Spider, V, 608, VI, 419; and sapphire, VI, 305; sign of pest, VI, 501; web as amulet, VI, 221
Spies, Joannes, pr Frankfurt, VI, 191
Spina, Bartholomew, V, 71, VI, 538
Spine, anointed, V, 470
Spinning-jenny, V, 35
Spira, Petrus, pr Messina, VI, 27
Spiringus, Ioannes, physician, V, 462
Spirit, corporeal, V, 87, 557, 641, VI, 225-9, 371, 396, 403, 407, 482-3; air transformed into, V, 511; alchemy and, VI, 243; animal, VI, 572; artery and, V, 47, VI, 381; blood and, V, 116; circulation of, VI, 329-31; classification of, as animal, natural and vital, V, 511, VI, 228-9; demon and, V,

486; diseased, VI, 211; divine or ethereal, V, 301, 559, VI, 228; dream and, VI, 481, 484; effect, of guilty conscience on, VI, 241; gem and, V, 457; imaginative, VI, 392; instrument of idea, V, 101-3; intellectual and moral qualities explained by, VI, 371; melancholy and, VI, 484; of metal, VI, 451, of natural things, V, 631, of plant, VI, 371, of sea, VI, 388, of star, VI, 387, of universe, VI, 507; prayer and, V, 106-7; radiation of, VI, 241; remedy for, V, 457; rotated in vertigo, V, 660; sun and, V, 301; underground, VI, 388; visual, V, 116, 475, VI, 286
Spirit, incorporeal, see Angel, Demon, Intelligence
Spirito, Lorenzo (1485), VI, 469
Spleen, V, 506, VI, 317
Spoleto, V, 255, 578, VI, 202
Sponnela, Clirosastre, astrologer, V, 169-70
Spontone, Ciro, VI, 506
Spontone, Gioanni Battista, VI, 506
Sprenger, Jacobus, cited, VI, 172, 531; and see *Malleus maleficarum*
Spring, see Bath, mineral, and Fountain
Springinklee, Hans, artist, V, 347
Spurge, poisonous herb, V, 29
Squarcialupus, Marcus, V, 656, VI, 183-5; cited, VI, 382
Squaring the circle, V, 292, 336, 407, VI, 33, 144, 443
Stabius, John, V, 160; complaint against Walther's executors, V, 339; life and works, V, 347; Werner and, V, 347-8
Stadius, John, V, 256, 303-4, VI, 598; attacked, V, 251; cited, V, 418, VI, 6, 131, 139; corrected, VI, 120, 137; *Ephemerides*, V, 232, 375, VI, 13-15, 18, 24, 60, 255; *Tabulae Bergenses*, V, 304, VI, 28-29, 119; tr Hermes, V, 303, VI, 158; Tycho Brahe on, V, 304
Stag, bone from heart of, V, 420, 454, 511, VI, 461; catches snakes, VI, 294; stone from tears of, V, 474; tip of tail, poisonous, V, 646; treatise on, VI, 311
Stampeus, Petrus Antonius, VI, 558
Stanhufius, Michael, *De meteoris* (1562), VI, 32, 489
Staphylinus (vermiform), VI, 268
Star, fixed, V, 171, 251, 265, 320, 370, VI, 29, 53-54, 90, 133; catalogue of, V, 343, VI, 54; color as clue to nature of, VI, 159; composition, VI, 357; distance, VI, 39, 53, 381; dog, V, 482, VI, 351; each a separate world, VI, 374; influence, V, 315, VI, 110, 351, 375, 435, 500; interaction of, VI, 375; light of, V, 29, 153, VI, 380; longitude and latitude of, VI, 64; magnitude, V, 315, VI, 110; make no sound, V, 153; number, V, 373, and terrestrial species, V, 658, and years of world, V, 373; observation of, V, 366, VI, 15, 82; orders of, VI, 110; Paracelsus on, rejected, V, 658; polar, V, 271, 495; position of, VI, 111, 140, verified, VI, 298, 327; refraction and, V, 366; rising and setting of, V, 349, VI, 64, 103; ruled by planets, VI, 434; tables of, V, 160, 263, 375; twinkling of, V, 32, 153; and see Sphere, eighth
Star, new, of 1572, V, 12, 248, 374, 397, VI, 39, 57, 67-69, 79, 96, 184, 376, 474; controversy as to, VI, 72, 97-98, 504-5; disappears, VI, 73; estimates of it thereafter, VI, 73, 81, 97; ignored, VI, 91; intellectual effect of, VI, 84, 407; not new, VI, 97-98, 358; parallax of, VI, 97, none, V, 248, VI, 67, 358; prediction from, VI, 69, 96, 184-5, 253; supernatural, VI, 69, 75, 96, 408
Star, new, of 1600, VI, 96; of 1604, VI, 96; of 1605, VI, 97, 169
Star of Bethlehem, see Bethlehem
Star of earth, V, 458
Stars, influence of, V, 107, 109, 140, 158, 235, 273-4, 318, 463, 473, 481, 510, 513, VI, 24, 86, 196, 417, 419, 445, 451, 503-4, 516, 571; after the fall, V, 239; by accident, VI, 181, 232, by aspect, V, 241, VI, 174, by heat, V, 552, VI, 174, 232, by influence, occult, V, 241, 272, 299, 643, 646, VI, 135, 188-9, 199, 203, 205, 252, 351, 435, by light, V, 272, 552, 643, VI, 174, 199, 232, 252, 379, by motion, V, 241, 252, 552, 643, 646, VI, 135, 174, 199, 232, 379, 435, by motion alone, VI, 205, 327, by rays, VI, 111, by spirits, VI, 387; changing, V, 665; difficult to measure, VI, 196,

204, to resist, VI, 157; fixed at creation, VI, 488; in four ways, V, 241; inferred from their colors, VI, 138; not inevitable, V, 215, VI, 161; not superficial, V, 272; not supernatural, VI, 121; on abnormal events, V, 192, 274, 290, 572, VI, 500, affairs, V, 172, 644, air, VI, 189, animal, V, 225, VI, 391; apparition, VI, 532, art, V, 134, 199, VI, 243, 392, and see Image, Autun, V, 307, bath, V, 435, VI, 209, bell, V, 107, bird, VI, 485, 543, body, V, 28, 140, 151, 160, 176, 264, 301, 393, 558, 634, VI, 167, 181, 439, Burgundy, V, 310, calamities, V, 163-4, characters, see, chemical remedy, VI, 243, Christ, see, church and state, V, 397-8, 401, compound, V, 290, 552, conflagration, final, V, 124, contingent event, VI, 125, 156-7, 172, 176, crops, V, 120, 172, cure, VI, 572, custom, VI, 500, day, critical, see, death, V, 172, demon, V, 84, 242, VI, 236, 426, disease, V, 120, 162-3, 280, 290, 351, 444, 572, 627-8, 638, 649, VI, 190, 199, 408, 423, 546, dream, V, 235, VI, 477, 482-3, 500, 512, 543, element, V, 290, 393, 400, 552-3, 644, VI, 129, 189-90, externals, V, 235, flood, see, foetus, V, 172, 236, VI, 203, 387, form, V, 290, 527, 559, 633, VI, 203, 368, 599, fortuitous event, V, 110, VI, 157, fortune, VI, 189, 204, fossil, V, 22, 27-28, future, VI, 10, gem, VI, 301, 316, generation, V, 157, 170, 247, 510, VI, 203, 205, 349, human, VI, 198, monstrous, V, 247-8, 510, VI, 203, spontaneous, V, 655, VI, 188, gold, VI, 304, hand, VI, 431, heat, V, 559, 572, herb, VI, 347, 570, denied, V, 294, VI, 259, history, V, 121, honors, VI, 204, human life, V, 398, 644, VI, 140, 199, 204, 351, 396-7, 417, human nature, V, 296, 572, 628, 639, 650, VI, 399, humors, V, 122, VI, 199, impotency, VI, 559, individual, VI, 240, inferiors, V, 42, 117, 158, 248, 633, VI, 159, 188-9, 199, 203, 349, 365, 368, 396, 434, 460, 499, intellect, V, 119, 177, 224, 242, VI, 94, 125, 131, 199, 203, 349, 351, 572, indirectly only, V, 58, 189, 242, interior of earth, VI, 396, knowledge, V, 53, land, V, 121, 553, law, V, 224, longevity, V, 121, VI, 403, magic, V, 83, 135, 573, VI, 336, 449-50, magnet, VI, 431, maniac, V, 242, marvel, V, 104, VI, 132, 203, matter, VI, 496-7, metal and mineral, V, 125, 249, 643-4, VI, 135, 199, 304, miracle, V, 107, 290, VI, 125, monarchy, VI, 344, monster, VI, 408, 413, 571, morals, V, 444, VI, 500, 572, motion, VI, 351, nationalism, V, 247-8, nature, V, 236-7, 400, VI, 165, 181, 450, new world, V, 167, 209, 212, VI, 346, occult virtue, V, 135, 296, 559, 561, 646, 655, 661, VI, 188, 205, 231, 354, 399, denied, VI, 189, 232, oracle, V, 104, papacy, see, pest, V, 161, 299, 398, 607-8, VI, 210-2, 220, physiognomy, V, 53, VI, 163-4, 167, poison, V, 481, VI, 209, politics, see Political, prayer, V, 117, prophet, V, 104, 213, VI, 477, 512, qualities, V, 109, 153, 203, VI, 109, 189, 203, 366, 379, religion, V, 108-9, 119, 124, 213, 215, 221, 224, 280-1, 572, VI, 125, 133, 174, 344, 512, 569, race, V, 394, region, V, 394, seer and sibyl, V, 105, soul, VI, 236, 435, 450, sublunar, see inferiors, sun and moon, VI, 375, sympathy and antipathy, VI, 351, 414, syphilis, V, 290, temperament, V, 398, VI, 190, tongues, gift of, VI, 176, war, V, 120, 299, 441, weapon ointment, VI, 240, weather, V, 120, 196, 199, 209, 216, 386-7, 572, VI, 15, 351, will excepted, V, 140, 151, 295, 312, VI, 94, 125, 174, 181, 199, 203, 349, 351, 379, 504, will inclined, V, 176, 235, 274, 400, 633, VI, 125, 181, 417-8; only general, V, 656, VI, 190, 199, 203, 205; varied, VI, 342

Stathmion, Christopher, Erastus against, V, 654-5; letters to, V, 379, 400, 654; prediction by, V, 400

Statue, V, 141; animated, V, 119; magic, V, 83; of Julius II, VI, 150; speaking, V, 83, and walking, V, 327; vital principle in, V, 91

Stauber, Laurentius, VI, 597

Stechmann, Johann, VI, 352

Steel, oil of, VI, 282

Steele, Robert (1917), VI, 219

Steganography, VI, 434

Steiff, K. (1881), V, 372
Steigerus, Ioannes, VI, 530
Steinheim, V, 65-66
Steinius, N. publisher, Frankfurt, VI, 316
Steinmann, J. pr Leipzig, VI, 502
Steinmetz, Valentin, VI, 184
Steinschneider, Moritz, V, 355
Stella, Erasmus, on gems, VI, 302-3
Stengel, Stenglen or Stenglin, Lucas, physician, V, 640-2
Stephanus, alchemist, V, 604, 623
Stephanus, medical, V, 430
Stephanus, pr Paris, V, 273, VI, 432
Stephanus, Henricus, pr Paris, V, 279, VI, 441
Stephanus, Robert, pr Paris, VI, 230
Stephen of Messina, tr, VI, 448
Stephen, king of Poland, V, 479, 482
Stereometry, V, 174
Sterpinus, John Michael, V, 546-7
Sterzi, G. V, 44
Stettin-Pomerania, duke of, dedic to, VI, 102
Stewart, William, bishop, V, 296
Stiborius, Andreas, V, 347-9
Sticados, an herb, VI, 262, 264
Stifelius, Michael, V, 392-3; cited, VI, 459
Stigelius, Ioannes, V, 380
Stigmata, VI, 571
Stimson, Dorothy (1917), VI, 43, 55
Stiphelius, see Stifelius
Stobaeus, VI, 449
Stöberl, see Stiborius
Stockelman, Johannes, pr Copenhagen, VI, 523
Stockholm, pr at, VI, 311
Stocmann, Erasmus (1604), VI, 39
Stoechas, an herb, VI, 262
Stoeffler, Johann, V, 326; *Almanach nova,* see *Ephemerides;* cited, V, 265, 374, VI, 11, 18, 21, 131; *Cosmographicae aliquot descriptiones,* V, 7; criticized, V, 200; dedic to, V, 379; *Elucidatio,* V, 334, 348; *Ephemerides,* V, 7, 209, 222-3, 232, 339, 348, 371, continued, V, 264, 372, 379; *Expurgatio,* V, 225-6; held responsible for fear of a flood, V, 181, 213, 225; influence, V, 331, 375; picture of, at age of 79, V, 264; quoted, V, 178, 181, 193-4, 198; story of his accident, V, 226, VI, 113
Stoic, VI, 227-8, 568
Stoius, Matthias, VI, 596
Stomach, each member of body has its own, V, 635; effect of drugs on, V, 663-4; muscles of, V, 505; worn over, VI, 315
Stone, book of 125, V, 548; broken by blood of goat, V, 559; can be broken, not cut, V, 555; disease, V, 146, VI, 212, 311, early death from, VI, 334, how caused? VI, 311, relieved, VI, 323, by an image, VI, 113, 303; in air, VI, 285, 366, animal, VI, 285, 307, 309-10, 323, bladder, V, 509, human body, VI, 269, 307, 408; over 400 voided, V, 432; sensitive, VI, 287; and see Bezoar, Gem
Storia della Università di Napoli, V, 74, 254, 274, VI, 492
Stork, chick burned alive as remedy, VI, 461; flight of, V, 145; love for its young, VI, 278
Storm, see Weather
Story, V, 446, VI, 26, 132, 504; animal, VI, 278; idle, VI, 281, incredible, V, 482; of apparitions, VI, 533; of feats of magic, VI, 536; stock, VI, 520; and see Astrologer, Travel, Witch
Strabo, criticized, V, 448
Straits of Gibraltar, V, 19-21
Straits of Magellan, VI, 345
Strasburg, V, 177, 317, 431, 436-7, 442, VI, 219, 520; astrology at, V, 324; bishop of, V, 437, VI, 123; clock in cathedral of, V, 323, VI, 88; pharmacist of, V, 267; preface from, V, 323; pr at, V, 57, 64-66, 79, 162, 173, 201, 203, 316, 322-3, 334, 356, 364, 373, 431-3, 443, 469, 528, 536-7, 541, 543, 600, 609, 622, 625, 641, VI, 55, 75, 88-89, 123, 244, 273, 433, 441, 467, 506; rainbows at, VI, 267; retired to, VI, 219; studied at, V, 397; taught at, V, 469, 607, VI, 503
Strata, observed by Leonardo da Vinci, V, 26, Palissy, V, 598
Strata, see Thomas a
Stratander, J. G. (1562), V, 609
Stratenus, William, M. D., VI, 87
Strauss, on sympathetic powder, V, 10
Streets, V, 85, 579; care of, VI, 579; see Paris, streets of

Striedinger, Ivo (1928), V, 549, VI, 245
Strigelius, Victorinus, VI, 595
Strobel, Geo. T., *Miscellaneen,* V, 202, 382-3, 387
Strubius, G. pr Wittenberg, VI, 4
Strunz, Franz (1937), V, 618
Struthius, Joseph, tr, V, 328
Stübler, Eberhard (1926), V, 500-1, 652
Stuchssen, Ioannes, pr Nürnberg, V, 354, 362
Student, average, V, 155; beginning, VI, 6, 11; dedic to, V, 225; dull, written down to, V, 154; enthusiasm of, V, 205; informs teacher, V, 45; joking with, VI, 487; method of, VI, 433; reaction against cramming, VI, 562; testify, VI, 468; to attain perfection, VI, 167, 429; wandering, VI, 254
Studi e Memorie per la Storia dell'Università di Bologna, VI, 153
Studien zur Geschichte der Medizin, V, 625
Studien zur Geschichte math. u. physikalischen Geographie, V, 353
Stueler, see Stella
Stupor, remedy for, V, 462
Sturio, a fish, VI, 257
Sturm, Johann, V, 324, VI, 596
Stuttgart, V, 269
Style, barbarous, VI, 208; distinctive, V, 378; fulsome, V, 590; of Cardan, V, 563, Croll, V, 649, Falloppia, VI, 208-9, Paracelsus, V, 619, Sanchez, VI, 561-2; overemphasized, V, 436; rhetorical, VI, 183-4, 506; vernacular, V, 477, 590, VI, 107; see Humanism
Styria, V, 223, VI, 191
Suardus, Paul, V, 460, 464
Suartzerd, Georg, VI, 597
Suavius, Leo, V, 636-40, VI, 475; compared with Dorn, V, 638-9; Wier against, VI, 406
Sublimation, V, 635, 643, 645, VI, 278
Submarine, V, 35, 585
Substance, V, 571; separate, V, 118-9, 135, VI, 477; and see Angel, Demon, Intelligence
Subtilis, Joh. Bapt., pr Naples, VI, 162
Success, essentials for, V, 363
Succha, Antonius, assistant to Vesalius, V, 524
Succinic acid, V, 650
Succubus, see Incubus and
Suchten, Alexander de, Paracelsist, V, 641
Suchten, John de, Paracelsist, V, 392, 640-2
Süddeutsch. Apotheker-Zeitung, VI, 266
Sudhoff, Karl, V, 417, 431, 439-40, 617-8, 629-30, 642; (1894), V, 439, 442, 474, 617, 625; (1902), V, 78-79, 162, 169, 173, 260, 296, 300, 302, 318, 323-4, 328, 356, 387, 434, 443, 572, VI, 106, 123, 126-8, 189, 431, 478-9; (1909), V, 407
Sueidewein, Johann, VI, 596
Suevus, Andrea, a teacher, V, 323
Suez, VI, 345
Suffocation, death from, predicted, V, 587
Suffumigation, V, 273, 574; against demons, VI, 338, 547, 558
Sugar cane, V, 453
Suicide, of an astrologer, V, 253
Suidas, VI, 32
Suiseth, Richard, V, 95-96; and see Calculator
Sulmona, VI, 139
Sulphate of potash, V, 650
Sulphur, VI, 334; as a remedy, V, 651, against demons, VI, 234; extracted alchemically, V, 132; generation of, V, 125; gold made from, VI, 634; name for, VI, 278; one of three principles, V, 626
Sulphuric acid, V, 34
Sulpitius (Sulpicius) Gallus, VI, 21
Sultan, Turkish, V, 206, 235
Sumatra, V, 453
Summa perfectionis, alchemical, V, 536-7
Summa textualis, alchemical, V, 623
Summers, Montague (1929), VI, 552
Summum bonum, VI, 350
Sun, V, 145, VI, 435; apogee of, VI, 24, 43, 53, 57; before sunrise, V, 560; comet and, VI, 381; declination of, see Ecliptic, obliquity of; distance of, V, 31, 110-11; genius of, V, 568; gold and, V, 33, 242; heat of, V, 32; herbs that turn towards, V, 495; influence, V, 301, greater than that of other planets, V, 191, affects their movement, V, 388, denied, V, 216, internal, V, 659; light from it or stars? V, 29,

VI, 375; mansions of, V, 309; moon and, V, 429, conjunctions and oppositions, V, 235, 245, 351, 608, VI, 197; movement of, VI, 182, that of blood compared to, V, 263; observation of, V, 366, VI, 61; perfect, VI, 564; position in universe, V, 424-5, VI, 374; six seen, V, 396; size, V, 25, 34, 53; souls from, V, 36; symbol of God, VI, 188; theory of, VI, 58; triple, V, 155, 239, VI, 486, 491; why looks larger when setting, V, 31, 32; worship, V, 425; and see Eclipse, Joshua, Revolution, Year
Sundial, VI, 471; cylindrical, V, 354; works on, V, 397
Sunstroke, V, 612
Superstition, V, 142-3, 309, VI, 135, 305, 520; attacked by an astrologer, V, 283; ecclesiastical, VI, 148, 549; in medicine, V, 47, 437-8, VI, 219-20, 232; of Cardan, V, 579, Paracelsus, V, 442; oriental, VI, 26; partial, V, 459-60, 653; popular, V, 509-10, 628, VI, 221, 404, 471-3, 503; ridiculed, V, 176
Surgeon and Surgery, V, 59-61, 288, 324, 465, 469, 531, 556, 598, VI, 254, 291, 463, 552, 559; death from, V, 322; forbidden to practise medicine, VI, 219-20; imperial, V, 391; low estimate of, V, 514, 522; moon and, V, 121; of later middle ages, V, 498; papal, V, 254; physician and, V, 513-4, 522, VI, 217, 311; practice, V, 509; taught, V, 44, 61, 499, VI, 290; training, V, 513-4; works on, V, 618, VI, 236, 321
Surius, Laurentius, V, 282, VI, 438, 459
Susius, Joannes Baptista, VI, 227
Suspension, VI, 233, 282; from neck, V, 249, 455-6, 560, 562, 646, VI, 294, 311, 321, 338, 419, by a thread, VI, 322; hidden, to cure remote patient, rejected, VI, 417; of Bible verses, V, 477, VI, 498; on tree, VI, 282; and see Amulet, Peony
Sutton, Henry, pr London, VI, 392
Swabia, V, 331
Swallow, ashes of, cure angina, V, 559, suffusion, VI, 235; cures its blinded young with an herb, VI, 260, disproved, V, 448; droppings of, VI, 358; palpitating heart of, for memory, V, 560; stone in gazzard of, VI, 310
Swallow-wort, see Chelidonia
Swamp, contagion from, V, 497; herbs found in, VI, 259
Swan, song, V, 146, VI, 284
Sweating sickness, V, 437, 497, VI, 394
Sweden, V, 376; king of, VI, 311, 537; queen of, VI, 42
Swertius, Franciscus (1628), VI, 45
Swine, see Pig
Swiss and Switzerland, V, 269, 331, 607, 612, 618, 652, VI, 89, 145, 157, 247, 440, 489; chronicle, V, 177; infantry, V, 164
Sword, against demons, VI, 405; drawn, V, 613; of three metals, VI, 404
Sybold, Henry, pr Strasburg, V, 79, 162, 528
Sycomancy, VI, 503
Sylvius, Jacobus, VI, 267; cited, V, 464, 647, VI, 252, 258, 272
Symbolica, VI, 502
Symbolism, V, 135, VI, 277; of colors, VI, 367-8
Symmetry, V, 17; of hand and body, V, 587
Symon, see Simon
Sympathetic powder, V, 10
Sympathy and antipathy, V, 390, 409, 424, VI, 234, 241, 282, 294, 297, 318, 350, 392, 397, 456; accepted, V, 481, 551, 561, 599, VI, 26, 128, 186, 287, 292, 323, 354, 419, 434, 460, 500, 508, 564, 601; analyzed, V, 571, VI, 414; examples of, V, 662, VI, 281-2, 416, 602; opposed, VI, 318; relation to magic, V, 574, VI, 426, 430, to occult virtue, V, 135, 527, 662, VI, 231, some denied, VI, 416; twenty kinds of, VI, 385
Symphorianus, see Curtius
Synesius of Cyrene, VI, 475, 478; cited, VI, 484, as an alchemist, V, 624
Synonym, VI, 278
Syphilis, V, 290, 454, VI, 212; account of, V, 62-63, 147, 254, 483, 497, 671-2; conjunctions and, V, 195, 227, 434, 489, VI, 187; foretold, V, 207; remedies for, V, 325, 459, 639, VI, 313; works on, V, 205-6, 324-5, 440, 442, 514, 544

Syphoning, VI, 294
Syracuse, VI, 63
Syriac, ignorance of, V, 134
Syrup, V, 289, 461, 642

Tabernacle, ten curtains of, VI, 432
Tables, V, 324; astrological, V, 172, 262-3, 345; astronomical, V, 160, 300, 343-4, 346, 355, 361, 372, 395, 423, 425, VI, 11, 16, 44-45, 57, 82, 184, 298; Bergenses, see Stadius; criticized, V, 282, V, 411, VI, 5, 53, 108; divining, VI, 503; emendation of, V, 412; Gregorian, VI, 57; inaccurate, V, 200-1; mathematical, V, 417; medical, VI, 268; of Barcelona, V, 344; of declinations of fixed stars, V, 160; of Leowitz, VI, 111-2; of longitudes, V, 557; of Magini, V, 251, VI, 57, 430; of oblique ascensions, V, 376; of physiognomy, VI, 510; of reference, V, 594; of sines, V, 357, 364, 376; of Vienna, V, 223, 332; resolutae, V, 359-60, VI, 82, 133; trigonometric, V, 415; Toledan, V, 300; and see Alfonsine, Prutenic, etc.
Taccola, Mariano di Giacomo, V, 34
Tacitus, the historian, VI, 199, 513
Tacitus, Joannes, dedic to, V, 333
Tacuinum, medical, V, 654
Tacuinus, Ioannes, pr Venice, V, 170, 537
Taddeo Alderotti, see Alderotti
Tafuri, G. B. (1744-1770), VI, 492, 600
Tages, VI, 504
Tagliana, Pietro, cardinal, V, 582
Tagus river, V, 585
Tahufer, Wolfgang, V, 658
Taisnier, Jean, V, 254, 580-88, VI, 118; cited, VI, 167; criticized, VI, 164, 201, 382; plagiarist, V, 4, 580-1; quoted, V, 580
Talc, V, 458
Tale, see Story
Taliacotius, Gaspar, anatomist, VI, 281
Talmud, V, 373, VI, 25, 444-6, 451, 454, 459
Tamarind, V, 467
Tamburini, Gino, V, 76
Tanacetum, an herb, VI, 262
Tanavete, an herb, VI, 262
Tangent, use of word, VI, 140
Tann, Josua von der, VI, 433
Tannhäuser, V, 229
Tannstetter, George Collimitius, V, 331, 348-9, 443; accused of errors, V, 225; *Artificium,* V, 316-7; cited, V, 323-4, 415; ed, V, 332, 347; extracted from, V, 443; *Libellus consolatorius,* V, 221-6, 332; *Scholia,* V, 388
Taormina, V, 215
Tarantula, V, 477
Tarnow, VI, 480
Tarragona, V, 174; pr at, VI, 96, 166, 428
Tartaglia, Nicolaus, criticized, VI, 137
Tartar, of Paracelsus, V, 626, 649
Tartary, V, 287, VI, 342
Tasso, Niccolò, count, V, 455
Taste, discussed, V, 390, 555, VI, 175, 354; identification by, V, 459, 463; of chemical, VI, 242, fish, VI, 271, herb, VI, 259, mineral, V, 593
Tatti, Giovanni (1561), VI, 217
Tauladanus, Robert, alchemist, V, 546-7
Taurellus, Nicolaus, VI, 191, 331-2
Taurus mountains, V, 19
Taxil, Jean (1614), VI, 97, 169-70
Taylor, Henry Osborn, V, 441
Tayssonière, G. de la, geomancer, VI, 472-3
Teaching, improved, V, 154; private, V, 44
Tech, duke of, VI, 76, 462
Technology, V, 34-35, 580-99
Teeth, see Tooth
Telemus, VI, 504
Telepathy, see Thought transference
Telephone, attempted, VI, 422
Telescope, V, 248, VI, 87, 190, 555
Telesia, bishop of, VI, 169
Telesio, Bernardino, V, 626, VI, 370-1; cited, VI, 48; forerun, V, 559; influence, VI, 374, 561
Temperament, V, 66, 237, 475, 557; forces affecting, VI, 204; knowledge of, VI, 190; properties of, V, 662; under stars, V, 398
Temple, William, Ramist, VI, 238
Templum Angelicae salutationis, Naples, V, 73
Tenaud or Thenaud, abbé, VI, 453
Teneriffe, peak of, V, 27, VI, 380
Terebinth, V, 461
Terence, notes on, VI, 498

Terminology, Arabic, V, 266, 278; astrological, V, 266, 269; astronomical, V, 161, 208; and see Name
Terminus (astrological), V, 216, 309, VI, 144; rejected, VI, 138
Terra sigillata, V, 420, 474
Terrae malum or Terrumalium, fruit of an herb, VI, 261
Tervisinus, Gaudentius, see Gaudentius of Treviso
Testicle, V, 47, 481, 507, VI, 364; edible, V, 609; removed by witchcraft, VI, 337, 546; single, V, 518, VI, 559
Testiculus, an herb, VI, 260-1
Tethya, a zoophyte, VI, 268
Tetragrammaton, V, 538, VI, 444-6, 463, 508
Teubner, Ioan. Car. (1725), V, 579
Teucer of Babylon, VI, 487
Teukesberg, Giva, VI, 164
Teutonic Knights, VI, 303
Text, revised and altered, V, 76-77, 81
Textbook, V, 130, 148-9, 152-5, 173; chemical, VI, 242-3; elementary, V, 5, 111; historical, of our childhood, VI, 275; new method in, V, 642, VI, 10; of anatomy, V, 500; of astrological medicine, VI, 127; of astronomy, V, 246, 331, 384-5, VI, 6-8, 10-12, 34-35, 40, 46-47; use of question and answer in, VI, 10, 34
Textual criticism, V, 142, 501-2, VI, 282, 492
Thadeus of Parma, V, 118
Thales, astrological foresight of, V, 389; cited, VI, 21
Theatinus, J. B., V, 71
Theatinus, Nicoletus Verniates, V, 71
Thebes, see Hephaestion of
Thebit ben Corat, V, 172; cited, V, 421, VI, 43, 62, 130, 361, on images, V, 533, length of year, VI, 26, motion of eighth sphere, V, 185, 333, VI, 17, 65; said to have added a tenth sphere, V, 333
Theft, V, 613; detected, V, 455, VI, 305, 440, 508, 542
Thelesphorus, VI, 75
Themar, V, 203
Themis, VI, 504
Themistius, cited, VI, 48
Themo Judeus, V, 23, 25, 33, VI, 284
Theodore Gaza, see Gaza
Theodoric (of Cervia?), V, 513
Theodoricus, Sebastian (1564), V, 154, VI, 34-35
Theodorus, alchemist, V, 623
Theodorus, M.D. of Basel, V, 609
Theodosian Code, V, 403
Theodosius, emperor, V, 244
Theodosius, VI, 82, 88; *Diebus*, V, 364; *Habitationibus*, V, 364; *Spherica*, V, 356, VI, 27
Theologian and Theology, V, 269, 282, 299, 378, 402, 504, 507, 547, 660, VI, 105, 116, 335-6, 377, 379, 429, 455, 491, 519, 540, 550; against Agrippa, V, 129; alone can bless, V, 316; Aristotelian, opposed, VI, 364, 520-1; astrology and, V, 58, 194, 198, 202, 233, 275-6, 279, 322, 397, VI, 135, 172, 174, 523, defended by, V, 197, 215, VI, 129, opposed by, VI, 16, 141, prediction by, VI, 361; astronomy and, VI, 28; bachelor of, V, 279; chiromancy and, V, 66, 252; cited, V, 101, 462, VI, 235, 378, 482; comet called supernatural by, V, 322; curious as to sex, V, 526; demon affirmed by, V, 82, VI, 337; doctor of, V, 116, 197, 252, 288, 446, 552, VI, 130, 462, 537, 556; dream and, VI, 482; Epicurean, V, 380; faculty of, V, 275, 279, 291, 345, and see Sorbonne; genitures of, VI, 597-8; Hebraic, VI, 456; humanism and, V, 8; intelligence and, VI, 413; licentiate of, V, 202; magic and, V, 660; master of, V, 201, VI, 63, 166, 487; mystic, V, 113; natural philosophy and, V, 42, 81, 91; on new star of 1572, VI, 67, 72; Orphic, V, 119; professor of, V, 67, 210, 215, 326, 397, 652, VI, 187, 346, 449, 524; rests on authority and faith, VI, 135; scholastic, attacked, V, 66, 175, 280-1, 285, 526, cited, VI, 97, 125; science and, V, 150-1, 276, 526, 652, 657, VI, 22, 54, 72, 76, 81, 239, 267, 290, 570, 572; studied, V, 86, 275, 397, 652, VI, 77, 201, 498; superstition of, VI, 240, 420; symbolic, VI, 444, 456; testimony of, VI, 279, 288; witchcraft and, VI, 527; works of, V, 440, VI, 346, 445, 524

Theomancy, VI, 454, 494-5
Theon of Alexandria, V, 292, 364, VI, 486
Theophilus, alchemist, V, 624
Theophrastus, V, 439; cited, V, 109, 460, 480, VI, 271, 303, 334, 399, 486, as an alchemist, V, 545, 624; criticized, V, 469, VI, 401, 519; lost works, V, 545; on plants, V, 141, 263, 273, comm. VI, 266
Theophrastus ab Hohenheim, see Paracelsus
Theophrastus Transsilvanus, V, 548
Theory of, see Medicine, Planet
Theosophy, VI, 434; and chemistry, VI, 438
Thephramancy, VI, 503
Therapeut, VI, 456
Theriac, V, 453, 484, 598, VI, 214, 230, 258, 553; preparation of, V, 470-1, VI, 225
Thesaurus exorcismorum (1608), VI, 558
Thesaurus pauperum, V, 5
Theses, at Ingolstadt, VI, 414, Jena, VI, 239, Montpellier, VI, 222-3, Paris, VI, 388; medical, VI, 222-3, 521; of Pico, VI, 431, 455, Russilianus, V, 78, Skalich, VI, 455-6; on magic, VI, 414, 534
Thessalus, V, 128
Thessaly, V, 203
Thetel, cited, VI, 300, 305; not cited, VI, 318
Theurgy, VI, 426, 459, 516, 532; false, VI, 193
Thevet, André, geographer, cited, VI, 361
Thibault, Jean, pr Antwerp, V, 128, 286, 288, VI, 478
Thiébaud, J. (1939), VI, 45
Thieme, Hugo, VI, 106
Thiers, VI, 221
Thirst, relieved, V, 611, VI, 316
Thirty Years War, V, 14
Thistle, eating a, V, 444
Thomas of Bologna, V, 622
Thomas of Cantimpré, VI, 276, 300; not cited, VI, 318
Thomas a Strata, V, 125
Thomasius, Matth. Binius, V, 170
Thomist, V, 175
Thorellus, Baldwinus, VI, 36
Thorn, V, 153
Thorndike, Lynn, V, 4, 85, 182, 291, 344, 471, VI, 50, 261, 279, 361, 436; T (1929), V, 40, 166, 260, 406, 481, 507, 552; T I, V, 291, 365, 419-20, 482, VI, 447, 562; T II, V, 63, 102, 148, 481, 600, 675, 678, VI, 218, 300, 361, 449, 480, 483; T III, V, 54, 190, 344, 364, 481, 622, VI, 351; T IV, V, 26, 121, 159, 168-9, 179, 203, 237, 240, 278, 335, 344, 356, 362, 379, 392, 492, 521, 537, 588, 673, VI, 289, 295, 304, 348, 401, 438, 440, 444, 487; T V, VI, 88, 388; T (1937), V, 64, 344, 547, 622, VI, 257
Thou, Christofle de, dedic to, VI, 526
Thou, J. A. de, V, 303, 331, 374, 398, 588, VI, 138, 191, 220, 227, 257, 325, 341, 373, 450, 478-9, 490, 499, 503
Thought, freedom of, opposed, VI, 395; and see Free thinking
Thought transference, V, 91, 606
Thriverus, H., V, 326
Thrones, VI, 451, 454, 551
Thuanus, see Thou, de
Thunder, V, 231-2; divination from, V, 420, 575-6, VI, 488; force in, V, 567; observed, V, 611
Thurecensis, V, 370, 600
Thuringia, VI, 254-5
Thurneisser, Leonhard, VI, 78-79, 245
Thylesius (1629), VI, 306
Thyodamas, VI, 504
Thyraeus, Petrus, S.J., VI, 533
Tibertus, see Antiochus Tibertus
Tichonius Affer, VI, 459
Tides, attributed to wind and spirit within the ocean, VI, 201, to subterranean channels, V, 30; disagreement as to, VI, 382; follow moon, V, 30, 192-3, VI, 128, 199, 383, denied, VI 205, doubted, V, 227, VI, 388; how explained by Cesalpino, VI, 327; like breathing, V, 29; like pulse, VI, 388; works on, V, 300, 314, 327, VI, 311, 475
Tigris-Euphrates, V, 19-20, 27, 30
Tiletanus, Io. Lod. pr Paris, V, 148, VI, 460
Time, VI, 124; and place, VI, 350, 410, 419; astronomical, V, 296; not ours to know, V, 223; specified, V, 203; told

by a suspended turquoise, VI, 322; and see Day, Election, Hour, Instant
Tincture, V, 632, 659, VI, 243, 434
Tinghi, Philip, pr Lyons, V, 326, VI, 45, 130
Tiraboschi, G. V, 44, 71, 204-5, 251, 254, 325, 336, 410, 488, 533, VI, 93, 123, 129, 154, 311, 313, 368, 373-4, 377
Tirano, V, 613
Tiraqueau, André, V, 143, 254, 289, 544, 618, VI, 227; quoted, VI, 207
Tiresias, VI, 504
Titelmann, Francis, *Compendium,* V, 147-52; criticized, V, 624; quoted, V, 139
Toad, dried, as antidote, VI, 388; found alive in stone, VI, 284; stone, V, 451, 478, VI, 232, 310, 323, how induced to void, VI, 282-3; used in alchemy, VI, 245, in witchcraft, VI, 337
Toast, V, 462
Tobias, and the angel, VI, 235, 357; and heart of a fish, VI, 547; cure of his father, VI, 358
Tocco, Felice (1892), VI, 424
Tocco and Vitelli (1891), VI, 424-7
Toepke, Gustav (1884-86), V, 402
Toledo, V, 269; choristers at, V, 582; magic at, V, 283; Nifo's prediction for, unsound, V, 211; submarine at, V, 585; Tables of, V, 300
Toledo, Anthonius, V, 159
Toledo, Francisco de, VI, 387
Toledo, see Gondisalvus of, James of
Toleration, religious, VI, 525, opposed, VI, 395
Toletus, Franciscus, see Toledo
Tolhopf, Johann, V, 406-7, 490
Tollin, Henri (1880), V, 288, 290
Tolm, VI, 436
Tomasini, J. P. (1629-30), V, 251, 303, VI, 122-3, 201-2, 369-70, 483
Tomeo, Niccolò Leonico, VI, 493
Tommaso da Ravenna, VI, 428
Tondinus, cited, V, 54; and see Tundinus
Tongue, gem placed beneath, V, 575; swollen, V, 459
Tongues, gift of, or speaking strange, V, 118, VI, 176, 439, 555
Toni, G. B. de (1923), V, 20, 29
Tonialus, J. J. dedic to, VI, 56
Tonsis, Ioannes de, patrician, preface to, VI, 336
Tooth, ache, V, 462, VI, 208; decay, V, 459; gigantic, V, 512; growth of, V, 511; hair and, V, 146; third set of, VI, 597; to soothe, VI, 311, 404
Top to toe order, VI, 217, 402, 602
Topaz, VI, 306
Topography, VI, 430
Toppi, Niccolo (1678), V, 74, VI, 492, 528
Tordesillas, V, 209
Torgau, VI, 269
Torme, Francisco de, VI, 166
Tornaesius, Ioannes, see Tournes, J. de
Tornieri, Iacomo, pr Rome, VI, 139
Torpedo, fish, power of, V, 101, 473, 477, 646, 663, VI, 206, 291, 565
Torquato, Antonio, see Arquato
Torquemada, cited, VI, 551
Torquetum, an astronomical instrument, V, 343-4, 365
Torre, Giambattista della, V, 489, VI, 62
Torrella, Gaspar, V, 179, VI, 488
Torrella, Jerome, VI, 304
Torrentinus, Laurentius, pr Florence, V, 273, VI, 226
Torres Villarroel, Diego de, VI, 166
Torresius, Joh., V, 134
Torrigiano, see Turrisianus
Torsianus, astrologer, VI, 36
Torture, V, 62, 312; confession to avoid, VI, 245; defied, V, 567; not dependable, V, 667; of Gaurico, V, 51, Raimondo, VI, 474, the innocent, V, 142; opposed, V, 578; seven times, VI, 174; use in witch trials, VI, 146, 336, 535, 539, 552; when justified, VI, 242
Toscanelli, Paolo dal Pozzo, V, 342, VI, 77
Tosius, Bartholomaeus, pr Rome, VI, 410
Toulouse, V, 269, VI, 431, 478-9; archbishop of, V, 300; execution of Vanini at, VI, 560; Parlement of, VI, 560; pr at, VI, 339-40, 463; Sanchez at, VI, 560-1; studied at, VI, 479, 531
Tourbillon, VI, 362
Tourette, Alexandre de la, see La Tourette

Tournes, Jean de, pr Lyons, V, 67-68, 398, 542, VI, 24, 479

Tournon, pr at, VI, 97, 169, 553; school at, VI, 382

Tours, pr at, V, 464, VI, 344

Toxites, Michael, V, 417, 619, 624, 641-2

Tozzi, Pietropaolo, pr Vicenza, VI, 162

Trachea, wound of, cured, V, 509

Tractationum philosophicarum tomus unus (1588), VI, 326

Tractatuum ex variis iuris interpretibus collectorum, VI, 432

Tradition, persistence of, VI, 276, 280-1, 401, 567-8

Tragacantha, V, 449

Tragus, Hieronymus, V, 443, VI, 255, 258, 261-3, 267, 273-4, 290, 353; omits magic virtues, VI, 292, yet watches on midsummer night, VI, 295

Tralles, see Alexander of

Transformation of Lot's wife, VI, 534; of men into beasts, V, 107-8, 660, VI, 337, 526, 539, 546, 548, denied, VI, 601, imagined, VI, 515-6, to be taken figuratively, VI, 477

Translation, faulty, by Evans, VI, 288, by Richter, V, 22, from Arabic, V, 450, of Euclid, V, 293, of Ptolemy, V, 336; from Arabic, VI, 449; from Greek, V, 3, 74, 257, 293, 304-5, 342-3, 364, 369, 400, 430, 482, 514, 530, VI, 112, 114, 120, 142, 154, 158, 255, 344, 368, 447-50, 460, 476, 478, 492; from vernaculars into Latin, V, 12, 51, 438, 545, 556, 601, 619, 625, 630, 644, VI, 7-8, 167, 187, 211, 215, 221, 274, 314, 316, 413, 530, 550; humanist, V, 336, 342-3; into Greek, VI, 460; into vernaculars, see English, French, German, Italian; medieval, V, 61-62, 263, 284, 365, 369-70, VI, 448, 476, criticized, V, 501-2, some works of Galen available only in, V, 437; old German, V, 391; Paracelsus, of, V, 417, 438, 618, 628, 630, 640; poetical, VI, 257; sixteenth century, V, 3, 74, 328, 437, 443, VI, 476; under assumed name, V, 112; urged, V, 185

Transmutation, of elements, V, 40, herbs, VI, 419, metals, see Alchemy

Transportation, magic, V, 83, VI, 336

Transubstantiation, V, 40, VI, 494-5

Transylvania, V, 155

Travel, V, 16, 170, 236, 581, 612-4, VI, 153, 254-5, 257, 332, 341, 433; material collected by, V, 650, VI, 420; medical instruction for, V, 609-12, 614, VI, 400; routes taken, V, 615-6; tales of, VI, 274; and see Vagabond

Treason, trial for, VI, 549

Treasure, found, VI, 416; hidden, V, 628, VI, 416, 542; problem of accidental unearthing of, V, 274; search for, V, 219, VI, 479, 498

Trebatius, Bernardinus, tr, VI, 447

Trebizond, see George of

Trechsel, pr Lyons, V, 342

Tree, VI, 289, 333; bark of, V, 476, VI, 284; gum of, V, 451-2; of life, V, 545-6, VI, 356; sign of pest, V, 608; to protect, VI, 282; work on, VI, 289

Trent, V, 582, VI, 518; and see Council of

Trepanning, V, 512

Trepidation, theory of, see Thebit ben Corat

Treves, archbishop of, VI, 537; pr at, VI, 537-8; and see Bernard of

Treviso, V, 63, 269, VI, 471, 493; pharmacist of, V, 548-9; pr at, VI, 447

Trial, see Treason, Witch

Triangle, VI, 39, 406, 454

Triangulation, V, 319

Tricasso, Giacomo, V, 63

Tricasso, Patricio, V, 63-65, 256, 587, VI, 131; condemned, VI, 163, 177; put on Index, VI, 147

Trick, V, 567, 574, VI, 429, 431, 434, 530, 601

Trier, see Treves

Trigonometry, V, 303, 415, VI, 82

Trigonus, see Triplicitas

Trimoille, madame de la, V, 309

Trincavelli, Victor, Aristotelian, VI, 229, 364, 449

Trinity, VI, 350, 427, 464; compared with Paracelsan principles, V, 658; in name of, VI, 404; nature and, VI, 341; proof of, VI, 454; represented by brain, liver and heart, VI, 362; Servetus on, V, 288

Trino, VI, 364

Tripe, V, 474

Triplicitas (astrological), V, 216, 309, 367, VI, 138, 144; change of, V, 278, 311, 415, VI, 69, 76, 117, 139, 174
Tripod, VI, 404
Tripoli, see Philip of
Trireme, V, 585
Trismegistus, see Hermes
Trithemius, V, 71, 91, 606, VI, 424, 598; Agrippa and, V, 130; Bouelles on, VI, 439-40; cited, VI, 504, 570; correspondence of, VI, 438-9; *Nepiachus*, VI, 439; quoted, VI, 437; represented as a necromancer, VI, 536, 598; *Scriptoribus*, V, 348; *Septem secundadeis*, V, 637, VI, 438, 441; *Steganographia*, V, 131, 136, 560, 562, 637-8, VI, 360, 439-40, 475, 521, 534
Triton, V, 143
Trium verborum, V, 538
Trochee, V, 461
Trojan war, VI, 142
Trompeta, Antonius Andreas, VI, 378
Trophonius, VI, 504
Trot, Bartholomew, bookseller, Lyons, V, 308
Trottus, Bernardus, VI, 51, 139
Trusianus, see Turrisianus
Truth, criteria of, V, 83, 566, 570, VI, 135, 278-81, 401, 415; love of, V, 52, 84, 467, 566; natural, VI, 238; of Bible, on science, VI, 356; of the mind and nature, VI, 395; twofold standard of, rejected, VI, 336
Trutvetter, Jodocus (1514), V, 149
Trygophorna, Caleb, VI, 105
Tubal Cain, V, 539
Tubercula, V, 280
Tübingen, V, 70, 348, VI, 37, 457; astronomy at, VI, 17, 29; Mundinus forbidden at, V, 500, 522; pr at, V, 153, 225, 264, 372, 412, VI, 3-5, 76, 79, 82, 123; relation of Melanchthon with, V, 379-80; studied at, V, 331, 383, 397, VI, 191; taught at, V, 114, 153, 371, VI, 16, 191, 341
Tuccius Tuccius (1585), V, 256
Tudor, Mary, queen of England, VI, 102, 196
Tuguriolum, V, 50
Tulle, V, 111
Tundinus, geomancer, V, 131; and see Tondinus
Tunis, V, 582
Turba philosophorum, V, 141, 538, 543, 623, 625
Turbith, V, 123
Turchi, Floriano, astrologer, V, 246
Turenne, viscount of, dedic to and horoscope of, VI, 161
Turin, V, 125, 546, VI, 217; archbishop of, V, 509; died at, VI, 227; pr at, V, 24, VI, 137, 258, 356, 372; taught at, VI, 212, 258
Turino, Andrea, physician, V, 260-1
Turk and Turkey, V, 470, VI, 353, 503; invasion by, V, 222, threatened, V, 224; pest in, VI, 185; prediction about, V, 230, 375, 410, 415, VI, 78, 80, 118; sect of, V, 206; union against, urged, V, 212, 243; and see Sultan
Turnebus, Adrian, VI, 38
Turner, William, naturalist, VI, 256-8, 261-3, 267, 271, 273, 279; misrepresented, VI, 287-8
Turnifer, Leonard, VI, 245
Turonensis, grossa, parva, herbs, VI, 263
Turque, Antoine de la, cited, VI, 361
Turquoise, does not change color in presence of poison, V, 478; ingredient in electuaries, VI, 314; loses beauty at owner's death and recovers it after it is worn by new owner, VI, 306, 322; saves its wearer from injury by breaking, VI, 186, 322
Turrecremata, cited, VI, 543
Turrel, Pierre, astrologer, V, 307-12
Turrisianus, *Plusquam commentator*, V, 40, 42, 170, 503-4, 513, VI, 229
Turrius, Baptista, see Torre, Giambattista della
Tursulum, an herb, VI, 262, 264
Tuscany, V, 19, VI, 338; grand-duke of, V, 642, VI, 126-7, 129, 332
Tutor, V, 228
Twins, argument from, against astrology, VI, 114, 204; differing fates of, V, 241, 272; geniture of the Farnese, V, 267; Siamese, V, 517
Tyana, see Apollonius of
Tyara, Petreius, despiser of astrology, VI, 194
Tyard, Pontus de, VI, 24, 119; career, VI, 106; cited, VI, 119; *Mantice*, V, 256, VI, 107-8, 493; *Univers*, VI, 24-26

Tycho Brahe, see Brahe
Tyrant, death of, predicted, V, 272
Tyre, king of, debate with Solomon, VI, 353
Tyrius, a clock-maker, V, 132
Tyrus, a snake, V, 474

Ubaldi, Guido, V, 50
Ubaldo del Monte, Guido (1579), VI, 109
Ubelin, Georg, V, 173, 437
Ubertino (of Casale?), VI, 75
Udine, V, 44
Uffenbach, Peter (1603), VI, 237; (1614), VI, 494
Ughelli, Ferd. (1717-22), VI, 528
Ugo, author of a chiromancy, V, 56-57
Ugo, medical, see Hugh of Siena
Ulcer, V, 227, 367; cure for, V, 621, 665, VI, 320, 323
Ulloa, Alfonso di, tr, VI, 390
Ulm, eclipse at, V, 216; pharmacist, of, VI, 267; pr at, V, 181, 348, 355, 674; written at, V, 658
Ulmus, Franciscus, of Poitiers, VI, 230
Ulmus, Ioannes Franciscus, see Olmo
Ulmus, Marcus Antonius, pr Venice, V, 529
Ulpian, jurist, VI, 537
Ulpian of Verona, VI, 493
Ulrich, administrator of Schwerin, VI, 535
Ulricherus, Geo. pr Strasburg, V, 316
Ulstad, Philip, *Coelum philosophorum*, V, 541-2, 602, 621; quoted, V, 532
Ulysses, V, 613
Umbilicomancy, V, 58, 511, 561
Umbilicus Veneris, VI, 309
Umbilicus, as amulet, VI, 292
Unger, Bernard, V, 114
Ungerer, Alfred (1922), VI, 88
Unguent, V, 273, 461, 636, 639, VI, 218; against vermin, V, 612; deceptive, VI, 477; demon and, VI, 477; for the memory, V, 607; from animal, V, 432; of alabaster, VI, 225; of exorcist, VI, 547; of magician, V, 478; of snake charmer, V, 473; of witches, VI, 420, 516, 571
Unicorn, V, 457; virtue of horn of, V, 264, 420, 476, 485, VI, 186, 315-6, denied, V, 665, VI, 232, 323
Unity of the Intellect, see Intellect
Universal, abandoned for particular, VI, 312, 354
Universe, see World
University, V, 4, 7, 78; botany in, VI, 266; failure at Nürnberg, V, 338, 393; failure to hold position in, V, 128; German, VI, 535; planned for Fano, V, 265-6; should have an observatory, VI, 17; trip to, V, 147; various, V, 123, 147; and see Academic, and names of particular universities and of subjects taught
Upsala, university of, V, 410
Ur of the Chaldees, VI, 520
Urania, V, 300-1
Uraniburg, V, 324; pr at, VI, 95
Urban VIII, bull against astrology, V, 247, VI, 145, 171-2, 175-7; detested astrology, VI, 175
Urbino, V, 95; cardinal of, V, 274; duchess of, V, 218; duke of, V, 246, dedic to, VI, 484, 517
Uriel, angel, invoked, VI, 508
Urinaire, VI, 524
Urine, bloody, V, 612; excessive, V, 10; of sacred animals in Egypt, VI, 353; retained, VI, 546; works on, V, 144; and see Uroscopy
Urkunden zur Geschichte der Universität Tübingen, V, 372
Uroscopy, V, 297, 465; carried to excess, V, 381; diagnosis with, alone, V, 436, diagnosis without, V, 308
Ursa Minor, V, 293
Ursel, pr at, V, 65-66, 540, VI, 286
Ursinus, Geo., *Prognostica*, V, 374-5
Ursinus, Ioannes, *Prosopoeia animalium*, VI, 257
Ursperg, abbot of, VI, 458
Ursus, N. R. (1588), VI, 55-56, 62
Usingen, see Bartholomew of
Utica, VI, 447
Utrecht, VI, 255; bishop of, VI, 102, 401; pr at, VI, 102; university of, VI, 87
Utrum, V, 14, 49
Uzielli, G. (1869), V, 28-29

Vacation, V, 86
Vacuum, V, 151; attraction exerted by, V, 551; between the stars, VI, 380;

existence of, denied, V, 658; inconsistent attitude of Leonardo da Vinci, V, 33; nature avoids, V, 495, VI, 384, 564-5; problem of, V, 146
Vadianus, Joachim (1531), V, 388; cited, VI, 509
Vagabond, intellectual, V, 8, 11, 127, 152, 169, 286, 288, 431, 439-40, VI, 22, 51, 423, 457
Vairus, Leonardus, VI, 528-9, 545; cited, V, 486, VI, 602
Val Camonica, V, 613
Valcurio, Georgius, VI, 596
Valencia, V, 269, VI, 95, 166, 373, 409, 428; archbishop of, V, 226; pr at, V, 535, VI, 96, 166, 304
Valentianus, Gregorius, cited, VI, 544
Valentianus, Ioannes, alchemist, V, 637
Valentinelli, J. (1868-1874), V, 169-70, 204
Valerandus de Bosco, alchemist, V, 623
Valeriano, Piero, *Litteratorum infelicitate,* V, 253, 313; on hieroglyphs, VI, 278, 447; *Sphere,* VI, 447
Valeriola, Franciscus, VI, 215
Valerius, Cornelius (1561), VI, 31; (1566), VI, 31-32
Valery, A. C. P. (1842), V, 488
Valescus de Taranta, *Philonium,* V, 629
Valesius, Franciscus, see Vallesius
Valgrisius, Vincent, pr Venice, V, 545, VI, 260
Valla, George, V, 6, 166, 343, 503
Valla, Lorenzo, V, 9
Valladolid, V, 582, VI, 129; pr at, VI, 129
Valle, Bartolomé de, VI, 165
Vallée or Vallensis, Robert, alchemist, V, 623
Vallesius (Valles de Covarruvias), Franciscus, VI, 258; cited, V, 486; *Sacra philosophia,* VI, 306, 355-60
Valtelline, V, 29
Valturius, Robertus, V, 34
Valverda, anatomist, V, 531
Van Gorp, Jan (1580), VI, 461
Vanini, Lucilio, death of, VI, 511; influence, VI, 511, 568; quoted, VI, 511; views of, VI, 568-72
Vannullo, Mercurio, VI, 470
Van Ortroy, see Ortroy
Vapor, V, 101, 107, 497
Vapovsky, Bernhard, letter to, V, 409
Varanus, Julius, V, 50
Varismann, Johann (1586), V, 481-4
Varnhagen (1872), V, 466
Vascosanus, Michael, pr Paris, V, 294, VI, 20
Vase, alchemical, see Instrument
Vassal, V, 172
Vasto, marchese of, VI, 485
Vatican, gardens, V, 325, 410; library, V, 407
Vaughn, astrologer, VI, 180
Vecchietti, Filippo (1790-96), V, 484, VI, 315
Vedova, Gius. (1832-36), V, 170, 545, VI, 202
Vegetation, growth accelerated, VI, 434; and see Herb
Vein, V, 29, 47, 523, 531, 562, VI, 329-32, 432
Velocity, see Motion
Velsius, Ioannes, VI, 598
Venamancy, V, 58
Venatorius, Thomas, V, 337, 369-70, 392
Vendôme, V, 152
Veneficia, VI, 545-6; natural and diabolical distinguished, VI, 234; put on Index, VI, 147
Venesection, see Phlebotomy
Venetian, see Venice
Venice, V, 94, 130, 206, 327, 447, VI, 452, 465; alchemy and, V, 539-40, 548-9, 604, VI, 245; astrology at, VI, 199-201; astronomical observations at, V, 257; bird's eye view of, V, 540; book center, VI, 452; Bruno at, VI, 427; buildings restored, V, 205; citizen of, VI, 510; composed at, V, 258; convent of, V, 517; Council of Ten, V, 250, 537, 539-40, VI, 557; doge of, V, 314, VI, 474; drugs at, V, 452, 455, 459, 461; fish and fisherman of, V, 597, 663; Gaurico and, V, 263, VI, 101; general of, V, 488; Grand Council of, VI, 474; harlots at, V, 527; hospital at, V, 517; Index of, see Index; Inquisition in, VI, 149; jeweler of, V, 456; knight of, VI, 200; medicine at, V, 488, 516, 630, VI, 429; nuncio to, VI, 551; of, V, 170, 624, VI, 105, 258, 364, 450; patrician of, V, 75, 79, 163, 606, VI, 154, 199, 349,

373, 436; pest at, VI, 185; Philologus at, V, 204; prediction concerning, V, 235, 240, 247; pr at, V, 4, 24, 38, 39, 44, 45-46, 55-56, 57, 64, 72-77, 79-80, 94, 96, 100, 114, 121, 144, 154, 157, 162-3, 165-6, 170, 179, 181, 183-4, 197, 218, 220, 233, 245-6, 250-1, 254, 259, 263-4, 269, 302, 306, 313-4, 325-6, 328, 335, 340, 342-3, 345-6, 364, 369, 391, 409, 419, 421, 445-6, 461, 464, 466, 479, 489, 493, 513-4, 528-9, 535-7, 539-40, 544-5, 547, 549, 555, 558, 572, 605, 607, 645, VI, 10, 25, 27, 40, 42, 47-48, 56, 60, 97, 100-1, 122, 124, 128, 137, 148, 155, 158-61, 164, 180, 198, 205, 208, 210, 213, 215, 217-8, 222, 224, 227-8, 258, 260, 266, 299, 300-1, 312-3, 325, 349, 364, 369, 371, 373, 376-7, 390, 393, 398, 405, 410, 414, 428-9, 431, 447-51, 458, 469, 471-6, 486, 492-3, 506, 510, 527-8, 544-5, 550, 556-7, 559, 599-600; public exorcist in, VI, 557; Rogati of, VI, 470; secret council of, VI, 201; senate of, V, 548, 645; Tables for, V, 251; taught at, V, 581; Turk and, V, 230; visited, V, 582, VI, 373; and see Paul of

Venosa, VI, 260

Ventilation, V, 497

Ventriloquism, VI, 520; and see Witch of Endor

Ventura, Cominus, pr Bergamò, V, 457

Venturi, G. B. (1797), V, 21

Venus, the planet, influence of, V, 58, 196, on comets, VI, 89, on divination, V, 575; orbit of, V, 425, VI, 20, 78; unusual in December, 1578, VI, 92

Verae alchemiae, see Gratarolo

Vergil, *Aeneid,* VI, 520, imitated, V, 254; as a magician, V, 118; cited, V, 443, VI, 281; *Georgics,* V, 609; weather signs from, V, 297, VI, 486

Vergil, Polydore, see Polydore

Vergilius, Ioannes, of Urbino, publisher, V, 95; and see Virgilius

Verhandlungen d. Natur. Ges. in Basel, V, 417, 629, 642

Verini, Francesco, VI, 522

Vermin, V, 612, VI, 275-6

Vernacular, increased use of, V, 5, 11-12; religious services in, VI, 528; scientific works in, VI, 273-4

Verniates of Chieti, see Theatinus

Veröffentlichungen des königl. Preuss. Meteor. Instituts, V, 178

Verona, V, 46, 59, 154, 269, 488, 505, 537-8, VI, 56, 124, 185, 224, 228; baths near, V, 537; bishop of, V, 264, VI, 558; margrave of, VI, 455; of, V, 264, VI, 147, 161, 209, 402, 492; patrician of, VI, 474; physician of, V, 324, 493, VI, 267; pr at, V, 265, VI, 161, 214, 514, 558

Verri, Pietro (1835), V, 161

Vertigo, V, 660, VI, 208

Verulanus, Ennius, cardinal, V, 259

Vervain, V, 483, 610, VI, 292, 546, 558

Vesalius, Andreas, V, 422, 550, VI, 329, 569; allusion to occult arts, V, 527-8; *Chirurgia magna,* V, 527, VI, 235; criticizes Galen, V, 525, 530; criticized, V, 529-31, VI, 213, 235; dedic to, V, 501; *Examen,* V, 530-1; Falloppia and, V, 529-31; Gemma Frisius and, V, 526; geniture of, VI, 105, 595; *Humani corporis fabrica,* V, 421, 441, 498, 518-20, 523-30, misleading preface, V, 522, plates, V, 519, reception, V, 528, VI, 9, 214; omissions, V, 45, 518-9; other works, V, 529; praised, V, 49; pupil of, V, 529, VI, 393; relation to past and contemporary anatomists, V, 516-9

Vespasian, VI, 435, 513

Vespucci, Amerigo, V, 422, 427; cited, VI, 433

Vespucci, Bartolomeo (1508), V, 164-5

Vesuvius, Mt. VI, 50

Vetter, Quido (1931), V, 429

Vettius Valens, VI, 130, 487

Via antiqua, V, 406

Vialardus, Franciscus Maria, VI, 373

Vianis, Bernardinus de, pr Venice, V, 263

Vice, V, 62

Vicenza, VI, 447; pr at, V, 343, VI, 162, 286, 431, 469, 550

Vicomercatus, Franciscus, *Principiis,* VI, 368; cited, VI, 48-49

Victor, Hieronymus, pr Vienna, V, 349, VI, 302

Vienna, VI, 457; astronomy at, V, 222, 366, 415; bishop of, VI, 491; dedic from, VI, 505; Engel at, V, 346; fall, predicted, V, 222; medicine at, VI, 128, 394; meteors at, V,

203; Paracelsus at, V, 440; plants near, VI, 184; pr at, V, 34, 174, 221, 322, 346, 353, 356, 375, VI, 302; Regiomontanus at, V, 366; studied at, V, 173, 385, 391; taught at, V, 160, 173, 224, 316, 322, 328, VI, 341; Tolhopf at, V, 407; university of, V, 345, 431, men of science at, V, 221, 567; visited, VI, 59
Vienne, archbishop of, V, 288; noble of, V, 310; pr at, VI, 257
Vierteljahrschrift f. Gesch. und Landeskunde Vorarlbergs, V, 391, 411, 413
Vignon, Eustathius, pr Venice, VI, 326
Viljeff, M., V, 366
Villach, VI, 490
Villalar, battle of, V, 209
Villanova, see Arnald of
Villanovanus, Michael, see Servetus
Villars, V, 296
Villaterius, Renatus, apothecary, V, 123, 125, 453
Villiers, Gilbert de, pr Lyons, V, 125
Villingen, see Georg Pictorius von
Villon, Antonius de, VI, 388
Vimacius or Vimacuus, Nicolaus Francus, V, 142
Vimercati, see Vicomercatus
Vincent of Beauvais, cited, V, 159, 406-7, 538, 547, VI, 300
Vincent, Peter, V, 400
Vinci, see Leonardo da
Vinegar, V, 458, 462, 635, VI, 429
Vinetus, Elias, V, 333, 379
Vintage, see Wine
Violati, pr Venice, VI, 431
Violet, V, 446, 608; oil of, V, 611
Viotto, Seth, pr Parma, V, 596
Viper, fat of, V, 451; generation of, V, 20, 551, VI, 186, 257, 281, 310, 348; oil of, VI, 219; only female, used in theriac, VI, 225; sympathy with murena, VI, 416
Virdung von Hassfurt, Johann, V, 160, 203; cited, V, 298, 323-4, VI, 6; criticized, V, 227; horoscope of Melanchthon, V, 401; own, VI, 596; reprinted, V, 203-4, VI, 158
Virgilius and the antipodes, VI, 436
Virgilius of Salzburg, verses against alchemy, V, 536
Virginia, VI, 276, 436
Virginity, bestows prophecy, VI, 481; required in divination, VI, 508
Virmius, see Virunius
Virtue, and vice, V, 20, 363; and see Occult
Virunius, Ludovicus Ponticus, VI, 493
Visconti, Zacharias, exorcist, VI, 558
Vision, see Eye and Eyesight
Visions, V, 87; death-bed, V, 568; false, feigned, and diabolical, VI, 532
Vistula, V, 425-6
Vitae selectae, V, 607
Vital faculty, VI, 229
Vitali, Bernardinus de, pr Venice, V, 144
Vitali, Lodovico, see Vitalis
Vitali, Matthias de, pr Venice, V, 144
Vitalis, Ludovicus, charged by Champier with error, V, 124; Cocles and, V, 61; description of, V, 241; prediction by, V, 213-4, 241-4; quoted, V, 234; *Terraemotu,* V, 241
Vitalism, V, 635, VI, 355, 386
Viterbo, V, 366, VI, 215; bishop of, V, 410; pr at, VI, 162
Vitex, VI, 277
Vitriol, V, 479, 651, VI, 243, 434
Vitriolum, V, 450
Vitriolum romanum, V, 450
Vitruvius, ed, V, 443; cited, V, 422
Vivaldus, Ludovicus, VI, 459
Vives, Ludovicus, cited, V, 227
Viviani, Ugo (1923), VI, 227, 328-9, 338
Vocabulary, V, 391; limited, V, 330
Voetius, Gisbertus (1665), V, 386, VI, 87, 183, 252, 560
Vögelin, Johann, astrology of, V, 322; cited, V, 328, VI, 381; mathematics of, V, 356, 386; pref. to, V, 391
Vogelius, Ewaldus, V, 648
Voice, origin of, V, 522; strange, VI, 532
Volaterranus, see Maffei
Volcano, V, 26-27, 592
Volckamer, Georg, dedic to, V, 359
Voltaire, V, 312
Volterra, see Maffei
Volumnius Rodulphus, see Rodulphus
Vomiting, V, 474, 479, VI, 223; best safeguard against poison, V, 485; muscles employed in, V, 505; often beneficial at sea, V, 614
Vortices, VI, 384
Voyage, fast sailing, V, 585; transatlantic, V, 553

Voyages of discovery (and New World), V, 558; astrological bearings of, V, 167, 212, VI, 346; ignored, V, 19, 122, 389; intellectual effect of, V, 9-10, 18-19, 167, 427, 490, 566, 614, VI, 12, 27, 42, 83, 319, 345-6, 436, 560, 564; interest in, V, 355, 358, 437, 488; monsters revealed by, VI, 275-6, 408; new bezoars, VI, 235, 275, 315, 335; new fauna, VI, 256, 274, 296; new flora, V, 453, 460, 463, VI, 225, 272, 274, 296, 332-3, 394, 533; new peoples, V, 577-8, VI, 564; noted, VI, 276; relation to science and magic, VI, 274-5; works on, V, 636; and see Columbus, Vespucci
Vuelius, ancient astrologer, VI, 130
Vulgar, against the, VI, 222; for sake of the, V, 105; and see Secrecy
Vulture, foot of, V, 478, 485; heart of, V, 610
Vuyrsung, Marcus, publisher, Augsburg, VI, 446

Wachter, Georg, publisher, Nürnberg, V, 356
Wackernagel, R. (1924), V, 177
Wadding, Luke, *Scriptores,* VI, 445
Waldeck assemblies, VI, 354
Walde-graue, Robert, pr Edinburgh, VI, 547
Waldseemüller, Martin, V, 173, 437
Walking-beam, V, 594
Wall, town, VI, 489
Wallis, John (1682), VI, 89
Walser, Ernst (1932), V, 287
Walsingham, secretary, VI, 219
Walter of Odington, V, 220, 633
Walther, Bartholomaeus, VI, 49, 366
Walther, Bernhard, V, 339-41, astronomical observations, V, 366; cited, VI, 11; house, V, 344; library, V, 339-40, 357, 360, 395
War, after new star of 1572, VI, 185; armies affected by a prediction, V, 329; Burgundian, VI, 89; civil, V, 222, VI, 409; decried, VI, 77; European, VI, 119; every fifty years, VI, 499; fear of, V, 180; German, of 1546, VI, 409; in Navarre, V, 208; Italian, V, 72, 95, 111, VI, 136; Italians outclassed in, V, 164; of 1503, V, 72; of Religion, V, 483, 589; opposed, V, 164, 277, 578; predicted or predictable, V, 202, 217, 235, 272, 290, 392, VI, 78, 144; prevalence of, V, 163, VI, 184, 441; Schmalkaldic, V, 397; signs of, VI, 501; Trojan, VI, 142; Turkish, VI, 142; unlucky in, V, 399
Warde, Wyllyam, tr (1558), VI, 215
Warmien, bishop of, V, 410
Wasp, VI, 290
Watch, carried, V, 614; spring, V, 567
Water, above the firmament, V, 213, VI, 82, 84-85, 342, 347-8, 354, 357; alchemical, V, 132-3, 465, 534, 544, 635, VI, 433; as matter, VI, 384; as medium in conception, V, 270; better for young than old, VI, 223; boiling, V, 145; circulation of, V, 22; effect on hydrophobia, V, 483, on poisons, V, 480; filtration of, V, 593; freezing of, VI, 373, 387; from side of Christ, V, 506-7, 526; heavier than earth, V, 569, VI, 83; holy, V, 213, VI, 154, 168, 404, 558; marvelous, VI, 420, 434; medicinal, V, 621, VI, 216, 218; mineral, VI, 243, exported, VI, 209; more healthful than wine, VI, 223; petrified, V, 141; potable, V, 593; probation, of, VI, 509; river, VI, 546; stagnant, V, 157; staying under, V, 22; subterranean, V, 588-93, VI, 284, 432; supreme, VI, 451; turned into wine, V, 611; unwholesome, V, 591, 611; used in divination, VI, 502; virtues of, V, 297; wholesome, V, 260; why used in baptism, V, 213; and see Aqua, Aqueduct, Clock, water, Earth and
Wavre, VI, 547
Wax, divination by, VI, 503; and see Agnus Dei, Image
Weale, A. publisher, London, V, 608
Wealth, demoralizing effect on the state, V, 243; increase of, V, 246; VI, 314; predicted, V, 587
Weapon ointment, VI, 239-40, 420, 525, 602; diabolical, VI, 536; rejected, VI, 416, 534
Weasel, VI, 255
Weather, altered by prayer to saint, V, 104, by ringing bells, V, 107, 231-2, by herbs, stones and exhalations, V, 106-7, 614; bad, V, 155, causes of,

V, 92; Buridan and, V, 156; cloudburst, VI, 489; comet and, VI, 92; conjunction of 1524 and, V, 193, 386; conjurers and, V, 283, VI, 154; medicine and, V, 323; observed and recorded, V, 156, 160, 231-2, 348, 353, 387, VI, 30; pest and, V, 497; prediction of, V, 6, 7, 160, 201, 224, 245, 265, 290-2, 296, 299, 328-9, 348, 361, 392, 611, VI, 30, 63, 95, 143, 155, 300, 412, 486-8, 496, a division of astrology, VI, 114, allowed, V, 655, VI, 187, 549-50, approved, V, 276, VI, 200, 417, 529, by boys, VI, 488, by days, V, 224, criticized, V, 191, from dream, VI, 488, not admitted, VI, 192, too uncertain, VI, 85, 144; protection against, VI, 169; signs, V, 48, 220-1, 249, 297, 463, 605, VI, 367, 397; storms from demons and witches, VI, 539, denied, VI, 536; very hot summer of 1540, VI, 255, of 1557, VI, 312; works on, V, 605-6

Webb, C. C. J. (1915), V, 94, 99

Wechel, Andreas, pr Paris, V, 301

Wechel, Andreas, heirs of, prs Frankfurt, VI, 494, 505

Wechel, Chr. pr Paris, V, 254, 291, 298, 301

Wecker, Jacob (1528-1586), VI, 215-6, 430

Weeping, VI, 230

Weickmoser, VI, 115

Weight, V, 146, 361; increased in alchemy, VI, 242

Weil, Erich (1932), V, 94

Weil, Ernst (1928), V, 464

Weimar, V, 224, 328, 400, VI, 457, 596

Weiss, Adam, teacher, V, 323

Weiss, E. (1888), V, 343

Weissenfels, V, 365, 394

Well, Artesian, V, 593; bucket, V, 595; deadly, V, 155

Wells, bishop of Bath and, V, 142

Werminghoff, A. (1921), V, 407

Werner, Johann, V, 337, 343; astrology of, V, 350-2; career, V, 349-53; cited, V, 357, VI, 11, 131; complaint against Walther, V, 339; criticized, by Beheim, V, 350, Copernicus, V, 353, 409-10, Nunes, VI, 35-36, Tycho Brahe, VI, 54; eleventh sphere of, VI, 17; prediction by, V, 350-1; quoted, V, 348; Stabius and, V, 347-8; works, *Canones*, V, 7, *Meteoroscopiis, V*, 353-4, 415, *Mutatione aurae*, V, 353, 368, *Triangulis*, V, 347, 350, 353-4, 414

Wernher, Adam, V, 203

Werwolf, V, 147, VI, 526, 547, 552; and see Lycanthropy

West Indies, VI, 275, 294, 315, 346, 420

Westphalia, treaty of, V, 14

Whale, not a fish, V, 570; sperm of, V, 470; to drive away, V, 614

Wheelbarrow, V, 595-6

Whirlwind, from cellar of haunted house, VI, 479

Wiberg, V, 642

Wickersheimer, E. (1923), V, 381; (1928), V, 345-6; (1929), V, 189; (1936), V, 39, 112, 124, 159, 300, VI, 473

Widmann, Johann, medical, V, 437

Widmanstad, Joh. Albert, V, 325, 410

Wier, Johann, V, 13; and Agrippa, V, 129, 137; *Commentitiis ieiuniis*, VI, 516; disagreed with, V, 636-7, VI, 535, 555; influence, VI, 517; *Lamiis*, VI, 406, 517, 527; *Praestigiis daemonum*, VI, 439, 515-6; Skalich and, VI, 456; Suavius and, VI, 406

Wife, V, 176, 202, 297, VI, 80, 116, 305

Wildenbergius, Hieronymus (1542), V, 153

Wilhelm, count Palatine, dedic to, VI, 45

Wilhelm III, duke of Saxony, V, 342

Wilhelm, Johann, von Laubenberg, dedic to, V, 355

Will, V, 151, VI, 350; freedom of, V, 93, VI, 166, 174, 181, 203, 301, 394, 496, 523; and see Astrology, Stars, influence of; last made, V, 204

Will, Georg Andreas (1755-58), V, 338, 359, 365, 370, 383, 396, 443, 658, VI, 60, 115, 126, 190, 229-30

Willenbrochius, Ioh., VI, 596

William of Aragon, V, 64, VI, 480

William of Auvergne, VI, 431

William of Conches, V, 157, 219, 600

William of England, V, 478

William, landgrave of Hesse, V, 12, 490, VI, 352

William of Hirsau, V, 600

William of Mirica (Nurice), V, 54, 586
William of Moerbeke, V, 54, 263
William of Piacenza, see William of Saliceto
William of St. Cloud, VI, 11
William of Saliceto, V, 506
Wimpheling, Jacob, V, 334
Wimpina, Conrad, cited, VI, 487
Winckler, Nicolaus Eberhard, VI, 133-5
Wind, VI, 355, 470; action upon mountains, V, 592; carries shellfish far inland, VI, 291; great, of 1551, VI, 489; lifts frogs and fish from water, V, 157; origin of, V, 157; raised by demon, VI, 479
Windischgraetz, V, 56
Windsor, V, 320
Wine, V, 446, 483-4, 579, 602, 605, 611, VI, 218, 435; drunk by goat, VI, 309, 314; employed in alchemy, V, 132, medicine, VI, 218, surgery, V, 509; hot and wet? V, 493; old not hotter than new, V, 465; prediction as to next vintage, V, 192; quenching metals in, V, 647; red, a cure for measles, VI, 393; spirit of, V, 602, 632; taken with, VI, 461; water more healthful, VI, 223
Winsemius, Vitus Ortel, see Ortel
Winsheim, see Theodoricus of
Winter, Robert, pr Basel, V, 529
Winterburg, Johann, pr Vienna, V, 346
Winterthur, VI, 459
Winzemius, Vitus, V, 405
Wirzius, Melchior, preface to, VI, 478
Wirsung, Marx, see Vuyrsung
Wissekerke, VI, 298
Witch and Witchcraft, V, 478, 666-7, VI, 233, 266, 427; belief in, V, 10, 105, 401, VI, 115, 287, 525, 545, 559; confessions of, V, 117, 576, 667, VI, 336, 535, 537-8; counter-magic against, VI, 338, 516, 523, decried, VI, 559; death attributed to, VI, 539; defended, V, 127, 653; deluded, VI, 515, 535, 539; disease attributed to, V, 477-8, 627, VI, 539, 546, 548; Endor, of, VI, 107-8, 359, 516, 529, 532; execution of, demanded, V, 660, 666, VI, 146, 201, 400, 405, 498, 525, 549; feared, VI, 201; flight through air, VI, 336, affirmed, VI, 352, 526, 539, 546, 548, denied, VI, 497, 536; hereditary tendency, VI, 538; heresy or not? VI, 515, 524; how dissolved, V, 118; ignored, VI, 519; illusion, regarded as an, VI, 515, 529; literature of, V, 13, 69-71, VI, 515, *et seq.;* loss of human form, VI, 352; met by Condé, VI, 491; number of, VI, 524; opposition to persecution of, VI, 515, 529, 538; powers of, VI, 539, 548; remedies for, VI, 428, 545, 559; remedies of, VI, 526, 539; require medical attention, V, 117, 477-8; sabbat, V, 117, VI, 146, 502, 525, 546, 549, 552, 555, denied, V, 576, VI, 571; safeguards against, VI, 404, 523; science and, VI, 335, 346, 351-2; storms, raised by? VI, 539, 548; stories of, V, 69, VI, 337, 502, 516, 526, 529, 539, 549, 551, laughed at, V, 576, VI, 522; tests of: cannot weep, VI, 337, 538, 548-9, 552, float in cold water, VI, 352, 535, 538, 548-9, objects under skin of, VI, 337, spots, insensible, VI, 522, 526, 535, 538, 548-9, 552, 554; rejected, VI, 516; trials of, VI, 522, procedure in, V, 576, VI, 336, 523, 526, 531, 535, 539, 549, 552, distinctions between Inquisition and secular courts, VI, 145-6; unguent of, VI, 420, 516, 571; vain hope of, V, 571; and see Demon, Sorcery
Witekind, Hermann, V, 404, VI, 40-41, 517
Witelo, V, 366, VI, 566; cited, V, 140, 421, 587, VI, 11, 20, 50, 78, 429; criticized, V, 305; ed., V, 349; misdated, VI, 130; on nature of demons, V, 86-89; quoted, 305-6
Witestein, see Wittesteyn
Withagius, Ioannes, pr Louvain, VI, 30
Wittenberg, V, 378; astrology at, V, 379, 384-6; born at, VI, 102; Bruno at, VI, 424-5; conduct of students at, V, 400; Faust at, VI, 536; Luther at, V, 438, VI, 558; mathematicians of, V, 405; orations at, V, 386-7, 390, 401; pr at, V, 154, 359, 376, 383, 385, 398, 404, 408, 414, VI, 4, 6, 10, 12, 19, 32, 34, 102-3, 118, 229, 364, 366, 461, 489-90, 493-4, 499, 506, 533-4; rector of, VI, 229; seminar at, V, 390; Skalich at, VI, 457; studied at, V, 298,

328, 341, 381, 384-6, 390, 394, 397, 402, 404, VI, 59, 123, 494; taught at, V, 154, 384-6, 397, VI, 34, 59, 73, 147, 229, 461, 494; three brothers of, VI, 507; university of, V, 338, 360, 379, 396, 412, 640, VI, 35, 493; visited, V, 383, VI, 191
Wittesteyn, Carolus, V, 644
Wittich, Paul (1580), V, 350, VI, 55, 90
Wohlwill, Emil (1904), V, 385
Wolf, antipathy between sheep and, VI, 416; belt of gut of, V, 559, VI, 501; deprives man of voice, affirmed and denied, V, 559-60, VI, 233, 301; discord between drums of sheepskin and wolfskin, VI, 241; dung of, medicinal, VI, 233; head or tail keeps out flies, VI, 282; invade a town, V, 608; mad, V, 484; right eye of, V, 610; transformation into, V, 660; see Lycanthropy and Werwolf
Wolf, Caspar, naturalist, VI, 254, 290-1
Wolf, Hieronymus, V, 185, 226, 383, VI, 105, 112-6, 194, 197, 202, 448, 596
Wolf, Reginald, pr London, VI, 392
Wolfenbüttel, VI, 253; pr at, V, 584, VI, 210
Wolfgang of Strasburg, pr, Cracow, V, 174
Wolkenstein, David, VI, 89
Wolsey, cardinal, V, 497
Wolsius, Reginald, dedic to, VI, 520
Woman, V, 57, 86, 268, VI, 301, 404, 479; adornment of, V, 455, 458-9; adultery, guilty of, V, 324; aphrodisiac for, V, 444; appetite for, V, 268; apparition of dead, VI, 469; bad luck from, V, 404; bearded, VI, 391; why not, VI, 428; baptizes, V, 509; chastity tested, VI, 429; childbirth eased, VI, 169, 218, 224; deceived and deceiving, VI, 236; diseases of, VI, 309; dominate, VI, 441; eat a root, VI, 261; fasting by, V, 478; forced to dance naked, VI, 421; gain and loss from, VI, 168; harlot, V, 62, 527; have sperm? V, 503; irrational, V, 97; is man hotter than? VI, 223; leprous, cured, VI, 252; married, amulet for, V, 176, to detect infidelity of, V, 305, 314, 324; menstruating, V, 487, VI, 220, 358, 402; mistress of a monk, V, 526; necromancy practiced by, VI, 468; nocturnal, V, 639; nourished on poison, see Poison; occult sense of, V, 599; old wife, V, 105, 316, 476, 630, VI, 237, 260, 404, 530, why fascinates? V, 487, VI, 286, 513; opinion of, VI, 221-2; patient, V, 482; personified as, V, 245; playful princess, VI, 472; prediction concerning, V, 241; prefer soldiers, V, 146; pregnant, V, 509, VI, 221; reading not for, V, 262; tenacious of old words and pronunciation, V, 145; virago, V, 510; vocabulary limited, V, 145; weakness and credulity of, VI, 515; wet-nurse, V, 316; whipped, VI, 526-7; who kill by glance, V, 473; and see Midwife
Womb, VI, 404; cells of, V, 509, 523, 526; death from prefocation of, V, 517; opened in post mortem, V, 509; and see Foetus
Wonneck, Johann, medical, V, 437
Wood, V, 555; oil from, V, 589-90; saw, V, 594; sprite, VI, 551; and see Forest
Wood, Casey A. (1935), V, 68
Woodcut, V, 124, 347, VI, 217
Woodstock, V, 320
Word, archaic or obsolete, V, 145; barbarous, VI, 527; cure by, censured, V, 283, 645, VI, 516, debated, VI, 233-4, 462; differences in meaning, VI, 491, 502; employed, VI, 404; holy, VI, 557; magic, V, 135; medical use of, illegal, VI, 234; odd, VI, 409; of Christ, V, 273; play upon, see Pun; power of, VI, 444, 479, questioned and denied, V, 100, 141, 478, 481-2, 573, VI, 33, 233-4, 358, 398, 408, 416, 462-3, 528, 571, 601, indirectly, affirmed, V, 103; verbal erudition attacked, VI, 565
Work, effect on temperament, VI, 204
World, book of, V, 150; book on, V, 152, VI, 350; center of, not a place of dignity, V, 429; depicted, VI, 471; diameter of, VI, 275; duration of, V, 373; end of, far off, V, 229, near, V, 396, VI, 69, 76, 117-8, 491, not in 1588, V, 374, not announced by conjunctions of 1524, V, 223, not predictable, V, 212, predicted, V, 218-9,

310-1, 342, 373-4, 392-3, VI, 134, signs of, VI, 75, and see Conflagration, final; eternity of, V, 108, VI, 125, 198, 410, 433, 551, denied, VI, 399, 433, 496; harmony of, VI, 26, 392, 406-7, 450, 454, 564; infinite, VI, 374; intellectual and physical, VI, 443; living being, a, VI, 384; new, see America, Antipodes, Voyages of discovery; old age of, VI, 29, 76, 92; parts of, V, 86, VI, 392; perfection of, VI, 350; plurality of, VI, 137, 374, 383, 427, denied, VI, 551; symmetry of, VI, 39; triple, VI, 406, of cabala, V, 134, 650, VI, 453, 455, 509; universal virtue of, V, 216; visible and celestial, VI, 443; see Soul for World soul

Worm, V, 135; cure of, V, 578, by mercury, VI, 224, 313; in deer, VI, 315, dog, V, 482, human body, V, 89, 451, 482, 599, VI, 403, rain, VI, 366; medicinal ingredient, VI, 216; powder of, VI, 388; sign of future crops, VI, 501; without feet, generated from putridity, VI, 290, in metal or rock, VI, 284; and see Earthworm

Worms, V, 402; pr at, V, 347

Wormwood, V, 483

Wotton, Edward, naturalist, VI, 258, 358

Wound, V, 59, VI, 223, 239-41, 287; from gunshot, V, 254, VI, 251; purges body of other bad humors, V, 145; reopens annually, V, 482; treatment of, V, 509, VI, 323, 420, 601

Wouters, see Valerius, Cornelius

Wreath, VI, 338

Wren, golden-crested, VI, 416

Wright, W. C. (1930), V, 493

Wrinkle, V, 459

Writing, secret, V, 638, VI, 434; and see Invisible

Wrong-headedness, V, 653

Wurtemberg, V, 652, VI, 191, 491; duke of, V, 631, VI, 46, 76, 80, 82, 316, 462, 537

Würzburg, V, 159, 345; bishop of, V, 342; pr at, V, 560

Würzelbaur, J. P. (1728), V, 366

Wyer, Robert, pr London, VI, 476

Xenocrates, cited, V, 83

Ximenes, Leonardo (1757), V, 257

Ydrid, alchemist, V, 623

Year, beginning of, V, 235, 243, VI, 118, 191, at Paris, V, 186, 279, 557, at Pisa, V, 326; Bolognese, V, 243-4; climacteric, V, 38, 268, 331, VI, 139-40, 202, 206, 357, 502, 546; critical, of world, VI, 76; Egyptian, VI, 139; enneatic, V, 268; fatal, VI, 138; leap, V, 54, 257, 492, VI, 209; length of, V, 411, VI, 36, 43, 45, 53, 58, 383, exact in Alfonsine Tables, VI, 36, 64-65; lord of the, VI, 138, 144; of Jubilee, V, 558; 1588, prediction as to, V, 373-4; see Revolution of

Yesid Constantinopolitanus, alchemist, V, 623

York, V, 227

Youth renewed, VI, 315, 551

Ypres, VI, 311

Zabarella, Iacopo (1589), VI, 369-70, 387, 435

Zabern, VI, 74, 79

Zacharias, V, 54

Zacharias, pope, VI, 551

Zachariel, spirit of Jupiter, VI, 441; see Sachiel

Zachius, Paulus, V, 10

Zadith ben Hamuel, see Senior

Zael or Zahel the Israelite, astrologer, V, 220, VI, 180, 301

Zalterius, Bologninus, pr Venice, V, 154, VI, 124

Zamberti, tr Euclid, V, 279, 293, 343

Zamora, see Núñez de

Zanardus, Michael, cited, VI, 172

Zanchius, Hieronymus, *De divinatione,* VI, 503

Zannetti, B, pr Rome, VI, 202, 569

Zannetti, Francesco, pr Rome, VI, 410

Zanzibar, VI, 346

Zara, V, 314

Zaragoza, V, 92; archbishop of, V, 623, VI, 167; pr at, VI, 96, 166

Zassenus, Servatius, bookseller, Louvain, V, 320

Zavattari, Edoardo (1923), VI, 371

Zazius, Franciscus, VI, 598

Zedler, J., *Universal Lexicon,* V, 303, 445-6, VI, 7, 45, 109, 123, 130, 156, 166, 256, 528, 533
Zeeland, V, 648, VI, 298
Zeg, V, 450
Zeitlösslin, an herb, VI, 274
Zeitschrift für Angewandte Chemie, V, 532
Zeitschrift für Math. u. Physik, V, 417
Zeitschrift für Naturwissenschaft, V, 443
Zeltner, C. G., V, 393
Zenarius, Damianus, pr Venice, VI, 56; heir, V, 250
Zeno, Greek philosopher, V, 523
Zeno, Antonio, discoverer of America, VI, 436
Zeno, Apostolo (1752), VI, 313
Zenocarus a Scauvuenburgo, Gulielmus, V, 410
Zentralblatt für Bibliothekswesen, V, 331, 352, 354-5, 359, 362
Zerbi, Gabriel, cited, V, 504, 507, 520; criticized, V, 505-6, 508, 511, 515; followers of, V, 506
Zetzner, Lazarus, pr Strasburg, V, 535, 540, 622, 648, VI, 61, 244, 433, 457
Ziegler, Jacob, V, 359, 370, 614; comm. V, 387; correspondence, V, 409
Zierikzee, V, 443, VI, 394
Ziletti, Giordano, pr Venice, V, 27, VI, 124-5, 180
Zilsel, Edgar (1940), V, 424
Zimara, Marco Antonio, VI, 48, 599-602
Zinner, E. (1934), V, 337, 339, 343, 348-9, 352-7, 364, 366; (1936), V, 341, 356, 361, 364; (1938), V, 165, 333-4, 337-42, 344-5, 348, 354-6, 358, 361-2, 364-5, 369-70, 374-5, 377, 407, VI, 60
Zittart, Heinrich, medical, V, 437
Zoar (Avenzoar), cited, VI, 315
Zobel, Theodoricus, canon, V, 66
Zodiac, division into houses, see House, astrological; division into signs, VI, 473; immobile, V, 282; influence of, V, 557, VI, 159, 429, 435, 508, on cities, VI, 124, parts of body, VI, 124, 128, 159, denied, VI, 200, 203; now displaced, V, 359; twelve angels and, VI, 508; twelve herbs and, V, 619; twofold, V, 185; and see Ecliptic
Zonca, Vittorio (1607), V, 35, 596
Zone, torrid, V, 31, 147; impassable, VI, 182
Zoophyte, VI, 436
Zoroaster, VI, 460-1; cited, VI, 141, 374, 406; existence denied, VI, 461; key of, VI, 459; magic and, V, 166, 533, VI, 477; Oracles of, VI, 601
Zorzi, see Giorgio
Zosimus, alchemist, V, 623-4
Zuccolo, Vitale (1590), VI, 377
Zuichemus, Viglius, VI, 598
Zurich, V, 362, 548, VI, 457; met at, VI, 267; minister at, VI, 530; pr at, V, 143, 420, 440, 470, 543, 589, 606, 621, VI, 265, 269, 291, 303-4, 531; schoolmates at, VI, 8; surgeon of, V, 324, VI, 254, 291; taught at, V, 153, VI, 478
Zvigger, Theodor, V, 484
Zwickau, VI, 302; taught at, VI, 498
Zwinger, Theodor, *Theatrum,* V, 59, 137, 418, 484, cited, VI, 284, 365, preface of 1562, V, 473
Zwingli, V, 37; tr, VI, 520
Zwinglian, VI, 148, 530

INDEX OF MANUSCRIPTS

Arezzo, Bibl. d. frat. di S. Maria, 389, V, 99
Arezzo, Bibl. d. frat. di S. Maria, 390, V, 100
Basel, Codices Faeschii, V, 401
Basel O.III.4, V, 379, 401, VI, 595
  O.IV.27, V, 372
  O.IV.32, V, 339, 372
Bern, Stadtbibliothek 353, V, 673-4, 677
Bologna, Bibl. Comunale (no shelf-mark), VI, 150
Bologna, University, 27, V, 170
Cambridge, Emmanuel 70, V, 674, 676
  Trinity 1035, V, 320
  Trinity 1081, V, 674
Cassel, Landesbibl. Chem. 8vo (2), VI, 161
Chicago, Art Institute 15.334, V, 355
Clermont-Ferrand 47, V, 674
Codice Atlantico, V, 16-17, 33-34
Davis and Orioli, LXVIII, 6, V, 85
Dresden F.67, V, 168
Erlangen 1227, V, 358
Escorial f.III.2, V, 43, 100
Escorial O.III.30, VI, 165
Escorial P.III.8, V, 674
Florence, Gaddi 663, V, 257
  Laurent. Plut. 84, cod. 22, V, 85
  Laurent. Plut. 89 sup., cod. 34, V, 326
  Laurent. Plut. 89 sup., cod. 35, V, 673, VI, 127
  Laurent. Plut. 89 sup., cod. 36, VI, 127
  Laurent. Plut. 89 sup., cod. 41, VI, 471
Florence, Riccard. L.II.XV, V, 325
  Riccard. L.II.XXV, VI, 473
  Riccard. 921, V, 674
  Riccard. 984, V, 533-4
  Riccard. 1221 F, V, 67
  Riccard. 1223 D.VI, VI, 522
Geneva, University, français 167, VI, 453
Gotha, chart. in fol. 152-155, VI, 266
London, British Museum,
  Harleian 3353, V, 673
  Royal 12.B.XV, V, 320
  Sloane 14, VI, 36
  Sloane 216, VI, 115, 121-3
  Sloane 696, VI, 469
  Sloane 1009, VI, 311
  Sloane 1437, VI, 473
  Sloane 1743, V, 320
  Sloane 1773, V, 320
  Sloane 2156, V, 86, 88
  Sloane 2561, VI, 476
  Sloane 2879, VI, 454, 474
  Sloane 3129, V, 180
  Sloane 3130, V, 180
  Sloane 3169, VI, 266-7
  Sloane 3188, VI, 392
  Sloane 3189, VI, 392
  Sloane 3190, VI, 393
  Sloane 3191, VI, 393
  Sloane 3437, V, 673, 675
  Sloane 3464, V, 676-7
  Sloane 3542, VI, 476
  Sloane 3677, VI, 393
  Sloane 3810, VI, 473
Lucca 1473, V, 253
Lyons 925, VI, 66
Lyons 1392, V, 112
Milan, Ambros. A.52.inf., V, 100
  A.71.inf., VI, 120
  A.153.inf., V, 273
  A.236.inf., V, 48-49
  D.201.inf., V, 100
  D.260.inf., VI, 123
  D.389.inf., VI, 438
  D.417.inf., V, 100
  D.461.inf., VI, 217
  G.289.inf., V, 55
  H.40.inf., VI, 311
  N.123.sup., V, 375
Montreal, McGill University, Osler 7618, VI, 163
Munich, CGM 151, V, 325, 410
  CLM 27, V, 343
  CLM 201, V, 100
  CLM 239, V, 100
  CLM 657, V, 674
  CLM 5043, VI, 441

CLM 19689, V, 348
CLM 19690, V, 676
CLM 24606, VI, 441
CLM 27083, V, 351
Naples VIII.F.55, V, 76-77
New York, Pierpont Morgan 722, V, 432
Pierpont Morgan, Leicester MS, V, 28
Nürnberg, Cent V app 8, V, 364
Cent V 15, V, 370
Math. fol. 652, V, 352
Orléans 244, V, 622
Oxford, All Souls 81, V, 676
Oxford, Bodleian,
Ashmole 186, V, 320
Ashmole 1471, V, 673
Canon.Misc. 23, V, 170
Canon.Misc. 24, V, 171
Canon.Misc. 109, V, 368
Digby 132, V, 348
Digby 143, V, 320
Rawlinson C.677, V, 676
Rawlinson D.1362, V, 673, 675
Oxford, Corpus Christi 190, V, 673
Oxford, New College 162, V, 676
Padua, Antoniana XXI, 497, V, 167
Paris, Arsenal 824, VI, 400
Arsenal 5028, V, 434
Bibliothèque Nationale,
6689, V, 274, VI, 181-2
7147, V, 285, 543
7156, VI, 421
7160A, V, 543
7163, V, 543
7169, V, 543
7236, V, 34
7417, V, 351, 368, 371
7420A, V, 674, 675
7443C, V, 371
7484, VI, 510
13004, V, 645
13008, V, 303
14011, V, 666
15125, V, 675
16650, V, 286
16660, V, 617
18504, V, 300
francais 2074, VI, 473
Paris, Institut de France,
A, V, 16
E, V, 16
F, V, 16
H, V, 29
Paris, Ste. Genevieve 2234, VI, 510
Philadelphia, John F. Lewis Collection 169, V, 432
Philadelphia, University of Pennsylvania, Edgar F. Smith MS, V, 641
Rome, Angelica 163, V, 259
Spaeth, A. Catalogue I, 203, V, 674
Strasburg 65 (Latin 63), VI, 489
Turin, CDII,i,II,17, VI, 109
Turin, CDV,i,II,29, VI, 109
Upsala, University, Greek 45, VI, 89
Upsala, University, Greek 46, VI, 89
Vatican City, Vatican library
Barberini lat. 271, V, 99
Barberini lat. 353, V, 99
Barberini lat. 921, VI, 171-2
Palatine lat. 1041, V, 142
Palat. lat. 1072, VI, 91
Palat. lat. 1264, V, 676
Palat. lat. 1375, V, 369
Palat. lat. 1892, V, 391, 640, 674, 676-7
Reg. Suev. 1319, VI, 473
Vatican lat. 3103, V, 407
3121, V, 675
3165, V, 552
3187, V, 324-5
3687, V, 265
3689, V, 268
3690, V, 268-9
3691, V, 268-9
5397, VI, 191-2
5733, V, 99
6253, VI, 156
6304, VI, 171
7180, V, 266, 274, VI, 173-4
Venice, S. Marco III, 7, V, 170
S. Marco VII, 14, V, 100
S. Marco VII, 37, V, 204
S. Marco VIII, 26, V, 169
S. Marco VIII, 89, V, 170
Vienna, Nationalbibliothek,
2525, V, 676
2945, VI, 489
3059, V, 675
3059*, V, 676
3276, V, 675
3292, V, 355
4007, V, 675
4417*, VI, 488
4756, V, 180, 247, 320, 351

4988, V, 172
5002, V, 167, 351-2
5280, V, 359, 370
5307, V, 674, 676-7
5503, V, 171
7433, V, 167
9616, VI, 492
10650, V, 351-2
Windsor, Royal, Fogli B, V, 33
Wolfenbüttel 84.1.Aug., V, 407
Würzburg, University, M.ch.q.59, V, 130

INDEX OF INCIPITS

Ad invictissimum principem Henricum .... V, 320
Antequam Antoni dulcissime ad divinae tuae .... V, 167
Artem chiromanticam ab excellentissima .... V, 56
Astronomia ut Plato .... VI, 191
Astrorum scientia et eorum effectus .... V, 247

Beatissimo ac sanctissimo nostro Paulo .... V, 266

Coeli et terrae Creator .... VI, 156
Contristatus erat Raymundus .... V, 536
Cum divina providentia cuncta .... V, 259
Cum Graecia longo et civili .... V, 380
Cum in omnibus artibus .... V, 379
Cum mecum diu ipse hesitans .... VI, 438
Cum preteritis diebus Romam venissem .... V, 85
Cum superiore anno dux potentissime .... V, 169

De recta nativitatis figura .... V, 170
Deus gloriose cum tue sublimis .... V, 536
Dubitandum quidem est maxime in scola .... V, 77
Dubitasti saepenumero Ioannes frater .... V, 648
Duo praecipua sunt et necessaria .... V, 320

Erecta nativitatis figura et per modos .... V, 170

Havea determinato Iulio Papa beatissimo .... V, 167
Hermes theologorum alchimistarumque pater .... V, 533
Hic tractatus quatuor complectitur .... VI, 510

In deiectione seminis humani .... V, 303
Inter astrologica iudicia scire .... VI, 36
Inter tam multas quam varias .... VI, 492

Madame le prince des philosophes .... V, 309
Magna diu questio fuit magna .... V, 265
Metoposcopia de lineis frontis .... VI, 510
Mi Baldasar excellentissime .... V, 76

Naturae mundique cano quae semina primum .... V, 254
Ne propriis in viribus .... V, 172
Non e dubio che per instinto .... VI, 471
Non senza admirabile causa .... V, 169

Omnes fere clades .... VI, 181
Omnes mundi mutaciones status negotia .... V, 171
Oneirocritica est in somniis .... VI, 510
Ordo naturae .... VI, 510

Parthorum reges ut auctor est Armeus ..... V, 188
Petistis ut scriberem vobis de rebus arduis ..... V, 86
Pour ce que plusieurs personnes ..... VI, 473
Primum autem de latenti rerum ..... V, 494
Ptolemeus solertissimus astrologie indagator ..... V, 197

Quamquam omnes philosophiae partes ..... V, 320
Queritur utrum astrologus possit scire ..... V, 198
Qui demonum notitiam expetunt ..... VI, 523
Quia in hoc libro de peste ..... V, 475
Quoniam ut ait Augustinus ..... V, 355
Quoniam vero summam totius operis ..... VI, 120
Quum multis ab hinc annis ..... V, 172

Radii ex septem planetis emissi ..... V, 303

Scito quod sapientes in miraculo ..... V, 534
Spondent quas non exhibent ..... V, 539
Superioribus his diebus ..... V, 351

Tollenda sunt de medio ..... V, 539

Ut de astrologiae antiquitate ..... VI, 172
Utrum stellarum et planetarum ..... V, 180

Verba Secretorum Hermetis ..... VI, 448

NOTE: SEE ALSO V, 673–78, APPENDIX 2, FOR INCIPITS OF WORKS OF CHIROMANCY, ARRANGED ALPHABETICALLY.